The University of Chicago School Mathematics Project

Precalculus and Discrete Mathematics

Second Edition

Teacher's Edition

Part 2, Chapters 7-13

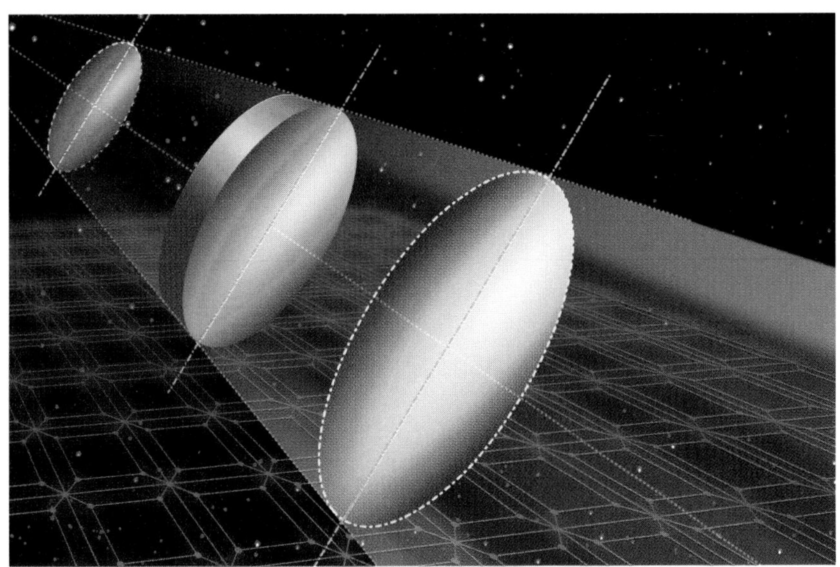

About the Cover In *Precalculus and Discrete Mathematics,* we prepare for calculus and preview the concepts of derivative and integral which are related to area and volume. The background contains a tessellation based on a network, a discrete graph, which represents the vertices of a rectangular solid.

Authors

Anthony L. Peressini John W. McConnell Zalman Usiskin
Susanna S. Epp Nils P. Ahbel David Witonsky
Kathleen A. Hollowell Susan Brown Wade Ellis, Jr.
John Sorteberg Denisse R. Thompson Dora Aksoy
Geoffrey D. Birky Greg A. McRill

Scott Foresman
Addison Wesley

Editorial Offices: Glenview, Illinois • Menlo Park, California
Sales Offices: Reading, Massachusetts • Atlanta, Georgia • Glenview, Illinois
Carrollton, Texas • Menlo Park, California
http://www.sf.aw.com

Contents

of Teacher's Edition

The complete Table of Contents for the Student Edition begins on page *vi*.

Your UCSMP Professional Sourcebook is found at the back of Part 1, starting on page T20.

ISBN: 0-673-45916-0

1 2 3 4 5 6 7 8 9—WO—0 5 0 4 0 3 0 2 0 1 0 0 9 9 9 8

CONTENTS

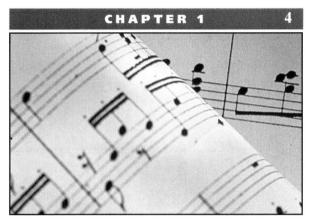

CHAPTER 5 282

Rational Numbers and Rational Functions

CHAPTER 6 348

Trigonometric Identities and Equations

CHAPTER 7 404

Recursion and Mathematical Induction

Chapter 7 Planner

Adapting to Individual Needs

The student text is written for the vast majority of students. The chart at the right suggests two pacing plans to accommodate the needs of your students. Students in the Full Course should complete the entire text by the end of the year. Students in the Minimal Course will spend more time when there are quizzes and more time on the Chapter Review. Therefore, these students may not complete all of the chapters in the text.

Options are also presented to meet the needs of a variety of teaching and learning styles. For each lesson, the Teacher's Edition provides a section entitled *Adapting to Individual Needs.* This section regularly includes **Optional Activities, Challenge** problems, **English Language Development** suggestions, and suggestions for providing **Extra Help.** The Teacher's Edition also frequently includes an **Error Alert,** an **Extension,** and an **Assessment** alternative. The options available in Chapter 7 are summarized in the chart below.

Chapter 7 Pacing Chart

Day	Full Course	Minimal Course
1	7-1	7-1
2	7-2	7-2
3	7-3	7-3
4	7-4	7-4
5	Quiz*; 7-5	Quiz*; begin 7-5.
6	7-6	Finish 7-5.
7	7-7	7-6
8	Quiz*; 7-8	7-7
9	7-9	Quiz*; begin 7-8.
10	Self-Test	Finish 7-8.
11	Review	7-9
12	Test*	Self-Test
13		Review
14		Review
15		Test*

*in the Teacher's Resource File

In the Teacher's Edition...

Lesson	Optional Activities	Extra Help	Challenge	English Language Development	Error Alert	Extension	Cooperative Learning	Ongoing Assessment
7-1	●	●	●		●	●	●	Written
7-2	●	●	●		●	●		Written
7-3	●	●	●		●	●	●	Group
7-4	●		●		●		●	Quiz
7-5	●	●	●		●	●	●	Written
7-6	●	●	●		●	●		Written
7-7	●	●			●	●	●	Quiz
7-8	●	●	●		●	●	●	Written
7-9	●	●	●		●	●		

In the Additional Resources...

	In the Teacher's Resource File							
Lesson	Lesson Masters	Teaching Aids*	Answer Masters	Technology Sourcebook	Assessment Sourcebook	Visual Aids**	Technology	Explorations Software
7-1	7-1	62, 65	7-1	Calc 11		62, 65, AM		
7-2	7-2	62	7-2			62, AM		
7-3	7-3	62	7-3			62, AM		
7-4	7-4	63	7-4		Quiz	63, AM		
7-5	7-5	63	7-5			63, AM		
7-6	7-6	63	7-6			63, AM		7-6
7-7	7-7	64, 66	7-7		Quiz	64, 66, AM		
7-8	7-8	64, 67, 68, 69	7-8			64, 67, 68, 69, AM		7-8
7-9		64	7-9			64, AM		
End of chapter					Tests			

*Teaching Aids are pictured on pages 404C.

**Visual Aids provide transparencies for all Teaching Aids and all Answer Masters.

Also available is the Study Skills Handbook which includes study-skill tips related to reading, note-taking, and comprehension.

Integrating Strands and Applications

	7-1	7-2	7-3	7-4	7-5	7-6	7-7	7-8	7-9
Mathematical Connections									
Number Sense	●	●	●	●	●	●	●	●	●
Algebra	●	●	●	●	●	●	●		
Logic and Reasoning	●	●	●	●	●	●	●	●	●
Patterns and Functions	●	●	●	●	●	●	●	●	●
Discrete Mathematics	●	●	●	●	●	●	●	●	●
Interdisciplinary and Other Connections									
Art						●			
Science		●		●					
Multicultural	●	●							
Technology	●	●	●			●		●	●
Consumer					●		●		
History	●								

Teaching and Assessing the Chapter Objectives

Chapter 7 Objectives (Organized into the SPUR catetgories—Skills, Properties, Uses, and Representations)	**Lessons**	**Progress Self-Test Questions**	**Chapter Review Questions**	**In the Teacher's Resource File** Chapter Test, Forms A and B	Chapter Test, Forms C	D
Skills						
A: Determine terms of a sequence which is defined either explicitly or recursively.	7-1	1	1-7		1	X
B: Conjecture explicit formulas for recursively defined sequences.	7-1	1	8-12			
C: Use summation notation to write sums.	7-2	3	13-18		2	
D: Rewrite sums recursively.	7-2	4	19-21		2	
E: Evaluate a finite or infinite geometric series.	7-6	6	22-25		4	X
Properties						
F: Prove that a recursively defined sequence has a particular explicit formula.	7-3	5	26-27			
G: Prove statements using the Principle of Mathematical Induction.	7-3, 7-4, 7-5, 7-7	8, 9, 10	28-35		3	
Uses						
H: Use recursive formulas to solve problems.	7-1	2	36-38			X
I: Execute algorithms on sets of numbers.	7-8	11	39-40		5	
Representations						
J: Interpret computer programs which calculate terms of sequences.	7-1, 7-3, 7-6	7	41-42		1	

Assessment Sourcebook
Quiz for Lessons 7-1 through 7-4
Quiz for Lessons 7-5 through 7-7
Chapter 7 Test, Forms A–D
Chapter 7 Test, Cumulative Form

TestWorks CD-ROM

Teaching Aids

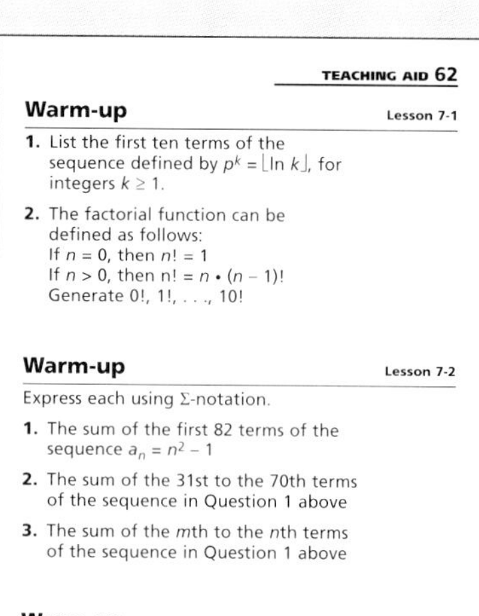

TEACHING AID 62

Warm-up
Lesson 7-1

1. List the first ten terms of the sequence defined by $p^k = \lfloor \ln k \rfloor$, for integers $k \geq 1$.
2. The factorial function can be defined as follows:
   If $n = 0$, then $n! = 1$
   If $n > 0$, then $n! = n \cdot (n - 1)!$
   Generate 0!, 1!, . . ., 10!

Warm-up
Lesson 7-2

Express each using Σ-notation.

1. The sum of the first 82 terms of the sequence $a_n = n^2 - 1$
2. The sum of the 31st to the 70th terms of the sequence in Question 1 above
3. The sum of the mth to the nth terms of the sequence in Question 1 above

Warm-up
Lesson 7-3

Suppose $p(k)$ is the statement $2^k > 2^{k-1}$.

1. Is the statement true when $k = 1$?
2. What is the statement $p(k + 1)$?
3. Explain why $p(k)$ implies $p(k + 1)$.

TEACHING AID 63

Warm-up
Lesson 7-4

1. Evaluate the first six terms of the sequence $a_n = 7^n - 1$.
2. What is the largest common factor of these six terms?
3. Prove that every term of the sequence is divisible by that factor.

Warm-up
Lesson 7-5

Let $S(n)$ be the statement $n! > 10^n$.

1. What is the smallest integer k for which $S(k)$ is true?
2. Explain: If $S(k)$ is true, then $S(k + 1)$ must be true.

Warm-up
Lesson 7-6

Consider the sequence defined by $a_n = \frac{3}{11}(1 - (.01)^n)$.

1. Write the first five terms of this sequence.
2. What is $\lim_{n \to \infty} a_n$?

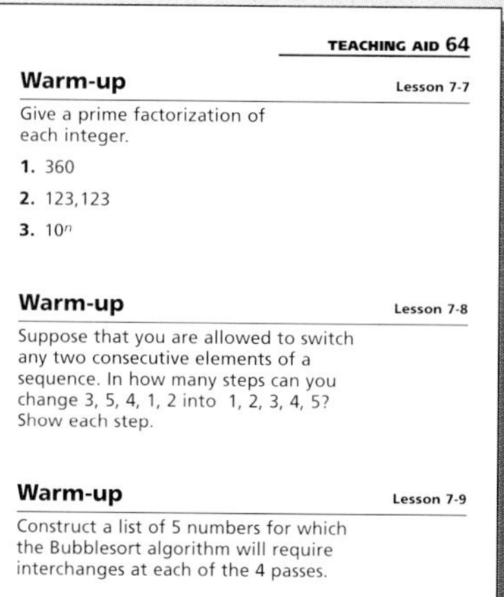

TEACHING AID 64

Warm-up
Lesson 7-7

Give a prime factorization of each integer.

1. 360
2. 123,123
3. 10^n

Warm-up
Lesson 7-8

Suppose that you are allowed to switch any two consecutive elements of a sequence. In how many steps can you change 3, 5, 4, 1, 2 into 1, 2, 3, 4, 5? Show each step.

Warm-up
Lesson 7-9

Construct a list of 5 numbers for which the Bubblesort algorithm will require interchanges at each of the 4 passes.

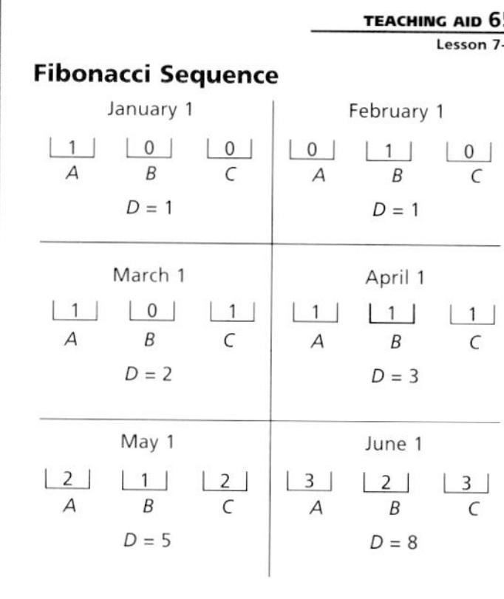

TEACHING AID 65
Lesson 7-1

Fibonacci Sequence

	A	B	C	D
January 1	1	0	0	D = 1
February 1	0	1	0	D = 1
March 1	1	0	1	D = 2
April 1	1	1	1	D = 3
May 1	2	1	2	D = 5
June 1	3	2	3	D = 8

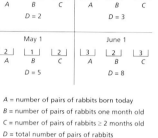

A = number of pairs of rabbits born today
B = number of pairs of rabbits one month old
C = number of pairs of rabbits $\geq$ 2 months old
D = total number of pairs of rabbits

TEACHING AID 66
Lessons 7-3, 7-7

Principles of Mathematical Induction

Principle of Mathematical Induction (Original Form)

Let $S(n)$ be a sentence in n. If
(1) $S(1)$ is true, and
(2) for all integers $k \geq 1$, the assumption that $S(k)$ is true implies that $S(k + 1)$ is true,
then $S(n)$ is true for all positive integers n.

Principle of Mathematical Induction (Strong Form)

Suppose that for each positive integer n, $S(n)$ is a sentence in n. If
(1) $S(1)$ is true, and
(2) for all integers $k \geq 1$, the assumption that $S(1), S(2), \ldots, S(k - 1), S(k)$ are all true implies that $S(k + 1)$ is also true,
then $S(n)$ is true for all integers $n \geq 1$.

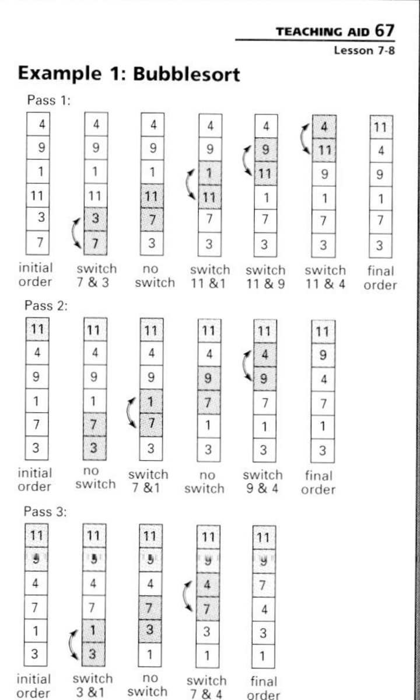

TEACHING AID 67
Lesson 7-8

Example 1: Bubblesort

Pass 1:

initial order	switch 7 & 3	no switch	switch 11 & 1	switch 11 & 9	switch 11 & 4	final order
4	4	4	4	4	4	11
9	9	9	9	9	11	4
1	1	1	1	11	9	9
11	11	11	11	1	1	1
3	3	7	7	7	7	7
7	7	3	3	3	3	3

Pass 2:

initial order	no switch	switch 7 & 1	no switch	switch 9 & 4	final order
11	11	11	11	11	11
4	4	4	4	4	9
9	9	9	9	9	4
1	1	1	7	7	7
7	7	7	1	1	1
3	3	3	3	3	3

Pass 3:

initial order	switch 3 & 1	no switch	switch 7 & 4	final order
11	11	11	11	11
9	9	9	9	9
4	4	4	4	7
7	7	7	7	4
1	1	3	3	3
3	3	1	1	1

TEACHING AID 68
Lesson 7-8

Example 2: Quicksort

Step 1: The list L contains more than one number, so continue to Step 2.

Step 2: $f = 7$ so compare 7 with the remaining numbers and group them into two sublists:
L_l = 3, 1, 4 and L_r = 11, 9.
L now looks like 3, 1, 4, 7, 11, 9.

Step 3: Use Quicksort to sort L_l = 3, 1, 4.
 Step 1: L_l contains more than one number, so continue.
 Step 2: $f = 3$, so divide L_l into $(L_l)_l = 1$ and $(L_l)_r = 4$. L_l is now 1, 3, 4.
 Step 3: Use Quicksort to sort $(L_l)_l$.
  Step 1: $(L_l)_l$ contains only one number, so it is already sorted.
 Step 4: Use Quicksort to sort $(L_l)_r$
  Step 1: $(L_l)_r$ contains only one number, sort is already sorted.
 Now L_l is sorted, and L looks like 1, 3, 4, 7, 11, 9.

TEACHING AID 69
Lesson 7-8

Example 2: Quicksort (continued)

Step 4: Use Quicksort to sort L_r = 11, 9.
 Step 1: L_r contains more than one number, so continue.
 Step 2: $f = 11$, so divide L_r into $(L_r)_l = 9$ and $(L_r)_r$ is empty. L_r is now 9, 11.
 Step 3: Quicksort to sort $(L_r)_l$.
  Step 1: $(L_r)_l$ contains only one number, so it is already sorted.
 Step 4: Use Quicksort to sort $(L_r)_r$.
  Step 1: $(L_r)_r$ contains no numbers, so it is already sorted.
 Now L_r is sorted, and L looks like 1, 3, 4, 7, 9,11.

Now L is sorted.

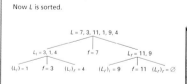

L = 7, 3, 11, 1, 9, 4
L_l = 3, 1, 4 | f = 7 | L_r = 11, 9
$(L_l)_l$ = 1 | f = 3 | $(L_l)_r$ = 4 | $(L_r)_l$ = 9 | f = 11 | $(L_r)_r = \varnothing$

Chapter Opener

Pacing

All lessons in this chapter are designed to be covered in one day. At the end of the chapter, you should plan to spend 1 day to review the Progress Self-Test, 1–2 days for the Chapter Review, and 1 day for a test. You may wish to spend a day on projects, and possibly a day is needed for quizzes. This chapter should therefore take 12–15 days. Spending more than 18 days on this chapter is not recommended; there is ample opportunity to review ideas in later chapters.

Using Pages 404–405

In theory, because no rule has been given for the sequence on page 405, the number in the blank cannot be determined. By saying "a simple pattern" we are suggesting that there is only one rule, but it is possible that there are others.

For instance, let $a_n - n$ and let $b_n = n^4 - 10n^3 + 35n^2 - 49n + 24$. Have students calculate the first four terms of each sequence and conjecture the fifth term. (Each sequence has first four terms 1, 2, 3, 4. However, while $a_5 = 5$, $b_5 = 29$.) For this reason we do not usually ask students to generate an explicit formula from terms of a sequence, unless there is additional information given, such as that the sequence is arithmetic.

The sequence on page 405 is discussed in **Example 3** of Lesson 7-1. In determining the correct number, students may recognize that the numbers in the second column are 1 less than a power of 2. Their guess would be $2^7 - 1 = 127$, which is

CHAPTER 7

404

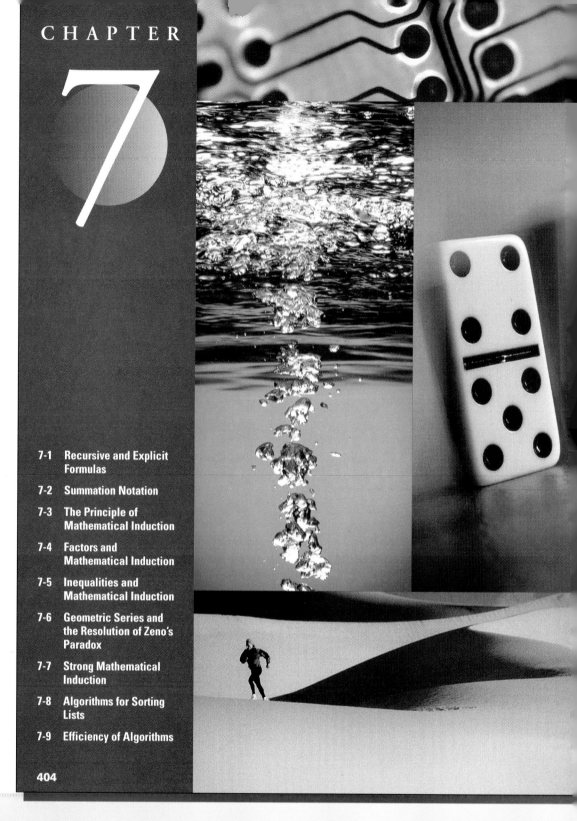

Chapter 7 Overview

The last few chapters have primarily dealt with precalculus topics. This chapter returns to topics in discrete mathematics, although mathematical induction is often a topic in precalculus courses. Almost all of the material of this chapter is specifically mentioned in the NCTM *Curriculum and Evaluation Standards* as part of the core curriculum for college bound students.

There are a number of reasons for the importance of this content. The kind of thinking that is used in recursion and in induction is a critical kind of thinking in solving many problems, in writing instructions or computer programs, and in viewing the ways in which objects are logically related. Mathematical induction is a powerful tool in proofs in virtually all branches of mathematics. The two ideas of recursion and induction are put together in this chapter in a way that points out the similarity of the ideas.

The first two lessons deal with recursion in the context of sequences. Students are expected to use the recursive definition of a sequence to generate the terms of the sequence and to conjecture an explicit formula for the sequence. Lesson 7-2 reviews summation notation.

We feel students often have too narrow a focus of the beauty and power of mathematical induction. Hence, Lessons 7-3 through

Recursion and Mathematical Induction

The numbers in the table below follow a simple pattern. What number belongs in the blank?

1	1
2	3
3	7
4	15
5	31
6	63
7	?

(Before reading even one more sentence, cover the rest of the page and try to determine this number.)

There are two quite different ways of working on this question. One way is to work *across*, seeing how the numbers in each row are related, and then determining what number is related to 7. This is what you often do when you find a rule for a function.

The second way is to work *down*, seeing how the numbers in the right column are related, and using the number 63 and possibly previous numbers to determine what number should go in the blank.

The kind of thinking in the second way is called *recursive thinking*. Recursive thinking is the use of previous elements in a sequence in a prescribed way to generate later ones. Computers, because of their capacity to repeat operations very quickly, are often programmed to apply ideas of recursion.

If you use recursive thinking on the above table, you can get successive entries in the right column without referring to the left column. After the first number, each number in the right column is one more than twice the number just above it.

In this chapter, you will learn how recursive thinking can be used in a variety of situations. You will also be introduced to *mathematical induction*, a method of proof that is related to thinking recursively. The methods you learn are used to tackle and solve important problems in mathematics, computer science, game theory, and many other fields.

correct. Others might find a pattern in the differences of consecutive terms.

You might poll the class: How many worked across? How many worked down? Working down uses recursive thinking.

Photo Connections

The photo collage makes real-world connections to the content of the chapter: recursion and mathematical induction.

Computer Circuitry: The computer's microprocessor processes and sorts bits of information by switching them from circuit to circuit. Lesson 7-8 deals with algorithms for sorting lists.

Bubbles: In "Bubblesort," which is discussed on page 450, numbers "bubble up" from bottom to top.

Dominoes: Mathematical induction, the topic of Lesson 7-3, is often illustrated by considering how a row of dominoes falls when the first domino is pushed over.

Runner: Zeno's Paradox about a runner trying to go from point A to point B, but never reaching point B, is discussed in Lesson 7-2.

Keyboard: The kind of thinking presented in this chapter is critical in writing computer programs. Students encounter computer programs throughout this chapter.

Chapter 7 Projects

At this time, you might want to have students look over the projects on pages 463–464.

7-7 illustrate many situations which are proved by using this technique. We do not necessarily expect students to master the use of induction in all of the contexts, but the discussion often helps students grasp the wide applicability of induction and gives them time to master its application to summations and divisibility.

Lesson 7-6 discusses the sum of the terms of a geometric sequence, including what it means to sum the terms of an infinite geometric sequence. The formula for the sum of the first n terms of a geometric sequence is proved using mathematical induction.

Lesson 7-7 discusses strong mathematical induction, which is used to prove (1) the number of moves required to assemble a jigsaw puzzle and (2) that every integer is either prime or a product of primes.

In Lesson 7-8 and 7-9, the ideas of recursion and iteration from the beginning of the chapter are applied to define computer sorting algorithms. The efficiency of such algorithms is studied, an important topic to users of computer time.

Students interested in Advanced Placement Computer Science will find recursion, sorting techniques, and analysis of efficiency of algorithms helpful.

Lesson 7-1

Objectives

A Determine terms of a sequence which is defined either explicitly or recursively.
B Conjecture explicit formulas for recursively defined sequences.
H Use recursive formulas to solve problems.
J Interpret computer programs which calculate terms of sequences.

Resources

From the ***Teacher's Resource File***
- Lesson Master 7-1
- Answer Master 7-1
- Teaching Aids
  62 Warm-up
  65 Fibonacci Sequence, for Optional Activity 2
- Technology Sourcebook
  Calculator Master 11

Additional Resources
- Visuals for Teaching Aids 62, 65

Teaching Lesson 7-1

Warm-up

1. List the first ten terms of the sequence defined by $p_k = \lfloor \ln k \rfloor$, for integers $k \geq 1$. **0, 0, 1, 1, 1, 1, 1, 2, 2, 2**
2. The factorial function can be defined as follows:
   If $n = 0$, then $n! = 1$
   If $n > 0$, then $n! = n \cdot (n - 1)!$
   Generate 0!, 1!, ... , 10!
   1, 1, 2, 6, 24, 120, 720, 5040, 40,320, 362,880, 3,628,800

LESSON

7-1 Recursive and Explicit Formulas

Finding Recursive Formulas for Sequences

It is easy to square an integer whose units digit (in base 10) is 1, such as 41. You know the square of the previous integer: $40^2 = 1600$. Then add 40 and 41 to 1600. The resulting sum, 1681, is the square of 41. This works because for all real numbers x,

$$\begin{aligned}(x + 1)^2 &= x^2 + 2x + 1\\ &= x^2 + x + (x + 1).\end{aligned}$$

Specifically, when $x = 40$, $\quad 41^2 = 40^2 + 40 + 41.$

The kind of thinking exemplified in this mental arithmetic is recursive, in the sense that a particular value in a sequence (in this case, the sequence of squares) is used to obtain the next value. You can use this thinking to obtain a recursive definition for the sequence of squares of the positive integers 1, 4, 9, 16, 25, ...

Definition
A **recursive formula for a sequence** consists of two statements:
(1) A specification of one or more initial terms of the sequence, called **initial conditions**;
(2) An equation that relates each subsequent term of the sequence to one or more of the previous terms, called a **recurrence relation**.

Not all initial conditions and recurrence relations determine a unique sequence. For instance, consider the sequence S with

$$\begin{cases} S_1 = 5 \\ S_{n+1} = 2S_{n-1}. \end{cases}$$

It is possible that S is the sequence 5, 5, 10, 10, 20, 20, . . . , or the sequence 5, 6, 10, 12, 20, 24, . . . , or many others. However, under certain circumstances a sequence is uniquely defined by a recursive formula.

Recursion Principle
Suppose that a recurrence relation defines x_{n+1} in terms of x_n and n for each integer $n \geq 1$. Then there is exactly one sequence X defined by this recurrence relation and the initial condition $x_1 = a$.

A proof of this principle is given in Lesson 7-3.

Lesson 7-1 Overview

Broad Goals This lesson reviews explicit and recursive formulas in a manner designed to set students up for mathematical induction.

Perspective The entire topic of recursion is one which will be quite familiar to students who have studied from previous UCSMP courses. Recursive definitions for sequences are given in Chapter 1 of UCSMP *Advanced Algebra* and are found also in *Functions, Statistics, and Trigonometry*. In those texts, it is assumed that the recursive definition results in a unique sequence; there is no Recursion Principle that gives criteria under which a recursive definition for a sequence yields a unique sequence. In this text, we state the principle explicitly because it is equivalent to the Principle of Mathematical Induction and it would not be consistent to ignore one while explicitly stating the other. In Lesson 7-3, the Recursion Principle is proved using mathematical induction. We introduce and use the Recursion Principle here because its thinking is the kind of thinking needed to understand mathematical induction.

Some sequences are more easily defined recursively than explicitly. Then, when an explicit formula is conjectured for a sequence, there is an obvious question: how can you tell if that formula is correct?

Example 1

Find a recursive formula for the sequence with explicit formula $a_n = n^2$.

Solution

A recursive formula has to have a first term and a recurrence relation expressing a_{n+1} in terms of previous terms. The first term of this sequence is 1. Since $a_n = n^2$, by substitution of $n + 1$ for n,

$$a_{n+1} = (n + 1)^2.$$

Now expand this power as was done at the top of page 406.

$$a_{n+1} = n^2 + 2n + 1$$

Substituting a_n for n^2 gives the recurrence relation. So a recursive formula for the sequence is

$$\begin{cases} a = 1 \\ a_{n+1} = a_n + (2n + 1) \quad \text{for all integers } n \geq 1. \end{cases}$$

Check

Let $n = 1$ in the recurrence relation. Then $a_{n+1} = a_2 = a_1 + 2 \cdot 1 + 1 = 1 + 2 + 1 = 4$, as it should be.

Recursive formulas are frequently used in computer programs to calculate and print out terms of sequences. Here are two programs to print out the first 100 terms of the above sequence of squares. One uses an explicit formula, the other, a recursive formula.

```
10 FOR N = 1 TO 100
20   TERM = N * N
30   PRINT TERM
40 NEXT N
50 END
```

```
10 TERM = 1
20 FOR N = 1 TO 100
30   PRINT TERM
40   TERM = TERM + 2 * N + 1
50 NEXT N
60 END
```

Sums lend themselves to recursion, since if you have $k + 1$ terms to be added and you know the sum of the first k of them, you need only add the last term to get the grand total. Any set of n terms to be added can be considered as the n terms $a_1, a_2, \ldots, a_n$ of a sequence. On page 408 is part of a computer program in BASIC which uses recursion to find the sum of n numbers A(1), A(2), . . . , A(N) that have already been entered into the computer's memory. Step 110 inputs the number of terms to be added so that the sum stops at the proper place. Step 120 is the initial condition and step 140 is the recurrence relation which gives the new sum.

Notes on Reading

Error Alert Throughout their study of mathematics, students have been applauded when they find a pattern for a sequence. They may have assumed that if the pattern works for the particular values of the given sequence, it will work always. Of course this is invalid reasoning, an example of improper induction. In this lesson, students see a procedure that enables such conjectures to be proved.

Examples 1–2 have students determine a recursive formula for a sequence given an explicit definition for it. **Examples 3–4** deal with the problem of finding an explicit formula for a sequence given a recursive definition for it. Students usually feel more accomplishment when they have found the explicit formula.

Students should see that the recurrence relation for the sequence of squares $a_n = n^2$ in **Example 1** is just a special case of the $(x + 1)^2 = x^2 + 2x + 1$ sentence true for all real numbers x. You might ask students to display their abilities at mental arithmetic by giving them the square of a two-digit integer x (say $45^2 = 2025$) and asking for the square of $x + 1$ ($46^2 = 2025 + 90 + 1 = 2116$).

Students who studied from UCSMP *Advanced Algebra* or *Functions, Statistics, and Trigonometry* will have distinguished programs that define sequences recursively from those that define them explicitly. For other students, you may want to have another example. Here are two programs that generate the same sequence. The first uses an explicit definition to generate 100 terms of the sequence defined by $a_n = n^2 + 5n + 4$.

This lesson gives one method: if the explicit formula generates a sequence with the same initial values and recursive relation as that of the given sequence, then by the Recursion Principle, they must be the same sequence.

In this rather painless way, the student is introduced to the two parts of a mathematical induction proof without the formal machinery of induction.

Optional Activities

Activity 1 Technology Connection
You might want to use *Technology Sourcebook, Calculator Master 11.* Students use a programmable calculator to observe how seemingly similar recurrence relations generate very different sequences.

Activity 2
Materials: **Teaching Aid 65**

At the end of the lesson, you may want students to explore the Fibonacci sequence. It was introduced by the Italian mathematician Leonardo of Pisa in 1202 in his book *Liber Abaci.* Here is the problem posed by Fibonacci that led to this sequence.

(Optional Activities continue on page 408.)

```
10 FOR N = 1 TO 100
20 AN = N^2 + 5 * N + 4
30 PRINT A
40 NEXT N
50 END
```

The second program uses a recursive definition to generate terms of the sequence defined by $a_1 = 10;\ a_{n+1} = a_n + 2n + 4$.

```
10 A = 10
15 PRINT A
20 FOR I = 2 TO 100
30 A = A + 2*I + 4
40 PRINT A
50 NEXT I
60 END
```

The sequence begins 10, 18, 28, 40, 54, ... The differences of consecutive terms form a linear sequence with slope 2; that is how the recursion relation in line 30 of the second program was found.

The sums $S_1, S_2, S_3, \ldots$ in **Example 2** form a sequence of partial sums, a concept defined formally in Lesson 7-6. To help students understand the solution, you may wish to write the following:

```
  ⋮
110 INPUT N
120 SUM = 0
130 FOR K = 1 TO N
140   SUM = SUM + A(K)
150 NEXT K
160 PRINT SUM
170 END
```

This program contains the idea behind the solution to the next example.

Example 2

Let S_n = the sum of the integers from 1 to n. For example, $S_5 = 1 + 2 + 3 + 4 + 5$. Find a recursive definition for S.

Solution

S_1 is the sum of the integers from 1 to 1, or simply 1. To develop the recurrence relation, note that, for example,

$$S_6 = 1 + 2 + 3 + 4 + 5 + 6 = S_5 + 6.$$

In general,

S_{n+1} = the sum of the integers from 1 to n + 1
= the sum of the integers from 1 to n, plus the integer n + 1
$= S_n + (n + 1)$.

Thus a recursive formula for S is

$$\begin{cases} S_1 = 1 \\ S_{n+1} = S_n + (n+1) & \text{for all integers } n \geq 1. \end{cases}$$

Sometimes it is easier to have a recursive formula for a sequence, while at other times it is easier to have an explicit formula. For instance, with the sequence 1, 3, 7, 15, 31, 63, . . . on page 405, a recursive formula can be used to calculate the next term. But if you wished the 100th term, an explicit formula would be more efficient.

Finding Explicit Formulas for Sequences

The most basic technique for conjecturing an explicit formula for a sequence that has been defined recursively is to find terms until you see a pattern emerging.

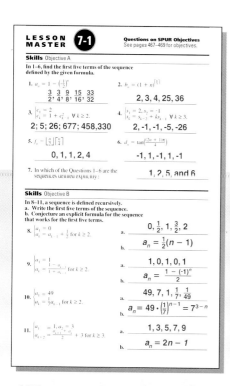

Optional Activity 2, continued

Suppose a certain breed of rabbit is infertile during its first month of life, but after two months and after every month thereafter each male-female pair of rabbits produces one additional male-female pair. Starting with one newly-born male-female pair and assuming that no rabbit dies, how many rabbit pairs will there be at the beginning of the nth month?

Keeping track of infertile, fertile, and baby rabbits is a hairy problem. A calendar as described on the next page may be helpful. This calendar is also provided on **Teaching Aid 65.** Assume that all births take place at 12:01 A.M. on the first of each month, beginning on January 1.

A = # pairs of rabbits born today
B = # pairs of rabbits one month old
C = # pairs of rabbits ≥ 2 months old
D = total # pairs of rabbits

LESSON MASTER 7-1

Questions on SPUR Objectives
See pages 467–469 for objectives.

Skills Objective A

In 1–6, find the first five terms of the sequence defined by the given formula.

1. $a_n = 1 - \left(-\frac{1}{2}\right)^n$ — $\frac{3}{2}, \frac{3}{4}, \frac{9}{8}, \frac{15}{16}, \frac{33}{32}$

2. $b_n = (1 + n)^{\lceil \frac{n}{3} \rceil}$ — 2, 3, 4, 25, 36

3. $\begin{cases} c_1 = 2 \\ c_k = 1 + c_{k-1}^2,\ \forall k \geq 2. \end{cases}$ — 2; 5; 26; 677; 458,330

4. $\begin{cases} s_1 = 2, s_2 = -1 \\ s_k = s_{k-2} + ks_{k-1},\ \forall k \geq 3. \end{cases}$ — 2, -1, -1, -5, -26

5. $f_n = \lfloor \frac{n}{2} \rfloor \lceil \frac{n}{4} \rceil$ — 0, 1, 1, 2, 4

6. $d_n = \tan\left(\frac{(2n+1)\pi}{4}\right)$ — -1, 1, -1, 1, -1

7. In which of the Questions 1–6 are the sequences defined explicitly? — 1, 2, 5, and 6

Skills Objective B

In 8–11, a sequence is defined recursively.
a. Write the first five terms of the sequence.
b. Conjecture an explicit formula for the sequence that works for the first five terms.

8. $\begin{cases} a_1 = 0 \\ a_k = a_{k-1} + \frac{1}{2} \text{ for } k \geq 2. \end{cases}$
a. $0, \frac{1}{2}, 1, \frac{3}{2}, 2$
b. $a_n = \frac{1}{2}(n - 1)$

9. $\begin{cases} a_1 = 1 \\ a_k = \frac{1 - a_{k-1}}{1 + a_{k-1}} \text{ for } k \geq 2. \end{cases}$
a. 1, 0, 1, 0, 1
b. $a_n = \frac{1 - (-1)^n}{2}$

10. $\begin{cases} a_1 = 49 \\ a_k = \frac{1}{7}a_{k-1} \text{ for } k \geq 2. \end{cases}$
a. $49, 7, 1, \frac{1}{7}, \frac{1}{49}$
b. $a_n = 49 \cdot \left(\frac{1}{7}\right)^{n-1} = 7^{3-n}$

11. $\begin{cases} a_1 = 1, a_2 = 3 \\ a_{k+2} = \frac{a_{k+1} + a_k}{2} + 3 \text{ for } k \geq 3. \end{cases}$
a. 1, 3, 5, 7, 9
b. $a_n = 2n - 1$

Example 3

The first six terms of a sequence T are 1, 3, 7, 15, 31, and 63, and a recursive formula for the sequence is $T_{k+1} = 2T_k + 1$ for all $k \geq 1$. Conjecture an explicit formula for T_k.

Solution

Each of these terms is one less than a power of 2.

$$\begin{aligned} T_1 &= 1 = 2^1 - 1 \\ T_2 &= 3 = 2^2 - 1 \\ T_3 &= 7 = 2^3 - 1 \\ T_4 &= 15 = 2^4 - 1 \\ T_5 &= 31 = 2^5 - 1 \\ T_6 &= 63 = 2^6 - 1 \end{aligned}$$

Thus an explicit formula for the sequence appears to be $T_k = 2^k - 1$.

You can prove that the explicit formula $T_k = 2^k - 1$ for the sequence is correct by showing that the sequence it defines satisfies the recursive formula.

Example 4

Prove that the kth term of the sequence T of Example 3 is $2^k - 1$.

Solution

Let S be the sequence defined by the formula $S_n = 2^n - 1$. It needs to be shown that S satisfies the recursive definition of the sequence. In Example 3, T is defined by

$$\begin{cases} T_1 = 1 \\ T_{k+1} = 2T_k + 1 & \text{for each integer } k \geq 1. \end{cases}$$

$S_1 = 2^1 - 1$, so S has the same initial condition as T.

For all n, $S_{n+1} = 2^{n+1} - 1$ — Substitute $n + 1$ for n in the formula for S.
$= 2 \cdot 2^n - 1$ — laws of exponents
$= 2 \cdot 2^n - 2 + 2 - 1$ — Subtract 2 and add 2.
$= 2 \cdot (2^n - 1) + 1$ — Distributive Property
$= 2 \cdot S_n + 1$. — Substitute using the formula for S_n.

So S satisfies the same recurrence relation as T. Since S and T have the same recursive definition, they are the same sequence.

In general, if you know a recursive formula for a sequence, then you can prove that an explicit formula is correct if you can show that the formula satisfies

(1) the initial condition or conditions, and
(2) the recurrence relation

of the recursive formula.

$S_5 = 1 + 2 + 3 + 4 + 5$
$S_6 = 1 + 2 + 3 + 4 + 5 + 6$

(the part $1 + 2 + 3 + 4 + 5$ of S_6 is bracketed and labeled S_5)

So $S_6 = S_5 + 6$. Thus, for $n = 5$, $S_{n+1} = S_n + (n + 1)$.

To lead into **Example 3**'s conclusion that for all k, $T_k = 2^k - 1$, you may wish to prove that the sequence defined recursively as

$$\begin{cases} a_1 = 2 \\ a_{n+1} = 2a_n \text{ for } n \geq 1 \end{cases}$$

has explicit definition $a_n = 2^n$. Be sure to write 2, 4, 8, 16, 32, … on the board! Seeing powers of two may help students recognize the explicit formula for T_k from the following table.

k	T_k
1	1
2	3
3	7
4	15
5	31

To prove that $T_k = 2^k - 1$ is the correct explicit formula, **Example 4** shows that this explicit formula leads to a sequence that has the same recursive definition. The Recursion Principle guarantees that the explicit formula will generate the identical sequence to that of the recursive formula.

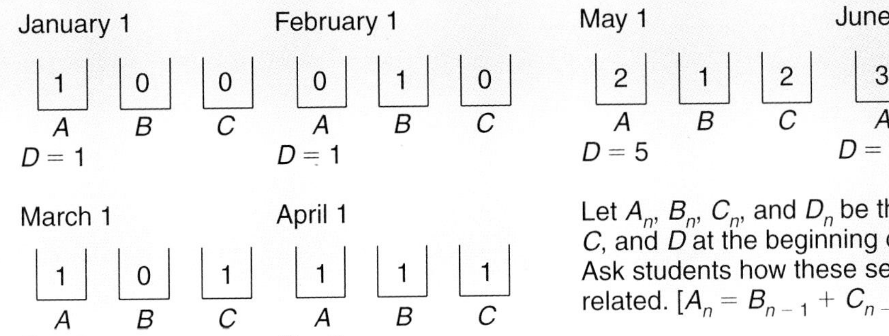

Let A_n, B_n, C_n, and D_n be the values of A, B, C, and D at the beginning of the nth month. Ask students how these sequences are related. $[A_n = B_{n-1} + C_{n-1} = D_{n-2}]$

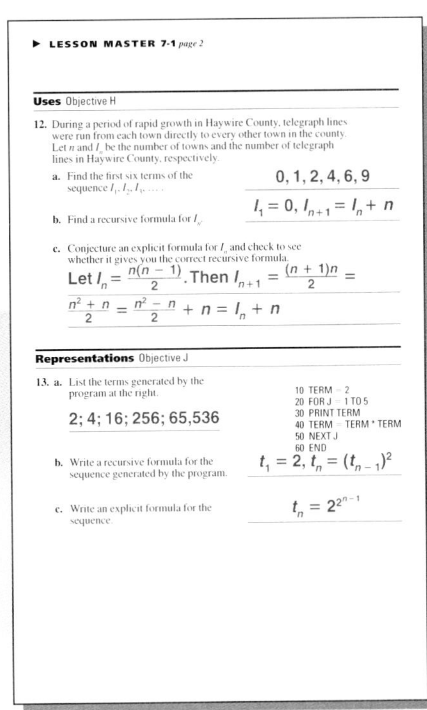

▸ **LESSON MASTER 7-1** *page 2*

Uses Objective H

12. During a period of rapid growth in Haywire County, telegraph lines were run from each town directly to every other town in the county. Let n and l_n be the number of towns and the number of telegraph lines in Haywire County, respectively.
   a. Find the first six terms of the sequence $l_1, l_2, l_3, \ldots$. — 0, 1, 2, 4, 6, 9
   b. Find a recursive formula for l_n. — $l_1 = 0$, $l_{n+1} = l_n + n$
   c. Conjecture an explicit formula for l_n and check to see whether it gives you the correct recursive formula.
   Let $l_n = \frac{n(n-1)}{2}$. Then $l_{n+1} = \frac{(n+1)n}{2} = \frac{n^2 + n}{2} = \frac{n^2 - n}{2} + n = l_n + n$

Representations Objective J

13. a. List the terms generated by the program at the right. — 2; 4; 16; 256; 65,536

```
10 TERM = 2
20 FOR J = 1 TO 5
30 PRINT TERM
40 TERM = TERM * TERM
50 NEXT J
60 END
```

   b. Write a recursive formula for the sequence generated by the program. — $t_1 = 2$, $t_n = (t_{n-1})^2$
   c. Write an explicit formula for the sequence. — $t_n = 2^{2^{n-1}}$

Error Alert After covering the examples in the lesson, some students might incorrectly conclude that all recursive formulas show a single initial condition. Point out that the definition on page 406 stipulates that one *or more* initial terms of the sequence might be given. Then direct them to the recursive formula for the Fibonacci sequence in **Question 8.**

Additional Examples

1. Find a recursive formula for the sequence with explicit formula $a_n = n^3$. $\mathbf{a_1 = 1;\ a_{n+1} = a_n + 3n^2 + 3n + 1}$ **for all integers** $\mathbf{n \geq 1}$
2. Let S_n = sum of the squares of the integers from 1 to *n*. For example,
   $$S_4 = 1^2 + 2^2 + 3^2 + 4^2.$$
   Find a recursive definition for *S*. $\mathbf{S_1 = 1;\ S_{n+1} = S_n + (n+1)^2}$ **for all integers** $\mathbf{n \geq 1}$
3. Suppose
   $$\begin{cases} a_1 = 2 \\ a_{n+1} = 3a_n + 2. \end{cases}$$
   Conjecture an explicit formula for a_n. $\mathbf{a_n = 3^n - 1}$ **for all integers** $\mathbf{n \geq 1}$
4. Prove that the explicit formula in Additional Example 3 is correct. **Let *s* be the sequence defined by** $\mathbf{s_n = 3^n - 1}$**. Then**
   $s_1 = 3^1 - 1 = 2;$
   $s_{n+1} = 3^{n+1} - 1$
   $= 3 \cdot 3^n - 3 + 3 - 1$
   $= 3(3^n - 1) + 2$
   $= 3s_n + 2$
   $\therefore s_{n+1} = 3s_n + 2$
   Thus, by the Recursion Principle, since *s* satisfies the same recursive definition as *a*, the sequences are identical.

1) $s_1 = 11,\ s_{k+1} = s_k + 4,$ $\forall$ **integers** $k \geq 1$

2) $t_1 = 0,\ t_{k+1} = t_k + 2k + 1,$ $\forall$ **integers** $k \geq 1$

5a) 1, 2, 5, 10, 17, 26
b) $t_n = n^2 - 2n + 2$

6a) 3, 7, 11, 15, 19, 23
b) $t_n = 4n - 1$

7a)
```
10 FOR N = 1 TO 50
20 TERM = SIN(3.1415*N/2)
30 PRINT TERM
40 NEXT N
50 END
```

8b) 1, 3, 4, 7, 11, 18, 29, 47, 76, 123
c) 1, 3, 8, 21, 55, 144, 377, 987, 2584, 6765; The sequence is the even terms of the Fibonacci sequence.

QUESTIONS

Covering the Reading

In 1 and 2, find a recursive formula for the sequence *s* with the given explicit formula. **See left.**

1. $s_n = 4n + 7$

2. $t_k = k^2 - 1$

3. Find a sequence not in this lesson satisfying the recursive formula
$$\begin{cases} S_1 = 5 \\ S_{n+1} = 2S_{n-1} \end{cases}.$$
Sample: $\mathbf{S = 5, 7, 10, 14, 20, 28, \ldots}$

4. What part of the Recursion Principle does the recursive formula of Question 3 not satisfy? **There is more than one sequence satisfying the recurrence relation.**

In 5 and 6, a recursive definition for a sequence is given. **a.** Write the first six terms of the sequence *t*. **b.** Find an explicit formula which works for the six terms. **c.** If possible, use the idea of Example 4 to prove that the explicit formula is correct. **a, b) See left. c) See margin.**

5. $\begin{cases} t_1 = 1 \\ t_{k+1} = t_k + 2k - 1 \end{cases}$ for all integers $k \geq 1$

6. $\begin{cases} t_1 = 3 \\ t_{k+1} = t_k + 4 \end{cases}$ for all integers $k \geq 1$

7. a. Write a program to print out the first fifty terms of the sequence defined by $a_n = \sin\left(\frac{\pi}{2} n\right)$, beginning with a_1. **See left.**

b. Give the first 10 terms of this sequence.
1, 0, -1, 0, 1, 0, -1, 0, 1, 0

Applying the Mathematics

8. a. The **Fibonacci sequence** *F* is defined as follows:
$$\begin{cases} F_1 = 1 \\ F_2 = 1 \\ F_{n+1} = F_n + F_{n-1} \quad \text{for } n \geq 2. \end{cases}$$
Calculate the first ten terms of *F*. **1, 1, 2, 3, 5, 8, 13, 21, 34, 55**

b. The Lucas sequence *L* has the same recurrence relation as *F*, but $L_1 = 1$ and $L_2 = 3$. Calculate the first ten terms of *L*. **See left.**

c. A third sequence *P* is defined as the product of corresponding terms of *F* and *L*. That is, for all *n*, $P_n = F_n \cdot L_n$. Calculate the first ten terms of P_n and describe what you get.

Adapting to Individual Needs

Extra Help

Subscript notation still may confuse some students. Build on the presentation in Lesson 2-8. Remind students that S_k is equivalent to $S(k)$. For students who are confused about S_{k+1}, ask what integer comes after *k*. [$k + 1$]

Additional Answers

5. c. $\mathbf{t_1 = 1^2 - 2(1) + 2 = 1}$**, so the initial condition is met.** $\mathbf{t_{n+1}}$
$\mathbf{= (n + 1)^2 - 2(n + 1) + 2}$
$\mathbf{= n^2 + 2n + 1 - 2n - 2 + 2}$
$\mathbf{= (n^2 - 2n + 2) + 2n - 1}$
$\mathbf{= t_n + 2n - 1}$**, so the recursive relationship is satisfied. Therefore, the explicit formula is correct.**

6. c. $\mathbf{t_1 = 4(1) - 1 = 3}$**, so the initial condition is met.** $\mathbf{t_{n+1}}$
$\mathbf{= 4(n + 1) - 1}$
$\mathbf{= 4n + 4 - 1 = t_n + 4}$**, so the recursive relationship is satisfied. Therefore, the explicit formula is correct.**

9) $1, \frac{1}{2}, \frac{1}{3}, \frac{1}{4}, \frac{1}{5}, \frac{1}{6}$; $a_n = \frac{1}{n}$, ∀ integers $n \geq 1$

9. Let $a_1, a_2, a_3, \ldots$ be the sequence defined below. Write the first six terms of the sequence and determine an explicit formula that is suggested by the pattern of numbers you obtain. **See left.**

$$\begin{cases} a_1 = 1 \\ a_{k+1} = \dfrac{a_k}{1 + a_k} & \forall \text{ integers } k \geq 1 \end{cases}$$

10a) 1, 1, 1, 1, 1, 1; $a_n = 1$, ∀ integers $n \geq 1$
b) 1, 2, 1, 2, 1, 2; $a_n = 1$, ∀ odd integers $n > 0$; $a_n = 2$, ∀ even integers $n > 1$
c) $1, c-1, 1, c-1, 1, c-1$; $a_n = 1$, ∀ odd integers $n > 0$; $a_n = c - 1$, ∀ even integers $n > 1$

10. Repeat the directions of Question 9 for each sequence. **See left.**

a. $\begin{cases} a_1 = 1 \\ a_{k+1} = -a_k + 2 & \forall \text{ integers } k \geq 1 \end{cases}$

b. $\begin{cases} a_1 = 1 \\ a_{k+1} = -a_k + 3 & \forall \text{ integers } k \geq 1 \end{cases}$

c. $\begin{cases} a_1 = 1 \\ a_{k+1} = -a_k + c & \forall \text{ integers } k \geq 1, \text{ where } c \text{ is a constant} \end{cases}$

11a) $a_1 = 2$; $a_{k+1} = 3a_k + 2$, ∀ integers $k \geq 1$
b) $a_n = 3^n - 1$, ∀ integers $n \geq 1$, conjectured from 2, 8, 26, 80, ...

11. Consider the program below.

```
10 TERM = 2
20 PRINT TERM
30 FOR I = 2 TO 100
40   TERM = TERM * 3 + 2
50   PRINT TERM
60 NEXT I
```

a. Write a recursive definition for the sequence printed by the computer.
b. Find the values of enough terms to conjecture an explicit formula for the sequence. (Hint: Each value is 1 less than something.)
c. Prove that the explicit formula is correct using the method of Example 4. **See margin.** **a, b) See left.**

12. A sequence s is defined recursively as follows:

$$\begin{cases} s_1 = \frac{1}{2} \\ s_{k+1} = s_k + \dfrac{1}{2^{k+1}} & \forall \text{ integers } k \geq 1. \end{cases}$$

a. Write the first six terms of this sequence. $\frac{1}{2}, \frac{3}{4}, \frac{7}{8}, \frac{15}{16}, \frac{31}{32}, \frac{63}{64}$
b. Conjecture an explicit formula for s_n. $s_n = \frac{2^n - 1}{2^n}$, ∀ integers $n \geq 1$

Review

13. Consider the function f defined by $f(x) = \frac{2x^2 + 4}{x^2 - 9}$. **See margin.**
a. Use limit notation to describe the end behavior of f.
b. Classify any discontinuities as removable or essential.
c. Find the equations of all asymptotes to the graph of f. *(Lessons 5-4, 5-5)*

In 14 and 15, rewrite the expression as a single fraction in factored form. *(Lesson 5-1)* **See left.**

14. $\left[\frac{k(k+1)}{2}\right]^2 + (k+1)^3$ **15.** $\frac{n}{n+1} + \frac{1}{(n+1)(n+2)}$

14) $\frac{(k+1)^2(k+2)^2}{4}$

15) $\frac{n+1}{n+2}$, for $n \neq -1$, $n \neq -2$

Notes on Questions

Question 1 By the method used in **Example 1,** students would find the recurrence relation by writing
$S_{n+1} = 4(n+1) + 7$
$= 4n + 4 + 7$
$= 4n + 7 + 4$
$= S_n + 4.$
Suggest that writing out a few terms and inspecting the results may be helpful: $S_1 = 11$, $S_2 = 15$, $S_3 = 19$, $S_4 = 23$, ... So each term is 4 more than its predecessor. Thus $S_{n+1} = S_n + 4$.

Question 7 Relate the results to the periodicity of the sine function. (This sequence picks key values of the function, ignoring all that is in between.) A graph will be useful.

Question 10 Although **part c** generalizes **parts a and b,** the sequences look quite different.

Question 11 Students here focus on obtaining a recursive definition from a computer program and then generating an explicit formula. A computer is not needed.

Questions 14–15 These questions provide algebraic skill review needed for doing proofs based on the Principle of Mathematical Induction.

Additional Answers

11. c. $a_1 = 3^1 - 1 = 2$, so the initial condition is met.
$a_{n+1} = 3^{n+1} - 1 = 3 \cdot 3^n - 1$
$= 3 \cdot 3^n - 3 + 3 - 1$
$= 3(3^n - 1) + 2 = 3a_n + 2$, so the recursive relationship is met. Therefore, the explicit formula is correct.

13. a. $\lim_{x \to \infty} f(x) = 2$; $\lim_{x \to -\infty} f(x) = 2$
b. There are essential discontinuities at $x = 3$ and $x = -3$.
c. $x = 3$, $x = -3$, $y = 2$

Follow-up for Lesson 7-1

Practice

For more questions on SPUR Objectives, use **Lesson Master 7-1** (shown on pages 408–409).

Assessment

Written Communication Have students **work in pairs.** Ask each student to create an explicit formula for a sequence. Have students write the recursive formula for his or her partner's explicit formula. Repeat the activity, asking students to begin with a recursive formula. [Students write recursive and explicit formulas for sequences.]

Extension

History Connection Archimedes (287–212 B.C.) developed the following recursion formulas for the areas and perimeters of inscribed and circumscribed regular polygons: If a_n and A_n are respectively the areas of regular polygons of n sides inscribed in and circumscribed about a circle, then $a_{2n} = \sqrt{a_n A_n}$ and $A_{2n} = \frac{2A_n a_{2n}}{A_n + a_{2n}}$. If p_n and P_n are perimeters of regular polygons of n sides inscribed in and circumscribed about a circle, then $p_{2n} = \sqrt{p_n P_{2n}}$ and $P_{2n} = \frac{2P_n p_n}{P_n + p_n}$. Archimedes used these formulas to develop the best approximation to π known until his time. Ask students to prove these recursion formulas. Then, beginning with equilateral triangles or hexagons, they should use the formulas to approximate π.

Project Update Project 2, *The Collatz Conjecture,* Project 4, *Exploring the Fibonacci Sequence,* and Project 6, *Generating Sequences with Matrices,* on pages 463–464 relate to the content of this lesson.

16a) Sample:

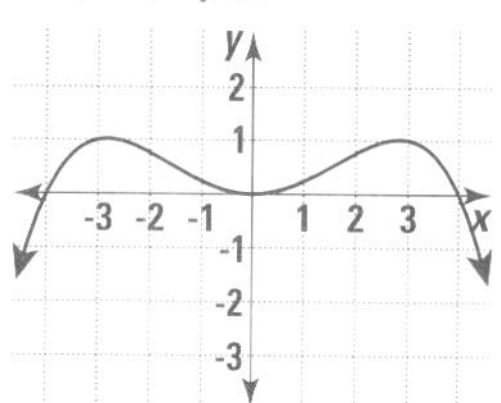

18ai) $\frac{1}{3}, \frac{4}{9}, \frac{13}{27}, \frac{40}{81}$; $a_n = \frac{1}{2}\left(1 - \left(\frac{1}{3}\right)^n\right)$, ∀ integers $n \geq 1$

ii) $\frac{1}{4}, \frac{5}{16}, \frac{21}{64}, \frac{85}{256}$; $a_n = \frac{1}{3}\left(1 - \left(\frac{1}{4}\right)^n\right)$, ∀ integers $n \geq 1$

16. a. Sketch the graph of an even function g such that $\lim_{x \to \infty} g(x) = -\infty$ and g is increasing on the interval $0 \leq x \leq 3$. **See left.**

b. What is the smallest number of relative maxima that g can have? *(Lessons 2-2, 2-3, 2-4)* **2**

17. Consider the universal statement:

$$\forall \text{ real numbers } x,\ p(x) \Rightarrow q(x).$$

a. Under what circumstances will the universal statement be false?

b. Suppose $p(x)$ is $(x + 3)^2 = 49$, and $q(x)$ is $x = 4$. *True or false,* ∀ *real numbers* x, $p(x) \Rightarrow q(x)$. *(Lessons 1-1, 1-3)* **False**

a) **If there exists an x such that $p(x)$ is true and $q(x)$ is false.**

Exploration

18. Extend Question 12 in the following way.

a. List the first four terms of each sequence and conjecture an explicit formula. **See left.**

i. $\begin{cases} a_1 = \frac{1}{3} \\ a_{k+1} = a_k + \frac{1}{3^{k+1}} & \text{for integers } k \geq 1 \end{cases}$

ii. $\begin{cases} a_1 = \frac{1}{4} \\ a_{k+1} = a_k + \frac{1}{4^{k+1}} & \text{for integers } k \geq 1 \end{cases}$

b. Conjecture an explicit formula for the sequence defined by

$$\begin{cases} a_1 = \frac{1}{c} \\ a_{k+1} = a_k + \frac{1}{c^{k+1}} & \text{for integers } k \geq 1 \text{ and constant integer } c \neq 0. \end{cases}$$

Does your formula work for noninteger values of c?

$a_n = \frac{1}{c-1} \cdot \left(1 - \left(\frac{1}{c}\right)^n\right)$; **yes, the formula works for all noninteger numbers $c \neq 0$ or 1.**

Adapting to Individual Needs

Challenge

Have students verify the explicit formula for the Fibonacci sequence

$$S_n = \frac{(1 + \sqrt{5})^n - (1 - \sqrt{5})^n}{2^n\sqrt{5}}$$

for as many values of n as they can.

Setting Up Lesson 7-2

Ask how many students are familiar with summation notation. You may wish to review **Examples 1–2** on page 414 before assigning Lesson 7-2. This will enable you to cover the lesson easily in a single period.

LESSON

7-2 Summation Notation

Infinite Sums

The Greek philosopher Zeno of Elea lived around 450 B.C. and is famous for his paradoxes. One of them involves a runner who is trying to go from point A to point B. Zeno pointed out that the runner would first have to go half the distance, then half the remaining distance, and so forth. Suppose the runner travels at a constant speed, taking one minute to go half the distance from A to B. It will then take $\frac{1}{2}$ minute to go half of the remaining distance, $\frac{1}{4}$ minute to go half of the new remaining distance, and so forth, as shown below.

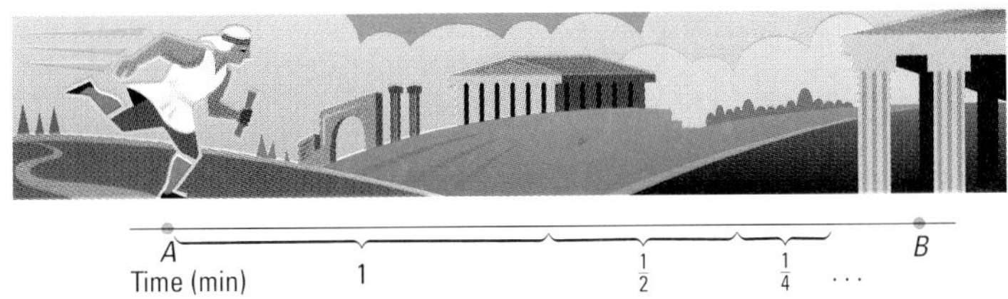

A, B; Time (min): 1, $\frac{1}{2}$, $\frac{1}{4}$ . . .

Zeno observed that the total time required for the runner to reach point B would have to equal the sum of an *infinite* collection of positive numbers:

$$1 + \frac{1}{2} + \frac{1}{4} + \frac{1}{8} + \ldots.$$

Zeno argued that such an infinite sum could not equal a finite number and therefore the runner could never reach point B. This argument is called a *paradox*, one of **Zeno's paradoxes**, because obviously runners do get from point A to point B.

What Is Summation Notation?

Summation notation, or *sigma notation*, is very convenient for concisely representing sums such as that arising from this paradox of Zeno. This notation uses the symbol Σ, the Greek capital letter sigma. Sigma is used because it is the Greek version of S, the first letter of the word *sum*. The numbers to be added are thought of as consecutive terms of a sequence.

❶ **Definition (Summation Notation)**

$$\sum_{i=m}^{n} a_i = a_m + a_{m+1} + \ldots + a_n$$

The symbol $\sum_{i=m}^{n} a_i$ is read "the sum of the numbers a_i from $i = m$ to $i = n$." The expression $a_m + a_{m+1} + \ldots + a_n$ is called the **expanded form** of $\sum_{i=m}^{n} a_i$, and the variable i is called the **index** of this sum.

Lesson 7-2

Objectives

C Use summation notation to write sums.

D Rewrite sums recursively.

Resources

From the ***Teacher's Resource File***
- Lesson Master 7-2
- Answer Master 7-2
- Teaching Aid 62: Warm-up

Additional Resources
- Visual for Teaching Aid 62

Teaching Lesson 7-2

Warm-up

Express each using Σ-notation.

1. The sum of the first 82 terms of the sequence $a_n = n^2 - 1$ $\sum_{i=1}^{82}(i^2 - 1)$
2. The sum of the 31st to the 70th terms of the sequence in Question 1 above $\sum_{i=31}^{70}(i^2 - 1)$
3. The sum of the mth to the nth terms of the sequence in Question 1 above $\sum_{i=m}^{n}(i^2 - 1)$

Notes on Reading

❶ The definition of summation notation given on this page is more advanced than we might give if students had never seen the symbol Σ before. If this is a new symbol for

Lesson 7-2 Overview

Broad Goals This lesson completes the prerequisites for the understanding of the mathematical induction proofs to be introduced in the next lesson. We expect that students have seen and used the Σ symbol before; the key new idea is to express $\sum_{i=1}^{n+1}$ in terms of $\sum_{i=1}^{n}$ and the $(n + 1)$st term.

Perspective Zeno's paradox is introduced as a vehicle for presenting a sum. Did Zeno actually think that the runner would not get from point A to point B? There is a tendency to think that the ancients were not as smart as we. Of course Zeno knew that people get from point A to point B. He was showing that the formal logic and mathematics of his time were insufficient for dealing with the infinite, in this case, with an infinite sum.

A paradox of Zeno related to the paradox with which this lesson opens is sometimes called the Dichotomy. In order to traverse a distance, the runner has to go halfway. To go halfway, the runner has to go a quarter of the way. To go a quarter of the way, the runner has to go an eighth of the way. And so on. Since the runner has to satisfy infinitely many of these conditions, the runner will never get started!

your students, then you might wish to put in an intermediate definition: $\sum_{i=1}^{n} a_i = a_1 + a_2 + \ldots + a_n$.

Remind students that the purpose of summation notation is to simplify and unclutter an expression, not make it more complex!

Error Alert It is important for students to understand that the index variable is the only variable for which values are substituted when the expanded form is written. That is, $\sum_{i=1}^{4} i = 1 + 2 + 3 + 4 = 10$ but $\sum_{i=1}^{4} (i + c) = (1 + c) + (2 + c) + (3 + c) + (4 + c) = 10 + 4c$ and $\sum_{i=5}^{10} k = k + k + k + k + k + k = 6k$.

In the examples above, c and k respectively, are not indices of summation and thus do not assume the range of integer values over which the sum is computed.

Although i is used as the index throughout the reading, point out to students that a variety of variables are used as indices in the problems.

Example 1

Write $\sum_{i=1}^{4} 3i$ in expanded form and find the value of this sum.

Solution

In this example, $a_i = 3i$ for each integer i. $\sum_{i=1}^{4} 3i$ is the sum of all the numbers $3i$ as i takes on integer values from 1 to 4. Consequently,

$$\begin{aligned}\sum_{i=1}^{4} 3i &= 3 \cdot 1 + 3 \cdot 2 + 3 \cdot 3 + 3 \cdot 4 \qquad \text{expanded form}\\ &= 3 + 6 + 9 + 12\\ &= 30.\end{aligned}$$

Writing Sums in More Than One Way

A given sum can be expressed in summation notation in more than one way. The index i of the sum can be replaced by any other variable without changing the meaning of the sum as long as the replacement is made every place in the sum where the index occurs. For example,

$$\sum_{i=2}^{5} 2^i = \sum_{n=2}^{5} 2^n = 2^2 + 2^3 + 2^4 + 2^5.$$

Furthermore, this sum can be denoted by

$$\sum_{i=1}^{4} 2^{i+1}$$

because $\quad 2^{1+1} + 2^{2+1} + 2^{3+1} + 2^{4+1} = 2^2 + 2^3 + 2^4 + 2^5.$

In the next example, the upper value of the index variable is itself a variable.

Example 2

Consider the summation $\sum_{k=1}^{n} \frac{n+1}{n+k}$.

a. Write the expanded form of the summation for $n = 1$.
b. Write the expanded form for $n = 4$, and approximate its value.
c. Write the expanded form for arbitrary n.

Solution

a. The index variable k varies from 1 to 1, so it takes on only the single value 1:

$$\sum_{k=1}^{1} \frac{1+1}{1+k} = \frac{1+1}{1+1}.$$

b. $$\begin{aligned}\sum_{k=1}^{4} \frac{4+1}{4+k} &= \frac{4+1}{4+1} + \frac{4+1}{4+2} + \frac{4+1}{4+3} + \frac{4+1}{4+4}\\ &= \frac{5}{5} + \frac{5}{6} + \frac{5}{7} + \frac{5}{8} \approx 3.173\end{aligned}$$

c. The index variable k varies from 1 to n.

$$\begin{aligned}\sum_{k=1}^{n} \frac{n+1}{n+k} &= \frac{n+1}{n+1} + \frac{n+1}{n+2} + \frac{n+1}{n+3} + \ldots + \frac{n+1}{n+n}\\ &= 1 + \frac{n+1}{n+2} + \frac{n+1}{n+3} + \ldots + \frac{n+1}{2n}\end{aligned}$$

Optional Activities

For students adept at BASIC programming and the definition for summation notation, you may wish to ask them to write a BASIC segment which achieves the same purpose as $\sum_{i=M}^{N}$ notation. Then have the students share the BASIC program with the class.

[Sample program:
```
90   REM ASSUME ARRAY
     A(M), A(M + 1), ..., A(N) IS IN
     MEMORY
100  LET SUM = 0
110  FOR I = M TO N STEP 1
120  LET SUM = SUM + A(I)
130  NEXT I
140  PRINT
150  PRINT "THE SUM IS "; SUM]
```

In summation notation, the sum of the integers from 1 to n, $1 + 2 + 3 + \dots + n$, can be written as $\sum_{i=1}^{n} i$. You saw a recursive formula for this sum S_n in the last lesson.

$$\begin{cases} S_1 = 1 \\ S_{n+1} = S_n + (n + 1) \quad \text{for } n \geq 1 \end{cases}$$

In summation notation, the recurrence relation is

$$\sum_{i=1}^{n+1} i = \sum_{i=1}^{n} i + (n + 1).$$

More generally, consider a sum from the mth term to the $(k + 1)$st term.

$$\begin{aligned} \sum_{i=m}^{k+1} a_i &= a_m + a_{m+1} + \dots + a_k + a_{k+1} \\ &= [a_m + a_{m+1} + \dots + a_k] + a_{k+1} \\ &= \left(\sum_{i=m}^{k} a_i\right) + a_{k+1} \end{aligned}$$

This recurrence relation is satisfied by any sum. Replacing $\sum_{i=m}^{k+1} a_i$ by $\left(\sum_{i=m}^{k} a_i\right) + a_{k+1}$ is referred to as "writing the sum recursively."

QUESTIONS

Covering the Reading

In 1 and 2, a summation is given. **a.** Write the sum in expanded form. **b.** Evaluate the sum. **See left.**

1. $\sum_{k=0}^{3} (k^2 + 3k - 2)$ **2.** $\sum_{n=-4}^{-1} 2^n$

3. *True or false.* $\sum_{p=3}^{8} 4p = \sum_{k=3}^{8} 4k$. Justify your answer in one or two sentences. **See left.**

4. Write $1^2 + 2^2 + 3^2 + \dots + 43^2$ using summation notation. $\sum_{i=1}^{43} i^2$

5. Consider the sum $\frac{1}{2} + \frac{1}{3} + \frac{1}{4} + \dots + \frac{1}{k+1}$.
a. Write using summation notation.
b. Write the sum recursively.

6. Note that the terms of the sequence of times in Zeno's Paradox are powers of $\frac{1}{2}$. **See margin.**
a. Use summation notation to write the sum of the first 5 terms.
b. Use summation notation to write the sum of the first n terms.

7. Refer to Example 2.
a. Find the value of the sum if $n = 3$. $\frac{37}{15} \approx 2.47$
b. Write $\sum_{k=n-1}^{n+1} \frac{n+1}{n+k}$ in expanded form.
$\frac{n+1}{2n-1} + \frac{n+1}{2n} + \frac{n+1}{2n+1}$

1a) $-2 + 2 + 8 + 16$
b) 24

2a) $2^{-4} + 2^{-3} + 2^{-2} + 2^{-1}$
b) $\frac{15}{16}$

3) True, the only difference is that different letters are used for the indices.

5a) $\sum_{j=1}^{k} \frac{1}{j+1}$

b) $\begin{cases} S_1 = \frac{1}{2}, \\ S_{n+1} = S_n + \frac{1}{n+1}, \\ \forall \text{ integers } n \geq 1 \end{cases}$

You could expand **Example 1** to note the identity $\sum_{i=1}^{n} k \cdot f(i) = k \sum_{i=1}^{n} f(i)$. Here, $\sum_{i=1}^{4} 3i = 3\sum_{i=1}^{4} i$. Have students expand both expressions and add to convince themselves of the reasonableness of the identity.

There is nothing highlighted in the last paragraph of the lesson, and it may be ignored by students, but it is quite important for mathematical induction to be able to express the sum "to $k + 1$" in terms of the sum "to k." **Questions 5, 8b, and 9** cover this idea. Here is another example: Let $a_i = 3i + 1$. Then

$$\begin{aligned} \sum_{i=1}^{k+1} a_i &= (3 \cdot 1 + 1) + (3 \cdot 2 + 1) + \dots \\ &+ (3 \cdot k + 1) + [3(k + 1) + 1] \\ &= \left(\sum_{i=1}^{k} a_i\right) + a_{k+1}. \end{aligned}$$

Notes on Questions

Questions 5, 8b, and 9 These questions prepare students for the inductive step in proofs using the principle of Mathematical Induction.

Additional Answers

6. a. $\sum_{k=0}^{4} \left(\frac{1}{2}\right)^k$

b. $\sum_{j=0}^{n-1} \left(\frac{1}{2}\right)^j$

Adapting to Individual Needs

Extra Help

If students are not familiar with summation notation, you may wish to begin more slowly than with the definition on page 413. Start first with a few examples in expanded form. Point out that there is a pattern in the expansion that can be expressed with a variable whose values increase by 1. The final step is an expression in summation notation.

You may wish to use the following.

Example: $1 + 2 + 3 + 4 + 5 = \sum_{i=1}^{5} i$

Example: $2 + 4 + 8 + 16 + 32 = 2^1 + 2^2 + 2^3 + 2^4 + 2^5 = \sum_{i=1}^{5} 2^i$

Example: $\frac{1}{2} + \frac{1}{4} + \frac{1}{8} + \frac{1}{16} + \frac{1}{32} = \frac{1}{2^1} + \frac{1}{2^2} + \frac{1}{2^3} + \frac{1}{2^4} + \frac{1}{2^5} = \sum_{i=1}^{5} \frac{1}{2^i}$

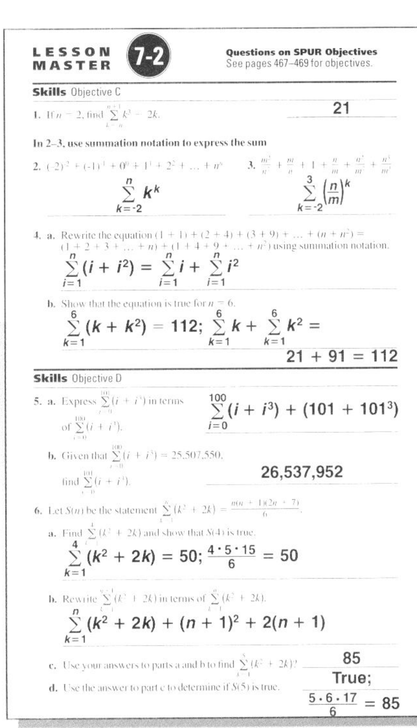
LESSON MASTER 7-2 **Questions on SPUR Objectives** See pages 467–469 for objectives.

Skills Objective C

1. If $n = 2$, find $\sum_{k=n}^{n+1} k^3 - 2k$. **21**

In 2–3, use summation notation to express the sum

2. $(-2)^{-2} + (-1)^{-1} + 0^0 + 1^1 + 2^2 + \dots + n^n$ $\sum_{k=-2}^{n} k^k$

3. $\frac{m^2}{n^2} + \frac{m}{n} + 1 + \frac{n}{m} + \frac{n^2}{m^2} + \frac{n^3}{m^3}$ $\sum_{k=-2}^{3} \left(\frac{n}{m}\right)^k$

4. a. Rewrite the equation $(1 + 1) + (2 + 4) + (3 + 9) + \dots + (n + n^2) = (1 + 2 + 3 + \dots + n) + (1 + 4 + 9 + \dots + n^2)$ using summation notation.
$\sum_{i=1}^{n} (i + i^2) = \sum_{i=1}^{n} i + \sum_{i=1}^{n} i^2$

b. Show that the equation is true for $n = 6$.
$\sum_{k=1}^{6} (k + k^2) = 112;\ \sum_{k=1}^{6} k + \sum_{k=1}^{6} k^2 = 21 + 91 = 112$

Skills Objective D

5. a. Express $\sum_{i=0}^{101} (i + i^3)$ in terms of $\sum_{i=0}^{100} (i + i^3)$. $\sum_{i=0}^{100} (i + i^3) + (101 + 101^3)$

b. Given that $\sum_{i=0}^{100} (i + i^3) = 25{,}507{,}550$, find $\sum_{i=0}^{101} (i + i^3)$. **26,537,952**

6. Let $S(n)$ be the statement $\sum_{k=1}^{n} (k^2 + 2k) = \frac{n(n+1)(2n+7)}{6}$.

a. Find $\sum_{k=1}^{4} (k^2 + 2k)$ and show that $S(4)$ is true.
$\sum_{k=1}^{4} (k^2 + 2k) = 50;\ \frac{4 \cdot 5 \cdot 15}{6} = 50$

b. Rewrite $\sum_{k=1}^{n+1} (k^2 + 2k)$ in terms of $\sum_{k=1}^{n} (k^2 + 2k)$.
$\sum_{k=1}^{n} (k^2 + 2k) + (n + 1)^2 + 2(n + 1)$

c. Use your answers to parts a and b to find $\sum_{k=1}^{5} (k^2 + 2k)$? **85**

d. Use the answer to part c to determine if $S(5)$ is true. **True;** $\frac{5 \cdot 6 \cdot 17}{6} = 85$

Additional Examples

1. Write $\sum_{i=1}^{4}(4i + i^2)$ in expanded form and find the value of this sum.
$\sum_{i=1}^{4}(4i + i^2) =$
$(4 \cdot 1 + 1^2) + (4 \cdot 2 + 2^2) +$
$(4 \cdot 3 + 3^2) + (4 \cdot 4 + 4^2) =$
$5 + 12 + 21 + 32 = 70$

2. Consider the sum $\sum_{k=1}^{n} \frac{n(k+1)}{(k+2)}$.
   a. Write the expanded form of the sum for $n = 1$.
   $\sum_{k=1}^{1} \frac{n(k+1)}{(k+2)} = \frac{1(1+1)}{(1+2)}$
   b. Write the expanded form of the sum for $n = 4$, and approximate its value.
   $\sum_{k=1}^{4} \frac{n(k+1)}{(k+2)} = \frac{4(1+1)}{(1+2)} +$
   $\frac{4(2+1)}{(2+2)} + \frac{4(3+1)}{(3+2)} + \frac{4(4+1)}{(4+2)} =$
   12.2
   c. Write the expanded form of the sum for arbitrary n.
   $\sum_{k=1}^{n} \frac{n(k+1)}{(k+2)} = \frac{n(1+1)}{(1+2)} +$
   $\frac{n(2+1)}{(2+2)} + \frac{n(3+1)}{(3+2)} + \ldots + \frac{n(n+1)}{(n+2)}$

Notes on Questions

Question 11 This question illustrates a general property for summation notation:

$\sum_{i=1}^{n}[a\,f(i) + b\,g(i)] =$

$a\sum_{i=1}^{n} f(i) + b\sum_{i=1}^{n} g(i)$

Question 20 This question gives practice in the algebraic manipulation needed for proving some statements using the Principle of Mathematical Induction.

8a) 1; 5: 14; 30
b) $\sum_{i=1}^{k+1} i^2 = 1^2 + 2^2 + \ldots + k^2 + (k+1)^2 = (1^2 + 2^2 + \ldots + k^2) + (k+1)^2 = \left(\sum_{i=1}^{k} i^2\right) + (k+1)^2$

10) $\sum_{j=1}^{4} (j^2 + j - 4)$

13) Sample: Let $a_n = 1$ $\forall n$. Then $\sum_{n=1}^{4} (a_n)^2 = 1^2 + 1^2 + 1^2 + 1^2 = 4$, and $\left(\sum_{n=1}^{4} a_n\right)^2 = (1 + 1 + 1 + 1)^2 = 16$

8. Consider the sequence defined by $a_i = i^2$. **See left.**
   a. Compute $\sum_{i=1}^{n} a_i$ for $n = 1, 2, 3$, and 4.
   b. Explain why $\sum_{i=1}^{k+1} i^2 = \left(\sum_{i=1}^{k} i^2\right) + (k+1)^2$ for each integer $k \geq 1$.

9. Write the sum $\sum_{i=1}^{k+1} i(i-1)$ recursively. $\left(\sum_{i=1}^{k} i(i-1)\right) + (k+1)k$

Applying the Mathematics

10. Express the sum in Question 1 in summation notation with an index j that varies from 1 to 4. **See left.**

11. Determine whether or not $\sum_{i=1}^{4} (i^3 + 5i) = \sum_{i=1}^{4} i^3 + 5\sum_{i=1}^{4} i$. **It does.**

12. Show that $\sum_{k=1}^{5} \left(\frac{1}{k} - \frac{1}{k+1}\right) = 1 - \frac{1}{6}$. (Hint: This problem is easier if you do not simplify the terms.) **See margin.**

13. Find a sequence S with $\sum_{n=1}^{4} (S_n^2) \neq \left(\sum_{n=1}^{4} S_n\right)^2$. **See left.**

14. Consider the computer program below.

```
10 SUM = 0
20 FOR I = -5 TO 5
30   SUM = SUM + .1 * (I/10)^2
40 NEXT I
50 PRINT SUM
60 END
```

In summation notation, write the expression this program evaluates.
$\frac{1}{1000}\sum_{i=-5}^{5} i^2$

Review

15. Tell whether the definition of the sequence $a_n = \begin{cases} 1 \text{ if } n \text{ is even} \\ -1 \text{ if } n \text{ is odd} \end{cases}$ is recursive or explicit, and write the first six terms of the sequence. *(Lesson 7-1)* **explicit; -1, 1, -1, 1, -1, 1**

16. a. Explain why there is no sequence that satisfies the recursive definition
$\begin{cases} x_1 = 0 \\ x_{n+1} = \frac{1}{x_n} \quad \text{for all integers } n \geq 1. \end{cases}$
a) x_2 is not defined since $x_2 = \frac{1}{0}$.
   b. Why does this not contradict the Recursion Principle? *(Lesson 7-1)*
   The definition defines the first term and defines each successive term in terms of the preceding term.

Adapting to Individual Needs

Challenge
In a book of tables find formulas for simplifying $\sum_{i=1}^{n} i^k$, for $k = 1$ through 10. (The first 3 of these will be discussed in Lessons 7-3 and 7-4.)
a. Each formula is a polynomial. What is the degree? [$k + 1$]
b. Which of these polynomials is divisible by $n + 1$? by $2n + 1$? [All; when k is even]

Additional Answers

12. $\sum_{k=1}^{5}\left(\frac{1}{k} - \frac{1}{k+1}\right)$
$= \left(1 - \frac{1}{2}\right) + \left(\frac{1}{2} - \frac{1}{3}\right) + \left(\frac{1}{3} - \frac{1}{4}\right) + \left(\frac{1}{4} - \frac{1}{5}\right) + \left(\frac{1}{5} - \frac{1}{6}\right)$
$= 1 + \left(-\frac{1}{2} + \frac{1}{2}\right) + \left(-\frac{1}{3} + \frac{1}{3}\right) + \left(-\frac{1}{4} + \frac{1}{4}\right) + \left(-\frac{1}{5} + \frac{1}{5}\right) - \frac{1}{6}$
$= 1 + 0 + 0 + 0 + 0 - \frac{1}{6} = 1 - \frac{1}{6}$

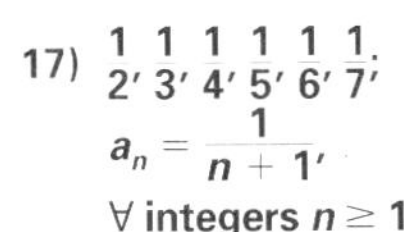
17) $\frac{1}{2}, \frac{1}{3}, \frac{1}{4}, \frac{1}{5}, \frac{1}{6}, \frac{1}{7}$; $a_n = \frac{1}{n+1}$, $\forall$ integers $n \geq 1$

17. Consider the sequence defined recursively by

$$\begin{cases} a_1 = \frac{1}{2} \\ a_{k+1} = \frac{k+1}{k+2} a_k \quad \forall \text{ integers } k \geq 1. \end{cases}$$

Write the first six terms of the sequence and conjecture an explicit formula for a_n. *(Lesson 7-1)* **See left.**

18. Newton's Law of Cooling states that the change in temperature of an object per unit of time is equal to a constant multiplied by the temperature difference between the object and the surrounding air. Suppose that a cake is removed from a 325°F oven and placed in a 75°F room. The cake's temperature decreases each minute by an amount equal to .05 times the difference in temperature between the cake and the room at the beginning of the minute. Let T_k be the temperature of the cake at the beginning of the kth minute. **a) See margin.**

a. Write a recursive definition for the sequence $T_1, T_2, T_3, \ldots$.

b. Use the result from part **a** to find the cake's temperature (to the nearest degree) at the beginning of the fifth minute. *(Lesson 7-1)* **279°**

19. Prove: $\forall$ *real numbers x and y*, $\sin^2 x - \sin^2 y = \cos^2 y - \cos^2 x$. *(Lesson 6-2)* **See margin.**

20. Write the following expression as a single fraction in factored form: $\frac{k}{2k+1} + \frac{1}{(2k-1)(2k+1)}$. *(Lesson 5-1)* $\mathbf{\frac{2k^2 - k + 1}{(2k+1)(2k-1)}}$

21. Let $f(k) = k + 1$ and $g(k) = \frac{k(k+1)}{2}$ for all real numbers k. Write a formula for $g \circ f$. *(Lesson 3-2)* $\mathbf{(g \circ f)(k) = \frac{(k+1)(k+2)}{2}}$

Exploration

22. Find out something about a paradox of Zeno that is different from the paradox mentioned in this lesson. **Sample: The Arrow Paradox states that an arrow never moves, because at each instant the arrow is in a fixed position. Another of Zeno's paradoxes, known as the Paradox of Achilles and the Tortoise, is frequently summarized as follows. Achilles, who could run 10 yards per second, competed against a tortoise which ran 1 yard per second. In order to make the race more fair, the tortoise was given a headstart of 10 yards. Zeno's argument, that Achilles could never pass the tortoise, was based on the "fact" that whenever Achilles reached a certain point where the tortoise had been, the tortoise would have moved ahead of that point.**

Practice

For more questions on SPUR Objectives, use **Lesson Master 7-2** (shown on page 415).

Assessment

Written Communication Have students choose one of **Questions 5, 6,** or **9** in Lesson 7-1. Then have them use summation notation to designate the sum of the first six terms of the sequence. [Students use summation notation to write sums.]

Extension

Have students generalize their solution to **Question 12.** That is, have them find $\sum_{k=1}^{n} \left(\frac{1}{k} - \frac{1}{k+1}\right)$. $[1 - \frac{1}{n+1}]$

Additional Answers

18. a. $T_1 = 325$, $T_{k+1} = 0.95T_k + 3.75$, $\forall$ integers $k \geq 1$

19. Left side $= \sin^2 x - \sin^2 y$
$= (1 - \cos^2 x) - (1 - \cos^2 y)$
$= 1 - \cos^2 x - 1 + \cos^2 y$
$= \cos^2 y - \cos^2 x$
$=$ Right side
$\therefore \forall$ real numbers x and y, $\sin^2 x - \sin^2 y = \cos^2 y - \cos^2 x$.

Setting Up Lesson 7-3

You may wish to use Lesson 7-3 as a two-day lesson. On the first day, you may want to discuss the lesson up to **Example 3.** Have students complete **Questions 1–8** for homework. On the second day, discuss **Example 3** and have students complete **Questions 9–17.** Be careful not to spend more than a couple of days on this lesson. Students will have opportunities in the remainder of the chapter to practice mathematical induction.

To prepare students for the use of a sequence of statements in Lesson 7-3, let $p(n)$ be the sentence $\sum_{k=1}^{n} (2k - 1) = n^2$.

1. Show that $p(1)$ is true. $[\sum_{k=1}^{1} (2k - 1) = 2(1) - 1 = 1^2]$
2. Write $p(i)$. $[\sum_{k=1}^{i} (2k - 1) = i^2]$
3. Write $p(i + 1)$. $[\sum_{k=1}^{i+1} (2k - 1) = (i + 1)^2]$

Lesson 7-3

Objectives

F Prove that a recursively defined sequence has a particular explicit formula.
G Prove statements involving sums using the Principle of Mathematical Induction.
J Interpret computer programs which calculate terms of sequences.

Resources

From the ***Teacher's Resource File***
- Lesson Master 7-3
- Answer Master 7-3
- Teaching Aid 62: Warm-up

Additional Resources
- Visual for Teaching Aid 62

Teaching Lesson 7-3

Warm-up

Suppose $p(k)$ is the statement $2^k > 2^{k-1}$.

1. Is the statement true when $k = 1$? **Yes**
2. What is the statement $p(k + 1)$? $\mathbf{2^{k+1} > 2^k}$
3. Explain why $p(k)$ implies $p(k + 1)$. **If $2^k > 2^{k-1}$, then $2 \cdot 2^k > 2 \cdot 2^{k-1}$. Thus $2^{k+1} > 2^k$.**

LESSON

7-3

The Principle of Mathematical Induction

Induction Is Not Mathematical Induction

Induction is the use of inductive reasoning to arrive at a generalization. We pointed out in Lesson 1-7 that induction is not a valid method of proof but it is very useful in coming up with conjectures. In Lesson 7-1, we used induction to conjecture that the sequence with $T_1 = 1$ and $T_{k+1} = 2T_k + 1$ had the explicit formula $T_n = 2^n - 1$. Then we used *de*duction to prove that this formula did in fact hold for all integers n.

Mathematical induction is not the same as induction. Mathematical induction refers to a valid proof argument form that is closely related to recursion.

The idea of mathematical induction is often illustrated as follows. Imagine a row of dominoes lined up in such a way that for each integer $k \geq 1$, if the kth domino falls over then it causes the $(k + 1)$st domino to fall over also. Now what happens if you push the first domino over? All the dominoes will fall.

The *Principle of Mathematical Induction* is a postulate of logic. It cannot be deduced from the logical principles you studied in Chapter 1.

> **Principle of Mathematical Induction**
> Let $S(n)$ be a sentence in n. If
> (1) $S(1)$ is true, and
> (2) for all integers $k \geq 1$, the assumption that $S(k)$ is true implies that $S(k + 1)$ is true, then $S(n)$ is true for all positive integers n.

Lesson 7-3 Overview

Broad Goals This lesson introduces mathematical induction and uses the Principle of Mathematical Induction to deduce some summation formulas.

Perspective The Principle of Mathematical Induction is, in some sense, a statement that modus ponens can be used infinitely many times simultaneously. Because it involves the infinite, and other logical principles do not, it is independent of them. Thus, in rigorous developments of mathematics from first principles, some postulate equivalent to the Principle of Mathematical Induction is needed. Some books assume the *well-ordering principle,* that every nonempty set of positive integers has a least element, and then deduce mathematical induction. We go directly to mathematical induction because the background has been set up for it in the preceding lessons. The analogy between recursive definitions and mathematical induction is drawn and the Recursion Principle proved. In this lesson, mathematical induction is employed to prove a formula for the sum of the first n odd integers and for the sum of a particular sequence of reciprocals.

The Two Steps of Mathematical Induction

Verification of (1) (pushing the first domino) is called the **basis step** of the induction, and verification of (2) (if the kth domino falls, so will the $(k + 1)$st) is called the **inductive step**. Note that (2) is a universal conditional statement. It is proved with a direct proof. You

> *suppose* that $S(k)$ is true for a particular but arbitrarily chosen integer $k \geq 1$,

and then you

> *show* that the supposition that $S(k)$ is true implies that $S(k + 1)$ is true.

The supposition that $S(k)$ is true is called the **inductive assumption**.

Example 1

Use the Principle of Mathematical Induction to prove that the sum of the first n positive odd integers is n^2. That is, prove that

$$1 + 3 + 5 \ldots + (2n - 1) = n^2 \qquad \text{for all integers } n \geq 1,$$

or in summation notation,

$$\sum_{i=1}^{n} (2i - 1) = n^2 \qquad \text{for all integers } n \geq 1.$$

Solution

First identify $S(n)$. In this case $S(n)$ is $\sum_{i=1}^{n} (2i - 1) = n^2$.

(1) Basis step: Show that $S(1)$ is true.
When $n = 1$, the left side of $S(1)$ is $2 \cdot 1 - 1$, which is 1, and the right side is 1^2. Hence the two sides of the equation are equal when $n = 1$, and so $S(1)$ is true.

(2) Inductive step: Show that the assumption that $S(k)$ is true implies that $S(k + 1)$ is true.
Suppose that $S(k)$ is true for a particular but arbitrarily chosen integer $k \geq 1$. That is, suppose

$$S(k): \sum_{i=1}^{k} (2i - 1) = k^2. \quad \text{This is the inductive assumption.}$$

Now deduce $S(k + 1)$, where

$$S(k + 1): \sum_{i=1}^{k+1} (2i - 1) = (k + 1)^2.$$

Begin with the left side of $S(k + 1)$, and use algebra and the inductive assumption to transform it into the right side of $S(k + 1)$.

$$\sum_{i=1}^{k+1} (2i - 1) = \left(\sum_{i=1}^{k} (2i - 1)\right) + 2(k + 1) - 1 \qquad \text{Write the sum recursively.}$$

$$= \left(\sum_{i=1}^{k} (2i - 1)\right) + 2k + 1 \qquad \text{Simplify.}$$

$$= k^2 + (2k + 1) \qquad \text{Use the inductive assumption (the supposition that } S(k) \text{ is true).}$$

$$= (k + 1)^2 \qquad \text{Factor.}$$

Therefore, for all integers $k \geq 1$, if $S(k)$ is true, then $S(k + 1)$ is true. Thus, from (1) and (2) above, using the Principle of Mathematical Induction, $S(n)$ is true for all integers $n \geq 1$.

Notes on Reading

In order to understand mathematical induction, students need (1) to apply the $S(n)$ notation of propositions and (2) to realize the significance of the two parts of the induction proof. Both of these prerequisites are new. Students have seen the notation of (1) since Lesson 1-1 and their work with recursive definitions makes (2) more reasonable. Still, the form of mathematical induction proofs is different from other proofs students have encountered, and the algebraic manipulation is also different, and so mathematical induction is often difficult for students the first time they study it. Do not expect mastery at first. You should have almost two weeks between this lesson and the test.

Begin by clarifying the language. *Improper induction* is the invalid argument form by which a generalization is made from specific examples. The *Principle of Mathematical induction* is the valid argument form studied in this lesson. A proof utilizing the Principle of Mathematical Induction is called a *mathematical induction* proof, or a proof "by mathematical induction." All of these terms are sometimes called *induction.* When a mathematician speaks of "reasoning by induction," what is always meant is "by mathematical induction."

The two steps needed for a mathematical induction proof are given on page 418. The basis step provides a starting point, an instance for which $S(n)$ is known to be true. The inductive statement is a universal conditional statement. The inductive assumption, that $S(k)$ is true for some arbitrarily chosen $k \geq 1$, is used to show that $S(k + 1)$ is true. Once the universal conditional statement is known to be true, it can be used with the basis step to create a series of simultaneous

Optional Activities

After students have done several of the problems in the lesson, show them this "proof" and ask them to identify the error.

Conjecture: For all integers $n \geq 1$,

$$\sum_{i=1}^{n} p^i = \frac{p^{n+1} - 1}{p - 1}$$

Proof: Suppose $\sum_{i=1}^{k} p^i = \frac{p^{k+1} - 1}{p - 1}$

We need to show $\sum_{i=1}^{k+1} p^i = \frac{p^{k+2} - 1}{p - 1}$.

$$\sum_{i=1}^{k+1} p^i = \frac{p^{k+1} - 1}{p - 1} + p^{k+1}$$

$$= \frac{p^{k+1} - 1}{p - 1} + \frac{p^{k+1}(p - 1)}{p - 1}$$

$$= \frac{p^{k+1} - 1 + p^{k+2} - p^{k+1}}{p - 1}$$

$$= \frac{p^{k+2} - 1}{p - 1}$$

[The basis step, when $n = 1$, has not been tested. When it is, we get $p = p + 1$, which is not true! This error emphasizes the importance of the basis step, which students so many times omit.]

modus ponens arguments. In this way, $S(n)$ is shown to be true for all positive integers greater than or equal to the value of n used in the basis step.

Take advantage of the comparison with recursive definitions on page 420. You may also liken the Principle of Mathematical Induction to climbing an infinite staircase. To prove that you'll be able to make that climb you must do two things:

1. Show that you can climb the first step.
2. Assuming that you can climb the kth step show that you'll be able to climb step $k + 1$ also.

Students may be quite familiar with a set of dominoes so arranged that pushing one will topple the entire set. There are toys with this property and people have been shown on television who have arranged thousands of dominoes in this way. The weakness of the domino metaphor is that it takes time for all the dominoes to fall, whereas when the Principle of Mathematical Induction is applied, the truth of $S(n)$ for all integers $n \geq 1$ is established simultaneously.

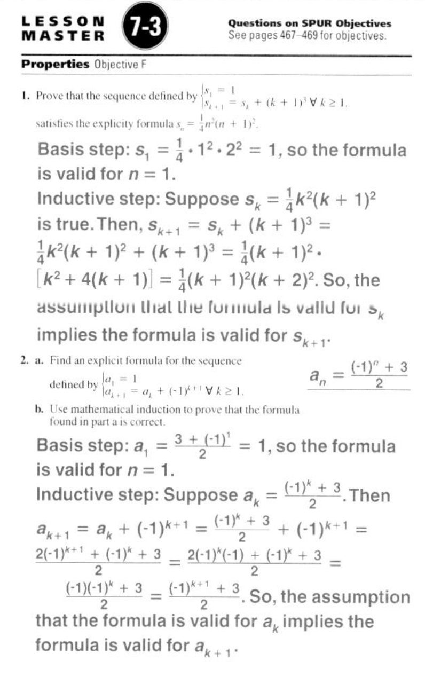

LESSON MASTER 7-3 **Questions on SPUR Objectives** See pages 467–469 for objectives.

Properties Objective F

1. Prove that the sequence defined by $\begin{cases} s_1 = 1 \\ s_{k+1} = s_k + (k+1)^3 \ \forall k \geq 1. \end{cases}$ satisfies the explicity formula $s_n = \frac{1}{4}n^2(n+1)^2$.

Basis step: $s_1 = \frac{1}{4} \cdot 1^2 \cdot 2^2 = 1$, so the formula is valid for $n = 1$.
Inductive step: Suppose $s_k = \frac{1}{4}k^2(k+1)^2$ is true. Then, $s_{k+1} = s_k + (k+1)^3 = \frac{1}{4}k^2(k+1)^2 + (k+1)^3 = \frac{1}{4}(k+1)^2 \cdot [k^2 + 4(k+1)] = \frac{1}{4}(k+1)^2(k+2)^2$. So, the assumption that the formula is valid for s_k implies the formula is valid for s_{k+1}.

2. a. Find an explicit formula for the sequence defined by $\begin{cases} a_1 = 1 \\ a_{k+1} = a_k + (-1)^{k+1} \ \forall k \geq 1. \end{cases}$ $a_n = \frac{(-1)^n + 3}{2}$

b. Use mathematical induction to prove that the formula found in part a is correct.

Basis step: $a_1 = \frac{3 + (-1)^1}{2} = 1$, so the formula is valid for $n = 1$.
Inductive step: Suppose $a_k = \frac{(-1)^k + 3}{2}$. Then $a_{k+1} = a_k + (-1)^{k+1} = \frac{(-1)^k + 3}{2} + (-1)^{k+1} = \frac{2(-1)^{k+1} + (-1)^k + 3}{2} = \frac{2(-1)^k(-1) + (-1)^k + 3}{2} = \frac{(-1)(-1)^k + 3}{2} = \frac{(-1)^{k+1} + 3}{2}$. So, the assumption that the formula is valid for a_k implies the formula is valid for a_{k+1}.

Mathematical Induction and the Recursion Principle

Proving by mathematical induction is quite similar to the thinking behind the Recursion Principle. Compare the processes.

Mathematical Induction	Recursion Principle
$S(n)$ is a proposition.	*a_n is a term of a sequence.*
Basis step: $S(1)$ is true.	Initial condition: a_1 has a particular value.
Inductive step: $S(k + 1)$ is proved from $S(k)$.	Recurrence relation: a_{k+1} is defined in terms of a_k.
Result: $S(n)$ is true for all integers $n \geq 1$.	Result: a_n is defined for all integers $n \geq 1$.

Because of the similarity between them, it is natural to use mathematical induction to prove the Recursion Principle. Here is the principle restated and with its mathematical induction proof.

Recursion Principle
Suppose that a recurrence relation defines x_{n+1} in terms of x_n and n for each integer $n \geq 1$. Then there is exactly one sequence X defined by this recurrence relation and the initial condition $x_1 = a$.

Proof
Suppose that there is a second sequence Y in which $y_1 = a$ and y_{n+1} is defined by the same recurrence relation as x_{n+1}. We need to show that $x_n = y_n$ for all positive integers n. Thus in the situation here, $S(n)$ is the statement $x_n = y_n$.

(1) Basis step: Show that $S(1)$ is true.
$S(1)$ is the statement $x_1 = y_1$. It is true because $x_1 = a$ and $y_1 = a$. That is, both sequences have the same initial condition.

(2) Inductive step: Show that the assumption that $S(k)$ is true implies that $S(k + 1)$ is true.
$S(k)$ is the statement that $x_k = y_k$. Since the sequences have the same recurrence relation and since x_{k+1} is defined in terms of x_k and k, and y_{k+1} is defined in terms of y_k and k, $x_{k+1} = y_{k+1}$. Thus $S(k + 1)$ is true.

By the Principle of Mathematical Induction, $S(n)$ is true for every positive integer n. Consequently, $x_n = y_n$ for all integers n. So the sequences X and Y are identical. So there cannot be two different sequences defined by this recurrence relation and initial condition.

Although the correctness of an explicit formula for a recursively defined sequence can be proved using the Recursion Principle, it is very common to use a mathematical induction proof to achieve the same purpose. On the next page is the problem of Example 4, Lesson 7-1, recast in the language of mathematical induction.

420

Adapting to Individual Needs

Extra Help

Alternate Approach For some students **Example 1**'s use of Σ-notation is somewhat overwhelming. Some initial expansions will be helpful. Detail the Σs needed. An example is given below.

$S(n)$ is $\sum_{i=1}^{n}(2i - 1) = (2 \cdot 1 - 1) + (2 \cdot 2 - 1) + (2 \cdot 3 - 1) + \ldots + (2 \cdot n - 1) = n^2$.

We are to prove that $S(n)$ is true for all integers $n \geq 1$.

$S(1)$ is $\sum_{i=1}^{n}(2 \cdot i - 1) = 2 \cdot 1 - 1 = 1^2$

$S(k)$ is $\sum_{i=1}^{k}(2i - 1) = (2 \cdot 1 - 1) + (2 \cdot 2 - 1) + (2 \cdot 3 - 1) + \ldots + (2k - 1) = k^2$,

which is assumed true in the inductive assumption.

Example 2

The sequence 1, 3, 7, 15, 31, 63, . . . is defined recursively as follows:

$$\begin{cases} T_1 = 1 \\ T_{k+1} = 2T_k + 1 \quad \text{for all integers } k \geq 1. \end{cases}$$

Use mathematical induction to prove that an explicit formula for the sequence is

$$T_n = 2^n - 1 \qquad \text{for all integers } n \geq 1.$$

Solution

In this case, $S(n)$ is the explicit formula $T_n = 2^n - 1$.

(1) Basis step: Show that $S(1)$ is true.

When $n = 1$, the formula is $T_1 = 2^1 - 1 = 1$. This agrees with the recursive definition of the sequence. Hence $S(1)$ is true.

(2) Inductive step: Show that the assumption that $S(k)$ is true implies that $S(k + 1)$ is true.

Suppose that $S(k)$ is true for a particular but arbitrarily chosen integer $k \geq 1$. That is, suppose

$S(k)$: $T_k = 2^k - 1$. inductive assumption

Now deduce $S(k + 1)$, where

$S(k + 1)$: $T_{k+1} = 2^{k+1} - 1$.

Transform the left side of $S(k + 1)$ into the right side using the inductive assumption.

$T_{k+1} = 2T_k + 1$	recursive definition of the sequence
$= 2(2^k - 1) + 1$	Substitute from the inductive assumption.
$= 2^{k+1} - 2 + 1$	Distributive Property
$= 2^{k+1} - 1$	Simplify.

Therefore, for all integers $k \geq 1$, if $S(k)$ is true, then $S(k + 1)$ is true.

Thus, from (1) and (2) above, using the Principle of Mathematical Induction, $S(n)$ is true for all integers $n \geq 1$.

Starting Mathematical Induction at an Integer Other Than 1

Above, the Principle of Mathematical Induction was stated as a way to deduce that a proposition $S(n)$ is true for all natural numbers 1, 2, 3, ... However, the set of integers for which $S(n)$ is defined or true need not start at 1. To prove $S(n)$ is true for all integers $\geq m$, begin by proving that $S(m)$ is true, and then prove that for all integers $k \geq m$, the assumption that $S(k)$ is true implies that $S(k + 1)$ is true. Example 3 illustrates this technique.

Error Alert Students have trouble understanding the inductive step. It bothers them that we assume the formula to be true for $n = k$. Relate this step to the domino experiment. It is akin to placing the dominoes carefully. If we place the dominoes so that the kth domino causes the $(k + 1)$st domino to fall, then all the dominoes will fall if we just topple the first. Giving the push is akin to showing the statement $S(1)$ is true.

After completing a proof by mathematical induction, be sure to summarize why the proof is complete. Students may not realize that they have completed the proof.

The formula for **Example 1** can be illustrated as shown below.

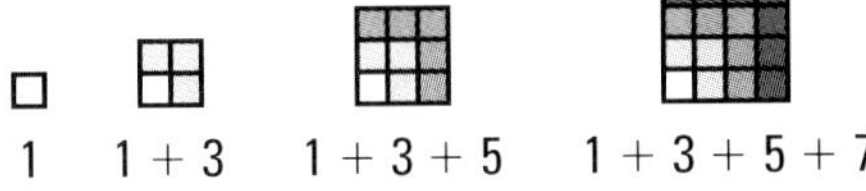

1 $\quad 1 + 3 \quad 1 + 3 + 5 \quad 1 + 3 + 5 + 7$

Notice that in **Examples 1–3**, we explicitly write the statement $S(n)$. At that point we have not established that $S(n)$ is true for any value of n. Before beginning, it is good to write down the statement $S(1)$ to be used in the basis step, the inductive assumption $S(k)$ and the conclusion $S(k + 1)$ to be proved from the assumption.

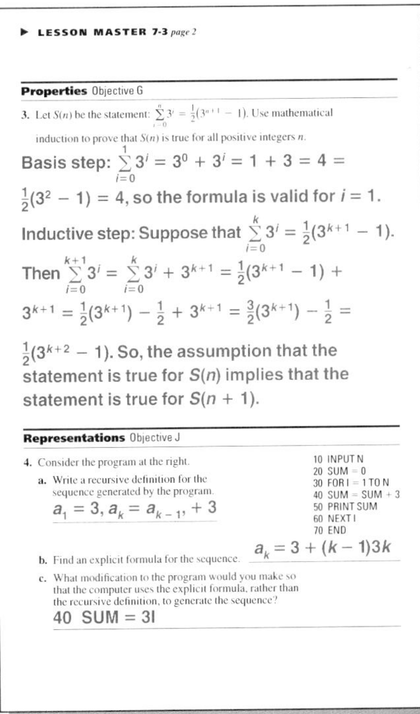

▶ **LESSON MASTER 7-3** *page 2*

Properties Objective G

3. Let $S(n)$ be the statement: $\sum_{i=0}^{n} 3^i = \frac{1}{2}(3^{n+1} - 1)$. Use mathematical induction to prove that $S(n)$ is true for all positive integers n.

Basis step: $\sum_{i=0}^{1} 3^i = 3^0 + 3^i = 1 + 3 = 4 = \frac{1}{2}(3^2 - 1) = 4$, so the formula is valid for $i = 1$.

Inductive step: Suppose that $\sum_{i=0}^{k} 3^i = \frac{1}{2}(3^{k+1} - 1)$. Then $\sum_{i=0}^{k+1} 3^i = \sum_{i=0}^{k} 3^i + 3^{k+1} = \frac{1}{2}(3^{k+1} - 1) + 3^{k+1} = \frac{1}{2}(3^{k+1}) - \frac{1}{2} + 3^{k+1} = \frac{3}{2}(3^{k+1}) - \frac{1}{2} = \frac{1}{2}(3^{k+2} - 1)$. So, the assumption that the statement is true for $S(n)$ implies that the statement is true for $S(n + 1)$.

Representations Objective J

4. Consider the program at the right.

```
10 INPUT N
20 SUM = 0
30 FOR I = 1 TO N
40 SUM = SUM + 3
50 PRINT SUM
60 NEXT I
70 END
```

a. Write a recursive definition for the sequence generated by the program.
$a_1 = 3, a_k = a_{k-1}, + 3$

b. Find an explicit formula for the sequence. $a_k = 3 + (k - 1)3k$

c. What modification to the program would you make so that the computer uses the explicit formula, rather than the recursive definition, to generate the sequence?
40 SUM = 3I

$S(k + 1)$ is $\sum_{j=1}^{k+1} (2i - 1) = (2 \cdot 1 - 1) + (2 \cdot 2 - 1) + (2 \cdot 3 - 1) + \ldots + (2k - 1) + (2(k + 1) - 1) = (k + 1)^2$, which must be proved from the inductive assumption.

The left side of $S(k + 1)$ is $S(k) + 2k + 1 = k^2 + (2(k + 1) - 1) = k^2 + 2k - 1 = (k + 1)^2$. The substitution of k^2 for most of the expansion of $S(k + 1)$ is effective.

To prove the inductive step in **Example 1** to be true, many students may benefit from the following:

1. Expand $S(k)$'s summation expression.
2. Expand $S(k + 1)$'s summation expression.
3. Replace most of the expansion of $S(k + 1)$'s summation expression with the corresponding explicit expression of $S(k)$ (since this is assumed true).
4. Simplify the result of step 3 to show equality with the desired result.

The recursive use of summation from **Lesson 7-2** is used in **Examples 1 and 3** to rewrite the statement for $S(k+1)$ so that the inductive assumption can be used.

Example 2 returns to the discussion of recursively defined sequences in Lesson 7-1. Here we show how mathematical induction can be used to prove that the explicit formula conjectured for the sequence is correct. Students need to realize that because the sequence is defined recursively, $S(k+1)$ follows easily from $S(k)$.

Example 3 helps students realize that the basis step is not necessarily the verification that $S(1)$ is true. In this particular instance, $n = 2$ is the first integer for which the given statement is defined.

Additional Examples

1. By using the Principle of Mathematical Induction, prove that, for all integers $n \geq 1$, $\sum_{i=1}^{n} \frac{1}{i(i+1)} = \frac{n}{n+1}$.
   Let $S(n)$ be the equation above. When $n = 1$, both sides equal $\frac{1}{2}$, so $S(1)$ is true. If $S(k)$ is true for a particular but arbitrarily chosen integer $k \geq 1$, then $\sum_{i=1}^{k} \frac{1}{i(i+1)} = \frac{k}{k+1}$. Now begin with the left side of $S(k+1)$. $\sum_{i=1}^{k+1} \frac{1}{i(i+1)} = \sum_{i=1}^{k} \frac{1}{i(i+1)} + \frac{1}{(k+1)(k+2)} = \frac{k}{k+1} + \frac{1}{(k+1)(k+2)} = \frac{k^2+2k+1}{(k+1)(k+2)} = \frac{(k+1)^2}{(k+1)(k+2)} = \frac{k+1}{k+2}$ So, $S(k+1)$ is true. Now applying the Principle of Mathematical Induction, $S(n)$ is true for all $n \geq 1$.

2. A sequence t is defined recursively by $\begin{cases} t_1 = 2 \\ t_{n+1} = 3t_n + 2 \text{ for all } n > 1) \end{cases}$ Prove that $t_n = 3^n - 1$ for all integers $n \geq 1$.

Example 3

Use mathematical induction to prove

$$\frac{1}{2 \cdot 1} + \frac{1}{3 \cdot 2} + \frac{1}{4 \cdot 3} + \frac{1}{5 \cdot 4} + \ldots + \frac{1}{n(n-1)} = \frac{n-1}{n} \quad \text{for all integers } n \geq 2;$$

that is, prove that

$$\sum_{i=2}^{n} \frac{1}{i(i-1)} = \frac{n-1}{n} \quad \text{for all integers } n \geq 2.$$

Solution

Note that the summation begins with $i = 2$. In fact $\frac{1}{i(i-1)}$ is undefined for $i = 0$ and $i = 1$.

The statement $S(n)$ is $\sum_{i=2}^{n} \frac{1}{i(i-1)} = \frac{n-1}{n}$.

(1) Basis step: Show that $S(2)$ is true.

When $n = 2$, the left side of $S(2)$ is

$$\sum_{i=2}^{2} \frac{1}{i(i-1)} = \frac{1}{2(2-1)} = \frac{1}{2}$$

and the right side is $\frac{2-1}{2} = \frac{1}{2}$, also. Hence $S(2)$ is true.

Many people like to show that more than one value of $S(n)$ is true. This is not required in a mathematical induction proof but can help you have faith in the result. Here is $S(3)$:

$$\sum_{i=2}^{3} \frac{1}{i(i-1)} = \frac{2}{3}.$$

The left side is $\frac{1}{2 \cdot 1} + \frac{1}{3 \cdot 2}$, which equals $\frac{1}{2} + \frac{1}{6}$, which is $\frac{2}{3}$, so it checks.

(2) Inductive step: Show that the assumption that $S(k)$ is true implies that $S(k+1)$ is true.

Suppose that $S(k)$ is true for a particular but arbitrarily chosen integer $k \geq 2$, where

$$S(k): \sum_{i=2}^{k} \frac{1}{i(i-1)} = \frac{k-1}{k}. \quad \text{This is the inductive assumption.}$$

Now show that $S(k+1)$ is true, where

$$S(k+1): \sum_{i=2}^{k+1} \frac{1}{i(i-1)} = \frac{(k+1)-1}{k+1}.$$

▶

Adapting to Individual Needs

Challenge

1. Give an example of a proposition for which the Inductive Step can be shown to be true, but the Basis Step cannot be proven, so the proposition is false. [Sample: $n = n + 1$ for all n]
2. Give an example of a proposition for which the Basis Step can be shown to be true, but the Inductive Step cannot be proven, so the proposition is false. [Sample: $n^2 = n$, for all n]

Then have students share their work with the class so the significance of the chosen examples can be discussed.

Begin with the left side of $S(k+1)$ and use algebra and the inductive assumption to transform it into the right side of $S(k+1)$:

$\sum_{i=2}^{k+1} \frac{1}{i(i-1)} = \left(\sum_{i=2}^{k} \frac{1}{i(i-1)}\right) + \frac{1}{(k+1)(k+1-1)}$	Write the sum recursively.
$= \frac{k-1}{k} + \frac{1}{(k+1)k}$	Substitute from the inductive assumption.
$= \frac{(k+1)(k-1)}{(k+1)k} + \frac{1}{(k+1)k}$	Equivalent Fractions Property
$= \frac{k^2-1+1}{(k+1)k}$	Add fractions with a common denominator.
$= \frac{k^2}{(k+1)k}$	Simplify.
$= \frac{k}{k+1}$	Equivalent Fractions Property
$= \frac{(k+1)-1}{k+1}$	Rewrite in the form of $S(k+1)$.

Therefore, for all integers $k \geq 2$, $S(k)$ implies $S(k+1)$.

Thus, from (1) and (2) above, using the Principle of Mathematical Induction, $S(n)$ is true for all integers $n \geq 2$.

QUESTIONS

Covering the Reading

1b) **Assume that $S(k)$ is true for a particular but arbitrarily chosen integer $k \geq 1$ where $S(k)$: $\sum_{i=1}^{k} (2i-1) = k^2$**

1. Refer to Example 1, which proves the following statement:

$$1 + 3 + 5 + \ldots + (2n-1) = n^2 \quad \text{for all integers } n \geq 1.$$

   a. Identify the basis step. **$1 = 1^2$**
   b. Write the inductive assumption. **See left.**

2. Consider the equation **See margin.**

$$S(n): \sum_{i=1}^{n} 2i = n(n+1) \quad \text{for all integers } n \geq 1.$$

   a. Show that $S(1)$ is true.
   b. Write $S(k)$ and $S(k+1)$.
   c. Show that for any integer $k \geq 1$, $S(k) \Rightarrow S(k+1)$.
   d. What can you conclude from the results of parts **a–c**?

In 3–5, $S(n)$ is given. **a.** Write $S(1)$, $S(3)$, and $S(5)$. **b.** Which of these are true and which are false? **c.** Write $S(k+1)$. **See margin.**

3. $S(n)$: *3 is a factor of* $n^3 + 2n$.

4. $S(n)$: $n^2 + 4 < (n+1)^2$

5. $S(n)$: $\sum_{i=1}^{n} (3i-2) = \frac{n(3n-1)}{2}$

$S(n)$ is the statement that $t_n = 3^n - 1$. $S(1)$ is the statement that $t_1 = 3^1 - 1 = 2$. This is true by the recursive definition. Suppose $S(k)$ is true. Then $t_{k+1} = 3t_k + 2 = 3(3^k - 1) + 2 = 3^{k+1} - 1$. So $S(k+1)$ is true. Thus, by the Principle of Mathematical Induction, $S(n)$ is true for all $n \geq 1$.

3. Use mathematical induction to prove that $5 + 7 + 9 + \ldots + [5 + 2(n-1)] = n(n+4)$ for all integers $n \geq 1$. Let $S(n)$ be the above equation. $S(1) = 5 = 1 \cdot (1+4)$, so $S(1)$ is true. Suppose $S(k)$ is true. Then $5 + 7 + 9 + \ldots + [5 + 2(k-1)] = k(k+4)$. Add $5 + 2k$ to each side so that the left side becomes the left side of $S(k+1)$. Then $5 + 7 + 9 + \ldots + [5 + 2k] = k(k+4) + 5 + 2k = k^2 + 6k + 5 = (k+1)(k+1+4)$. So $S(k) \Rightarrow S(k+1)$ and, by the Principle of Mathematical Induction, $S(n)$ is true for all $n \geq 1$.

Notes on Questions

Question 1 This question may help identify students' difficulties with the content of the lesson.

Question 2 This question can serve as a model for mathematical induction. Focus on the induction steps. Work out all the algebra.

Questions 3–5 These questions help with needed steps in mathematical induction without going through complete proofs.

Question 4 This inequality shows that statements of the form $S(n)$ need not be addition formulas or equations.

Additional Answers

2. a. $\sum_{i=1}^{1} 2i = 2(1) = 2$ and $1(1+1) = 2$, so $S(1)$ is true.

b. $S(k)$: $\sum_{i=1}^{k} 2i = k(k+1)$;
$S(k+1)$: $\sum_{i=1}^{k+1} 2i = (k+1)(k+2)$

c. $\sum_{i=1}^{k+1} 2i = \sum_{i=1}^{k} 2i + 2(k+1) = k(k+1) + 2(k+1) = (k+1)(k+2)$, so $S(k+1)$ is true.

d. $S(n)$ is true $\forall$ integers $n \geq 1$.

3. a. $S(1)$: 3 is a factor of 3; $S(3)$: 3 is a factor of 33; $S(5)$: 3 is a factor of 135.

b. All are true.

c. $S(k+1)$: 3 is a factor of $(k+1)^3 + 2(k+1)$.

4. a. $S(1)$: $5 < 4$; $S(3)$: $13 < 16$; $S(5)$: $29 < 36$

b. $S(1)$ is false. $S(3)$ and $S(5)$ are true.

c. $S(k+1)$: $(k+1)^2 + 4 < (k+2)^2$

5. a. $S(1)$: $1 = \frac{1(2)}{2}$; $S(3)$: $1 + 4 + 7 = \frac{3(8)}{2}$; $S(5)$: $1 + 4 + 7 + 10 + 13 = \frac{5(14)}{2}$

b. All are true.

c. $S(k+1)$: $\sum_{i=1}^{k+1} (3i-2) = \frac{(k+1)(3k+2)}{2}$

Notes on Questions

Questions 6 and 10 If students have trouble, do **Question 6** first and ask them to complete **Question 10** by themselves. **Question 6** provides a start for **Question 10.**

(Notes on Questions continue on page 426.)

Additional Answers

7. b. **Assume that $S(k)$ is true for a particular but arbitrarily chosen integer $k \geq 1$.**
$S(k)$: $1^2 + 2^2 + \ldots + k^2 = \frac{k(k+1)(2k+1)}{6}$. Show that $S(k+1)$: $1^2 + 2^2 + \ldots + k^2 + (k+1)^2 = \frac{(k+1)(k+2)(2(k+1)+1)}{6}$ is true.

$1^2 + 2^2 + \ldots + k^2 + (k+1)^2$
$= \frac{k(k+1)(2k+1)}{6} + (k+1)^2$
$= \frac{k(k+1)(2k+1) + 6(k+1)^2}{6}$
$= \frac{(k+1)(k(2k+1) + 6(k+1))}{6}$
$= \frac{(k+1)(2k^2+7k+6)}{6}$
$= \frac{(k+1)(k+2)(2k+3)}{6}$
$= \frac{(k+1)(k+2)(2(k+1)+1)}{6}$

c. **Since $S(1)$ is true and $S(k) \Rightarrow S(k+1)$, by mathematical induction, $S(n)$ is true $\forall$ integers $n \geq 1$.**

8. c. **Let $S(n)$: $a_n = \frac{(3^n - 1)}{2}$ $\forall$ integers $n \geq 1$.**

(1) $a_1 = \frac{3^1 - 1}{2} = 1$. This agrees with the recursive formula, hence $S(1)$ is true.

(2) Assume $S(k)$: $a_k = \frac{3^k - 1}{2}$ is true for some integer $k \geq 1$. Show $S(k+1)$: $a_{k+1} = \frac{3^{k+1} - 1}{2}$ is true. $a_{k+1} = 3a_k + 1 = 3\left(\frac{3^k - 1}{2}\right) + 1 = \frac{3^{k+1} - 3 + 2}{2} = \frac{3^{k+1} - 1}{2}$. Therefore, for all integers $k \geq 1$, if $S(k)$ is true, then $S(k+1)$ is true. Thus, from (1) and (2) above, using the Principle of Mathematical Induction, $S(n)$ is true for all integers $n \geq 1$. Hence, the explicit formula describes the same sequence as the recursive formula.

6a) $\frac{1(1+1)}{2}$
b) $1 + 2 + 3 + \ldots + k = \frac{k(k+1)}{2}$
c) $1 + 2 + 3 + \ldots + k + k + 1 = \frac{(k+1)(k+2)}{2}$
d) $1 + 2 + 3 + \ldots + k + k + 1$
e) use inductive assumption
f) $\frac{k(k+1) + 2(k+1)}{2}$
g) $\frac{(k+1)(k+2)}{2}$
h) The Principle of Mathematical Induction

7a) $S(1)$: $1^2 = \frac{(1)(2)(3)}{6}$, so $S(1)$ is true.

6. Fill in the missing steps in the following proof of the formula for the sum of the first n integers: **See left.**

$$1 + 2 + 3 + \ldots + n = \frac{n(n+1)}{2} \quad \textit{for all integers } n \geq 1.$$

Proof: Let $S(n)$ be the equation $\sum_{i=1}^{n} i = \frac{n(n+1)}{2}$.

(1) Show that $S(1)$ is true.
When $n = 1$, the left side of the equation is 1 and the right side is <u>**a.**</u> which also equals 1. Hence the equation is true for $n = 1$ and so $S(1)$ is true.

(2) Show that the assumption that $S(k)$ is true implies that $S(k+1)$ is true.
Suppose $S(k)$ is true for a particular but arbitrarily chosen integer $k \geq 1$, where $S(k)$: <u>**b.**</u> This is the inductive assumption.

We must show that $S(k)$ being true implies that $S(k+1)$ is true, where $S(k+1)$: <u>**c.**</u>.

Begin with the left side of $S(k+1)$ and use the inductive assumption to transform it to obtain the right side of $S(k+1)$.

<u>**d.**</u> $= \sum_{i=1}^{k} i + k + 1$	Write the sum recursively.
$= \frac{k(k+1)}{2} + (k+1)$	<u>**e.**</u>
$= \frac{k(k+1)}{2} + \frac{2(k+1)}{2}$	Equivalent Fractions Property
$=$ <u>**f.**</u>	Add fractions with a common denominator.
$=$ <u>**g.**</u>	Factor out $k + 1$.
$= \frac{(k+1)((k+1)+1)}{2}$	Rewrite.

Thus, if the inductive assumption $S(k)$ is true, then $S(k+1)$ is true.

From (1) and (2) above, you can conclude that $S(n)$ is true for all integers $n \geq 1$ by <u>**h.**</u>.

Applying the Mathematics

7. Consider the equation

$$S(n)\text{: } 1^2 + 2^2 + 3^2 + \ldots + n^2 = \frac{n(n+1)(2n+1)}{6}.$$

Consider the steps of a mathematical induction proof that $S(n)$ is true for all integers $n \geq 1$.

a. Write and verify the basis step. **See left.**
b. Show that for any integer $k \geq 1$, $S(k) \Rightarrow S(k+1)$. **See margin.**
c. Complete the proof. **See margin.**

9. **$S(n)$: $a_n = 2n^2 - 1$ $\forall$ integers $n \geq 1$. (1) $a_1 = 1$ from the recursive definition; $a_1 = 2 \cdot 1^2 - 1 = 1$ from the explicit definition. Hence, $S(1)$ is true. (2) Assume $S(k)$: $a_k = 2k^2 - 1$ for some integer $k \geq 1$. Show $S(k+1)$: $a_{k+1} = 2(k+1)^2 - 1$ is true. $a_{k+1} = a_k + 4k + 2 = 2k^2 - 1 + 4k + 2 = 2(k^2 + 2k + 1) - 1 = 2(k+1)^2 - 1$. Therefore, $S(k+1)$ is true if $S(k)$ is true, and (1) and (2) prove by the Principle of Mathematical Induction that the explicit formula does describe the sequence.**

8a) 1, 4, 13, 40, 121
b) 1, 4, 13, 40, 121

8. a. Write out the first 5 terms of the sequence defined recursively by **See left.**

$$\begin{cases} a_1 = 1 \\ a_{k+1} = 3a_k + 1 \quad \text{for all integers } k \geq 1. \end{cases}$$

b. Write out the first five terms of the sequence defined explicitly by the formula **See left.**

$$b_n = \frac{3^n - 1}{2} \quad \text{for all integers } n \geq 1.$$

c. Use mathematical induction to verify that the explicit formula describes the same sequence as the recursive formula. (Hint: Follow the model of Example 2.) **See margin.**

9. Consider the sequence 1, 7, 17, 31, . . . defined recursively by

$$\begin{cases} a_1 = 1 \\ a_{k+1} = a_k + (4k + 2) \quad \text{for all integers } k \geq 1. \end{cases}$$

Use mathematical induction to prove that an explicit formula for this sequence is

$$a_n = 2n^2 - 1 \quad \text{for all integers } n \geq 1.$$ **See margin.**

10. Use mathematical induction to prove that $S(n)$ is true for all integers $n \geq 1$ where

$$S(n)\text{: } \sum_{i=1}^{n} (3i - 2) = \frac{n(3n - 1)}{2}.$$

(Hint: Follow the steps of Question 2.) **See margin.**

Review

11. Use summation notation to rewrite the sum. *(Lesson 7-2)*

$$\frac{1}{n} + \frac{2}{n} + \frac{3}{n} + \ldots + \frac{n}{n} \quad \sum_{i=1}^{n} \frac{i}{n}$$

12. a. Write the sum $\sum_{i=-3}^{n} (i^2 + i)$ in expanded form.

b. Find the value of the sum in part **a** when $n = 2$. *(Lesson 7-2)*

See left.

12a) $(-3)^2 + -3 + (-2)^2 + (-2) + (-1)^2 + (-1) + \ldots + n^2 + n$
b) 16

13. Recall that $\lfloor x \rfloor$ denotes the floor of x, the greatest integer that is less than or equal to x. Consider the sequence defined by:

$$\begin{cases} a_1 = 1 \\ a_k = a_{\lfloor (k+1)/2 \rfloor} + a_{\lfloor k/2 \rfloor} \quad \forall \text{ integers } k \geq 2. \end{cases}$$

a. Write the first six terms of the sequence. **1, 2, 3, 4, 5, 6**

b. Conjecture an explicit formula for the sequence. *(Lesson 7-1)* **See left.**

13b) Sample: $a_n = n$, for all integers $n \geq 1$

14. a. Graph $y = \cos x$ on the interval $0 \leq x \leq \pi$.

b. Graph the line $y = x$ on the same set of axes.

c. Form the graph of $y = \cos^{-1} x$ on the interval $-1 \leq x \leq 1$ by reflecting the graph of $y = \cos x$ across the line $y = x$.

d. Evaluate without using a calculator. *(Lessons 2-6, 6-7)*

i. $\cos^{-1}\left(\frac{\sqrt{2}}{2}\right)$ $\frac{\pi}{4}$ ii. $\cos^{-1}\left(\frac{1}{2}\right)$ $\frac{\pi}{3}$ iii. $\cos^{-1}\left(\frac{-\sqrt{3}}{2}\right)$ $\frac{5\pi}{6}$

a–c) See left.

14a–c)

y
3
$y = \cos^{-1} x$
$y = x$
1
-1 1 3 x
-1
$y = \cos x$

Follow-up for Lesson 7-3

Practice

For more questions on SPUR Objectives, use **Lesson Master 7-3** (shown on pages 420–421).

Assessment

Group Assessment You may wish to complete **Question 10** as a class. Have two or three students volunteer to put the proof on the board and have the other students critique the proof. [Assess students' understanding of mathematical induction.]

(Follow-up continues on page 426.)

10. (1) $\sum_{i=1}^{1}(3i - 2) = 3 \cdot 1 - 2 = 1$ **and** $\frac{1 \cdot (3 - 1)}{2} = 1$**. Hence, $S(1)$ is true.**

(2) Assume $S(k)$: $\sum_{i=1}^{k}(3i - 2) = \frac{k(3k - 1)}{2}$ **is true for some integer $k \geq 1$. Show $S(k + 1)$:** $\sum_{i=1}^{k+1}(3i - 2) = \frac{(k + 1)(3(k + 1) - 1)}{2}$ **is true. Now** $\sum_{i=1}^{k+1}(3i - 2)$

$$= \sum_{i=1}^{k}(3i - 2) + 3(k + 1) - 2$$

$$= \frac{3k^2 - k + 6k + 2}{2}$$

$$= \frac{3k^2 + 5k + 2}{2} = \frac{(k + 1)(3k + 2)}{2}$$

$$= \frac{(k + 1)(3(k + 1) - 1)}{2}.$$

The inductive step is true. Thus, (1) and (2) prove by the Principle of Mathematical Induction that $S(n)$ is true for all integers $n \geq 1$.

Extension

Example 1, Question 2, and **Question 5** are examples of arithmetic series. Challenge students to prove by mathematical induction that

$$\sum_{i=1}^{n}[a + (i - 1)d] = \frac{n[2a + (n-1)d]}{2}$$

where a and d are real numbers. Have students give the specific values of a and d for which the above formula becomes **Example 1, Question 2,** and **Question 5,** respectively. [For $k = 1$, $[a + (1 - 1)d] = \frac{1[2a + (1 - 1)d]}{2}$, so $a = \frac{2a}{2}$ is true. Assume $\sum_{i=1}^{n}[a + (i - 1)d] = \frac{n[2a + (n-1)d]}{2}$ for some $n = k$. $\sum_{i=1}^{k+1}[a + (i - 1)d]$

$$= \sum_{i=1}^{k}[a + (i - 1)d] + a + (k + 1 - 1)d$$

$$= \frac{k[2a + (k - 1)d]}{2} + a + kd$$

$$= \frac{2ka + k(k - 1)d + 2a + 2kd}{2}$$

$$= \frac{2ka + k^2d - kd + 2a + 2kd}{2}$$

$$= \frac{(k + 1)(2a + kd)}{2}$$, so the statement is true for $n = k + 1$, and therefore, by induction, true for all n.
Example 1: $a = 1$, $d = 2$;
Question 2: $a = 2$, $d = 2$;
Question 5: $a = 1$, $d = 3$.]

Project Update Project 4, *Exploring the Fibonacci Sequence,* and Project 6, *Generating Sequences with Matrices,* on page 464 relate to the content of this lesson.

Notes on Questions

Question 15 Inform students that adding and subtracting the same number, as is done in **part c,** is not a trick but a rather common mathematical procedure. They may recall doing this when completing the square.

15a) Since $x - y$ is a factor of $x^4 - y^4$, and $x^4 - y^4$ is a factor of $x^5 - xy^4 = x(x^4 - y^4)$, then by the Transitive Property of Factors, $x - y$ is a factor of $x^5 - xy^4$.
b) $xy^4 - y^5 = y^4(x - y)$
c) Since $x - y$ is a factor of $x^5 - xy^4$ by part **a** and $x - y$ is a factor of $xy^4 - y^5$ by part **b**, then $x - y$ is a factor of $(x^5 - xy^4) + (xy^4 - y^5)$ by the Factor of a Polynomial Sum Theorem.

15. **a.** Given that $x - y$ is a factor of $x^4 - y^4$, explain why $x - y$ is a factor of $x^5 - xy^4$. See left.
b. Factor $xy^4 - y^5$. See left.
c. Use parts **a** and **b** to explain why $x - y$ is a factor of $x^5 - xy^4 + xy^4 - y^5$. *(Lesson 4-1)* See left.

16. *True or false.* If k is an odd integer, then 2 is a factor of $3k^2 + k + 2$. *(Lesson 4-1)* True

Exploration

17. Consider the computer program in BASIC below.

```
10 INPUT N
20 PRINT N
30 N = N + 1
40 GOTO 20
50 END
```

Explain how this program models the Principle of Mathematical Induction.
The program contains an initial condition in line 10 and a recurrence relation in line 30. Given an infinite amount of time and computer memory, it would print all the integers greater than N − 1.

Setting Up Lesson 7-4

Be certain to discuss **Question 15** of Lesson 7-3. This brings back the vocabulary word "factor."

LESSON

7-4

Factors and Mathematical Induction

Mathematical induction is a widely applicable method of proof. In the last lesson, you saw that it can be used to prove a wide variety of formulas involving sums. Mathematical induction can also be used to prove divisibility properties.

Recall from Chapter 4 that if m and n are integers, then m is a *factor* of n if and only if $n = m \cdot k$ for some integer k. In Chapter 4 this idea was used to prove some fundamental properties of divisibility, which are repeated below.

Factor of an Integer Sum Theorem
For all integers a, b, and c, if a is a factor of b and a is a factor of c, then a is a factor of $b + c$.

Transitive Property of Integer Factors
For all integers a, b, and c, if a is a factor of b and b is a factor of c, then a is a factor of c.

Applying Mathematical Induction to Prove a Property of Divisibility

Example 1

Prove that for every positive integer n, 3 is a factor of $n^3 + 2n$.

Solution

Let $S(n)$ be the sentence: 3 is a factor of $n^3 + 2n$.

(1) Basis step: Show that $S(1)$ is true.
$S(1)$ is the statement: 3 is a factor of $1^3 + 2 \cdot 1$. Since $1^3 + 2 \cdot 1 = 3$, and 3 is a factor of 3, $S(1)$ is clearly true.

(2) Inductive step: Show that $S(k)$ implies $S(k + 1)$ for all integers $k \geq 1$.
Assume that $S(k)$ is true for some particular but arbitrarily chosen positive integer k. That is, assume

$S(k)$: 3 is a factor of $k^3 + 2k$. This is the inductive assumption.

Now it must be shown that $S(k + 1)$ is true, where

$S(k + 1)$: 3 is a factor of $(k + 1)^3 + 2(k + 1)$.

Expanding $(k + 1)^3$ and $2(k + 1)$, the expression in $S(k + 1)$ becomes

$$k^3 + 3k^2 + 3k + 1 + 2k + 2$$

which can be regrouped as

$$(k^3 + 2k) + 3k^2 + 3k + 3.$$

▸

Lesson 7-4

Objectives

G Prove statements involving factors using the Principle of Mathematical Induction.

Resources

From the ***Teacher's Resource File***
- Lesson Master 7-4
- Answer Master 7-4
- Teaching Aid 63: Warm-up
- Assessment Sourcebook: Quiz for Lessons 7-1 through 7-4

Additional Resources
- Visual for Teaching Aid 63

Teaching Lesson 7-4

Warm-up

1. Evaluate the first six terms of the sequence $a_n = 7^n - 1$. **6, 48, 342, 2400, 16,806, 117,648**
2. What is the largest common factor of these six terms? **6**
3. Prove that every term of the sequence is divisible by that factor. **Let $S(n)$: a_n is divisible by 6. Then $S(1)$ is true, since 6 is divisible by 6. If $S(k)$ is true, then $7^k - 1$ is divisible by 6. So $7(7^k - 1)$ is divisible by 6. So $7^{k+1} - 7$, or $7^{k+1} - 6 - 1$ is divisible by 6. Since 6 is divisible by 6, the sum $6 + (7^{k+1} - 6 - 1) = 7^{k+1} - 1$ is divisible by 6, and $S(k + 1)$ is true. Using the Principle of Mathematical Induction, 6 is a factor of $7^n - 1$ for all positive integers n.**

Notes on Reading

Ask students for numerical examples of both the Factor of an Integer Sum Theorem and the Transitive Property of Integer Factors. They need to understand these theorems thoroughly in order to understand the examples and questions in which they are needed.

In Lesson 4-1, students completed proofs about factors using the definition of a factor and the basic properties of divisibility. In this lesson, students see proofs about

Lesson 7-4 Overview

Broad Goals Students have seen two methods for proving divisibility theorems: (1) use the definition of factor and properties of divisibility; (2) use modular arithmetic. Mathematical induction becomes method (3). The purpose of this lesson is to practice mathematical induction in this context.

Perspective In this lesson, students see that the same steps are involved in mathematical induction proofs regardless of the context of the proofs. Students still need to verify the basis step, and still need to prove that $S(k + 1)$ is true if the inductive assumption $S(k)$ is true. The difference in this lesson is that in proving that $S(k + 1)$ is true, students will need to use the properties of divisibility from earlier chapters that are reviewed at the beginning of this lesson.

factors that use mathematical induction. While induction is not necessary for all these proofs, it is a very powerful technique that can be applied to situations where the previous techniques are not applicable.

In **Example 1** and in a number of the problems in the remainder of this chapter, students need to expand an expression of the form $(k + 1)^3$. Hence, it may be worthwhile to review the formula:
$(a + b)^3 = a^3 + 3a^2b + 3ab^2 + b^3$.

It is likely that **Example 1** will seem more straightforward to students than **Examples 2–3**. In the latter two examples, the hardest part for students is generally knowing what term needs to be added and subtracted to obtain $S(k + 1)$ in the proper form.

Some students respond well to using the definition of factor explicitly. In the inductive step of the proof of **Example 2,** use the following:
3 divides $4^k - 1$ means $\exists$ an integer m such that $4^k - 1 = 3m$.
Then the proof becomes

$$\begin{aligned} 4^{k+1} - 1 &= 4(4^k) - 1 \\ &= 4(4^k - 1 + 1) - 1 \\ &= 4(4^k - 1) + 4(1) - 1 \\ &= 4(3m) + 3 = 3(4m + 1) \end{aligned}$$

which, because $4m + 1$ is an integer, is divisible by 3. Thus $4^{k+1} - 1$ is also divisible by 3.

LESSON MASTER 7-4

Questions on SPUR Objectives
See pages 467–469 for objectives.

Properties Objective G

In 1–3, use mathematical induction to prove that the statement is true. Samples are given.

1. For all integers a, a is a factor of $(a + 1)^n - 1$ $\forall$ positive integers n.
$(a + 1)^1 - 1 = a + 1 - 1 = a$, and a is a factor of a. Assume that a is a factor of $(a + 1)^k - 1$. Then $(a + 1)^{k+1} - 1 = (a + 1)(a + 1)^k - 1 = a(a + 1)^k + (a + 1)^k - 1$. By the inductive assumption, a is a factor of $(a + 1)^k$. a is clearly a factor of $a(a + 1)^k$. So, a is a factor of $(a + 1)^{k+1} - 1$. Thus, the assumption that a is a factor of $(a + 1)^k - 1$ implies that a is a factor of $(a + 1)^{k+1} - 1$.

2. 2 is a factor of $n^2 + n$ for all positive integers n.
$1^2 + 1 = 1 + 1 = 2$, and 2 is a factor of 2. Assume that 2 is a factor of $k^2 + k$. Then $(k + 1)^2 + (k + 1) = k^2 + 2k + 1 + k + 1 = (k^2 + k) + 2(k + 1)$. By the inductive assumption, 2 is a factor of $k^2 + k$. 2 is clearly a factor of $2(k + 1)$. So, 2 is a factor of $(k + 1)^2 + (k + 1)$. Thus, the assumption that 2 is a factor of $k^2 + k$ implies that 2 is a factor of $(k + 1)^2 + (k + 1)$.

3. 4 is a factor of $n^4 + n^2$ for all positive integers n.
$1^4 + 1^2 + 2 \cdot 1 = 1 + 1 + 2 = 4$, and 4 is a factor of 4. Assume that 4 is a factor of $k^4 + k^2 + 2k$. Then $(k + 1)^4 + (k + 1)^2 + 2(k + 1) = k^4 + 4k^3 + 6k^2 + 4k + 1 + k^2 + 2k + 1 + 2k + 2 = (k^4 + k^2 + 2k) + 4(k^3 + k^2 + k + 1) + 2k^2 + 2k$. By the inductive assumption, 4 is a factor of $k^4 + k^2 + 2k$. 4 is clearly a factor of $4(k^3 + k^2 + k + 1)$. Since $2k^2 + 2k = 2k(k + 1)$ and either k or $k + 1$ is even, 4 is a factor of $2k^2 + 2k$, and thus a factor of the entire expression. Thus, the assumption that the statement is true for k implies that the statement is true for $k + 1$.

By the inductive assumption, 3 is a factor of $k^3 + 2k$. The remaining terms in the sum all have a factor of 3. So, by the Factor of an Integer Sum Theorem, 3 is a factor of $(k^3 + 2k) + 3k^2 + 3k + 3$ and so $S(k + 1)$ is true.

From (1) and (2), using the Principle of Mathematical Induction,

$$S(n)\text{: 3 is a factor of } n^3 + 2n$$

is true for all integers $n \geq 1$.

In the next example, some manipulation must be done before the factorization needed in the proof becomes evident.

Example 2

Prove that for every positive integer n,

3 is a factor of $4^n - 1$.

Solution

Let $S(n)$: 3 is a factor of $4^n - 1$.

(1) Show that $S(1)$ is true.

$S(1)$ is the statement 3 is a factor of $4^1 - 1$. Since $4^1 - 1 = 3$, $S(1)$ is true.

(2) Show that the assumption that $S(k)$ is true implies that $S(k + 1)$ is true.
Assume that $S(k)$ is true for some positive integer k. That is, assume

$$S(k)\text{: 3 is a factor of } 4^k - 1.$$

It must be shown that this assumption implies $S(k + 1)$ is true where

$$S(k + 1)\text{: 3 is a factor of } 4^{k+1} - 1.$$

Transform the expression in $S(k + 1)$ so that it contains the expression in $S(k)$. This can be done using the fact that you can subtract 1 from a number and then add 1 without changing the value of the number.

$$\begin{aligned} 4^{k+1} - 1 &= 4(4^k) - 1 && \text{Properties of Exponents} \\ &= 4(4^k - 1 + 1) - 1 && \text{Add and subtract 1.} \\ &= 4(4^k - 1) + 4(1) - 1 && \text{Distributive Property} \\ &= 4(4^k - 1) + 3 \end{aligned}$$

1 The inductive assumption states that 3 is a factor of $4^k - 1$. Since $4^k - 1$ is a factor of $4(4^k - 1)$, by the Transitive Property of Integer Factors, 3 is then a factor of $4(4^k - 1)$. Since 3 is also a factor of itself, by the Factor of an Integer Sum Theorem, 3 is a factor of $4(4^k - 1) + 3$. Therefore, 3 is a factor of $4^{k+1} - 1$, and so $S(k + 1)$ is true.

From (1) and (2) above, using the Principle of Mathematical Induction, 3 is a factor of $4^n - 1$ for all positive integers n.

Optional Activities

Cooperative Learning After completing the lesson, you might have students **work in groups** and use the Principle of Mathematical Induction to prove that for all positive integers n

$$\left(1 + \frac{3}{1}\right)\left(1 + \frac{5}{4}\right) \ldots \left(1 + \frac{2n + 1}{n^2}\right) = (n + 1)^2.$$

[$S(1)$ *is* $\left(1 + \frac{3}{1}\right) = (1 + 1)^2$, which is true. If $S(k)$ is true, then $S(k + 1)$ can be written as $(k + 1)^2\left(1 + \frac{2(k + 1) + 1}{(k + 1)^2}\right)$, which equals $(k + 1)^2 + 2(k + 1) + 1 = [(k + 1) + 1]^2 = (k + 2)^2$. Thus $S(k + 1)$ is true if $S(k)$ is true. So by the Principle of Mathematical Induction, $S(n)$ is true for all integers $n \geq 1$.]

Adding and Subtracting k to Show Factors

You may have viewed the adding and subtracting of 1 in the middle of Example 2 as a trick. But there is a saying among some problem solvers: If an idea is used once, it is a trick; but if it is used twice, then it is a *technique*. In Lesson 7-1 we added 2 and subtracted 2 in proving the explicit formula for the sequence 1, 3, 7, 15, 31, ...

In Example 3, the technique of adding and subtracting a number is used to show that $x - y$ is a factor of $x^n - y^n$ for all n. Here xy^k is subtracted and then added again.

Example 3

Use the Principle of Mathematical Induction to prove that $x - y$ is a factor of $x^n - y^n$ for each positive integer n.

Solution

Here

$$S(n): x - y \text{ is a factor of } x^n - y^n.$$

(1) Show that $S(1)$ is true.

$S(1)$ is the statement $x - y$ is a factor of $x^1 - y^1$, which is certainly true.

(2) Show that the assumption that $S(k)$ is true implies that $S(k + 1)$ is true.
Assume that $S(k)$ is true for some integer $k \geq 1$.
That is, assume

$$S(k): x - y \text{ is a factor of } x^k - y^k$$

is true.

It must be shown that this assumption implies that $S(k + 1)$ is true, where

$$S(k + 1): x - y \text{ is a factor of } x^{k+1} - y^{k+1}.$$

Begin with $x^{k+1} - y^{k+1}$ and subtract and add xy^k so that the expression becomes a sum of terms clearly divisible by $x - y$.

$$x^{k+1} - y^{k+1} = x^{k+1} - xy^k + xy^k - y^{k+1} \quad \text{Subtract and add } xy^k.$$
$$= x(x^k - y^k) + y^k(x - y) \quad \text{Factor.}$$

Certainly $x - y$ is a factor of $y^k(x - y)$. By the inductive assumption, $x - y$ is a factor of $x^k - y^k$. Since $x^k - y^k$ is a factor of $x(x^k - y^k)$, by the Transitive Property of Integer Factors, $x - y$ is a factor of $x(x^k - y^k)$. According to the Factor of a Polynomial Sum Theorem, since $x - y$ is a factor of each term, $x - y$ is a factor of the sum. So $x - y$ is a factor of $x^{k+1} - y^{k+1}$.

From (1) and (2), using the Principle of Mathematical Induction, $S(n)$ is true for all positive integers n.

The result in Example 3 shows, for instance, that because $5 = 7 - 2$, 5 is a factor of $7^n - 2^n$ for each natural number n. It also shows that, for any real number a, $a - 1$ is a factor of $a^n - 1$ for every natural number n. Note that Example 2 is the special case of this when $a = 4$.

❶ Emphasize the comments following **Example 2.** Mathematical proofs often involve considerable creativity. Even though the structure of proofs by mathematical induction are the same, creativity is needed to make connections between the expressions in $S(k)$ and $S(k + 1)$.

Additional Examples

1. Prove that for every positive integer n, 5 is a factor of $n^5 + 4n$. **$S(1)$ is the statement that 5 is a factor of $1^5 + 4(1) = 5$, which is true. Assume $S(k)$: 5 is factor of $k^5 + 4k$. Now consider the expression in $S(k + 1)$: $(k + 1)^5 + 4(k + 1) = k^5 + 5k^4 + 10k^3 + 10k^2 + 5k + 1 + 4(k + 1) = k^5 + 4k + 5(k^4 + 2k^3 + 2k^2 + k + 1)$, and since by the inductive assumption, $k^5 + 4k$ is divisible by 5, the entire expression is divisible by 5. Thus $S(k) \Rightarrow S(k + 1)$ and so by the Principle of Mathematical Induction $S(n)$ is true for all integers $n \geq 1$.**

(Additional Examples continue on page 430.)

▶ **LESSON MASTER 7-4** *page 2*

4. Suppose that the functions f and g are such that $f(x)$ and $g(x)$ are both integers whenever x is an integer. Suppose further that the integer is a factor of $f(n)$ when $n \geq 5$ and is a factor of $g(n)$ when $n \geq 9$. For what values of n can you be sure that n is a factor of the given expression?

a. $f(n) + g(n)$ $\quad$ $n \geq 9$

b. $f(n) \cdot g(n)$ $\quad$ $n \geq 5$

5. Prove that $x + y$ is a factor of $x^{2n} - y^{2n}$ ∀ positive integers n. (Hint: In the inductive step, add and subtract x^2y^{2k}).

True when $n = 1$; $S(1)$: $x^2 - y^2 = (x - y)(x + y)$
Assume true for $n = k$; $S(k)$: $(x + y)$ is a factor of $x^{2k} - y^{2k}$

$S(k + 1)$: $x^{2(k+1)} - y^{2(k+1)}$
$= x^{2k+2} - y^{2k+2}$
$= x^{2k+2} + x^2y^{2k} - x^2y^{2k} - y^{2k+2}$
$= (x^{2k}x^2 - x^2y^{2k}) + (x^2y^{2k} - y^{2k}y^2)$
$= x^2(x^{2k} - y^{2k}) + y^{2k}(x^2 - y^2)$

$x + y$ is a factor of $x^{2k} - y^{2k}$ by the inductive assumption and is therefore a factor of $x^2(x^{2k} - y^{2k})$. It is also a factor of $x^2 + y^2$, as proved in the base case, and is therefore a factor of $y^{2k}(x^2 - y^2)$. By the Factor of an Integer Sum Theorem, $x + y$ is a factor of $x^{2(k+1)} - y^{2(k+1)}$. Thus, the assumption $S(k)$ implies $S(k + 1)$ is true.

Adapting to Individual Needs

Challenge

Refer students to **Question 10.** Ask them to consider whether or not $2m$ is a factor of $T = m^n(3^n - 2^n)$ for all integers $n \geq 2$. For example, if $m = 5$, is 10 a factor of $5^n(3^n - 2^n)$? [no] If $m = 6$, is 12 a factor of $6^n(3^n - 2^n)$? [yes] Ask them to make a conjecture about the values of m for which the statement will be true. [For positive even integer values of m, $2m$ is a factor of $m^n(3^n - 2^n)$ for $n \geq 2$.] Then, ask them to prove this conjecture. [If m is even and $n \geq 2$, then ∃ a positive integer k with $m = 2k$. So $T = m^n(3^n - 2^n) = 2k \cdot m^{n-1}(3^n - 2^n) = 2m \cdot k \cdot m^{n-2}(3^n - 2^n)$. Since $n \geq 2$, m^{n-2} is an integer. So T is divisible by $2m$. If m is odd, then $T = m^n(3^n - 2^n)$ is a product of the odd number m^n and the odd number $3^n - 2^n$. So T is odd. ∴ T is not divisible by the even number $2m$.]

2. Prove that for every positive integer n, 5 is a factor of $6^n - 1$. $S(1)$ is that 5 is a factor of $6^1 - 1 = 5$, which is true. Assume $S(k)$. Now $6^{k+1} - 1 = 6(6^k) - 1$ $= 6(6^k - 1) + 5 = 6(5m) + 5$ (by the inductive assumption) $= 5(6m + 1)$, so the expression in $S(k + 1)$ is divisible by 5, and so $S(k + 1)$ is true if $S(k)$ is true. So by the Principle of Mathematical Induction $S(n)$ is true for all integers $n \geq 1$.

Notes on Questions

Questions 3–4 These questions lead students through the induction proofs before asking them to complete an entire proof on their own in **Questions 5–8.**

Question 11 Error Alert Help students see that it is often easier to get results into the desired form if factors are not expanded.

Additional Answers

3. a. $S(1)$: 2 is a factor of 2; since $2 \cdot 1 = 2$, $S(1)$ is true. $S(13)$: 2 is a factor of 158; since $2 \cdot 79 = 158$, $S(13)$ is true. $S(20)$: 2 is a factor of 382; $2 \cdot 191 = 382$, so $S(20)$ is true.
   b. $S(k)$: 2 is a factor of $k^2 - k + 2$. $S(k + 1)$: 2 is a factor of $(k + 1)^2 - (k + 1) + 2$.
   d. $k^2 + k + 2 = (k^2 - k + 2) + 2k$; 2 is a factor of $k^2 - k + 2$ and $2k$, so 2 is a factor of $(k + 1)^2 - (k + 1) + 2$ by the Factor of an Integer Sum Theorem.
   e. 2 is a factor of $n^2 - n + 2$ $\forall$ integers $n \geq 1$.
5. Since $9 - 3 = 6$, substituting $x = 9$ and $y = 3$ into the result of Example 3 yields $9 - 3 = 6$ is a factor of $9^n - 3^n \; \forall \; n \geq 1$.
6. Since $13 - 1 = 12$, substituting $x = 13$ and $y = 1$ into the result of Example 3 gives $13 - 1 = 12$ is a factor of $13^n - 1^n \; \forall \; n \geq 1$.

2) $(n + 1)^2 + (n + 1) = n^2 + 3n + 2 = (n^2 + n) + 2(n + 1)$. It is clear that 2 is a factor of $2(n + 1)$. Since 2 is also a factor of $n^2 + n$, then 2 will be a factor of their sum, $(n^2 + n) + (2(n + 1))$, by the Factor of a Polynomial Sum Theorem.

4a) Since 5 is a factor of $6^1 - 1 = 5$, $S(1)$ is true.
b) $S(k)$: 5 is a factor of $6^k - 1$.
c) $S(k + 1)$: 5 is a factor of $6^{k+1} - 1$.
d) $6^{k+1} - 1 = 6 \cdot 6^k - 1 = 6 \cdot 6^k - 6 + 5 = 6(6^k - 1) + 5$; 5 is a factor of $6^k - 1$ and of 5, so 5 is a factor of their sum. Thus, $S(k + 1)$ is true. Hence, $S(n)$: 5 is a factor of $6^n - 1 \; \forall \; n \geq 1$ is true by the Principle of Mathematical Induction.

QUESTIONS

Covering the Reading

1. Show that when $n = 3$, 16 is a factor of $5^n - 4n - 1$. $5^3 - 4 \cdot 3 - 1 = 112 = 16 \cdot 7$, so 16 is a factor.
2. Show that if 2 is a factor of $n^2 + n$, then 2 is a factor of $(n + 1)^2 + (n + 1)$. (Hint: Expand $(n + 1)^2 + (n + 1)$ and regroup.) See left.
3. Consider the sentence: $S(n)$: *2 is a factor of* $n^2 - n + 2$.
   a. Show that $S(1)$, $S(13)$, and $S(20)$ are all true.
   b. Write $S(k)$ and $S(k + 1)$.
   c. Expand the expression in $S(k + 1)$ from part **b** and simplify the expanded expression. $k^2 + k + 2$
   d. Use appropriate regrouping to show that for all k, $S(k) \Rightarrow S(k + 1)$.
   e. What can you conclude from the results of parts **a–d**?
   a, b, d, e) See margin.
4. Let $S(n)$ be the sentence: *5 is a factor of* $6^n - 1$. Prove that $S(n)$ is true for every positive integer n, using the following steps. See left.
   a. Show that $S(1)$ is true.
   b. Write the inductive assumption $S(k)$.
   c. Write $S(k + 1)$.
   d. Use the fact that $6^{k+1} - 1 = 6(6^k - 1) + 5$ to complete the proof.

In 5 and 6, use the result of Example 3 to show that the statement below is true.

5. 6 is a factor of $9^n - 3^n$ for all positive integers n. See margin.
6. 12 is a factor of $13^n - 1$ for all positive integers n. See margin.

Applying the Mathematics

7. Let $S(n)$ be the sentence: *3 is a factor of* $n^3 + 14n + 3$. Use the Principle of Mathematical Induction to prove that $S(n)$ is true for all positive integers $n \geq 1$. See margin.
8. Prove that 6 is a factor of $n^3 + 11n$ for all positive integers n. Use the theorem: $\forall$ positive integers n, 6 is a factor of $3n(n + 1)$. See margin.
9. Using results from this lesson, prove in one line that See margin.

   $\forall$ *positive integers* $n \geq 1$, *3 is a factor of* $2^{2n} - 1$.
10. Given $S(n)$: *8 is a factor of* $12^n - 8^n$. See margin.
    a. Determine whether $S(1)$, $S(2)$, and $S(3)$ are true.
    b. $12^n - 8^n$ is in the form $x^n - y^n$ as in Example 3. However, $8 \neq 12 - 8$. What, if anything, can you conclude about $S(n)$ based on the result of that example?
    c. Use the factorization

    $$\begin{aligned} 12^n - 8^n &= 4^n \cdot 3^n - 4^n \cdot 2^n \\ &= 4^n(3^n - 2^n) \end{aligned}$$

    to prove that $S(n)$ is true for all integers $n \geq 2$. (You do not need to use mathematical induction.)

7. $S(1)$ is true since $1^3 + 14 \cdot 1 + 3 = 18 = 3 \cdot 6$. Assume $S(k)$: 3 is a factor of $k^3 + 14k + 3$. Show $S(k + 1)$: 3 is a factor of $(k + 1)^3 + 14(k + 1) + 3$ is true. $(k + 1)^3 + 14(k + 1) + 3 = k^3 + 3k^2 + 17k + 18 = (k^3 + 14k + 3) + 3k^2 + 3k + 15$. Since 3 is a factor of $k^3 + 14k + 3$ and $3(k^2 + k + 5)$, $S(k + 1)$ is true. Hence, 3 is a factor of $n^3 + 14n + 3 \; \forall$ integers $n \geq 1$ by the Principle of Mathematical Induction.
8. (1) 6 is factor of $1^3 + 11 = 12 = 2 \cdot 6$, hence $S(1)$ is true. (2) Assume $S(k)$: 6 is a factor of $k^3 + 11k$ is true for some positive integer k. Show $S(k + 1)$: 6 is a factor of $(k + 1)^3 + 11(k + 1)$ is true. Now $(k + 1)^3 + 11(k + 1) = k^3 + 3k^2 + 3k + 1 + 11k + 11 = (k^3 + 11k) + 3k(k + 1) + 12$. Because 6 is a factor of $k^3 + 11k$ by the inductive assumption, a factor of $3k(k + 1)$ by the theorem, and a factor of 12, it follows that 6 is a factor of $(k + 1)^3 + 11(k + 1)$. Since $S(1)$ is true and $S(k) \Rightarrow S(k + 1)$, by the Principle of Mathematical Induction, 6 is a factor of $n^3 + 11n$, $\forall$ integers $n \geq 1$.
9. Sample: By Example 3 with $x = 2^2$ and $y = 1$, $x - y = 3$ is a factor of $x^n - y^n = 2^{2n} - 1$.
10. a. $S(1)$: false. $S(2)$ and $S(3)$: true.
    b. All we can conclude is that $S(2)$ and $S(3)$ are true.
    c. $12^n - 8^n = 4^n(3^n - 2^n)$. 8 is a factor of 4^n if $n \geq 2$. Hence, $S(n)$ holds if $n \geq 2$.

Review

11. Use mathematical induction to prove: $\sum_{i=1}^{n} i^3 = \left[\frac{n(n+1)}{2}\right]^2$ for all integers $n \ge 1$. *(Lesson 7-3)* **See margin.**

12. Prove: The sequence 5, 7, 11, 19, 35, . . ., defined recursively by

$$\begin{cases} T_1 = 5 \\ T_{k+1} = 2T_k - 3 \quad \forall \text{ integers } k \ge 1 \end{cases}$$

has explicit formula $T_n = 2^n + 3 \quad \forall$ integers $n \ge 1$. *(Lessons 7-1, 7-3)*
See margin.

13. Determine whether or not the equation below is true. *(Lesson 7-2)*
True

$$\sum_{j=-2}^{3} \frac{1}{3^j} = \sum_{j=-2}^{3} 3^{j-1}$$

16a)

In 14 and 15, show that the equation is an identity. **See margin.**

14. $\cos^4 x - \sin^4 x = \cos(2x)$ *(Lesson 6-6)*

15. $\frac{a^4 - b^4}{a - b} = a^3 + a^2b + ab^2 + b^3$ *(Lesson 4-3)*

16. Define a function f by $f(x) = (.7)^x$. *(Lesson 2-7)*

a. Use an automatic grapher to graph f. **See left.**

b. What is $\lim_{x \to \infty} (.7)^x$? **0**

c. Find the smallest integer n such that $(.7)^n < .01$. **13**

d. Use the answer to part **b** to find $\lim_{x \to \infty} \frac{1 - (.7)^x}{1 - .7}$. $\mathbf{\frac{10}{3}}$

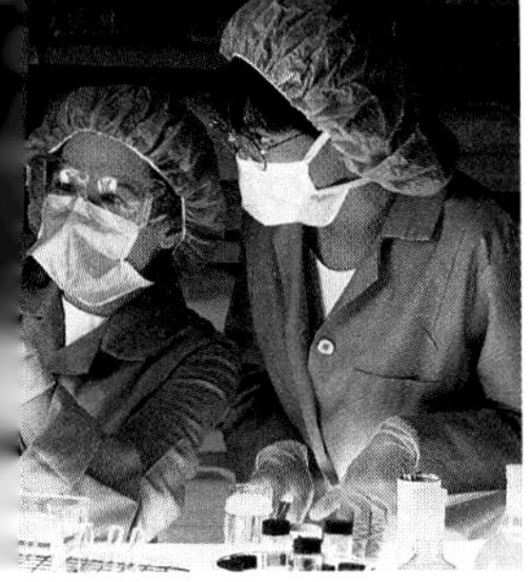

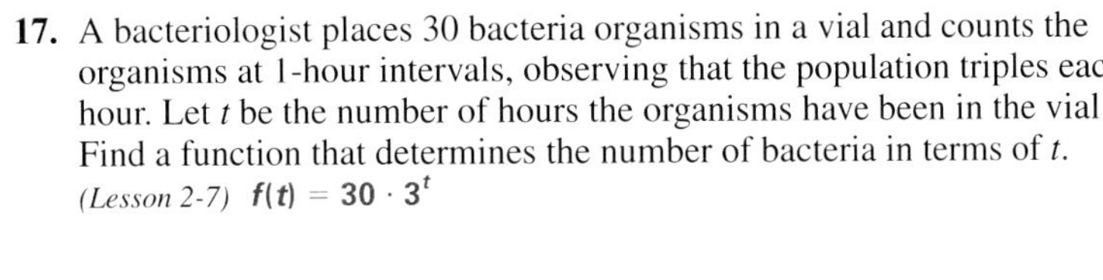

17. A bacteriologist places 30 bacteria organisms in a vial and counts the organisms at 1-hour intervals, observing that the population triples each hour. Let t be the number of hours the organisms have been in the vial. Find a function that determines the number of bacteria in terms of t. *(Lesson 2-7)* $\mathbf{f(t) = 30 \cdot 3^t}$

Exploration

18. Find several polynomials in n (like the ones in Example 1 or Question 7) which have 3 as a factor for all integers $n \ge 1$.
Samples: $n^4 + 2n^2$, $n^3 + 14n$, $n(n+1)(n+2) = n^3 + 3n^2 + 2n$

Follow-up for Lesson 7-4

Practice

For more questions on SPUR Objectives, use **Lesson Master 7-4** (shown on pages 428–429).

Assessment

Quiz A quiz covering Lessons 7-1 through 7-4 is provided in the *Assessment Sourcebook.*

12. Let $S(n)$: $T_n = 2^n + 3$. $T_1 = 2^1 + 3 = 5$ which agrees with the recursive definition, hence $S(1)$ is true. Assume $S(k)$: $T_k = 2^k + 3$ is true for some integer k. Show $S(k+1)$: $T_{k+1} = 2^{k+1} + 3$ is true. $T_{k+1} = 2T_k - 3 = 2(2^k + 3) - 3 = 2^{k+1} + 6 - 3 = 2^{k+1} + 3$. Since $S(1)$ is true and $S(k) \Rightarrow S(k+1)$, by the Principle of Mathematical Induction $S(n)$ is true for all $n \ge 1$. Hence, the explicit formula correctly defines the sequence.

14. right side $= \cos 2x$
$= \cos^2 x - \sin^2 x$ — Formula for cos $(2x)$
$= (\cos^2 x - \sin^2 x) \cdot 1$ — Multiplication by 1
$= (\cos^2 x - \sin^2 x)(\cos^2 x + \sin^2 x)$ — Pythagorean Identity
$= \cos^4 x - \sin^4 x$ — Multiplication
$=$ left side
Therefore, $\cos^4 x - \sin^4 x = \cos(2x)$ by the Transitive Property.

15. left side $= \frac{a^4 - b^4}{a - b}$
$= \frac{(a^2 - b^2)(a^2 + b^2)}{a - b}$ — Factoring
$= \frac{(a - b)(a + b)(a^2 + b^2)}{a - b}$ — Factoring
$= (a + b)(a^2 + b^2)$ — Division
$= a^3 + a^2b + ab^2 + b^3$ — Multiplication
Therefore, by the Transitive Property, $\frac{a^4 - b^4}{a - b} = a^3 + a^2b + ab^2 + b^3$, when $a \ne b$.

11. $S(1)$ is true because $\sum_{i=1}^{1} i^3 = 1^3 = 1$ and $\left[\frac{1(1+1)}{2}\right]^2 = 1^2 = 1$. Assume $S(k)$: $\sum_{i=1}^{k} i^3 = \left[\frac{k(k+1)}{2}\right]^2$ is true for some integer $k \ge 1$. Show that $S(k+1)$: $\sum_{i=1}^{k+1} i^3 = \left[\frac{(k+1)(k+2)}{2}\right]^2$ is true. Now $\sum_{i=1}^{k+1} i^3 = \sum_{i=1}^{k} i^3 + (k+1)^3 = \left[\frac{k(k+1)}{2}\right]^2 + (k+1)^3 = \frac{k^2(k+1)^2}{4} + \frac{4(k+1)^3}{4} = \frac{(k+1)^2[k^2 + 4(k+1)]}{4} = \frac{[(k+1)(k+2)]^2}{4}$. Since $S(1)$ is true and $S(k) \Rightarrow S(k+1)$, by the Principle of Mathematical Induction, $S(n)$ is true for all integers $n \ge 1$.

Lesson 7-5

Objectives

G Prove statements involving inequalities using the Principle of Mathematical Induction.

Resources

From the ***Teacher's Resource File***
- Lesson Master 7-5
- Answer Master 7-5
- Teaching Aid 63: Warm-up

Additional Resources
- Visual for Teaching Aid 63

Teaching Lesson 7-5

Warm-up

Let $S(n)$ be the statement $n! > 10^n$.

1. What is the smallest integer k for which $S(k)$ is true? **25**
2. Explain: If $S(k)$ is true, then $S(k + 1)$ must be true. **Sample: The left and right sides are products of n factors. To go from $S(k)$ to $S(k + 1)$, if $k \geq 25$, the left side is multiplied by a number larger than 10, while the right is multiplied by 10. So, if the left side begins larger than the right, it will remain larger.**

Notes on Reading

The key in all mathematical induction proofs is the move from $S(k)$ to $S(k + 1)$. In **Examples 1–2,** this requires multiplying both sides of the inequality by an appropriate number, which can be found by writing out $S(k)$ and $S(k + 1)$ to see how they are related. Since in these cases the

LESSON

7-5 Inequalities and Mathematical Induction

Mathematical induction can be used to prove many statements that you may have accepted without proof when you first saw them. Example 1 uses the Transitive Property of Inequality (if $a < b$ and $b < c$, then $a < c$) to deduce another inequality.

Example 1

Prove: For all integers $n \geq 1$, if $0 < x < 1$, then $x^n < 1$.

Solution

Let $S(n)$ be the statement: If $0 < x < 1$, then $x^n < 1$.
Basis step: $S(1)$ is the statement if $0 < x < 1$, then $x^1 < 1$, which is true since $p \Rightarrow p$ always.

Inductive step: We wish to show that $S(k) \Rightarrow S(k + 1)$ for all integers $k \geq 1$.

Assume $S(k)$. So if $0 < x < 1$, then $x^k < 1$ — definition of $S(n)$

$x \cdot x^k < x$ — M_x

$x^{k+1} < x$ — Product of Powers Property

But $x < 1$. So by the Transitive Property of Inequality,

$x^{k+1} < 1$.

Thus $S(k) \Rightarrow S(k + 1)$. So, by the Principle of Mathematical Induction, $S(n)$ is true for all integers $n \geq 1$.

Some inequalities that are not so obvious can be proved by mathematical induction.

Example 2

Prove: For all integers $n \geq 1$, $3^n \geq 1 + 2n$.

Solution

Let $S(n)$ be: $3^n \geq 1 + 2n$.
Basis step: $S(1)$ is $3^1 \geq 1 + 2 \cdot 1$, or $3 \geq 3$, which is true.

Inductive step: We need to show that $3^k \geq 1 + 2k \Rightarrow 3^{k+1} \geq 1 + 2(k + 1)$ for all integers $k > 1$. The ideas in Example 1 will help.

Assume $S(k)$. Then $3^k \geq 1 + 2k$ — definition of $S(k)$

$3 \cdot 3^k \geq 3(1 + 2k)$ — M_3

$3^{k+1} \geq 3 + 6k$ — Product of Powers Property, Distributive Property

Lesson 7-5 Overview

Broad Goals This lesson applies mathematical induction to inequalities.

Perspective This brief lesson is designed to offer another day of practice doing mathematical induction proofs. Although the contexts of the proofs are different, no new theorems are needed.

Optional Activities

After discussing **Examples 1–2,** ask students to prove the following:
For all integers $n \geq 1$, $(a + 1)^n \geq 1 + an$.
[$S(1)$ is true. Assuming $S(k)$: $(a + 1)^k \geq 1 + ak$, prove $S(k + 1)$: $(a + 1)^{k+1} \geq 1 + a(k + 1) = ak + a + 1$. Multiply both sides of $S(k)$ by $a + 1$: $(a + 1)^{k+1} \geq (1 + ak)(a + 1) = 1 + a(k + 1) + a^2k \geq 1 + a(k + 1)$. So, by the Principle of Mathematical Induction, $S(n)$ is true for all integers $n \geq 1$.]

Additional Answers, page 433

4. **Let $S(n)$ be the statement: if $x > 0$, then $x^n > 0$. $S(1)$: $x^n = x^1 = x$; since $0 < x$, $S(1)$ is true. Assume $S(k)$. So if $x > 0$, then $x^k > 0$.**
 $x \cdot x^k > 0 \cdot x$ — M_x, and $x > 0$
 $x^{k+1} > 0$ — Product of Powers Property
 Thus, $S(k) \Rightarrow S(k + 1)$. So, by the Principle of Mathematical Induction, $S(n)$ is true for all integers $n \geq 1$.

We want $1 + 2(k + 1)$ on the right, which is $3 + 2k$. So we need $3 + 6k > 3 + 2k$. But this follows because $6 > 2$ and k is positive. So $6k > 2k$, and so $3 + 6k > 3 + 2k$. Thus,

$3^{k+1} \geq 3 + 2k$	Transitive Property of Inequality
$3^{k+1} \geq 1 + 2(k + 1)$	Distributive Property, Commutative Property of Addition

Thus $S(k) \Rightarrow S(k + 1)$. So, by the Principle of Mathematical Induction, $S(n)$ is true for all integers $n \geq 1$.

QUESTIONS

Covering the Reading

1. State the Transitive Property of Inequality.
 If $a < b$, and $b < c$ then $a < c$.

In 2 and 3, refer to Example 1.

2. Identify each statement. See left.
 a. $S(1)$
 b. $S(3)$
 c. $S(k) \Rightarrow S(k + 1)$

3. In the inductive step, $x^k < 1$ implies $x \cdot x^k < x$. Why is the sense of the inequality not changed? The sense of the inequality is not changed because $x > 0$.

4. Prove: For all integers $n \geq 1$, if $x > 0$, then $x^n > 0$.
 See margin.

In 5 and 6, refer to Example 2.

5. Identify each statement. See margin.
 a. $S(1)$
 b. $S(2)$
 c. $S(k) \Rightarrow S(k + 1)$

6. Disprove: For all integers $n \geq 1$, $3^n > 1 + 2n$. See left.

7. Prove: For all integers $m \geq 1$, $2^m \geq 1 + m$. See margin.

Applying the Mathematics

In 8 and 9, prove using the Principle of Mathematical Induction. See margin.

8. For all integers $n \geq 9$, $2^n > 40n$.

9. For all integers $t \geq 3$, $3t^2 \geq 9t$.

2a) basis step: $S(1)$ is the statement: If $0 < x < 1$, then $x^1 < 1$.
b) $S(3)$: If $0 < x < 1$, then $x^3 < 1$
c) inductive step: Assume $S(k)$. So if $0 < x < 1$, by multiplication, $x \cdot x^k < x \cdot 1$ which implies $x^{k+1} < x$. But $x \leq 1$ so by the Transitive Property, $x^{k+1} < 1$. Thus $S(k) \Rightarrow S(k + 1)$

6) Let $n = 1$. Then $3^1 = 3$ and $1 + 2(1) = 3$, so $3 > 3$ gives a contradiction. So we can conclude that the statement is false.

left side is taken to the kth and $(k + 1)$st powers, multiplying by k is a natural thing to do.

Additional Examples

1. Prove: For all integers $n \geq 1$, if $x > 1$, *then* $x^n > 1$. **Sample: Let $S(n)$ be the statement: If $x > 1$, then $x^n > 1$. $S(1)$ is the statement: If $x > 1$, then $x > 1$, which is true. Suppose $S(k)$ is true. Then if $x > 1$, $x^k > 1$. Multiplying both sides by x, $x^{k+1} > x$, and since $x > 1$, $x^{k+1} > 1$ by the Transitive Property of Inequality. Thus $x^{k+1} > 1$, so $S(k + 1)$ is true. So, by the Principle of Mathematical Induction, $S(n)$ is true for all integers $n \geq 1$.**
2. Prove : For all integers $n \geq 6$, $3^{n-2} > 2^n$. **Sample: Let $S(n)$ be the statement: $3^{n-2} > 2^n$. $S(6)$ is the statement: $3^4 > 2^6$, which is true. Suppose $S(k)$ is true. Then $3^{k-2} > 2^k$. Multiplying both sides by 3, $3^{k-1} > 3 \cdot 2^k$. But since $3 > 2$ and 2^k is positive for all k, $3 \cdot 2^k > 2 \cdot 2^k$. Finally, $2 \cdot 2^k = 2^{k+1}$. Consequently, $3^{k-1} > 2^{k+1}$ by the Transitive Property of Inequality and Substitution, so $S(k + 1)$ is true. So, by the Principle of Mathematical Induction, $S(n)$ is true for all integers $n \geq 6$.**

Notes on Questions

Question 6 Error Alert Some students may forget that to disprove a statement they need only one counterexample! This question shows that the $\geq$ sign in **Example 2** cannot be replaced by the $>$ sign.

5. a. Basis step: $S(1)$: $3^1 \geq 1 + 2(1) \Rightarrow 3 \geq 3$
 b. $S(2)$: $3^2 \geq 1 + 2(2) \Rightarrow 9 \geq 5$
 c. Inductive step: $S(k)$: $3^k \geq 1 + 2k$; $3 \cdot 3^k \geq 3(1 + 2k)$ by multiplication. But $3 \cdot 3^k = 3^{k+1} \geq 3(1 + 2k) \geq 1 + 2(k + 1)$. Thus $S(k) \Rightarrow S(k + 1)$

7. Let $S(m)$ be the statement: $2^m \geq 1 + m$. $S(1)$: $2^1 = 2 \geq 2 = 1 + 1$, so $S(1)$ is true. Assume $S(k)$. Then

$2^k \geq k + 1$ — Definition of $S(k)$
$2 \cdot 2^k \geq 2(1 + k)$ — M_2
$2^{k+1} \geq 2 + 2k$ — Product of Powers and Distributive Property
$2^{k+1} \geq 1 + (k + 1) + k$ — Distributive Prop.
$2^{k+1} \geq 1 + (k + 1)$ — Transitive Prop., since $k \geq 1$

Thus, $S(k) \Rightarrow S(k + 1)$. So by the Principle of Mathematical Induction, $S(m)$ is true for all integers $m \geq 1$.

8. Let $S(n)$ be the statement $2^n > 40n$.
 $S(9)$: $2^9 = 512 > 360 = 40(9)$, so $S(9)$ is true.
 Assume $S(k)$: $2^k > 40k$. Then
 $2 \cdot 2^k > 2(40k)$ — M_2
 $2^{k+1} > 40(2k)$ — Product of Powers
 $2^{k+1} > 40(k + 1) + 40(k - 1)$ — Distributive Property
 $2^{k+1} > 40(k + 1)$ — Transitive Property, since $(k - 1) > 0$.
 Thus, $S(k) \Rightarrow S(k + 1)$. So, by the Principle of Mathematical Induction, $S(n)$ is true for all integers $n \geq 9$.

9. See Additional Answers at the back of this book.

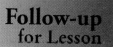

Notes on Questions

Question 14 Ask students if the inequalities are true for *any* negative integers *n*. [No]

Follow-up for Lesson 7-5

Practice

For more questions on SPUR Objectives, use **Lesson Master 7-5** (shown below).

Assessment

Written Communication Have students **work in pairs.** Ask each student to write a true statement similar to those in **Examples 1–2.** Then have partners use the Principle of Mathematical Induction to prove each other's premise. [Students prove inequality statements using the Principle of Mathematical Induction.]

Extension

To extend **Example 2,** ask each half of the class to prove one of the following for all integers $n \geq 1$: $4^n \geq 1 + 3n$ or $5^n \geq 1 + 4n$. [Proofs are similar to the Solution for **Example 2** on page 432.]

Additional Answers

10–11. See Additional Answers at the back of this book.

LESSON MASTER 7-5 — **Questions on SPUR Objectives** See pages 467–469 for objectives.

Properties Objective G

In 1–3, prove the statement using the Principle of Mathematical Induction.

1. For all integers $n \geq 1$, if $0 < a < 1$, then $0 < a^n < 1$. Basis step: If $0 < a < 1$, then $0 < a^1 < 1$, since $a^1 = a$.
Inductive step: Assume that $0 < a^k < 1$. Then $0 = a \cdot 0 < a \cdot a^k = a^{k+1} < a \cdot 1$, or $0 < a^{k+1} < a$, since $a > 0$. $0 < a^{k+1} < a$ and $a < 1 \Rightarrow 0 < a^{k+1} < 1$. So, the assumption that the inequalities are true for a^k implies that these inequalities are true for a^{k+1}.

2. For all integers $p \geq 2$, $4^p > p^2 + 2p + 1$.
Basis step: $4^2 = 16 > 2^2 + 2 \cdot 2 + 1 = 9$
Inductive step: Assume that $4^k > k^2 + 2k + 1$ for $k \geq 1$. Then $4^{k+1} = 4 \cdot 4^k > 4(k^2 + 2k + 1) = 4k^2 + 8k + 4 = (k^2 + 2k + 1) + 2(k + 1) + 1 + (3k^2 + 4k) = (k + 1)^2 + 2(k + 1) + 1 + (3k^2 + 4k) > (k + 1)^2 + 2(k + 1) + 1$. So, the assumption that the inequality is true for *k* implies that the inequality is true for $k + 1$.

3. For all integers $n \geq 1$ and all real θ such that $\cos\theta \neq 0$, $|\sec^n\theta| \geq |\cos^n\theta|$.
Basis step: $\cos\theta \neq 0 \Rightarrow 0 < |\cos\theta| \leq 1 \Rightarrow |\sec\theta| = \left|\frac{1}{\cos\theta}\right| = \frac{1}{|\cos\theta|} \geq 1 \geq |\cos\theta|$
Inductive step: Assume that $|\sec^k\theta| \geq |\cos^k\theta|$. Then $|\sec^{k+1}\theta| = |\sec\theta||\sec^k\theta| \geq |\sec\theta| \cdot |\cos^k\theta| \geq |\cos\theta||\cos^k\theta| = |\cos^{k+1}\theta|$. So, the assumption that the inequality is true for *k* implies that the inequality is true for $k + 1$.

4. a. *True or false.* For all integers $n \geq 1$, if $x > y$, then $x^n > y^n$. False
   b. If your answer to part a is "true," give a proof. If your answer is "false," give a counterexample.
   Sample: $-2 > -3$, but $(-2)^2 < (-3)^2$.

Review

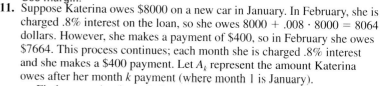

10. Prove: *For every positive integer n, 3 is a factor of* $n^3 + 14n$. *(Lesson 7-4)* See margin.

11. Suppose Katerina owes \$8000 on a new car in January. In February, she is charged .8% interest on the loan, so she owes $8000 + .008 \cdot 8000 = 8064$ dollars. However, she makes a payment of \$400, so in February she owes \$7664. This process continues; each month she is charged .8% interest and she makes a \$400 payment. Let A_k represent the amount Katerina owes after her month *k* payment (where month 1 is January).
   a. Find a recursive formula for the sequence $A_1, A_2, A_3, \ldots$.
   b. Use the recursive formula and a calculator to see how much she owes in May. *(Lesson 7-1)*
   See margin.

12. On the same set of axes, sketch the graphs of $y = \tan x$ and $y = \cot x$ for $-2\pi \leq x \leq 2\pi$, and explain how the graphs are related. *(Lesson 5-7)* See below.

13. Find numbers *x* and *y* such that $x \equiv 5 \pmod 7$ and $y \equiv 3 \pmod 7$.
   a. For the *x* and *y* you found, to what number (mod 7) is *xy* congruent?
   b. Must everyone get the same answer you got for part **a**? *(Lesson 4-5)*
   See left.

13a) Sample: $x = 12$ and $y = 10$, $xy = 120$ and $120 \pmod 7 \equiv 1 \pmod 7$
b) Yes. $xy \pmod 7 \equiv 1 \pmod 7$

Exploration

14. Are the inequalities in Examples 1 and 2 true for all negative integers *n*? Why or why not? **The inequality in Example 1 does not hold for all negative integers *n*, since if $x = .5$ and $n = -1$ then $x^n = 2$, which is greater than 1.**
The inequality in Example 2 is true for all negative integers *n*, since 3^n is always positive for $n < 0$ and $1 + 2n$ is always negative for $n < 0$. So, $3^n \geq 1 + 2n$ for all integers $n < 0$.

12)

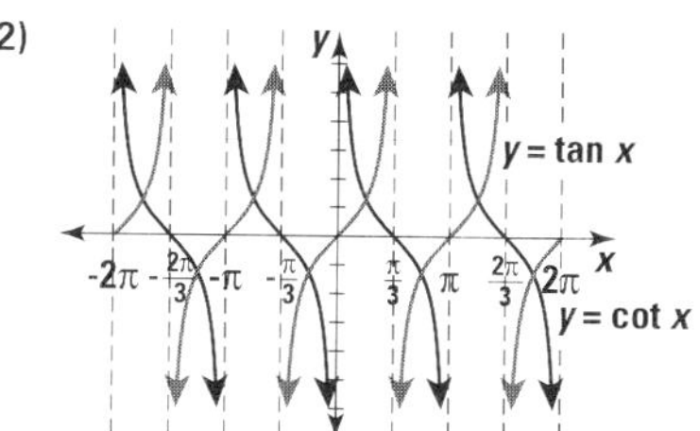

The graphs are related because $\cot x = -\tan\left(x - \frac{\pi}{2}\right)$, so $\cot x$ represents the transformation $T_{-1, \frac{\pi}{2}}$ applied to $\tan x$.

Adapting to Individual Needs

Extra Help

Some students may have trouble following how the Transitive Property of Inequality is used in **Example 2.** First point out that the Transitive Property of Inequality given at the beginning of the lesson can be rewritten using greater than signs: If $c > b$ and $b > a$, then $c > a$. Then identify the two key statements in the example: $3^{k+1} \geq 3 + 6k$ and $3 + 6k > 3 + 2k$. Now students should follow the reasonableness of $3^{k+1} \geq 3 + 2k$.

Challenge

$S(n)$: If *p* and *q* are any rational numbers such that $p < q$, then there exist *n* rational numbers such that $p < r_1 < r_2 < \ldots < r_n < q$. Have students prove $S(n)$ is true $\forall$ *n*. [$S(1)$ is easily verified by letting $r_1 = \frac{p+q}{2}$. Assume $S(k)$ is true. Letting $r_{k+1} = \frac{r_k + q}{2}$ verifies $S(k + 1)$ since r_{k+1} is between r_k and *q* so is not equal to any of the other r_i. Therefore, $S(n)$ is true for all *n*.]

LESSON

7-6

Geometric Series and the Resolution of Zeno's Paradox

Finite and Infinite Series

The indicated sum of consecutive terms of a sequence is called a **series**. If the sequence is finite, then the sum

$$\sum_{i=1}^{n} a_i = a_1 + a_2 + \ldots + a_n$$

is called a **finite series**. If the sequence is infinite, then there are infinitely many terms to add. The sum is denoted by

$$\sum_{i=1}^{\infty} a_i = a_1 + a_2 + \ldots$$

and is called an **infinite series**.

For example, if

$$a_i = \left(\tfrac{1}{2}\right)^i$$

then $$\sum_{i=0}^{10} \left(\tfrac{1}{2}\right)^i = 1 + \tfrac{1}{2} + \tfrac{1}{4} + \tfrac{1}{8} + \ldots + \tfrac{1}{1024}$$

is a finite series, while $$\sum_{i=0}^{\infty} \left(\tfrac{1}{2}\right)^i = 1 + \tfrac{1}{2} + \tfrac{1}{4} + \tfrac{1}{8} + \ldots$$

❶ is an infinite series. In fact, this is the infinite series from Zeno's Paradox in Lesson 7-2.

In stating his paradox about the impossibility of moving from point A to point B, Zeno argued that the sum of an infinite series must be infinite. Of course, he knew you could get from point A to point B, but he wanted to demonstrate that the logic and mathematics of his time could not deal with this situation. In this lesson, you will see how mathematicians today deal with such an infinite summation. To do so, we first consider finite series.

Finite Geometric Series

A finite **geometric series** is the sum of consecutive terms of a geometric sequence. The simplest such series has first term 1 and is the sum of the first n powers of the constant ratio r. There is a simple formula for this sum.

Theorem (Sum of the First n Powers)
If $r \neq 1$, then
$$1 + r + r^2 + \ldots + r^{n-1} = \frac{1 - r^n}{1 - r} \quad \forall \text{ integers } n \geq 1.$$

Lesson 7-6

Objectives

E Evaluate a finite or an infinite geometric series.

J Interpret computer programs which calculate terms of sequences.

Resources

From the ***Teacher's Resource File***
- Lesson Master 7-6
- Answer Master 7-6
- Teaching Aid 63: Warm-up

Additional Resources
- Visual for Teaching Aid 63
- Exploration 7-6

Lesson 7-6

Warm-up

Consider the sequence defined by $a_n = \frac{3}{11}(1 - (.01)^n)$.

1. Write the first five terms of this sequence. .27, .2727, .272727, .27272727, $.27272727\overline{27}$
2. What is $\lim_{n\to\infty} a_n$? $\frac{3}{11}$, or $.\overline{27}$

Notes on Reading

❶ You can use Zeno's paradox (Lesson 7-2) as a basis for writing partial sums and their values:

$S_1 = 1 \qquad = 1 + 0$

$S_2 = 1 + \frac{1}{2} \qquad = 1 + \frac{1}{2}$

$S_3 = 1 + \frac{1}{2} + \frac{1}{4} \qquad = 1 + \frac{3}{4}$

$S_4 = 1 + \frac{1}{2} + \frac{1}{4} + \frac{1}{8} \qquad = 1 + \frac{7}{8}$

$S_5 = 1 + \frac{1}{2} + \frac{1}{4} + \frac{1}{8} + \frac{1}{16} \qquad = 1 + \frac{15}{16}$

.
.
.

$S_n = 1 + \frac{1}{2} + \frac{1}{4} + \frac{1}{8} + \ldots + \frac{1}{2^{n-1}} = 1 + \frac{2^n - 1}{2^n}$

Since $2^n - 1 < 2^n$ always, $\frac{2^n - 1}{2^n} < 1$ $\Rightarrow 1 + \frac{2^n - 1}{2^n} < 2 \Rightarrow S_n < 2$ always!

Lesson 7-6 Overview

Broad Goals In the preceding lessons, mathematical induction has been used in proofs of rather specific results. In this lesson, the general problem of the evaluation of a finite geometric series is attacked, and part of its solution involves a mathematical induction proof. Then, by taking the limit, infinite geometric series can be evaluated and Zeno's paradox from Lesson 7-2 can be resolved.

Perspective Beginning with **Example 2** of **Lesson 7-1,** students have been working with series. Summation notation is a way of compactly expressing the terms of a series. In this lesson we formally define series and focus our attention on geometric series.

(Overview continues on page 436.)

The Evaluation of a Finite Geometric Series Theorem was known at the time of Euclid and is included as Proposition 35 of Book IX of his *Elements*. Here is a translation from Carl Boyer's *A History of Mathematics* (New York: John Wiley, 1968).

"If as many numbers as we please be in continued proportion, and there be subtracted from the second and the last numbers equal to the first, then as the excess of the second is to the first, so will the excess of the last be to all those before it." In algebraic terms, that means for a geometric sequence g with first term g_1 and common ratio r, $\frac{g_{n+1} - g_1}{S_n} = \frac{g_2 - g_1}{g_1}$ is equivalent to $S_n = \frac{g_1 - g_1 r^n}{1 - r}$.

Encourage students to be careful in their language when talking about infinite summation. Students need to grasp the concept that the infinite sum is the limit of the sequence of partial sums. This notion of the limit of the sequence of partial sums is an important concept in calculus that will be utilized in the study of the integral in Chapter 13.

Proof

The proof uses mathematical induction. Here $S(n)$ is the equation $1 + r + r^2 + \ldots + r^{n-1} = \frac{1 - r^n}{1 - r}$, where r is a real number and $r \neq 1$.

(1) Basis step: $S(1)$ is the statement $1 = \frac{1 - r^1}{1 - r}$. When $r \neq 1$, the right side equals 1, so $S(1)$ is true.

(2) Inductive step: Assume $S(k)$ is true. That is, assume $1 + r + r^2 + \ldots + r^{k-1} = \frac{1 - r^k}{1 - r}$. We must show that $S(k + 1)$ is true, where $S(k + 1)$ is the statement $1 + r + r^2 + \ldots + r^k = \frac{1 - r^{k+1}}{1 - r}$. We begin with the left side and show that it equals the right side.

$$1 + r + r^2 + \ldots + r^{k-1} + r^k = \frac{1 - r^k}{1 - r} + r^k \quad \text{inductive assumption, } A_{r,k}$$

$$= \frac{1 - r^k}{1 - r} + \frac{(1 - r)r^k}{1 - r} \quad \text{common denominator}$$

$$= \frac{1 - r^k + r^k - r^{k+1}}{1 - r} \quad \text{adding fractions, Distributive Property}$$

$$= \frac{1 - r^{k+1}}{1 - r} \quad \text{Opposites add to zero.}$$

Therefore, if $S(k)$ is true, then $S(k + 1)$ is true.

Since $S(1)$ is true and for all $k \geq 1$, $S(k) \Rightarrow S(k + 1)$, then by the Principle of Mathematical Induction, $S(n)$ is true for all integers $n \geq 1$.

Example 1

Find the sum of $1 + 3 + 9 + 27 + \ldots + 3^{10}$.

Solution

Here $r = 3$ and $n = 11$. So the sum is $\frac{1 - 3^{11}}{1 - 3} = \frac{3^{11} - 1}{2}$. A calculator shows this number to be 88,573.

Multiplying both sides of the formula for the Sum of the First n Powers by the number a results in a formula for the sum of the terms of any finite geometric sequence.

Zeno of Elea
(c. 495–c. 430 B.C.)

Theorem (Evaluation of a Finite Geometric Series)

If a is any real number and r is any real number other than 1, then for all integers $n \geq 1$,

$$a + ar + ar^2 + \ldots + ar^{n-1} = a\left(\frac{1 - r^n}{1 - r}\right).$$

Example 2

In Zeno's Paradox as given in Lesson 7-2, after going half the distance, then half the remaining distance, and so forth for n repetitions, the runner will have traveled the following number of minutes:

$$1 + \frac{1}{2} + \frac{1}{4} + \frac{1}{8} + \ldots + \frac{1}{2^{n-1}}.$$

a. Simplify this sum.
b. Calculate the sum for $n = 5$, 10, and 20.

Lesson 7-6 Overview, continued

It is possible that students will have seen the formula for the evaluation of a finite geometric series. In earlier UCSMP courses, students will have seen this proof:

$$\begin{aligned} S &= a + ar + ar^2 + ar^3 + ar^4 + \ldots + ar^{n-1} \\ -rS &= \quad - ar - ar^2 - ar^3 - ar^4 - \ldots - ar^{n-1} - ar^n \\ \hline S - rS &= a - ar^n \\ S(1 - r) &= a(1 - r^n) \\ S &= \frac{a(1 - r^n)}{1 - r} \text{ if } r \neq 1. \end{aligned}$$

This proof is sometimes not considered rigorous under today's mathematical standards because an infinite distributive property is used to get from S to $-rS$, and because there is an infinite subtraction. That is why we use mathematical induction in this lesson.

Solution

a. Use the Formula for the sum of the terms of a finite geometric sequence, with $a = 1$ and $r = \frac{1}{2}$.

$$1 + \frac{1}{2} + \frac{1}{4} + \frac{1}{8} + \ldots + \frac{1}{2^{n-1}} = \frac{1 - \left(\frac{1}{2}\right)^n}{1 - \frac{1}{2}} = \frac{1 - \frac{1}{2^n}}{\frac{1}{2}} = 2\left(1 - \frac{1}{2^n}\right)$$

b. For $n = 5$, the sum equals $2\left(1 - \frac{1}{2^5}\right) = 1.9375$.

For $n = 10$, the sum equals $2\left(1 - \frac{1}{2^{10}}\right) \approx 1.9980$.

For $n = 20$, the sum equals $2\left(1 - \frac{1}{2^{20}}\right) \approx 1.999998$.

Infinite Geometric Series

The expressions calculated in Example 2b are the sums of the first five, ten, and twenty terms of the infinite geometric series $1 + \frac{1}{2} + \frac{1}{4} + \frac{1}{8} + \ldots$. Such sums are called *partial sums*. Given any sequence of numbers $a_1, a_2, a_3, \ldots$, the **partial sums** of the sequence are the numbers

$$a_1, \quad a_1 + a_2, \quad a_1 + a_2 + a_3, \quad a_1 + a_2 + a_3 + a_4, \ldots.$$

We denote the sequence of partial sums by $S_1, S_2, S_3, \ldots$. Then

$$S_1 = a_1 = \sum_{i=1}^{1} a_i$$
$$S_2 = a_1 + a_2 = \sum_{i=1}^{2} a_i$$
$$S_3 = a_1 + a_2 + a_3 = \sum_{i=1}^{3} a_i$$
$$S_4 = a_1 + a_2 + a_3 + a_4 = \sum_{i=1}^{4} a_i$$
$$\vdots$$
$$S_n = a_1 + a_2 + a_3 + \ldots + a_n = \sum_{i=1}^{n} a_i$$
$$\vdots$$

In Example 2b above, the partial sums appear to get closer and closer to 2 as n gets larger and larger. If the numbers $S_1, S_2, S_3, \ldots$ approach a finite limit as n gets larger and larger without bound, then the infinite sum is defined to equal this limit.

> **Definition**
> Let $a_1, a_2, a_3, \ldots$ be an infinite sequence of numbers and let $S_n = \sum_{i=1}^{n} a_i$. Then the **infinite sum** $\sum_{k=1}^{\infty} a_k = \lim_{n\to\infty} S_n = \lim_{n\to\infty} \sum_{k=1}^{n} a_k$, provided this limit exists and is finite.

It appears that the infinite sum

$$1 + \frac{1}{2} + \frac{1}{4} + \frac{1}{8} + \ldots = \sum_{k=0}^{\infty} \frac{1}{2^k} = 2.$$

In the statement of the Sum of the First n Powers Theorem on page 435, students may ask why the last term on the left side is not r^n. In response, mention that we wish to have a formula for the first n terms and rewrite the left side as $r^0 + r^1 + r^2 + \ldots + r^{n-1}$ and point out that this series has exactly n terms. To further make this point, you can write the series in summation notation $\sum_{i=1}^{n} r^{i-1}$, which shows the n terms.

In the proof of the Evaluation of an Infinite Geometric Series Theorem, you may wish to point out two properties of limits that are used implicitly.

$\lim_{n\to\infty}[(\frac{a}{1-r})(1 - r^n)] = (\frac{a}{1-r})\lim_{n\to\infty}(1 - r^n)$ uses $\lim_{n\to\infty} k \cdot f(n) = k\lim_{n\to\infty} f(n)$, and

$(\frac{a}{1-r})\lim_{n\to\infty}(1 - r^n) = (\frac{a}{1-r})(1 - 0)$ uses $\lim_{n\to\infty}(k - f(n)) = \lim_{n\to\infty} k - \lim_{n\to\infty} f(n)$.

Optional Activities

Activity 1 Technology Connection
Materials: Explorations software

Students may use *Exploration 7-6, Finite Geometric Series,* as an alternative to **Example 1** in Lesson 7-6. Students can input the first term, the common ratio, and the number of terms. The program will show the first ten terms and the sum of the geometric series. Students can enter the common ratio as a fraction or as a decimal.

Activity 2 A ball drops 20 feet and rises each time to a height $\frac{3}{4}$ of the previous height. Have students determine how far the ball will travel up and down before coming to rest. [140 ft]

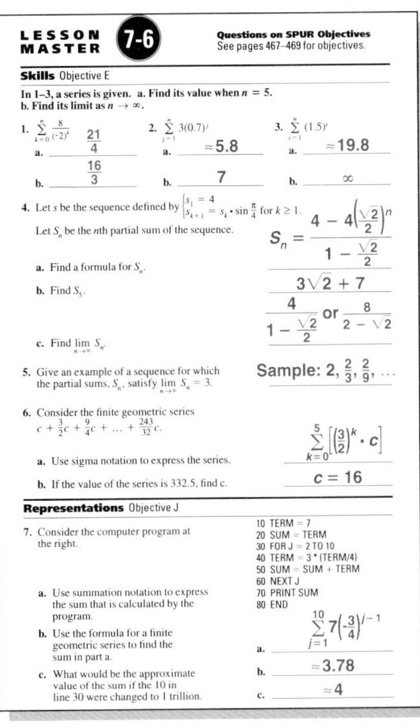
LESSON MASTER 7-6 Questions on SPUR Objectives
See pages 467–469 for objectives.

Skills Objective E

In 1–3, a series is given. a. Find its value when $n = 5$. b. Find its limit as $n \to \infty$.

1. $\sum_{k=0}^{n} \frac{8}{(-2)^k}$ a. $\frac{21}{4}$ b. $\frac{16}{3}$

2. $\sum_{j=1}^{n} 3(0.7)^j$ a. ≈ 5.8 b. 7

3. $\sum_{i=1}^{n} (1.5)^i$ a. ≈ 19.8 b. ∞

4. Let s be the sequence defined by $\begin{cases} s_1 = 4 \\ s_{k+1} = s_k \cdot \sin\frac{\pi}{4} \text{ for } k \ge 1. \end{cases}$
Let S_n be the nth partial sum of the sequence.
 a. Find a formula for S_n. $S_n = \dfrac{4 - 4\left(\frac{\sqrt{2}}{2}\right)^n}{1 - \frac{\sqrt{2}}{2}}$
 b. Find S_5. $3\sqrt{2} + 7$
 c. Find $\lim_{n\to\infty} S_n$. $\dfrac{4}{1 - \frac{\sqrt{2}}{2}}$ or $\dfrac{8}{2 - \sqrt{2}}$

5. Give an example of a sequence for which the partial sums, S_n, satisfy $\lim_{n\to\infty} S_n = 3$. Sample: $2, \frac{2}{3}, \frac{2}{9}, \ldots$

6. Consider the finite geometric series $c + \frac{3}{2}c + \frac{9}{4}c + \ldots + \frac{243}{32}c$.
 a. Use sigma notation to express the series. $\sum_{k=0}^{5}\left[\left(\frac{3}{2}\right)^k \cdot c\right]$
 b. If the value of the series is 332.5, find c. $c = 16$

Representations Objective J

7. Consider the computer program at the right.

```
10 TERM = 7
20 SUM = TERM
30 FOR J = 2 TO 10
40 TERM = 3 * (TERM/4)
50 SUM = SUM + TERM
60 NEXT J
70 PRINT SUM
80 END
```

 a. Use summation notation to express the sum that is calculated by the program. $\sum_{j=1}^{10} 7\left(-\frac{3}{4}\right)^{j-1}$
 b. Use the formula for a finite geometric series to find the sum in part a. ≈ 3.78
 c. What would be the approximate value of the sum if the 10 in line 30 were changed to 1 trillion. ≈ 4

Have students express the last sentence of the reading part of the lesson on page 439 in if-then language. [*If the limit of the sequence of partial sums exists, then the terms of the sequence approach zero.*]

The text shows that the converse is not true. To convince students that $\sum_{i=1}^{\infty} \frac{1}{i} = 1 + \frac{1}{2} + \frac{1}{3} + \frac{1}{4} + ... + \frac{1}{n} + ...$ has no finite limit, suggest grouping:

$$\underbrace{1}_{1} + \underbrace{\frac{1}{2} + \frac{1}{3} + \frac{1}{4}}_{>1} +$$

$$\underbrace{\frac{1}{5} + \frac{1}{6} + \frac{1}{7} + \frac{1}{8} + \frac{1}{9} + \frac{1}{10} + \frac{1}{11} + \frac{1}{12}}_{>1} + ...$$

We may group the terms of $\sum_{i=1}^{\infty} \frac{1}{i}$ into clusters whose sums are all 1 or more. Thus $\sum_{i=1}^{\infty} \frac{1}{i}$ has no finite limit.

Additional Examples

1. a. Evaluate $1 + 5 + 25 + 125 + ... + 5^{10}$ **$\frac{1 - 5^{11}}{1 - 5} = 12{,}207{,}031$**
   b. If I give you 1 penny today, double the amount tomorrow, and keep doubling every day for one 30-day month, how many pennies would you have received from me? **$\frac{1 - 2^{30}}{1 - 2} =$ 1,073,741,823 pennies which equals \$10,737,418.23.**

The proof of this depends on the following property of real numbers with absolute value less than 1. If $|b| < 1$, then $\lim_{n\to\infty} b^n = 0$. This agrees with what we found in Lesson 2-7 to be the end behavior of the exponential function $f(x) = b^x$ when $0 < b < 1$:

$$\lim_{x\to\infty} b^x = 0.$$

That is, the graph of f approaches the x-axis as x becomes larger and larger without bound. Thus when $0 < r < 1$,

$$\lim_{n\to\infty} r^n = 0.$$

Since for any integer n, $|r^n| = |(-r)^n|$, it is also the case that $\lim_{n\to\infty} r^n = 0$ when $-1 < r < 0$. These facts enable infinite geometric series to be evaluated.

Theorem (Evaluation of an Infinite Geometric Series)
If a is any real number and r is a real number with $0 < |r| < 1$, then

$$\sum_{k=0}^{\infty} ar^k = \frac{a}{1-r}.$$

Proof
Suppose a is any real number and r is a real number with $0 < |r| < 1$.

$\sum_{k=0}^{\infty} ar^k = \lim_{n\to\infty} \sum_{k=0}^{n} ar^k$	definition of infinite summation
$= \lim_{n\to\infty} \left[a\left(\frac{1-r^n}{1-r}\right)\right]$	Evaluation of a Finite Geometric Series Theorem
$= \lim_{n\to\infty} \left[\left(\frac{a}{1-r}\right)(1-r^n)\right]$	Rewrite.
$= \frac{a}{1-r} \lim_{n\to\infty} (1-r^n)$	Factor out the constant $\frac{a}{1-r}$.
$= \frac{a}{1-r}(1-0)$	$\lim_{n\to\infty} r^n = 0$
$= \frac{a}{1-r}$	

With the above theorem, the infinite series arising from Zeno's Paradox can be evaluated.

Example 3

Evaluate the infinite series $\sum_{k=0}^{\infty} \left(\frac{1}{2}\right)^k = 1 + \frac{1}{2} + \frac{1}{4} + \frac{1}{8} + \ldots + \frac{1}{2^n} + \ldots.$

Solution

This is an infinite geometric series with first term $a = 1$ and constant ratio $r = \frac{1}{2}$. By the theorem, the sum is $\frac{a}{1-r} = \frac{1}{1-\frac{1}{2}} = 2$.

The result of Example 3 agrees with common sense and resolves Zeno's Paradox. If it takes the runner one minute to go halfway from A to B, it takes two minutes to go all the way.

Optional Activities

Activity 3 Have students generalize **Question 12** to explain why all repeating decimals are rational numbers. If students need more practice with the method first, have them create some repeating decimals of their own, write them as the sum of a finite decimal and an infinite geometric series, and then find their sums. [All repeating decimals can be written as the sum of a rational number s and the infinite series $a + ar + ar^2 + ... + ar^n + ...$ where a is a rational number (and r is a negative integer power of 10. Since $|r| < 1$, the series converges to $\frac{a}{1-r}$. $1 - r$ is rational since both 1 and r are rational, so the quotient is rational since the quotient of two rational numbers is rational. Adding s keeps the sum rational.]

Activity 4 Ask students to research the p-series $\sum_{n=1}^{\infty} \frac{1}{n^p}$, and to answer the following.

1. When $p = 1$, the series is called the harmonic series. Why is that? [Musical strings with lengths in the ratios $\frac{1}{2}$, $\frac{1}{4}$, and $\frac{2}{3}\left(=\frac{1}{2}+\frac{1}{6}\right)$, were seen to produce pleasant tones. Mathematics was studied with music in ancient times, and these ratios came to be called harmonic.]

Not all sequences of partial sums of a given infinite series approach a finite limit. For instance, consider the following sum of terms of a geometric sequence with $r > 1$:

$$1 + 2 + 4 + 8 + \ldots + 2^n + \ldots.$$

Since the terms of this geometric sequence become larger and larger, the sequence of corresponding partial sums approaches infinity, not a finite limit. A necessary condition for the limit of partial sums to exist and be finite is that the terms of the given sequence approach zero. But this is not sufficient. For the infinite harmonic series

$$\sum_{i=1}^{\infty} \frac{1}{i} = 1 + \frac{1}{2} + \frac{1}{3} + \frac{1}{4} + \frac{1}{5} + \ldots + \frac{1}{n} + \ldots$$

$\lim_{n\to\infty} \frac{1}{n} = 0$, but the partial sums of the series have no finite limit.

QUESTIONS

Covering the Reading

In 1 and 2, find the sum of the geometric series.

1. $1 + 2.5 + 6.25 + 15.625 + \ldots + (2.5)^7$ **≈ 1016.6**

2. $\sum_{i=1}^{n-1} \frac{3}{2^i}$ **$6 - 6\left(\frac{1}{2}\right)^n$**

3. Given the sequence $a_1, a_2, a_3, \ldots$ with $a_k = \frac{1}{k}$ for each integer $k \ge 1$. Let $S_1, S_2, S_3, \ldots$ denote the sequence of corresponding partial sums. Find S_3, S_4, and S_5. **$S_3 = \frac{11}{6}$, $S_4 = \frac{25}{12}$, $S_5 = \frac{137}{60}$**

4. In the lesson, it was shown that if $0 < r < 1$, then $\lim_{n\to\infty} r^n = 0$.
   a. If $r = \frac{1}{2}$, how large must n be to ensure that $r^n < .001$?
   b. Calculate r^n for this value of n. **≈ 0.00098**
   c. If $r = .99$, how large must n be to ensure that $r^n < .001$?
   $n \ge 688$ a) $n \ge 10$

5. a. Find the sum $\frac{4}{3} + \frac{4}{3^2} + \frac{4}{3^3} + \ldots + \frac{4}{3^{20}}$. **≈ 2**
   b. Find $\sum_{k=0}^{\infty} \frac{4}{3^k}$. **6**

6. Find the sum of the infinite geometric sequence $100 + 80 + 64 + \frac{256}{5} + \frac{1024}{25} + \ldots.$ **500**

7. Is the value of $\sum_{k=0}^{\infty} \left(\frac{10}{9}\right)^k$ finite? Why or why not?
   No, it diverges since the ratio $r = \frac{10}{9} > 1$ and $\lim_{k\to\infty} \left(\frac{10}{9}\right)^k = \infty \ne 0$.

Applying the Mathematics

8. An infinite series is called **convergent** if it has a finite limit, **divergent** otherwise. **See left.**
   a. Give an example of a convergent series.
   b. Give an example of a divergent series.

8a) Sample: $\sum_{n=0}^{\infty} \frac{1}{5^n}$

b) Sample: $\sum_{n=0}^{\infty} \left(\frac{3}{2}\right)^n$

2. Zeno's runner of Lesson 7-2, after reaching a midpoint, always has half the remaining distance to run.

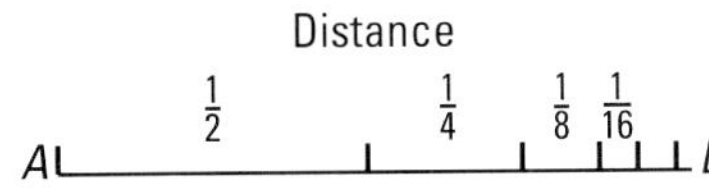

For n repetitions, the fraction of distance from A to B that he has run is $D_n = \frac{1}{2} + \frac{1}{4} + \frac{1}{8} + \ldots + \frac{1}{2^n}$.

a. Simplify this sum. **$D_n = 1 - \frac{1}{2^n}$ or $\frac{2^n - 1}{2^n}$**

b. Calculate this sum for $n = 5$, 10, and 20. **$D_5 = \frac{31}{32} = 0.96875$, $D_{10} = \frac{1023}{1024} \approx 0.9990234375$, $D_{20} \approx \frac{1,048,575}{1,048,576} \approx 0.9999990463$**

3. Evaluate the infinite series $\frac{1}{2} + \frac{1}{4} + \frac{1}{8} + \ldots + \frac{1}{2^n} + \ldots.$ **1**

Notes on Questions

Question 4 Solving these inequalities requires the use of logarithms. Students may need to be reminded of this inequality-solving technique. This question helps to prepare students for understanding the ε-δ (epsilon-delta) proofs that they may see in calculus.

Question 8 This question introduces the definitions of convergent and divergent series. It is useful for students to understand the meaning of these terms.

2. Look at the sequence of partial sums for the harmonic series. Do you think it converges? [It happens not to converge.]
3. For what values of p does the p-series converge? [$p > 1$]

Adapting to Individual Needs

Extra Help

Some students will need constant reminders of the distinction between *sequence* and *series*: *Sequence* is used to refer a function whose domain is a set of consecutive integers, while *series* means the indicated sum of consecutive terms of a sequence. Point out that sometimes we refer to a sequence of series, as in the phrase *sequence of partial sums* (finite series) discussed following **Example 2.**

Challenge

Have students use a series to show that $.\overline{9} = 1$. $\left[.\overline{9} = \sum_{k=0}^{\infty} .9(.1)^k = \frac{.9}{1 - .1} = 1\right]$

Notes on Questions

Question 11 Error Alert
Ask students to write out the first five terms of both the sequence (the changing values of TERM) and the partial sums of the series (the changing values of SUM) associated with this question. Some students will carelessly mix the two.

Question 17 Writing $\sum_{k=1}^{\infty} \frac{6}{k^2}$ as $6\sum_{k=1}^{\infty} \frac{1}{k^2}$ and evaluating $6(\frac{1}{1^2} + \frac{1}{2^2} + \frac{1}{3^2} + \frac{1}{4^2} + \ldots)$ will be easier.

Follow-up for Lesson 7-6

Practice

For more questions on SPUR Objectives, use **Lesson Master 7-6** (shown on page 437).

Assessment

Written Communication Have students give examples of two infinite geometric series, one with a finite limit and one without. Then ask them to explain how they determined the limits of their examples. [Students show understanding of the evaluation of infinite geometric series.]

9a) $a\left(\frac{1-r^n}{1-r}\right) = a \cdot \frac{-1}{-1} \cdot \frac{1-r^n}{1-r} = a\left(\frac{r^n-1}{r-1}\right)$
c) the right side
d) the left side

10) $p\left(\frac{3^{n+2}-1}{3-1}\right) = \frac{p}{2}(3^{n+2}-1)$

11a) $a_1 = 3$, $a_k = \frac{1}{2}a_{k-1}$, for all integers $2 \le k \le 25$.
b) $a_n = 3\left(\frac{1}{2}\right)^{n-1}$
c) $\sum_{j=1}^{25} \left(\frac{1}{2}\right)^{j-1}$
f) The result confirms **d** and **e**.

12a) $6.2 + \frac{71}{10^4} + \frac{71}{10^7} + \frac{71}{10^{10}} + \ldots + \frac{71}{10^{4+3(n-1)}}$

9. a. Explain why, for all real numbers a and r with $r \neq 1$, **a, c, d) See left.**

$$a\left(\frac{1-r^n}{1-r}\right) = a\left(\frac{r^n-1}{r-1}\right).$$

b. Evaluate the left and right sides of the equation in part **a** for $a = 1$ and for both $r = 2$ and $r = \frac{1}{2}$. **See margin.**

c. Which side of the equation is easier to evaluate when $r > 1$?

d. Which side of the equation is easier to evaluate when $r < 1$?

10. Find the sum $p + 3p + 3^2p + \ldots + 3^{n+1}p$. **See left.**

11. Consider the computer program below.

```
10 TERM = 3
20 SUM = 3
30 FOR K = 2 TO 25
40   TERM = TERM * .5
50   SUM = SUM + TERM
60 NEXT K
70 PRINT SUM
80 END
```

a. Write a recursive definition for the sequence whose terms are stored in the variable TERM. **See left.**

b. Write an explicit formula for the sequence. **See left.**

c. Use summation notation to write the sum that is calculated by the program. **See left.**

d. Use the formula for the sum of the terms of a finite geometric series to find the sum in part **c**. **≈ 5.99999982**

e. Suppose line 30 is modified by changing 25 to larger and larger integers, running the program each time. The printed answer will get closer and closer to what number? **6**

f. Run the program to confirm your answers to parts **d** and **e**. **See left.**

12. a. Write the infinite repeating decimal $6.2071071071\ldots = 6.2\overline{071}$ as the sum of a finite decimal and an infinite geometric series. **See left.**

b. Add the decimal and the series to find a simple fraction equal to the infinite decimal. $\frac{62009}{9990}$

Review

13. Prove: For every positive integer n, if $x > 1$, then $x^n > 1$. *(Lesson 7-5)* **See margin.**

14. Consider the equation

$$S(n): \sum_{k=1}^{n} [k(k+1)] = \frac{n(n+1)(n+2)}{3}.$$ **See margin.**

a. Verify that $S(3)$ is true.

b. Use mathematical induction to prove that $S(n)$ is true for all integers $n \ge 1$. *(Lesson 7-3)*

440

Additional Answers

9. b. $a = 1, r = 2$:
left side $= 1 \cdot \left(\frac{1-2^n}{-1}\right) = 2^n - 1$,
right side $= 1 \cdot \left(\frac{2^n-1}{1}\right) = 2^n - 1$;

$a = 1, r = \frac{1}{2}$:
left side $= 1 \cdot \left(\frac{1-\left(\frac{1}{2}\right)^n}{\frac{1}{2}}\right) = 2 - 2\left(\frac{1}{2}\right)^n$,
right side $= 1 \cdot \left(\frac{\left(\frac{1}{2}\right)^n - 1}{-\left(\frac{1}{2}\right)}\right) = 2 - 2\left(\frac{1}{2}\right)^n$

13. Let $S(n)$: if $x > 1$, then $x^n > 1$ ∀ integers $n \ge 1$.
$S(1)$: $x^1 = x > 1$, is true since x is greater than 1.
Assume $S(k)$. If $k > 1$, then $x^k > 1$.

$x \cdot x^k > x \cdot 1$	M_x
$x^{k+1} > x$	Product of Powers
$x^{k+1} > 1$	Transitive Property

Thus $S(k) \Rightarrow S(k+1)$. So by the Principle of Mathematical Induction, $S(n)$ is true for all positive integers n.

15a)

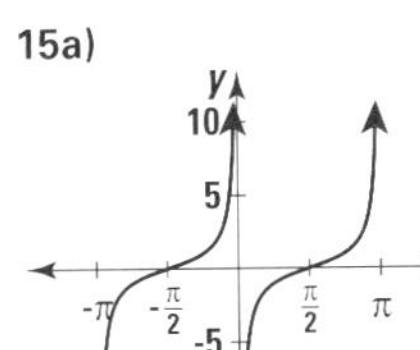

The graph has shifted $\frac{\pi}{2}$ units to the right.

18a) $4, \frac{-4}{3}, \frac{4}{5}, \frac{-4}{7}, \frac{4}{9}, \frac{-4}{11}$

15. a. Graph $y = \tan\left(\theta - \frac{\pi}{2}\right)$ on the interval $-\pi \le \theta \le \pi$. How is this graph related to the parent graph $y = \tan\theta$? **See left.**

b. Solve the equation $\tan\left(\theta - \frac{\pi}{2}\right) \le 1$ on the interval $-\pi \le \theta \le \pi$. *(Lessons 3-8, 5-7, 6-8)* $-\pi < \theta \le -\frac{\pi}{4}$ **or** $0 < \theta \le \frac{3\pi}{4}$

16. Solve for q: $\frac{1}{25} + \frac{1}{q} = \frac{1}{10}$. *(Lesson 5-8)* $\frac{50}{3}$

Exploration

17. a. Use a computer or programmable calculator to approximate $\sum_{k=1}^{\infty} \frac{6}{k^2}$.

b. Find the square root of your answer to part **a**. **3.141**

c. What do you think the exact value of the answer to part **b** is? π

a) **about 9.867**

18. Define a sequence by $a_k = \frac{(-1)^{k+1} \cdot 4}{2k - 1}$.

a. Find the first six terms of the sequence. **See left.**

b. Write a program to print the corresponding partial sums S_n for $n = 1, 2, 3, \ldots, 100$. Note that the terms of S alternately increase and decrease. **See below.**

c. Use your program to approximate $\sum_{k=1}^{\infty} \frac{(-1)^{k+1} \cdot 4}{2k - 1}$. A good approximation can be obtained by averaging two consecutive partial sums, such as S_{10000} and S_{10001}. **3.141594**

d. What do you think the exact value of the answer to part **c** is? π

b)
```
10 SUM = 0
20 FOR TERM = 1 TO 100
30 LET A = (-1)^(TERM + 1)*4/(2*TERM - 1)
40 SUM = SUM + A
50 PRINT SUM
60 NEXT TERM
70 END
```

Extension

Discuss what happens to an infinite geometric series when the common ratio is -1. Ask students for their views. You might compare them with the views of Euler. Euler thought that the sum
$S = 1 - 1 + 1 - 1 + 1 - 1 + \ldots$
was $\frac{1}{2}$, arguing as follows:
Grouping one way, $(1 - 1) + (1 - 1) + (1 - 1) + \ldots = 0$.
Grouping a second way, $1 - 1 + 1 - 1 + 1 - 1 + \ldots = 1 + (-1 + 1) + (-1 + 1) + (-1 + 1) + \ldots = 1$.
The average is $\frac{1}{2}$.
Two arguments confirm Euler's answer:
Let $S = 1 - 1 + 1 - 1 + 1 - 1 + \ldots$
Then $S = 1 - (1 - 1 + 1 - 1 + 1 - 1 + \ldots)$, so $S = 1 - S \Rightarrow 2S = 1 \Rightarrow S = \frac{1}{2}$.
Ignoring the stipulation that $|r| < 1$ in the formula for a infinite geometric sequence,
$S = \frac{a}{1 - r} = \frac{1}{1 - (-1)} = \frac{1}{2}$.
However, today we would say that the series has no limit.

Project Update Project 1, *Amortizations,* Project 3, *Zeno's Paradoxes*, and Project 5, *Geometric Sequences*, on pages 463–464, relate to the content of this lesson.

14. a. $S(3)$: $\sum_{i=1}^{3} i(i + 1) = \frac{3 \cdot 4 \cdot 5}{3}$.
Does $1 \cdot 2 + 2 \cdot 3 + 3 \cdot 4 = 4 \cdot 5$? Does $2 + 6 + 12 = 20$? Does $20 = 20$? Yes. Hence, $S(3)$ is true.

b. $S(1)$: $1 \cdot 2 = \frac{1 \cdot 2 \cdot 3}{3}$, which is true.

Assume $S(k)$: $\sum_{i=1}^{k} i(i + 1) = \frac{k(k + 1)(k + 2)}{3}$ is true for some integer $k \ge 1$. Show that $S(k + 1)$: $\sum_{i=1}^{k+1} i(i + 1) = \frac{(k + 1)(k + 2)(k + 3)}{3}$ is true.

$\sum_{i=1}^{k+1} i(i + 1) = \sum_{i=1}^{k} i(i + 1) + (k + 1)(k + 2)$
$= \frac{k(k + 1)(k + 2)}{3} + (k + 1)(k + 2)$
$= (k + 1)(k + 2)\left(\frac{k}{3} + 1\right)$
$= \frac{(k + 1)(k + 2)(k + 3)}{3}$.

Hence, $S(n)$ holds $\forall$ integer $n \ge 1$.

Lesson 7-7

Objectives

G Prove statements using the Strong Form of the Principle of Mathematical Induction.

Resources

From the ***Teacher's Resource File***
- Lesson Master 7-7
- Answer Master 7-7
- Assessment Sourcebook: Quiz for Lessons 7-5 through 7-7
- Teaching Aids
  64 Warm-up
  66 Principles of Mathematical Induction

Additional Resources
- Visuals for Teaching Aids 64, 66

Teaching Lesson 7-7

Warm-up

Give a prime factorization of each integer.

1. 360 $2^3 \cdot 3^2 \cdot 5$
2. 123,123 $3 \cdot 7 \cdot 11 \cdot 13 \cdot 41$
3. 10^n $2^n \cdot 5^n$

(Note: Because the prime factorization is unique up to the order of its factors, every student should have the same prime factorization.)

LESSON

7-7 *Strong Mathematical Induction*

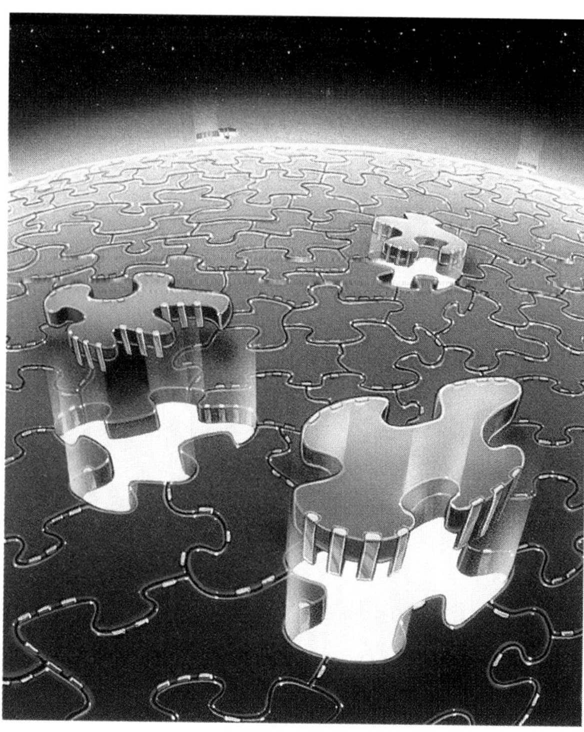

Puzzling Question. *If a jigsaw puzzle has one thousand pieces, how many moves are needed to assemble it?* *See Example 1.*

What Is Strong Mathematical Induction?

When defining a sequence recursively, sometimes the recurrence relation requires that you know more than one previous term (as in the Fibonacci sequence, in which a_{n+1} is defined in terms of a_n and a_{n-1}). Similarly, the inductive step in some mathematical induction proofs requires an inductive assumption that more than $S(k)$ is true. This modified inductive assumption results in what is called the *strong form of mathematical induction*, or *strong mathematical induction*.

> **Principle of Mathematical Induction (Strong Form)**
> Suppose that for each positive integer n, $S(n)$ is a sentence in n. If
> (1) $S(1)$ is true, and
> (2) for all integers $k \geq 1$, the assumption that $S(1), S(2), \ldots, S(k-1), S(k)$ are all true implies that $S(k+1)$ is also true,
> then $S(n)$ is true for all integers $n \geq 1$.

The Strong Form of Mathematical Induction given above differs from the original form in Lesson 7-3 only in the inductive step. In the inductive step in the Strong Form, you are allowed to use the assumption that *all* of the statements $S(1), S(2), \ldots, S(k-1), S(k)$ are true in order to prove that $S(k+1)$ is true. These two forms of mathematical induction are logically equivalent in the sense that the validity of either form implies the validity of the other. (The proof is beyond the scope of this course.)

Lesson 7-7 Overview

Broad Goals This lesson provides examples of the use of the Strong Form of Mathematical Induction.

Perspective The Strong Form of Mathematical Induction is akin to defining the nth term of a sequence recursively in terms of any of the preceding terms. That is, in the strong form, the truth of a proposition $S(x)$ for any values of $x \leq k$ can be used to deduce the truth of the proposition $S(k+1)$.

Mathematically, the two forms of mathematical induction are equivalent; each can be proved from the other; and in practice each is called simply "mathematical induction," but for learning purposes it is effective to separate them.

An Application to Jigsaw Puzzles

In this lesson there are three proofs which utilize strong mathematical induction. The first proof involves assembling a jigsaw puzzle. The process can be thought of as a game in which a *move* consists of putting together two *blocks*, each consisting of one or more individual puzzle pieces, to form a larger block. Before reading on, try to answer these questions: If the puzzle has n pieces, how many moves are needed? Does the number of moves depend on how you put the puzzle together?

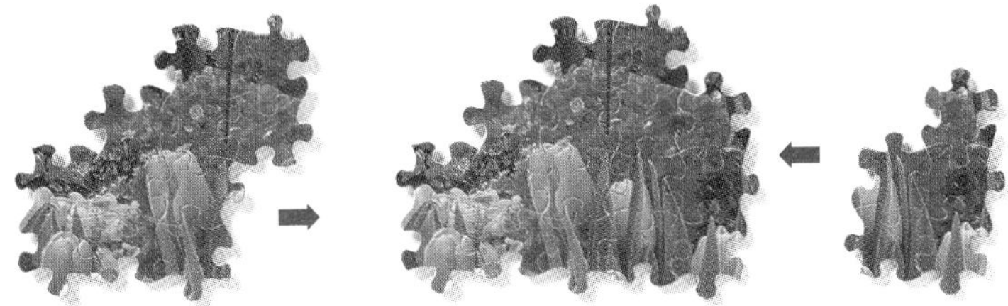

To many people, the answers are not obvious. Although there are many different ways to assemble a given jigsaw puzzle, the *number* of moves that are needed is always the same!

Example 1

Prove: $\forall$ positive integers n, the number of moves necessary to assemble any jigsaw puzzle with n pieces is $n - 1$.

Solution

Let $S(n)$ be the sentence: *Any assembly of a jigsaw puzzle with n pieces requires n − 1 moves.*

(1) Show that $S(1)$ is true.

$S(1)$: Any assembly of a jigsaw puzzle with 1 piece requires 0 moves.

A jigsaw puzzle with only one piece is already assembled and so no moves are required for its assembly. Therefore $S(1)$ is true. (Since a two-piece puzzle requires 1 move for its assembly, $S(2)$ is true also.)

(2) Show that the assumption that $S(1), S(2), \dots, S(k)$ are all true implies that $S(k + 1)$ is true.

Assume that for some integer $k \geq 1$, $S(1), S(2), \dots, S(k - 1), S(k)$ are all true. This means if a jigsaw puzzle has k or fewer pieces, then the number of moves required for any assembly of that puzzle is 1 less than the number of pieces.

Show that this assumption implies that $S(k + 1)$ is true:

$S(k + 1)$: Any assembly of a jigsaw puzzle with $k + 1$ pieces requires k moves.

Now a jigsaw puzzle with $k + 1$ pieces has been assembled by some finite sequence of moves. The last move in this sequence put together two blocks. If r and s are the numbers ▸

Notes on Reading

The strong form of mathematical induction is not always found in texts at this level. The examples and theorems in this lesson show the power of the strong form of the Principle of Mathematical Induction. Students are led from the seemingly trivial theorem about jigsaw puzzles to the powerful part of the Fundamental Theorem of Arithmetic.

Teaching Aid 66 with the statements of the original form and strong form of mathematical induction is provided so that students can easily see the distinction.

For some students (and teachers), the jigsaw puzzle result of **Example 1** is so obvious that they wonder why a proof is needed. For others, the result is not obvious at all. You may wish to point out that implicit in **Example 1** is the assumption that no mistakes are made in building the puzzle, that is, that no pieces are incorrectly connected.

If you used the infinite staircase analogy given in the Teacher Notes for Lesson 7-3, the inductive step in Strong Mathematical Induction becomes: Assuming that you have reached all of the first k steps, show that you can also climb step $k + 1$. You might think of it as including climbers who take two or three or any number of stairs at a time.

Optional Activities

To conclude the lesson, have students make up a recursively defined sequence like the ones in **Questions 5–6,** make a conjecture about the sequence, and then prove their assertion. [Students may build off of **Question 5** by defining a_1 and a_2 to be multiples of 3 and asserting that every term in the sequence is a multiple of 3. Building off **Question 6,** students may define $a_1 = 2$ and $a_2 = 4$, and $a_{k+1} = a_{k-1} + 3a_k$ for $k \geq 2$ and assert that every term of the sequence is an even integer.]

❶ The first paragraph following **Example 1** is an important variant of strong induction. The original definition of strong induction specifies $n = 1$. The corresponding idea with the original form of mathematical induction is found in **Example 3** of Lesson 7-3, Additional Example 3 in these Teacher Notes to Lesson 7-3, and in many of the problems of Lesson 7-5. In essence, you don't have to push over the first domino to begin induction. You may begin at the qth domino.

Some students may note that **Example 2** is basically a repeated (forever) application of a theorem that the sum of any three odd numbers is also odd.

of pieces in these two blocks, then r + s is the total number of pieces in the puzzle. That is, r + s = k + 1. Hence both r and s are integers from 1 to k, inclusive.

These two final blocks of pieces can be thought of as completed jigsaw puzzles with r and s pieces, and so by the inductive assumption, these two blocks required r − 1 and s − 1 moves for their assembly. Therefore, the total number of moves required for the assembly of the puzzle with k + 1 pieces is

$$\underbrace{(r-1) + (s-1)}_{\text{moves to assemble two blocks}} + \underset{\text{move to put the two blocks together}}{1}$$

$= r + s - 1$

$= (k + 1) - 1$ because $r + s = k + 1$

$= k.$

It follows that S(k + 1) is true, which completes the inductive step. Therefore, by the Strong Form of the Principle of Mathematical Induction, S(n) is true for every positive integer n.

❶ As with the original form of mathematical induction, strong mathematical induction does not have to begin with $n = 1$. Also the basis step may require establishing the proof of $S(n)$ for more than one particular value of n. So the basis step can be replaced by

> $S(a), S(a + 1), S(a + 2), \ldots, S(b)$ are true for some particular integers a and b.

Then in the inductive step, $k \geq a$ and $S(a), S(a + 1), S(a + 2), \ldots, S(b)$ are assumed true.

An Application to Divisibility

Consider the sequence defined recursively by

$$\begin{cases} a_1 = 1 \\ a_2 = 1 \\ a_3 = 1 \\ a_{k+1} = a_k + a_{k-1} + a_{k-2} & \text{for } k \geq 3. \end{cases}$$

Using successive substitution to calculate a_4, a_5, a_6, and a_7 yields

$$\begin{aligned} a_4 &= a_3 + a_2 + a_1 = 1 + 1 + 1 = 3 \\ a_5 &= a_4 + a_3 + a_2 = 3 + 1 + 1 = 5 \\ a_6 &= a_5 + a_4 + a_3 = 5 + 3 + 1 = 9 \\ a_7 &= a_6 + a_5 + a_4 = 9 + 5 + 3 = 17. \end{aligned}$$

A reasonable conjecture would be that every term in the sequence is odd.

Strong mathematical induction can be used to prove this conjecture. The inductive step uses the recurrence relation $a_{k+1} = a_k + a_{k-1} + a_{k-2}$, but

LESSON MASTER  **7-7**

Questions on SPUR Objectives
See pages 467–469 for objectives.

Properties Objective G

1. Let $S(n)$ be a sentence in n. Suppose that $S(1)$ is false. Also suppose that for all integers $k \geq 1$, the assumption that $S(1), S(2), \ldots S(k-1), S(k)$ are all false implies that $S(k+1)$ is also false. What can you conclude? Explain your answer.

   Sample: It is true that $S(n)$ is false for all integers n. The Strong Form of Mathematical Induction requires a statement of truth.

In 2–4, use the Strong Form of Mathematical Induction.

2. Let a be the sequence defined by

   $$\begin{cases} a_1 = bq \\ a_2 = cq \\ a_{k+1} = da_k + ea_{k-1} \ \forall k \geq 2, \end{cases}$$

   where b, c, d, e, and q are all integers. Prove that q is a factor of every term of the sequence.

   Sample: By definition q is a factor of a_n for $n = 1$ and $n = 2$. Assume that q is a factor of $a_1, a_2, \ldots$, and a_k for $k \geq 2$. Then $a_k = rq$ for some integer r, and $a_{k-1} = sq$, for some integer s. So, $a_{k+1} = da_k + ea_{k-1} = drq + esq = (dr + es)q$; and thus q is a factor of a_{k+1}. So, the assumption that q is a factor of $a_1, a_2, \ldots$, and a_k implies that q is a factor of a_{k+1}.

Adapting to Individual Needs

Extra Help

If the jigsaw puzzle results of **Example 1** are not obvious to your students, you might consider this experiment relating to the jigsaw puzzle problem. Bring in several pieces of a puzzle and have students count the number of moves to assemble those pieces for different numbers of puzzle pieces. Students might be able to conjecture the relationship that is proved in **Example 1.**

this relation is only valid for $k \geq 3$. Thus, the inductive step (showing that $S(1), \ldots, S(k)$ are true implies $S(k+1)$ is true) can only be done for $k \geq 3$. This is like showing that in a row of dominoes, each falling domino, starting with the third one, causes the next one to fall. You must still show that the first three dominoes fall. Thus, in the proof which follows, the basis step shows that $S(1)$, $S(2)$, and $S(3)$ are true.

Example 2

Prove that all of the terms of the sequence defined on page 444 are odd.

Solution

The following is to be proved for all natural numbers n.

$$S(n)\text{: } a_n \text{ is an odd integer.}$$

(1) Show that $S(1)$, $S(2)$, and $S(3)$ are true.
$S(1)$, $S(2)$, and $S(3)$ are the statements that a_1, a_2, and a_3 are odd integers. The initial conditions $a_1 = 1$, $a_2 = 1$, and $a_3 = 1$ imply that they are. So $S(1)$, $S(2)$, and $S(3)$ are true.

(2) Show that the assumption that $S(1), S(2), \ldots, S(k-1), S(k)$ are all true for some integer $k \geq 3$ implies that $S(k+1)$ is true.
Assume that $a_1, a_2, \ldots, a_{k-1}, a_k$ are all odd integers. We must show that a_{k+1} is an odd integer where $a_{k+1} = a_k + a_{k-1} + a_{k-2}$. From the definition of odd, an integer m is odd if and only if it can be written as $m = 2t + 1$ for some integer t. Thus, since a_k, a_{k-1}, and a_{k-2} are all odd, there are integers p, q, and r such that

$$a_k = 2p + 1,\ a_{k-1} = 2q + 1,\ a_{k-2} = 2r + 1.$$

Substituting into the recurrence relation

$$\begin{aligned} a_{k+1} &= a_k + a_{k-1} + a_{k-2} \\ a_{k+1} &= (2p + 1) + (2q + 1) + (2r + 1) \\ &= 2(p + q + r + 1) + 1. \end{aligned}$$

Since $p + q + r + 1$ is an integer, then $2(p + q + r + 1)$ is an even integer, and it follows that a_{k+1} has the form of an odd integer. Thus, if $S(1), S(2), \ldots, S(k)$ are all true, $S(k+1)$ is true.

Therefore, by the Strong Form of the Principle of Mathematical Induction, the statement

$$S(n)\text{: } a_n \text{ is an odd integer}$$

is true for all positive integers n.

An Application to Prime Numbers

Some important theorems require strong mathematical induction for their proofs. On the next page it is used to prove a statement that is part of the Fundamental Theorem of Arithmetic.

Most of the proofs that students are expected to complete using the Strong Form of Induction will relate to properties of recursively defined sequences, such as in **Example 2.** Students need to realize that in such situations the basis step may involve verifying the property for more than one specific statement.

Be careful that you do not allow the class to get bogged down at this point. By now students should have the basics of mathematical induction proofs even though they may still have some problems in final execution of the technique. There are still two more lessons in the chapter to provide opportunities for further practice.

▶ LESSON MASTER 7-7 *page 2*

Sample proofs are given.

3. Let a be the sequence defined by

$$\begin{cases} a_1 = 7q \\ a_2 = 13q^2 \\ a_{k+1} = 4qa_k + 10q^2a_{k-1}\ \forall\, k \geq 2, \end{cases}$$

where q is an integer.

Prove that q^n is a factor of $a_n\ \forall\, n \geq 1$.

For $S(n)$ use $S(n)$: q^n is a factor of a_n. $S(1)$: $a_1 = 7q$ is true. $S(2) = a_2 = 13q^2$ is true. $S(k)$: $a_k = 4qa_{k-1} + 10q^2a_{k-2}$ is true for $k = 2, 3, \ldots k$. $S(k+1) = 4qa_k + 10q^2a_{k-1} = 4q \cdot q^kp(q) + 10q^2q^{k-1}r(q)$, where $p(q)$ and $r(q)$ are the other factors, $= q^{k+1}(4p(q) + 10r(q))$.
So by the Strong Form of the Principle of Mathematical Induction, $S(n)$ is true for all n.

4. Let b be the sequence defined by

$$\begin{cases} b_1 = 1 \\ b_2 = 2 \\ b_{k+1} = k(b_k + b_{k-1})\ \forall\, k \geq 2. \end{cases}$$

Prove that $b_n = n!$ for all positive integers n.

$b_1 = 1 = 1!$, $b_2 = 2 = 2 \cdot 1 = 2!$, so $b_n = n!$ for $n = 1$ and $n = 2$.

Assume that $b_i = i!$ for $i = 1, 2, \ldots, k$. Then, $b_{k+1} = k(b_k + b_{k-1}) = k(k! + (k-1)!) = k(k(k-1)! + (k-1)!) = k(k-1)!(k+1) = k!(k+1) = (k+1)!$. Thus, the assumption that the statement is true for all positive integers less than $k+1$ implies that the statement is true for $k+1$.

❷ The reason that Strong Mathematical Induction is needed in the proof of the theorem in this lesson is that the factors of a given number are never one less than the number but may, in different situations, be any number less than the given number. Thus there needs to be the ability to connect $S(k+1)$ to any of the $S(i)$, $i = 1$ to k, that precede it.

Additional Examples

1. The "We're All Siblings Society" is sponsoring a hands-across-your-town campaign. Their goal is to have citizens in each community form a hand-holding chain linking together diverse groups. Between each two people there will be a flag. Assuming that no person in the chain holds hands with himself (herself), how many flags will be needed when there are n people in the chain? Prove the result.
$n - 1$; Let $S(n)$: $n - 1$ flags are needed for a chain of n people. $S(1) = 0$ and $S(2) = 1$ obviously. Assume for some integer k, $S(1)$ through $S(k)$ are all true. Now a chain of $k + 1$ people is formed by joining chains of r and s people, where $r + s = k + 1$ and since $r \le k$ and $s \le k$, by the inductive assumption these chains hold $r - 1$ and $s - 1$ flags. One more flag is necessary to join them, so for $k + 1$ people, $1 + (r - 1) + (s - 1) = (r + s) - 1 = (k + 1) - 1 = k$ flags are needed. Thus, by the Strong Form of the Principle of Mathematical Induction, $S(n)$ is true for all integers $n \ge 1$.

Theorem ❷
Every positive integer $n \ge 2$ is either a prime or a product of primes.

(The Fundamental Theorem of Arithmetic also states that the prime factorization is unique.)

Proof
Let $S(n)$ be the sentence *n is a prime or a product of primes.*
The Strong Form of the Principle of Mathematical Induction is used, starting with $n = 2$.
(1) Show that $S(2)$ is true.
$S(2)$ is the statement *2 is a prime or a product of primes.* Clearly $S(2)$ is true because 2 is a prime.
(2) Show that the assumption that $S(2), S(3), \ldots, S(k)$ are all true implies that $S(k+1)$ is true.
Assume that $S(2), S(3), \ldots, S(k-1), S(k)$ are all true.
That is, assume that

Every integer from 2 to k, inclusive, is either a prime or a product of primes.

It needs to be shown that this assumption implies that $S(k+1)$ is true, where

$S(k+1)$: *$k + 1$ is a prime or a product of primes.*

Now, there are two possibilities: either $k + 1$ is prime or it is not prime. If $k + 1$ is prime, then $S(k+1)$ is true. If $k + 1$ is not prime, then $k + 1 = a \cdot b$ where a and b are positive integers greater than 1 and less than $k + 1$. Therefore, a and b are integers from 2 to k, inclusive, and so the inductive assumption implies that both a and b are either primes or products of primes. Consequently, $k + 1 = a \cdot b$ is also a product of primes, and so $S(k+1)$ is true in this case also.

It follows that $S(n)$ must be true for all integers $n \ge 2$ by the Strong Form of the Principle of Mathematical Induction.

QUESTIONS

Covering the Reading

1. Explain the difference between the Strong Form of Mathematical Induction and the original form. **See margin.**

2. A 4-piece jigsaw puzzle is shown at the right.
One way to put it together is to combine 1 and 3, then combine 2 and 4, then join the blocks.
a. Describe two other ways of putting the puzzle together. **See left.**
b. How many steps are needed for each of your ways? **3**

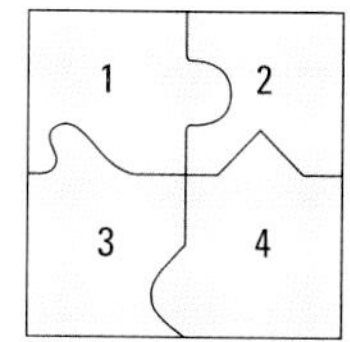

2a) Sample: Combine 1, 2, and 3, then join 4; combine 1 and 3, then join 4, then join 2.

Additional Answers
1. **In the Strong Form of Mathematical Induction, the assumption that each of $S(1), S(2), \ldots, S(k)$ are true is used to show that $S(k+1)$ is true. In the original form, only the assumption that $S(k)$ is true is used to prove $S(k+1)$ is true.**

3) The 7-piece and 13-piece blocks needed 6 and 12 steps respectively, by the inductive assumption. That is 18 steps; joining them is the 19th step.

4a) 2, 2, 4, 8, 14

b) i) $S(n)$: a_n is an even integer

ii) $a_1 = 2$, $a_2 = 2$, $a_3 = 4$ are even integers

iii) $a_1, a_2, \ldots, a_k$ are all even integers. Prove that a_{k+1} is an even integer.

iv) $a_{k+1} = a_k + a_{k-1} + a_{k-2}$. a_k, a_{k-1}, and a_{k-2} are all even integers by the inductive assumption. So there exist integers p, q, and r such that $a_k + a_{k-1} + a_{k-2} = 2p + 2q + 2r$. By the Factor of an Integer Sum Theorem, $a_k + a_{k-1} + a_{k-2}$ is then also an even integer. And so a_{k+1} is an even integer.

v) The sum of any even integers is even.

3. The last move in putting together a 20-piece jigsaw puzzle was to combine a block of 7 pieces and a block of 13 pieces. Explain how strong mathematical induction tells you that the last move was the 19th move made. **See left.**

4. A sequence is defined recursively as follows: **See left.**

$$\begin{cases} a_1 = 2 \\ a_2 = 2 \\ a_3 = 4 \\ a_{k+1} = a_k + a_{k-1} + a_{k-2} & \text{for } k \geq 3. \end{cases}$$

a. Compute the first five terms of this sequence.

b. Complete the steps below to prove, using the Strong Form of Mathematical Induction, that the terms of this sequence are all even integers.

i. Write the statement $S(n)$.

ii. Verify the basis step.

iii. Write the inductive assumption and the statement that must be proved assuming it.

iv. Use part **iii** and the Factor of an Integer Sum Theorem to complete the inductive step.

v. What can you conclude from the results of parts **ii–iv**?

Applying the Mathematics

5. Consider the sequence defined recursively as follows:

$$\begin{cases} a_1 = 5 \\ a_2 = 15 \\ a_{k+1} = a_k + a_{k-1} & \text{for } k \geq 2. \end{cases}$$

a. Write the first four terms of the sequence. **5, 15, 20, 35**

b. Use the Strong Form of Mathematical Induction to prove that every term of the sequence is a multiple of 5. (Hint: Use the Factor of an Integer Sum Theorem.) **See margin.**

6. Consider the sequence defined recursively as follows:

$$\begin{cases} a_1 = 3 \\ a_2 = 5 \\ a_{k+1} = a_{k-1} + 2a_k & \text{for } k \geq 2. \end{cases}$$

Prove that every term of the sequence is an odd integer.

$a_1 = 3$ and $a_2 = 5$ are odd integers. Assume $a_1, a_2, \ldots, a_k$ are all odd integers. $a_{k+1} = a_{k-1} + 2a_k$, where $a_{k-1} = 2q + 1$ and $a_k = 2r + 1$ for some integers q and r. Then $a_{k+1} = 2q + 1 + 2(2r + 1) = 2q + 4r + 3 = 2(q + 2r + 1) + 1$ so a_{k+1} is odd. Hence, by the Strong Form of Mathematical Induction, every term in the sequence is an odd integer.

Note that Additional Example 1 is equivalent to **Example 1** in the lesson. Another equivalent problem is the number of cuts needed to split a long licorice stick among n people. $[n - 1]$

2. Consider the sequence defined recursively by

$$\begin{cases} a_1 = 2 \\ a_2 = 4 \\ a_{k+1} = 7a_k + a_{k-1} & \text{for } k \geq 2. \end{cases}$$

Prove that all terms of this sequence are even.

Let $S(n)$: a_n is even. $S(1)$ and $S(2)$ are true from the initial conditions of the sequence. Assume for some integer k, $S(1)$ through $S(k)$ are all true. By this inductive assumption, there are integers r and s such that $a_{k+1} = 7a_k + a_{k-1} = 7(2r) + 2s = 2(7r + s)$, so a_{k+1} is even. So $S(k + 1)$ is true. Thus, by strong induction, $S(n)$ is true for all integers $n \geq 1$.

Notes on Questions

Question 4 Compare this question to **Example 2.**

Questions 5–6 Cooperative Learning Have students **work in groups** on one of these proofs and assign the other one for homework. Invite one student from each group to put the group's proof on the board, and then discuss the correctness of the proofs.

Additional Answers

5. b. $a_1 = 5$ and $a_2 = 15$ are multiples of 5. Assume $a_1, a_2, \ldots, a_k$ are all multiples of 5. Show that a_{k+1} is a multiple of 5. Now $a_{k+1} = a_k + a_{k-1}$. 5 is a factor of a_k and a_{k-1}, so by the Factor of an Integer Sum Theorem it is factor of their sum, a_{k+1}. Hence, by the Strong Form of Mathematical Induction, a_n is a multiple of 5 $\forall$ integers $n \geq 1$.

Notes on Questions

Question 10 Students should recognize that this sequence is a geometric sequence.

Question 11 Error Alert Ask students for the domain of this identity. $\left[\left\{x: x \neq \frac{n\pi}{2}, n \text{ an integer}\right\}\right]$

Question 12 Consumer Connection What if the manufacturer switches to cylindrical cans with radii equal to their heights? [If the radius is r, $P(x) = 0.15\pi r^3 - .50\pi r$. A can with radius $\frac{10}{3}$ inches yields a net income of zero; smaller cans yield a loss, larger cans yield a profit.]

Question 14 Students may notice that $a_{k+1} = a_k + a_{k-1}$ for $k \geq 2$ is the recurrence relation for a generalized Fibonacci Sequence. Invite students to write a program that will ask for the input of the first two terms of such a sequence and then generate as many terms as desired. It is useful if one wishes to check hypotheses.

7a) $S(2)$: $L_2 = F_3 + F_1$. $3 = 2 + 1$, so $S(2)$ is true. $S(3)$: $L_3 = F_4 + F_2$. $4 = 3 + 1$, so $S(3)$ is true.
b) $\forall$ integers j such that $2 \leq j \leq k$, $L_j = F_{j+1} + F_{j-1}$
c) $S(k+1)$: $L_{k+1} = F_{k+2} + F_k$
d) $L_{k+1} = L_k + L_{k-1} = (F_{k+1} + F_{k-1}) + (F_k + F_{k-2})$
e) $L_{k+1} = (F_{k-1} + F_{k-2}) + (F_{k+1} + F_k) = F_{k+2} + F_k$

7. Recall, from the Questions in Lesson 7-1, that the *Lucas sequence L* has the same recurrence relation as the Fibonacci sequence F but it has different initial conditions. It is described recursively as follows:

$$\begin{cases} L_1 = 1 \\ L_2 = 3 \\ L_{k+1} = L_k + L_{k-1} \quad \text{for integers } k \geq 2. \end{cases}$$

Complete the steps below to show that $S(n)$: $L_n = F_{n+1} + F_{n-1}$ is true for all integers $n > 2$, using strong mathematical induction. **See left.**

a. Show that $S(2)$ and $S(3)$ are true.
b. Write the inductive assumption.
c. Write $S(k+1)$.
d. Use the inductive assumption and the recursive definition of the Lucas sequence to rewrite L_{k+1} as a sum of four terms of the Fibonacci sequence.
e. Regroup the result from part **d** and use the recursive definition of the Fibonacci sequence to finish the inductive step.

Review

8. Calculate each infinite sum. *(Lesson 7-6)*
a. $\sum_{k=0}^{\infty}\left[3\cdot\left(\frac{2}{3}\right)^k\right]$ **9** **b.** $3 + \sum_{k=0}^{\infty} 2\cdot\left(\frac{2}{3}\right)^k$ **9**

9. Use mathematical induction to prove that $n^3 + 3n^2 + 2n$ is divisible by 3 for all integers $n \geq 1$. *(Lesson 7-4)* **See margin.**

10. Given the sequence defined recursively as follows: **See margin.**

$$\begin{cases} a_1 = 4 \\ a_{k+1} = 3\cdot a_k \quad \text{for } k \geq 1. \end{cases}$$

Prove that $a_n = 4\cdot 3^{n-1}$ is an explicit formula for the sequence. *(Lesson 7-3)*

11. a. Use an automatic grapher to graph $y = \csc x \sec x - \cot x$.
b. Use the graph in part **a** and your knowledge of the graphs of trigonometric functions to conjecture an identity: $\csc x \sec x - \cot x =$ __?__. **tan x**
c. Prove the identity in part **b**. *(Lessons 6-1, 6-2)*
a, c) See margin.

12. A manufacturer produces cubical boxes with lids. The boxes cost 25 cents per square inch of surface area to make. For each box sold the manufacturer receives 15 cents per cubic inch of volume.
a. Assume that the manufacturer is able to sell every box made. Express the net income received for each box as a polynomial function $P(x)$, where x is the length of a side in inches. $P(x) = 0.15x^3 - 1.5x^2$
b. What size box yields a net income of zero? **10″ × 10″ × 10″**
c. Do larger boxes yield a positive profit? **Yes**
d. Does the manufacturer incur a loss if smaller boxes are made? **Yes**
(Lessons 3-1, 3-3, 3-7)

13. Solve $\sqrt{(x-1)(x+5)} = \sqrt{x+5}$ over the reals. *(Lesson 3-3)*
$x = -5, 2$

Additional Answers

9. Let $S(n)$: $n^3 + 3n^2 + 2n$ is divisible by 3. Then $S(1)$: $1^3 + 3 \bullet 1^2 + 2 \bullet 1$ is divisible by 3. $1 + 3 + 2 = 6$, which is divisible by 3, so $S(1)$ is true. Assume $S(k)$: $k^3 + 3k^2 + 2k$ is divisible by 3 is true for some integer $k \geq 1$. Show $S(k+1)$: $(k+1)^3 + 3(k+1)^2 + 2(k+1)$ is divisible by 3 is true.
$(k+1)^3 + 3(k+1)^2 + 2(k+1) =$
$k^3 + 3k^2 + 3k + 1 + 3k^2 + 6k + 3 + 2k + 2 =$
$k^3 + 6k^2 + 11k + 6 = (k^3 + 3k^2 + 2k) + 3(k^2 + 3k + 2)$. $k^3 + 3k^2 + 2k$ is divisible by 3 by the inductive assumption, and $3(k^2 + 3k + 2)$ is divisible by 3; thus their sum is divisible by 3. Therefore, by mathematical induction, $n^3 + 3n^2 + 2n$ is divisible by 3 $\forall$ integers $n \geq 1$.

10. $S(n)$: $a_n = 4(3)^{n-1}$. $S(1)$: $a_1 = 4(3)^0$. $a_1 = 4$, so $S(1)$ is true. Assume $S(k)$: $a_k = 4(3)^{k-1}$ is true. Show $S(k+1)$: $a_{k+1} = 4(3)^k$ is true. $a_{k+1} = 3a_k = 3(4 \bullet 3^{k-1}) = 4 \bullet 3^k$. By mathematical induction, $S(n)$ is true for all integers $n \geq 1$. Hence, $a_n = 4(3)^{n-1}$ is an explicit formula for the sequence.

14a) a_1 and a_2 must be multiples of 7.
b) a_1 and a_2 must be multiples of m.
c) a_1 and a_2 are multiples of m. Assume a_1 and a_2, ..., a_k are multiples of m. $a_{k+1} = a_k + a_{k-1}$. Because a_{k-1} and a_k are multiples of m, their sum, a_{k+1}, is also a multiple of m by the Factor of a Polynomial Sum Theorem. By the Strong Form of Mathematical Induction, every term in the sequence is a multiple of m.

Exploration

14. Consider a sequence a that satisfies the recurrence relation $a_{k+1} = a_k + a_{k-1}$ $\forall$ integers $k \geq 2$. **See left.**

a. Of what form must a_1 and a_2 be so that every term of the sequence $a_1, a_2, a_3, \ldots$ is a multiple of 7?

b. Of what form must a_1 and a_2 be so that every term is a multiple of m?

c. Prove that if a_1 and a_2 are of the form specified in part **b**, then every term is a multiple of m.

15. a. Adapt the Recursion Principle from Lesson 7-1 so that it parallels strong mathematical induction.

b. Use strong mathematical induction to prove your adaptation of the principle.

a) Suppose that a recurrence relation defines x_{n+1} in terms of x_n, $x_{n-1}, \ldots, x_1$, and n for each integer $n \geq 1$. Then there is exactly one sequence defined by this recurrence relation and the initial condition $x_1 = a$.

b) Suppose there is a second sequence y for which $y_1 = a$ and y_{n+1} is defined by the same recurrence relation and as x_{n+1}. Let $S(n)$ be the statement $x_n = y_n$. (1) Because $x_1 = a$, and $y_1 = a$, $x_1 = y_1$, So $S(1)$ is true. (2) Assume $S(1), S(2), \ldots, S(k)$ are true. Then $x_1 = y_1, x_2 = y_2, \ldots, x_k = y_k$. The sequences have the same recurrence relation; y_{k+1} is defined in terms of $y_1, \ldots, y_k$ and k; and x_{k+1} is defined in terms of $x_1, \ldots, x_k$ and k; so $x_{k+1} = y_{k+1}$. Thus, $S(k+1)$ is true. By (1), (2), and the Strong Form of Mathematical Induction, $S(n)$ is true for all $n \geq 1$. Therefore, the adapted Recursion Principle is proved.

Follow-up for Lesson 7-7

Practice

For more questions on SPUR Objectives, use **Lesson Master 7-7** (shown on pages 444–445).

Assessment

Quiz A quiz covering Lessons 7-5 through 7-7 is provided in the *Assessment Sourcebook.*

Extension

Have students make up a recursively defined sequence like the ones in **Questions 5–6,** make a conjecture about the sequence, and then prove their assertion. [Students may build off of **Question 5** by defining a_1 and a_2 to be multiples of 3 and asserting that every term in the sequence is a multiple of 3. Building off **Question 6,** students may define $a_1 = 2$ and $a_2 = 4$, $a_{k+1} = a_{k-1} + 3a_k$ for $k \geq 2$ and assert that every term of the sequence is an even integer.]

Project Update Project 4, *Exploring the Fibonacci Sequence,* on page 464, relates to the content of this lesson.

11. a.

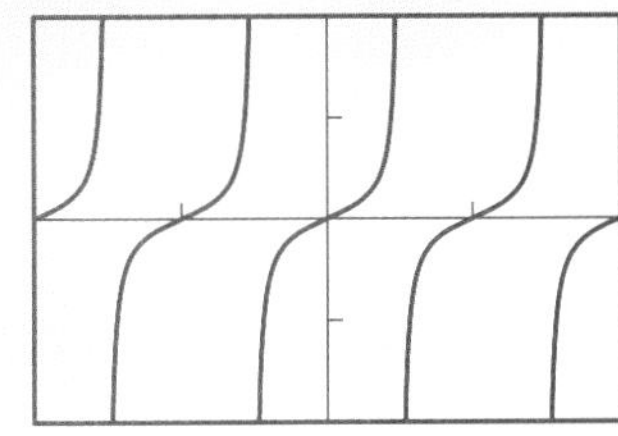

$-2\pi \leq x \leq 2\pi$, x-scale $= \pi$
$-10 \leq y \leq 10$, y-scale $= 5$

c. left side

$= \csc x \sec x - \cot x$

$= \frac{1}{\sin x} \bullet \frac{1}{\cos x} - \frac{\cos x}{\sin x}$ — Definition of cosecant, secant, and cotangent

$= \frac{1}{\sin x \cos x} - \frac{\cos^2 x}{\sin x \cos x}$ — Multiplication

$= \frac{1 - \cos^2 x}{\sin x \cos x}$ — Subtraction of Fractions

$= \frac{\sin^2 x}{\sin x \cos x}$ — Pythagorean Identity

$= \frac{\sin x}{\cos x}$ — Simplifying fractions

$= \tan x$ — Definition of tangent

= right side

Therefore, $\csc x \sec x - \cot x = \tan x$ $\forall$ x for which both sides are defined.

Lesson 7-8

Objectives

I Execute algorithms on sets of numbers.

Resources

From the ***Teacher's Resource File***
- Lesson Master 7-8
- Answer Master 7-8
- Teaching Aids
  64 Warm-up
  67 Example 1, Bubblesort
  68, 69 Example 2, Quicksort

Additional Resources
- Visuals for Teaching Aids 64, 67, 68, 69
- Exploration 7-8

Teaching Lesson 7-8

Warm-up

Suppose that you are allowed to switch any two consecutive elements of a sequence. In how many steps can you change 3, 5, 4, 1, 2 into 1, 2, 3, 4, 5? Show each step.
Sample: 7 steps: 35412 → 35142 → 31542 → 13542 → 13524 → 13254 → 12354 → 12345

LESSON

7-8 *Algorithms for Sorting Lists*

Computers are often employed to arrange or sort a given list of items in some desired order. Arranging a list of names in alphabetical order or a list of numbers in increasing order can be a tedious job if the lists are very long. *Sorting algorithms* provide the computer with the necessary instructions to carry out this task. This lesson describes and compares two computer sorting algorithms. It also shows how the Principle of Mathematical Induction can be used to verify that an algorithm does the job it is supposed to do.

Bubblesort

❶ Suppose you are given a list of n numbers to arrange in increasing order. One algorithm for accomplishing this task is called *Bubblesort*. Bubblesort makes successive passes through the list *from the bottom to the top*. In each pass, successive pairs of adjacent numbers are compared; if the number on the bottom is larger than the one on top, the two are exchanged; otherwise, they are left as is. One result of the first pass is that the largest number "bubbles up" to the top; a result of the second pass is that the next larger number ends up second to the top. After the nth pass, the n top numbers in the list are called the *sorted section* of the list; the rest make up the *unsorted section*.

Example 1

Apply the Bubblesort algorithm to arrange the list 7, 3, 11, 1, 9, 4 in increasing order.

Solution

Imagine the numbers in the list written in a column starting at the bottom and going up to the top. For example, the list 7, 3, 11, 1, 9, 4 would appear as follows.

4
9
1
11
3
7

▶

Lesson 7-8 Overview

Broad Goals The purpose of this lesson is to exhibit two sorting algorithms and compare their properties.

Perspective Sorting is one of the most basic operations that can be done with data. Examples of sorting are alphabetizing, putting in numerical order, putting in order of dates, or ordering by size or by some code. Two sorting algorithms are discussed here: Bubblesort, an iterative algorithm, in that the same procedure is repeated again and again; and Quicksort, a recursive algorithm, because the algorithm calls upon a smaller version of itself. Because Quicksort is a recursive algorithm, one can use mathematical induction to prove that Quicksort does the job claimed for it.

Computers also use similar algorithms to alphabetize lists. Because a computer assigns numerical values to the letters of the alphabet, a program similar to that for the sorting algorithms can be used to arrange lists alphabetically. Sorting Algorithms is a mandatory topic in Advanced Placement Computer Science (APCS). If your school offers this course, ask your APCS teacher if he/she has a program that shows visually a variety of sorting algorithms. Your class may be astounded at the time difference required by Bubblesort

The effect of the first pass is shown below. In each case, the numbers in the green boxes are compared. At the end of the first pass, the number in the top, purple box is in its correct position. Therefore, it is now in the sorted section of the list.

Pass 1:

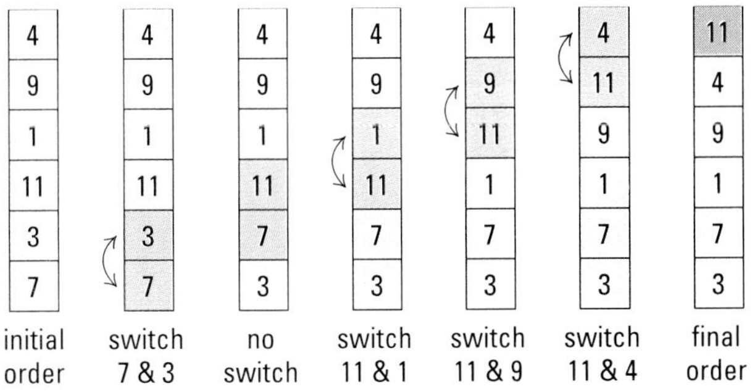

initial order	switch 7 & 3	no switch	switch 11 & 1	switch 11 & 9	switch 11 & 4	final order
4	4	4	4	4	4	11
9	9	9	9	9	11	4
1	1	1	1	11	9	9
11	11	11	11	1	1	1
3	3	7	7	7	7	7
7	7	3	3	3	3	3

At the end of the first pass the numbers in the list are in the order

3, 7, 1, 9, 4, 11.

For each succeeding pass, the unsorted numbers are compared. The successive comparisons are shown in the green boxes. Those in the purple boxes are in the sorted section of the list.

Pass 2:

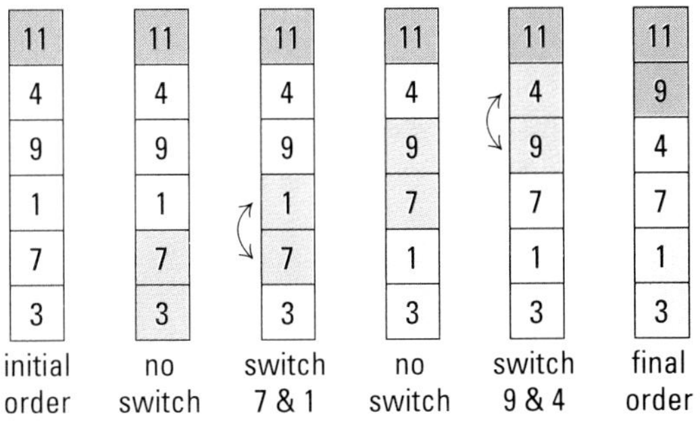

initial order	no switch	switch 7 & 1	no switch	switch 9 & 4	final order
11	11	11	11	11	11
4	4	4	4	4	9
9	9	9	9	9	4
1	1	1	7	7	7
7	7	7	1	1	1
3	3	3	3	3	3

At the end of the second pass the numbers in the list are in the order

3, 1, 7, 4, 9, 11.

Pass 3:

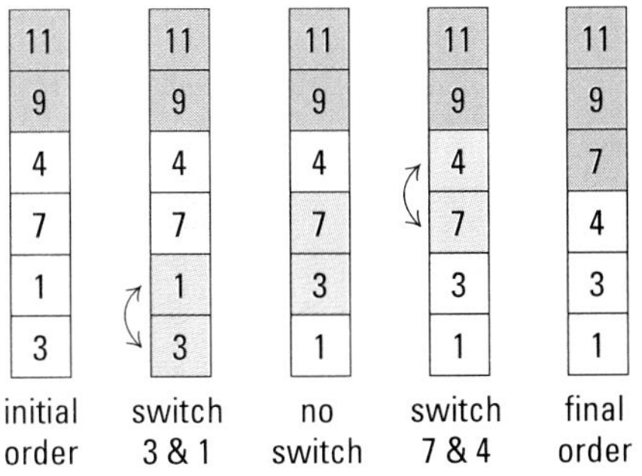

initial order	switch 3 & 1	no switch	switch 7 & 4	final order
11	11	11	11	11
9	9	9	9	9
4	4	4	4	7
7	7	7	7	4
1	1	3	3	3
3	3	1	1	1

Notes on Reading

Students may wonder why they are asked to use one of the text algorithms to sort a small list of numbers. We use a small list for illustrative purposes only. Such algorithms would only be used with fairly long lists of numbers to be sorted. However, long lists are not practical for understanding the mechanics of the algorithms.

❶ The writing of the list of numbers in Bubblesort from bottom to top will confuse some students. The reason it is written in this way is that the name "Bubblesort" is a more apt description of what occurs during the sorting process when the larger numbers "bubble up" through the list. **Teaching Aid 67** is provided so that you can more easily explain the algorithm.

Some versions of Bubblesort will end when a pass through the remaining list produces no switches. That list is in order.

Error Alert Some students may be confused by the notation used in the Quicksort Algorithm. Point out that $(L_l)_l$ is the left sublist of the previous left sublist, and $(L_l)_r$ is the right sublist of the previous left sublist. Similarly explain $(L_r)_l$ and $(L_r)_r$.

Point out to students that in each sublist the first number will be placed in the correct position relative to the numbers in that sublist. The "divide and conquer" strategy of Quicksort keeps approximately halving the size of the lists used, making the process ever easier.

(slow) versus Quicksort (fast) to sort a large list of numbers.

Students who are interested in sorting techniques and recursion will find a wealth of information in *Algorithms + Data Structures = Programs,* by Niklaus Wirth (Prentice-Hall, 1976). The author is the creator of both Pascal and Modula II. The book is a classic in its field. The University of Toronto Library has an excellent film (also available in VCR format) called "Sorting Out Sorts." It provides excellent visual examples of a wide variety of sorting techniques along with analyses of efficiency, as discussed in the next lesson.

❷ In the use of the Quicksort Algorithm in **Example 2,** double subscripts are used to name the lists. Students may need some help in interpreting such lists. **Teaching Aids 68** and **69** are provided for this purpose. Encourage students to read from the rightmost subscript to the leftmost. For instance, $(M_l)_r$ is the right sublist of the left sublist from the previous step.

Additional Examples

1. Repeat the instructions for **Example 1** using the list 6, 5, 4, 2, 3, 1. Reading top to bottom, here are the steps:
   Pass 1:
   1,3,2,4,5,6
   1,3,2,4,6,5
   1,3,2,6,4,5
   1,3,6,2,4,5
   1,6,3,2,4,5
   6,1,3,2,4,5
   Pass 2:
   6,1,3,2,5,4
   6,1,3,5,2,4
   6,1,5,3,2,4
   6,5,1,3,2,4
   Pass 3:
   6,5,1,3,4,2
   6,5,1,4,3,2
   6,5,4,1,3,2
   Pass 4:
   6,5,4,1,3,2 (stays same)
   6,5,4,3,1,2
   Pass 5:
   6,5,4,3,2,1

Ask students if a list in exactly reverse order to that desired is the worst case for Bubblesort to handle. [Yes]

At the end of the third pass the numbers in the list are in the order

1, 3, 4, 7, 9, 11,

which is in increasing order.

You can stop here if you are executing the algorithm by hand. However, if you program a computer for the algorithm, it will continue to execute the last two passes without performing any interchanges between boxes. There are many lists of 6 numbers which would require all five passes in Bubblesort to achieve the required arrangement.

The general algorithm can be described as follows:

Bubblesort Algorithm
To arrange a list L of numbers in increasing order:

Step 1: If L contains only one number (or no numbers), then L is already sorted, so stop. Otherwise, let the "unsorted section of the list" be the entire list and the "sorted section of the list" be empty.
Step 2: Make a pass through the unsorted section of L from bottom to top. Compare pairs of successive numbers and switch the numbers in the pair if the bottom number of the pair is greater than the top one. (At the end of each pass, the greatest of the unsorted numbers is at the top of the unsorted section of L. This number becomes the bottom of the sorted section of L.)
Step 3: If the unsorted section of L contains more than one number, repeat step 2; otherwise stop.

Bubblesort is an example of an **iterative algorithm**. The term *iterative* refers to the fact that the same steps are **iterated**, that is, repeated over and over.

Quicksort

Another sorting algorithm, called *Quicksort*, is a **recursive algorithm**, in the sense that during its execution it makes use of, or "calls on," itself. Quicksort sorts a list by assuming that smaller lists can be sorted. It arranges a list of real numbers in increasing order by performing the following steps:

Quicksort Algorithm
To arrange a list L in increasing order of numbers:

Step 1: If L contains only one number (or no numbers), then L is already sorted, so stop. Otherwise, continue with Steps 2 through 4.
Step 2: Divide L into two *sublists* by comparing the first number f in L with the remaining numbers. Place those numbers that are less than or equal to f in a *left sublist* L_ℓ and those that are greater than f in a *right sublist* L_r. Then place f between L_ℓ and L_r. The list is now L_ℓ, f, L_r.
Step 3: Use Quicksort to sort L_ℓ.
Step 4: Use Quicksort to sort L_r.

Optional Activities

Activity 1 Technology Connection
Materials: *Explorations* software

Students may use *Exploration 7-8, Sorting Algorithms,* to compare two sorting algorithms, Quicksort and Bubblesort. Students can enter a list of numbers, then choose a type of sort. The program will demonstrate the algorithm for each sort, step-by-step. Students can compare the number of passes and the steps for each algorithm.

Activity 2 Alternate Approach Have students **work in pairs**. Give one student in each pair twenty 3-by-5 index cards and ask that the cards be numbered 1 to 20. Have students shuffle the cards and spread them out in a row in front of them. Select either Bubblesort or Quicksort. As one student keeps rereading the algorithm, the other student applies it until the cards are in order. Then students reverse roles. Many students enjoy this activity and develop a good understanding of both algorithms.

The action of the Quicksort algorithm on the original list of Example 1 is described below.

Example 2

❷ Apply the Quicksort algorithm to the list $L = 7, 3, 11, 1, 9, 4$.

Solution

Step 1: The list L contains more than one number, so continue to Step 2.

Step 2: $f = 7$ so compare 7 with the remaining numbers and group them into two sublists:

$$L_\ell = 3, 1, 4 \qquad \text{and} \qquad L_r = 11, 9.$$

L now looks like

$$3, 1, 4, 7, 11, 9.$$

Step 3: Use Quicksort to sort $L_\ell = 3, 1, 4$.

Step 1: L_ℓ contains more than one number, so continue.

Step 2: $f = 3$, so divide L_ℓ into

$$(L_\ell)_\ell = 1 \qquad \text{and} \qquad (L_\ell)_r = 4.$$

L_ℓ is now 1, 3, 4.

Step 3: Use Quicksort to sort $(L_\ell)_\ell$.

Step 1: $(L_\ell)_\ell$ contains only one number, so it is already sorted.

Step 4: Use Quicksort to sort $(L_\ell)_r$.

Step 1: $(L_\ell)_r$ contains only one number, so it is already sorted.

Now L_ℓ is sorted, and L looks like

$$1, 3, 4, 7, 11, 9.$$

Step 4: Use Quicksort to sort $L_r = 11, 9$.

Step 1: L_r contains more than one number, so continue.

Step 2: $f = 11$, so divide L_r into

$$(L_r)_\ell = 9 \qquad \text{and} \qquad (L_r)_r \text{ is empty.}$$

L_r is now 9, 11.

Step 3: Use Quicksort to sort $(L_r)_\ell$.

Step 1: $(L_r)_\ell$ contains only one number, so it is already sorted.

Step 4: Use Quicksort to sort $(L_r)_r$.

Step 1: $(L_r)_r$ contains no numbers, so it is already sorted.

Now L_r is sorted, and L looks like

$$1, 3, 4, 7, 9, 11.$$

Now L is sorted.

Notice that step 1 is the basis step for the recursion. In steps 3 and 4, the algorithm calls upon itself.

The diagram below illustrates the action of the Quicksort algorithm on the list given in Example 2.

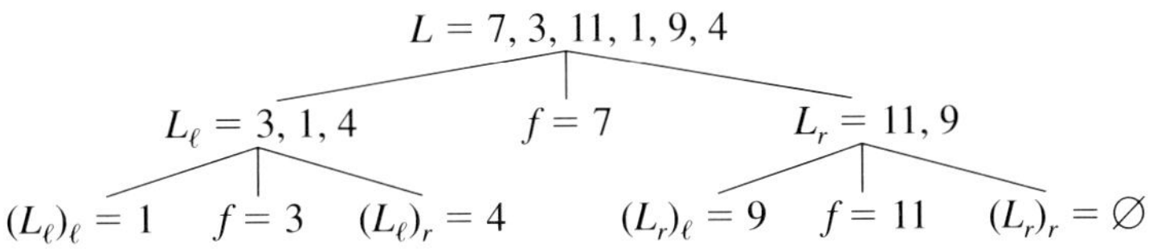

Adapting to Individual Needs

Extra Help Students may enjoy and benefit from a live application of Bubblesort. Ask 8 or 10 students to write their last name in large letters on a sheet of paper. Invite them to come up to the front of the room, mix them randomly (or in last-to-first order alphabetically), and have them sort themselves using the Bubblesort Algorithm. Have the unsorted list one step away from the front of the room and the sorted list against the wall. Repeat with another group of students. Have students verbally summarize the algorithm.

2. Apply Quicksort to the list $M = 6, 5, 4, 2, 3, 1$
$M_l = 5, 4, 2, 3, 1$; $f = 6$; M_r is empty so is sorted. Sort 5, 4, 2, 3, 1; here $M_l = 4, 2, 3, 1$; $f = 5$; M_r is empty so is sorted. Sort 4, 2, 3, 1; here $M_l = 2, 3, 1$; $f = 4$; M_r is empty so is sorted. Sort 2, 3, 1; here $M_l = 1$; $f = 2$; $M_r = 3$, and they are sorted. The sorted list is 1, 2, 3, 4, 5, 6.

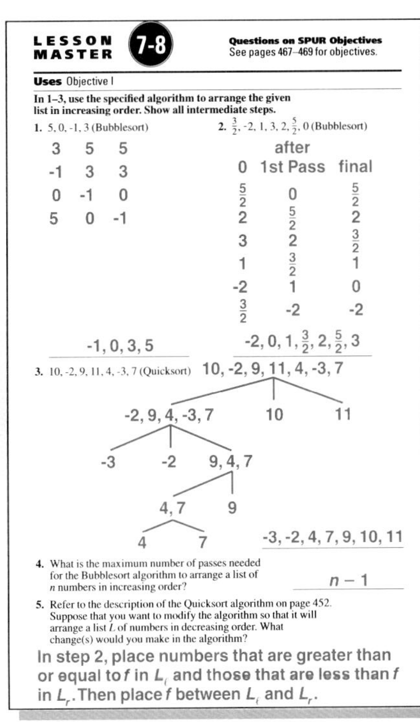

LESSON MASTER 7-8 **Questions on SPUR Objectives** See pages 467–469 for objectives.

Uses Objective I

In 1–3, use the specified algorithm to arrange the given list in increasing order. Show all intermediate steps.

1. 5, 0, -1, 3 (Bubblesort)

3	5	5
-1	3	3
0	-1	0
5	0	-1

-1, 0, 3, 5

2. $\frac{3}{2}, -2, 1, 3, 2, \frac{5}{2}, 0$ (Bubblesort)

	after 1st Pass	final
0		
$\frac{5}{2}$	0	$\frac{5}{2}$
2	$\frac{5}{2}$	2
3	2	$\frac{3}{2}$
1	$\frac{3}{2}$	1
-2	1	0
$\frac{3}{2}$	-2	-2

$-2, 0, 1, \frac{3}{2}, 2, \frac{5}{2}, 3$

3. 10, -2, 9, 11, 4, -3, 7 (Quicksort) 10, -2, 9, 11, 4, -3, 7

-2, 9, 4, -3, 7 10 11

-3 -2 9, 4, 7

4, 7 9

4 7

-3, -2, 4, 7, 9, 10, 11

4. What is the maximum number of passes needed for the Bubblesort algorithm to arrange a list of n numbers in increasing order? $n - 1$

5. Refer to the description of the Quicksort algorithm on page 452. Suppose that you want to modify the algorithm so that it will arrange a list L of numbers in decreasing order. What change(s) would you make in the algorithm?

In step 2, place numbers that are greater than or equal to f in L_ℓ and those that are less than f in L_r. Then place f between L_ℓ and L_r.

Notes on Questions

Questions 5, 6, 8, 9 Require students to list all the intermediate steps when performing the given algorithms. Otherwise, there is no way of knowing that the algorithm has been applied properly.

Question 8 Every time a number smaller than the first number in the list is encountered, exchange that number with the first number.

Follow-up for Lesson 7-8

Practice

For more questions on SPUR Objectives, use **Lesson Master 7-8** (shown on page 453).

Assessment

Written Communication Using a list of 5, 6, 7, or 8 numbers, have students **work in pairs,** one partner following the directions for **Question 5** and the other following the directions for **Question 6.** Then have students work together to check and compare their results. [Students apply the Bubblesort and Quicksort algorithms.]

Extension

Sorting is a major topic in Computer Science. Below are the names of a dozen sorting algorithms.

1. Insertion Sort
2. Selection Sort
3. Exchange (Bubblesort) Sort
4. Tree Sort
5. Heapsort
6. Quicksort
7. Shellsort
8. Merge Sort
9. Shakersort
10. Natural Mergesort
11. Balanced Mergesort
12. Polyphase Sort

Ambitious students or groups of students could explore these as a project, comparing the efficiencies (see Lesson 7-9) and appropriateness of application.

Based on the descriptions of these algorithms and the preceding examples, it is reasonable to believe that either of these algorithms will always succeed in arranging any list of n numbers in increasing order. Strong mathematical induction can be used to *prove* that the Quicksort algorithm does what it is supposed to do.

Quicksort Theorem
For each integer $n \geq 0$, the Quicksort algorithm arranges any list of n distinct real numbers in increasing order.

Proof
Let $S(n)$ be the sentence

The Quicksort algorithm arranges any list of n distinct real numbers in increasing order.

The inductive step of the proof uses Steps 3 and 4 of the algorithm, which are executed only if $n \geq 2$. Therefore, the basis step must show that both $S(0)$ and $S(1)$ are true.

(1) Show $S(0)$ and $S(1)$ are true.
Any list containing no number or only one number is already arranged in increasing order and Quicksort leaves it alone. Therefore, $S(0)$ and $S(1)$ are true.

(2) Show that the assumption that $S(0), \dots, S(k)$ are true implies that $S(k+1)$ is true.
Assume that statements $S(0), \dots, S(k)$ are true for some integer $k \geq 1$; that is, assume that the Quicksort algorithm arranges any list of up to k distinct numbers in increasing order. It must be shown that Quicksort can then arrange any list of $k + 1$ numbers in increasing order. Let L be any list of $k + 1$ distinct real numbers. Since $k \geq 1$, Step 2 of the Quicksort algorithm applied to the list L places the first number f of L in the correct position relative to the numbers in the left sublist L_ℓ and the right sublist L_r. Because L_ℓ and L_r both contain k or fewer numbers, the inductive assumption implies that Steps 3 and 4 of the Quicksort algorithm will arrange them in increasing order. Once the numbers of L_ℓ are arranged in increasing order to the left of f and the numbers of L_r are arranged in increasing order to the right of f, the entire list L is in increasing order. Therefore, $S(k+1)$ is true, assuming that $S(0), S(1), \dots, S(k)$ are true.

Hence, by strong mathematical induction, $S(n)$ is true for all integers $n \geq 0$.

Quicksort and Bubblesort show that more than one algorithm may be available to solve a given problem. The question arises as to which algorithm is better. This question is the subject of the next lesson.

Adapting to Individual Needs

Challenge
Have students prepare a handout for their classmates which provides instructions for sorting lists in ascending or descending order using a calculator. Be sure that students identify the calculator for which the handout is written. Students should include examples and instructions about key strokes.

QUESTIONS

Covering the Reading

1a) 2 and 5
b) 2 and 5 are not exchanged.
2a) 2 and 5
b) 5 is placed in L_r

In 1 and 2, the given algorithm is applied to the list 2, 5, 3, 8. **a.** Determine the first two numbers compared. **b.** Specify the action taken as a result of that comparison. See left.

1. Bubblesort

2. Quicksort

3. Write the list 9, 1, 6, 4 after the first pass of Bubblesort. 1, 6, 4, 9

4. Suppose Quicksort is applied to the list 9, 1, 6, 4. What are the results of Step 2 of Quicksort? $f = 9$, $L_\ell = \{1, 6, 4\}$, $L_r = \varnothing$

5) 5, -7, 1.5, -1, 13, 6 Initial order;
-7, 1.5, -1, 5, 6, 13 After first pass;
-7, -1, 1.5, 5, 6, 13 After second pass

In 5 and 6, use the specified algorithm to arrange the list 5, -7, 1.5, -1, 13, 6 in increasing order. Show intermediate results of each step.

5. Bubblesort See left.

6. Quicksort See margin.

Applying the Mathematics

7) If no interchanges are necessary, adjacent numbers are in order. Hence, by the Transitive Property, the entire list is in order.

7. Suppose that no interchanges are necessary during a given pass in the Bubblesort algorithm. Explain why the list at that pass must already be in increasing order. See left.

8. The following algorithm finds the smallest number in a list of n distinct numbers. Compare the first number in the list successively to the remaining numbers. When a number smaller than the first is encountered, place it in front of the rest of the list and continue making successive comparisons with it. The number that is in the first position in the list after the last comparison is the smallest number in the list. This is called the *Filterdown algorithm*. See margin.

a. Apply the Filterdown algorithm to the list 7, 9, 4, 6, -4, 5, 0 and write the intermediate list after each rearrangement of the list.

b. Construct an algorithm for arranging a list in increasing order that uses Filterdown as a "subalgorithm."

9. Construct a list of 6 numbers for which the Bubblesort algorithm will require interchanges at each of the 5 passes. Sample: 6, 5, 4, 3, 2, 1

In 10 and 11, when calculating efficiencies of sorting algorithms, the maximum number of *comparisons* necessary for a list of n numbers is usually considered. Based on this definition, determine which one of the algorithms, Bubblesort or Quicksort, is more efficient for sorting the indicated list.

10. the list of Example 1 Quicksort

11. the list of Questions 1 and 2 Quicksort

Review

12. Prove: If $x \geq 1$, then $x^n \geq x$ for all positive integers n. *(Lesson 7-5)* See margin.

13. Find integers q and r such that $57 = 4q + r$ and $0 \leq r < 4$. *(Lesson 4-2)* $q = 14$, $r = 1$

Additional Answers

8. a. 7, 9, 4, 6, -4, 5, 0 initial order
4, 7, 9, 6, -4, 5, 0
-4, 4, 7, 9, 6, 5, 0

b. Apply the Filterdown algorithm to the list. The smallest number is now in front. Apply Filterdown to the sublist which includes all but the first number. Apply Filterdown to the sublists which are successively one element smaller. Continue until the list is exhausted.

12. Let $S(n)$ be the statement: if $x \geq 1$, then $x^n \geq x$.
$S(1)$: $x^1 = x \geq x$, which is true.
Assume $S(k)$.
$x^k \geq x$ Inductive assumption
$x \cdot x^k \geq x \cdot x$ M_x
$x^{k+1} \geq x^2$ Product of Powers and Simplification
$x^{k+1} \geq x$ Since $x^2 \geq x$ for $x \geq 1$, and the Transitive Property
Therefore, $S(k) \Rightarrow S(k+1)$. Hence, by the Principle of Mathematical Induction, $S(n)$ is true for all integers $n \geq 1$.

Additional Answers

6.

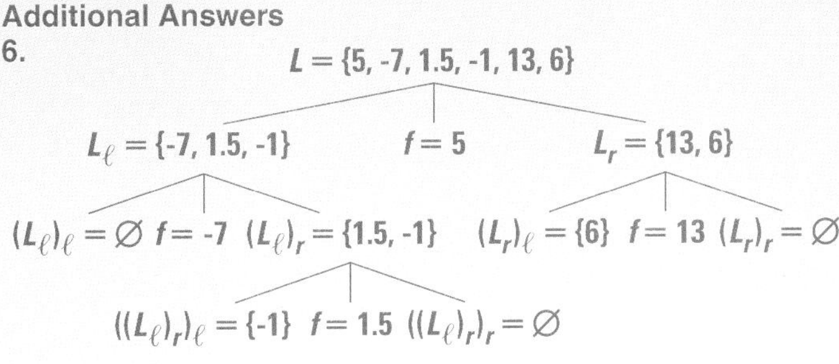

$L = \{5, -7, 1.5, -1, 13, 6\}$
$L_\ell = \{-7, 1.5, -1\}$
$f = 5$
$L_r = \{13, 6\}$
$(L_\ell)_\ell = \varnothing$ $f = -7$ $(L_\ell)_r = \{1.5, -1\}$
$(L_r)_\ell = \{6\}$ $f = 13$ $(L_r)_r = \varnothing$
$((L_\ell)_r)_\ell = \{-1\}$ $f = 1.5$ $((L_\ell)_r)_r = \varnothing$

Additional Answers

14. a_1 and a_2 are even. Assume $a_1, a_2, \ldots a_k$ are all even. Show that a_{k+1} is even. $a_{k+1} = c \cdot a_k + a_{k-1} = c(2p) + 2r = 2(cp + r)$ for some integers p and r. Since $cp + r$ is an integer by closure properties, a_{k+1} is even. Therefore, a_n is even for all integers $n \geq 1$ by the Strong Form of Mathematical Induction.

16. Prove $S(n)$: $\sum_{i=1}^{n} \frac{1}{i(i+1)} = \frac{n}{n+1}$ for all integers $n \geq 1$.

$S(1)$: $\sum_{i=1}^{1} \frac{1}{i(i+1)} = \frac{1}{1+1}$ is true.

Assume $S(k)$: $\sum_{i=1}^{k} \frac{1}{i(i+1)} = \frac{k}{k+1}$ is true.

Show that $S(k+1)$: $\sum_{i=1}^{k+1} \frac{1}{i(i+1)} = \frac{k+1}{k+2}$ is true.

$$\sum_{i=1}^{k+1} \frac{1}{i(i+1)} = \sum_{i=1}^{k} \frac{1}{i(i+1)} + \frac{1}{(k+1)(k+2)} = \frac{k}{k+1} + \frac{1}{(k+1)(k+2)} = \frac{k(k+2)}{(k+1)(k+2)} + \frac{1}{(k+1)(k+2)} = \frac{(k+1)^2}{(k+1)(k+2)} = \frac{k+1}{k+2}.$$

So by mathematical induction, $S(n)$ is true $\forall$ integers $n \geq 1$.

18. The argument is valid. The three premises are: (1) $p \Rightarrow q$, (2) $q \Rightarrow r$, (3) $\sim r$. By the Transitive Property and statements (1) and (2), $p \Rightarrow r$. Then by modus tollens and (3), $\sim p$. This is the conclusion, and so the argument is valid.

15a) $A_2 = \frac{1}{4}$, $A_3 = \frac{1}{16}$

b) $A_k = \frac{1}{4^{k-1}}$, for integers $k \geq 1$

c) $\left(\frac{4}{3}\right)\left(1 - \left(\frac{1}{4}\right)^n\right)$

d) $\frac{4}{3}$

14. Let c be any integer and define a sequence recursively by

$$\begin{cases} a_1 = 2 \\ a_2 = 2 \\ a_{k+1} = ca_k + a_{k-1} & \text{for integers } k \geq 2. \end{cases}$$

Use strong mathematical induction to prove: **See margin.**

$\forall$ *integers* $n \geq 1$, a_n *is even.* *(Lesson 7-7)*

15. The figure at the right is formed from an infinite sequence of squares where the side of each square is half as long as the side of the preceding square. Let A_k be the area of square k, and let $A_1 = 1$. **See left.**

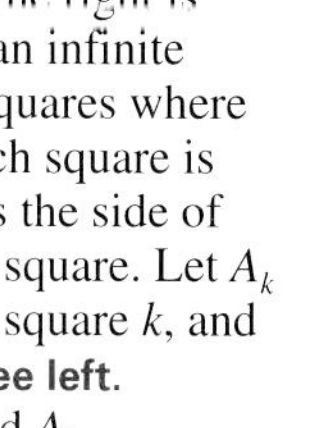

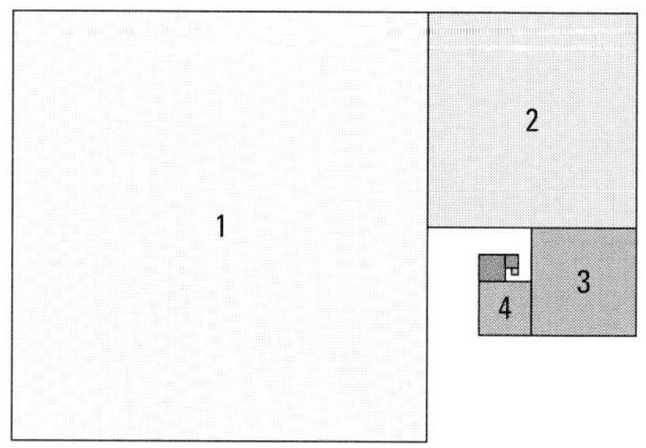

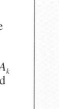

a. Find A_2 and A_3.

b. Write an explicit formula for A_k.

c. Find a formula for $\sum_{k=1}^{n} A_k$, the sum of the areas of the first n squares.

d. Find the total area of the figure. *(Lesson 7-6)*

16. Prove: For all integers $n \geq 1$, **See margin.**

$$\frac{1}{1 \cdot 2} + \frac{1}{2 \cdot 3} + \frac{1}{3 \cdot 4} + \ldots + \frac{1}{n(n+1)} = \frac{n}{n+1};$$

that is, $$\sum_{i=1}^{n} \frac{1}{i(i+1)} = \frac{n}{n+1}.$$ *(Lesson 7-3)*

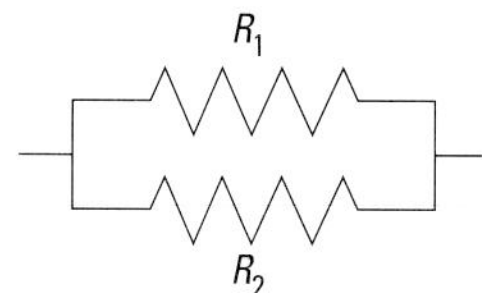

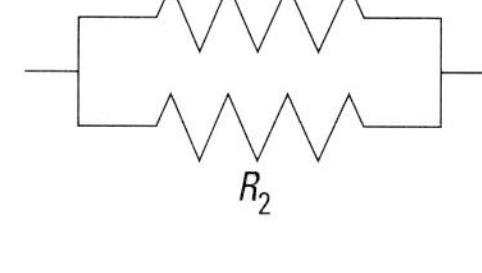

17. The equivalent resistance R of two resistors R_1 and R_2 connected in parallel is given by the equation

$$\frac{1}{R} = \frac{1}{R_1} + \frac{1}{R_2}.$$

a. Solve this equation for R. $R = \frac{R_1 R_2}{R_1 + R_2}$

b. Find R if $R_1 = 7$ ohms and $R_2 = 10$ ohms. *(Lesson 5-8)* $\frac{70}{17} \approx$ **4.12 ohms**

18. Determine whether the argument below is valid or invalid. Justify your reasoning. **See margin.**

If it is Thanksgiving, then dinner includes turkey.
If dinner includes turkey, then dinner includes potatoes.
Dinner does not include potatoes.
$\therefore$ *It is not Thanksgiving.* *(Lessons 1-6, 1-7)*

Exploration

19. Consider a list of 5 letters: a, b, c, d, e. Arrange these letters in an order that requires 4 passes of the Bubblesort algorithm to rearrange them in alphabetical order. How many such orderings are there?
Sample: *e, d, c, b, a*; there are 24 such orderings. The only restriction is that *a* must be the last letter in the list.

Setting Up Lesson 7-9

Discuss **Questions 10–11** to introduce the ideas of efficiency and comparing algorithms.

LESSON

7-9 *Efficiency of Algorithms*

Several different algorithms may be available to solve a given problem. How do you choose among these algorithms? Sometimes the best choice might be the simplest one to do by hand or the simplest one to program on a computer. This may be the case for "small" problems that do not require a large number of calculations or comparisons. However, "large" problems might force you to consider other features of the algorithm, such as how much computer time or computer memory it would require. Such features are measures of the *efficiency* of an algorithm.

How Is the Efficiency of an Algorithm Calculated?

In this lesson, the **efficiency** of an algorithm is the maximum number $E(n)$ of *significant operations* necessary for the algorithm to solve the given problem if it is of *size n*. This is not a precise definition of efficiency until size and significant operations are defined for the given problem. These two ideas are usually easy to identify in specific problems. For instance, consider the familiar algorithm for adding two multi-digit positive integers.

A reasonable way to measure the size of an addition problem would be to use the maximum number of digits in either of the two positive integers that are added. Using this measure, the size of the addition problem 372 + 457 is 3. Now apply the algorithm.

Given Problem		Step 1		Step 2		Step 3
				1		
372		372		372		372
+ 457	→	457	→	457	→	457
		9		29		829

Each step of the addition algorithm involves the addition of single-digit numbers to produce a digit in the sum, and sometimes a "carry" digit of 1. It is reasonable to regard these single-digit additions as the significant operations for this algorithm and the "carries" as insignificant because they are by-products of the additions.

With these meanings of size and significant operations, for the addition algorithm,

$$E(3) = 3$$

because at most 3 single-digit additions are required to add two 3-digit numbers.

❶ Two Algorithms for Computing Powers

Algorithms can differ greatly in their efficiency. Consider now the problem of computing x^n for some real number x and some positive integer n. Compare the two algorithms on page 458.

Lesson 7-9

Objectives

There are no SPUR Objectives for any reading lesson.

Resources

From the ***Teacher's Resource File***
- Answer Master 7-9
- Teaching Aid 64: Warm-up

Additional Resources
- Visual for Teaching Aid 64

Warm-up

Construct a list of 5 numbers for which the Bubblesort algorithm will require interchanges at each of the 4 passes. **Answers will vary.**

Notes on Reading

Efficiency of algorithms is an area of interest to any user of valuable computer time. Clearly, cost requirements demand that the most efficient algorithm be used if all other factors are equal.

❶ For the two algorithms for calculating powers, students can get a concrete feel for the efficiency of the algorithms by performing calculations on their calculator. Have students compute 3^{12} by multiplying $3 \cdot 3 \cdot 3 \cdot 3 \cdot 3 \cdot 3 \cdot 3 \cdot 3 \cdot 3 \cdot 3 \cdot 3 \cdot 3$. Then have students compute 3^2, 3^4, and 3^8 by squaring.

Lesson 7-9 Overview

Broad Goals This reading lesson begins with an introduction to the notions of size of a problem and the efficiency of an algorithm for solving that problem. The efficiency of two algorithms for computing x^n are compared, and then the efficiency of Bubblesort and Quicksort are compared.

Perspective If you have never dealt with these ideas before, you may be surprised that series, logarithms, and the floor function are involved here. The algorithms for computing x^n are mentioned also in Lesson 8-6 when computing powers of complex numbers.

Optional Activities

Have students find an old book which explains how to calculate the square root of a number using an algorithm similar to long division. Ask students to compute the square root of a positive integer (not a perfect square) using the algorithm. Also, ask students to comment on the process!

Make sure students understand that 3^4 is obtained by squaring 3^2 and that 3^8 is obtained by squaring 3^4. Now 3^{12} can be computed as $3^4 \cdot 3^8$.

Students should keep track of the number of computations needed in each case. Such an experiment may help them understand the importance of efficiency in dealing with extremely large powers.

Error Alert Throughout the discussion of the multiplication algorithms, be sure students do not confuse the number of factors with the number of multiplications. The efficiency is determined by counting the number of multiplications, which for any given product is one less than the number of factors.

❷ If you have any students taking computer science, they may already have studied the measure of efficiency of algorithms in their classes. A function with the same overall end behavior as the function *E* used in this lesson is called the "Big O" ("oh", not "zero"), for Order of efficiency. For instance, because the end behavior of Bubblesort is like that of a quadratic polynomial, the efficiency of Bubblesort is said to be of the order of n^2, written as $O(n^2)$. For Quicksort the efficiency is of the order $O(n \log_2 n)$.

First Algorithm for computing x^n: repeated multiplication.
Multiply x repeatedly $n - 1$ times. That is, x^n is the nth term of the sequence defined recursively by

$$a_1 = x \text{ and } a_{k+1} = x \cdot a_k \qquad \text{for } k \geq 1.$$

This algorithm requires $n - 1$ multiplications. For instance, to calculate 7^{32}, it would take 31 multiplications.

$$7 \cdot 7 = 7^2; 7 \cdot 7^2 = 7^3; 7 \cdot 7^3 = 7^4; \text{ and so on.}$$

If the size of the problem is taken to be n and the significant operations are the required multiplications, then the efficiency of this algorithm is

$$E(n) = n - 1$$

because it requires $n - 1$ multiplications.

The second algorithm is more difficult to explain but it is surprisingly efficient. It is based on the fact that certain powers can be calculated quickly. With it, 7^{32} can be calculated in only five multiplications:
$7 \cdot 7 = 7^2; 7^2 \cdot 7^2 = 7^4; 7^4 \cdot 7^4 = 7^8; 7^8 \cdot 7^8 = 7^{16}; 7^{16} \cdot 7^{16} = 7^{32}$.

Second Algorithm for computing x^n: writing n as a sum of powers of 2.
Write n as a sum of powers of 2. (This is equivalent to writing n in base 2.)
Calculate x^n for those powers by repeatedly squaring. Then multiply the powers.

For example, to calculate x^{43}, note that

$$43 = 101011_2 = 2^5 + 2^3 + 2^1 + 2^0 = 32 + 8 + 2 + 1.$$

So $$x^{43} = x^{32} \cdot x^8 \cdot x^2 \cdot x.$$

The computation of x^{43} by this algorithm requires 5 multiplications to produce

$$x^2, x^4, x^8, x^{16}, x^{32}$$

and then 3 more to combine powers for a total of 8 multiplications.

Notice that computing x^n for any integer n from $2^5 = 32$ to $2^6 - 1 = 63$ would require the 5 multiplications necessary to produce

$$x^2, x^4, x^8, x^{16}, x^{32}$$

and then at most 5 additional multiplications to form x^n.

Of course, the second algorithm is more complicated to describe than the first. However, it is more efficient. For a given exponent n, the greatest power of 2 needed is 2^p,

where $$2^p \leq n < 2^{p+1}.$$

To solve for p, take the logarithm to base 2 of each part.

$$p \leq \log_2 n < p + 1$$

Adapting to Individual Needs

Extra Help

Before discussing the general formula for the efficiency of the second algorithm, some students may need more details to understand why, after computing x^2, x^4, x^8, x^{16}, and x^{32}, at most five additional multiplications are needed to compute x^n for $2^5 = 32 \leq n < 2^6 - 1 = 63$. You may wish to share the table at the right with your students. The 1s indicate the factors needed to produce the specific number x^n. For example, $x^{34} = x^{32} \cdot x^2$.

	x^{32}	x^{16}	x^8	x^4	x^2	x^1
x^{32}	1	0	0	0	0	0
x^{33}	1	0	0	0	0	1
x^{34}	1	0	0	0	1	0
x^{35}	1	0	0	0	1	1

.
.
.

Students should recognize that this analysis produces the binary numbers from 32 to 63.

As the table can verify, each of these numbers can be represented by at most six digits when written in base 2. Hence, at most six of the factors x, x^2, x^4, x^8, x^{16}, and x^{32} (five multiplications) are needed to produce x^n for $32 \leq n < 63$.

Therefore, the exponent p is the greatest integer less than or equal to $\log_2 n$; that is,

$$p = \lfloor \log_2 n \rfloor.$$

Once p has been determined, p multiplications are needed to compute

$$x^2, x^4, x^8, \ldots, x^{(2^p)},$$

and then at most p additional multiplications to compute x^n. Therefore, because the multiplications are taken as the only significant operations, the efficiency of the second algorithm is

$$\begin{aligned} E(n) &= p + p \\ &= 2p \\ &= 2\lfloor \log_2 n \rfloor. \end{aligned}$$

For large values of n, $E(n)$ for the second algorithm is a much smaller number than $E(n)$ for the first algorithm. The second algorithm is more efficient. For example, for x^{1000}, the first algorithm requires 999 multiplications while the second requires at most

$$2\lfloor \log_2 1000 \rfloor = 2 \cdot 9 = 18$$

multiplications. This is the sense in which the second algorithm is more efficient than the first.

❷ Comparing Efficiencies of Bubblesort and Quicksort

For the Bubblesort and Quicksort algorithms considered in the last lesson, a natural interpretation for the size n of a problem is the number n of items in the list, and the significant operations are the comparisons of numbers in the list. We will define the efficiency $E(n)$ of this algorithm to be the number of comparisons necessary to arrange the list.

For Bubblesort, a formula for $E(n)$ is not difficult to derive. Recall that to sort a list of n real numbers, Bubblesort makes (at most) $n - 1$ passes through the list. In the first pass, it makes $n - 1$ comparisons; in the second pass, it makes $n - 2$ comparisons; and so on to the $(n - 1)$st pass, in which it makes only one comparison. Thus the total number of comparisons it makes is

$$E(n) = \underset{\text{Pass 1}}{(n-1)} + \underset{\text{Pass 2}}{(n-2)} + \ldots + \underset{\text{Pass }(n-2)}{2} + \underset{\text{Pass }(n-1)}{1}.$$

Thus, $E(n)$ is the sum of the first $n - 1$ natural numbers. From Lesson 7-3, this sum is known to be $\frac{(n-1)[(n-1)+1]}{2}$, which is $\frac{n(n-1)}{2}$.

Quicksort was invented in 1960 by C.A.R. Hoare. It is quite a useful invention, for it can be shown that the efficiency of the Quicksort algorithm is approximately $n(\log_2 n - 2)$, which is significantly better than that of Bubblesort. The efficiency of algorithms can translate into the computer time required for execution of the algorithm. Suppose that a computer is capable of executing one million significant operations per second. The table on page 460 lists approximate execution times for the various efficiency functions $E(n)$ seen in this lesson and for various values of n.

You can use these values to have students determine the respective time multiplier if the number of items to be sorted is doubled for each.
For Bubblesort,

$$\begin{aligned} E(2n) &\approx O((2n)^2) \\ &= 4n^2 \\ &\approx 4(E(n)) \end{aligned}$$

For Quicksort,

$$\begin{aligned} E(2n) &\approx O(2n(\log_2 (2n))) \\ &= O(2n + 2n\log_2 n) \\ &\approx 2n + 2E(n) \end{aligned}$$

Thus, for Bubblesort, needed time is quadrupled. For Quicksort, it is somewhat more than doubled.

Adapting to Individual Needs

Challenge

The series $1 + x + \frac{x^2}{2!} + \frac{x^3}{3!} + \ldots + \frac{x^n}{n!}$ can be used to approximate e^x. The desired degree of accuracy can be obtained by adding more terms until the output does not change in the required decimal place. Have students use this series to approximate e^1, e^2, and e^3, to 4 decimal places. [2.7183, 7.3891, 20.0855]

Notes on Questions

Questions 1–4 You may wish to discuss with students best-case and worst-case scenarios for calculating the efficiency of an algorithm. For example:

Question 1 The efficiency of the algorithm is the same regardless of the given numbers.

Question 2 The efficiency of the algorithm is best if there are no carries; worst if there is a carry in every digit.

Questions 3–4 The efficiency $E(n) = n - 1$ for all n in the repeated multiplication algorithm; for the sums of powers, $E(n)$ is best if n is itself a power of 2.

Question 5 Compare this to the efficiency of Quicksort. As the number of items to be sorted increases tenfold repeatedly, how does the efficiency of Bubblesort compare to that of Quicksort? [Bubblesort's efficiency is multiplied by 100; Quicksort's by about 33.]

Question 8 Students are given an "add zero" hint to help in the inductive step.

Question 11b Ask students to generalize their indicated sum to any finite arithmetic sequence a_n. Then ask them to derive an explicit formula for $\sum_{i=1}^{n}[a_1 + (i-1)d]$.

Question 14 Complex numbers are the focus of the next chapter.

(Notes on Questions continue on page 462.)

Algorithm	$E(n)$	$n = 100$	$n = 1000$	$n = 10{,}000$	$n = 1{,}000{,}000$
x^n: repeated multiplication	$n - 1$	.0001 sec	.001 sec	.01 sec	1 sec
x^n: n as sum of powers of 2	$2\lfloor \log_2 n \rfloor$	.000012 sec	.000018 sec	.000026 sec	.000038 sec
Bubblesort: n numbers	$\frac{n(n-1)}{2}$	.005 sec	.5 sec	50 sec	139 hours!
Quicksort: n numbers	$n(\log_2 n - 2)$	.0005 sec	.008 sec	.11 sec	18 seconds

Since computers often have to calculate powers and sort lengthy lists, improved algorithms are literally quite valuable—they save time and thereby save money.

QUESTIONS

Covering the Reading

In 1 and 2, refer to the addition of 372 and 457, as shown in the lesson.

1. Using the same meanings for size and significant operations, what is the efficiency of the addition algorithm for adding two positive integers with at most n digits each? $E(n) = n$

2. If each carry is also considered to be a significant operation, compute the efficiency. $E(n) = 2n - 1$

3. Compare the efficiencies of the two algorithms of this lesson for calculating each power. See left.

a. x^{10} **b.** x^{10000}

3a) repeated multiplication: 9; sum of powers of 2: 6
b) repeated multiplication: 9999; sum of powers of 2: 26

4. The second algorithm discussed in this lesson for computing x^n requires successive comparisons of 2, 2^2, 2^3, and so on, with n until a positive p is found so that

$$2^p \le n < 2^{p+1}.$$

a. How many comparisons are needed for this? p

b. If these comparisons are also regarded as significant operations for the algorithm, compute the efficiency $E(n)$ of the second algorithm. See left.

4b) $3\lfloor \log_2 n \rfloor$

5. What is the efficiency of the Bubblesort algorithm if it is used to arrange 1000 numbers in increasing order? $E(1000) = 499{,}500$

6. Suppose the efficiency of an algorithm is given by the formula

$$E(n) = n^3.$$

If a computer can execute one million significant operations per second, calculate the execution time for each value of n.

a. $n = 100$
b. $n = 1000$
c. $n = 1{,}000{,}000$

a) 1 second b) 1000 seconds or ≈ 16.67 minutes
c) 10^{12} seconds or ≈ 31,710 years

Additional Answers, page 461

7.
$L = \{7, -3, 2, -6, 10, 5\}$
$L_\ell = \{-3, 2, -6, 5\}$ $f = 7$ $L_r = \{10\}$
$(L_\ell)_\ell = \{-6\}$ $f = -3$ $(L_\ell)_r = \{2, 5\}$
$((L_\ell)_r)_\ell = \varnothing$ $f = 2$ $((L_\ell)_r)_r = \{5\}$

Review

7. Apply the Quicksort algorithm to arrange the following list in increasing order: 7, -3, 2, -6, 10, 5. Show the intermediate results of each step. *(Lesson 7-8)* **See margin.**

8. Use mathematical induction to show that 16 is a factor of $5^n - 4n - 1$ for all integers $n \geq 1$. (Hint: In the inductive step, use the fact that $5^{k+1} = 5(5^k - 4k - 1 + 4k + 1) = 5(5^k - 4k - 1) + 20k + 5$.) *(Lesson 7-4)* **See margin.**

9. A sequence is defined recursively as follows:

$$\begin{cases} a_1 = 5 \\ a_{k+1} = a_k + 6k + 8 \quad \forall\, k \geq 1. \end{cases}$$

Show that an explicit formula for the sequence is $a_n = 3n^2 + 5n - 3$. *(Lessons 7-1, 7-3)* **See margin.**

10) Left side =
$-1 + 4 + 13 + 26 + 43 = 85$
Right side =
$2(0 + 1 + 4 + 9 + 16) + 3(0 + 1 + 2 + 3 + 4) - (1 + 1 + 1 + 1 + 1) =$
$2(30) + 3(10) - 5 =$
85

10. Show that $\sum_{i=0}^{4} (2i^2 + 3i - 1) = 2\sum_{i=0}^{4} i^2 + 3\sum_{i=0}^{4} i - \sum_{i=0}^{4} 1$. *(Lesson 7-2)*
See left.

11. In an auditorium, each row of seats contains 5 more seats than the row in front of it. The first row has 34 seats and there are 27 rows.
    a. If a_n is the number of seats in row n, write an explicit formula for a_n.
    b. Use summation notation to describe the total number of seats in the auditorium. *(Lessons 7-1, 7-2)* **$\sum_{n=1}^{27} (34 + 5(n - 1))$**
    a) $a_n = 34 + 5(n - 1)$

12. Consider the function h defined by $h(x) = \frac{5x + 3}{x - 4}$.
    a. Use division to express this function rule in another form. **See left.**
    b. Identify any horizontal or oblique asymptotes to the graph and give the appropriate equations. **$y = 5$**
    c. Give the equation of any vertical asymptote. **$x = 4$**
    d. Sketch a graph of the function. *(Lessons 5-4, 5-5)* **See left.**

12a) $h(x) = 5 + \frac{23}{x - 4}$
d)

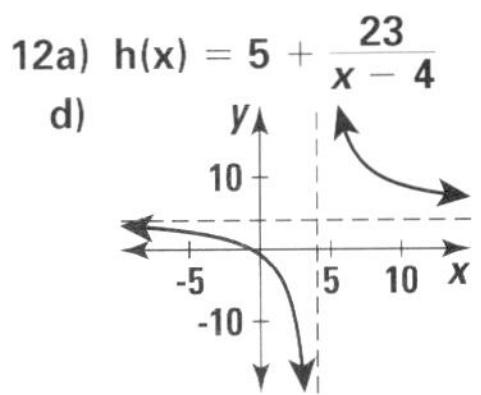

13. a. Write a logical expression to describe the network below.

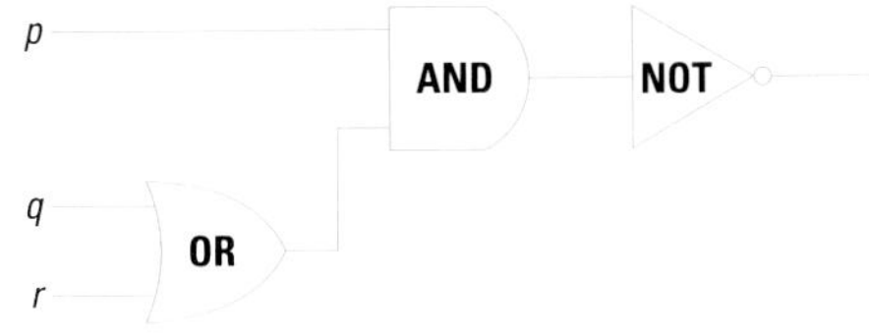

not (p and (q or r))

    b. Give a set of input values for p, q, and r which will yield an output value of 1. *(Lesson 1-4)* **Sample: $p = 0$, $q = 1$, $r = 0$**

14. Compute. *(Previous course)*
    a. $(6 - 4i) + (-5 + i)$ **$1 - 3i$**
    b. $(6 - 4i) - (-5 + i)$ **$11 - 5i$**
    c. $(6 - 4i) \cdot (-5 + i)$ **$-26 + 26i$**

Follow-up for Lesson 7-9

Extension

Refer students to **Question 6.** Have them conjecture which algorithm would be more efficient, one whose efficiency formula is $E(n) = n \log n$ or one whose efficiency formula is $E(n) = n\sqrt{n}$. Encourage students to find the execution time for different values of n: $n = 100$, $n = 1000$, and $n = 1{,}000{,}000$, assuming that the computer executes one million significant operations per second. [The algorithm with efficiency formula $E(n) = n \log n$ is more efficient. For $E(n) = n \log n$, if $n = 100$, $E(n) = .0002$ sec; if $n = 1000$, $E(n) = .003$ sec; if $n = 1{,}000{,}000$, $E(n) = 6$ sec. For $E(n) = n\sqrt{n}$ if $n = 100$, $E(n) = .001$ sec; if $n = 1000$, $E(n) = .032$ sec; if $n = 1{,}000{,}000$, $E(n) = 1000$ sec $\approx$ 17 min.]

Additional Answers

9. Let $S(n)$: $a_n = 3n^2 + 5n - 3$. For $n = 1$, the formula yields $a_1 = 3 \cdot 1^2 + 5 \cdot 1 - 3 = 5$. This agrees with the initial condition, so $S(1)$ is true. Assume $S(k)$: $a_k = 3k^2 + 5k - 3$ is true for some positive integer k. Show that $S(k + 1)$: $a_{k+1} = 3(k + 1)^2 + 5(k + 1) - 3$ is true. $a_{k+1} = 3(k + 1)^2 + 5(k + 1) - 3 = (3k^2 + 5k - 3) + 6k + 8 = a_k + 6k + 8$. This agrees with the recursive formula, so $S(k + 1)$ is true. Hence, by mathematical induction, $S(n)$ is true for all integers $n \geq 1$, and so the explicit formula for the sequence is $3n^2 + 5n - 3$.

8. $S(n)$: $5^n - 4n - 1$ is divisible by 16. $S(1)$: $5^1 - 4(1) - 1$ is divisible by 16. $S(1)$ is true since 0 is divisible by 16. Assume $S(k)$: $5^k - 4k - 1$ is divisible by 16 for some positive integer k. Show that 16 is a factor of $5^{k+1} - 4(k + 1) - 1$. $5^{k+1} - 4(k + 1) - 1$
$= 5(5^k - 4k - 1 + 4k + 1) - 4(k + 1) - 1$
$= 5(5^k - 4k - 1) + 20k + 5 - 4(k + 1) - 1$
$= 5(5^k - 4k - 1) + 16k$.
16 is a factor of $5^k - 4k - 1$ (by the inductive assumption) and a factor of $16k$. Hence, by the Factor of an Integer Sum Theorem, 16 is also a factor of $5(5^k - 4k - 1) + 16k$. Therefore, by mathematical induction, $5^n - 4n - 1$ is divisible by 16 for all positive integers n.

Notes on Questions

Question 15 This question is a "must" for any computer science students in your class. Analysis of the efficiency of algorithms is a challenging topic in computer science, yet this is a very accessible question.

Question 16 *Selection Sort* is an iterative algorithm designed to find the *k*th smallest of a set of numbers. *Selection Sort* works by finding the smallest element, then the second smallest element (by finding the smallest of the elements remaining after the smallest is omitted), and so forth. One special case of selection sort occurs in the determination of the median of a set of numbers.

Merge Sort is a recursive algorithm which works as follows. The first half of the list of numbers is sorted using merge sort, then the second half is sorted. Finally, the two halves are merged into a single sorted list. For more information on these and other algorithms and their efficiency, see Robert Sedgewick's text *Algorithms* (Addison-Wesley, 1988).

Other sorting algorithms are mentioned on page 454 in the *Extension* for Lesson 7-8.

15c) Each of the n digits of the second number are multiplied by up to n digits of the first number. Hence, there are at most n^2 multiplications.

e) $E(n) = n^2 + 2n$; For the problem, $n = 2$, so the efficiency should be 8. All four multiplication steps shown, must be carried out, as well as the four column additions. $4 + 4 = 8$, so the algorithm checks.

Exploration

15. An algorithm for multiplying two positive integers with at most n digits each is illustrated in the following diagram for $n = 2$.

						2										
34		34		34		34		34		34		34		34		34
× 52	→	52	→	52	→	52	→	52	→	52	→	52	→	52	→	52
		8		68		68		68		68		68		68		68
						0		170		170		170		170		170
										8		68		768		1768

a. Take the size of a given multiplication to be the maximum number of digits in either of the two numbers being multiplied. What is the size of the problem in the illustration above? **2**

b. What is the size of the problem if 48 is multiplied by 186? **3**

c. If single-digit multiplications are taken to be significant operations, show that there are at most n^2 multiplications. **See left.**

d. Also take the single-digit additions of the partial products to be significant operations. You must determine the maximum number of columns that must be added. The first partial product can have at most $n + 1$ digits so there are at most $n + 1$ columns in that row. Each row below it can have at most 1 additional column of digits. Use this information to determine the maximum number of single-digit additions. **$2n$ column additions**

e. Use parts **c** and **d** to determine a formula for the efficiency of the algorithm. Verify that the formula works for the problem illustrated here. **See left.**

16. Two other sorting algorithms are Selection and Merge. Look up Selection sort and Merge sort in a computer science book and find formulas for their efficiency $E(n)$. Compare their efficiency with that of Bubblesort and Quicksort for various values of n. **See margin.**

"There's a throwback for you. He checks all his answers with pencil and paper."

Additional Answers

**16. For Merge Sort, $E(n) = n \log_2 n$.
For Selection Sort, $E(n) = 2n$.
Approximate $E(n)$:**

	$n = 10$	$n = 100$	$n = 10{,}000$	$n = 1{,}000{,}000$
Merge Sort	33	664	133,000	2×10^7
Selection Sort	20	200	20,000	2×10^6
Bubblesort	45	4950	5×10^7	5×10^{11}
Quicksort	13	464	113,000	1.8×10^7

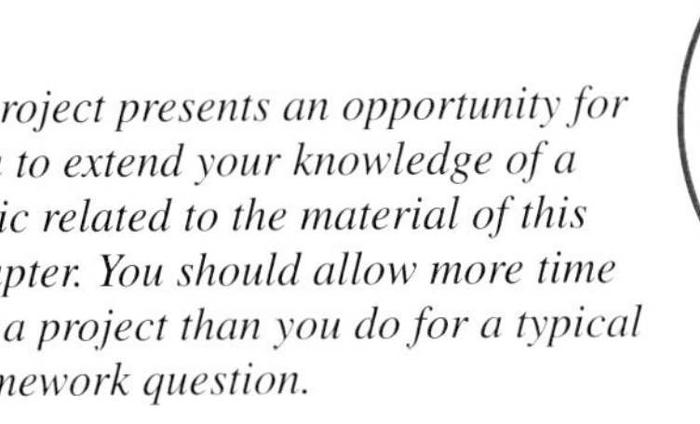

A project presents an opportunity for you to extend your knowledge of a topic related to the material of this chapter. You should allow more time for a project than you do for a typical homework question.

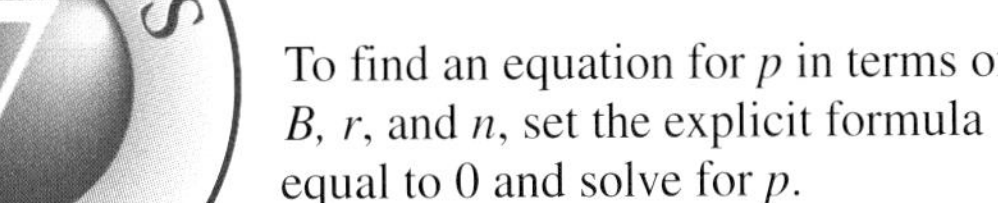

1 Amortizations

Suppose a car is purchased with \$5,000 borrowed at an annual interest rate of 12% (that is, a monthly rate of 1%). The loan is paid off in monthly installments of \$166 each. In other words, each month after the car is purchased, the amount owed (balance) is equal to the balance in the previous month, plus 1% of that balance in interest, minus the payment of \$166. Let A_n be the amount owed n months after the car is purchased.

a. Calculate A_1, A_2, and A_3.

b. Write a recursive definition for the sequence A.

c. Show that $A_3 =$
$1.01^3 \cdot 5000 - 1.01^2 \cdot 166 - 1.01 \cdot 166 - 166$.
(Hint: Find a numeric expression for A_1; do not calculate its value. Then substitute it into the recurrence relation to find an expression for A_2. Repeat this again to find an expression for A_3.)

d. Show that $A_3 =$
$5000 \cdot 1.01^3 - 166(1.01^0 + 1.01^1 + 1.01^2)$.

e. Conjecture a similar expression for A_n.

f. Use your knowledge of geometric series to rewrite the expression in parentheses in part **e** to obtain an explicit formula for A_n.

g. Use your formula from part **f** to find the amount owed on the car after 3 years.

h. Generalize the above by using the same steps to find an explicit formula for the balance after n months when \$$B$ are borrowed at a monthly interest rate of r.

i. Suppose you know B and r, and you wish to calculate the amount p of the monthly payment so that the loan will be paid off after n months. (This is called amortizing the loan over n months.) To find an equation for p in terms of B, r, and n, set the explicit formula equal to 0 and solve for p.

j. Estimate how much money you would need to borrow to buy a car of your choosing, and find out the typical interest rate for a car loan. Use the formula from part **i** to calculate your monthly payment in order to pay off the loan in 3 years. How much would you pay altogether over the 3 years? How much more than the actual amount borrowed would this be?

2 The Collatz Conjecture

A famous unsolved problem involves the computer program shown below. Let N be a positive integer.

```
10 INPUT N
15 PRINT "START WITH";N
20 LET X = N
22 IF X = 1 THEN GOTO 30
25 IF X = 1 THEN END
30 IF X/2 = INT(X/2) THEN GOTO 50
35 X = 3 * X + 1
40 PRINT X
45 GOTO 25
50 X = X/2
55 PRINT X
60 GOTO 25
```

a. Describe what this program does in general.

b. Investigate the outputs of this program for a variety of values of N. As of 1997, no one knew whether this program always generates the final value of X that you found or whether it takes on new values indefinitely for some N or whether it returns to some previously taken value and then loops.

c. This problem was posed in 1953 by Byrone Thwaites, but is sometimes called the Collatz Conjecture after a German mathematician who posed a similar problem in the 1930s. Use the Internet or books to find out some of the work that has been done on this problem.

Chapter 7 Projects

The projects relate chiefly to the content of the lessons of this chapter as follows:

Project	Lesson(s)
1	7-6
2	7-1
3	7-6
4	7-1, 7-3, 7-7
5	7-6
6	7-1, 7-3

1 Amortizations The process in this project shows the way that loan payments are calculated.

2 The Collatz Collection The Collatz Conjecture is also known as the $3n + 1$ problem. To entice some students into considering this project, you might run through the program for the integers 1 to 10.

$1 \to 4 \to 2 \to 1$
$2 \to 1$
$3 \to 10 \to 5 \to 16 \to 8 \to 4 \to 2 \to 1$
4 has been done above, with 1
5 has been done above, with 3
$6 \to 3$, which has been done
$7 \to 22 \to 11 \to 34 \to 17 \to 52 \to 26 \to 13 \to 40 \to 20 \to 10 \to 5$, which has been done
8 has been done with 3
$9 \to 28 \to 14 \to 7$, which has been done
10 has been done with 7

3 Zeno's Paradoxes Any encyclopedia is a place to start.

4 Exploring the Fibonacci Sequence The number and variety of patterns involving the Fibonacci numbers is so great that there exists a journal, *The Fibonacci Quarterly,* wholly devoted to properties of them and related sequences.

Possible Responses

1. a. $A_1 = 5000 + 50 - 166 = \$4{,}884$
$A_2 = 4884 + 48.84 - 166 = 4766.84$
$A_3 = 4766.84 + 47.6684 - 166 = \$4{,}648.51$

b. $A_n = A_{n-1} + 0.1A_{n-1} - 166 = 1.01A_{n-1} - 166$

c. $A_3 = 1.01A_2 - 166 = 1.01(1.01A_1 - 166) - 166$
$= 1.01(1.01(1.01A_0 - 166) - 166) - 166$
$= 1.01(1.01(1.01 \cdot 5000 - 166) - 166) - 166$
$= 1.01(1.01^2 \cdot 5000 - 1.01 \cdot 166 - 166) - 166$
$= 1.01^3 \cdot 5000 - 1.01^2 \cdot 166 - 1.01 \cdot 166 - 166$

d. Factoring out 166 from the formula in part c.
$A_3 = 5000 \cdot 1.01^3 - 166(1.01^2 + 1.01 + 1)$
$= 5000 \cdot 1.01^3 - 166(1.01^2 + 1.01^1 + 1.01^0)$
$= 5000 \cdot 1.01^3 - 166(1.01^0 + 1.01^1 + 1.01^2)$

e. Conjecture:
$A_n = 5000 \cdot 1.01^n - 166(1.01^0 + 1.01^1 + \ldots + 1.01^{n-1})$

f. $A_n = 5000 \cdot 1.01^n - 166\left(\frac{1 - 1.01^n}{1 - 1.01}\right)$
$= 5000 \cdot 1.01^n - 166\left(\frac{1 - 1.01^n}{-0.01}\right)$
$= 5000 \cdot 1.01^n + 16600(1 - 1.01^n)$

g. $A_3 = 5000 \cdot 1.01^3 + 16600(1 - 1.01^3) = 4648.5084 \approx \$4{,}648.51$

(Responses continue on page 464.)

5 Geometric Sequences This is a purely mathematical project.

6 Generating Sequences with Matrices This mathematical project is more difficult than Project 5.

Additional Responses, page 463
Project 1, continued

1. h. Following the same steps, $A_n = B \cdot (1 + r)^n + \frac{166}{r}(1 - (1 + r)^n)$.
   i. $0 = B \cdot (1 + r)^n + \frac{P}{r}(1 - (1 + r)^n)$
   $\frac{P}{r}(1 - (1 + r)^n) = -B \cdot (1 + r)^n$
   $P = \frac{-rB \cdot (1 + r)^n}{1 - (1 + r)^n}$
   j. Sample: The annual interest rate is 10%, and I would need to borrow \$8000 to buy the car I want. The monthly rate, r, is approximately 0.8333%.
   $P = \frac{-rB \cdot (1 + r)^n}{1 - (1 + r)^n}$
   $= \frac{-0.008333 \cdot 8000 \cdot (1.008333)^{36}}{1 - 1.008333^{36}}$
   $= \frac{-70.6664 \cdot 1.372457}{1 - 1.372457}$
   $= \frac{-96.986592}{-0.372457} =$ \$260.40/mo.
   After 3 years, I would have paid 36 • (260.40) = \$9,374.40, \$1,374.40 more than I borrowed.
2. a. The program asks for an initial value, then, based on a recursive definition, outputs terms of a sequence. If a term is 1, the sequence terminates; otherwise, the next term is computed using the following rule:
   $a_{k+1} = \begin{cases} 3a_k + 1, \text{ when } a_k \text{ is odd} \\ \frac{a_k}{2} \text{ when } a_k \text{ is even} \end{cases}$

(continued)

3 Zeno's Paradoxes

Look up some of Zeno's other paradoxes and write a report on them.

4 Exploring the Fibonacci Sequence

Below are some interesting sums involving the terms of the Fibonacci sequence F, which is defined as

$$\begin{cases} F_1 = 1 \\ F_2 = 1 \\ F_{k+1} = F_k + F_{k-1} & \text{for integers } k \geq 2. \end{cases}$$

a. Write the first 12 terms of this sequence.

In parts **b–d**, follow these 4 steps.

i. Fill in the blanks.
ii. Based on the results, form a conjecture, $S(n)$, about the sum in the nth row.
iii. Show that $S(n)$ is true for some n other than those shown.
iv. Use the Principle of Mathematical Induction to prove that $S(n)$ is true for all natural numbers.

b.
$1^2 = 1 \cdot 1$
$1^2 + 1^2 = 1 \cdot 2$
$1^2 + 1^2 + 2^2 = 2 \cdot 3$
$1^2 + 1^2 + 2^2 + 3^2 = 3 \cdot$ _?_
$1^2 + 1^2 + 2^2 + 3^2 + 5^2 =$ _?_
$1^2 + 1^2 + 2^2 + 3^2 + 5^2 + 8^2 =$ _?_

c.
$1 + 1 = 2$
$1 + 1 + 2 = 4$
$1 + 1 + 2 + 3 =$ _?_
$1 + 1 + 2 + 3 + 5 =$ _?_
$1 + 1 + 2 + 3 + 5 + 8 =$ _?_

d.
$1^2 + 1^2 = 2$
$1^2 + 2^2 =$ _?_
$2^2 + 3^2 =$ _?_
$3^2 + 5^2 =$ _?_
$5^2 + 8^2 =$ _?_

e. Investigate some sums of your own choosing. Prove that any patterns you find are valid for all natural numbers.

5 Geometric Sequences

A square has sides of length s. An infinite sequence of squares is formed by placing the vertices of each one at the midpoints of the sides of the previous one.

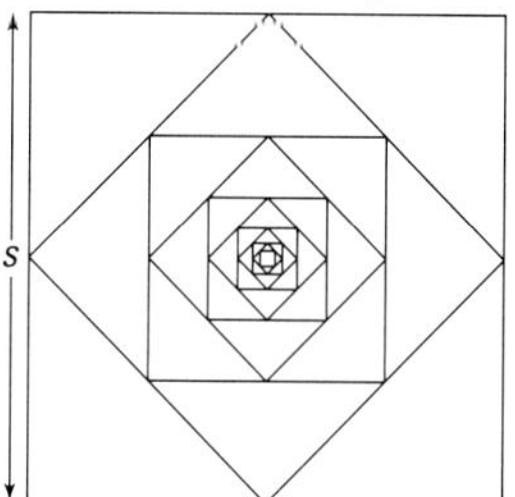

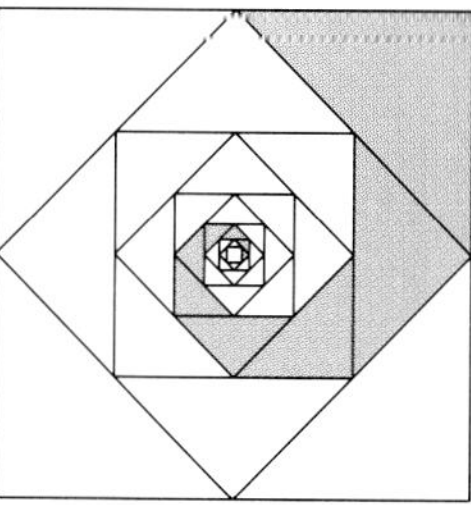

a. Find the sum of the perimeters of the squares, if possible.
b. Find the area of the shaded region (shown above at the right), if possible.
c. Form a similar sequence using some other regular polygon, and try to repeat parts **a** and **b**.

6 Generating Sequences with Matrices

Let $M = \begin{bmatrix} 1 & 1 \\ 1 & 0 \end{bmatrix}$.

a. Calculate M^2, M^3, M^4, M^5, and M^6.
b. Make a conjecture which relates M^n to the Fibonacci sequence for integers $n \geq 2$.
c. Prove your conjecture by using the Principle of Mathematical Induction.
d. Find the first six terms of a sequence that is analogously related to the powers of the matrix $\begin{bmatrix} 2 & 1 \\ 1 & 0 \end{bmatrix}$.
e. Find a recursive formula for the sequence you found in part **d**.
f. Generalize by finding a recursive formula for the sequence related to the powers of $\begin{bmatrix} a & 1 \\ 1 & 0 \end{bmatrix}$, where a is any real number.

b. Sample:

N	Output
3	10, 5, 16, 8, 4, 2, 1
4	2, 1
5	8, 4, 2, 1
6	3, 10, 5, 16, 8, 4, 2, 1
7	22, 11, 34, 17, 52, 26, 13, 40, 20, 10, 5, 16, 8, 4, 2, 1

3. Sample: There are 4 paradoxes attributed to Zeno. (1) The dichotomy paradox discussed in this book, where to travel a certain distance you must first travel one half that distance. This leads to an infinite division and a conclusion that you never reach the end point. (2) In the Achilles and tortoise paradox Achilles travels at a faster rate than the tortoise. The tortoise is given a head-start in race. The false conclusion reached is that Achilles can never catch the tortoise because once he has moved to the place the tortoise was, the tortoise will have moved. (3) In the arrow paradox we conclude that we cannot distinguish between a moving and stationary arrow, since at any instant it is indistinguishable from a stationary arrow at that point. (4) Another paradox results from the division of space and time.
4. See Additional Answers at the back of this book.

SUMMARY

A recursive formula for a sequence consists of an initial condition or conditions and a recurrence relation that describes how to obtain a term of the sequence from one or more preceding terms. After using the recursive formula to calculate the first several terms of a sequence, one may see a pattern for an explicit formula for the sequence. If correct, the explicit formula can be proved true by showing that it satisfies the recursive formula.

A series is the indicated sum of consecutive terms of a sequence. Summation notation is a shorthand way of indicating the sum. $\sum_{i=m}^{n} a_i$ means $a_m + a_{m+1} + \ldots + a_{n-1} + a_n$. For the sequence $a_1, a_2, a_3, \ldots$, the nth partial sum S_n is defined by $S_n = \sum_{i=1}^{n} a_i$. If the sequence of partial sums $S_1, S_2, S_3, \ldots$ has a limit, then the value of the infinite series $\sum_{i=1}^{\infty} a_i$ is defined to be $\lim_{n\to\infty} S_n$. Infinite series help to resolve one of Zeno's paradoxes. The value of an infinite geometric series with first term a and common ratio r is $\frac{a}{1-r}$ for $0 < |r| < 1$.

An important proof technique, mathematical induction, can be used to show that some statements $S(n)$ are true for all positive integers n. To use induction, you first show that $S(1)$ is true. Then you show that if the inductive assumption $S(k)$ is true, then $S(k + 1)$ is also true. The Strong Form of Mathematical Induction is a variant of this technique; its inductive assumption is that $S(1), S(2), \ldots, S(k)$ are all true. The two forms of the Principle of Mathematical Induction are used in this chapter to prove properties of sums, factors, inequalities, recursively defined sequences, and algorithms.

Some computer algorithms are iterative; they repeat the same procedure again and again to solve a problem. Others are recursive; they solve a problem by reducing it to smaller and smaller versions of itself. Two algorithms for sorting lists are Bubblesort, which is iterative, and Quicksort, which is recursive. Quicksort is the more efficient algorithm.

VOCABULARY

Below are the most important terms and phrases for this chapter. You should be able to give a definition and a specific example of each and a precise definition for those marked with an asterisk (*).

Lesson 7-1
* recursive formula for a sequence, initial condition(s), recurrence relation
Recursion Principle
Fibonacci sequence

Lesson 7-2
Zeno's Paradox
* summation notation, $\sum_{i=m}^{n} a_i$, expanded form, index

Lesson 7-3
* Principle of Mathematical Induction
* basis step, inductive step
* inductive assumption

Lesson 7-6
series, finite series, infinite series
* geometric series
Sum of the First n Powers Theorem
Evaluation of a Finite Geometric Series
partial sum
* infinite sum, $\sum_{k=1}^{\infty} a_k$
Evaluation of an Infinite Geometric Series
convergent
divergent

Lesson 7-7
* Principle of Strong Mathematical Induction

Lesson 7-8
sorting algorithm
Bubblesort, Quicksort
iterate
iterative algorithm
recursive algorithm
Quicksort Theorem

Summary

The Summary gives an overview of the entire chapter and provides an opportunity for students to consider the material as a whole. Thus, the Summary can be used to help students relate and unify the concepts presented in the chapter.

Vocabulary

Terms, symbols, and properties are listed by lesson to provide a checklist of concepts a student must know. Emphasize to students that they should read the vocabulary list carefully before starting the Progress Self-Test. If students do not understand the meaning of a term, they should refer back to the indicated lesson.

Additional Responses, page 464

5. a. Let $p(i)$ = the perimeter of the ith square.
$p(1) = 4s$
$p(2) = 4\frac{s}{2}\sqrt{2} = 2\sqrt{2}s$
$p(3) = 4\frac{\sqrt{2}s}{4}\sqrt{2} = 2s$
$p(4) = 4\frac{s}{4}\sqrt{2} = \sqrt{2}s$
$p(5) = 4\frac{\sqrt{2}s}{8}\sqrt{2} = s$
$p(6) = 4\frac{s}{8}\sqrt{2} = \frac{\sqrt{2}}{2}s$
It can be seen that $p(i)$ is a geometric sequence with $p(k+1) = \frac{\sqrt{2}}{2}p(k)$. So with $p(1) = 4s$ and $r = \frac{\sqrt{2}}{2}$, the sum $\sum_{i=1}^{\infty} p(i)$ is $\frac{4s}{1-\frac{\sqrt{2}}{2}} = \frac{4s}{\frac{2-\sqrt{2}}{2}} = \frac{8s}{2-\sqrt{2}} = \frac{8s(2+\sqrt{2})}{2} = 4s(2+\sqrt{2}) = (8+4\sqrt{2})s$.

b. Let $A(i)$ = the area of the triangle.
$A(1) = \frac{1}{2}\left(\frac{s}{2}\right)^2 = \frac{s^2}{8}$
$A(2) = \frac{1}{2}\left(\frac{\sqrt{2}s}{4}\right)^2 = \frac{s^2}{16}$
$A(3) = \frac{1}{2}\left(\frac{s}{4}\right)^2 = \frac{s^2}{32}$
$A(4) = \frac{1}{2}\left(\frac{\sqrt{2}s}{8}\right)^2 = \frac{s^2}{64}$
$A(5) = \frac{1}{2}\left(\frac{s}{8}\right)^2 = \frac{s^2}{128}$
It can be seen that $A(i)$ is a geometric sequence with $A(k+1) = \frac{1}{2}A(k)$. So with $A(1) = \frac{s^2}{8}$ and $r = \frac{1}{2}$, the sum $\sum_{i=1}^{\infty} A(i)$ is $\frac{\frac{s^2}{8}}{1-\frac{1}{2}} = \frac{\frac{s^2}{8}}{\frac{1}{2}} = \frac{s^2}{4}$.

Project Responses continue in Additional Answers at the back of this book.

Progress Self-Test

For the development of mathematical competence, feedback and correction, along with the opportunity to practice, are necessary. The Progress Self-Test provides the opportunity for feedback and correction; the Chapter Review provides additional opportunities and practice. We cannot overemphasize the importance of these end-of-chapter materials. It is at this point that the material 'gels' for many students, allowing them to solidify skills and understanding. In general, student performance should be markedly improved after these pages.

Assign the Progress Self-Test as a one-night assignment. Worked-out *solutions* for all questions are in the Selected Answers section of the student book. Encourage students to take the Progress Self-Test honestly, grade themselves, and then be prepared to discuss the test in class.

Advise students to pay special attention to those Chapter Review questions (pages 467–469) that correspond to questions missed on the Progress Self-Test.

Additional Answers

2. $r_1 = 5$, $r_n = 3r_{n-1}$, for $n \geq 2$

5. Let $S(n)$: $c_n = 3 \cdot 2^n - 3$. $S(1)$: $c_1 = 3 \cdot 2^1 - 3$. This matches the recursive definition since $c_1 = 3$, so $S(1)$ is true. Assume $S(k)$: $c_k = 3 \cdot 2^k - 3$ is true for some arbitrary integer k. Show that $S(k+1)$: $c_{k+1} = 3 \cdot 2^{k+1} - 3$ is true. From the recursive definition, $c_{k+1} = 2c_k + 3 = 2(3 \cdot 2^k) - 3 = 3 \cdot 2^{k+1} - 3$. Therefore, $S(k+1)$ is true. Hence, by mathematical induction, $S(n)$ is true for all $n \geq 1$, and so the explicit formula $c_n = 3 \cdot 2^n - 3$ yields the correct definition of the sequence.

8. Let $S(n)$: $\sum\limits_{i=1}^{n} i^2 = \frac{n(n+1)(2n+1)}{6}$.

(1) $\sum\limits_{i=1}^{1} i^2 = 1^2 = 1$, $\frac{1 \cdot 2 \cdot 3}{6} = 1$

so $S(1)$ *is* true. (2) Assume that $S(k)$ is true for an arbitrary integer $k \geq 1$ where $S(k)$:

$\sum\limits_{i=1}^{k} i^2 = \frac{k(k+1)(2k+1)}{6}$.

PROGRESS SELF-TEST

2, 5, 8, 9) See margin. 4, 7, 10) See below.

Take this test as you would take a test in class. Then check the test yourself using the solutions at the back of the book.

1. a. Find the first five terms of this recursively defined sequence: **1, 2, 4, 8, 16**

$$\begin{cases} a_1 = 1 \\ a_2 = 2 \\ a_{k+1} = 3a_k - 2a_{k-1} \quad \text{for integers } k \geq 2. \end{cases}$$

b. Conjecture an explicit formula for this sequence. $a_n = 2^{n-1}$ **∀ integers** $n \geq 1$

2. Someone started a rumor and told it to 5 other people. Each person who heard it told it to 3 friends who then told it to 3 other friends, and so forth. Let r_n be the number of people who hear the rumor on the nth telling. Write a recursive formula for the sequence r.

3. *Multiple choice.* Which of the following describes the sum **c**

$2 + 4 \cdot 2 + 8 \cdot 3 + 16 \cdot 4 + 32 \cdot 5 + 64 \cdot 6$?

(a) $\sum\limits_{i=1}^{6} i^2$ (b) $\sum\limits_{i=1}^{6} 2^{i-1} \cdot i^2$

(c) $\sum\limits_{i=1}^{6} 2^i \cdot i$ (d) $\sum\limits_{i=0}^{6} 2^i \cdot (i-1)$

4. Rewrite $\sum\limits_{i=1}^{k+1} i^2$ recursively in terms of $\sum\limits_{i=1}^{k} i^2$.

5. Prove that the sequence defined recursively by

$$\begin{cases} c_1 = 3 \\ c_{k+1} = 2c_k + 3 \quad \forall \text{ integers } k \geq 1 \end{cases}$$

has the explicit formula $c_n = 3 \cdot 2^n - 3$ for all integers $n \geq 1$.

4) $\sum\limits_{i=1}^{k+1} i^2 = \left(\sum\limits_{i=1}^{k} i^2\right) + (k+1)^2$

6. Evaluate each series.

a. $\sum\limits_{k=0}^{10} 2\left(\frac{1}{3}\right)^k$ **≈ 2.9999831**

b. $\sum\limits_{k=0}^{\infty} 2\left(\frac{1}{3}\right)^k$ **3**

7. Consider the computer program below, which prints out terms of a sequence.

```
10 B = 1
20 FOR J = 1 TO 10
30 B = 2 * B + 5
40 PRINT B
50 NEXT J
60 END
```

a. Does it use an explicit or a recursive formula?
b. Write the formula it uses.

8. Use the Principle of Mathematical Induction to prove that

$\sum\limits_{i=1}^{n} i^2 = \frac{n(n+1)(2n+1)}{6}$ ∀ integers $n \geq 1$.

9. Prove that 4 is a factor of $2n^2 + 2n + 8$ for all positive integers n.

10. What is the form of the inductive assumption in the Strong Form of Mathematical Induction?

11. Use the Quicksort Algorithm to sort the list 8, 3, 10, 7, 1 in increasing order. Show the results of each step.

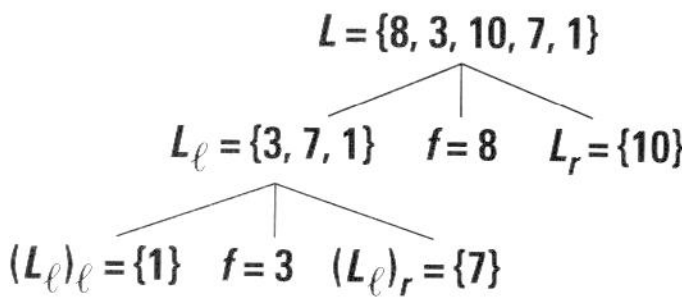

The sorted list is 1, 3, 7, 8, 10.

7a) recursive
b) $b_1 = 1$; $b_{j+1} = 2b_j + 5$ for $j \geq 1$

10) Assume $S(1), S(2), \ldots, S(k)$ are true for some integer $k \geq 1$.

Now use the assumption that $S(k)$ is true to prove $S(k+1)$ is true:

$\sum\limits_{i=1}^{k+1} i^2 = \left(\sum\limits_{i=1}^{k} i^2\right) + (k+1)^2$

$= \frac{k((k+1)(2k+1))}{6} + \frac{6(k+1)^2}{6} = \frac{k+1}{6} \cdot (2k^2 + k + 6k + 6) = \frac{(k+1)(k+2)(2k+3)}{6} = \frac{(k+1)((k+1)+1)(2(k+1)+1)}{6}$. Hence, $S(n)$ is true for all integers $n \geq 1$ by the Principle of Mathematical Induction.

9. Let $S(n)$: 4 is a factor of $2n^2 + 2n + 8$. (1) $2 \cdot 1^2 + 2 \cdot 1 + 8 = 12$ and 4 is a factor of 12, so $S(1)$ is true. (2) Assume $S(k)$ is true. That is, 4 is a factor of $2k^2 + 2k + 8$ for some arbitrary integer $k \geq 1$. Show $S(k+1)$ is true. $2(k+1)^2 + 2(k+1) + 8 = 2k^2 + 4k + 2 + 2k + 2 + 8 = (2k^2 + 2k + 8) + 4k + 4 = (2k^2 + 2k + 8) + 4(k+1)$. 4 is a factor

CHAPTER REVIEW

Questions on SPUR Objectives

SPUR stands for **S**kills, **P**roperties, **U**ses, and **R**epresentations. The Chapter Review questions are grouped according to the SPUR Objectives for this chapter.

SKILLS DEAL WITH THE PROCEDURES USED TO GET ANSWERS.

Objective A: *Determine terms of a sequence which is defined either explicitly or recursively. (Lesson 7-1)*

In 1–5, find the first five terms of the sequence defined by the indicated formula. **4, 5) See margin.**

1. $a_n = 3^n + 4$ **7, 13, 31, 85, 247**
2. $f_n = \frac{(n+1)(2n+1)(3n-5)}{6}$ **$-2, \frac{5}{2}, \frac{56}{3}, \frac{105}{2}, 110$**
3. $b_n = 2 \cdot \left\lfloor \frac{n}{2} \right\rfloor$ **0, 2, 2, 4, 4**
4. $\begin{cases} a_1 = 2 \\ a_{k+1} = \frac{k}{k+2} a_k & \text{for } k \geq 1 \end{cases}$
5. $\begin{cases} a_1 = 3 \\ a_2 = 5 \\ a_{k+1} = 2a_k - 4a_{k-1} & \text{for } k \geq 2 \end{cases}$
6. Find t_{10} for the sequence defined by $t_n = 6(n-3) + 9$. **51**
7. Let c be a real number, and define a sequence by $\begin{cases} a_1 = 3c \\ a_{k+1} = a_k - c & \text{for } k \geq 1. \end{cases}$ Find a_7. **$-3c$**

Objective B: *Conjecture explicit formulas for recursively defined sequences. (Lesson 7-1)*

In 8–10, a recursive definition for a sequence is given. **a.** Write the first five terms of the sequence. **b.** Conjecture an explicit formula for the sequence which works for the first five terms. **See margin.**

8. $\begin{cases} a_1 = 3 \\ a_{k+1} = a_k + 2 & \text{for } k \geq 1 \end{cases}$
9. $\begin{cases} a_1 = 1 \\ a_{k+1} = \frac{a_k}{k+1} & \text{for } k \geq 1 \end{cases}$
10. $\begin{cases} a_1 = 3 \\ a_{k+1} = 2 - a_k & \text{for } k \geq 1 \end{cases}$
11. Write an explicit formula for I_n, the sum of the first n positive even integers. **$I_n = n(n+1)$**
12. Consider the sequence defined recursively by $\begin{cases} a_1 = 1 \\ a_2 = 2 \\ a_{k+1} = 2a_k - a_{k-1} & \text{for } k \geq 2. \end{cases}$
    a. List the first five terms. **1, 2, 3, 4, 5**
    b. Conjecture an explicit formula for a_n. **$a_n = n$**
    c. Repeat parts **a** and **b** if $a_1 = 2$ and $a_2 = 4$. **2, 4, 6, 8, 10; $a_n = 2n$**

Objective C: *Use summation notation to write sums. (Lesson 7-2)* **13a, 16–18) See margin.**

13. a. Write the sum $\sum_{k=-3}^{n} (n+k)$ in expanded form.
    b. Find the value of the sum in part **a** if $n = 2$. **9**
14. *True or false.* **False**
    $$\sum_{k=0}^{3} [(k+1)]^2 = \left[\sum_{k=0}^{3} (k+1)\right]^2$$
15. Define a sequence for all positive integers n by $a_n = \frac{1}{9-2n}$. Find $\sum_{k=1}^{7} a_n$. **$\frac{1}{7}$**

In 16 and 17, write using summation notation.

16. $2 \cdot 1 + 2 \cdot 2 + 2 \cdot 3 + 2 \cdot 4 + 2 \cdot 5 + 2 \cdot 6$
17. $\frac{1}{-n} + \frac{1}{-n+1} + \frac{1}{-n+2} + \ldots + \frac{1}{-3} + \frac{1}{-2} + \frac{1}{-1}$
18. It can be shown that the statement
    $S(n)$: $1 \cdot 2 + 2 \cdot 3 + 3 \cdot 4 + \ldots + n(n+1) = \frac{n(n+1)(n+2)}{3}$
    is true for all integers $n \geq 1$.
    a. Rewrite $S(n)$ using summation notation.
    b. Verify that $S(4)$ is true.

Chapter 7 Review

Resources

From the ***Teacher's Resource File***
- Answer Master for Chapter 7 Review
- Assessment Sourcebook: Chapter 7 Test, Forms A–D; Chapter 7 Test, Cumulative Form

Additional Resources
- TestWorks CD-ROM

The main objectives for the chapter are organized in the Chapter Review under the four types of understanding this book promotes–Skills, Properties, Uses, and Representations.

Whereas end-of-chapter material may be considered optional in some texts, in UCSMP *Precalculus and Discrete Mathematics* we have selected these objectives and questions with the expectation that they will be covered. Students should be able to answer these questions with about 85% accuracy after studying the chapter.

You may assign these questions over a single night to help students prepare for a test the next day, or you may assign the questions over a two-day period. If you work the questions over two days, then we recommend assigning the *evens* for homework the first night so that students get feedback in class the next day, then assigning the *odds* the night before the test, because answers are provided to the odd-numbered questions.

of $2k^2 + 2k + 8$ by the inductive assumption, and 4 is clearly a factor of $4(k+1)$. Hence, 4 is a factor of $2(k+1)^2 + 2(k+1) + 8$ by the Factor of an Integer Sum Theorem. Thus, $S(n)$ is true for all positive integers n by mathematical induction. So 4 is a factor of $2n^2 + 2n + 8$ for all positive integers n.

Additional Answers, page 467

4. $2, \frac{2}{3}, \frac{1}{3}, \frac{1}{5}, \frac{2}{15}$
5. 3, 5, -2, -24, -40
8. a. 3, 5, 7, 9, 11
   b. $a_n = 2n + 1$ for all integers $n \geq 1$
9. a. $1, \frac{1}{2}, \frac{1}{6}, \frac{1}{24}, \frac{1}{120}$
   b. $a_n = \frac{1}{n!}$ for all integers $n \geq 1$
10. a. 3, -1, 3, -1, 3
    b. $a_n = \begin{cases} 3 & \text{when } n \text{ is odd} \\ -1 & \text{when } n \text{ is even} \end{cases}$
13. a. $(n-3) + (n-2) + \ldots + (n+n)$
16. $\sum_{i=1}^{6} 2i$
17. $\sum_{i=1}^{n} -\frac{1}{i}$
18. a. $S(n)$: $\sum_{i=1}^{n} i(i+1) = \frac{n(n+1)(n+2)}{3}$
    b. $S(4)$: $\sum_{i=1}^{4} i(i+1) = \frac{4(5)(6)}{3}$; $1 \cdot 2 + 2 \cdot 3 + 3 \cdot 4 + 4 \cdot 5 = 40$ and $\frac{4(5)(6)}{3} = 40$, so $S(4)$ is true.

It is effective to ask students which questions they still do not understand and use the day or days as a total class discussion of the material which the class finds most difficult.

Assessment

Evaluation The Assessment Sourcebook provides five forms of the Chapter 7 Test. Forms A and B present parallel versions in a short-answer format. Forms C and D offer performance assessment. The fifth test is Chapter 7 Test, Cumulative Form. About 50% of this test covers Chapter 7, 25% of it covers Chapter 6, and 25% of it covers earlier chapters.

For information on grading, see *General Teaching Suggestions: Grading* in the *Professional Sourcebook,* which begins on page T20 in the Teacher's Edition.

Feedback After students have taken the test for Chapter 7 and you have scored the results, return the tests to students for discussion. Class discussion of the questions that caused trouble for the most students can be very effective in identifying and clarifying misunderstandings. You might want to have them write down the items they missed and work, either in groups or at home, to correct them. It is important for students to receive feedback on every chapter test, and we recommend that students see and correct their mistakes before proceeding too far into the next chapter.

CHAPTER SEVEN

Objective D: *Rewrite sums recursively.* *(Lesson 7-2)* **19a, 19c, 20a, 20c, 21, 23) See margin.**

19. Let $S(k)$ be the statement *The sum of the first k positive even integers is $k(k+1)$.*

a. Write $S(k)$ using summation notation.

b. What is the 101st term of the sum? **202**

c. If the sum of the first 100 terms is 10100, find the sum of the first 101 terms in two different ways.

20. The sum of the first n positive integer powers of 3 is given by the formula $\frac{3}{2}(3^n - 1)$. That is,

$$\sum_{i=1}^{n} 3^i = \frac{3}{2}(3^n - 1).$$

a. Show that this formula works for $n = 4$.

b. Use your result from part **a** to find the sum of the first 5 terms. **120 + 243 = 363**

c. Show that if $n = 5$ is substituted into $\frac{3}{2}(3^n - 1)$, the result agrees with part **b**.

21. Rewrite $\sum_{j=1}^{k+1} (j-1)(2j+1)$ in terms of $\sum_{j=1}^{k} (j-1)(2j+1)$.

Objective E: *Evaluate a finite or an infinite geometric series.* *(Lesson 7-6)*

22. Find the value of $\sum_{k=0}^{10} \left(\frac{2}{3}\right)^k$. **≈ 2.9653**

23. a. Write a formula that evaluates $\sum_{k=0}^{n} \frac{t}{4^k}$.

b. Use your answer to part **a** to find $\sum_{k=0}^{10} \frac{2}{4^k}$.

24. Find $\sum_{k=0}^{\infty} \frac{3}{5^k}$. $\frac{15}{4}$

25. Define a geometric sequence by

$$\begin{cases} a_1 = 2 \\ a_{k+1} = .8a_k \quad \forall \text{ integers } k \ge 1. \end{cases}$$

Let S_n be the nth partial sum of the sequence.

a. Find a formula for S_n. $S_n = 10\left(1 - \left(\frac{4}{5}\right)^n\right)$

b. What is S_7? **≈ 7.9029**

c. Find $\lim_{n\to\infty} S_n$. **10**

PROPERTIES DEAL WITH THE PRINCIPLES BEHIND THE MATHEMATICS.

26–35) See margin.

Objective F: *Prove that a recursively defined sequence has a particular explicit formula.* *(Lesson 7-3)*

26. Prove that the sequence defined by

$$\begin{cases} a_1 = 4 \\ a_{k+1} = 3a_k + 4 \quad \forall k \ge 1 \end{cases}$$

has explicit formula $a_n = 2 \cdot 3^n - 2$.

27. Consider the sequence defined by

$$\begin{cases} b_1 = 0 \\ b_{k+1} = b_k + 2k \quad \forall k \ge 1. \end{cases}$$

a. Find the first five terms of the sequence.

b. Prove that it has the explicit formula $b_n = n(n-1)$.

Objective G: *Prove statements using the Principle of Mathematical Induction.* *(Lessons 7-3, 7-4, 7-5, 7-7)*

In 28–33, use mathematical induction to prove that $S(n)$ is true for all natural numbers n.

28. $S(n)$: $3 + 7 + 11 + \ldots + (4n - 1) = n(2n + 1)$

29. $S(n)$: $\sum_{i=1}^{n} 3i(i+2) = \frac{n(n+1)(2n+7)}{2}$

30. $S(n)$: *3 is a factor of* $n^3 + 14n$.

31. $S(n)$: *If* $n \ge 2$, *3 is a factor of* $2n^3 - 5n$.

32. $S(n)$: *If* $0 \le x \le 1$, *then* $0 \le x^n \le x$.

33. $S(n)$: *If* $n \ge 2$, *then* $4^n > 4n$.

34. Consider $S(n)$ below, which is to be proved for all integers $n \ge 1$ by mathematical induction.

$$S(n): \left(1 - \frac{1}{2}\right)\left(1 - \frac{1}{3}\right)\left(1 - \frac{1}{4}\right) \ldots \left(1 - \frac{1}{n+1}\right) = \frac{1}{n+1}$$

a. Verify the basis step.

b. Write the inductive assumption.

c. Write the statement $S(k+1)$.

d. Use the Principle of Mathematical Induction to complete the proof that $S(n)$ is true for all integers $n \ge 1$.

35. Define the sequence b by

$$\begin{cases} b_1 = 0 \\ b_2 = 4 \\ b_{k+1} = b_k + 3b_{k-1} \quad \text{for } k \ge 2. \end{cases}$$

a. Find the first five terms.

b. Use the Strong Form of the Principle of Mathematical Induction to prove that *4 is a factor of b_n ∀ integers $n \ge 1$.*

Additional Answers

19. a. $S(k)$: $\sum_{i=1}^{k} 2i = k(k+1)$

c. $10100 + 202 = 10302$ and $101(102) = 10302$

20. a. $3 + 9 + 27 + 81 = 120$ and $\frac{3}{2}(3^4 - 1) = \frac{3}{2}(81 - 1) = 120$, so the formula works for $n = 4$.

c. $\frac{3}{2}(3^5 - 1) = \frac{3}{2}(243 - 1) = \frac{3}{2} \cdot 242 =$ 363, which agrees with part b.

21. $\sum_{j=1}^{k+1} (j-1)(2j+1) = \left[\sum_{j=1}^{k} (j-1)(2j+1)\right] + (k)(2k+3)$

23. a. $\frac{4t}{3}\left(1 - \left(\frac{1}{4}\right)^{n+1}\right)$

b. ≈ 2.6667

26. Let $S(n)$: $a_n = 2 \cdot 3^n - 2$ for all integers $n \ge 1$. (1) $S(1)$: $a_1 = 2 \cdot 3^1 - 2$. $a_1 = 4$, so $S(1)$ is true. (2) Assume $S(k)$: $a_k = 2 \cdot 3^k - 2$ is true for some arbitrary integer $k \ge 1$. Show that $S(k+1)$: $a_{k+1} = 2 \cdot 3^{k+1} - 2$ is true. From the recursive definition, $a_{k+1} = 3a_k + 4 = 3(2 \cdot 3^k - 2) + 4 = 2 \cdot 3^{k+1} - 6 + 4 = 2 \cdot 3^{k+1} - 2$. Hence, by mathematical induction, $S(n)$ is true for all integers $n \ge 1$, and the explicit formula is correct.

27. a. 0, 2, 6, 12, 20

b. Let $S(n)$: $b_n = n(n-1)$ for all integers $n \ge 1$. (1) $S(1)$: $b_1 = 1(1-1)$. $b_1 = 0$, so $S(1)$ is true. (2) Assume $S(k)$: $b_k = k(k-1)$ is true for some arbitrary integer $k \ge 1$. Show that $S(k+1)$: $b_{k+1} = (k+1)((k+1)-1)$ is true.

USES DEAL WITH APPLICATIONS OF MATHEMATICS IN REAL SITUATIONS.

36, 37a, 38a, 39a, 40) See margin.

Objective H: *Use recursive formulas to solve problems.* (*Lesson 7-1*)

36. Imagine n towns, each of which is connected to each of the others by a telecommunications cable. Let C_n be the number of such cables.

a. Find C_2, C_3, and C_4.

b. Write a recurrence relation for C_{k+1} in terms of C_k.

c. Use your answers to parts **a** and **b** to find how many cables are needed to connect eight towns.

37. At the beginning of month 1, a homeowner owes $80,000 on a house. At the beginning of each month thereafter, 1% interest is added to the amount owed, and then the homeowner pays off $900 of the loan. Let A_n represent the amount owed in the nth month.

a. Write a recursive definition for the sequence $A_1, A_2, A_3, \ldots$.

b. Find the amount owed in the sixth month. $79,489.90

38. Recall that a binary number is a string of digits, each of which is a 0 or a 1. Each such digit is called a **bit**. Let b_n represent the number of different binary numbers possible using n bits.

a. Write a recursive definition for the sequence $b_1, b_2, b_3, \ldots$.

b. How many binary numbers can be stored by a computer in a **byte**, which consists of 8 bits? 256

Objective I: *Execute algorithms to sort sets of numbers.* (*Lesson 7-8*)

39. a. Apply the Bubblesort algorithm to the list 1, 3, 5, 2, 4. Show intermediate results of each step.

b. Suppose we change the rule for interchanges in the Bubblesort algorithm to: interchange two adjacent numbers if the lower one is smaller than the upper one. What will the final list be if this version is applied to the list in part **a**? 5, 4, 3, 2, 1

40. Apply the Quicksort algorithm to the list 21, 1, 8, 13, 1, 5. Show intermediate results of each step. See margin.

REPRESENTATIONS DEAL WITH PICTURES, GRAPHS, OR OBJECTS THAT ILLUSTRATE CONCEPTS.

41a, c, d, 42b) See margin.

Objective J: *Interpret computer programs which calculate terms of sequences.* (*Lessons 7-1, 7-3, 7-6*)

41. Consider the program below.

```
10 TERM = 1
20 PRINT TERM
30 SUM = TERM
40 FOR K = 2 TO 20
50   TERM = TERM/2
60   PRINT TERM
70   SUM = SUM + TERM
80 NEXT K
90 PRINT SUM
100 END
```

a. Write the recursive definition for the sequence whose terms it stores in the variable TERM.

b. Write an explicit formula for the sequence in part **a**. $a_n = \left(\frac{1}{2}\right)^{n-1}$ $\forall$ integers $n \geq 1$

c. Use summation notation to write the sum ultimately stored in SUM.

d. Write a formula that could be used to calculate this sum directly.

42. Consider the computer program below.

```
10 FOR N = 1 TO 5
20   A = 3 * N + 7
30   PRINT A
40 NEXT N
50 END
```

10, 13, 16, 19, 22

a. Write the terms generated by this program.

b. Does the computer program use a recursive or an explicit formula? Explain.

c. Write the formula it uses. $a_n = 3n + 7$

Additional Answers

29. (1) $S(1)$: $\sum_{i=1}^{1} 3i(i+2) = \frac{1 \cdot 2 \cdot 9}{2}$. $3 \cdot 1(1+2) = 9$ and $\frac{1 \cdot 2 \cdot 9}{2} = 9$, so $S(1)$ is true.

(2) Assume that $S(k)$: $\sum_{i=1}^{k} 3i(i+2) = \frac{k(k+1)(2k+7)}{2}$ is true for some arbitrary integer $k \geq 1$.

Show $S(k+1)$: $\sum_{i=1}^{k+1} 3i(i+2) = \frac{(k+1)(k+2)(2(k+1)+7)}{2}$ is true.

$\sum_{i=1}^{k+1} 3i(i+2) = \left(\sum_{i=1}^{k} 3i(i+2)\right) + 3(k+1)(k+3) =$

$\frac{k(k+1)(2k+7)}{2} + (k+1)(3k+9)$

$= \frac{k(k+1)(2k+7)}{2} + \frac{2(k+1)(3k+9)}{2}$

$= \left(\frac{k+1}{2}\right)(2k^2 + 7k + 6k + 18)$

$= \left(\frac{k+1}{2}\right)(k+2)(2k+9)$

$= \frac{(k+1)(k+2)(2(k+2)+7)}{2}$

By Mathematical Induction, $S(n)$ is true $\forall$ integers $n \geq 1$.

30. (1) $S(1)$: 3 is a factor of $1^3 + 14(1)$. $1^3 + 14(1) = 15$, so $S(1)$ is true. (2) Assume $S(k)$: 3 is a factor of $k^3 + 14k$ is true for some integer $k \geq 1$. Show that $S(k+1)$: 3 is a factor of $(k+1)^3 + 14(k+1)$ is true. Expanding, $(k+1)^3 + 14(k+1)$ $= (k^3 + 3k^2 + 3k + 1) + (14k + 14)$ $= (k^3 + 14k) + (3k^2 + 3k + 15)$ $= (k^3 + 14k) + 3(k^2 + k + 5)$. By the inductive assumption, 3 is a factor of $k^3 + 14k$, and 3 is a factor of $3(k^2 + k + 5)$. So, 3 is a factor of their sum by the Factor of an Integer Sum Theorem. By mathematical induction, $S(n)$ is true $\forall$ integers $n \geq 1$.

31–42. See Additional Answers at the back of this book.

From the recursive definition, $b_{k+1} = b_k + 2k = k(k-1) + 2k =$ $k^2 + k = (k+1)k = (k+1)((k+1)-1)$. Hence, by mathematical induction, $S(n)$ is true $\forall$ integers $n \geq 1$, and the explicit formula is correct.

28. Let $S(n)$: $3 + 7 + 11 + \ldots + (4n-1) = n(2n+1)$. (1) $S(1)$: $3 = 1(2 \cdot 1 + 1)$. $S(1)$ is true. (2) Assume $S(k)$: $3 + 7 + 11 + \ldots + (4k-1) = k(2k+1)$ is true for some arbitrary integer $k \geq 1$. Show that $S(k+1)$: $3 + 7 + 11 + \ldots + (4k-1) + (4(k+1)-1) = (k+1)(2(k+1)+1)$ is true. From the inductive assumption, $3 + 7 + 11 + \ldots + (4k-1) + (4(k+1)-1) =$ $k(2k+1) + (4(k+1)-1) =$ $2k^2 + k + 4k + 3 = (k+1)(2k+3)$ $= (k+1)(2(k+1)+1)$ Hence, by mathematical induction, $S(n)$ is true for all integers $n \geq 1$.

Chapter 8 Planner

Adapting to Individual Needs

The student text is written for the vast majority of students. The chart at the right suggests two pacing plans to accommodate the needs of your students. Students in the Full Course should complete the entire text by the end of the year. Students in the Minimal Course will spend more time when there are quizzes and more time on the Chapter Review. Therefore, these students may not complete all of the chapters in the text.

Options are also presented to meet the needs of a variety of teaching and learning styles. For each lesson, the Teacher's Edition provides a section entitled *Adapting to Individual Needs.* This section regularly includes **Optional Activities, Challenge** problems, **English Language Development** suggestions, and suggestions for providing **Extra Help.** The Teacher's Edition also frequently includes an **Error Alert,** an **Extension,** and an **Assessment** alternative. The options available in Chapter 8 are summarized in the chart below.

Chapter 8 Pacing Chart

Day	Full Course	Minimal Course
1	8-1	8-1
2	8-2	8-2
3	8-3	8-3
4	8-4	8-4
5	Quiz*; 8-5	Quiz*; begin 8-5.
6	8-6	Finish 8-5.
7	8-7	8-6
8	8-8	8-7
9	Quiz*; 8-9	8-8
10	8-10	Quiz*; begin 8-9.
11	Self-Test	Finish 8-9.
12	Review	8-10
13	Test*	Self-Test
14		Review
15		Review
16		Test*

*in the Teacher's Resource File

In the Teacher's Edition...

Lesson	Optional Activities	Extra Help	Challenge	English Language Development	Error Alert	Extension	Cooperative Learning	Ongoing Assessment
8-1	●	●	●		●	●	●	Group
8-2	●	●	●		●	●		Written
8-3	●	●	●		●	●		Oral
8-4	●	●	●		●	●		Quiz
8-5	●	●	●		●	●	●	Written
8-6	●	●	●	●	●	●	●	Written
8-7	●	●	●		●	●	●	Written
8-8	●	●	●		●	●		Quiz
8-9	●	●	●		●	●	●	Oral
8-10	●	●	●		●	●	●	

In the Additional Resources...

	In the Teacher's Resource File							
Lesson	Lesson Masters	Teaching Aids*	Answer Masters	Technology Sourcebook	Assessment Sourcebook	Visual Aids**	Technology	Explorations Software
8-1	8-1	70	8-1			70, AM		
8-2	8-2	70, 73, 74	8-2			70, 73, 74, AM		8-2
8-3	8-3	70, 75, 76	8-3			70, 75, 76, AM		8-3
8-4	8-4	70, 77, 78	8-4		Quiz	70, 77, 78, AM		8-4
In-class Activity			8-5					
8-5	8-5	71, 79, 80	8-5	Calc 12		71, 79, 80, AM		
8-6	8-6	71, 73, 74, 81	8-6			71, 73, 74, 81, AM		
8-7	8-7	71, 82, 83	8-7			71, 82, 83, AM		
8-8	8-8	72	8-8		Quiz	72, AM		
8-9	8-9	72, 84, 85	8-9			72, 84, 85, AM		
8-10		72, 86	8-10			72, 86, AM		
End of chapter					Tests			

*Teaching Aids are pictured on pages 470C and 470D.

**Visual Aids provide transparencies for all Teaching Aids and all Answer Masters.

Also available is the Study Skills Handbook which includes study-skill tips related to reading, note-taking, and comprehension.

Integrating Strands and Applications

	8-1	8-2	8-3	8-4	8-5	8-6	8-7	8-8	8-9	8-10
Mathematical Connections										
Number Sense	●	●			●	●	●	●	●	●
Algebra	●	●	●	●	●	●	●	●	●	●
Geometry	●	●	●	●			●			
Measurement	●	●								
Logic and Reasoning		●		●		●	●	●		●
Patterns and Functions	●	●	●	●	●	●	●	●	●	●
Discrete Mathematics	●					●	●			●
Interdisciplinary and Other Connections										
Art										●
Science	●	●	●	●	●	●			●	●
Social Studies						●				●
Multicultural	●	●						●		
Technology		●	●	●	●		●	●	●	●
Literature										●

Teaching and Assessing the Chapter Objectives

Chapter 8 Objectives (Organized into the SPUR catetgories—Skills, Properties, Uses, and Representations)	**Lessons**	**Progress Self-Test Questions**	**Chapter Review Questions**	**In the Teacher's Resource File** **Chapter Test, Forms A and B**	**Chapter Test, Forms C**	**D**
Skills						
A: Express complex numbers in binomial, rectangular, polar and trigonometric form.	8-1, 8-3	1	1-9		1	
B: Perform operations with complex numbers.	8-1, 8-3	3	10-22		1	
C: Convert between polar and rectangular representations of points.	8-2	2	23-26		3	
D: Find powers and roots of complex numbers.	8-6, 8-7	7	27-34		2	
E: Find all zeros, and their multiplicities, of a given polynomial.	8-8, 8-9	8	35-38		4	
Properties						
F: Prove or verify properties of complex numbers.	8-1, 8-3, 8-6	9	39-43			
G: Use the properties of polynomials to find or describe their zeros.	8-8, 8-9	10	44-49		4	
Uses						
H: Use complex numbers to solve AC circuit problems.	8-1	4	50-52			
Representations						
I: Graph complex numbers and verify the Geometric Addition and Geometric Multiplication Theorems.	8-1, 8-2, 8-3	5	53-59			
J: Sketch graphs of polar equations.	8-4, 8-5	11, 12	60-65		5	X
K: Use DeMoivre's Theorem to graph powers and roots of complex numbers.	8-6, 8-7	6, 7	66-69		2	X

Assessment Sourcebook
Quiz for Lessons 8-1 through 8-4
Quiz for Lessons 8-5 through 8-8

Chapter 8 Test, Forms A–D
Chapter 8 Test, Cumulative Form

TestWorks CD-ROM

TEACHING AID 70

Warm-up
Lesson 8-1

Solve each of these equations.

1. $x^2 + 4x + 3 = 0$ **2.** $x^2 - 4x + 3 = 0$

3. $x^2 + 2x + 3 = 0$ **4.** $x^2 + 2x + 10 = 0$

Warm-up
Lesson 8-2

Suppose $A = (1, 0)$ and $B = (0, 0)$. Find the measure of $\angle ABC$ in degrees for the given value of C.

1. $C = (\cos 65°, \sin 65°)$

2. $C = (-2, -2)$

3. $C = (72, -36)$

Warm-up
Lesson 8-3

Solve each of the equations for the complex number z.

1. $4 + 5i + z = -3 - 8i$ **2.** $\frac{z}{9 + 6i} = 1 - 7i$

Warm-up
Lesson 8-4

Let G_1 be the graph of $y = \sin x$, G_2 be the graph of $y = 2 \sin x$, G_3 be the graph of $y = 2 + \sin x$, and G_4 be the graph of $y = \sin 2x$. Describe how G_2, G_3, and G_4 are related to G_1.

TEACHING AID 71

Warm-up
Lesson 8-5

Carefully graph the eleven points (r, θ) satisfying $r = 6 \cos 2\theta$, when $\theta = 0°$, $\pm 10°$, $\pm 20°$, $\pm 30°$, $\pm 40°$ and $\pm 45°$.

Warm-up
Lesson 8-6

Let $z = 2 + 3i$.

1. Calculate z^2, z^3, and z^4.
2. Find the distance of the graphs of z, z^2, z^3, and z^4 from the origin.
3. Predict what the distance of z^5 will be from the origin. Check your prediction by calculating z^5 and its distance from the origin.
4. Generalize Question 3.

Warm-up
Lesson 8-7

Which of the following are 8th roots of 1?

1. 1 **2.** -1

3. i **4.** $-i$

5. $\frac{\sqrt{2} + i\sqrt{2}}{2}$ **6.** $\cos 60° + i \sin 60°$

7. $1 - i$ **8.** $[1, 225°]$

TEACHING AID 72

Warm-up
Lesson 8-8

1. Find all solutions to the equation $(2x + 25)(x^2 + x + 6) = 0$.

2. Find a 3rd degree polynomial equation that has the same solutions as the equation of Question 1.

Warm-up
Lesson 8-9

1. Find all solutions to the equation $x^3 + x^2 + x + 1 = 0$.

2. Write a polynomial equation whose zeros are 1, -1, i, and $-i$.

Warm-up
Lesson 8-10

Enter 3 into your calculator set to radians. Repeatedly press the sine key, writing down the values you get rounded to the nearest thousandth.

1. Give a recursive definition for the sequence you are creating.

2. Conjecture the limit of the nth term of this sequence as $n \to \infty$.

TEACHING AID 73
Lessons 8-2, 8-6

Polar Grid

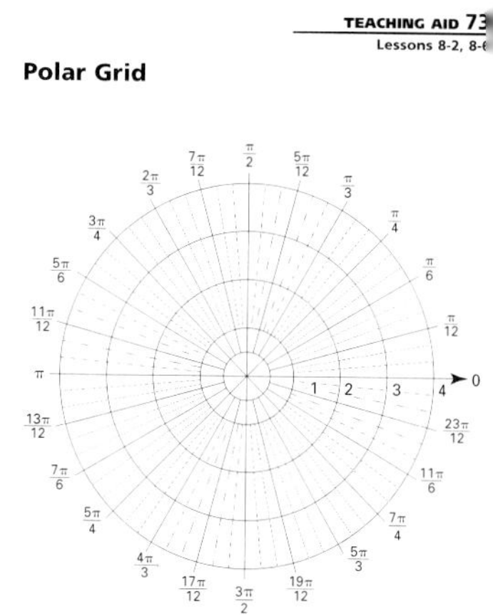

TEACHING AID 74
Lessons 8-2, 8-6

Polar Grids

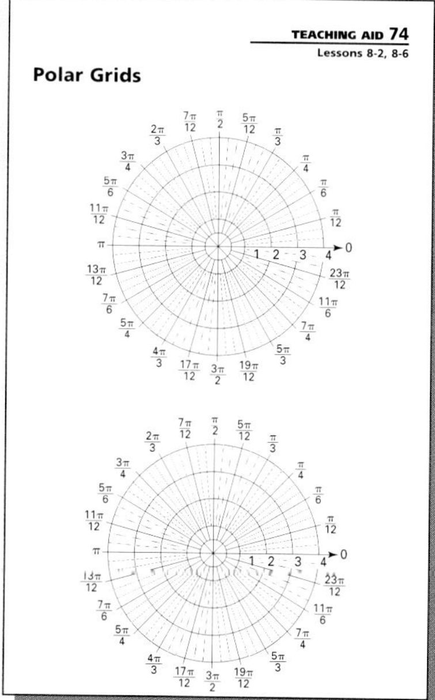

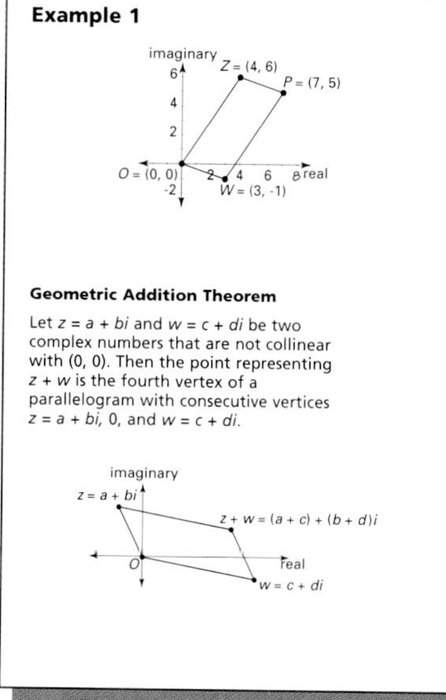

TEACHING AID 75
Lesson 8-3

Example 1

Geometric Addition Theorem

Let $z = a + bi$ and $w = c + di$ be two complex numbers that are not collinear with (0, 0). Then the point representing $z + w$ is the fourth vertex of a parallelogram with consecutive vertices $z = a + bi$, 0, and $w = c + di$.

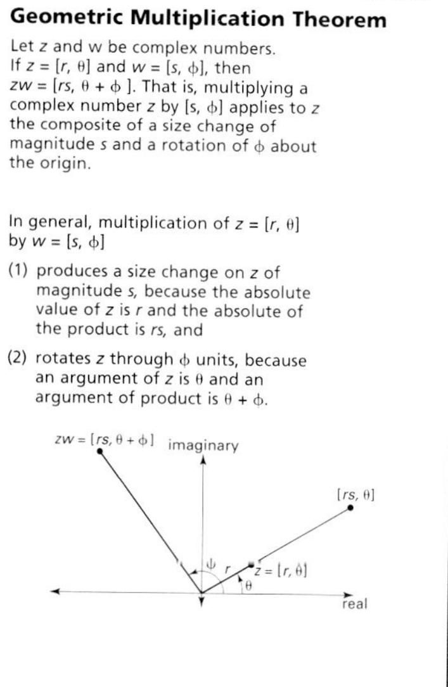

TEACHING AID 76
Lesson 8-3

Geometric Multiplication Theorem

Let z and w be complex numbers. If $z = [r, \theta]$ and $w = [s, \phi]$, then $zw = [rs, \theta + \phi]$. That is, multiplying a complex number z by $[s, \phi]$ applies to z the composite of a size change of magnitude s and a rotation of ϕ about the origin.

In general, multiplication of $z = [r, \theta]$ by $w = [s, \phi]$

(1) produces a size change on z of magnitude s, because the absolute value of z is r and the absolute of the product is rs, and

(2) rotates z through ϕ units, because an argument of z is θ and an argument of product is $\theta + \phi$.

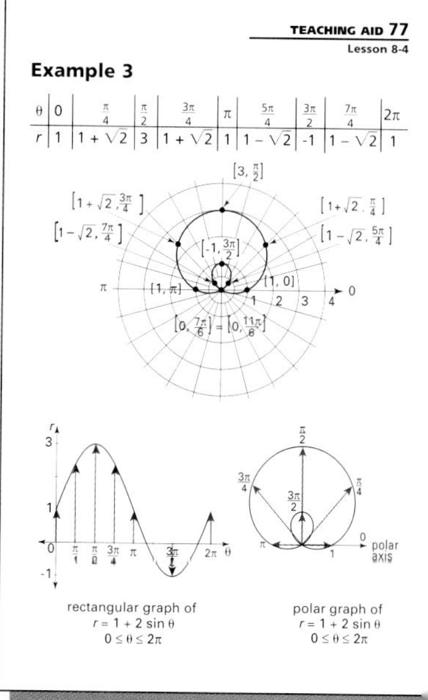

TEACHING AID 77
Lesson 8-4

Example 3

θ	0	$\frac{\pi}{4}$	$\frac{\pi}{2}$	$\frac{3\pi}{4}$	π	$\frac{5\pi}{4}$	$\frac{3\pi}{2}$	$\frac{7\pi}{4}$	2π
r	1	$1 + \sqrt{2}$	3	$1 + \sqrt{2}$	1	$1 - \sqrt{2}$	-1	$1 - \sqrt{2}$	1

rectangular graph of $r = 1 + 2 \sin \theta$, $0 \le \theta \le 2\pi$

polar graph of $r = 1 + 2 \sin \theta$, $0 \le \theta \le 2\pi$

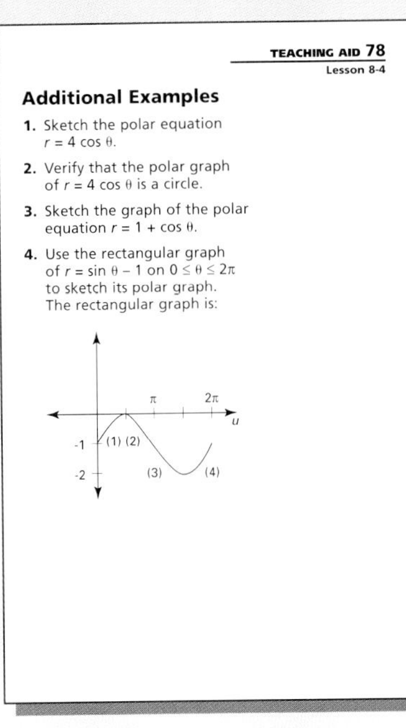

TEACHING AID 78
Lesson 8-4

Additional Examples

1. Sketch the polar equation $r = 4\cos\theta$.
2. Verify that the polar graph of $r = 4\cos\theta$ is a circle.
3. Sketch the graph of the polar equation $r = 1 + \cos\theta$.
4. Use the rectangular graph of $r = \sin\theta - 1$ on $0 \le \theta \le 2\pi$ to sketch its polar graph. The rectangular graph is:

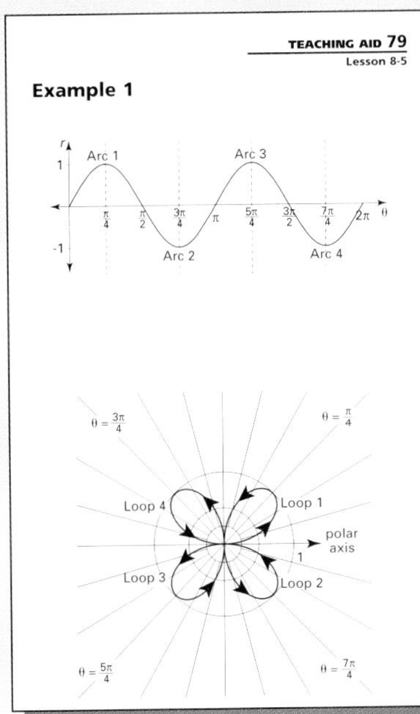

TEACHING AID 79
Lesson 8-5

Example 1

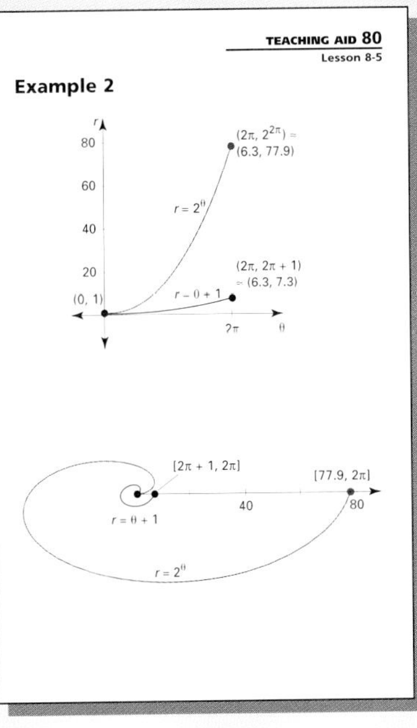

TEACHING AID 80
Lesson 8-5

Example 2

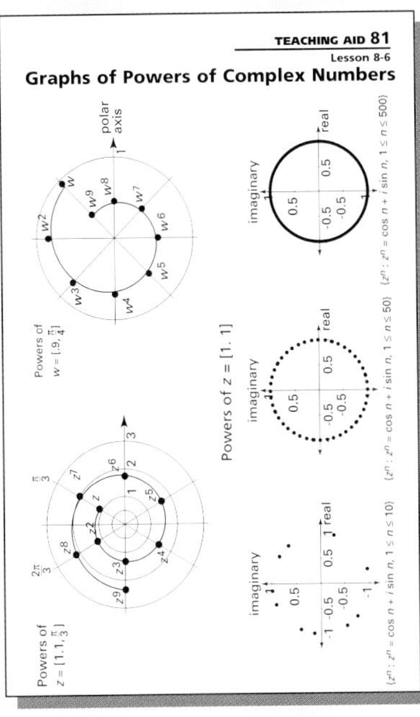

TEACHING AID 81
Lesson 8-6

Graphs of Powers of Complex Numbers

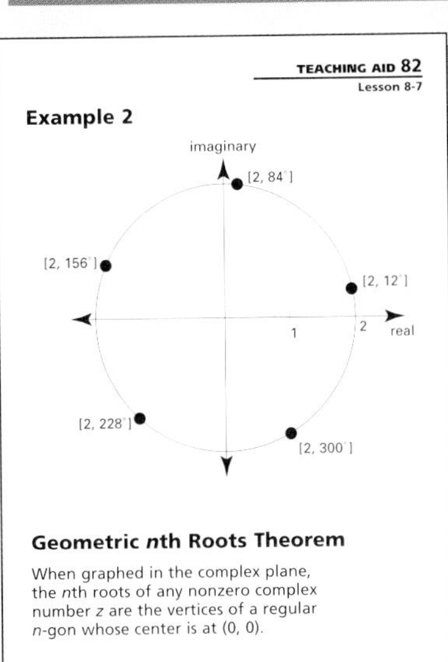

TEACHING AID 82
Lesson 8-7

Example 2

Geometric nth Roots Theorem

When graphed in the complex plane, the nth roots of any nonzero complex number z are the vertices of a regular n-gon whose center is at (0, 0).

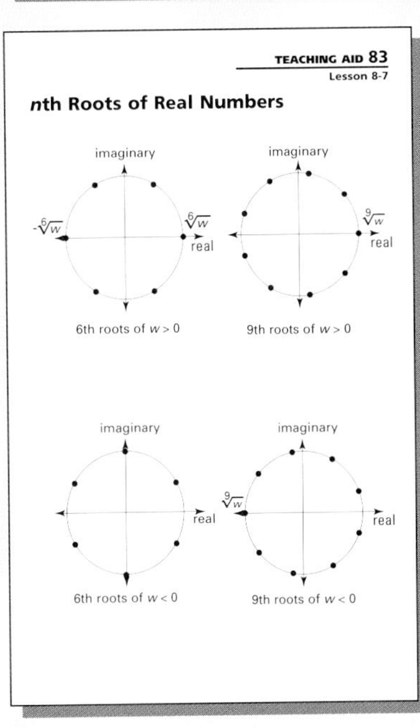

TEACHING AID 83
Lesson 8-7

nth Roots of Real Numbers

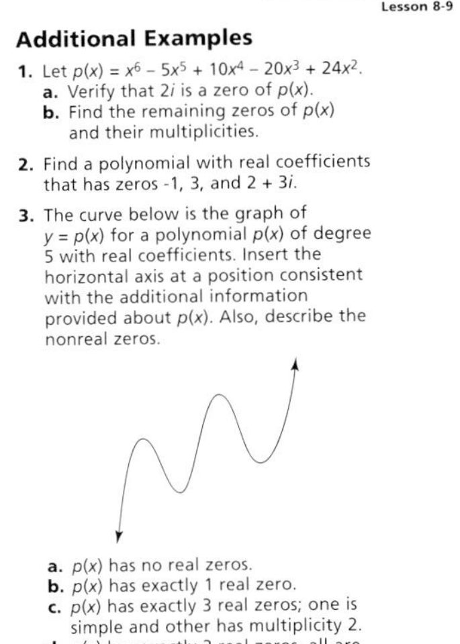

TEACHING AID 84
Lesson 8-9

Additional Examples

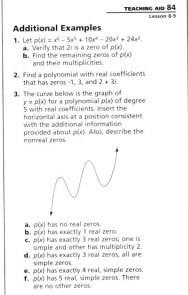

1. Let $p(x) = x^6 - 5x^5 + 10x^4 - 20x^3 + 24x^2$.
   a. Verify that $2i$ is a zero of $p(x)$.
   b. Find the remaining zeros of $p(x)$ and their multiplicities.
2. Find a polynomial with real coefficients that has zeros -1, 3, and $2 + 3i$.
3. The curve below is the graph of $y = p(x)$ for a polynomial $p(x)$ of degree 5 with real coefficients. Insert the horizontal axis at a position consistent with the additional information provided about $p(x)$. Also, describe the nonreal zeros.
   a. $p(x)$ has no real zeros.
   b. $p(x)$ has exactly 1 real zero.
   c. $p(x)$ has exactly 3 real zeros; one is simple and other has multiplicity 2.
   d. $p(x)$ has exactly 3 real zeros, all are simple zeros.
   e. $p(x)$ has exactly 4 real, simple zeros.
   f. $p(x)$ has 5 real, simple zeros. There are no other zeros.

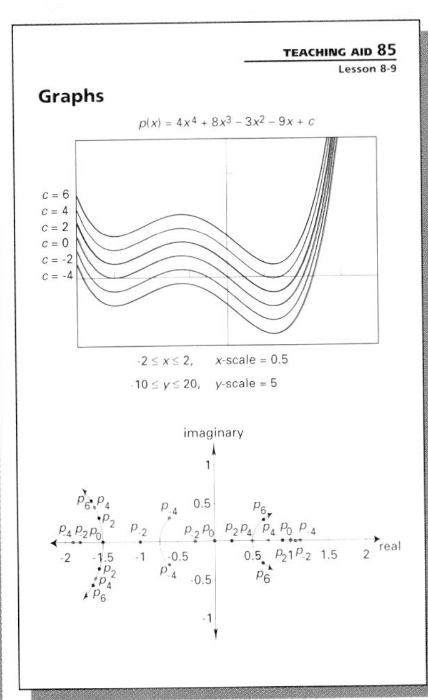

TEACHING AID 85
Lesson 8-9

Graphs

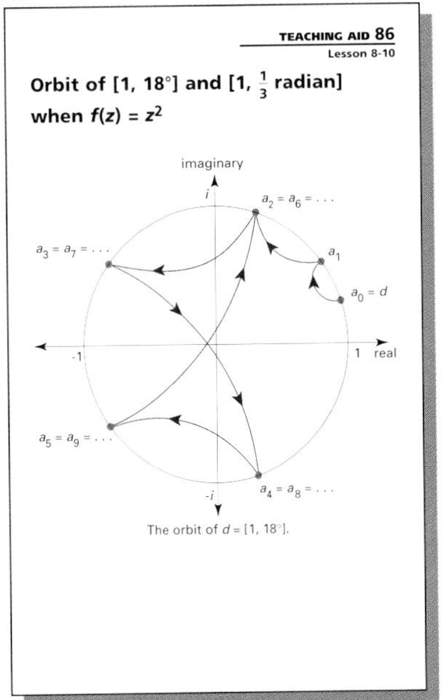

TEACHING AID 86
Lesson 8-10

Orbit of [1, 18°] and [1, $\frac{1}{3}$ radian] when $f(z) = z^2$

The orbit of d = [1, 18°].

Chapter Opener

Pacing

All lessons in this chapter are designed to be covered in one day. At the end of the chapter, you should plan to spend 1 day to review the Progress Self-Test, 1–2 days for the Chapter Review, and 1 day for a test. You may wish to spend a day on projects, and possibly a day is needed for quizzes and the In-class Activity. This chapter should therefore take 13–16 days. Spending more than 18 days on this chapter is not recommended; there is review in later chapters.

Using Pages 470–471

Discuss Euler's Theorem that $e^{i\pi} + 1 = 0$. Point out that it contains the most important constants of mathematics (e, i, π, 0, and 1), and operations of addition, multiplication, and exponentiation. Rewritten as $e^{i\pi} = -1$ we see the astounding fact that a transcendental number (e) raised to an imaginary power ($i\pi$) equals a real number (-1). (A transcendental number is one that cannot be a solution to a polynomial equation with integer coefficients.)

In this chapter are many wonderful and beautiful theorems that connect algebra and geometry through the graphing of complex numbers and through polar coordinates. Also here are some of the newer ideas in mathematics, chaos and fractals.

CHAPTER 8

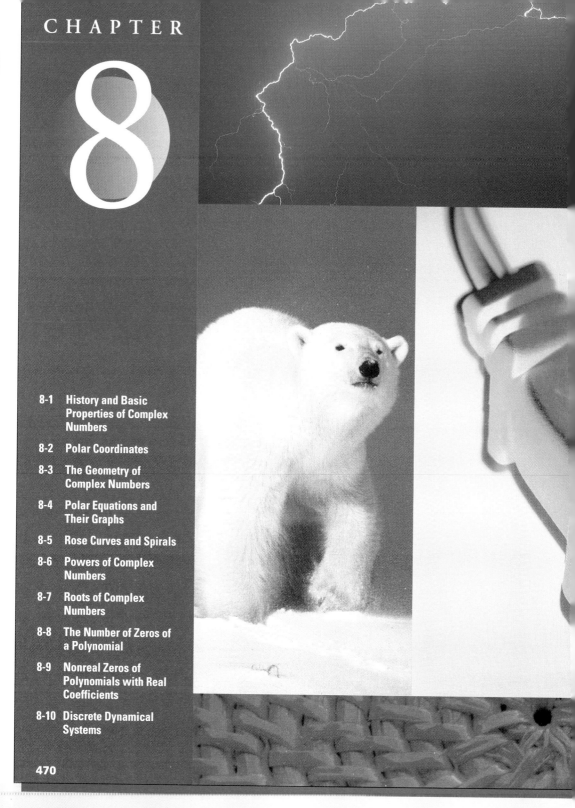

Chapter 8 Overview

The opening page of this chapter describes the variety of elementary uses of complex numbers students will see in this chapter, including the geometry of complex numbers, the Fundamental Theorem of Algebra, and the use of complex numbers in studying discrete dynamical systems. Polar coordinates are exceedingly useful in this look at complex numbers, and they also allow some beautiful curves to be graphed. For this reason, the two ideas are intertwined here.

There are many reasons for giving such a varied look. First, the previous exposure students have had to complex numbers will likely have been only as solutions to quadratic and other polynomial equations. The numbers are often perceived as artificial because no context is given for the polynomials or their solutions. The word "imaginary" does not help to convey a greater sense of reality! Second, students do not often see the benefits of a coordinate system different from the rectangular system with which they are so familiar. Polar coordinates are not only important and beautiful in their own right, but they expand a student's vision to think even about other possible coordinate systems.

Immediately in this chapter there is an application to electronics, and complex numbers are graphed in the rectangular coordinate plane. Then, after the introduction of the

Polar Coordinates and Complex Numbers

Your first use of complex numbers such as i and $2 + 3i$, and the use that came first historically, was probably as solutions to equations like $x^2 + 6 = 0$ that have no real solutions. Mathematicians of the 16th, 17th, and 18th centuries knew of no other uses for complex numbers, and were uncomfortable with them. Euler's discovery of the relationship $e^{i\pi} + 1 = 0$, and Gauss' proof in 1797 of the Fundamental Theorem of Algebra, helped mathematicians to realize that complex numbers play a unique role in mathematics. Casper Wessel in that same year, and Jean Robert Argand in 1806, showed that complex numbers can be associated with points on the plane. This led to using complex numbers to represent geometric and physical objects such as a chambered nautilus and quantities such as forces, velocities, and flows.

Complex numbers today have a variety of uses, all stemming from their algebraic origins and their geometric interpretations. They are associated with transformations, they can be used to describe some beautiful geometric figures, and they can have the properties of vectors. They have become important in many areas of mathematics and science, including electrical, acoustical, and aeronautical engineering. During the 1970s, the words *chaos* and *fractal* entered the mathematician's vocabulary and a new area of mathematics called dynamical systems arose, producing new applications for complex numbers.

In this chapter, complex numbers are represented by rectangular coordinates and polar coordinates. Polar coordinates have applications far beyond complex numbers. Some plane curves, such as those pictured below, have very complicated rectangular coordinate equations but rather simple polar coordinate equations.

Photo Connections

The photo collage makes real-world connections to the content of the chapter: polar coordinates and complex numbers.

Lightning: In Lesson 8-10 mathematical models used to forecast the weather are discussed.

Nautilus shell: A chambered nautilus shell is shaped like a logarithmic spiral. Rose curves and spirals are discussed in Lesson 8-5.

Polar bear: Polar coordinate grids, a background of circles and rays emanating from the pole, are commonly used for plotting points and sketching curves in polar coordinates. Polar equations and their graphs are discussed in Lesson 8-4.

Electrical plug: Complex numbers are used in the study of electricity. Ohm's Law, relating impedance to voltage and current, is discussed in Lesson 8-1.

Basket: The coils of a basket with a constant distance between successive coils resemble the spirals of Archimedes, discussed in Lesson 8-5.

Chapter 8 Projects

At this time, you might want to have students look over the projects on pages 542–543.

polar coordinate system, addition and multiplication of complex numbers are seen to have simple geometric interpretations. Addition is particularly easy to see in rectangular coordinates; multiplication is more easily interpreted in polar coordinates.

Some curves have simpler equations in polar coordinates than they have in rectangular coordinates; these include certain lines, some circles, cardioids, rose curves, and spirals. The purpose of the two lessons devoted to graphing curves in polar coordinates is to display the power of this coordinate system while giving students practice and experience working in it.

The chapter then completes the geometric look at operations on complex numbers by considering their powers and roots using DeMoivre's Theorem. Following this is a look again at the zeros of polynomials, extending the work of Chapter 4.

The reading lesson displays the application of complex numbers to the analysis of certain discrete dynamical systems.

Students who have had previous UCSMP courses will have seen the use of complex numbers in solving equations and should have encountered the Fundamental Theorem of Algebra. Students who studied the last chapter of *Functions, Statistics, and Trigonometry* will have seen most of the content of this chapter.

Lesson 8-1

Objectives

A Express complex numbers in binomial and rectangular form.
B Perform operations with complex numbers.
F Prove or verify properties of complex numbers.
H Use complex numbers to solve AC circuit problems.
I Graph complex numbers.

Resources

From the ***Teacher's Resource File***
- Lesson Master 8-1
- Answer Master 8-1
- Teaching Aid 70: Warm-up

Additional Resources
- Visual for Teaching Aid 70

Teaching Lesson 8-1

Warm-up

Solve each of these equations.
1. $x^2 + 4x + 3 = 0$ $x = -1$ or $x = -3$
2. $x^2 - 4x + 3 = 0$ $x = 1$ or $x = 3$
3. $x^2 + 2x + 3 = 0$
$x = -1 - i\sqrt{2}$ or $x = -1 + i\sqrt{2}$
4. $x^2 + 2x + 10 = 0$
$x = -1 - 3i$ or $x = -1 + 3i$

LESSON 8-1 History and Basic Properties of Complex Numbers

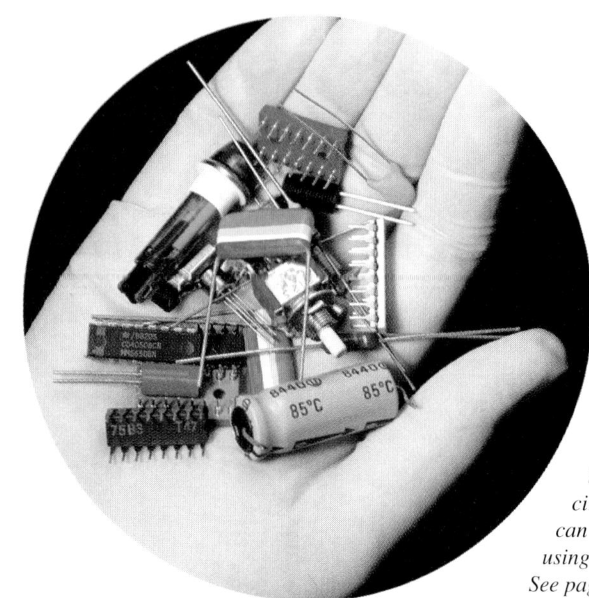

Simply Complex. *Electronic components such as resistors and capacitors regulate impedance in AC circuits. Their effect can be represented using complex numbers.* *See page 477.*

The Work of Cardano

The development of complex numbers had its origin in the search for methods to solve polynomial equations. Prior to the 1500s, quadratic equations without real solutions such as

$$x^2 + 1 = 0$$

were regarded as "unsolvable." The quadratic formula

$$x = \frac{-b \pm \sqrt{b^2 - 4ac}}{2a}$$

had been used (in a more primitive notation) long before 1500 to solve quadratic equations

$$ax^2 + bx + c = 0$$

for cases in which $b^2 - 4ac$ is positive. However, Girolamo Cardano, a 16th century Italian mathematician, seems to have been the first to treat the quadratic formula expressions

$$-\frac{b}{2a} + \frac{\sqrt{b^2 - 4ac}}{2a} \qquad -\frac{b}{2a} - \frac{\sqrt{b^2 - 4ac}}{2a}$$

as numbers even when $b^2 - 4ac$ is negative. He did this by adopting the following algebraic rules for the square roots of negative numbers.

(1) $\sqrt{-1} \cdot \sqrt{-1} = -1$
(2) For any positive real number d, $\sqrt{-d} = \sqrt{d}\sqrt{-1}$.
(3) Multiplication is associative and commutative.

Using these rules, he could carry out computations as in Example 1.

Lesson 8-1 Overview

Broad Goals This lesson covers the terminology, the four fundamental operations, and the graphing associated with complex numbers. The operations are applied in the formula $I = \frac{V}{Z}$ relating current I, voltage V, and impedance Z.

Perspective For operating on complex numbers, the binomial form $a + bi$ of a complex number is quite convenient.

For graphing on a horizontal coordinate system, writing or thinking of $a + bi$ as the ordered pair (a, b) is needed.

Some books refer to what we call imaginary numbers as *pure imaginary numbers.* Some books use the term imaginary number to refer to any complex number whose imaginary part is nonzero. Since it is unfortunate that any of these numbers are called "imaginary," we have tried to limit the scope of the term.

It is expected that the operations with complex numbers have previously been studied, but graphing and the applications may be new.

Example 1

Multiply $\sqrt{-25} \cdot \sqrt{-16}$.

Solution

Simplify each square root first by using rule (2) on page 472.

$$\sqrt{-25} = \sqrt{25}\sqrt{-1} = 5\sqrt{-1}$$
$$\sqrt{-16} = \sqrt{16}\sqrt{-1} = 4\sqrt{-1}$$

Then apply rules (1) and (3).

$$\sqrt{-25} \cdot \sqrt{-16} = 5\sqrt{-1} \cdot 4\sqrt{-1} = 20\sqrt{-1}\sqrt{-1} = -20$$

Later Contributors to Vocabulary and Symbolism

To deal with the quadratic formula expressions that combined real numbers and square roots of negative numbers, Cardano applied his rules with the algebraic rules for combining binomials to "numbers" of the form

$$a + b\sqrt{-1}$$

where a and b are real numbers. For example, to add $3 + 2\sqrt{-1}$ to $-1 + 5\sqrt{-1}$, he combined "like" terms of these binomials.

$$\left(3 + 2\sqrt{-1}\right) + \left(-1 + 5\sqrt{-1}\right) = (3 + (-1)) + (2 + 5)\sqrt{-1}$$
$$= 2 + 7\sqrt{-1}$$

Similarly, to multiply these two numbers, he used the product formula for binomials and the fact that $\left(\sqrt{-1}\right)^2 = -1$.

$$\left(3 + 2\sqrt{-1}\right) \cdot \left(-1 + 5\sqrt{-1}\right) = -3 - 2\sqrt{-1} + 15\sqrt{-1} + 10\left(\sqrt{-1}\right)^2$$
$$= (-3 - 10) + (-2 + 15)\sqrt{-1}$$
$$= -13 + 13\sqrt{-1}$$

Square roots of negative numbers were later given the name *imaginary numbers* by Descartes in the early 1600s, and, in 1777, Euler introduced the symbol i for $\sqrt{-1}$. An **imaginary number** is defined to be a number of the form bi, where b is a real number and the **imaginary unit** i satisfies $i^2 = -1$. Gauss later introduced the modern name, *complex numbers*, for these numbers.

René Descartes (1596–1650), in an oil painting by Frans Hals

Definitions

A **complex number** is a number that can be written in the form $a + bi$ where a and b are real numbers and $i^2 = -1$. The **real part** of $a + bi$ is a and the **imaginary part** is b.

❶ The variable z is commonly used to represent a complex number. If $z = 2 - 3i$, the real part of z is 2 and the imaginary part is -3. The set of real numbers and the set of imaginary numbers are subsets of the set of complex numbers. Any real number a can be expressed as $a + 0i$. Any imaginary number bi can be expressed as $0 + bi$.

Notes on Reading

Error Alert In general, when working with radicals with negative radicands, the negative numbers must be removed from the radicands by writing $\sqrt{-n}$ as $i\sqrt{n}$ before performing any manipulations on them, as **Example 1** illustrates. Point out that if you try to apply the Square Root of a Product Theorem in **Example 1,** you obtain $\sqrt{-25} \cdot \sqrt{-16} = \sqrt{400} = 20$, which is incorrect. Hence, *you must simplify the radicals first.* Then you may apply the familiar rules to the square roots of nonnegative real numbers.

You may also wish to point out that we do **Example 1** as we do because we have not yet defined i. After defining i, students can do **Example 1** in this alternate way: $\sqrt{-25} = \sqrt{25}\sqrt{-1} = 5i$ and $\sqrt{-16} = \sqrt{16}\sqrt{-1} = 4i$. Then $\sqrt{-25} \cdot \sqrt{-16} = 5i \cdot 4i = 20i^2 = 20(-1) = -20$.

There are three cases concerning square roots of products:

1. If $a \geq 0$ and $b \geq 0$, then $\sqrt{a}\sqrt{b} = \sqrt{ab}$.
2. If either $a < 0$ or $b < 0$, but not both, then $\sqrt{a}\sqrt{b} = \sqrt{ab}$;
3. If both $a < 0$ and $b < 0$, then $\sqrt{a}\sqrt{b} = -\sqrt{ab}$.

We discourage memorizing these cases. When b is positive, it is easy to rewrite $\sqrt{-b}$ as $i\sqrt{b}$ and proceed from there.

❶ **Error Alert** Some people think the imaginary part of the complex number $a + bi$ is bi. This would cause difficulty for interpreting the imaginary part of (a, b). Students may have difficulty believing that a single variable z can represent a complex number because they typically see complex numbers written with two variables (e.g., $a + bi$). Graphing helps to see that a complex number is a single entity. This geometrical representation of complex numbers is a theme throughout the chapter. Do not ignore it here.

Optional Activities

As an extension of **Question 13,** ask students if a similar relationship holds for $z - w$, $w - z$, zw, $\frac{z}{w}$, and $\frac{w}{z}$. That is, when the results are plotted with 0, z, and w, does a parallelogram form? Have them justify their answers. [A parallelogram forms with $z - w$ and with $w - z$, but not with the product or quotient. $z - w = 9 + 10i$, and the slopes of the sides of the parallelogram formed are $\frac{10}{9}$ and 4. $w - z = -9 - 10i$, and the slopes of the sides of the parallelogram are $\frac{10}{9}$ and $\frac{2}{7}$.]

Students should not memorize the definitions of addition and multiplication of complex numbers. They need only to use the distributive property twice, remember that $\sqrt{-1}\sqrt{-1} = -1$, and combine like terms. The operations are completely consistent with what one would expect.

❷ We assume without proof that all of the field axioms apply to the set of complex numbers; in fact, these axioms are used to motivate the definitions of the operations on complex numbers. Note that the set of complex numbers is not ordered; that is, given two complex numbers, you cannot say that one is less than the other.

In **Lesson 5-6,** students learned that to rationalize a denominator of the form $a + \sqrt{b}$, one could multiply both numerator and denominator by $a - \sqrt{b}$. Then b was positive. The process of rewriting the quotient in **Example 2** can be viewed as extending this procedure to instances where b is negative. Specifically, the given fraction equals $\frac{6 + 7\sqrt{-1}}{8 + 5\sqrt{-1}}$ or $\frac{6 + \sqrt{-49}}{8 + \sqrt{-25}}$ and both numerator and denominator are multiplied by $8 - 5\sqrt{-1}$ or $8 - \sqrt{-25}$.

Two complex numbers $a + bi$ and $c + di$ are **equal** if and only if $a = c$ and $b = d$. Thus, the complex numbers $2 + 3i$ and $3 + 2i$ are not equal even though they are both constructed from the same two real numbers, 2 and 3.

Operations with Complex Numbers

Addition, subtraction, and multiplication of two complex numbers, $z = a + bi$ and $w = c + di$, are defined to be similar to the corresponding operations for binomials and use the property that $i^2 = -1$.

Definitions

Let a, b, c, and d be real numbers and let $z = a + bi$ and $w = c + di$. Then:

$z + w = (a + c) + (b + d)i$ **(Addition)**

$zw = (ac - bd) + (ad + bc)i.$ **(Multiplication)**

❷ With these customary definitions of addition and multiplication, the complex numbers satisfy the **field properties**. Specifically, addition and multiplication are closed, commutative, and associative. There is an identity ($0 = 0 + 0i$) for addition and a different identity ($1 = 1 + 0i$) for multiplication. Every complex number $z = a + bi$ has an additive inverse ($-z = -a - bi$), and every nonzero complex number z has a multiplicative inverse $\frac{1}{z}$. Finally, multiplication is distributive over addition. We say that, with the definitions of addition and multiplication given above, the complex numbers form a field, the **field of complex numbers**.

Girolamo Cardano (1501–1576), in a woodcut from the cover of his Practica Arithmatice, 1539

The consequences of forming a field are that all of the familiar operations (addition, subtraction, multiplication, division, and integer powers) can be done with complex numbers just as they are done with real numbers, in the manner used by Cardano.

Subtraction and division of complex numbers are defined as they are with real numbers: For all complex numbers z and w, $z - w = z + -w$ and, when $w \neq 0$, $\frac{z}{w} = z \cdot \frac{1}{w}$. As one consequence of these definitions, rational expressions involving complex numbers can be dealt with in the same way as rational expressions involving real numbers. For instance, if a fraction has a complex number in its denominator, a process akin to rationalizing the denominator can be used to rewrite the number in $a + bi$ form.

Example 2

Express the quotient $\frac{6 + 7i}{8 + 5i}$ in $a + bi$ form.

Solution

Think of the denominator as $8 + 5\sqrt{-1}$. Its conjugate is $8 - 5\sqrt{-1}$, or $8 - 5i$. Multiply both the numerator and denominator by $8 - 5i$.

▶

LESSON MASTER 8-1 **Questions on SPUR Objectives** See pages 547–549 for objectives.

Skills Objective A

In 1–3, give the real part and the imaginary part of the complex number.

1. $18 - 13i$ real 18 imaginary -13
2. $-i$ real 0 imaginary -1
3. $\sqrt{7}$ real $\sqrt{7}$ imaginary 0

In 4 and 5, write the complex number as an ordered pair.

4. $7 + 9i$ (7, 9)
5. $-i + \sqrt{5}$ ($\sqrt{5}$, -1)

In 6 and 7, write the complex number in $a + bi$ form.

6. (0, -8) $-8i$
7. $(-\frac{2}{3}, 1)$ $-\frac{2}{3} + i$

Skills Objective B

In 8–13, perform the indicated operation and write the answer in $a + bi$ form.

8. $(6 - i) - (10 + 7i)$ $-4 - 8i$
9. $(1 + 6i)(3 - 4i)$ $27 + 14i$
10. $\frac{\sqrt{-72}}{3}$ $2\sqrt{2}i$
11. $\frac{9 - 2i}{2 + 5i}$ $\frac{8}{29} - \frac{49}{29}i$
12. $\frac{7i}{2 + 2i} + 1 - 12i$ $\frac{11}{4} - \frac{41}{4}i$
13. $(-5 + 8i)^2$ $-39 - 80i$

In 14 and 15, solve the equation and express the solution in $a + bi$ form.

14. $-5 + 6i = v + 8 - i$ $v = -13 + 7i$
15. $w^2 = -19$ $w = \pm\sqrt{19}i$

Properties Objective F

16. Verify that $2 - i$ is a solution of $z^2 - 4z + 5 = 0$.
$(2 - i)^2 - 4(2 - i) + 5 = 4 - 4i + i^2 - 8 + 4i + 5 = 4 - 4i - 1 - 8 + 4i + 5 = 0$

17. Let $z = a + bi$ and $w = c + di$. Prove that $\overline{z + w} = \bar{z} + \bar{w}$.
$z + w = (a + c) + (b + d)i$, so $\overline{z + w} = (a + c) - (b + d)i$. But $\bar{z} = a - bi$ and $w = c - di$, so $\bar{z} + \bar{w} = (a - bi) + (c - di) = (a + c) + (b + d)i$

Adapting to Individual Needs

Extra Help

As you cover the operations with complex numbers, students might benefit from a more detailed discussion of field properties. Given a set of numbers and two operations (usually addition and multiplication, but this need not be the case), a field is formed if and only if there exists

1. closure of both operations
2. commutativity of both operations
3. associativity of both operations
4. the distributive law
5. identities (zero and one) for the operations
6. an additive inverse of each number
7. a multiplicative inverse of each nonzero number.

Under addition and multiplication, the reals form a field, as do the rationals. Complex numbers, with addition and multiplication as defined in the lesson, also form a field.

$$\frac{6+7i}{8+5i} = \frac{6+7i}{8+5i} \cdot \frac{8-5i}{8-5i} \qquad \text{because } \frac{8-5i}{8-5i} = 1$$
$$= \frac{48-30i+56i-35i^2}{64-25i^2}$$
$$= \frac{48+26i+35}{64+25} \qquad \text{because } i^2 = -1$$
$$= \frac{83+26i}{89}$$
$$= \frac{83}{89} + \frac{26}{89}i$$

Conjugate Complex Numbers

Note that $8 + 5i$ and $8 - 5i$ are a pair of complex numbers of the form $a + bi$ and $a - bi$. The numbers in such a pair are called **complex conjugates** of each other. We denote the conjugate of z by $\bar{z}$. So if $z = a + bi$, then $\bar{z} = a - bi$.

The product of a complex number and its complex conjugate is always real.

Example 3

Prove: $\forall$ complex numbers z, $z \cdot \bar{z}$ is a real number.

Solution

Let $z = a + bi$, where a and b are real numbers. Then $\bar{z} = a - bi$.

$$z \cdot \bar{z} = (a+bi)(a-bi)$$
$$= a^2 - abi + abi - b^2i^2$$
$$= a^2 - b^2(-1) \qquad \text{because } i^2 = -1$$
$$= a^2 + b^2$$

Since a and b are real, $a^2 + b^2$ is also real. Thus, $z \cdot \bar{z}$ is a real number.

The result of Example 3 provides a way to factor the polynomial $x^2 + y^2$ over the field of complex numbers. For all complex numbers x and y, $x^2 + y^2 = (x + yi)(x - yi)$. Thus some polynomials that are prime over the set of polynomials with real coefficients can be factored if complex coefficients are allowed.

Graphing Complex Numbers

Complex numbers were viewed as a mathematical curiosity without application outside of mathematics until Caspar Wessel in 1797 and Jean Robert Argand in 1806 independently developed a graphical representation for complex numbers.

To graph the complex number $z = a + bi$, write it as the ordered pair (a, b) where the first coordinate represents the real part and the second coordinate represents the imaginary part. Thus, the complex numbers $z = 3 - 5i$ and $w = -4 + 6i$ can be represented as the ordered pairs (3, -5) and (-4, 6), respectively.

Some calculators have operations on complex numbers built in. Some symbol manipulation software, *Derive* among them, ask the user to select the domain for factoring polynomials. Allowable choices include factoring over polynomials with rational, radical, and complex number coefficients. Thus, depending upon the domain of coefficients, $x^2 + 5$ could be prime or could be factored as $(x + i\sqrt{5})(x - i\sqrt{5})$. This idea will be discussed again in **Lesson 8-9** when we point out that nonreal zeros of polynomials with real coefficients come in conjugate complex number pairs.

To assist students in proving theorems such as those in **Example 3** and **Questions 16 and 20,** suggest that they begin as follows. If the theorem involves only one complex number, represent it as $z = a + bi$. If two complex numbers are involved, represent one as $z_1 = a + bi$ and the other as $z_2 = c + di$ or $z_1 = a_1 + b_1i$, $z_2 = a_2 + b_2i$.

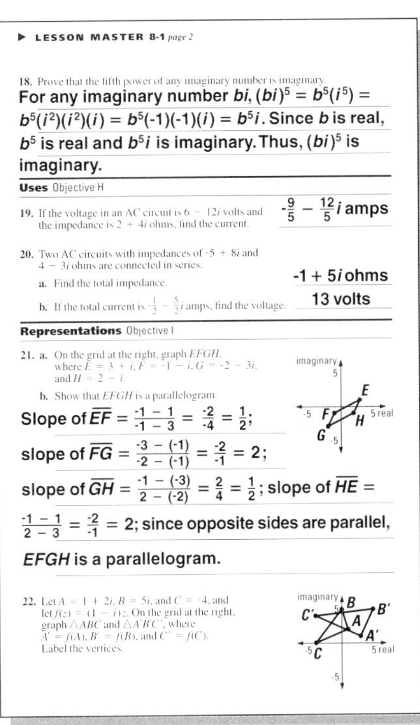
▸ LESSON MASTER 8-1 *page 2*

18. Prove that the fifth power of any imaginary number is imaginary.
For any imaginary number bi, $(bi)^5 = b^5(i^5) = b^5(i^2)(i^2)(i) = b^5(-1)(-1)(i) = b^5i$. Since b is real, b^5 is real and b^5i is imaginary. Thus, $(bi)^5$ is imaginary.

Uses Objective H

19. If the voltage in an AC circuit is $6 - 12i$ volts and the impedance is $2 + 4i$ ohms, find the current. **$-\frac{9}{5} - \frac{12}{5}i$ amps**

20. Two AC circuits with impedances of $-5 + 8i$ and $4 - 3i$ ohms are connected in series.
a. Find the total impedance. **$-1 + 5i$ ohms**
b. If the total current is $\frac{1}{2} - \frac{5}{2}i$ amps, find the voltage. **13 volts**

Representations Objective I

21. a. On the grid at the right, graph $EFGH$, where $E = 3 + i$, $F = -1 - i$, $G = -2 - 3i$, and $H = 2 - i$.
b. Show that $EFGH$ is a parallelogram.
Slope of $\overline{EF} = \frac{-1-1}{-1-3} = \frac{-2}{-4} = \frac{1}{2}$; slope of $\overline{FG} = \frac{-3-(-1)}{-2-(-1)} = \frac{-2}{-1} = 2$; slope of $\overline{GH} = \frac{-1-(-3)}{2-(-2)} = \frac{2}{4} = \frac{1}{2}$; slope of $\overline{HE} = \frac{-1-1}{2-3} = \frac{-2}{-1} = 2$; since opposite sides are parallel, $EFGH$ is a parallelogram.

22. Let $A = 1 + 2i$, $B = 5i$, and $C = -4$, and let $f(z) = (1 - i)z$. On the grid at the right, graph $\triangle ABC$ and $\triangle A'B'C'$, where $A' = f(A)$, $B' = f(B)$, and $C' = f(C)$. Label the vertices.

Adapting to Individual Needs

Challenge

Show that $\frac{\sqrt{2}+\sqrt{-2}}{2}$ is a square root of i.

$$\left[\left(\frac{\sqrt{2}+\sqrt{-2}}{2}\right)^2 = \frac{2+2\sqrt{2}\sqrt{-2}-2}{4} = \frac{4i}{4} = i\right]$$

Additional Examples

1. Multiply $\sqrt{-36}\sqrt{-9}$. **-18**
2. Express the quotient $\frac{7 + 2i}{3 - 5i}$ in $a + bi$ form. **$\frac{11}{34} + \frac{41}{34}i$**
3. Prove: $\forall$ complex numbers z, $z + \bar{z}$ is a real number equal to twice the real part of z. **Let $z = a + bi$. Then $\bar{z} = a - bi$, and so $z + \bar{z} = a + bi + a - bi = 2a$.**
4. If the total voltage across a circuit is 20 volts and the current is $2 + i$ amps, find the impedance. **$\frac{20}{2 + i} = 8 - 4i$ ohms**

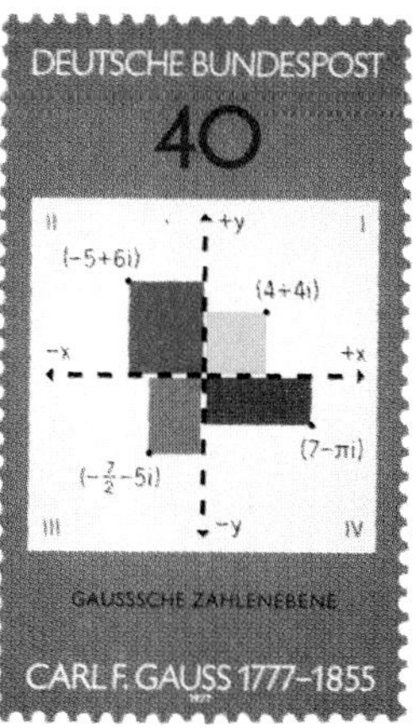

In this way, complex numbers can be identified with points in a plane just as real numbers can be identified with points on a number line. This plane, called the **complex plane**, is constructed like the ordinary coordinate plane. The horizontal axis is the **real axis**, and the vertical axis perpendicular to it is the **imaginary axis**.

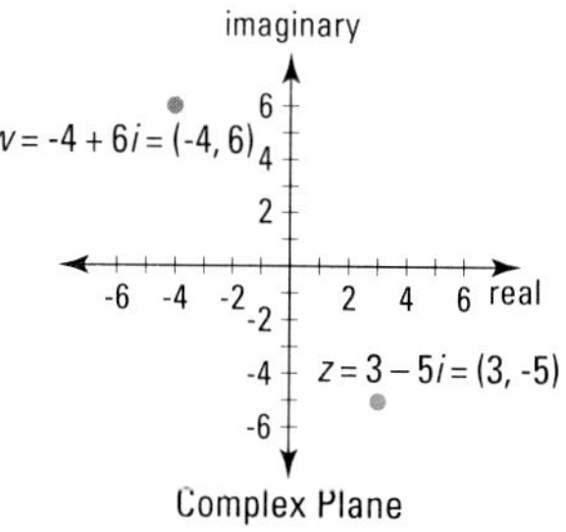

Complex Plane

Notice that the origin in the complex plane represents the complex number $0 = 0 + 0i$. Further, because all real numbers $a + 0i$ have coordinates $(a, 0)$, all real numbers are graphed on the real axis. Similarly all imaginary numbers $0 + bi$ are plotted on the imaginary axis because they have coordinates $(0, b)$. Finally, the point in the complex plane that represents the complex conjugate $\bar{z} = a - bi$ is the reflection image over the real axis of the point representing $z = a + bi$. Four complex numbers are graphed on the German postage stamp at the left.

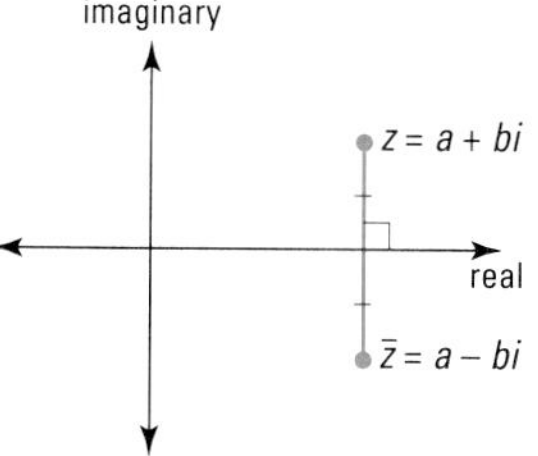

Complex numbers are commonly used in electronics to represent quantities such as voltage, current, and impedance when dealing with alternating current (AC). **Voltage** refers to the electrical potential between two points in an electrical circuit and is measured in volts. **Current**, which is measured in amps, refers to the rate of flow of electric charge through a circuit. **Impedance**, which is measured in ohms, refers to the opposition to the flow of current caused by components called resistors, coils, and capacitors. The total impedance in a circuit is represented by a complex number whose real part indicates the opposition to current flow due to resistors, and whose imaginary part indicates the opposition due to coils and capacitors. For example, suppose a circuit contains resistors with impedance 8 ohms, and coils and capacitors with impedance -3 ohms. Then the total impedance in the circuit is given by $8 - 3i$.

Impedance is related to voltage and current according to Ohm's Law,

$$I = \frac{V}{Z},$$

where I is current (measured in amps), V is voltage, and Z is impedance. Also, if two circuits are connected in **series**—that is, in such a way that current flows through one circuit and then through the other—the total impedance and total voltage are found by adding the impedances and voltages of the individual circuits, respectively.

476

Example 4

Suppose two AC circuits are connected in series, one with an impedance of -5 + 7i ohms and the other with an impedance of 8 − 13i ohms.

a. Find the total impedance.

b. If the voltage across the two circuits is 15 volts, find the current.

Solution

a. The total impedance is the sum of the individual impedances, or

$$(-5 + 7i) + (8 - 13i) = 3 - 6i \text{ ohms.}$$

b. Substituting into Ohm's Law yields

$$\begin{aligned} I &= \frac{V}{Z} = \frac{15}{3 - 6i} \\ &= \frac{15(3 + 6i)}{(3 - 6i)(3 + 6i)} \\ &= \frac{45 + 90i}{45} \\ &= 1 + 2i \text{ amps.} \end{aligned}$$

QUESTIONS

Covering the Reading

1. Who was the first to work with complex numbers expressed in the given notation, and in what century did this happen?
   a. $a + bi$ **Leonhard Euler; 18th**
   b. $a + b\sqrt{-1}$ **Cardano; 16th**
   c. (a, b) **Wessel; 18th**

2. Rewrite using i notation.
   a. $\sqrt{-64}$ **$8i$**
   b. $\sqrt{-20}$ **$\sqrt{20}i = 2\sqrt{5}i$**

3. Simplify each product.
   a. $\sqrt{-9} \cdot \sqrt{-49}$ **-21**
   b. $\sqrt{-8} \cdot \sqrt{-2}$ **-4**

4. Identify the real and imaginary parts of the complex number $8 - 7i$.
   real = 8; imaginary = -7

5. Rewrite $10 + \sqrt{-225}$ in $a + bi$ form. **$10 + 15i$**

6. **a.** *True or false.* If a number is real, then it is complex. **True**
   b. Is the converse true? **No**

In 7 and 8, perform the indicated operations and write the result in $a + bi$ form.

7. $(7 - 6i) + (-4 + 2i)$ **$3 - 4i$**

8. $\frac{14 + 6i}{7}$ **$2 + \frac{6}{7}i$**

9. Let $z = 2 - i$ and $w = 3 + 2i$.
   a. Compute $z \cdot w$ and write the answer in $a + bi$ form. **$8 + i$**
   b. Write the complex conjugate of your answer to part **a**. **$8 - i$**
   c. Find $\bar{z}$. **$2 + i$**
   d. Find $\bar{w}$. **$3 - 2i$**
   e. Multiply your answers to parts **c** and **d**. Write the result in $a + bi$ form. Compare with your answer to part **b**.
   $8 - i$; they are equal.

Notes on Questions

Question 6 Some mathematicians do not consider the set of real numbers to be a subset of the set of complex numbers. They consider the set of real numbers to be a set with operations isomorphic to a subset of the set of complex numbers and the operations on them. The question is philosophical: whether isomorphism means two sets are identical but just represented differently; or whether it means they are different sets.

Question 9 As they go through the parts of this question, students are demonstrating the theorem $\overline{z \cdot w} = \bar{z} \cdot \bar{w}$. You may wish to verbalize it as "the conjugate of a product equals the product of the conjugates." Ask if a corresponding result holds true for products of irrational numbers like $5 + 3\sqrt{2}$ and $3 + 4\sqrt{2}$ and their conjugates. [Yes.]

Notes on Questions

Question 13 This question introduces the geometric interpretation of addition of complex numbers. This topic is covered in more detail in **Lesson 8-3.**

Question 17 This question anticipates some of the work in **Lesson 8-8.** Ask students to use division to determine the other solution of the polynomial equation.

Question 18 This question foreshadows the determination of complex solutions that is investigated in **Lesson 8-8.** In class you may wish to ask students to find the solutions of $x^2 + 9 = 0$ and $x^2 + 4 = 0$. Factoring over the set of polynomials with complex coefficients is a fun way to do this.

Question 20 Remind students that because the statement is a biconditional, proofs of two if-then statements are required.

Question 25 This question anticipates some of the work in **Lesson 8-8.** Students have probably seen the sum and product theorems for quadratics with real solutions.

11a–d)

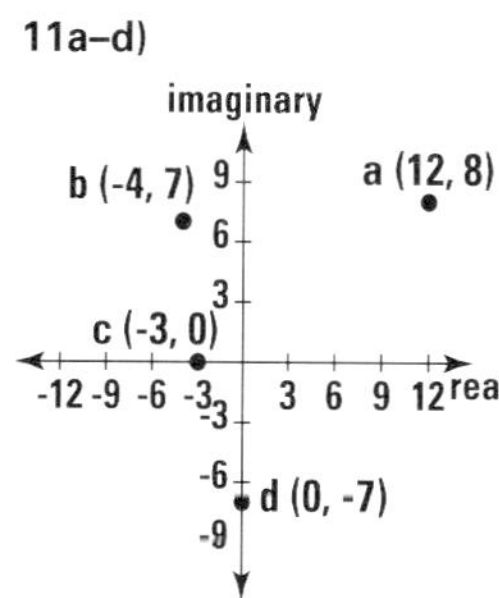

13b)

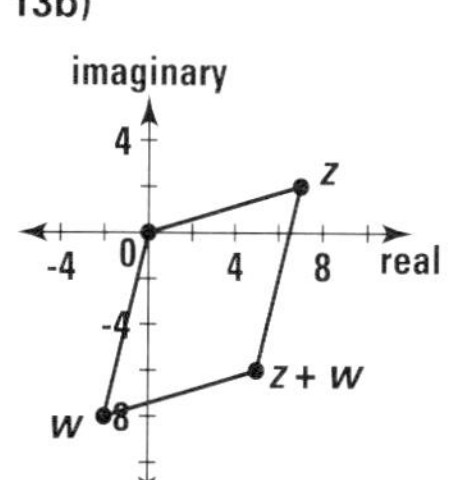

Transistor circuit boards contain resistors and other electronic components.

16) For two imaginary numbers mi and ni, $mi + ni = (m + n)i$. Since m and n are real, $m + n$ is real, and $(m + n)i$ is an imaginary number.

10. Express $\frac{5i}{4 - 3i}$ in $a + bi$ form. **$-\frac{3}{5} + \frac{4}{5}i$**
11. Rewrite each complex number as an ordered pair and graph it in the complex plane. **a–d) See left for graphs.**
    a. $12 + 8i$ **(12, 8)**
    b. $-4 + 7i$ **(-4, 7)**
    c. -3 **(-3, 0)**
    d. $-7i$ **(0, -7)**
12. Two AC circuits with impedances of $9 - i$ ohms and $-5 + 3i$ ohms are connected in series.
    a. Find the total impedance. **$4 + 2i$ ohms**
    b. If the voltage across the two circuits is 6 volts, find the current. **$\frac{6}{5} - \frac{3}{5}i$**

Applying the Mathematics

13. Let $z = 7 + 2i$ and $w = -2 - 8i$.
    a. Compute $z + w$. **$5 - 6i$**
    b. Plot 0, z, w, and $z + w$ in the complex plane. **See left.**
    c. The points you have plotted in part **b** are vertices of a quadrilateral. What kind of quadrilateral is it? How do you know? **parallelogram; sample: slopes of opposite sides are equal**
14. Determine the values for x and y that make the following equation true:
    $$12 + xi = (3 + y) + 7i.$$ **$x = 7$, $y = 9$**
15. In an AC circuit, the voltage across the resistors is 15 volts, and the voltage across the coils and capacitors is 18 volts, so that the total voltage is given by $15 + 18i$. The current is 6 amps.
    a. Find the impedance. **$\frac{5}{2} + 3i$ ohms**
    b. If the circuit actually consists of two circuits connected in series, and the impedance of one of those circuits is $2.5 - 2i$, find the impedance of the other. **$5i$ ohms**
16. Prove or disprove:
    The sum of any two imaginary numbers is an imaginary number. **See left.**
17. Show that $1 + i$ is a solution of $z^2 - 2z + 2 = 0$. **See margin.**
18. Find all four solutions of the equation
    $$x^4 + 13x^2 + 36 = 0$$
    by factoring. **$\pm 3i$, $\pm 2i$**
19. If $z = 5 - 2i$, find $\frac{1}{z}$ and express the result in $a + bi$ form. Check by multiplying $z \cdot \frac{1}{z}$. **$\frac{5}{29} + \frac{2}{29}i$. See margin for check.**
20. Prove that $z = \bar{z}$ if and only if z is a real number. **See margin.**

Review

21. Use proof by contradiction to prove that there is no smallest integer. *(Lesson 4-7)* **See margin.**

Additional Answers

17. $(1 + i)^2 - 2(1 + i) + 2 =$
$1 + i + i + i^2 - 2 - 2i + 2 =$
$1 + i + i - 1 - 2 - 2i + 2 = 0$
So $1 + i$ is a solution of $z^2 - 2z + 2 = 0$.

19. $\frac{5}{29} + \frac{2}{29}i$; $z \cdot \frac{1}{z} = (5 - 2i)(\frac{5}{29} + \frac{2}{29}i) =$
$\frac{25}{29} + \frac{10}{29}i - \frac{10}{29}i - \frac{4}{29}i^2 = \frac{25}{29} + \frac{4}{29} = 1$

20. Let $z = a + bi$. Then $\bar{z} = a - bi$. By definition of equality for complex numbers, $a + bi = a - bi$ if and only if $a = a$ and $b = -b$, then $2b = 0$ and $b = 0$. So $z = a + bi = a + 0i$, and z is a real number.

21. Suppose there is a smallest integer, s. Then $s - 1 < s$, and $s - 1$ is an integer. This contradicts the assumption that s is the smallest integer. So the assumption is false, and there is no smallest integer.

22. Use the definition of absolute value to fill in the blanks:
 a. $x > 5$ or $x < -5$ if and only if $|x|$ __?__. > 5
 b. $-4 < x < 2$ if and only if $|x + 1|$ __?__. *(Lesson 3-9)* < 3

23. The conversion formula between the two most common measures of temperature, Celsius and Fahrenheit, is

$$C = \frac{5}{9}(F - 32).$$

The numerical values for the same temperature on the two scales are usually quite different, for example, 68° F = 20° C.
 a. There is one temperature whose numerical value on both scales is the same. Find this temperature. **-40°**
 b. Suppose that a reading in degrees Fahrenheit is considered close to its Celsius reading if the readings differ by no more than 5°. Find the range of temperatures whose Fahrenheit and Celsius readings are close to each other. *(Lessons 3-1, 3-8)* **$-51.25°F \le t \le -28.75°F$**

24a) **domain:** $\{x: 2 \le x \le 5\}$; **range:** $\{y: 1 \le y \le 2\}$

b)

reflection image of graph of $y = f(x)$

$y = f(x)$

24. Refer to the increasing function f graphed below.
 a. Give the domain and range of f. **See left.**
 b. Reflect the graph of $y = f(x)$ across the line $y = x$. **See left.**
 c. Find the domain and range of the function represented by the reflection image. **domain: $\{x: 1 \le x \le 2\}$; range: $\{y: 2 \le y \le 5\}$**
 d. How are f and the function in part **c** related? *(Lessons 2-1, 2-2, 3-2)* **They are inverses.**

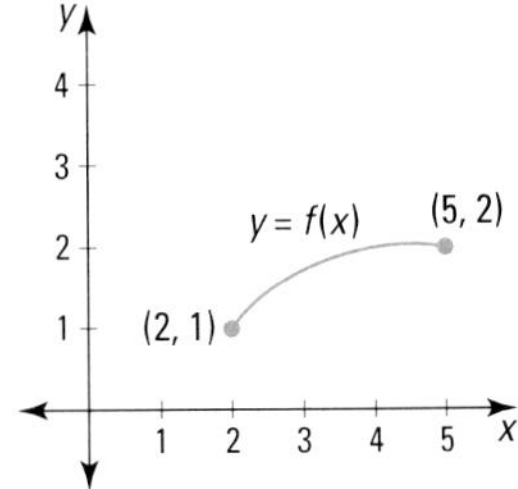

Exploration

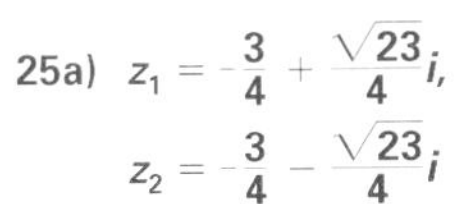

25a) $z_1 = -\frac{3}{4} + \frac{\sqrt{23}}{4}i$, $z_2 = -\frac{3}{4} - \frac{\sqrt{23}}{4}i$

25. a. Solve the quadratic equation $2x^2 + 3x + 4 = 0$. Call your solutions z_1 and z_2. **See left.**
 b. How are z_1 and z_2 related? **They are complex conjugates.**
 c. Compute $z_1 + z_2$ and z_1z_2. How are the sum and product related to the coefficients of the given equation? $z_1 + z_2 = -\frac{3}{2}$, $z_1 \cdot z_2 = 2$
 d. Generalize parts **b** and **c** and, if possible, prove your generalization.

For $ax^2 + bx + c = 0$, the roots are $z_1 = \frac{-b + \sqrt{b^2 - 4ac}}{2a}$ and $z_2 = \frac{-b - \sqrt{b^2 - 4ac}}{2a}$. So $z_1 + z_2 = \frac{-2b}{2a} = -\frac{b}{a}$.

$z_1 \cdot z_2 = \frac{b^2 - (b^2 - 4ac)}{4a^2} = \frac{4ac}{4a^2} = \frac{c}{a}$.

Follow-up for Lesson 8-1

Practice

For more questions on SPUR Objectives, use **Lesson Master 8-1** (shown on pages 474–475).

Assessment

Group Assessment Write two complex numbers on the board. Then have the students work independently to find both possible quotients of the two complex numbers, expressing each in $a + bi$ form. Have students compare their answers and discuss any differences. [Students express the quotient of complex numbers in $a + bi$ form.]

Extension

Get groups together to examine the counterparts of **Question 16** for the operations with imaginary numbers. Then ask the same questions with nonimaginary nonreal complex numbers. [The set of imaginary numbers is not closed under any of the operations; nor is the set of nonimaginary nonreal complex numbers.]

Project Update Project 5, *Matrix Representations of Complex Numbers,* Project 6, *Quaternions,* and Project 8, *Applications of Complex Numbers,* on pages 542–543, relate to the content of this lesson.

Lesson 8-2

Objectives

C Convert between polar and rectangular representations of points.

I Graph complex numbers and verify the Geometric Addition and Geometric Multiplication Theorems.

Resources

From the ***Teacher's Resource File***

- Lesson Master 8-2
- Answer Master 8-2
- Teaching Aids
  70 Warm-up
  73 Large Polar Coordinate Grid
  74 Polar Grids

Additional Resources

- Visuals for Teaching Aids 70, 73, 74
- Exploration 8-2

Teaching Lesson 8-2

Warm-up

Suppose $A = (1, 0)$ and $B = (0, 0)$. Find the measure of $\angle ABC$ in degrees for the given value of C.

1. $C = (\cos 65°, \sin 65°)$ **65°**

2. $C = (-2, -2)$ **225°**

3. $C = (72, -36)$
$\tan^{-1} -0.5 \approx -26.57°$

LESSON

8-2 Polar Coordinates

Star Trails. *This time-lapse photograph shows how stars appear to move in the night sky about a pole. It was taken in Botswana at 19° south latitude.*

People had observed since ancient times that stars at night seem to rotate around a point in the sky; that point was called a *pole*. When, in 1543, Copernicus published his theory that Earth orbits around the sun once a year and spins on its axis once each day, the points on Earth which intersect the axis were naturally called the north and south poles.

Maps of polar regions, like the one on page 482 of the north pole, show lines radiating from the pole. These lines, which on Earth are longitude lines, are identified by their degree measure from some reference line. On the map, the circles of latitude are concentric. *Polar coordinates* in the plane use a grid similar to that found in the map.

Constructing a Polar Coordinate System

To construct a polar coordinate system in a plane, first select a point O to be the **pole** of the system. Then select a line through O to be the **polar axis**. Coordinatize this line so that O has coordinate 0. Usually the polar axis is drawn to be horizontal, as shown below. Any point P in the plane different from the pole has **polar coordinates $[r, \theta]$** if and only if, under a rotation of θ about the pole O, P is the image of the point with coordinate r.

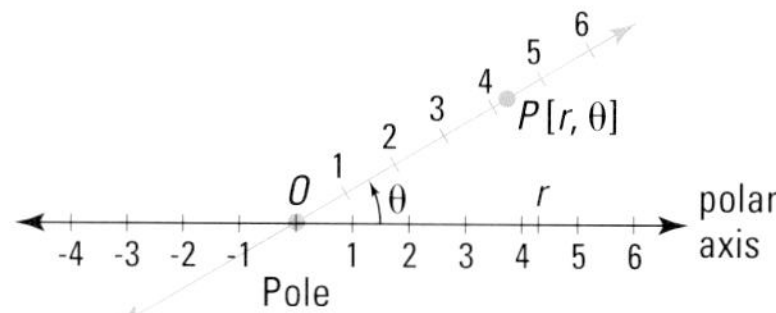

480

Lesson 8-2 Overview

Broad Goals This lesson introduces polar coordinates and discusses relationships of polar coordinates $[r, \theta]$ to rectangular coordinates (x, y) for the same point.

Perspective Coordinate systems provide a link between algebra and geometry. The choice of system is similar to the choice of fraction or decimal representation for rational numbers; it does not change the object; it merely represents it differently.

Jakob Bernoulli, a member of the famous family of brilliant Swiss mathematicians and scientists, introduced the concept of polar coordinates in 1691. Students may wish to read about this extraordinary family and their many contributions to both mathematics and science.

We consistently use brackets [,] to represent polar coordinates in order to distinguish them from the parentheses (,) used for rectangular coordinates.

A tricky aspect of polar coordinates is that the same point may have many polar coordinates. $[r, \theta] = [r, \theta + 2\pi n] = [-r, \theta + (2n + 1)\pi]$ $\forall$ integers n. This is analogous to the fact that the same rational number has many different representations as fractions. This property of polar coordinates is critical to understanding the graphs of curves in Lessons 8-4 and 8-5.

In the graph on page 480, it looks as if P is the image of the point with coordinate about 4.3 under a rotation of about 30°, so $r \approx 4.3$ and $\theta \approx \frac{\pi}{6} = 30°$, and P has approximate polar coordinates $\left[4.3, \frac{\pi}{6}\right]$ or [4.3, 30°]. The brackets [ ] are used to distinguish polar from rectangular coordinates.

Every rotation of θ yields the same image as a rotation of $\theta + 2\pi n$ (in radians) or $\theta + 360n$ (in degrees), where n is any integer. So, unlike the situation with rectangular coordinates, a point has more than one polar coordinate representation. For the point P, three other representations are $\left[4.3, \frac{13\pi}{6}\right]$, [4.3, -330°], and $\left[4.3, -\frac{11\pi}{6}\right]$. Since points on the polar axis can have negative coordinates, r can be negative, as Example 1 shows.

❶

Example 1

a. Plot the point $Q = \left[-5, \frac{3\pi}{4}\right]$.

b. Give different polar coordinates $[r, \theta]$ for Q in which $r > 0$.

Solution

a. Rotate the polar axis $\frac{3\pi}{4}$ about O and look for the point with coordinate -5.

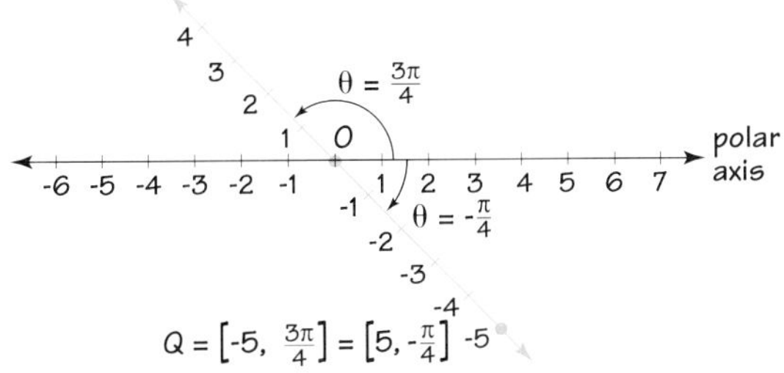

$Q = \left[-5, \frac{3\pi}{4}\right] = \left[5, -\frac{\pi}{4}\right]$

b. A rotation of $-\frac{\pi}{4}$ will bring the point with coordinate 5 on the polar axis to the same position. So $Q = \left[5, -\frac{\pi}{4}\right]$ is another possible representation for point Q.

In any polar coordinate system, the pole O has polar coordinates $[0, \theta]$ for *any* number θ. Thus, [0, 0], [0, 30°], and $\left[0, \frac{\pi}{2}\right]$ are three of the infinitely many polar coordinate representations of the pole.

The possible polar coordinates for a point other than the pole are summarized in the following theorem.

❷

Theorem

For any particular values of r and θ, the following polar coordinate representations name the same point.

a. $[r, \theta]$

b. $[r, \theta + 2\pi n]$, $\forall$ integers n

c. $[-r, \theta + (2n + 1)\pi]$, $\forall$ integers n

Notes on Reading

The primary objectives of this lesson are to help students to gain facility with plotting points on a polar grid and with conversions between the rectangular and polar representations of a point in the plane. Both of these skills require practice. Note immediately that we use brackets for polar form and parentheses for rectangular form; if you have not made this distinction before, be careful to make it here. Clarity will pay off.

❶ **Error Alert** Some students find it difficult to plot points $[r, \theta]$ when $r < 0$. Suggest that they view the polar axis as a spinner. You may fasten a thin, coordinatized stick with a thumbtack to the pole of a sheet of polar graph paper. Rotating the stick by the angle θ and using its coordinatization for r will help students master polar plotting. We have provided **Teaching Aids 73 and 74** to assist you: a big polar grid for demonstration of graphing to the class and a page with smaller polar grids to duplicate for students to use on their homework.

❷ In interpreting the first theorem of this lesson, remind students that "$\forall$ integers n" allows n to be positive, negative, or zero. Some texts use the notation $\theta \pm 2\pi k$, where k is a positive integer, to emphasize that any integer multiple of 2π can be added to or subtracted from θ. We are able to avoid the $\pm$ sign by allowing n to be negative.

Optional Activities

Activity 1 Technology Connection
Materials: Explorations software

Students may use *Exploration 8-2, Polar and Rectangular Coordinates,* as an alternative to **Example 3** in Lesson 8-2. Students can enter a point in polar coordinates or rectangular coordinates and convert to the opposite format. The students can observe their chosen point on a rectangular coordinate grid and on a polar grid.

Activity 2 Have students prove that the graph of $r = n$, where n is a real number, is always a circle. Ask them what happens if n is negative. [$r = \sqrt{x^2 + y^2} = n$, so $x^2 + y^2 = n^2$, which is the equation of a circle with center (0,0) and radius n. If n is negative, the same equation results, so $r = 5$ and $r = -5$ have identical graphs, circles centered at the origin with radius 5.] Then have students prove that the graph of $\theta = a$, where a is a real number, is always a line. [$\theta = \tan^{-1}(\frac{y}{x}) = a$. Taking the tangent of both sides, $\frac{y}{x} = \tan a$, so $y = (\tan a)x$. Therefore $\theta = a$ is a line with slope $\tan a$ and y-intercept 0.]

If students are bothered by the existence of more than one pair of polar coordinates for the same point, make the analogy with fraction and decimal representations of rational numbers, as pointed out in the Perspectives for this lesson.

When discussing **Example 2,** you might wish to point out the following analogy. With rectangular coordinates, the point (2, 5) is the intersection of the line $x = 2$ with the line $y = 5$. In polar coordinates, when $r > 0$, students may think of the point $[3, \frac{5\pi}{12}]$ as the intersection of the circle of radius $r = 3$ with the ray $\theta = \frac{5\pi}{12}$.

❸ You may wish to use a reference triangle to verify the Polar-Rectangular Conversion theorem. For simplicity select θ such that $0 < \theta < \frac{\pi}{2}$. Draw a segment from the pole to [r, q] and segments from [r, q] to [r, 0] and [0, 0] to [r, 0] to create a right △ OAB as pictured below. From right triangle trigonometry, $\cos\theta = \frac{OA}{OB}$, $\sin\theta = \frac{AB}{OB}$ or $\cos\theta = \frac{x}{r}$, $\sin\theta = \frac{y}{r}$ or $x = r\cos\theta$, $y = r\sin\theta$.

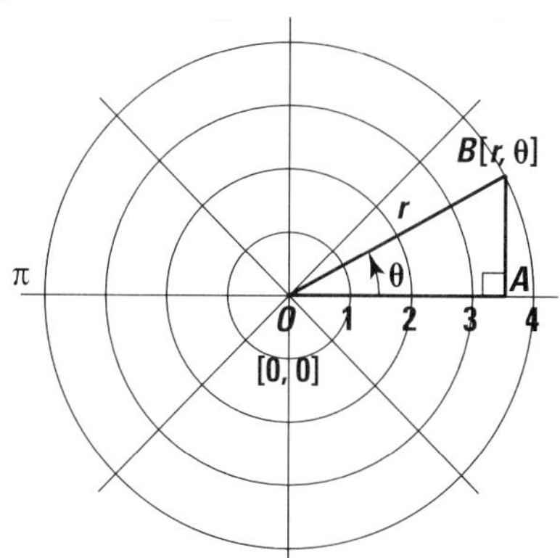

Polar Coordinate Grids

The **polar grid** pictured at the right is very helpful for plotting points and sketching curves in polar coordinates and is commonly used.

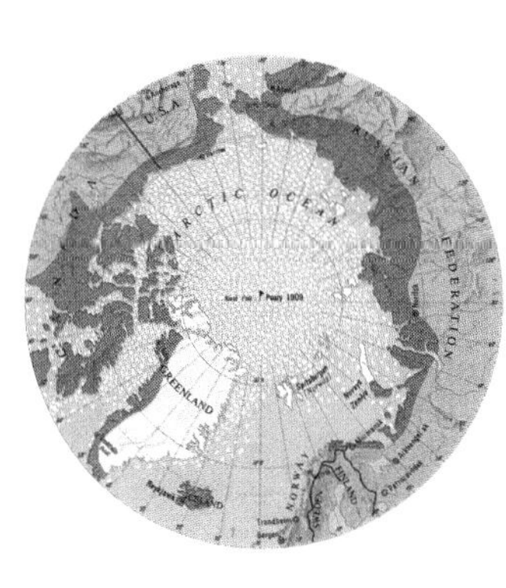

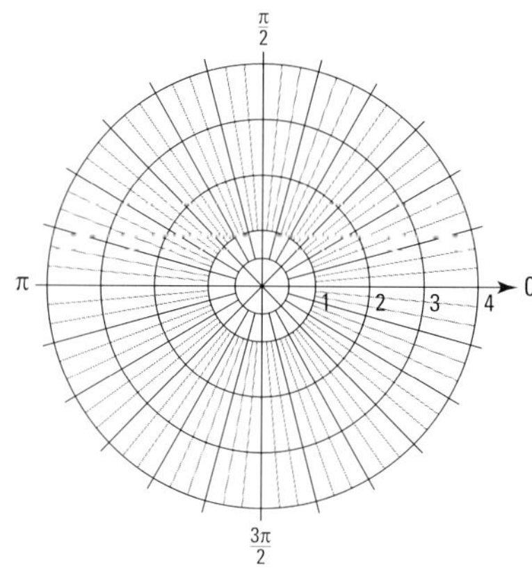

Each of the concentric circles in the grid represents a value of r, and each ray from the pole represents a value of θ. When plotting using polar coordinates, you should identify the positive polar axis with an arrow and put a scale on it to indicate values of r.

Example 2

Use the same polar grid for all three parts.

a. Plot the points $Q_1 = \left[-2.4, \frac{\pi}{2}\right]$ and $Q_2 = \left[2.1, \frac{-7\pi}{3}\right]$.

b. Sketch all solutions $[r, \theta]$ to the equation $r = 3$.

c. Sketch all solutions $[r, \theta]$ to the equation $\theta = \frac{5\pi}{12}$.

Solution

a. To plot Q_1, go to -2.4 on the polar axis (to the left of the pole) and rotate that point $\frac{\pi}{2}$ about the pole.
To plot Q_2, go to 2.1 on the polar axis and rotate that point $-\frac{7\pi}{3}$ about the pole.

b. The equation $r = 3$ describes the circle of radius 3 centered at the pole. That circle is drawn in orange.

c. $\theta = \frac{5\pi}{12}$ is the line obtained by rotating the polar axis by $\frac{5\pi}{12}$. That line is drawn in green.

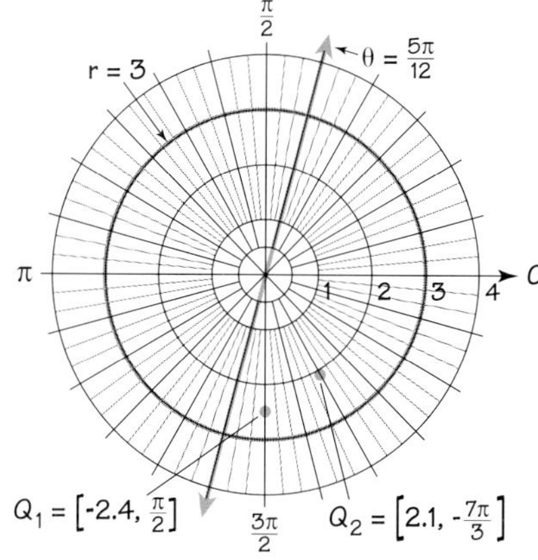

Adapting to Individual Needs

Extra Help

Many scientific calculators can do conversions between rectangular and polar coordinates. One calculator has shift register keys Po(x, y) and Rec(r, θ) for this purpose. Another has these conversions in the MATH menu. Ask your students if their calculators have this capacity.

Challenge

Derive a formula for the distance between the points $[r_1, \theta_1]$ and $[r_2, \theta_2]$ in terms of r_1, r_2, θ_1, and θ_2. [Use the Law of Cosines to get: $d = \sqrt{r_1^2 + r_2^2 - 2r_1r_2\cos(\theta_1 - \theta_2)}$]

Often polar and rectangular coordinate systems are superimposed on the same plane. Then the polar axis coincides with the x-axis and the pole is the origin. When this is done, you can use trigonometry to find the unique rectangular coordinate representation for any point whose polar coordinate representation is known.

Example 3

Find the rectangular coordinates of the point $P = \left[3, \frac{5\pi}{6}\right]$.

Solution

First plot P as shown here.

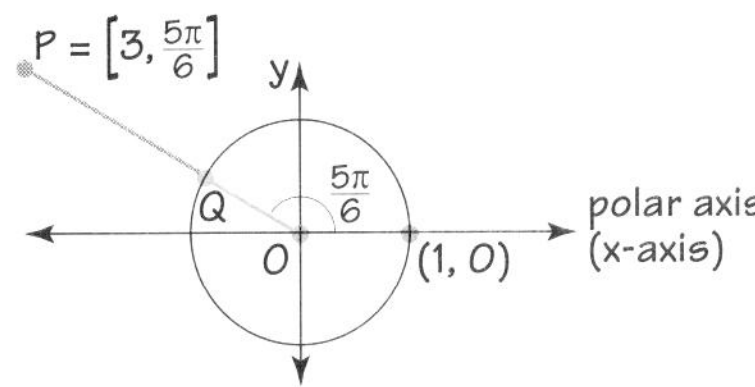

Let Q be $\left[1, \frac{5\pi}{6}\right]$, where the unit circle intersects $\overrightarrow{OP}$. Notice that $Q = R_{\frac{5\pi}{6}}(1, 0)$. So, by definition of the cosine and sine, $Q = \left(\cos \frac{5\pi}{6}, \sin \frac{5\pi}{6}\right)$. Because $P = \left[3, \frac{5\pi}{6}\right]$, P is three times as far from the origin as Q, so $P = \left(3 \cos \frac{5\pi}{6}, 3 \sin \frac{5\pi}{6}\right)$.

Thus $P = \underbrace{\left[3, \frac{5\pi}{6}\right]}_{\text{polar}} = \underbrace{\left(3 \cos \frac{5\pi}{6}, 3 \sin \frac{5\pi}{6}\right) = \left(-\frac{3\sqrt{3}}{2}, \frac{3}{2}\right)}_{\text{rectangular}}$

Check

Both $P = \left[3, \frac{5\pi}{6}\right]$ and $\left(-\frac{3\sqrt{3}}{2}, \frac{3}{2}\right)$ are in the 2nd quadrant, closer to the x-axis than the y-axis.

The procedure used in Example 3 generalizes to the following result.

3 **Polar-Rectangular Conversion Theorem**

If $[r, \theta]$ is a polar coordinate representation of a point P, then the rectangular coordinates (x, y) of P are given by

$$x = r \cos \theta \quad \text{and} \quad y = r \sin \theta.$$

Proof

If P is the pole, then $P = (0, 0)$. The theorem holds because $x = 0 = 0 \cdot \cos \theta$ and $y = 0 = 0 \cdot \sin \theta$ for any θ.

For all points but the pole, the argument of Example 3 applies. It is left for you to generalize.

The conversion from rectangular coordinates of a point to polar coordinates by use of the Rectangular to Polar conversion formulas $r^2 = x^2 + y^2$ and $\tan \theta = \frac{y}{x}$ offers the opportunity to remind students that the equation $\tan \theta = c$ always has infinitely many solutions because the tangent function is periodic. This confirms the idea that a point can have infinitely many polar coordinates. However, if students use the inverse tangent key on their calculator to solve this equation, only the solution in the interval $-\frac{\pi}{2} < \theta < \frac{\pi}{2}$ is displayed because the $\tan^{-1}$ function selects this value from among the infinitude of solutions to $\tan \theta = c$.

Additional Examples

1. a. Plot the point $P = \left[2, -\frac{\pi}{4}\right]$

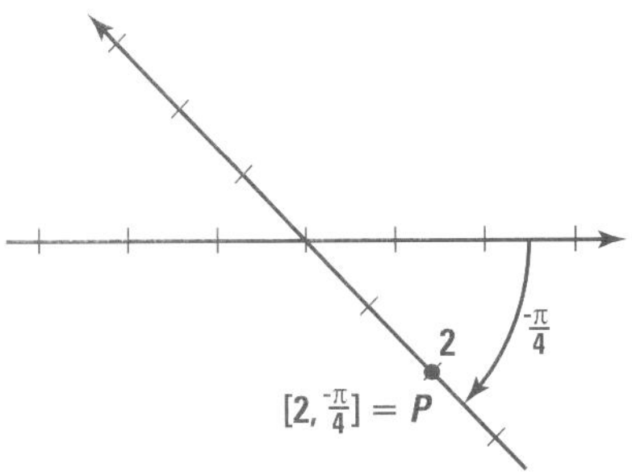

b. Give a different polar representation $[r, \theta]$ for P in which $r > 0$ and $\theta > 0$.
Sample: $\left[2, \frac{7\pi}{4}\right]$

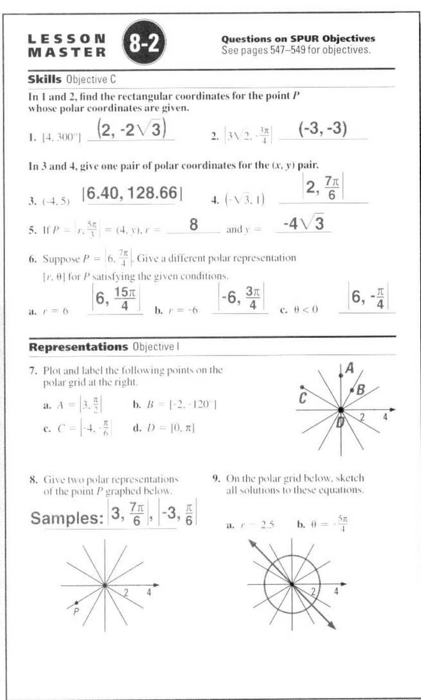

LESSON MASTER 8-2

Questions on SPUR Objectives
See pages 547–549 for objectives.

Skills Objective C

In 1 and 2, find the rectangular coordinates for the point P whose polar coordinates are given.

1. $[4, 300°]$ $\left(2, -2\sqrt{3}\right)$
2. $\left[3\sqrt{2}, -\frac{3\pi}{4}\right]$ $(-3, -3)$

In 3 and 4, give one pair of polar coordinates for the (x, y) pair.

3. $(-4, 5)$ $[6.40, 128.66]$
4. $(-\sqrt{3}, 1)$ $\left[2, \frac{7\pi}{6}\right]$
5. If $P = \left[r, \frac{5\pi}{3}\right] = (4, y)$, $r =$ 8 and $y =$ $-4\sqrt{3}$
6. Suppose $P = \left[6, \frac{7\pi}{4}\right]$. Give a different polar representation $[r, \theta]$ for P satisfying the given conditions.
   a. $r = 6$ $\left[6, \frac{15\pi}{4}\right]$ b. $r = -6$ $\left[-6, \frac{3\pi}{4}\right]$ c. $\theta < 0$ $\left[6, -\frac{\pi}{4}\right]$

Representations Objective I

7. Plot and label the following points on the polar grid at the right.
   a. $A = \left[3, \frac{\pi}{2}\right]$ b. $B = [-2, -120°]$
   c. $C = \left[-4, -\frac{\pi}{6}\right]$ d. $D = [0, \pi]$
8. Give two polar representations of the point P graphed below.
   Samples: $\left[3, \frac{7\pi}{6}\right]$, $\left[-3, \frac{\pi}{6}\right]$
9. On the polar grid below, sketch all solutions to these equations.
   a. $r = 2.5$ b. $\theta = -\frac{5\pi}{4}$

2. Do all parts on the same polar grid.
   a. Plot the points $Q_1 = [-3.2, \frac{3\pi}{4}]$ and $Q_2 = [3.8, \frac{7\pi}{6}]$.
   b. Sketch all solutions $[r, \theta]$ to the equation $r = 2.4$.
   c. Sketch all solutions $[r, \theta]$ to the equation $\theta = \frac{13\pi}{12}$.

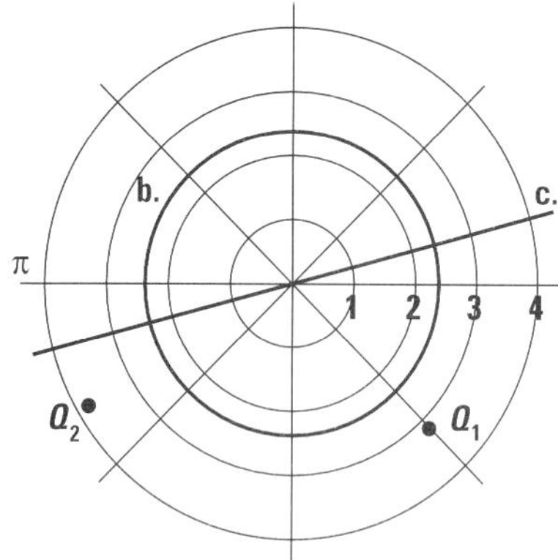

3. Find the rectangular coordinates of the point P with polar coordinates $[5, \frac{\pi}{6}]$.
   $(5 \cos \frac{\pi}{6}, 5 \sin \frac{\pi}{6}) = (\frac{5\sqrt{3}}{2}, \frac{5}{2})$
   Students with scientific calculators that do polar → rectangular conversions should check their solution with the calculator.
4. Find 3 different polar coordinate representations for the point whose rectangular coordinates are (5, -12). **Samples:**
   $[13, \tan^{-1}(-\frac{12}{5})] \approx [13, -67.4]$, $\approx [13, 292.6]$, $\approx [-13, 112.6]$

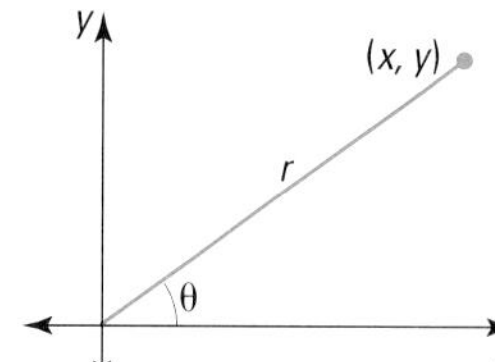

Translating from rectangular to polar coordinates is also possible. To obtain a general formula, we solve the following system for r and θ.

$$\begin{cases} x = r \cos \theta \\ y = r \sin \theta \end{cases}$$

To find θ, notice that

$$\frac{y}{x} = \frac{r \sin \theta}{r \cos \theta} = \tan \theta.$$

There are many possible values of θ, leading to the many possible polar representations. For a given point, the values of θ differ by multiples of π (or 180°).

To solve the above system for r, notice that

$$x^2 + y^2 = (r \cos \theta)^2 + (r \sin \theta)^2 = r^2(\cos^2 \theta + \sin^2 \theta) = r^2 \cdot 1 = r^2.$$

So $\qquad r = \pm\sqrt{x^2 + y^2}.$

This confirms that r can be positive or negative. The choice for r (and for θ) depends on the quadrant in which the point is located.

Example 4

Find 3 different polar coordinate representations for the point whose rectangular coordinates are (-3, 4).

Solution

$r = \pm\sqrt{(-3)^2 + 4^2} = \pm 5$ and $\tan \theta = -\frac{4}{3}$.

A calculator shows

$$\theta = \tan^{-1}\left(-\frac{4}{3}\right) \approx -53°.$$

So $\qquad \theta \approx -53° + 180°n.$

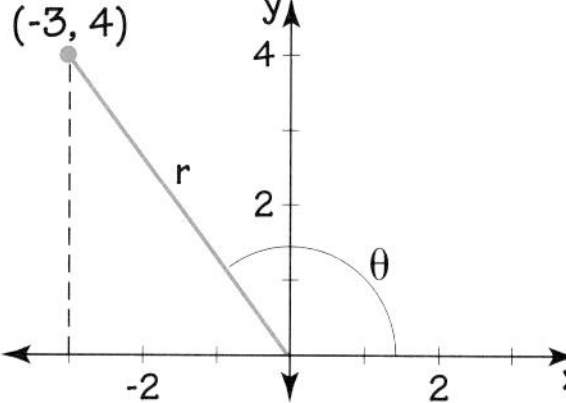

Since the point is in the second quadrant, one representation is [-5, -53°]. From this, you can obtain the other polar coordinate representations: [5, 127°], [-5, 307°], and so on.

The general relationships that govern the conversion between rectangular and polar coordinates are summarized below.

Polar to Rectangular	Rectangular to Polar
$x = r \cos \theta$	$r^2 = x^2 + y^2$
$y = r \sin \theta$	$\tan \theta = \frac{y}{x}$

In Lesson 8-1, the complex number $z = a + bi$ was plotted in the complex plane by writing it as the ordered pair (a, b). Polar coordinates provide another way of representing complex numbers $a + bi$ as $[r, \theta]$, where $r = \sqrt{a^2 + b^2}$ and $\tan \theta = \frac{b}{a}$. Both these ways are quite useful, as you will see throughout the rest of this chapter.

Additional Answers

3. a. **By case b of the polar coordinate representation theorem in this lesson, $[4, \frac{\pi}{3}] = [4, \frac{\pi}{3} + 2(-1)\pi] = [4, -\frac{5\pi}{3}]$. Then by case b again, $[4, -\frac{5\pi}{3} + 2k\pi]$ for any integer k is a polar coordinate representation of $[4, \frac{\pi}{3}]$.**
   b. **By case c of the polar coordinate representation theorem in this lesson, $[4, \frac{\pi}{3}] = [-4, \frac{\pi}{3} + \pi] = [-4, \frac{4\pi}{3}]$. So by case b, $[-4, \frac{4\pi}{3} + 2k\pi]$ for any integer k is a polar coordinate representation of $[4, \frac{\pi}{3}]$.**

QUESTIONS

Covering the Reading

1a–d)

1. Plot all the points on the same polar grid. See left.
   a. [2, 300°] **b.** [-4, 100°] **c.** $\left[0, \frac{\pi}{6}\right]$ **d.** $\left[1, \frac{5\pi}{3}\right]$

2. Suppose $P = \left[2, \frac{7\pi}{6}\right]$. Give a different polar coordinate representation $[r, \theta]$ for P satisfying the given conditions. Samples are given.
   a. $r = 2$ $\left[2, \frac{19\pi}{6}\right]$ **b.** $r = -2$ $\left[-2, \frac{\pi}{6}\right]$ **c.** $\theta < 0$ $\left[2, -\frac{5\pi}{6}\right]$

3. Explain why the points are polar coordinate representations of $\left[4, \frac{\pi}{3}\right]$.
   a. $\left[4, -\frac{5\pi}{3} + 2k\pi\right]$ for any integer k
   b. $\left[-4, \frac{4\pi}{3} + 2k\pi\right]$ for any integer k a, b) See margin.

4a, b)

4. On the same polar grid, sketch all solutions to these equations.
   a. $r = 2$ **b.** $\theta = \frac{2\pi}{3}$ a, b) See left.

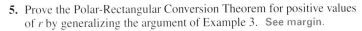

5. Prove the Polar-Rectangular Conversion Theorem for positive values of r by generalizing the argument of Example 3. See margin.

In 6 and 7, find the rectangular coordinates for the point P whose polar coordinates are given.

6. $\left[4, \frac{3\pi}{2}\right]$ (0, -4) 7. [2.3, -42°] ≈ (1.7, -1.5)

In 8 and 9, give one pair of polar coordinates for each (x, y) pair.

8. (5, 2) ≈ $[\sqrt{29}, 21.8°]$ 9. (-2, -3) ≈ $[-\sqrt{13}, 56.3°]$

Applying the Mathematics

10. A boat in distress is 4.2 km east and 8.5 km south of a ship. **a.** If the ship wishes to help the boat, in what direction should it sail? **b.** If the ship can make 25 $\frac{\text{km}}{\text{h}}$, how long will it take to reach the boat?
    a) 26.3° East of South b) ≈ .38 hours or ≈ 23 minutes

11. Let $P = \left[3, \frac{\pi}{6}\right]$. Find one pair of polar coordinates for the image of P under the given transformation. Samples are given.
    a. reflection over the polar axis $\left[3, \frac{11\pi}{6}\right]$
    b. reflection over the line $\theta = \frac{\pi}{2}$ $\left[3, \frac{5\pi}{6}\right]$
    c. rotation of $\frac{2\pi}{3}$ radians about the pole $\left[3, \frac{5\pi}{6}\right]$

12. Example 4 could be interpreted as getting polar coordinate representations of what complex number? $-3 + 4i$

13. Give polar coordinates for each complex number. Samples are given.
    a. (1, 0) [1, 0°] **b.** i [1, 90°] **c.** $11i$ [11, 90°]

Notes on Questions

Question 2 Elicit enough responses so students see the patterns, that for a fixed value of r all correct values of θ differ by multiples of 2π, and when r is converted to its opposite the value of θ changes by an odd multiple of π.

Question 4a Using $r = \sqrt{x^2 + y^2}$ and $r = 2$, ask students to convert the polar equation $r = 2$ to its corresponding rectangular form. They should get $x^2 + y^2 = 4$, which they should recognize is the equation of the circle with center at the origin and radius 2. Point out that $r = 2$ is a much simpler equation than $x^2 + y^2 = 4$. Also note that because θ does not appear in the equation $r = 2$, θ can be any real number. (This is analogous to an equation $x = h$ for a vertical line, where the nonappearance of y allows it to be any real number.)

Question 4b Note that the polar equation of any line through the pole is of the form $\theta = c$. The rectangular form for such a line is $y = mx$. Ask for the relationship between m and c. ($m = \tan c$)

Questions 7–9 It is useful to give exact answers before giving the approximate values.
For **Question 7:**
(2.3 cos (-42°), 2.3 sin (-42°)) ≈ (1.7, -1.5);
Question 8:
$[\sqrt{29}, \tan^{-1}\frac{2}{5}] \approx [5.4, 21.8°]$;
Question 9:
$[-\sqrt{13}, \tan^{-1}\frac{3}{2}] \approx [-3.6, 56.3°]$.

Question 8 Ask students to write expressions that will generate all possible polar coordinates for these two points. ($[\sqrt{29}, \tan^{-1} 0.4 + 2\pi n]$ or $[-\sqrt{29}, \tan^{-1} 0.4 + \pi n]$)

Questions 12, 13, and 17 The questions provide an introduction to the polar representation of complex numbers, in anticipation of Lesson 8-3.

5. Given any point $P = [r, \theta]$. First plot P and $Q = [1, \theta] = (\cos \theta, \sin \theta)$. Because $[r, \theta]$ is r times as far from the origin as Q, its rectangular coordinates are $(r \cos \theta, r \sin \theta)$. Thus, the rectangular coordinates of P are given by $x = r \cos \theta$ and $y = r \sin \theta$.

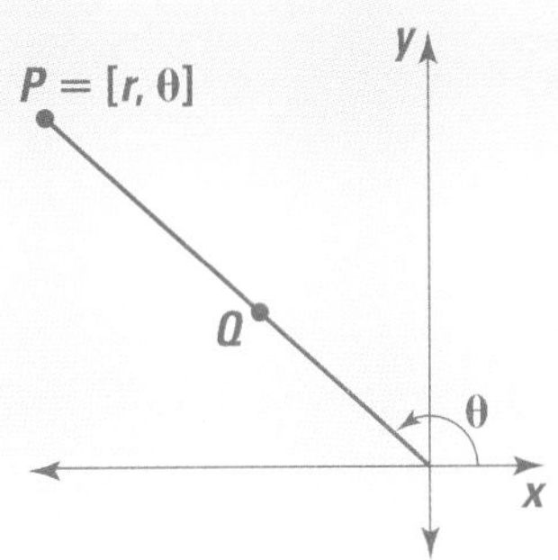

Notes on Questions

Question 19 You may summarize **part a** as "conjugate of a sum is the sum of the conjugates," and **parts b and c** similarly. These illustrate what may be called distributive properties of conjugation over addition, multiplication, and division.

Follow-up for Lesson 8-2

Practice

For more questions on SPUR Objectives, use **Lesson Master 8-2** (shown on page 483).

Assessment

Written Communication Have students **work in pairs.** Ask each student to make up one problem like **Example 3** and one like **Example 4.** Have students solve their partner's problems. [Students convert between rectangular and polar representations of points.]

Extension

In **Question 11,** ask students to generalize their answer to the images of any point $P = [r, \theta]$. Then have them consider other transformations. In polar coordinates, size changes are easy, but translations are very difficult.

Project Update Project 2, *Three-Dimensional "Polar" Coordinates,* on page 542, relates to the content of this lesson.

Additional Answers

19. a. $z + w = (6 - 3i) + (2 + 4i) = 8 + i$, so $\overline{z + w} = 8 - i$. $\overline{z} = 6 + 3i$ and $\overline{w} = 2 - 4i$. So $\overline{z} + \overline{w} = (6 + 3i) + (2 - 4i) = 8 - i$. $\therefore \overline{z + w} = \overline{z} + \overline{w}$

b. $z \cdot w = (6 - 3i)(2 + 4i) = 24 + 18i$. So $\overline{z \cdot w} = 24 - 18i$. $\overline{z} \cdot \overline{w} = (6 + 3i)(2 - 4i) = 24 - 18i$. $\therefore \overline{z \cdot w} = \overline{z} \cdot \overline{w}$.

c. $\frac{z}{w} = \frac{(6 - 3i)}{(2 + 4i)} = 0 - \frac{3}{2}i$, so $\overline{\left(\frac{z}{w}\right)} = 0 + \frac{3}{2}i$. $\frac{\overline{z}}{\overline{w}} = \frac{6 + 3i}{2 - 4i} = 0 + \frac{3}{2}i$. $\therefore \overline{\left(\frac{z}{w}\right)} = \frac{\overline{z}}{\overline{w}}$.

15) $P_1 = [3, 0°]$, $P_2 = [3, 30°]$, $P_3 = [3, 90°]$, $P_4 = [3, 120°]$, $P_5 = [3, 195°]$, $P_6 = [3, 240°]$, $P_7 = [3, 285°]$; $r = 3$

16) $Q_1 = \left[-4, \frac{\pi}{6}\right]$, $Q_2 = \left[-3, \frac{\pi}{6}\right]$, $Q_3 = \left[-2, \frac{\pi}{6}\right]$, $Q_4 = \left[-1, \frac{\pi}{6}\right]$, $Q_5 = \left[0, \frac{\pi}{6}\right]$, $Q_6 = \left[1, \frac{\pi}{6}\right]$, $Q_7 = \left[2, \frac{\pi}{6}\right]$, $Q_8 = \left[3, \frac{\pi}{6}\right]$, $Q_9 = \left[4, \frac{\pi}{6}\right]$; $\theta = \frac{\pi}{6}$

21a) $\frac{400h}{26 + h}$

Nature's Light Show. *Northern lights result from high-energy solar particles that penetrate Earth's magnetic field. They are more visible near the magnetic poles.*

14. When the coordinates of P are written in polar form, $\theta = \frac{\pi}{6}$. When the coordinates are written in rectangular form, $x = 5$. Find polar and rectangular coordinates for P. $\left[\frac{10\sqrt{3}}{3}, \frac{\pi}{6}\right]$; $\left(5, \frac{5\sqrt{3}}{3}\right)$

In 15 and 16, the rays are equally spaced around the pole. Give polar coordinates for each labeled point on the graph. Then write an equation that r and θ satisfy.

15. See left.

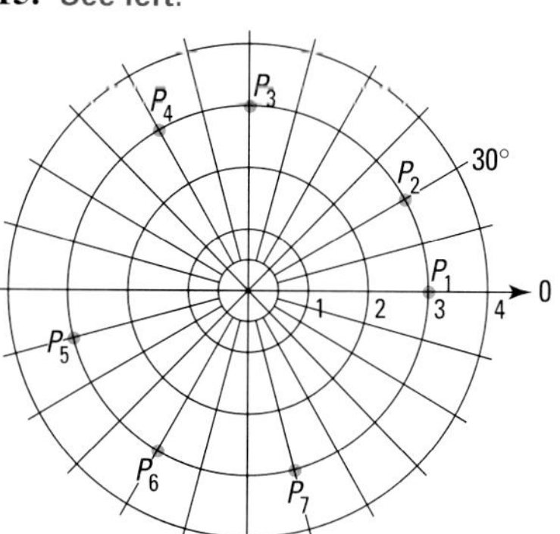

16. See left.

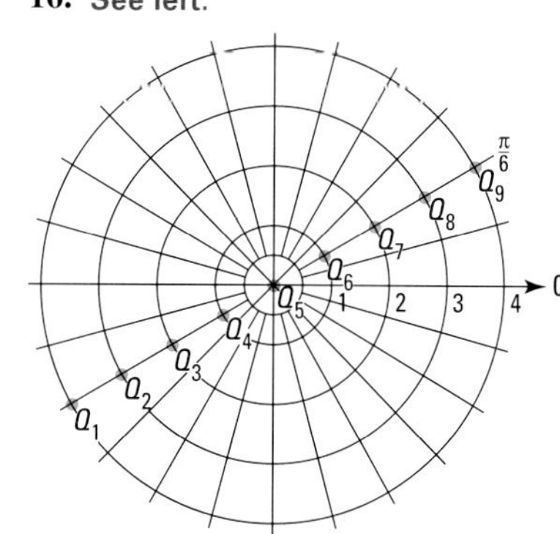

17. What complex number is represented by the point P_6 in Question 15? $-1.5 + (-1.5\sqrt{3})i$

Review

18. If the voltage across an AC circuit is $10 - 15i$ volts and the impedance is $-4 + 6i$ ohms, find the current. *(Lesson 8-1)* $-\frac{5}{2}$ amps

19. Let $z = 6 - 3i$ and $w = 2 + 4i$. Verify the following algebraic properties of the complex conjugate of z and w. *(Lesson 8-1)*
 a. $\overline{z + w} = \overline{z} + \overline{w}$ b. $\overline{z \cdot w} = \overline{z} \cdot \overline{w}$ c. $\overline{\left(\frac{z}{w}\right)} = \frac{\overline{z}}{\overline{w}}$
 a–c) See margin.

20. a. Expand $\cos(\theta + \phi)$. $\cos\theta\cos\phi - \sin\theta\sin\phi$
 b. Expand $\sin(\theta + \phi)$. *(Lessons 6-4, 6-5)* $\sin\theta\cos\phi + \cos\theta\sin\phi$

21. Suppose a person drives 8,000 miles per year with a car that averages 26 miles/gallon. Assume that gasoline costs \$1.30/gallon.
 a. Find a single fraction that gives the amount of money this person would save in a year by improving the gas mileage by h miles/gallon.
 b. By how much must the gas mileage improve to save \$80 a year? *(Lesson 5-4)* 6.5 mpg
 a) See left.

22. Prove that the points (-1, 0), (-5, -5), (-11, -5), and (-7, 0) are vertices of a parallelogram. *(Previous course)* See margin.

Exploration

23. On Earth, where are the north and south *magnetic* poles? See margin.

22. Let the vertices in clockwise order be $A(-1, 0)$, $B(-5, -5)$, $C(-11, -5)$, and $D(-7, 0)$. The slope of $\overline{AD} = 0$; the slope of $\overline{BC} = 0$. The slope of $\overline{AB} = \frac{-5 - 0}{-5 - (-1)} = \frac{5}{4}$; the slope of $\overline{DC} = \frac{-5 - 0}{-11 - (-7)} = \frac{5}{4}$. Since $ABCD$ is composed of two pairs of parallel lines, it is a parallelogram.

23. The north magnetic pole lies just north of North America and west of Greenland and is about latitude 76° N and longitude 101° W on Bathurst Island in Canada. The south magnetic pole is in Antarctica and is about latitude 66° S and longitude 140° E, just off the coast of Antarctica due south of Australia. The locations of both magnetic poles vary over time.

LESSON 8-3

The Geometry of Complex Numbers

The arithmetic operations with complex numbers can be interpreted geometrically using rectangular and polar coordinate systems in the complex plane.

A Geometric Picture of Addition

Consider first the addition of complex numbers. If $z = a + bi$ and $w = c + di$, then their sum is

$$z + w = (a + c) + (b + d)i.$$

Since $z = (a, b)$ and $w = (c, d)$, in rectangular coordinates, this addition is

$$(a, b) + (c, d) = (a + c, b + d).$$

There is a simple geometric interpretation for this addition.

Example 1

Let $z = 4 + 6i$ and $w = 3 - i$. Plot the points z, w, and $z + w$ in the complex plane and verify that the points representing z, 0, w, and $z + w$ are consecutive vertices of a parallelogram.

Solution

In this case,

$$\begin{aligned} z &= 4 + 6i = (4, 6) = Z \\ 0 &= 0 + 0i = (0, 0) = O \\ \text{and} \quad w &= 3 - i = (3, -1) = W \\ \text{So} \quad z + w &= (4 + 6i) + (3 - i) = 7 + 5i \\ &= (7, 5) = P \end{aligned}$$

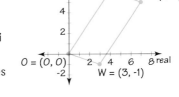

The four points Z, O, W, and P are vertices of a quadrilateral, as shown at the right. To prove that $ZOWP$ is a parallelogram, find slopes of pairs of opposite sides.

$$\text{slope of } \overline{OZ} = \frac{6 - 0}{4 - 0} = \frac{3}{2} \qquad \text{slope of } \overline{WP} = \frac{5 - (-1)}{7 - 3} = \frac{3}{2}$$

Thus $\overline{OZ} \parallel \overline{WP}$.

$$\text{slope of } \overline{ZP} = \frac{5 - 6}{7 - 4} = -\frac{1}{3} \qquad \text{slope of } \overline{OW} = \frac{-1 - 0}{3 - 0} = -\frac{1}{3}$$

So $\overline{ZP} \parallel \overline{OW}$. Therefore, $ZOWP$ is a parallelogram.

The slope calculations in Example 1 can be carried out for any nonzero complex numbers $z = (a, b)$, $w = (c, d)$ and $z + w = (a + c, b + d)$, provided that $a \neq 0$ and $c \neq 0$. The result is the theorem on page 488, whose proof is left as Question 2.

Lesson 8-3

Objectives

- **A** Express complex numbers in binomial, rectangular, polar and trigonometric form.
- **B** Perform operations with complex numbers.
- **F** Prove or verify properties of complex numbers.
- **I** Graph complex numbers and verify the Geometric Addition and Geometric Multiplication Theorems.

Resources

From the ***Teacher's Resource File***

- Lesson Master 8-3
- Answer Master 8-3
- Teaching Aids
  - 70 Warm-up
  - 75 Example 1 and the Geometric Addition Theorem
  - 76 The Geometric Multiplication Theorem

Additional Resources

- Visuals for Teaching Aids 70, 75, 76
- Exploration 8-3

Teaching Lesson 8-3

Warm-up

Solve each of the equations for the complex number z.

1. $4 + 5i + z = -3 - 8i$ **$-7 - 13i$**

2. $\frac{z}{9 + 6i} = 1 - 7i$ **$51 - 57i$**

Lesson 8-3 Overview

Broad Goals This lesson provides visual representations of addition and multiplication of complex numbers.

Perspective The addition of complex numbers, following the rule $(a, b) + (c, d) = (a + c, b + d)$, is isomorphic to vector addition, and so there is a parallelogram geometric representation identical to that for vectors. We call this the Geometric Addition Theorem. The less-known Geometric Theorem shows the beauty of multiplication of complex numbers in polar coordinates: $[r, \theta] \cdot [s, \phi] = [rs, \theta + \phi]$.

The Geometric Addition and Multiplication Theorems have interpretations in the language of geometric transformations. Adding a complex number (a, b) translates the graph of complex numbers a units to the right and b units up. Multiplying by a complex number $[r, \theta]$ performs the composite of a size change of magnitude r and a rotation of θ.The Geometric Multiplication Theorem is useful for understanding the geometry of powers and roots in Lessons 8-6 and 8-7.

The connection between the polar and rectangular forms of complex numbers is given by the trigonometric form, a binomial form $a + bi$ in which both a and b are written in terms of r and θ.

Notes on Reading

Science Connection By this time of the year, students with experience in physics have almost certainly done vector addition both algebraically and geometrically with parallelograms. Note that complex number addition has the same structure; it is isomorphic.

Point out that it is usually easiest to multiply and divide complex numbers if they are in polar form, a little harder it they are in trigonometric form only because there is more to write, and relatively hardest if they are in $a + bi$ form. This may bother students, for they were taught $a + bi$ form first. However, $a + bi$ form is easiest for addition and subtraction and ties in better with work on polynomials.

Teaching Aid 75 is given with the statement of the Geometric Addition Theorem and the drawing of **Example 1. Teaching Aid 76** contains the various statements of the Geometric Multiplication Theorem and the example that follows it.

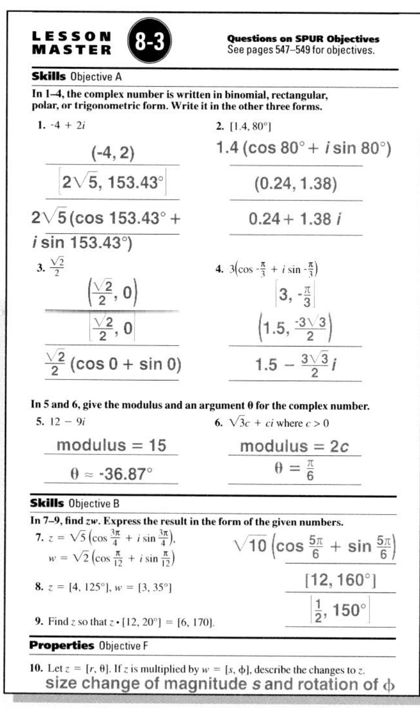

LESSON MASTER 8-3 Questions on SPUR Objectives

See pages 547–549 for objectives.

Skills Objective A

In 1–4, the complex number is written in binomial, rectangular, polar, or trigonometric form. Write it in the other three forms.

1. $-4 + 2i$

   $(-4, 2)$

   $[2\sqrt{5}, 153.43°]$

   $2\sqrt{5}(\cos 153.43° + i \sin 153.43°)$

2. $[1.4, 80°]$

   $1.4(\cos 80° + i \sin 80°)$

   $(0.24, 1.38)$

   $0.24 + 1.38i$

3. $\frac{\sqrt{2}}{2}$

   $\left(\frac{\sqrt{2}}{2}, 0\right)$

   $\left[\frac{\sqrt{2}}{2}, 0\right]$

   $\frac{\sqrt{2}}{2}(\cos 0 + \sin 0)$

4. $3\left(\cos -\frac{\pi}{3} + i \sin -\frac{\pi}{3}\right)$

   $\left[3, -\frac{\pi}{3}\right]$

   $\left(1.5, \frac{-3\sqrt{3}}{2}\right)$

   $1.5 - \frac{3\sqrt{3}}{2}i$

In 5 and 6, give the modulus and an argument θ for the complex number.

5. $12 - 9i$

   modulus = 15

   $\theta \approx -36.87°$

6. $\sqrt{3}c + ci$ where $c > 0$

   modulus = $2c$

   $\theta = \frac{\pi}{6}$

Skills Objective B

In 7–9, find zw. Express the result in the form of the given numbers.

7. $z = \sqrt{5}\left(\cos \frac{3\pi}{4} + i \sin \frac{3\pi}{4}\right)$, $w = \sqrt{2}\left(\cos \frac{\pi}{12} + i \sin \frac{\pi}{12}\right)$

   $\sqrt{10}\left(\cos \frac{5\pi}{6} + \sin \frac{5\pi}{6}\right)$

8. $z = [4, 125°]$, $w = [3, 35°]$

   $[12, 160°]$

9. Find z so that $z \cdot [12, 20°] = [6, 170]$.

   $\left[\frac{1}{2}, 150°\right]$

Properties Objective F

10. Let $z = [r, \theta]$. If z is multiplied by $w = [s, \phi]$, describe the changes to z.

    size change of magnitude s and rotation of ϕ

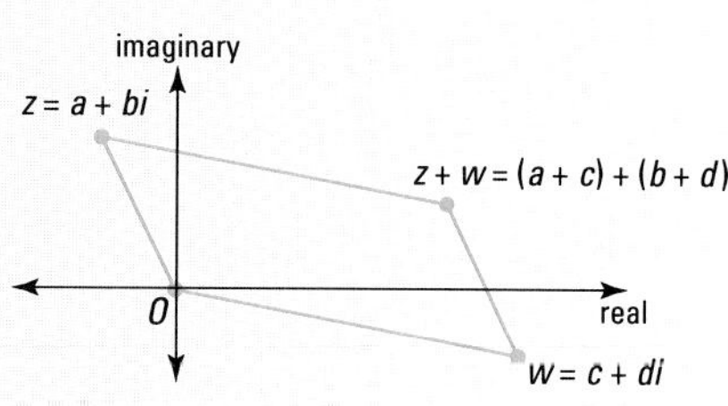

Geometric Addition Theorem
Let $z = a + bi$ and $w = c + di$ be two complex numbers that are not collinear with (0, 0). Then the point representing $z + w$ is the fourth vertex of a parallelogram with consecutive vertices $z = a + bi$, 0, and $w = c + di$.

Row, Row, Row Your Kayak... *The velocity of the stream and the force of the paddler are vectors that combine to determine the velocity of the kayak.*

If you have studied vectors in a science class or a previous mathematics course, you may recognize that the rules for adding complex numbers are the same as those for vectors. In this book, vectors are studied in Chapter 12.

Another geometric interpretation of addition of complex numbers uses the language of transformations. Adding a complex number $z = (a, b)$ to a complex number w applies the translation a units horizontally and b units vertically to w.

Polar Form of a Complex Number

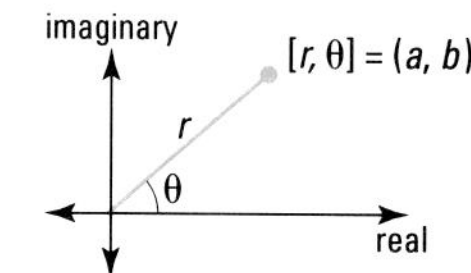

Multiplication of complex numbers can also be interpreted geometrically, but it is easier with polar coordinates. Let $[r, \theta]$ with $r \geq 0$ be the polar coordinates for (a, b) or $a + bi$. Then, from Lesson 8-2 you know that

$$r = \sqrt{a^2 + b^2} \quad \text{and} \quad \tan \theta = \frac{b}{a}.$$

Since the period of the tangent function is π, there are always two values of θ between 0 and 2π that satisfy $\tan \theta = \frac{b}{a}$. The correct value is obtained by examining the quadrant in which (a, b) is located.

Example 2

Find the polar coordinates $[r, \theta]$ of $2 - 3i$ with $r \geq 0$ and $0 \leq \theta \leq 2\pi$.

Solution

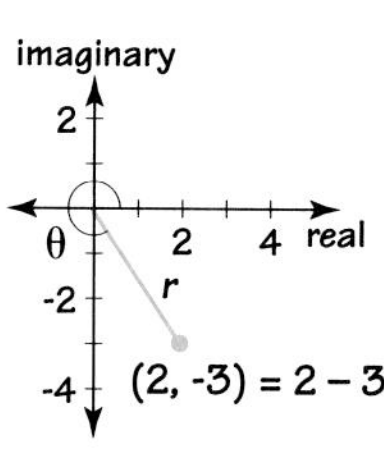

(2, -3) is a point in the 4th quadrant.

$$r = \sqrt{2^2 + (-3)^2} = \sqrt{13}$$

$\tan \theta = \frac{-3}{2} = -1.5$, so $\theta \approx -.983$ and a polar coordinate representation is $[\sqrt{13}\ -.983]$. But this value of θ is not between 0 and 2π. Add 2π to get $\theta \approx -.983 + 2\pi \approx 5.3$. Thus, approximate polar coordinates for $2 - 3i$ are $[\sqrt{13}, 5.3]$.

488

Optional Activities

Activity 1 Technology Connection
Materials: *Explorations* software

Students may use *Exploration 8-3, Addition of Complex Numbers,* as an alternative to **Example 1** in Lesson 8-3. Students can designate two points in the complex plane. They can observe the algebraic and graphical results of adding their chosen points. The slope of each side of the parallelogram created by connecting the points is also computed.

Activity 2 Refer students to **Questions 16–17.** Ask them what complex number z they should use and what operation they should perform to produce each transformation.

1. rotation of $\triangle ABC$ by $\frac{\pi}{3}$
   [Multiply each vertex by $[1, \frac{\pi}{3}] = \frac{1}{2} + \frac{3}{2}i$.]
2. scale change of $\triangle ABC$ by a factor of 5
   [Multiply each vertex by $[5, 0] = 5$.]

For any complex number z, the distance from z to the origin is called the **absolute value** or **modulus** of z, and is written $|z|$. If $z = [r, \theta]$, then $|z| = |r|$. This generalizes the idea of absolute value of real numbers. If $z = a + bi$, then $|z| = \sqrt{a^2 + b^2}$.

When $z = [r, \theta]$ and $r > 0$, the form $[r, \theta]$ is called a **polar form** of z, and θ is called an **argument** of z. A complex number has infinitely many polar forms, but if $z = [r_1, \theta_1] = [r_2, \theta_2]$, with $r_1 > 0$ and $r_2 > 0$, then $|z| = r_1 = r_2$ and $\theta_1 = \theta_2 \pmod{2\pi}$. That is, the arguments θ_1 and θ_2 differ by a multiple of 2π.

Point out that the proof of the Geometric Multiplication Theorem begins with the rectangular representation of complex numbers, converts the numbers to trigonometric form, and then elegantly expresses the final result in rectangular form. Each form has advantages and disadvantages in terms of calculations and/or proofs. Note that recognizing the expanded forms of sin $(\theta + \phi)$ and cos $(\theta + \phi)$ is crucial in completing the proofs. This may surprise students, and it exemplifies the unity of mathematics. Hidden and proved in this proof is a theorem for multiplying complex numbers written in trigonometric form: $[r(\cos\theta + i\sin\theta)] \cdot [s(\cos\phi + i\sin\phi)] = rs[\cos(\theta + \phi) + i\sin(\theta + \phi)]$. Emphasize: To multiply two complex numbers, multiply their absolute values and add their arguments.

Trigonometric Form of a Complex Number

In Lesson 8-2, you saw conversion from polar coordinates to rectangular coordinates.

If $\quad (a, b) = [r, \theta]$, then $a = r\cos\theta$ and $b = r\sin\theta$.

Substituting, $\quad a + bi = r\cos\theta + (r\sin\theta)i$

$\quad = r(\cos\theta + i\sin\theta)$.

If $r > 0$, then the expression $r(\cos\theta + i\sin\theta)$ is called a **trigonometric form of the complex number**. Like polar coordinates, the trigonometric form denotes a complex number in terms of its absolute value and argument. But unlike polar coordinates, a complex number in trigonometric form is still in $a + bi$ form. This makes the trigonometric form quite useful.

Example 3

Write the complex number $-2 - 2\sqrt{3}\,i$ in trigonometric form.

Solution

First find r and θ.

$$r = \sqrt{(-2)^2 + (-2\sqrt{3})^2} = \sqrt{4 + 12} = 4$$

$$\tan\theta = \left(\frac{-2\sqrt{3}}{-2}\right) = \sqrt{3}$$

Since $-2 - 2\sqrt{3}\,i$ is in the 3rd quadrant,

$$\theta = \frac{\pi}{3} + \pi = \frac{4\pi}{3}.$$

Therefore, $-2 - 2\sqrt{3}\,i = 4\left(\cos\frac{4\pi}{3} + i\sin\frac{4\pi}{3}\right)$.

imaginary
real
$(-2, -2\sqrt{3})$
4

The trigonometric form of a complex number is not unique. You can add $2\pi n$ to the argument for any integer n. So,

$$\forall \text{ integers } n,\ -2 - 2\sqrt{3}\,i = 4\left(\cos\left(\frac{4\pi}{3} + 2\pi n\right) + i\sin\left(\frac{4\pi}{3} + 2\pi n\right)\right).$$

You have now seen four ways of writing complex numbers.

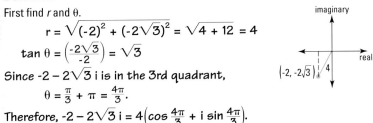

form:	binomial		rectangular		polar		trigonometric
	$a + bi$	=	(a, b)	=	$[r, \theta]$	=	$r(\cos\theta + i\sin\theta)$
	real part a		imaginary part b		absolute value $\lvert r\rvert$		argument $\theta \pm 2\pi n$

Adapting to Individual Needs

Extra Help

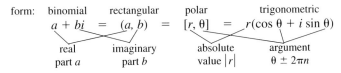

Some students might have difficulty determining θ when converting from the rectangular form to the trigonometric form of a complex number. Emphasize that it is important first to determine in which quadrant the graph of the complex number lies.

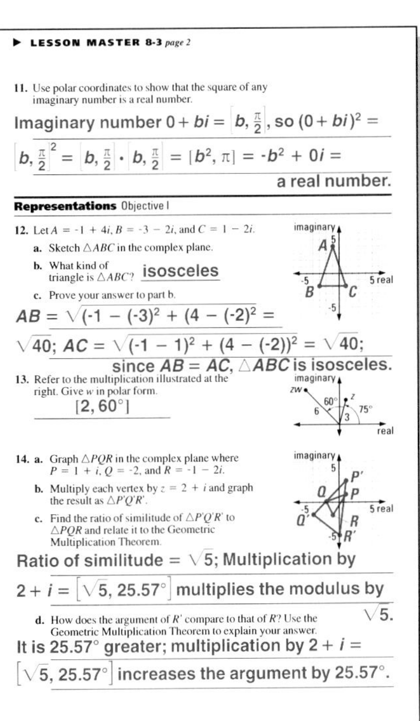

▶ **LESSON MASTER 8-3** *page 2*

11. Use polar coordinates to show that the square of any imaginary number is a real number.

Imaginary number $0 + bi = \left[b, \frac{\pi}{2}\right]$, so $(0 + bi)^2 = \left[b, \frac{\pi}{2}\right]^2 = \left[b, \frac{\pi}{2}\right] \cdot \left[b, \frac{\pi}{2}\right] = [b^2, \pi] = -b^2 + 0i =$ a real number.

Representations Objective I

12. Let $A = -1 + 4i$, $B = -3 - 2i$, and $C = 1 - 2i$.
   a. Sketch $\triangle ABC$ in the complex plane.
   b. What kind of triangle is $\triangle ABC$? isosceles
   c. Prove your answer to part b.

$AB = \sqrt{(-1 - (-3)^2 + (4 - (-2)^2} = \sqrt{40}$; $AC = \sqrt{(-1 - 1)^2 + (4 - (-2))^2} = \sqrt{40}$; since $AB = AC$, $\triangle ABC$ is isosceles.

13. Refer to the multiplication illustrated at the right. Give w in polar form.
   $[2, 60°]$

14. a. Graph $\triangle PQR$ in the complex plane where $P = 1 + i$, $Q = -2$, and $R = -1 - 2i$.
   b. Multiply each vertex by $z = 2 + i$ and graph the result as $\triangle P'Q'R'$.
   c. Find the ratio of similitude of $\triangle P'Q'R'$ to $\triangle PQR$ and relate it to the Geometric Multiplication Theorem.

Ratio of similitude $= \sqrt{5}$; Multiplication by $2 + i = [\sqrt{5}, 25.57°]$ multiplies the modulus by $\sqrt{5}$.

   d. How does the argument of R' compare to that of R? Use the Geometric Multiplication Theorem to explain your answer.

It is 25.57° greater; multiplication by $2 + i = [\sqrt{5}, 25.57°]$ increases the argument by 25.57°.

By the end of this lesson, students will have seen four ways of writing complex numbers: $a + bi$ binomial form; rectangular coordinate form (a, b); trigonometric form $r(\cos \theta + i \sin \theta)$; and polar form $[r, \theta]$. In the last two forms, $r \geq 0$ (so that later we can obtain nth roots without any confusion). It is a good idea to summarize these forms and their names at this point. (A fifth common form is the exponential form $re^{i\theta}$, but this form is not discussed in this book.)

Additional Examples

1. If $z = -2 + 3i$ and $w = 5 - 2i$, show that the graphs of z, 0, w, and $z + w$ are vertices of a parallelogram.
   Let $P = z + w = (3, 1)$.
   Now $Z = (-2, 3)$, $O = (0, 0)$, and $W = (5, -2)$.
   Slope of $\overline{OZ} = \frac{3-0}{-2-0} = -\frac{3}{2}$
   Slope of $\overline{WP} = \frac{1--2}{3-5} = -\frac{3}{2}$
   $\therefore \overline{OZ} \parallel \overline{WP}$
   Slope of $\overline{ZP} = \frac{1-3}{3--2} = -\frac{2}{5}$
   Slope of $\overline{OW} = \frac{-2-0}{5-0} = -\frac{2}{5}$
   $\therefore \overline{ZP} \parallel \overline{OW}$
   $\therefore ZOWP$ is a parallelogram.
2. Find the polar coordinates $[r, \theta]$ of $z = -7 - i$ with $r \geq 0$ and $0 \leq \theta \leq 2\pi$. **$[5\sqrt{2}, \pi + \tan^{-1}(\frac{1}{7})] \approx [5\sqrt{2}, 3.283]$**
   If possible, have students check this result with a scientific calculator having polar rectangular conversion built in.
3. Write the complex number $-5\sqrt{3} + 5i$ in trigonometric form. **$10(\cos \frac{5\pi}{6} + i \sin \frac{5\pi}{6})$**

A Geometric Picture of Multiplication

The trigonometric form of complex numbers makes it possible to deduce the following geometric interpretation of multiplication of complex numbers.

Geometric Multiplication Theorem
Let z and w be complex numbers. If $z = [r, \theta]$ and $w = [s, \phi]$, then $zw = [rs, \theta + \phi]$. That is, multiplying a complex number z by $[s, \phi]$ applies to z the composite of a size change of magnitude s and a rotation of ϕ about the origin.

Proof
Since $z = [r, \theta]$ and $w = [s, \phi]$, in trigonometric form $z = r(\cos \theta + i \sin \theta)$ and $w = s(\cos \phi + i \sin \phi)$. Then

$$\begin{aligned} z \cdot w &= r(\cos \theta + i \sin \theta) \cdot s(\cos \phi + i \sin \phi) \\ &= rs[(\cos \theta \cos \phi - \sin \theta \sin \phi) + i(\cos \theta \sin \phi + \sin \theta \cos \phi)]. \end{aligned}$$

Now apply the trigonometric identities for $\sin(\theta + \phi)$ and $\cos(\theta + \phi)$.

$$z \cdot w = rs[\cos(\theta + \phi) + i \sin(\theta + \phi)]$$

Now translate back into polar form.

$$z \cdot w = [rs, \theta + \phi]$$

For example, if $z = [4, 132°]$ and $w = [3, 95°]$, then the polar form of the product $z \cdot w$ is $[4 \cdot 3, 132° + 95°] = [12, 227°]$.

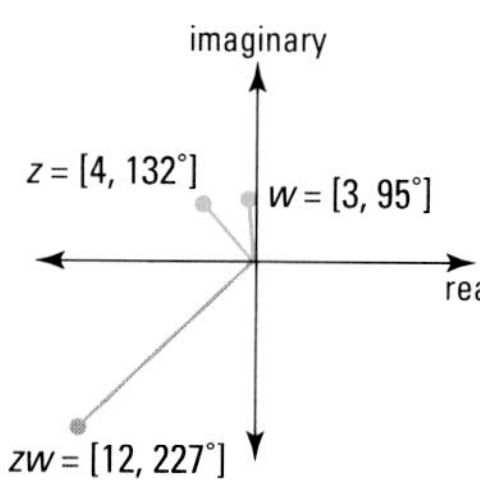

In general, multiplication of $z = [r, \theta]$ by $w = [s, \phi]$

(1) produces a size change on z of magnitude s, because the absolute value of z is r and the absolute of the product is rs, and

(2) rotates z through ϕ units, because an argument of z is θ and an argument of the product is $\theta + \phi$.

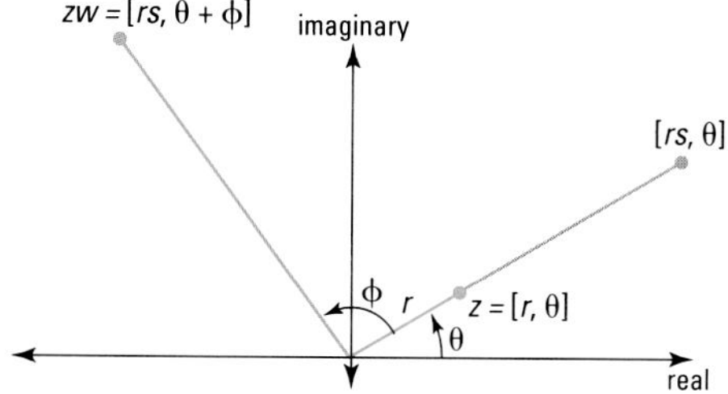

Adapting to Individual Needs

Challenge
Have students answer the following.
1. If $z = [r, \theta]$, give the polar and trigonometric forms of $\overline{z}$. [Polar: $\overline{z} = [r, -\theta]$; trigonometric: $\overline{z} = r(\cos \theta - i \sin \theta)$]
2. Describe, geometrically, $r \cdot z$, where r is a real number and z is a complex number. [All points on the line through (0, 0) and z.]
3. Let $z = a + bi$, where $a \neq 0$ and $b \neq 0$.
   a. Describe the polygon whose vertices are z, $\overline{z}$, $-z$, and $-\overline{z}$. [vertices of a rectangle]
   b. Square each of the above 4 numbers and describe the graphs of their squares. [only 2 points]
   c. Does $z^2 = (\overline{z})^2$? [No]
   d. Are z^2 and $(\overline{z})^2$ conjugates? [Yes]

3a) $\left[3\sqrt{2}, \frac{3\pi}{4}\right]$
b) $3\sqrt{2} \cdot \left(\cos\frac{3\pi}{4} + i\sin\frac{3\pi}{4}\right)$

4a) $\left[\frac{\sqrt{3}}{3}, 30°\right]$
b) $\frac{\sqrt{3}}{3}(\cos 30° + i\sin 30°)$

5a) $\approx [5, 127°]$
b) $\approx 5(\cos 127° + i\sin 127°)$

6)

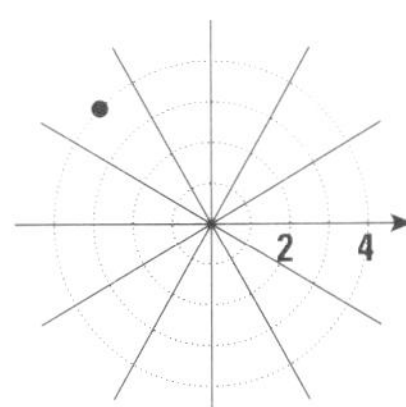

7)

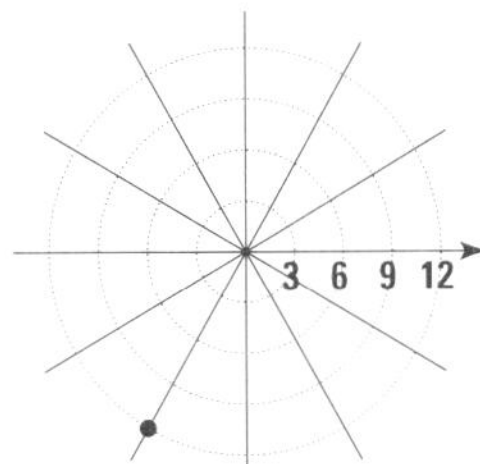

8)

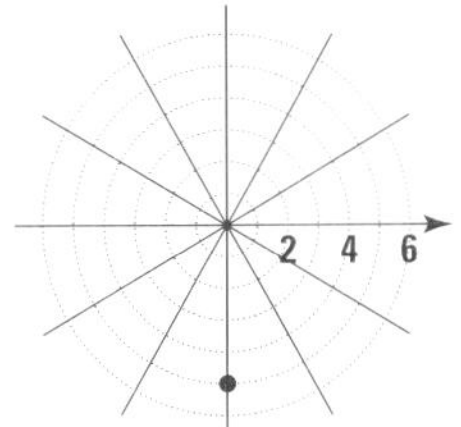

QUESTIONS

Covering the Reading

1. Verify the Geometric Addition Theorem for the complex numbers $z = 7 + 3i$ and $w = 4 - 9i$. **See margin.**

2. Prove the Geometric Addition Theorem for the complex numbers $z = a + bi$ and $w = c + di$, when $a \neq 0$ and $c \neq 0$. **See margin.**

In 3–5, a complex number in $a + bi$ form is given. **a.** Write the number in polar form. **b.** Write the number in trigonometric form. **3–5) See left.**

3. $-3 + 3i$
4. $\frac{1}{2} + \frac{1}{2\sqrt{3}}i$
5. $-3 + 4i$

In 6–8, graph the number on the same complex plane. **See left.**

6. $4\left(\cos\frac{3\pi}{4} + i\sin\frac{3\pi}{4}\right)$

7. $12\left(\cos\left(-\frac{2\pi}{3}\right) + i\sin\left(-\frac{2\pi}{3}\right)\right)$

8. $5\left(\cos\frac{3\pi}{2} + i\sin\frac{3\pi}{2}\right)$

10) $50\left(\cos\frac{7\pi}{6} + i\sin\frac{7\pi}{6}\right)$

In 9–11, find zw. Express results in the form of the given numbers.

9. $z = [3, 150°]$ $w = [2, 60°]$ **[6, 210°]**

10. $z = 10\left(\cos\frac{11\pi}{12} + i\sin\frac{11\pi}{12}\right)$ $w = 5\left(\cos\frac{\pi}{4} + i\sin\frac{\pi}{4}\right)$ **See above.**

11. $z = 2 + 3i$ $w = -4 + i$ **$-11 - 10i$**

12. Illustrate the multiplication of $z = 3(\cos 65° + i\sin 65°)$ by $w = 5(\cos 40° + i\sin 40°)$ with a diagram showing the appropriate size transformation and rotation. **See margin.**

13. Give the modulus and an argument θ for the imaginary number $-3i$. **modulus: 3, argument: 270°**

Applying the Mathematics

14. Recall this theorem from geometry: If the diagonals of a quadrilateral have the same midpoint, then the quadrilateral is a parallelogram. Use this theorem to provide an alternative proof that *ZOWP* in Example 1 is a parallelogram. **See margin.**

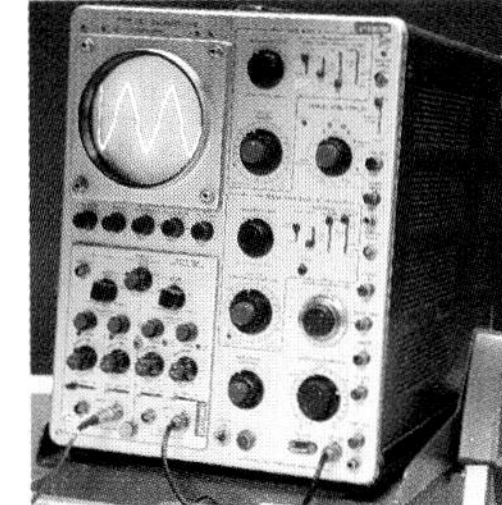

15. The AC circuit in Example 4 of Lesson 8-1 has a current of $w = 1 + 2i$ amps. This can be interpreted as follows. If an oscilloscope were connected to the circuit in order to graph the rate of flow of electrons over time, a sine curve would result. The amplitude of the sine curve would be equal to $|w|$, and the phase shift would be equal to $-\theta$ where θ is the argument of w.
    a. Find $|w|$ and $-\theta$. **$|w| = \sqrt{5}$, $-\theta \approx -63.4°$**
    b. Graph the sine curve with this amplitude and phase shift, and period 2π. **See margin.**

Notes on Questions

Questions 3–5 For a good check, ask students to evaluate the sines and cosines of the trigonometric form and then simplify. The result should be the $a + bi$ form. You might also ask students to put these in rectangular form. And then, put all the answers in a table with each row representing one of the questions and each column representing one of the forms.

Questions 6–8 These are easiest if students express each in $[r, \theta]$ form.

12.

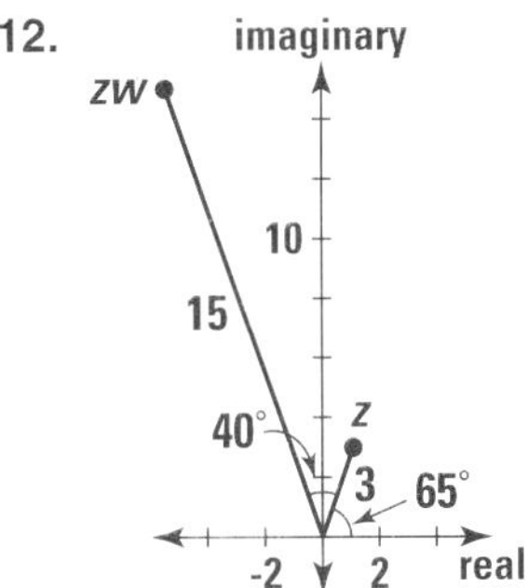

14. The midpoint of $\overline{ZW} = \left(\frac{4+3}{2}, \frac{6+(-1)}{2}\right) = \left(\frac{7}{2}, \frac{5}{2}\right)$.
The midpoint of $\overline{PO} = \left(\frac{7+0}{2}, \frac{5+0}{2}\right) = \left(\frac{7}{2}, \frac{5}{2}\right)$.
Since the diagonals have the same midpoint, *ZOWP* is a parallelogram.

15. b.

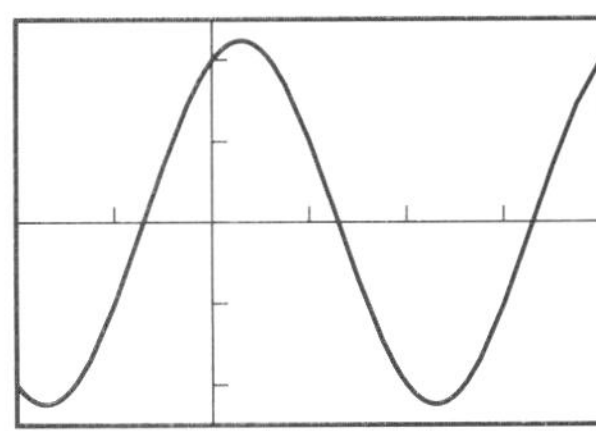

$-\pi \le x \le 2\pi$, x-scale $= \frac{\pi}{2}$
$-2.5 \le y \le 2.5$, y-scale $= 1$

Additional Answers

1. $z = 7 + 3i = (7, 3) = Z$; $O = 0 + 0i = (0, 0) = O$, $w = 4 - 9i = (4, -9) = W$; $z + w = 11 - 6i = (11, -6) = P$; slope of $\overline{OZ} = \frac{3-0}{7-0} = \frac{3}{7}$; slope of $\overline{WP} = \frac{-6-(-9)}{11-4} = \frac{3}{7}$; so $\overline{OZ} // \overline{WP}$; slope of $\overline{ZP} = \frac{-6-3}{11-7} = -\frac{9}{4}$; slope of $\overline{OW} = \frac{-9-0}{4-0} = -\frac{9}{4}$; and so $\overline{ZP} // \overline{OW}$. Therefore, the figure is a parallelogram.

2. $z = a + bi = (a, b) = Z$; $O = 0 + 0i = (0, 0) = O$; $w = c + di = (c, d) = W$; $z + w = (a + c) + (b + d)i = (a + c, b + d) = P$. The slope of $\overline{OZ} = \frac{b-0}{a-0} = \frac{b}{a}$; slope of $\overline{WP} = \frac{b+d-d}{a+c-c} = \frac{b}{a}$, and so $\overline{OZ} // \overline{WP}$. The slope of $\overline{ZP} = \frac{b+d-b}{a+c-a} = \frac{d}{c}$; slope of $\overline{OW} = \frac{d-0}{c-0} = \frac{d}{c}$, and so $\overline{ZP} // \overline{OW}$. Therefore, the figure is a parallelogram.

Notes on Questions

Question 16 Be sure to make connections between this question and the Geometric Multiplication Theorem. Have students draw an accurate diagram and measure and compare arguments and moduli of points and their images. Ask what in the problem is equal to the ratio of similitude and why this is so.

Question 21 Ask students for a geometric interpretation of this result. [If the graph of the complex number z is not on the real axis, then z, 0, the conjugate of z, and the sum of z and its conjugate are four vertices of a rhombus whose line of symmetry is the real axis. If the graph of z is on the real axis—that is, if z is real—then it equals its conjugate and the sum is graphed on the real axis.]

Question 22 Error Alert Students who answer $\frac{5\pi}{8}$ have neglected to consider the range of the inverse sine function, that is, the domain of the restricted sine function.

Follow-up for Lesson 8-3

Practice

For more questions on SPUR Objectives, use **Lesson Master 8-3** (shown on pages 488–489).

Assessment

Oral Communication Have students explain their work in **Questions 9–11** and then comment on the relative difficulty of the three exercises. [Students compare the methods of multiplying complex numbers in rectangular, trigonometric, and polar forms.]

Extension

In **Questions 25–26,** invite students to prove their theorems. Graphs should accompany the proofs.

Project Update Project 5, *Matrix Representations of Complex Numbers,* and Project 8, *Applications of Complex Numbers,* on pages 542–543, relate to the content of this lesson.

16b) $AB = \sqrt{5}$, $BC = 2$, and $AC = \sqrt{17}$ while $A'B' = 5$, $B'C' = \sqrt{20}$, and $A'C' = \sqrt{85}$. Then $\frac{A'C'}{AC} = \frac{\sqrt{85}}{\sqrt{17}} = \sqrt{5}$, $\frac{A'B'}{AB} = \frac{5}{\sqrt{5}} = \sqrt{5}$, and $\frac{B'C'}{BC} = \frac{\sqrt{20}}{2} = \sqrt{5}$. So the triangles are similar by the SSS Similarity Theorem.

17a) $E' = 5 + i$, $F' = 1 + 4i$, $G' = 3 + 6i$. $EF = 5$, $EG = \sqrt{29}$, $FG = 2\sqrt{2}$, while $E'F' = 5$, $E'G' = \sqrt{29}$, and $F'G' = 2\sqrt{2}$. So $\triangle EFG \cong \triangle E'F'G'$ by the SSS Congruence Theorem.

18a) $|12 - 15i| = \sqrt{12^2 + (-15)^2} = \sqrt{144 + 225} = \sqrt{369} = 3\sqrt{41}$, and $3|4 - 5i| = 3\sqrt{4^2 + (-5)^2} = 3\sqrt{16 + 25} = 3\sqrt{41}$.

b) Proof: $|cz| = |ca + cbi| = \sqrt{c^2a^2 + c^2b^2} = \sqrt{c^2(a^2 + b^2)} = |c|\sqrt{a^2 + b^2} = |c||a + bi| = |c||z|$

16. Consider the triangle in the complex plane with vertices $A = 3 + i$, $B = 2 - i$ and $C = 2 - 3i$.

a. Multiply each of the vertices by $z = 1 + 2i$ to obtain points A', B', and C'. $A' = 1 + 7i$, $B' = 4 + 3i$, $C' = 8 + i$

b. Show that the triangles ABC and $A'B'C'$ are similar. See left.

c. What is the ratio of similitude? $\sqrt{5}$

17. Consider the triangle in the complex plane with vertices at $E = 4$, $F = 3i$, and $G = 2 + 5i$. Add the complex number $1 + i$ to each of the vertices E, F, and G to obtain points E', F', and G'.

a. Show that $\triangle E'F'G'$ is congruent to $\triangle EFG$. (Hint: Find lengths of corresponding sides.) See left.

b. Describe the geometric transformation which maps $\triangle EFG$ onto $\triangle E'F'G'$. $T_{1,1}$

18. a. Show that $|12 - 15i| = 3\,|4 - 5i|$. See left.

b. Generalize part **a** and prove your generalization. $\forall$ real numbers c and complex numbers $z = a + bi$, $|cz| = |c| \cdot |z|$. See left for proof.

Review

19. a. Graph all solutions to the equation $r = 4$ on a polar grid. See margin.

b. What equation in x and y do all such solutions satisfy? *(Lesson 8-2)* $x^2 + y^2 = 16$

20. Simplify $(18 - \sqrt{-100}) + (-4 + 3\sqrt{-36})$. *(Lesson 8-1)* $14 + 8i$

21. Prove or disprove: *For all complex numbers, the sum of the number and its complex conjugate is a real number.* *(Lesson 8-1)* See margin.

22. Find the exact value of $\sin^{-1}(\sin \frac{5\pi}{8})$. *(Lesson 6-7)* $\frac{3\pi}{8}$

23. Given the graph at right.

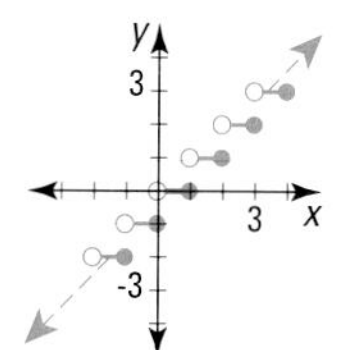

a. Does the graph represent a function? Yes

b. If so, identify its domain and range. If not, why not? *(Lessons 2-1, 2-2)* domain: the set of real numbers; range: the set of integers

24. Complete the square to find the center and radius of the circle with equation $x^2 + 2x + y^2 - 4y = 4$. *(Previous course)* center = (-1, 2), radius = 3

Exploration

25. What could be a Geometric Subtraction Theorem? See below.

26. What could be a Geometric Division Theorem? See margin.

25) Let $z = a + bi$ and $w = c + di$ be two complex numbers that are not collinear with the origin. Then the point representing $z - w$ is the fourth vertex of a parallelogram with consecutive vertices $z = a + bi$, 0, and $w = c + di$.

Additional Answers

19. a.

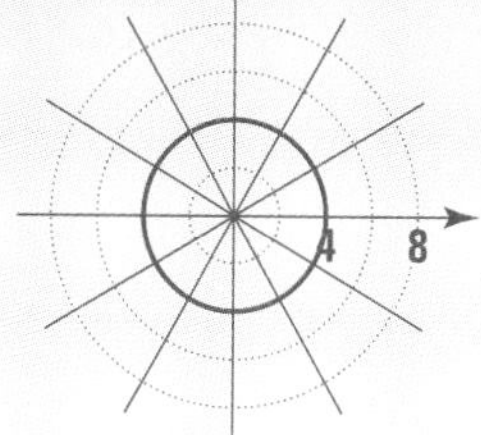

21, 26. See Additional Answers at the back of this book.

Setting Up Lesson 8-4

Discuss **Question 24** to bring back the idea of completing the square. This process is used in **Example 2** of Lesson 8-4.

LESSON

8-4 Polar Equations and Their Graphs

In the last lesson, you saw a connection between complex numbers and polar coordinates, but polar coordinates have a beautiful geometry on their own.

Polar Equations for Circles

In Lesson 8-2, you saw that circles centered at the origin have very simple equations in polar coordinates. Some other circles also have simple polar equations, as Examples 1 and 2 show.

Example 1

Sketch the graph of the set of points $[r, \theta]$ which satisfy the polar equation $r = 2 \sin \theta$.

Solution

Construct a table of ordered pairs $[r, \theta]$ that satisfy the equation. Then plot these points on a polar grid and connect successive points with a smooth curve.

θ	$r = 2 \sin \theta$
0	0
$\pi/6$	1
$\pi/4$	$\sqrt{2}$
$\pi/3$	$\sqrt{3}$
$\pi/2$	2
$2\pi/3$	$\sqrt{3}$
$3\pi/4$	$\sqrt{2}$
$5\pi/6$	1
π	0
$7\pi/6$	-1
$5\pi/4$	$-\sqrt{2}$
$4\pi/3$	$-\sqrt{3}$
$3\pi/2$	-2
$5\pi/3$	$-\sqrt{3}$
$7\pi/4$	$-\sqrt{2}$
$11\pi/6$	-1
2π	0

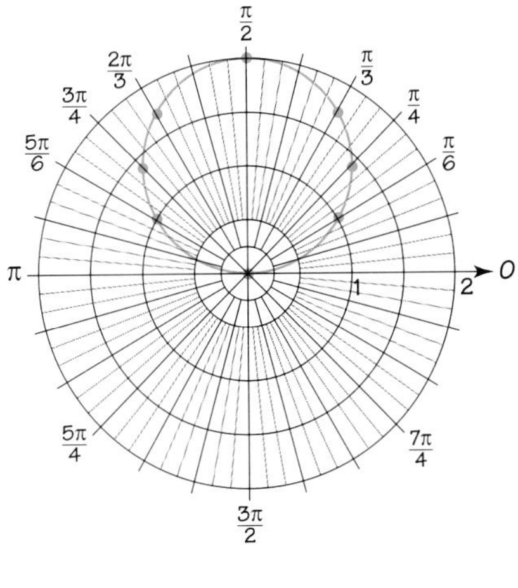

Notice that when $\pi < \theta < 2\pi$, r is negative and so these points coincide with points plotted when $0 \le \theta \le \pi$. This indicates it would have been sufficient to plot points $[r, \theta]$ when $0 \le \theta \le \pi$. Also, since the sine function has period 2π, no other values of θ need be considered.

The graph in Example 1 can be proved to be a circle by applying the conversion formulas between rectangular and polar coordinates.

Lesson 8-4

Objectives

J Sketch graphs of polar equations.

Resources

From the ***Teacher's Resource File***
- Lesson Master 8-4
- Answer Master 8-4
- Assessment Sourcebook: Quiz for Lessons 8-1 through 8-4
- Teaching Aids
  70 Warm-up
  77 Example 3
  78 Additional Examples

Additional Resources
- Visuals for Teaching Aids 70, 77, 78
- Exploration 8-4

Teaching Lesson 8-4

Warm-up

Let G_1 be the graph of $y = \sin x$, G_2 be the graph of $y = 2 \sin x$, G_3 be the graph of $y = 2 + \sin x$, and G_4 be the graph of $y = \sin 2x$. Describe how G_2, G_3, and G_4 are related to G_1. **G_2 is the image of G_1 under a vertical stretch of magnitude 2; G_3 is the image of G_1 under a vertical translation of 2 units, and G_4 is the image of G_1 under a horizontal scale change of magnitude $\frac{1}{2}$.**

Lesson 8-4 Overview

Broad Goals This is the first of two lessons on graphs of polar equations: any graph of a set of polar coordinate ordered pairs $[r, \theta]$ satisfying an equation in r and θ.

Perspective Two methods are given here for sketching graphs of polar equations. The first method is to use a table of values, as students have done many times for equations in x and y. The second method is to graph the *rectangular* coordinates (r, θ) first, and use the rectangular graph to sketch the polar graph. The latter method is especially useful if an automatic grapher is not available or does not produce polar graphs easily. When students are already familiar with the appearance of rectangular graphs of equations such as $r = \sin \theta$, $r = \cos \theta + 1$, $r = \sin 3\theta$, and $r = \theta$, this method can be used to sketch polar graphs by hand almost as quickly (although not as accurately) as they can be plotted on an automatic grapher.

Some figures have rather simple equations in either rectangular or polar coordinates. For instance, the polar equation $r = 2 \sin \theta$ has the same graph as the rectangular equation $x^2 + (y - 1)^2 = 1$. But even a simple change in the polar equation to $r = 1 + 2 \sin \theta$ leads to a curve (a cardioid) whose equation in rectangular coordinates is quite complicated.

(Overview continues on page 494.)

Notes on Reading

Sketching the polar graph of an equation $r = f(\theta)$ by constructing a table of values and then plotting the points listed in the table, as is done in **Example 1,** is relatively easy for students because this procedure is essentially the same as the one that they learned in beginning algebra for graphing functions in rectangular coordinates. The second method in this lesson, using the graph of the rectangular equation to get the polar graph, takes advantage of students knowledge of rectangular graphs.

Some students may notice a pattern in the right column of the table on page 493: $\sqrt{0}, \sqrt{1}, \sqrt{2}, \sqrt{3}, \sqrt{4}$. This is just happenstance!

Students may have difficulty plotting those points for which $r < 0$. To help, use a transparent ruler on **Teaching Aid 77.** To plot the point $[-\sqrt{2}, \frac{5\pi}{4}]$, place the ruler along the $\theta = \frac{5\pi}{4}$ ray. The point will be $\sqrt{2} \approx 1.4$ from the origin on the ray opposite $\theta = \frac{5\pi}{4}$. The ruler will locate this ray.

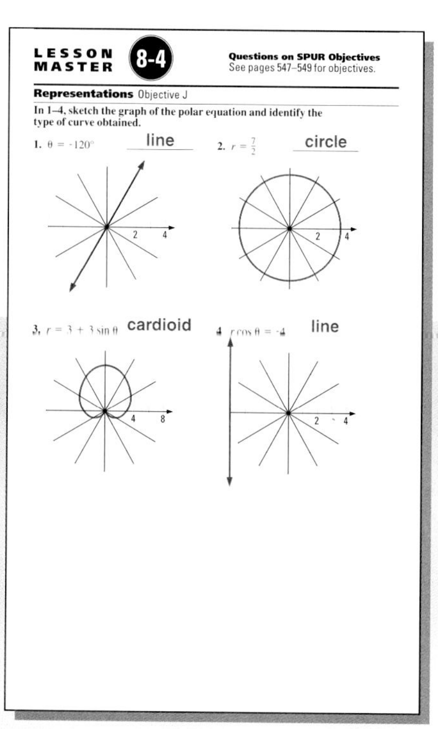
LESSON MASTER 8-4 Questions on SPUR Objectives
See pages 547–549 for objectives.

Representations Objective J

In 1–4, sketch the graph of the polar equation and identify the type of curve obtained.

1. $\theta = -120°$ line
2. $r = \frac{7}{2}$ circle
3. $r = 3 + 3\sin\theta$ cardioid
4. $r\cos\theta = -4$ line

Example 2

Prove that the graph of $r = 2 \sin \theta$ is a circle.

Solution

The idea is to convert the polar equation into a rectangular equation whose graph is known. There are three conversion formulas:

$$r^2 = x^2 + y^2, \qquad y = r\sin\theta, \qquad \text{and} \qquad x = r\cos\theta.$$

The first two of these are useful here. Solving for $\sin\theta$ in the second formula, $\sin\theta = \frac{y}{r}$. Substituting, the given polar equation

$$r = 2\sin\theta$$

becomes $r = 2\frac{y}{r}$.

So $r^2 = 2y$.

Substituting for r^2 using the first conversion formula,

$$x^2 + y^2 = 2y.$$

This is an equation for a circle. To find its center and radius, complete the square.

$$x^2 + y^2 - 2y = 0$$

$$x^2 + (y^2 - 2y + 1) = 1 \quad \text{Complete the square on } y.$$

$$x^2 + (y - 1)^2 = 1$$

This verifies that the polar graph of $r = 2\sin\theta$ is the circle with center (0, 1) and radius 1.

This procedure can be used to show that when a is any nonzero real number, the polar graphs of the equations $r = a\cos\theta$ and $r = a\sin\theta$ are circles.

Polar Equations for Limaçons

Example 3 shows that a seemingly minor change in the polar equation considered in Example 1 can result in a quite different polar graph.

Example 3

Sketch the graph of the polar equation $r = 1 + 2\sin\theta$.

Solution

Construct a table of values for this equation.

θ	0	$\frac{\pi}{4}$	$\frac{\pi}{2}$	$\frac{3\pi}{4}$	π	$\frac{5\pi}{4}$	$\frac{3\pi}{2}$	$\frac{7\pi}{4}$	2π
r	1	$1+\sqrt{2}$	3	$1+\sqrt{2}$	1	$1-\sqrt{2}$	-1	$1-\sqrt{2}$	1

Notice that r is negative when $\theta = \frac{5\pi}{4}$, $\theta = \frac{3\pi}{2}$, and $\theta = \frac{7\pi}{4}$. Also, $r = 0$ for those values of θ for which $1 + 2\sin\theta = 0$; that is, when $\sin\theta = -\frac{1}{2}$. In the interval

Lesson 8-4 Overview, continued

Despite the advantages associated with the fact that a point in the plane has many polar representations, one disadvantage is that extra care is needed when information about polar curves is derived from their equations. For example, the circles given by the polar equations $r = \sin\theta$ and $r = \cos\theta$ intersect at the pole and at point $[\frac{\sqrt{2}}{2}, \frac{\pi}{4}]$. But, only the point $[\frac{\sqrt{2}}{2}, \frac{\pi}{4}]$ satisfies the given polar equations simultaneously.

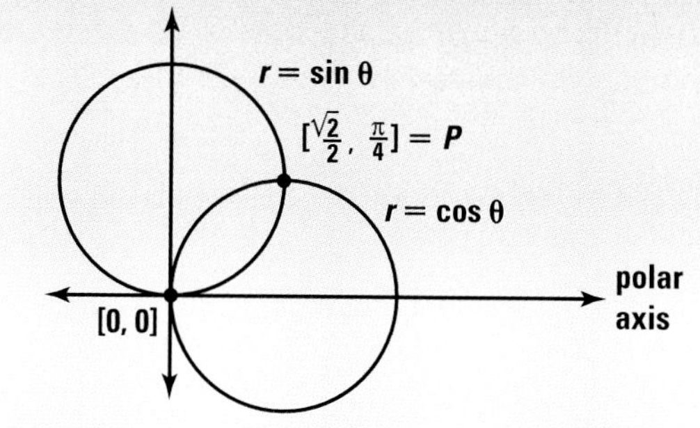

$0 \le \theta \le 2\pi$, $\sin \theta = -\frac{1}{2}$ when $\theta = \frac{7\pi}{6}$ or $\frac{11\pi}{6}$. Thus the value of r is negative throughout the interval $\frac{7\pi}{6} < \theta < \frac{11\pi}{6}$. When successive points in the table are plotted and connected with a smooth curve, a graph like the one below occurs.

❶

$\left[3, \frac{\pi}{2}\right]$ $\left[1+\sqrt{2}, \frac{3\pi}{4}\right]$ $\left[1+\sqrt{2}, \frac{\pi}{4}\right]$ $\left[1-\sqrt{2}, \frac{7\pi}{4}\right]$ $\left[1-\sqrt{2}, \frac{5\pi}{4}\right]$ $\left[-1, \frac{3\pi}{2}\right]$ $[1, 0]$ π $[1, \pi]$ 1 2 3 4 O $\left[0, \frac{7\pi}{6}\right] = \left[0, \frac{11\pi}{6}\right]$

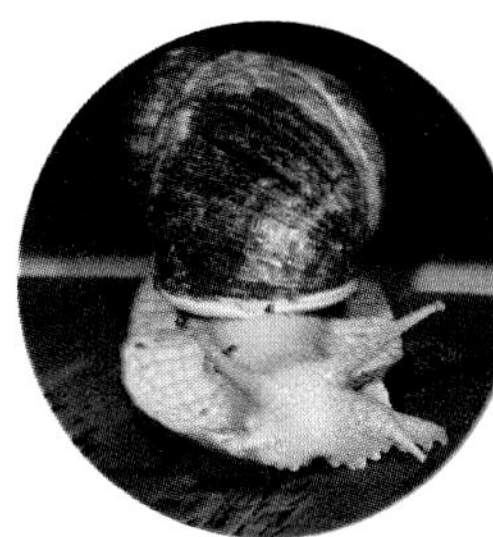

The polar graph of $r = 1 + 2 \sin \theta$ constructed in Example 3 is a type of curve known as a **limaçon** (pronounced lim′ə son′). Limaçon is an Old French word for "snail." The polar graphs of equations of the form

$$r = a + b \cos \theta \quad \text{or}$$
$$r = a + b \sin \theta,$$

where a and b are nonzero real numbers, are all limaçons. To have an inside loop like the limaçon in Example 3, r must be negative for some interval of values of θ; otherwise, the limaçon simply has a "dimple" like the graph of $r = 3 + 2 \sin \theta$ displayed at the right.

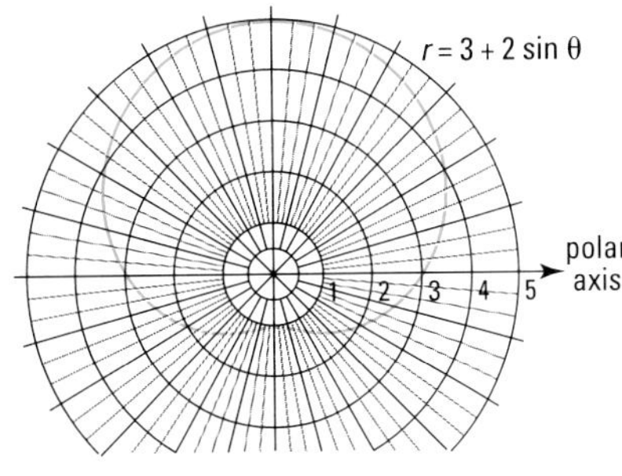

Rectangular and Polar Graphs of the Same Equation

The rectangular graph and the polar graph of a given equation $r = f(\theta)$ are usually strikingly different. For example, while the polar graph of $r = 1 + 2 \sin \theta$ is the limaçon of Example 3, the rectangular graph of this equation is a sine curve of amplitude 2 translated 1 unit up the vertical r-axis.

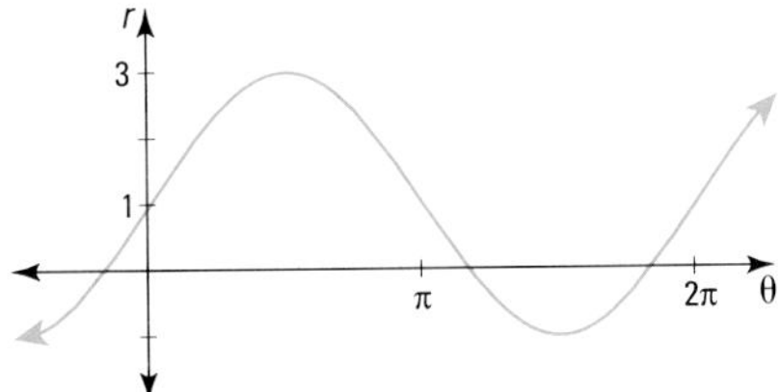

As polar graphs become more complicated, students may lose track of the sequencing of points to be plotted and connected. Suggest that they take the table of ordered pairs used in **Example 1** and divide it into four parts $0 \le \theta < \frac{\pi}{2}$, $\frac{\pi}{2} \le \theta < \pi$, $\pi < \theta \le \frac{3\pi}{2}$, and $\frac{3\pi}{2} < \theta \le 2\pi$. Use a different color pencil for each part of the table and the same color for sketching the graph. Doing this for an easy problem like that of **Example 1** will build a useful technique for succeeding in the more complicated and beautiful problems of the next section.

❶ **Error Alert** Students may think that because the graphs of $r = 2 \sin \theta$ or $r = 1 + 2 \sin \theta$ fail the vertical line test, that these are not functions. They may not realize that the Vertical Line Test is an artifact of the rectangular coordinate system. Functions in polar coordinates are of the form $f: \theta \to r$, and their graphs need not satisfy either a vertical or horizontal line test. Remind them of the definition of function.

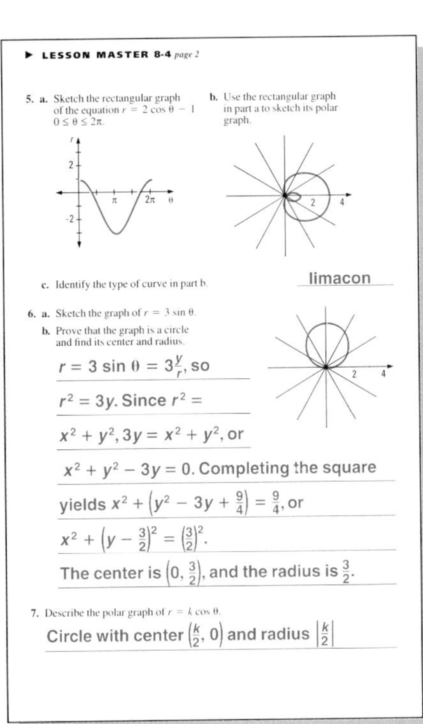

▶ **LESSON MASTER 8-4** *page 2*

5. a. Sketch the rectangular graph of the equation $r = 2 \cos \theta - 1$ $0 \le \theta \le 2\pi$.

   b. Use the rectangular graph in part a to sketch its polar graph.

   c. Identify the type of curve in part b. limacon

6. a. Sketch the graph of $r = 3 \sin \theta$.

   b. Prove that the graph is a circle and find its center and radius.

   $r = 3 \sin \theta = 3\frac{y}{r}$, so $r^2 = 3y$. Since $r^2 = x^2 + y^2$, $3y = x^2 + y^2$, or $x^2 + y^2 - 3y = 0$. Completing the square yields $x^2 + \left(y^2 - 3y + \frac{9}{4}\right) = \frac{9}{4}$, or $x^2 + \left(y - \frac{3}{2}\right)^2 = \left(\frac{3}{2}\right)^2$.

   The center is $\left(0, \frac{3}{2}\right)$, and the radius is $\frac{3}{2}$.

7. Describe the polar graph of $r = k \cos \theta$.

   Circle with center $\left(\frac{k}{2}, 0\right)$ and radius $\left|\frac{k}{2}\right|$

The pole is on both circles because one of its polar representations, [0, 0], satisfies $r = \sin \theta$ while another, $\left[0, \frac{\pi}{2}\right]$, satisfies $r = \cos \theta$. However, the non-uniqueness of polar representation is also the reason why the polar coordinate system provides effective (and beautiful) graphs of some equations, and this advantage outweighs the disadvantages that are involved.

Optional Activities

Technology Connection
Materials: Explorations software

Students may use *Exploration 8-4, Polar Graphs,* to do the In-class Activity prior to Lesson 8-5. Students can choose a polar equation and designate values for the constants a and b. The graph and a table of values are shown. An animation of a point as it moves around on the polar graph illustrates the creation of the graph.

Stress that even though ordered pairs are written $[r, \theta]$, θ is the independent variable and r is the dependent variable. Thus we write $r = f(\theta)$. Thus in polar coordinates, the independent variable is listed second, whereas in rectangular coordinates, the independent variable x is first. Be sure to point this out, or you will have some students writing $[\theta, r]$ ordered pairs and getting thoroughly confused.

You may wish to embellish upon the method of using a rectangular graph of $r = 1 + 2 \sin \theta$ to assist in sketching the polar graph. Use **Teaching Aid 78.** Divide the rectangular graphs into intervals of width $\frac{\pi}{2}$ and either number or draw each part of $y = 1 + 2 \sin \theta$ in a different color. Then use these parts to help sketch the polar graph of $y = 1 + 2 \sin \theta$, again numbering or drawing each part in the color used for the rectangular graphs. Use arrows to show that sequencing in the polar graph. Students find this technique very satisfying. Be sure to emphasize that the rectangular graph is for assistance—it is not the polar graph!

Additional Examples

1. Sketch the polar equation $r = 4 \cos \theta$. **The graph contains the following points: $[4, 0]$, $[2\sqrt{3}, \frac{\pi}{6}]$, $[2\sqrt{2}, \frac{\pi}{4}]$, $[2, \frac{\pi}{3}]$, $[0, \frac{\pi}{2}]$, $[-2, \frac{2\pi}{3}]$, $[-2\sqrt{2}, \frac{3\pi}{4}]$, $[-2\sqrt{3}, \frac{5\pi}{6}]$, $[-4, \pi]$, $[-2\sqrt{3}, \frac{7\pi}{6}]$, $[-2\sqrt{2}, \frac{5\pi}{4}]$, $[-2, \frac{4\pi}{3}]$, $[0, \frac{3\pi}{2}]$, $[2, \frac{5\pi}{3}]$, $[2\sqrt{2}, \frac{7\pi}{4}]$, $[2\sqrt{3}, \frac{11\pi}{6}]$, $[4, 2\pi]$.**

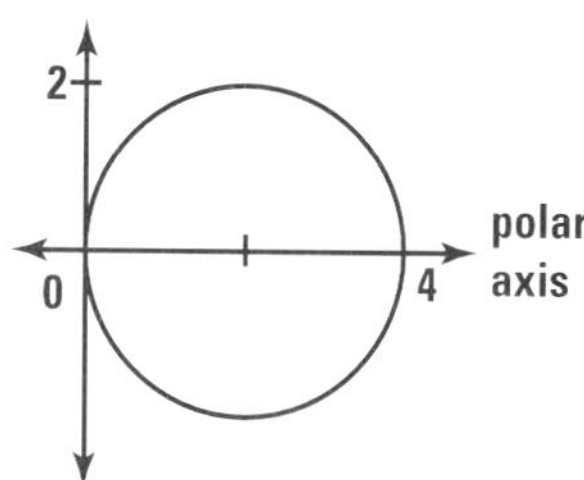

Although the polar and rectangular graphs of an equation $r = f(\theta)$ have very different appearances, there is a geometric relationship between the two that is very helpful for graphing polar equations. Examine the two figures below.

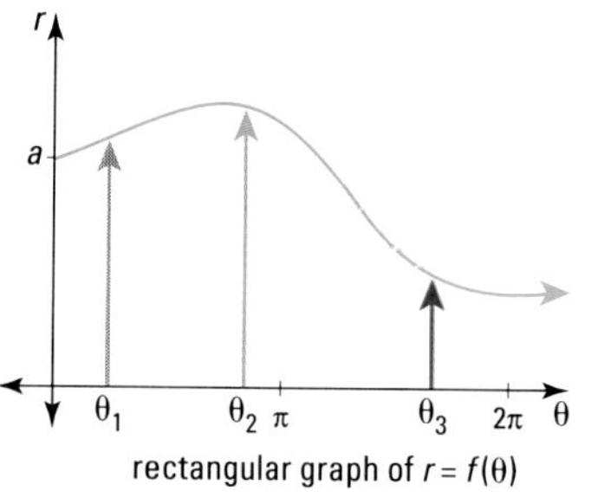

rectangular graph of $r = f(\theta)$

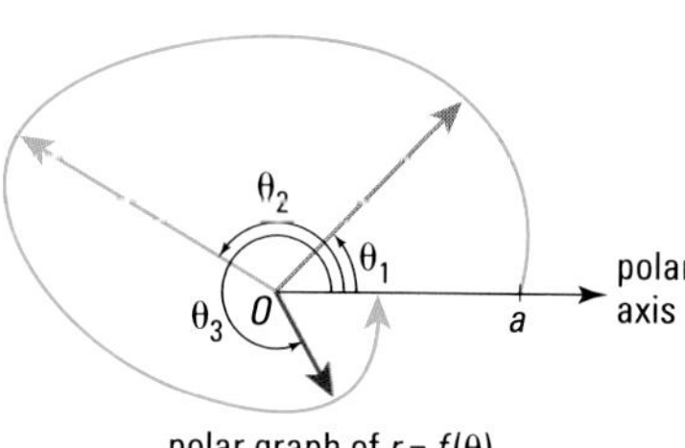

polar graph of $r = f(\theta)$

The vertical arrows in the rectangular graph correspond to the radial arrows in the polar graph. For each value of θ, the vertical arrow from the θ-axis to the rectangular graph of $r = f(\theta)$ corresponds to the length of the segment from the pole to the polar graph at an angle θ to the polar axis. Below, this relationship between the rectangular and polar graphs is illustrated for the equation $r = 1 + 2 \sin \theta$.

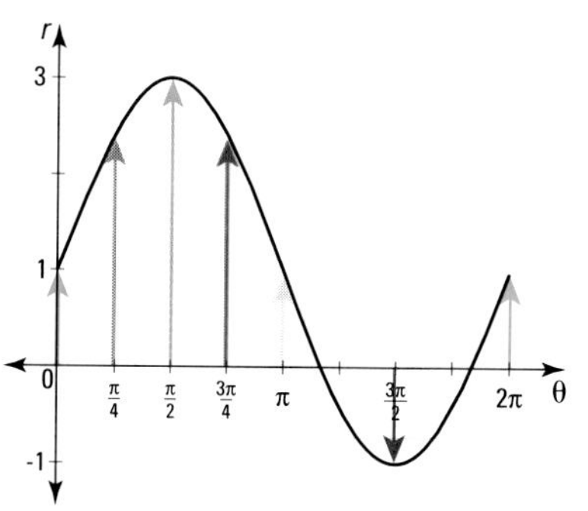

rectangular graph of $r = 1 + 2 \sin \theta$
$0 \le \theta \le 2\pi$

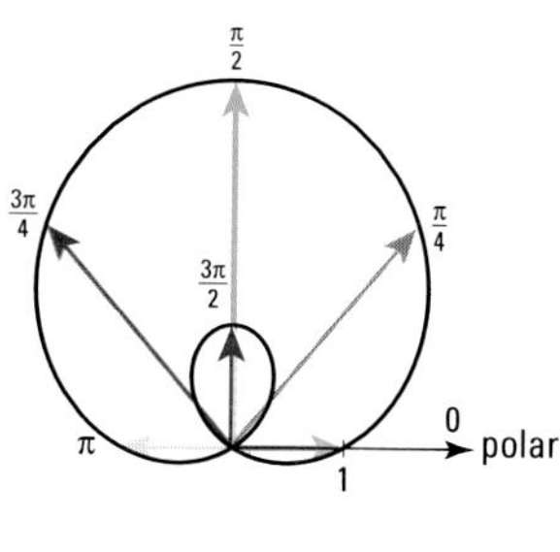

polar graph of $r = 1 + 2 \sin \theta$
$0 \le \theta \le 2\pi$

Using a Rectangular Graph To Draw a Polar Graph

Some automatic graphers plot polar graphs directly; others do not. If yours does not, you can still plot a polar graph if you take advantage of the relationship described above. One way to do this is to store a program in a grapher's memory that transforms the rectangular graph of an equation to the polar graph. Your teacher or the manual for the grapher may provide instructions for doing this. However, an automatic grapher can help you to sketch polar graphs even if it is not programmed to produce polar plots. The following example shows you how to do this.

Adapting to Individual Needs

Extra Help

You might want to "reuse" the table from **Example 1** when you cover **Example 3,** leading students to understand that they need to simply add 1 to each value of r. You should mention that not all of these points are needed to draw a good sketch.

Challenge

Tell students that $r = a + b \cos \theta$ and $r = a + b \sin \theta$ are limaçons. Have them answer the following questions.

1. Which of these curves are symmetric with respect to the vertical axis? $[r = a + b \sin \theta]$
2. Which of these curves are symmetric with respect to the horizontal axis? $[r = a + b \cos \theta]$

Example 4

Use the rectangular graph of $r = 3 + 2\cos\theta$ on $0 \le \theta \le 2\pi$ to sketch its polar graph.

$y = 3 + 2\cos x$

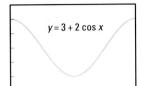

$0 \le x \le 2\pi$, x-scale $= \frac{\pi}{2}$
$0 \le y \le 6$, y-scale $= 1$

Solution

Because this is an equation of the form $r = a + b\cos\theta$, the polar graph will be a limaçon. Use a grapher to plot the rectangular graph of the equation.

Notice that as θ increases from 0 to 2π, the value of r decreases from its maximum value of 5 at $\theta = 0$ to its minimum value of 1 at $\theta = \pi$ and then it increases to its maximum value of 5 again at $\theta = 2\pi$. Consequently, in the corresponding polar graph, the lengths of the segments from the pole decrease from a maximum length of 5 at $\theta = 0$ to the minimum length of 1 at $\theta = \pi$ and then increase to a maximum length of 5 at $\theta = 2\pi$. Thus the polar graph of $r = 3 + 2\cos\theta$ can be sketched as below.

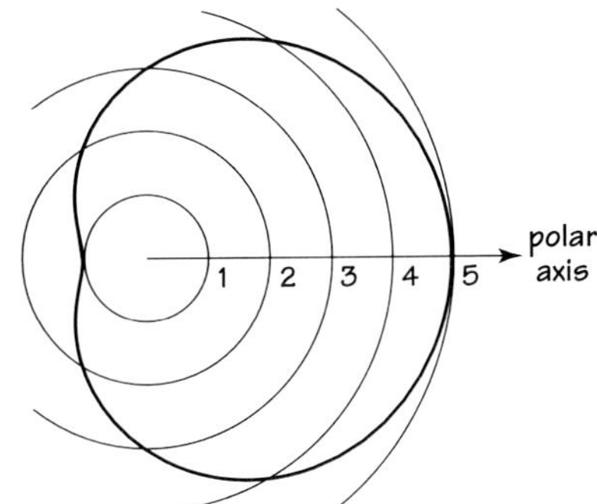

polar graph of $r = 3 + 2\cos\theta$ on $0 \le \theta \le 2\pi$

If you had sketched the graph of the equation in Example 4 on the interval $0 \le \theta \le \pi$, you would have obtained only the upper half of the limaçon and your graph would have had the shape below.

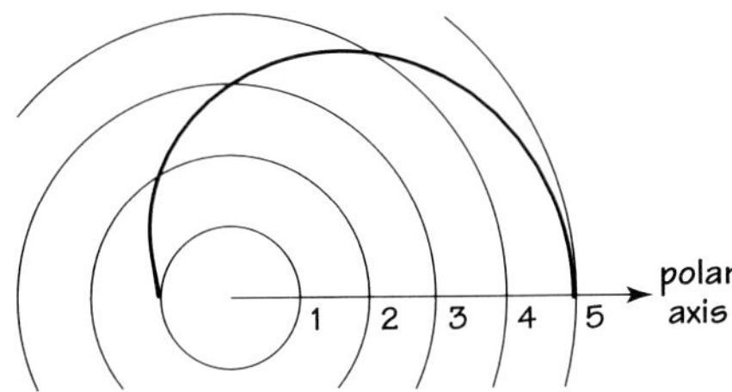

However, if you had sketched the same equation on an interval larger than $0 \le \theta \le 2\pi$, or on any interval whose length is greater than or equal to 2π radians, your polar graph would have looked like that in Example 4. This would have happened because the cosine function is periodic with period 2π, so the values of $r = 3 + 2\cos\theta$ repeat every 2π.

3. What roles do a and b play on the graph? [The length along the axis of symmetry is $a + b$ if $a \le b$ and $2a$ if $a \ge b$. The width along the other axis is $2a$.]

2. Verify that the polar graph of $r = 4\cos\theta$ is a circle. **Using the substitutions $r = \sqrt{x^2 + y^2}$; $\cos\theta = \frac{x}{\sqrt{x^2 + y^2}}$. Then $r = 4\cos\theta$ becomes $\sqrt{x^2 + y^2} = \frac{4x}{\sqrt{x^2 + y^2}}$ or $(x - 2)^2 + y^2 = 4$, which is a circle with center (2, 0) and radius 2.**

3. Sketch the graph of the polar equation $r = 1 + \cos\theta$. **Some points are on the graph are: $[0, 2]$, $[\frac{2 + \sqrt{3}}{2}, \frac{\pi}{6}]$, $[\frac{2 + \sqrt{2}}{2}, \frac{\pi}{4}]$, $[\frac{3}{2}, \frac{\pi}{3}]$, $[1, \frac{\pi}{2}]$, $[\frac{1}{2}, \frac{2\pi}{3}]$, $[\frac{2 - \sqrt{2}}{2}, \frac{3\pi}{4}]$, $[\frac{2 - \sqrt{3}}{2}, \frac{5\pi}{6}]$, $[0, \pi]$, $[\frac{2 - \sqrt{3}}{2}, \frac{7\pi}{6}]$, $[\frac{2 - \sqrt{2}}{2}, \frac{5\pi}{4}]$, $[\frac{1}{2}, \frac{4\pi}{3}]$, $[1, \frac{3\pi}{2}]$, $[\frac{3}{2}, \frac{5\pi}{3}]$, $[\frac{2 + \sqrt{2}}{2}, \frac{7\pi}{4}]$, $[\frac{2 + \sqrt{3}}{2}, \frac{11\pi}{6}]$, $[2, 2\pi]$.**

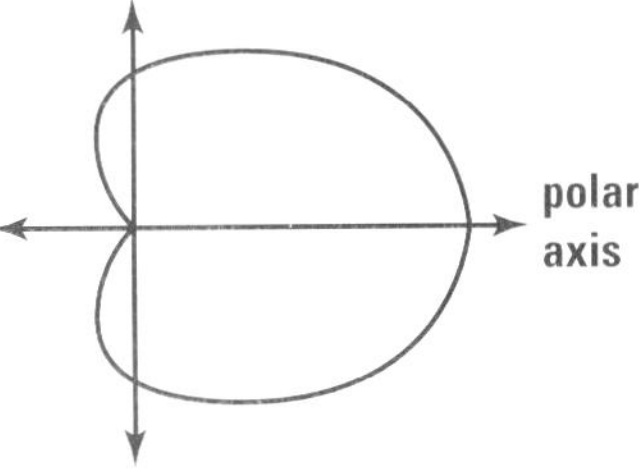

$r = 1 + \cos\theta$ is a cardioid.

4. Use the rectangular graph of $r = \sin\theta - 1$ on $0 \le \theta \le 2\pi$ to sketch its polar graph. **The rectangular graph is:**

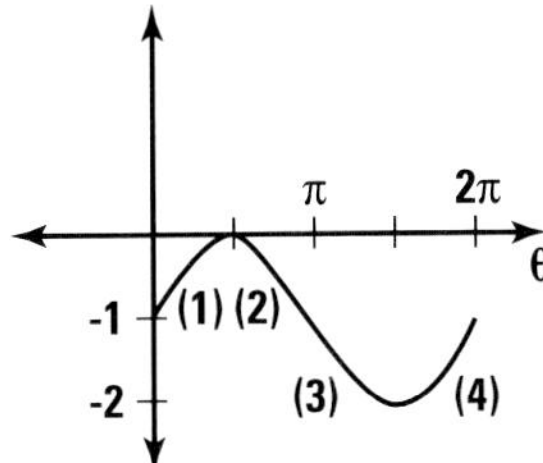

polar graph:

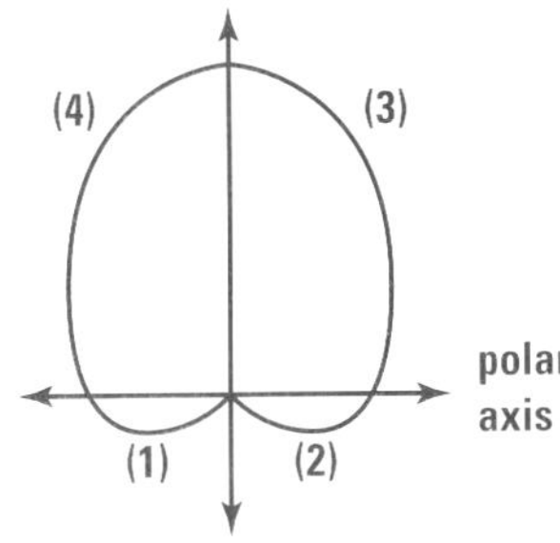

a cardioid

Notes on Questions

Question 10 A cardioid is a special limaçon (see **Question 19**). "Limaçon" is French for "snail." The little hook on the ç in "limaçon" is a cedilla, a diacritical mark in French to indicate that the *c* is pronounced like an *s* rather than like a *k*.

Question 14 Students should check their answer by checking that $\triangle ABC$ and its image are congruent.

Question 19 One instance of $a = b$ is found in **Question 10.**

Additional Answers

1.

θ	0	$\frac{\pi}{6}$	$\frac{\pi}{4}$	$\frac{\pi}{3}$	$\frac{\pi}{2}$	π	$\frac{3\pi}{2}$	2π
r	0	$\frac{3}{2}$	$\frac{3\sqrt{2}}{2}$	$\frac{3\sqrt{3}}{2}$	3	0	-3	0

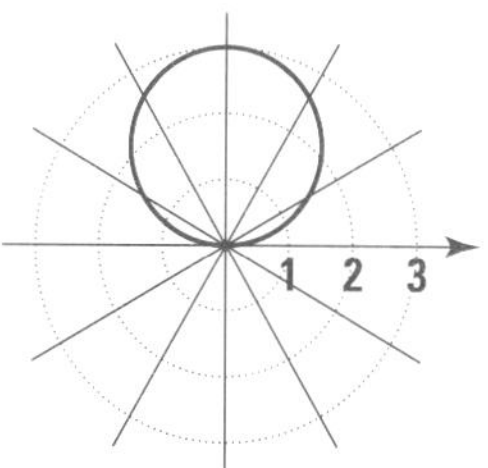

2.

θ	0	$\frac{\pi}{6}$	$\frac{\pi}{4}$	$\frac{\pi}{3}$	$\frac{\pi}{2}$	$\frac{3\pi}{4}$	π	$\frac{3\pi}{2}$	2π
r	6	$3\sqrt{3}$	$3\sqrt{2}$	3	0	$-3\sqrt{2}$	-6	0	6

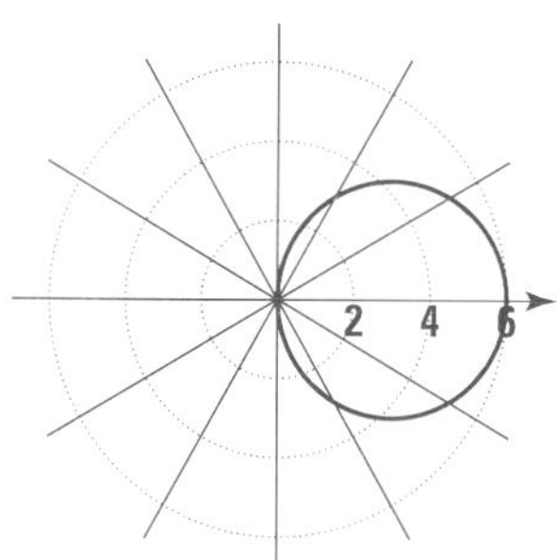

4.

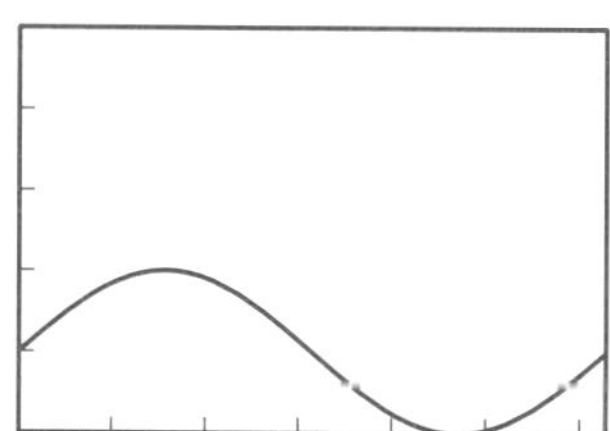

$0 \le x \le 2\pi$, x-scale = 1
$0 \le y \le 5$, y-scale = 1

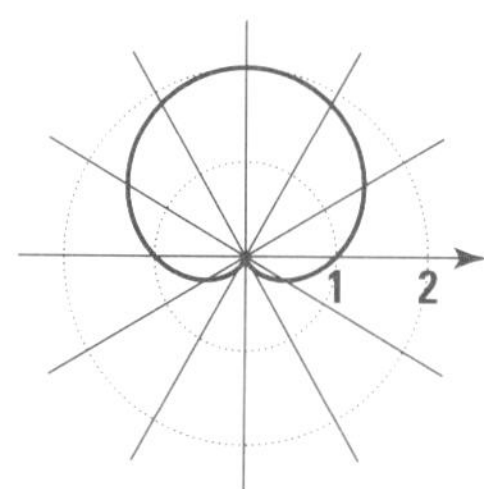

3) $r = 3 \sin \theta$
$\Rightarrow r = \frac{3y}{r}$ (Conversion formula)
$\Rightarrow r^2 = 3y$
$\Rightarrow x^2 + y^2 = 3y$ (Conversion formula)
$\Rightarrow (x^2) + \left(y - \frac{3}{2}\right)^2 = \frac{9}{4}$

This verifies that the curve in Question 1 is a circle and has center $\left(0, \frac{3}{2}\right)$ and radius $\frac{3}{2}$.

a philodendron with elongated heart-shaped leaves

7b)

QUESTIONS

Covering the Reading

In 1 and 2, use a table of values to sketch the polar graphs of the equation on the interval $0 \le \theta \le 2\pi$.

1. $r = 3 \sin \theta$ See margin.

2. $r = 6 \cos \theta$ See margin.

3. Prove that the curve in Question 1 is a circle, and find its center and radius. See left.

In 4 and 5, plot the rectangular graph of the given equation. Then use the rectangular graph of the equation to sketch the polar graph.

4. $r = 1 + \sin \theta \quad 0 \le \theta \le 2\pi$ See margin.

5. $r = 2 + 3 \cos \theta \quad 0 \le \theta \le 2\pi$ See margin.

6. The polar graph in Question 4 is a curve known as a _?_. limaçon

Applying the Mathematics

7. a. Convert the polar equation $r(\sin \theta + \cos \theta) = 1$ to rectangular coordinates by using the polar-rectangular conversion formulas.
b. Sketch the polar graph of the equation.
See left. a) $y + x = 1$

In 8 and 9, determine whether or not the function is periodic. If it is, describe an interval $\theta_1 \le \theta \le \theta_2$ that determines the complete graph of $r = f(\theta)$.

8. $r = \theta$
not periodic

9. $r = 2 \cos \theta + \sin 2\theta$
periodic, Sample: $0 \le \theta \le 2\pi$

10. The polar graph of $r = 1 + \cos \theta$ is a curve known as a **cardioid**. Carefully graph this curve and use the graph to explain how the curve got its name. See margin.

11. a. Without graphing, explain how the polar graph of $r = k \sin \theta$ is related to the polar graph of $r = \sin \theta$. See margin.
b. Describe the polar graph of $r = k \sin \theta$.
It is a circle with radius $\frac{k}{2}$ and center $\left(0, \frac{k}{2}\right)$.

Review

12. Illustrate the multiplication of $z = 2(\cos 150° + i \sin 150°)$ by $w = 5(\cos 40° + i \sin 40°)$ with a diagram showing the appropriate size transformation and rotation. *(Lesson 8-3)* See margin.

13. Suppose Z and W are the points in the plane that represent the complex numbers $z = 2 - i$ and $w = -1 + 3i$, respectively. Then the distance $ZW = 5$. Let $v = -\frac{7}{2} - 8i$, and suppose points Z' and W' represent $z + v$ and $w + v$, respectively.
a. What are the coordinates of Z' and W'? $Z' = \left(-\frac{3}{2}, -9\right)$, $W' = \left(-\frac{9}{2}, -5\right)$
b. What transformation maps Z to Z' and W to W'? $T_{-7/2, -8}$
c. Find $Z'W'$. *(Lesson 8-3)* 5

5.

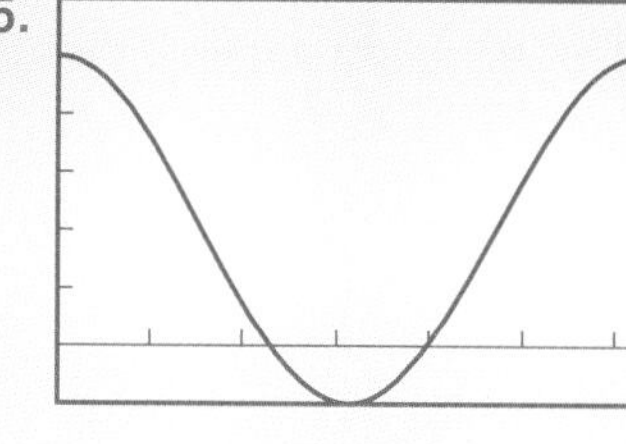

$0 \le x \le 2\pi$, x-scale = 1
$-1 \le y \le 6$, y-scale = 1

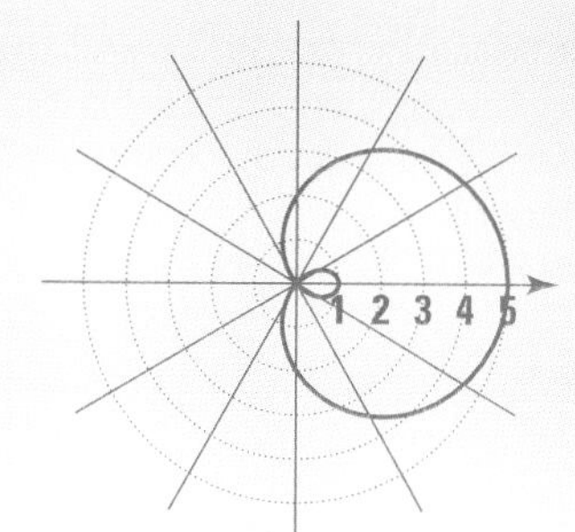

14a) $A' = [2, 90°]$,
$B' = [1, 195°]$,
$C' = [4, 330°]$

b)

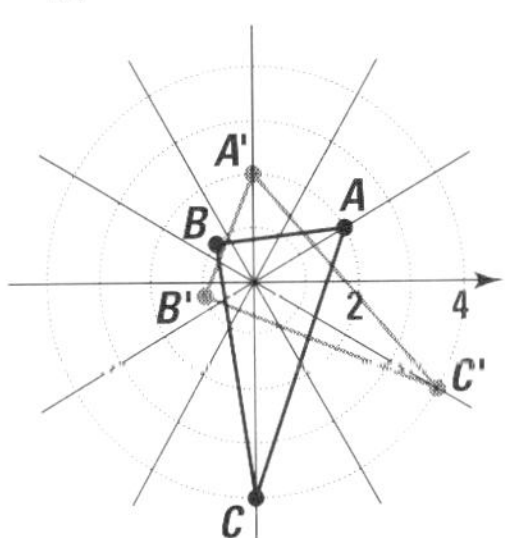

15b) They are complex conjugates.

19a)

$r = a + b\cos\theta$, where $a < b$

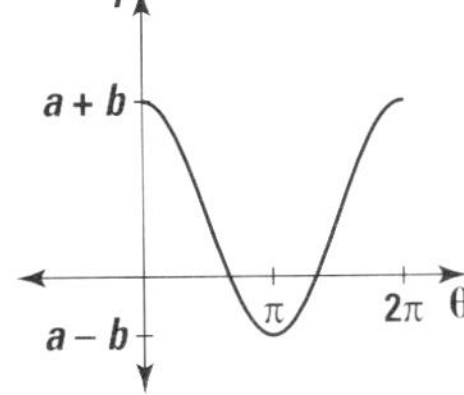

$r = a + b\cos\theta$, where $a = b$

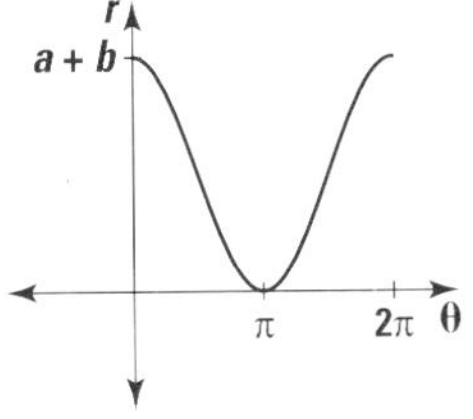

$r = a + b\cos\theta$, where $a > b$

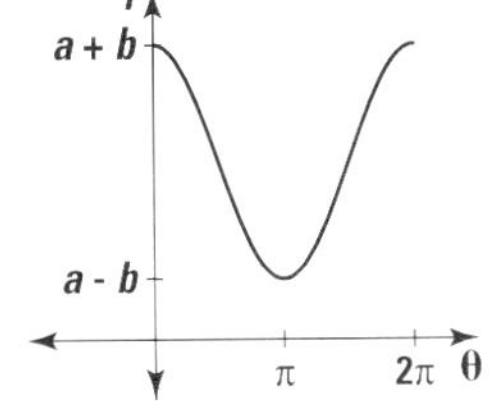

14. **a.** Consider $\triangle ABC$ with vertices $A = [2, 30°]$, $B = [1, 135°]$ and $C = [4, 270°]$. Rotate the triangle 60° about the pole and give polar coordinates for the new vertices.

b. Graph $\triangle ABC$ and its image on a polar grid. *(Lesson 8-2)*
a, b) See left.

15. Let $z = \frac{1}{2} + \frac{\sqrt{3}}{2}i$ and $w = \frac{1}{z}$.

a. Write w in $a + bi$ form. $\frac{1}{2} - \frac{\sqrt{3}}{2}i$

b. Compare z with w. **See left.**

c. Write z and w in polar form. How do they compare? *(Lessons 8-1, 8-2)*
$z = [1, \pi/3]$, $w = [1, -\pi/3]$; **their arguments are opposites.**

16. Let $z = -3 + 4i$, $v = 2 - i$, and $w = -3i$. Find the value of each expression below and write your answer in $a + bi$ form.

a. $\frac{v + w}{z}$ $-.88 + .16i$ **b.** $\frac{v}{z}$ $-.4 - .2i$ **c.** $\frac{w}{z}$ $-.48 + .36i$

d. Add the answers to parts **b** and **c**, and compare the sum to the answer to part **a**. *(Lesson 8-1)* **The sum, $-.88 + .16i$, is equal to the answer to part a.**

17. Write in summation notation: $\sum_{k=1}^{10} (k(2k + 1))$

$1 \cdot 3 + 2 \cdot 5 + 3 \cdot 7 + 4 \cdot 9 + \ldots + 10 \cdot 21$. *(Lesson 7-2)*

18. Is $\{(x, y): x^2 + y^2 = 9\}$ a function? Why or why not? *(Lesson 2-1)*
No, the graph of $x^2 + y^2 = 9$ is a circle, and it fails the vertical-line test for functions.

Exploration

19. Suppose that a and b are positive numbers.

a. Sketch rectangular graphs of $r = a + b\cos\theta$ for each of the following three cases. **See left.**
i. $a < b$ **ii.** $a = b$ **iii.** $a > b$

b. Sketch a polar graph of the equation in part **a** for each of the three cases. **See margin.**

c. Explain why the polar graphs for the three cases in part **a** have the following properties:
i. $a < b$; a limaçon with an inner loop
ii. $a = b$; a limaçon that includes the pole but with no inner loop (also called a cardioid)
iii. $a > b$; a limaçon that does not include the pole.
i) **Around $\theta = \pi$, r has negative values, causing a loop.**
ii) **If $a = b$, there are no negative values for θ.**
iii) **$r > 0$ for all θ.**

Follow-up for Lesson 8-4

Practice

For more questions on SPUR Objectives, use **Lesson Master 8-4** (shown on pages 494–495).

Assessment

Quiz A quiz covering Lessons 8-1 through 8-4 is provided in the *Assessment Sourcebook.*

Extension

Students may prove that the graphs of $r = a\sin\theta$ and $r = a\cos\theta$ are both circles with radius $\frac{a}{2}$. Then find their centers. [$r = a\sin\theta$ has corresponding rectangular equation $x^2 + (y - \frac{a}{2})^2 = (\frac{a}{2})^2$, so it has center $(0, \frac{a}{2})$ and radius $\frac{a}{2}$. $r = a\cos\theta$ has corresponding rectangular equation $(x - \frac{a}{2})^2 + y^2 = (\frac{a}{2})^2$, so it has center $(\frac{a}{2}, 0)$ and radius $\frac{a}{2}$.]

Project Update Project 1, *Polar Equations for Conic Sections,* on page 542, relates to the content of this lesson.

Additional Answers

10.

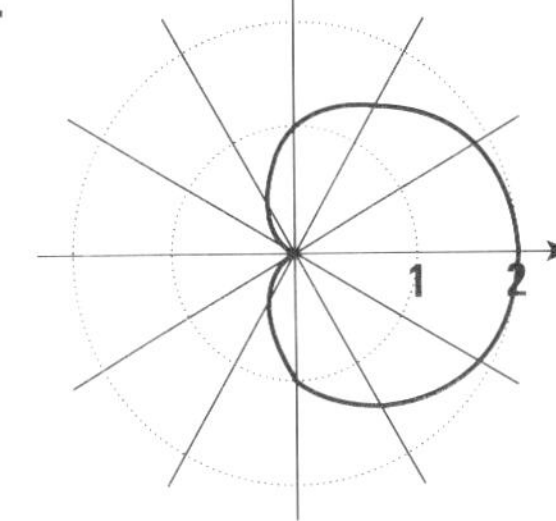

"Cardio-" is a prefix meaning "heart." Cardioid curves resemble hearts.

11. a. **The polar graph of $r = k\sin\theta$ is the graph of $r = \sin\theta$ taken through a scale change of k.**

12.

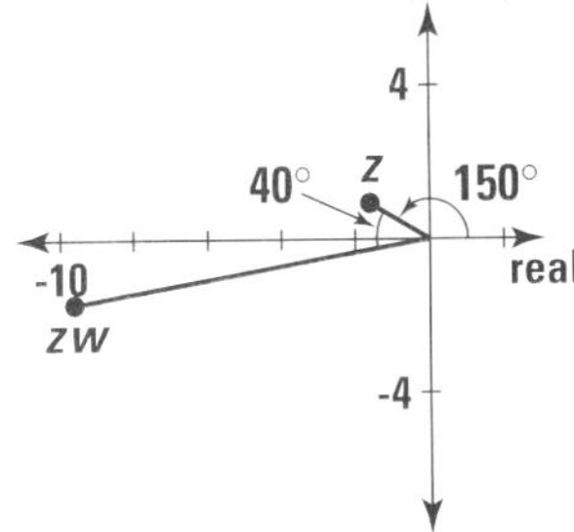

19. **See Additional Answers at the back of this book.**

Setting Up Lesson 8-5

Do the In-class Activity on page 500.

In-class Activity

Resources

From the ***Teacher's Resource File***
■ Answer Master 8-5

The result of **Part 2** is the polar equivalent of the Graph-Translation Theorem: If, in an equation relating r and θ, θ is replaced by $\theta - \phi$, then the graph is rotated ϕ.

When explaining **Part 3,** note that the trigonometric identity is not tied to any coordinate system. So, it can be used to explain graphs in any coordinate system.

The graphs in **Parts 4–5** usually surprise students. You can do these parts with Lesson 8-5.

Additional Answers

1. **Sample: Put calculator in Polar mode and enter equation using the y = key.**

2. a.

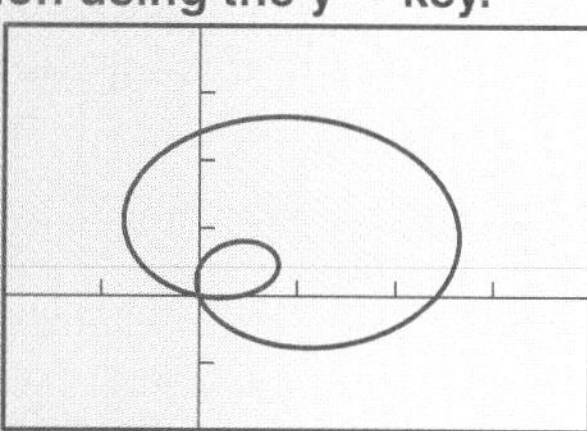

$0 \le \theta \le 2\pi$, θ-step $= \frac{\pi}{6}$
$-2 \le x \le 4$, x-scale = 1
$-2 \le y \le 4$, y-scale = 1

There is a rotation of $\frac{\pi}{4}$ units clockwise.

b. **The equation shows a horizontal translation $\frac{\pi}{4}$ units to the right.**

c. **It would rotate the graph in Example 3 by $\frac{\pi}{3}$.**

d. **The graph will be the same as the graph in Example 3 but, for $x > 0$, will be rotated clockwise if the angle is $(\theta + x)$ and counterclockwise if the angle is $(\theta - x)$.**

Introducing Lesson 8-5

Graphing Polar Equations Using Technology

IN-CLASS ACTIVITY

Work with one or two others to complete this activity.

1–5) See margin.

1 Determine how to enter a polar equation into your calculator or computer. Check that you can do so by graphing $r = 2 \sin \theta$ and comparing your graph with Example 1 of Lesson 8-4. Notice that your window now includes the interval for θ.

2 Graph $r = 1 + 2 \sin\left(\theta + \frac{\pi}{4}\right)$.
a. How is this graph related to the one in Example 3 of Lesson 8-4?
b. Explain why the result in part **a** occurs.
c. Predict what the graph of $r = 1 + 2 \sin\left(\theta - \frac{\pi}{3}\right)$ would look like.
d. Generalize the results of parts **a, b,** and **c**.

3 Graph $r = \cos \theta$ and $r = \sin \theta$. What trigonometric identity helps to explain why these graphs are related as they are?

4 **a.** Sketch the graph of $r = \tan \theta$.
b. This graph has asymptotes. What are the rectangular equations for the asymptotes?
c. Explain the asymptotes by determining a rectangular equation for the graph.

5 **a.** Sketch the graph of $r = \sec \theta$. (You will probably have to enter $\frac{1}{\cos\theta}$.)
b. Explain why the graph looks as it does.
c. Predict what the graph of $r = \csc \theta$ will look like, and check your prediction.

3. $\sin \theta = \cos (90° - \theta)$

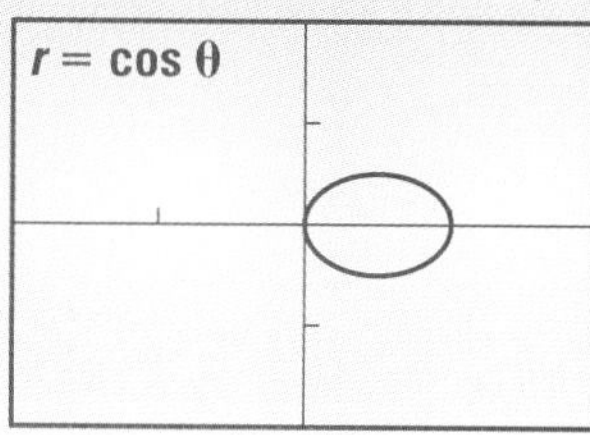

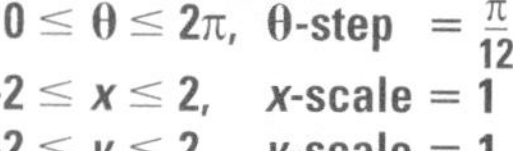

$0 \le \theta \le 2\pi$, θ-step $= \frac{\pi}{12}$
$-2 \le x \le 2$, x-scale = 1
$-2 \le y \le 2$, y-scale = 1

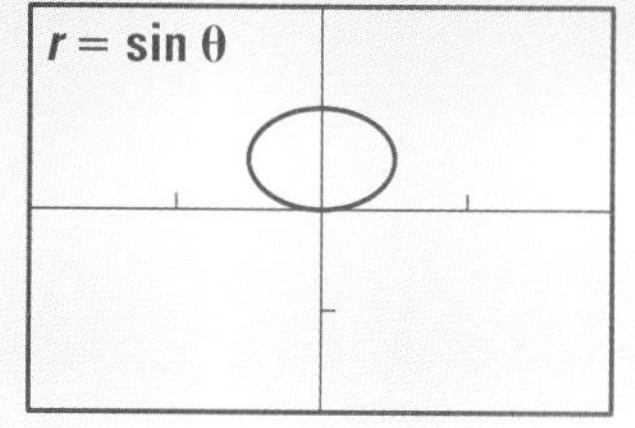

$0 \le \theta \le 2\pi$, θ-step $= \frac{\pi}{12}$
$-2 \le x \le 2$, x-scale = 1
$-2 \le y \le 2$, y-scale = 1

4. a.

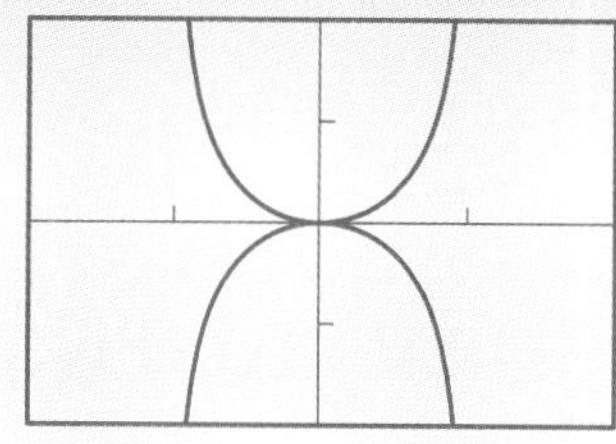

$0 \le \theta \le 2\pi$, θ-step $= \frac{\pi}{12}$
$-2 \le x \le 2$, x-scale = 1
$-2 \le y \le 2$, y-scale = 1

b. **$x = 1$, $x = -1$**

c. **$r = \tan \theta$ gives the rectangular equation $\sqrt{x^2 + y^2} = \frac{y}{x}$ which simplifies to $y^2 = \frac{-x^4}{x^2 - 1}$. The rectangular equation is undefined when $x = 1$ and $x = -1$, so $x = 1$ and $x = -1$ are equations of the asymptotes.**

5. **See Additional Answers at the back of this book.**

LESSON

8-5

Rose Curves and Spirals

Green Gentian. *The petals of many flowers such as this green gentian resemble rose curves.*

In the In-class Activity on the preceding page, you should have seen that the effect of replacing θ by $\theta - k$ in an equation of the form $r = f(\theta)$ is to rotate the graph by an amount k about the pole. It is natural to wonder what happens when θ is replaced by $a\theta$. The result is surprising and beautiful.

Rose Curves

Example 1

Sketch the polar graph of

$$r = \sin 2\theta \quad \text{for} \quad 0 \le \theta \le 2\pi.$$

Solution

The rectangular graph of $r = \sin 2\theta$ for $0 \le \theta \le 2\pi$ is given below.

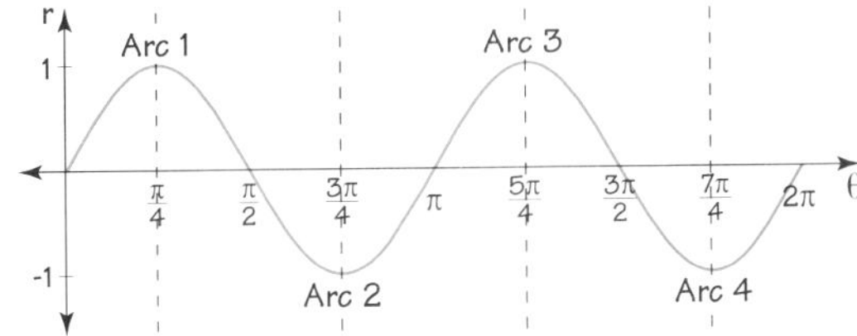

Lesson 8-5

Objectives

J Sketch graphs of polar equations.

Resources

From the ***Teacher's Resource File***
- Lesson Master 8-5
- Answer Master 8-5
- Teaching Aids
  71 Warm-up
  79 Example 1
  80 Example 2
- Technology Source Book
  Calculator Master 12

Additional Resources
- Visuals for Teachings 71, 79, 80

Teaching Lesson 8-5

Warm-up

Carefully graph the eleven points $[r, \theta]$ satisfying $r = 6 \cos 2\theta$, when $\theta = 0°, \pm10°, \pm20°, \pm30°, \pm40°$ and $\pm45°$. **The points all lie on one petal of a rose curve.**

Notes on Reading

Rose curves are surprising and gorgeous, so you may wish to spend an extra day on the *Extension* for this lesson, or combine that with the quiz on Lessons 8-1 to 8-4.

Lesson 8-5 Overview

Broad Goals This lesson discusses the polar graphs of equations whose rectangular coordinate graphs are known to students: simple trigonometric equations of the form $r = a \sin(n\theta)$, linear equations of the form $r = a\theta + b$, and exponential equations of the form $r = ab^{\theta}$. The results are rose curves, spirals of Archimedes, and logarithmic spirals, respectively.

Perspective The curves in this lesson not only show the power of polar coordinate representations but they are themselves beautiful and surprising. They can be graphed using either of the methods of Lesson 8-4.

When n is an even nonzero integer, the polar equations $r = a \cos(n\theta)$ and $r = a \sin(n\theta)$ describe rose curves with $2n$ petals.

When n is odd, these polar equations describe rose curves with n petals.

The graphs of the polar equations $r = a\theta + b$ and $r = ab^{\theta}$ are spirals of Archimedes and logarithmic spirals, respectively. While it might seem that the linear equation leading to the spiral of Archimedes is the more common, actually

(Overview continues on page 502.)

Teaching Aid 79 can be used as you discuss **Example 1** and the symmetry properties of polar graphs. Ask:

1. Suppose $r = f(\theta)$ and for all θ, $f(-\theta) = f(\theta)$. What kind of symmetry does the graph of f possess? [Symmetry to the line containing the polar axis]
2. Suppose $r = f(\theta)$ and for all θ, $f(\pi - \theta) = f(\theta)$. What kind of symmetry does the graph of f possess? [Symmetry to the line $\theta = \frac{\pi}{2}$.]
3. Suppose $r = f(\theta)$ and for all θ, $f(\pi + \theta) = f(\theta)$. What kind of symmetry does the graph of f possess? [Point symmetry to the pole] However, there is one caution: The converses of these sufficient conditions are not true. For instance, the polar graph of $r = \sin 2\theta$ for $0 \le \theta \le 2\pi$ is symmetric to the vertical line $\theta = \frac{\pi}{2}$ even though there exists a θ such that $f(\theta) \neq f(\pi - \theta)$.

Error Alert In **Example 1** students might think that the loops should be drawn counterclockwise about the pole as θ increases from 0 to 2π. Point out that this is not the case because $r \le 0$ for loops 2 and 4. Thus the points on these loops are a half-turn image of where they would be when $r \ge 0$.

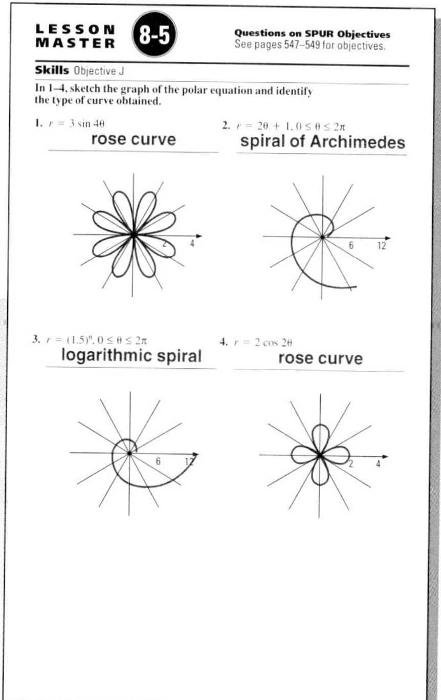
LESSON MASTER 8-5 Questions on SPUR Objectives
See pages 547–549 for objectives.

Skills Objective J

In 1–4, sketch the graph of the polar equation and identify the type of curve obtained.

1. $r = 3 \sin 4\theta$ rose curve

2. $r = 2\theta + 1, 0 \le \theta \le 2\pi$ spiral of Archimedes

3. $r = (1.5)^\theta, 0 \le \theta \le 2\pi$ logarithmic spiral

4. $r = 2 \cos 2\theta$ rose curve

The θ-axis divides this graph into 4 congruent arcs, each symmetric to one of the dotted vertical lines where θ is an odd multiple of $\frac{\pi}{4}$. Each of these arcs contributes one of the four congruent loops in the polar graph below.

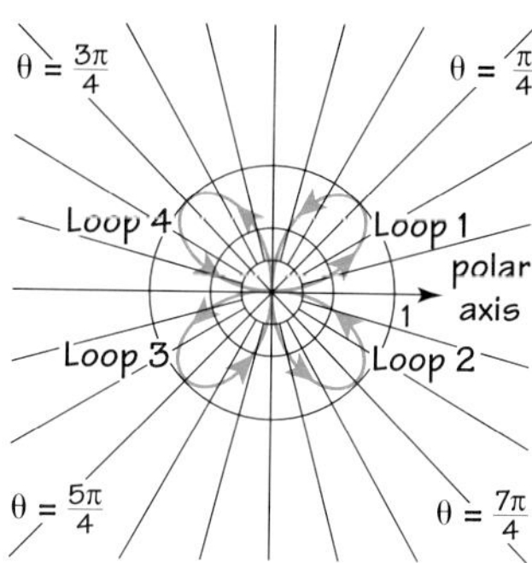

Because of the periodicity of the sine function, values of θ outside $0 \le \theta \le 2\pi$ produce no new points for the graph.

The beautiful polar graph in Example 1 is called a *four-leafed rose*. In general, the polar graphs of equations of the form

$$r = a \cos n\theta,\ a > 0,\ n \text{ a positive integer}$$

or

$$r = a \sin n\theta,\ a > 0,\ n \text{ a positive integer}$$

are called **rose curves**. The length of each *leaf* or *petal* is a and the number of leaves is determined by n. When n is even, the number of leaves is $2n$. When n is odd, the number of leaves is n. For example, the polar graph of the equation

$$r = 2 \cos 3\theta$$

is a 3-leafed rose and each leaf has length 2.

Tiger Flower, native to Mexico and Guatemala

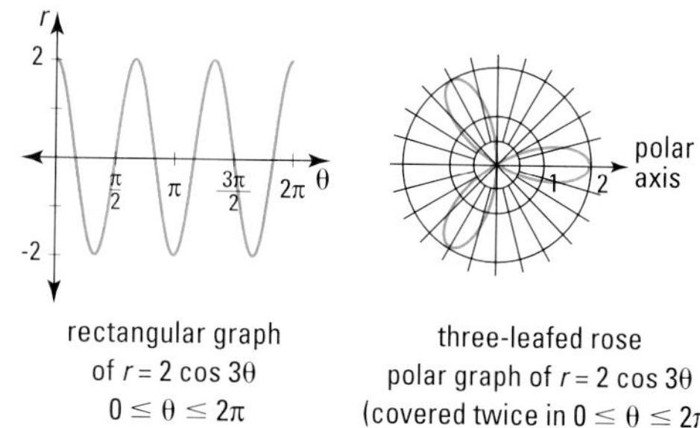

rectangular graph of $r = 2 \cos 3\theta$, $0 \le \theta \le 2\pi$

three-leafed rose polar graph of $r = 2 \cos 3\theta$ (covered twice in $0 \le \theta \le 2\pi$)

In determining the points that satisfy $r = 2 \cos 3\theta$, notice that values of r repeat with period $\frac{2\pi}{3}$ but the complete polar graph of $r = f(\theta)$ requires the entire interval $0 \le \theta \le \pi$. Therefore, you sometimes need to consider a larger interval than the period of the trigonometric function to obtain the complete polar graph.

Lesson 8-5 Overview, continued

the logarithmic spiral has more immediate applications. In Lesson 8-6, students will learn that the powers of a complex number b lie on such a spiral (the spiral $r = b^\theta$).

When a thick rope is coiled, the spiral it forms is a spiral of Archimedes because the distance between coils is constant. In animal growth, as in the horns of some species of sheep and the shells of some marine animals, the logarithmic spiral is found.

Optional Activities

Activity 1 Technology Connection
In *Technology Sourcebook, Calculator Master 12,* students use a graphics calculator to investigate how properties of rose curves and other polar graphs are determined by the equations for the graphs.

Example 2

Sketch the polar graphs of the following equations on the same polar coordinate grid:

$$r = \theta + 1, 0 \le \theta \le 2\pi \qquad \text{and} \qquad r = 2^{\theta}, 0 \le \theta \le 2\pi.$$

Solution

First sketch the rectangular graphs of the two equations on the same rectangular coordinate grid.

❶

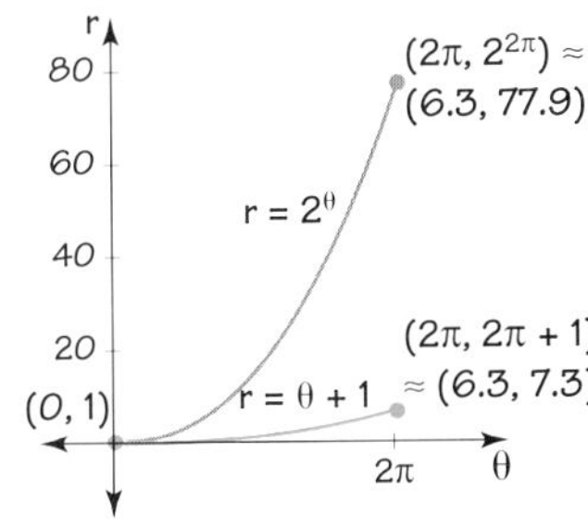

Both functions are increasing on the interval $0 \le \theta \le 2\pi$ and both have the value 1 at $\theta = 0$. But the exponential function described by $r = 2^{\theta}$ increases much more rapidly than the linear function with $r = \theta + 1$.

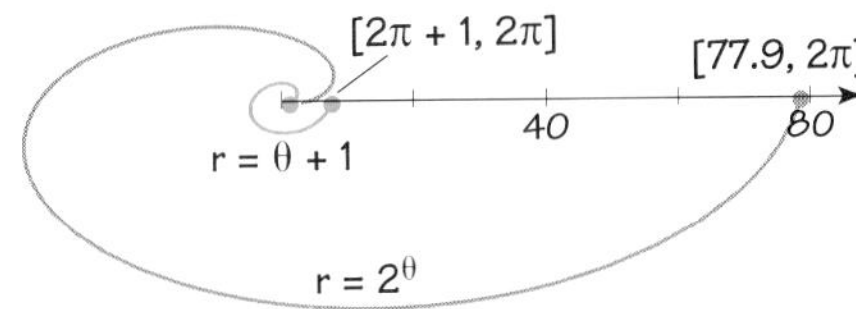

Both polar graphs are sections of spirals, but the polar graph of $r = 2^{\theta}$ expands as a spiral much more rapidly than that of $r = \theta + 1$.

The polar graphs of $r = \theta + 1$ and, more generally,

$$\{[r, \theta]: r = a\theta + b\}$$

where a is positive and b is nonnegative, are called **spirals of Archimedes**. They have the appearance of a coil of rope or hose with a constant distance between successive coils.

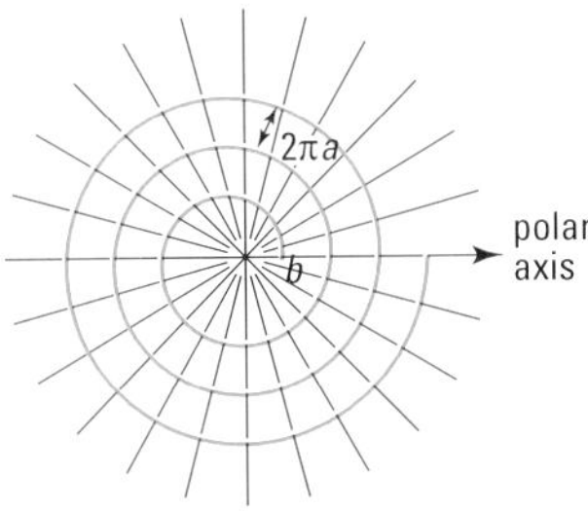

Spiral of Archimedes $r = a\theta + b$

❶ Teaching Aid 80 shows the diagrams for **Example 2.** The relationship between the spirals of Archimedes and logarithmic spirals has an analog for rectangular coordinates: If you plot $(x, \log y)$ in place of (x, y) for the exponential function $y = ab^x$, the resulting rectangular graph is a straight line instead of an exponential curve. It is this fact that underlies the use of semilog paper to plot experimental data that is expected to fit an exponential model. Students who studied *Functions, Statistics, and Trigonometry* will be familiar with this idea.

Activity 2 Ask students to write an equation for and make a polar graph of a rose with four petals and petal length 2. [$r = 2 \sin 2\theta$ or $r = 2 \cos 2\theta$] Then have them repeat the activity for a rose with three petals. [$r = 2 \sin 3\theta$ or $r = 2 \cos 3\theta$]

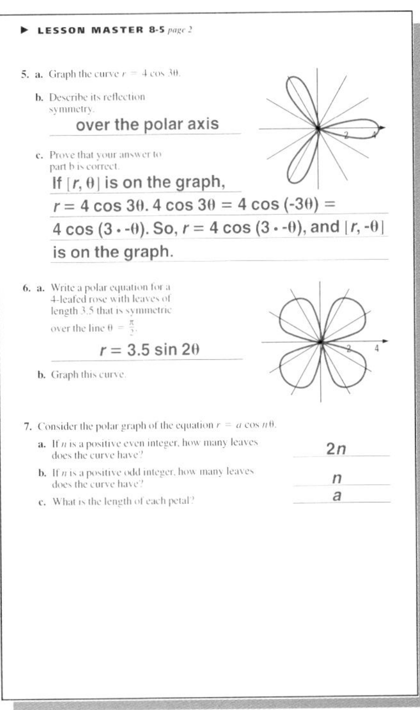

▶ **LESSON MASTER 8-5** *page 2*

5. a. Graph the curve $r = 4 \cos 3\theta$.

   b. Describe its reflection symmetry.
   over the polar axis

   c. Prove that your answer to part b is correct.
   If $[r, \theta]$ is on the graph, $r = 4 \cos 3\theta$. $4 \cos 3\theta = 4 \cos(-3\theta) = 4 \cos(3 \cdot -\theta)$. So, $r = 4 \cos(3 \cdot -\theta)$, and $[r, -\theta]$ is on the graph.

6. a. Write a polar equation for a 4-leafed rose with leaves of length 3.5 that is symmetric over the line $\theta = \frac{\pi}{2}$.
   $r = 3.5 \sin 2\theta$

   b. Graph this curve.

7. Consider the polar graph of the equation $r = a \cos n\theta$.

   a. If n is a positive even integer, how many leaves does the curve have? $2n$

   b. If n is a positive odd integer, how many leaves does the curve have? n

   c. What is the length of each petal? a

❷ **Science Connection** The nautilus (a relative of the squid) may have the most beautiful shell of all the sea animals. Like natural beehives, the regularity of these shells is astounding; they look as if they were crafted by machine.

Additional Examples

1. Sketch the polar graph of $r = 2 \cos 3\theta$ for $0 \le \theta \le 2\pi$.

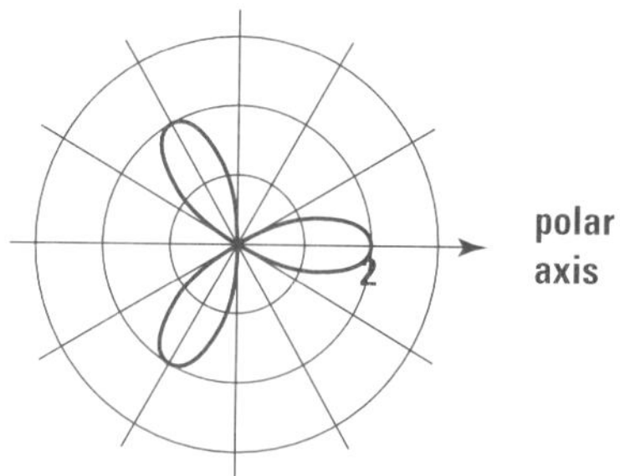

2. Sketch the polar graph of $r = \pi + \frac{\theta}{2}$ for $0 \le \theta \le 4\pi$.

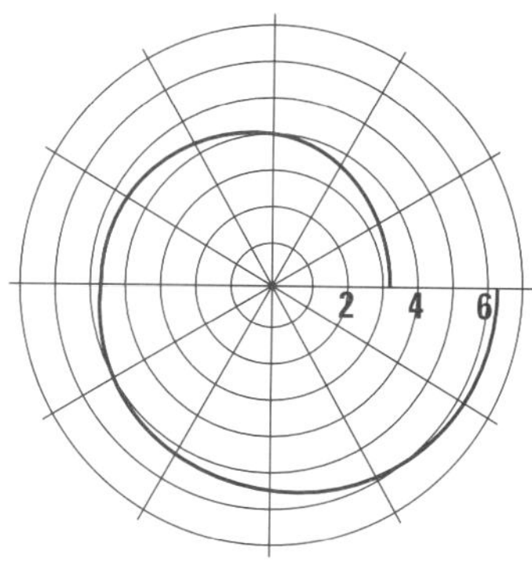

(Notes on Questions begin on page 506.)

In contrast, the polar graphs of $r = 2^\theta$ and, more generally,

$$\{[r, \theta]: r = ab^\theta\}$$

where $a > 0$ and $b > 1$, are called **logarithmic spirals**. The distance between successive coils of a logarithmic spiral is not constant as with spirals of Archimedes. Rather this distance d approaches ∞ as θ approaches ∞, and approaches 0 as θ approaches $-\infty$.

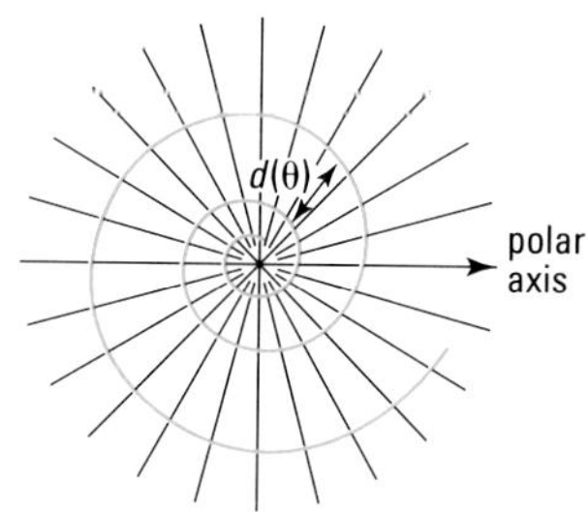

Logarithmic spirals derive their name from the fact that

$$r = ab^\theta$$
$$\Leftrightarrow \quad \log r = \log (ab^\theta)$$
$$\Leftrightarrow \quad \log r = \log a + (\log b)\theta,$$

which is of the form $\quad \log r = A + B\theta.$

Thus, if you plot $[\log r, \theta]$ in place of $[r, \theta]$ for the equation $r = ab^\theta$, the resulting polar graph is a spiral of Archimedes instead of a logarithmic spiral.

One very remarkable geometric property of the logarithmic spiral is that the angle ϕ between the tangent line to the polar graph of $r = ab^\theta$ and the radial line from the pole has the same measure at any point of the spiral.

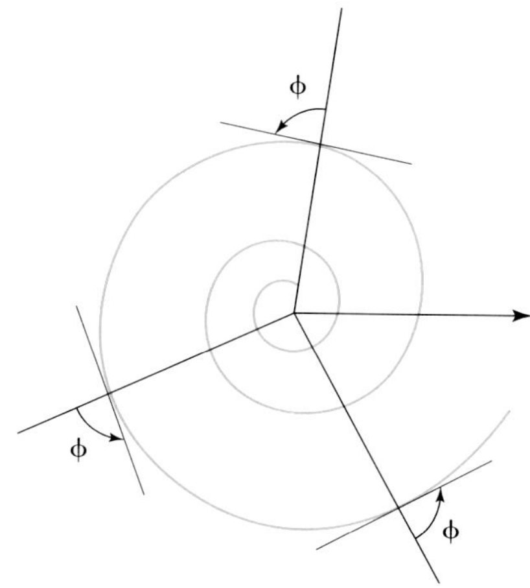

Adapting to Individual Needs

Extra Help

Some students may find it troublesome that the number of leaves depends on whether n is even or odd. Cover **Example 1** carefully and then have students follow the same procedure shown for $r = \sin 3\theta$, $r = \sin 4\theta$, and $r = \sin 5\theta$. Have them notice that in the interval $0 \le \theta < 2\pi$, there are $2n$ arcs in the sine curve. Then lead them to see that when n is even, each arc forms its own loop in the rose, so there are $2n$ loops. But when n is odd, the loops with negative r-values coincide with the loops with positive r-values. Hence, there are $\frac{2n}{2} = n$ loops.

One consequence of this property is that any two regions bounded by two lines intersecting at a fixed angle at the pole and two consecutive intercepted arcs of the spiral are similar.

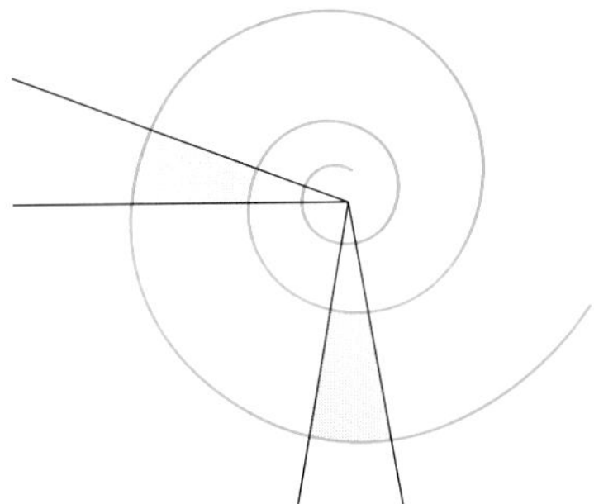

The shells of some sea creatures are shaped like logarithmic spirals for this reason. As the creature grows, the shell compartment expands in a way that allows the creature to retain its shape. Shown here is the shell of a chambered nautilus, cut in half to show its compartments.

❷

QUESTIONS

Covering the Reading

In 1–3, sketch the polar graph. **See left.**

1. $r = 4 \cos 5\theta$ **2.** $r = 3 \sin 2\theta$ **3.** $r = \cos 6\theta$

4. How would the graph of $r = \cos 6(\theta - \pi)$ compare to the graph in Question 3? **It will be the same since $\cos(\theta - \pi) = -\cos\theta$**

5. Give polar coordinates for five points on the graph of $r = \theta + 1$. **See left.**

6. Give polar coordinates for five points on the graph of $r = 2^{\theta}$. **Sample: $[1, 0]$, $\left[2^{\pi/6}, \frac{\pi}{6}\right]$, $\left[2^{\pi/4}, \frac{\pi}{4}\right]$, $\left[2^{\pi/2}, \frac{\pi}{2}\right]$, $[2^{\pi}, \pi]$**

1)

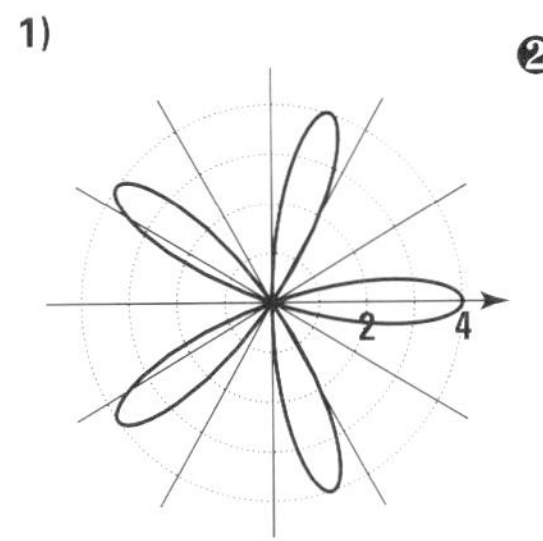

2)

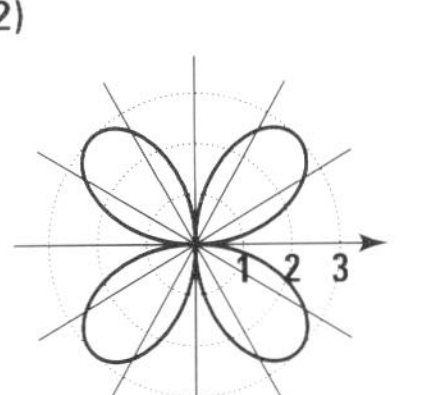

3)

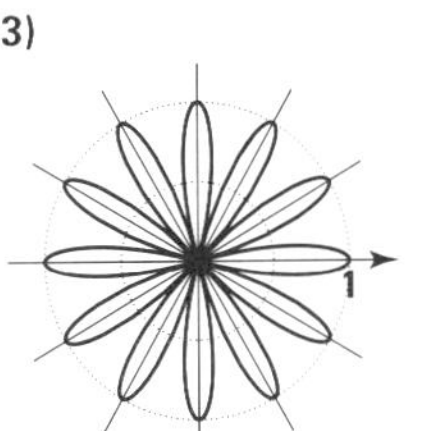

5) Sample: $[1, 0]$, $\left[\frac{\pi + 6}{6}, \frac{\pi}{6}\right]$, $\left[\frac{\pi + 4}{4}, \frac{\pi}{4}\right]$, $\left[\frac{\pi + 2}{2}, \frac{\pi}{2}\right]$, $[\pi + 1, \pi]$

Follow-up for Lesson 8-5

Practice

For more questions on SPUR Objectives, use **Lesson Master 8-5** (shown on pages 502–503).

Assessment

Written Communication Have students write the general form of the equations of polar graphs that yield rose curves, spirals of Archimedes, and logarithmic spirals. Then have the students give an example and polar graph of each. [Students show understanding of the equations and polar graphs of rose curves, spirals of Archimedes, and logarithmic spirals.]

Extension

Cooperative Learning You may wish to take an extra day to introduce students to other families of curves, such as the three shown below. Suggest that students **work in groups,** trying different values of a, and then seeing the effects of changing a on these graphs.

cissoid: $r = 2a \tan\theta \sin\theta$

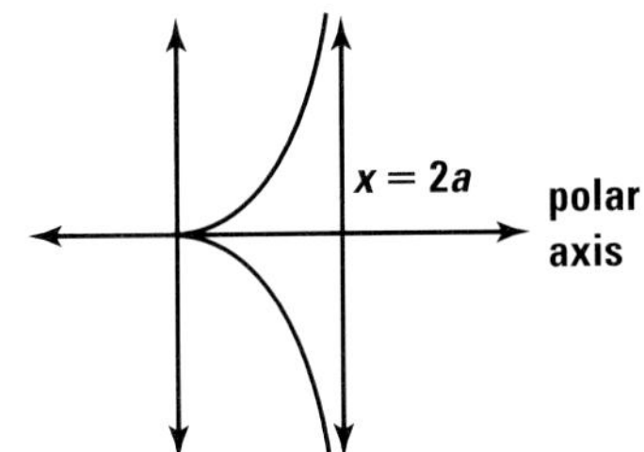

lemniscate: $r^2 = a^2 \cos 2\theta$

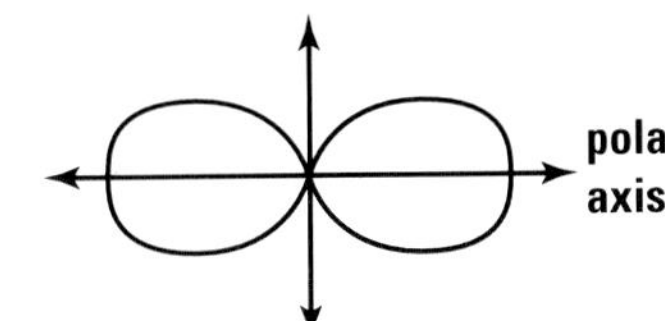

lituus: $r^2 = \frac{a^2}{\theta}$

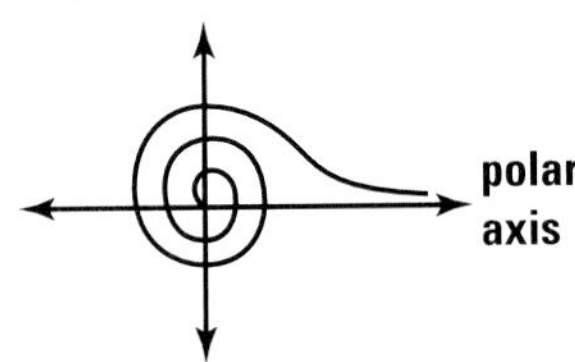

Project Update Project 1, *Polar Equations for Conic Sections,* and Project 4, *Spirals,* on page 542, relate to the content of this lesson.

Adapting to Individual Needs

Challenge

Have students answer the following.

1. Explore the graphs of $r = a \cos n\theta$ and $r = a \sin n\theta$ for noninteger values of n. Use a larger value than 2π for the maximum limit of θ. [Sample: $r = 4 \cos \frac{2}{3}\theta$ and $r = 4 \sin \frac{5}{3}\theta$ produce overlapping petals.]
3. Describe the results when the spiral $r = \theta$ is graphed on $-2\pi \le \theta \le 2\pi$ instead of $0 \le \theta \le 2\pi$. [two spirals in opposite directions]
4. Explore the graphs of the form $r = e^{\sin\theta} + a \cos n\theta$. [Sample: $r = e^{\sin\theta} - 2 \cos 4\theta$ produces a very nice butterfly.]

Notes on Questions

Question 9 This question shows that one can use polar graphs to test for identities just as rectangular graphs were used in Chapter 6.

Question 11 Although the graphs intersect at [0, 0], these coordinates do not satisfy $r = 4\cos\theta$. Instead, $[0, \frac{\pi}{2}]$ does.

Questions 12–13 These questions review complex numbers in preparation for Lesson 8-6.

Additional Answers

9\. b. $r = \sqrt{2}\cos\left(\theta - \frac{\pi}{4}\right)$
$= \sqrt{2}\left(\cos\theta\cos\frac{\pi}{4} + \sin\theta\sin\frac{\pi}{4}\right)$
$= \sqrt{2}\left(\cos\theta \cdot \frac{\sqrt{2}}{2} + \sin\theta \cdot \frac{\sqrt{2}}{2}\right)$
$= \cos\theta + \sin\theta$

c. $r = \cos\theta + \sin\theta$
$\Rightarrow r = \frac{x}{r} + \frac{y}{r} \Rightarrow r = \frac{x + y}{r}$
$\Rightarrow r^2 = x + y$
$\Rightarrow x^2 + y^2 = x + y$
$\Rightarrow x^2 - x + y^2 - y = 0$
$\Rightarrow x^2 - x + \frac{1}{4} + y^2 - y + \frac{1}{4} = \frac{1}{2}$
$\Rightarrow \left(x - \frac{1}{2}\right)^2 + \left(y - \frac{1}{2}\right)^2 = \left(\frac{1}{\sqrt{2}}\right)^2$

So, the graph is a circle.

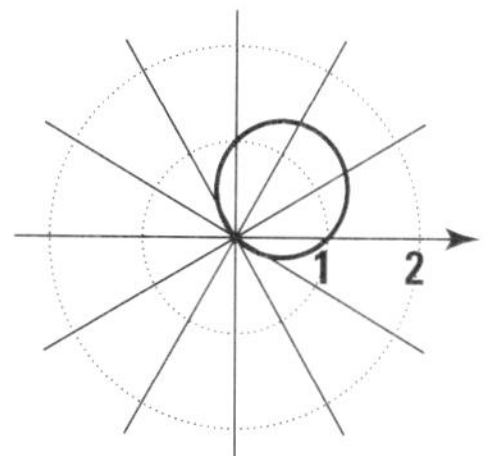

10.

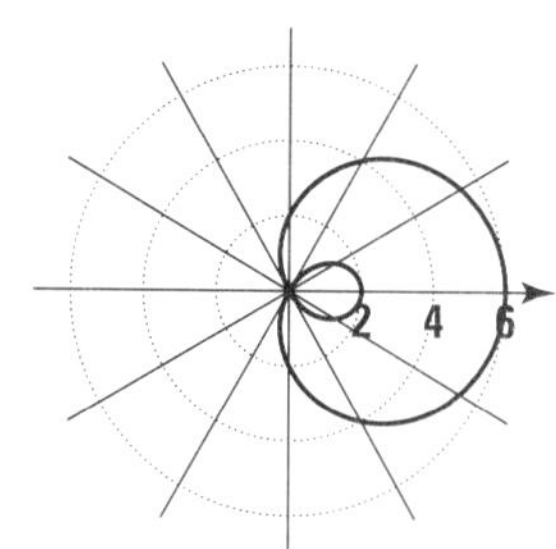

7b) Sample: $r = 2\cos 5\theta$

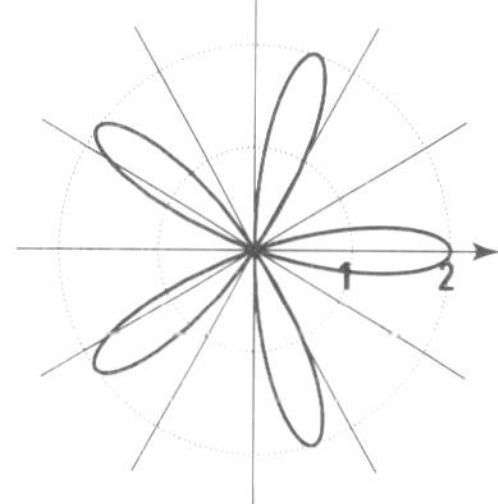

8)

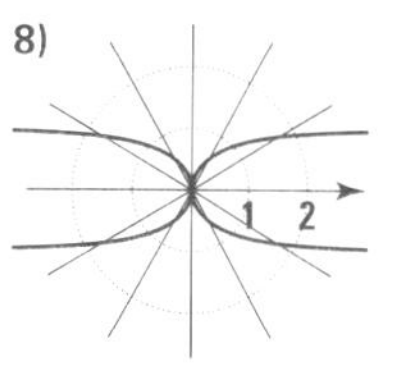

There are horizontal asymptotes because $\cot\theta$ is undefined when $\sin\theta = 0$.

9a)

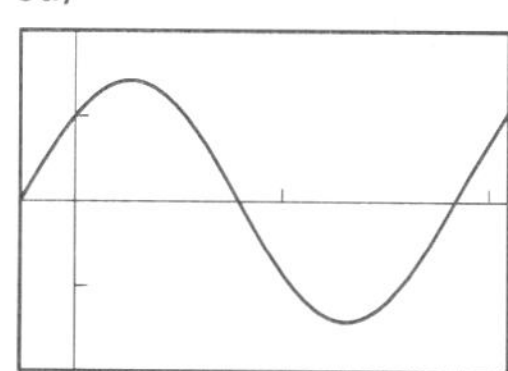

$-\frac{\pi}{4} \le x \le 2\pi$, x-scale = 3
$-2 \le y \le 2$, y-scale = 1

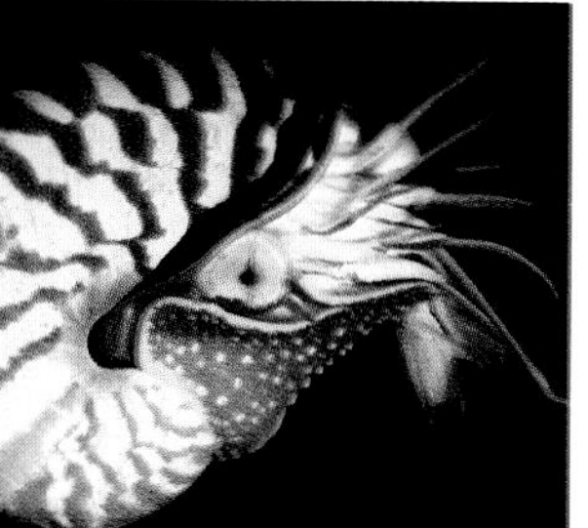

chambered nautilus

Applying the Mathematics

7. a. What is an equation for a five-leafed rose with leaves of length 2?
b. Graph this curve. See left.
a) $r = 2\sin 5\theta$ or $r = 2\cos 5\theta$

8. Sketch the graph of $r = \cot\theta$ and explain why it has the shape it does. See left.

9. a. Use an automatic grapher to plot the rectangular graphs of the equations $r = \cos\theta + \sin\theta$ and $r = \sqrt{2}\cos\left(\theta - \frac{\pi}{4}\right)$. See left.
b. Verify that the equations in part **a** are equivalent by using an appropriate identity. See margin.
c. Sketch the polar graph of $r = \cos\theta + \sin\theta$ and verify that it is a circle. See margin.

Review

10. Graph the curve $r = 2 + 4\cos\theta$ on a polar grid. *(Lesson 8-4)* See margin.

11. a. On a polar grid, sketch the curves $r = 4\cos\theta$ and $r = 4\sin\theta$.
b. Find the points of intersection of the two curves. *(Lessons 6-8, 8-4)*
a) See margin. b) [0, 0], $[2\sqrt{2}, \pi/4]$

12. a. A size change of magnitude $\frac{1}{2}$ followed by a rotation of $\frac{4\pi}{3}$ about the origin is equivalent to multiplication by what complex number?
b. Write your answer to part **a** in $a + bi$ form. $-\frac{1}{4} - \frac{\sqrt{3}}{4}i$
c. Use your answer to part **b** to find the images of the points $u = -2$, $v = 6$, $w = 6 + 4i$, and $z = -2 + 4i$ under the transformations described.
d. Graph the points u, v, w, and z and their images. *(Lessons 8-2, 8-3)*
a) $\frac{1}{2}\left(\cos\frac{4\pi}{3} + i\sin\frac{4\pi}{3}\right)$ c, d) See margin.

13. In an AC circuit, the current is $-4 + 3i$ amps and the impedance is $2 + 4i$ ohms.
a. Find the voltage across the circuit. $-20 - 10i$ volts
b. Suppose the circuit is connected in series with another circuit with voltage $11 + 8i$ volts. Find the total voltage. *(Lesson 8-1)* $-9 - 2i$ volts

14. The rectangle at the right is twice as wide as it is high. What are the measures of the acute angles formed by its diagonals? *(Previous course)* about 26.6° and 63.4°

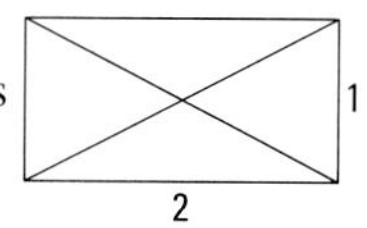

Exploration

15. Find out something about the chambered nautilus other than what is stated in this lesson. The chambered nautilus is also known as the pearly nautilus. It has a smooth, coiled shell 15–25 cm in diameter, consisting of 30 to 36 chambers; it lives in the outermost chamber.

11\. a. $r = 4\sin\theta$

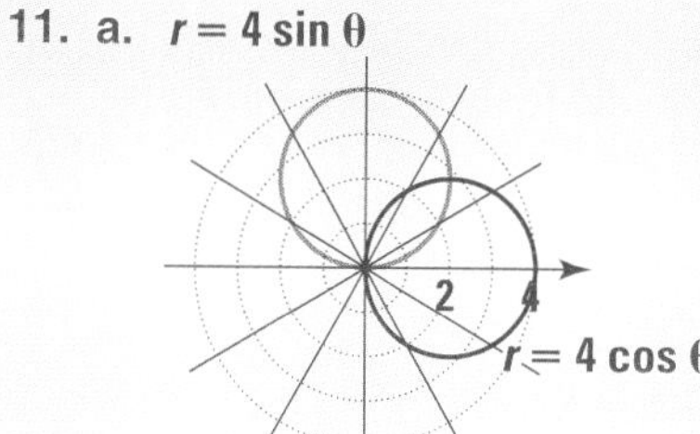

12\. c. $u' = \frac{1}{2} + \frac{\sqrt{3}}{2}i$, $v' = -\frac{3}{2} - \frac{3\sqrt{3}}{2}i$,
$w' = -\frac{3}{2} + \sqrt{3} + \left(-1 - \frac{3\sqrt{3}}{2}\right)i$,
$z' = \frac{1}{2} + \sqrt{3} + \left(\frac{\sqrt{3}}{2} - 1\right)i$

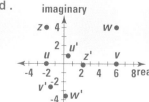

d. imaginary
z• 4 w•
2 u'
u z' v
-4 -2 2 4 6 8 real
v' -2
-4 w'

LESSON

8-6

Powers of Complex Numbers

❶ *Each spiral arm of this galaxy, NGC 6946, is like the spiral obtained in Example 2.*

Lessons 8-1 and 8-3 covered the algebraic and geometric properties of the two basic operations in the complex number field: addition and multiplication. Now we consider calculating positive integer powers of a complex number. The ability to find these powers provides all of the computational equipment needed to obtain values of polynomial functions involving complex numbers. Also, there is an interesting relationship between the powers of a complex number and one of the curves you studied in the last lesson.

Calculating the Powers of a Complex Number

Recall that in Lesson 7-9, two algorithms were given for the calculation of x^n for a given real number x and positive integer n. The first, using repeated multiplication, required $n - 1$ significant operations. The second required thinking of the integer n as a sum of powers of 2, but was more efficient because it required fewer steps.

Similarly, there is more than one way to calculate z^n for a given complex number z and positive integer n. For instance, one way to calculate z^9 when $z = (-1 + \sqrt{3}\,i)$ is to repeatedly square z to obtain z^2, z^4, and z^8, and then multiply z^8 by z to arrive at z^9. For most values of z and n, however, there is a more efficient way to obtain z^n. This way is based on the Geometric Multiplication Theorem, and utilizes a simple formula known as DeMoivre's (pronounced dee mwavs') Theorem, named after its discoverer, Abraham DeMoivre (1667–1754).

Lesson 8-6

Objectives

D Find powers of complex numbers.

F Prove or verify properties of complex numbers.

K Use DeMoivre's Theorem to graph powers of complex numbers.

Resources

From the ***Teacher's Resource File***

- Lesson Master 8-6
- Answer Master 8-6
- Teaching Aids
  - 71 Warm-up
  - 73 Large Polar Coordinate Grid
  - 74 Polar Grids
  - 81 Graphs of Powers of Complex Numbers

Additional Resources

- Visuals for Teaching Aids 71, 73, 74, 81

Teaching Lesson 8-6

Warm-up

Let $z = 2 + 3i$.

1. Calculate z^2, z^3, and z^4. **$-5 + 12i$, $-46 + 9i$, $-119 - 120i$**
2. Find the distance of the graphs of z, z^2, z^3, and z^4 from the origin. **$13^{1/2}$, 13, $13^{3/2}$, 169**
3. Predict what the distance of z^5 will be from the origin. Check your prediction by calculating z^5 and its distance from the origin. **$13^{5/2}$**
4. Generalize Question 3. **The distance of z^n from the origin is $13^{n/2}$.**

Notes on Reading

❶ **Science Connection** Galaxies are classified as spiral, elliptical, or irregular. Spiral galaxies have pinwheel-like arms that coil out from the center. Elliptical galaxies are spherical or spheroidal. Irregular galaxies have no definite shape.

Lesson 8-6 Overview

Broad Goals This is the second of three consecutive lessons with some of the most visually beautiful elegance of all elementary mathematics. DeMoivre's Theorem is proved and used to graphically display the integer powers of a complex number.

Perspective Students now have the background for both the algebra and the geometry of the powers of complex numbers. The algebra is given by DeMoivre's Theorem: $(r(\cos\theta + i\sin\theta))^n = r^n(\cos(n\theta) + i\sin(n\theta))$ in its common trigonometric form, and $[r, \theta]^n = [r^n, n\theta]$ in the simpler polar coordinate form. DeMoivre's Theorem is proved by induction.

The geometry is that, if the absolute value of a particular complex number is not 1, then the graphs of the powers of that

(Overview continues on page 508.)

DeMoivre's Theorem is so simple that students do not always appreciate how astounding it is. Point out that in $a + bi$ form, the first form known to mathematicians, this theorem is not at all obvious. It is only in the trigonometric and polar forms that the pattern is evident.

❷ To reinforce understanding of the theorem and its proof by induction, do a series of applications of the Geometric Multiplication Theorem. For example, to calculate $[3, 20°]^4$, we do

$[3, 20°] \cdot [3, 20°] = [9, 40°]$
$[3, 20°] \cdot [9, 40°] = [27, 60°]$
$[3, 20°] \cdot [27, 60°] = [81, 80°]$
But $[81, 80°] = [3^4, 4 \cdot 20°]$.
So $[3, 20°]^4 = [3^4, 4 \cdot 20°]$.

❸ **Error Alert** In Solution 2 of **Example 1,** some students may have difficulty understanding why $[512, 6\pi] = [512, 0]$. Remind them that we saw in Lesson 8-2 that $[r, \theta] = [r, \theta + 2\pi n]$, $\forall$ integers n. Here $r = 512$, $\theta = 0$ and $n = 3$.

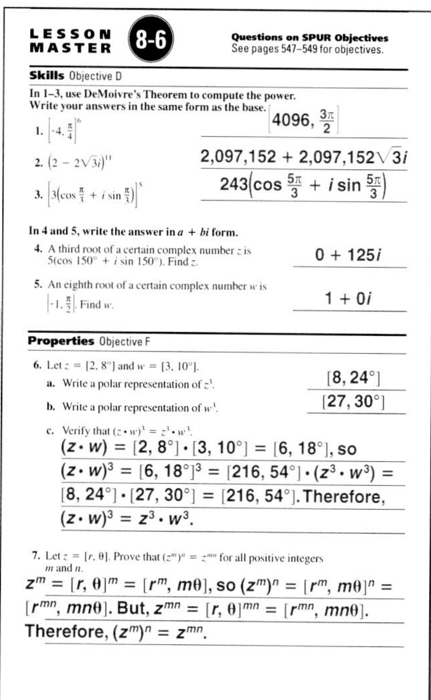

LESSON MASTER 8-6 **Questions on SPUR Objectives** See pages 547–549 for objectives.

Skills Objective D

In 1–3, use DeMoivre's Theorem to compute the power. Write your answers in the same form as the base.

1. $\left[-4, \frac{\pi}{4}\right]^6$ — $\left[4096, \frac{3\pi}{2}\right]$
2. $(2 - 2\sqrt{3}i)^{11}$ — $2{,}097{,}152 + 2{,}097{,}152\sqrt{3}i$
3. $\left[3\left(\cos\frac{\pi}{3} + i\sin\frac{\pi}{3}\right)\right]^5$ — $243\left(\cos\frac{5\pi}{3} + i\sin\frac{5\pi}{3}\right)$

In 4 and 5, write the answer in $a + bi$ form.

4. A third root of a certain complex number z is $5(\cos 150° + i\sin 150°)$. Find z. — $0 + 125i$
5. An eighth root of a certain complex number w is $\left[-1, \frac{\pi}{2}\right]$. Find w. — $1 + 0i$

Properties Objective F

6. Let $z = [2, 8°]$ and $w = [3, 10°]$.
   a. Write a polar representation of z^3. — $[8, 24°]$
   b. Write a polar representation of w^3. — $[27, 30°]$
   c. Verify that $(z \cdot w)^3 = z^3 \cdot w^3$.
   $(z \cdot w) = [2, 8°] \cdot [3, 10°] = [6, 18°]$, so $(z \cdot w)^3 = [6, 18°]^3 = [216, 54°] \cdot (z^3 \cdot w^3) = [8, 24°] \cdot [27, 30°] = [216, 54°]$. Therefore, $(z \cdot w)^3 = z^3 \cdot w^3$.

7. Let $z = [r, \theta]$. Prove that $(z^m)^n = z^{mn}$ for all positive integers m and n.
$z^m = [r, \theta]^m = [r^m, m\theta]$, so $(z^m)^n = [r^m, m\theta]^n = [r^{mn}, mn\theta]$. But, $z^{mn} = [r, \theta]^{mn} = [r^{mn}, mn\theta]$. Therefore, $(z^m)^n = z^{mn}$.

Abraham DeMoivre

DeMoivre's Theorem

DeMoivre's Theorem extracts a price for its efficiency. The complex number must be written in polar or trigonometric form in order to apply it easily.

DeMoivre's Theorem
(Polar Form) For all positive integers n, if $z = [r, \theta]$, then

$$z^n = [r^n, n\theta].$$

(Trigonometric Form) For all positive integers n, if $z = r(\cos\theta + i\sin\theta)$, then

$$z^n = r^n(\cos n\theta + i\sin n\theta).$$

❷ **Proof**
As is often the case when trying to show that a mathematical statement is true for all positive integers, mathematical induction is used. Given $z = [r, \theta]$, the truth of $S(n)$ must be proved for all positive integers n, where $S(n)$ is $z^n = [r^n, n\theta]$. First show that $S(1)$ is true.

$$S(1)\colon z^1 = [r^1, 1 \cdot \theta].$$

Since $z = [r, \theta]$, $S(1)$ is true.
Second show that for any positive integer k, the assumption $S(k)$ is true implies that $S(k + 1)$ is true.

Here $\quad S(k)\colon z^k = [r^k, k\theta]$.
and $\quad S(k + 1)\colon z^{k+1} = [r^{k+1}, (k + 1)\theta]$.
If $S(k)$ is true, then multiplying both sides by z yields

$z \cdot z^k = [r, \theta] \cdot [r^k, k\theta]$	substitution
$z^{k+1} = [r \cdot r^k, \theta + k\theta]$	Geometric Multiplication Theorem
$= [r^{k+1}, (k + 1)\theta]$	Product of Powers, Distributive Property

Thus, $S(k + 1)$ is true. Therefore, by the Principle of Mathematical Induction, $S(n)$ is true for all positive integers.

The next example shows how to use DeMoivre's Theorem to compute the power mentioned earlier.

Example 1

Compute z^9 when $z = -1 + \sqrt{3}i$.

Solution 1

Find a trigonometric form for z. If $z = r(\cos\theta + i\sin\theta)$, then

$$r = \sqrt{(-1)^2 + (\sqrt{3})^2} = \sqrt{4} = 2.$$

$\tan\theta = \frac{\sqrt{3}}{-1}$ and θ is in the second quadrant.

Therefore, $\theta = \frac{2\pi}{3}$, and so a trigonometric form of z is

$$z = 2\left(\cos\frac{2\pi}{3} + i\sin\frac{2\pi}{3}\right).$$

▸

Lesson 8-6 Overview, continued

number lie on a logarithmic spiral with $a = 1$, for if $[s, \phi]$ satisfies $r = b^\theta$, then $s = b^\phi$, and so $s^n = (b^\phi)^n = (b)^{n\phi}$. Thus $[s^n, n\phi]$ also satisfies $r = b^\theta$.

A hint of the idea of discrete dynamical systems described in Lesson 8-10 is found by graphing the powers of certain complex numbers with absolute value 1. These powers all lie on the unit circle.

Optional Activities

Cooperative Learning To engender an appreciation for the power of knowledge, you may wish to divide your class into 4 teams. Each team is to calculate and simplify $(1 - i)^{10}$ using a different algorithm. All groups must show all required work.

Team A: Expand $(1 - i)^{10}$ by rewriting it as $(1 - i)(1 - i) \ldots (1 - i)$ and multiplying.

Apply DeMoivre's Theorem with $r = 2$, $\theta = \frac{2\pi}{3}$, and $n = 9$.

$$z^9 = 2^9\left[\cos\left(9 \cdot \frac{2\pi}{3}\right) + i \sin\left(9 \cdot \frac{2\pi}{3}\right)\right]$$

Because $2^9 = 512$ and $9 \cdot \frac{2\pi}{3} = 6\pi \equiv 0 \pmod{2\pi}$, it follows that a simpler trigonometric form of z^9 is

$$z^9 = 512(\cos 0 + i \sin 0) = 512.$$

That is, $(-1 + \sqrt{3}i)^9$ is the real number 512.

Solution 2

❸ Use a polar form for z. If $z = [r, \theta]$, then find r and θ as in Solution 1. So a polar form of z is

$$z = \left[2, \frac{2\pi}{3}\right].$$

Apply DeMoivre's Theorem to find

$$z^9 = \left[2^9, 9 \cdot \frac{2\pi}{3}\right] = [512, 6\pi] = [512, 0] = 512.$$

Graphing the Powers of a Complex Number

The geometry of the sequence of successive powers of a complex number is quite beautiful.

Example 2

Suppose that $z = \left[1.1, \frac{\pi}{3}\right]$.

a. Use DeMoivre's Theorem to compute the successive powers: $z^2, z^3, z^4, z^5, z^6, z^7, z^8, z^9$.

b. Plot these points in the complex plane and draw a smooth curve through the successive points.

Solution

a. Here are the values of these complex numbers with r to two decimal places.

$$z^2 = \left[1.21, \frac{2\pi}{3}\right]$$
$$z^3 = \left[1.33, \frac{3\pi}{3}\right] = [1.33, \pi]$$
$$z^4 = \left[1.46, \frac{4\pi}{3}\right]$$
$$z^5 = \left[1.61, \frac{5\pi}{3}\right]$$
$$z^6 = \left[1.77, \frac{6\pi}{3}\right] = [1.77, 0]$$
$$z^7 = \left[1.95, \frac{7\pi}{3}\right] = \left[1.95, \frac{\pi}{3}\right]$$
$$z^8 = \left[2.14, \frac{8\pi}{3}\right] = \left[2.14, \frac{2\pi}{3}\right]$$
$$z^9 = \left[2.36, \frac{9\pi}{3}\right] = [2.36, \pi]$$

Team B: Express $(1 - i)^{10}$ in trigonometric form as $[\sqrt{2}(\cos(-45°) + i\sin(-45°))]^{10}$ and evaluate using repeated applications of $[r(\cos\theta + i\sin\theta)] \cdot [s(\cos\phi + i\sin\phi)] = [rs(\cos(\theta + \phi) + i\sin(\theta + \phi))]$.

Team C: Do repeated applications of the Geometric Multiplication Theorem for $[\sqrt{2}, -45°]^{10}$.

Team D: Use DeMoivre's Theorem to evaluate $[\sqrt{2}, -45°]^{10}$.

If there are some students who know the Binomial Theorem (to be discussed in Lesson 10-5), then have them constitute a 5th team to calculate $(1 - i)^{10}$. Be compassionate—make this a timed event. All teams should get $-32i$, but Team D should finish first.

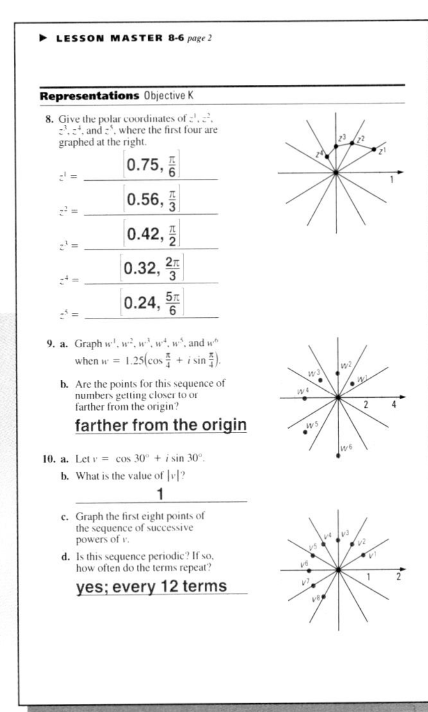

LESSON MASTER 8-6 page 2
Representations Objective K
8. Give the polar coordinates of z¹, z², z³, z⁴, and z⁵, where the first four are graphed at the right.
z¹ = 0.75, π/6
z² = 0.56, π/3
z³ = 0.42, π/2
z⁴ = 0.32, 2π/3
z⁵ = 0.24, 5π/6
9. a. Graph w¹, w², w³, w⁴, w⁵, and w⁶ when w = 1.25(cos π/4 + i sin π/4).
b. Are the points for this sequence of numbers getting closer to or farther from the origin?
farther from the origin
10. a. Let v = cos 30° + i sin 30°.
b. What is the value of |v|?
1
c. Graph the first eight points of the sequence of successive powers of v.
d. Is this sequence periodic? If so, how often do the terms repeat?
yes; every 12 terms

❹ **History Connection** Ferns were the most prominent form of plant life in the Carboniferous Period (260 million years ago). In fact, part of that period is called the "Age of the Fern."

In the discussion for graphing powers of z when $|z| = 1$, some students will need to be reminded that there are an infinite number of complex numbers whose absolute value is 1, unlike real numbers where there are only two such numbers. All these complex numbers lie on the unit circle. Like real numbers, complex numbers w and z satisfy the relation $|zw| = |z||w|$, so if two complex numbers have absolute value 1, so does their product. For this reason, the power of any complex number with absolute value 1 also has absolute value 1. Another way of seeing this is from DeMoivre's Theorem: $[1, \theta]^n = [1, n\theta]$. A generalization is found in **Question 14.**

Teaching Aid 81 contains the spiral outward of **Example 2,** the spiral inward of the powers of the complex number $w = [.9, \frac{\pi}{4}]$, and the first 10, 50, and 500 powers of $z = [1,1]$ as shown in the lesson.

b. Shown here are the graphs of these points in the complex plane.

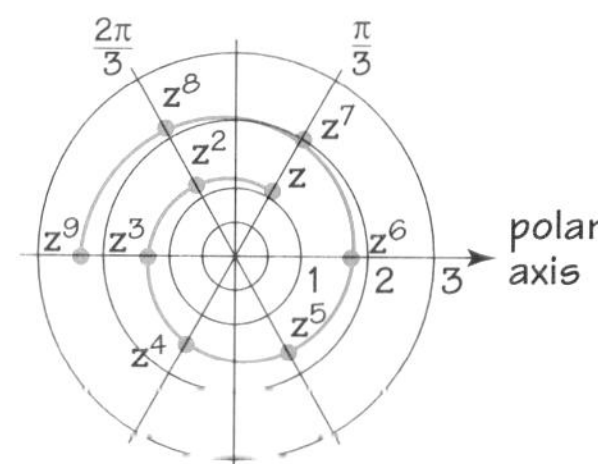

The curve looks like a spiral. In fact, all the powers of $z = \left[1.1, \frac{\pi}{3}\right]$ lie on the logarithmic spiral $r = (1.1)^{3\theta/\pi}$.

Example 3

Prove that the integer powers of $\left[1.1, \frac{\pi}{3}\right]$ lie on the logarithmic spiral with equation $r = 1.1^{3\theta/\pi}$.

Solution

By DeMoivre's Theorem, $\left[1.1, \frac{\pi}{3}\right]^n = \left[1.1^n, \frac{n\pi}{3}\right]$. Consequently, an integer power $[r, \theta]$ has $r = 1.1^n$ and $\theta = \frac{n\pi}{3}$.

Solving for n in terms of θ, $n = \frac{3\theta}{\pi}$. Substituting in the equation for r, $r = 1.1^{3\theta/\pi}$.

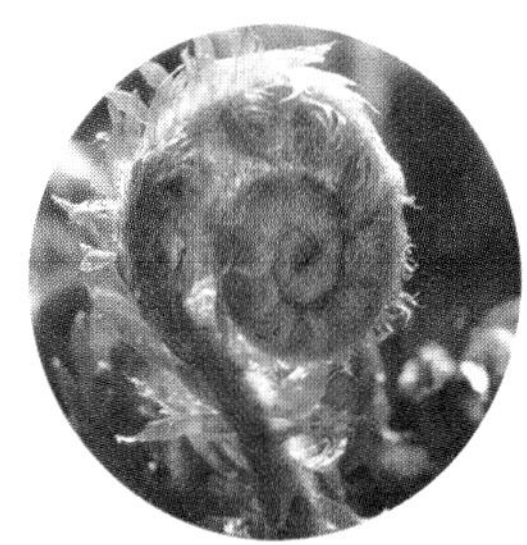

❹ *fern frond uncoiling in the spring*

In Example 2, the powers of $z = [r, \theta]$ are successively farther and farther from the origin because r, the absolute value of z, satisfies $r > 1$. Consequently, as n increases, so does r^n. When $r < 1$, the powers of $[r, \theta]$ spiral inward. For instance, at the right is the graph of the first through ninth powers of w where $w = .9\left(\cos\left(\frac{\pi}{4}\right) + i \sin\left(\frac{\pi}{4}\right)\right)$.

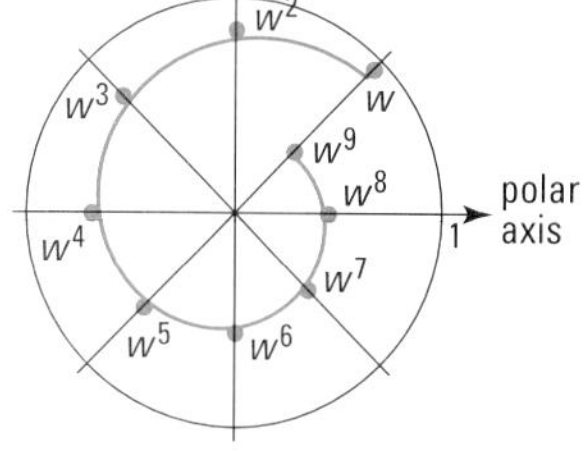

Graphing Powers of z when $|z| = 1$

If z is a complex number with $|z| = 1$, then $|z^n| = 1$ for all positive integers n. (You are asked to prove a more general form of this in Question 14.) This means that the graphs of the sequence of successive powers of z,

$$z, z^2, z^3, \ldots, z^k, \ldots$$

all lie on the circle of radius 1 centered at the origin (the unit circle).

This sequence of points is periodic for some choices of z. For example, if $z = 1$, then $z, z^2, z^3, \ldots$ is the constant sequence with all terms equal to 1. If $z = i$, then $z, z^2, z^3, \ldots$ is the sequence

$$i, -1, -i, 1, i, -1, -i, 1, \ldots$$

with period 4, since the sequence repeats itself every 4 terms.

Adapting to Individual Needs

Extra Help

Point out that the proof of DeMoivre's Theorem is given for the polar form. Explain that the proof of the trigonometric form could contain similar steps, or one could use the existing proof and convert between the two forms at the beginning and end of the proof.

English Language Development

The name "DeMoivre" has various pronunciations in common use. One French pronunciation is given in the lesson. Another is dee-mwavrs´, with the r unaccented. DeMoivre spent some time in England, and a British pronunciation used by some people is dee-moy´-vree.

There are values of z with $|z| = 1$ for which all terms of the sequence $z, z^2, z^3, \ldots$ are distinct points on the unit circle centered at the origin in the complex plane. For example, if $z = \cos 1 + i \sin 1$ (that is, the argument of z is 1 radian), then by DeMoivre's Theorem,

$$z^n = \cos n + i \sin n.$$

In this case, it can be shown that for each positive integer n, the value of z^n is different. The diagrams below show the graphs of the first 10, 50, and 500 points of this sequence.

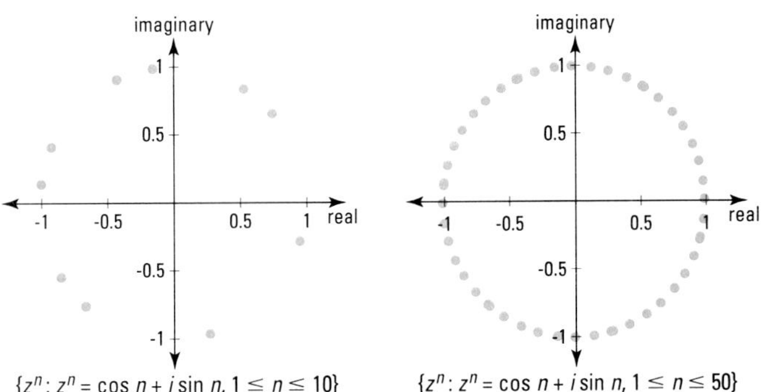

$\{z^n : z^n = \cos n + i \sin n, 1 \le n \le 10\}$ $\{z^n : z^n = \cos n + i \sin n, 1 \le n \le 50\}$

Not all points on the circle are included in the infinite sequence of powers of z, but it can be shown that given any point on the circle, there is some power of z that is as close as you wish to that point.

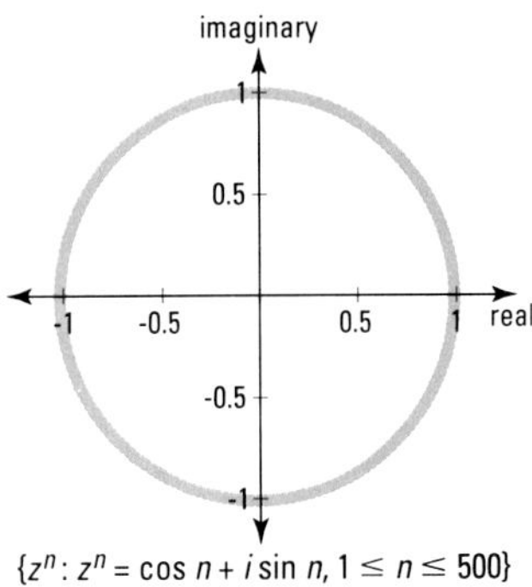

$\{z^n : z^n = \cos n + i \sin n, 1 \le n \le 500\}$

QUESTIONS

Covering the Reading

In 1–3, use DeMoivre's Theorem to compute the power. Write your answer in the same form as the base. **See left.**

1. $\left[3, \frac{\pi}{5}\right]^4$ **2.** $\left[6\left(\cos \frac{4\pi}{7} + i \sin \frac{4\pi}{7}\right)\right]^3$ **3.** $(2 + 2\sqrt{3}\, i)^5$

1) $\left[81, \frac{4\pi}{5}\right]$

2) $216\left(\cos \frac{12\pi}{7} + i \sin \frac{12\pi}{7}\right)$

3) $512 - 512\sqrt{3}\, i$

In 4 and 5, does the graph of the sequence of numbers get closer to or farther from the origin?

4. z^1, z^2, z^3, z^4, z^5 when $z = \frac{1}{3}\left(\cos\left(\frac{\pi}{7}\right) + i \sin\left(\frac{\pi}{7}\right)\right)$ **closer**

Additional Examples

1. Compute z^{11} when $z = \frac{1}{2} + \frac{\sqrt{3}}{2}i$.
$z = \cos \frac{\pi}{3} + i \sin \frac{\pi}{3} = [1, \frac{\pi}{3}]$, so $z^{11} = [1^{11}, \frac{11\pi}{3}] = [1, \frac{5\pi}{3}]$.

2. Suppose $z = [1.2, \frac{\pi}{2}]$. Compute the successive powers z^2 through z^9, and then plot them and z in the complex plane, and draw a smooth curve through the consecutive powers.
With r to two decimal places,
$z = [1.2, \frac{\pi}{2}]$, $z^2 = [1.44, \pi]$,
$z^3 = [1.73, \frac{3\pi}{2}]$, $z^4 = [2.07, 0]$,
$z^5 = [2.49, \frac{\pi}{2}]$, $z^6 = [2.99, \pi]$,
$z^7 = [3.58, \frac{3\pi}{2}]$, $z^8 = [4.30, 0]$,
$z^9 = [5.16, \frac{\pi}{2}]$.

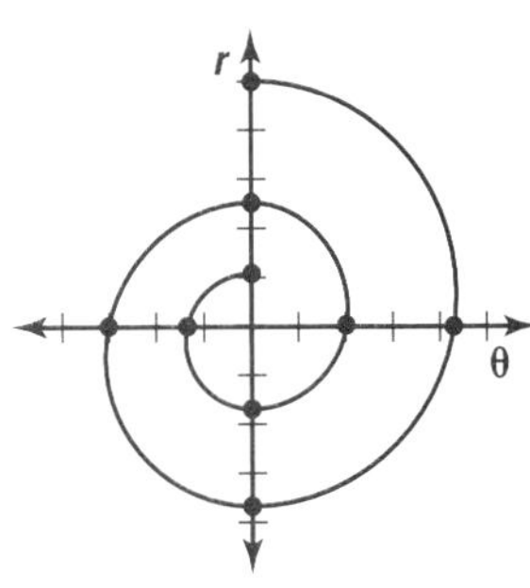

Adapting to Individual Needs

Challenge

Have students use DeMoivre's Theorem to give another proof of previously obtained identities.

1. $\cos 2\theta = \cos^2\theta - \sin^2\theta$
2. $\sin 2\theta = 2 \cos \theta \sin \theta$
3. $\cos 3\theta = \cos^3\theta - 3 \cos \theta \sin^2\theta$
4. $\sin 3\theta = 3 \cos^2\theta \sin \theta - \sin^3\theta$

[Expand $(\cos \theta + i \sin \theta)^2$ by ordinary multiplication and then by DeMoivre's Theorem. Equating the real parts gives the identity in Question 1. Equating the imaginary parts gives the identity in Question 2. Similarly, expanding $(\cos \theta + i \sin \theta)^3$ gives the last two identities.]

Notes on Questions

Questions 6, 7, 10, 15, and 16 Students need polar graph paper for these problems. You can duplicate either **Teaching Aid 73** with a large polar coordinate grid or **Teaching Aid 74** with smaller polar grids.

Question 12 This question anticipates Lesson 8-7.

Question 13 Is it obvious to students that all points on the graph of $z = [1.1, \frac{\pi}{3}]^n$ lie on exactly one of three lines? Ask them why. [The arguments of the powers are multiples of $\frac{\pi}{3}$. All these multiples lie on one of three lines.]

Question 14 Note that each side is a real number. You might want to check this by asking students to calculate $|z|^2$ and $|z^2|$ when $z = 3 + 4i$.
$[z^2 = -7 + 24i;\ |z|^2 = |z^2| = 25]$

Question 17 Remind students that many proofs concerning properties of complex numbers begin with "Let $z = a + bi$."

6)

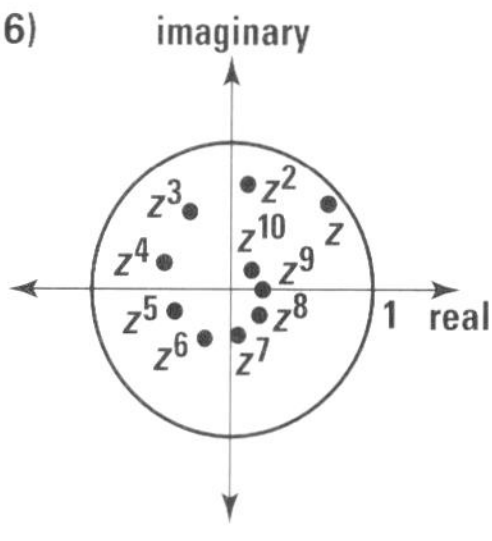

7)

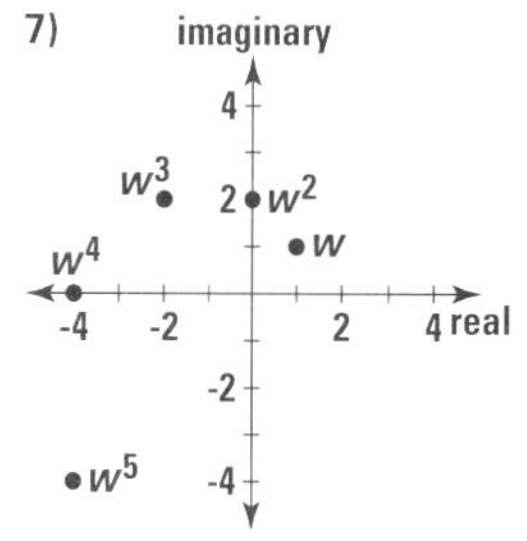

10)

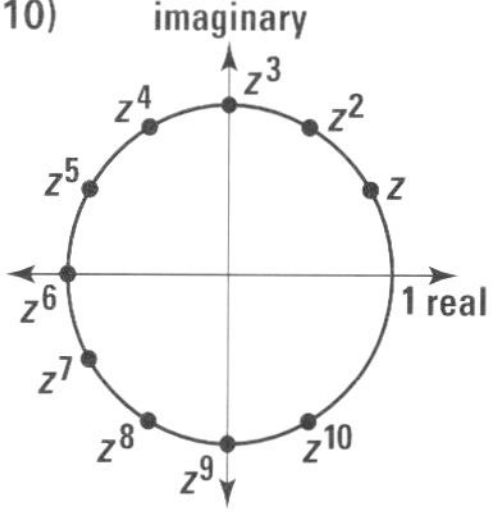

11b) $\left[4, \frac{\pi}{3}\right]^4 = \left[256, \frac{4\pi}{3}\right] = -128 - 128\sqrt{3}\,i$

13a) $z^7 = \left[2^7, \frac{14\pi}{3}\right]$, $z^{13} = \left[2^{13}, \frac{26\pi}{3}\right]$, $z^{19} = \left[2^{19}, \frac{38\pi}{3}\right]$, $z^{25} = \left[2^{25}, \frac{50\pi}{3}\right]$

b) $\frac{14\pi}{3} = \frac{2\pi}{3} + 2(2)\pi$; $\frac{26\pi}{3} = \frac{2\pi}{3} + 2(4)\pi$; $\frac{38\pi}{3} = \frac{2\pi}{3} + 2(6)\pi$; $\frac{50\pi}{3} = \frac{2\pi}{3} + 2(8)\pi$

5. w^1, w^2, w^3, w^4, w^5 when $w = \left[5, \frac{2\pi}{11}\right]$ **farther**

6. Graph $z^1, z^2, \ldots, z^{10}$ when $z = [.85, 40°]$. **See left.**

7. Graph w^1, w^2, w^3, w^4, and w^5 when $w = 1 + i$. **See left.**

8. Find an equation for the logarithmic spiral on which the powers in Question 7 lie. $r = (\sqrt{2})^{4\theta/\pi}$

9. Give the polar coordinates of the points w^3, w^6, and w^9 from the graph following Example 3. $w^3 = \left[.729, \frac{3\pi}{4}\right]$, $w^6 = \left[.53, \frac{3\pi}{2}\right]$, $w^9 = \left[.39, \frac{\pi}{4}\right]$

10. Graph the first 10 positive integer powers of $\left[1, \frac{\pi}{6}\right]$. **See left.**

Applying the Mathematics

11. a. Calculate $(2 + 2\sqrt{3}\,i)^4$ by thinking of it as $((2 + 2\sqrt{3}\,i)^2)^2$.

b. Check your work by converting $2 + 2\sqrt{3}\,i$ to polar form and using DeMoivre's Theorem. **See left.**

a) $-128 - 128\sqrt{3}\,i$

12. A fourth root of a certain complex number is $5(\cos 45° + i \sin 45°)$. Find the complex number. **-625**

13. Refer to Example 1.

a. Compute z^7, z^{13}, z^{19}, and z^{25}. **See left.**

b. Show that the argument for each of the powers in part **a** is of the form $\frac{2\pi}{3} + 2n\pi$, for some integer n. **See left.**

c. The powers z^1, z^7, z^{13}, z^{19}, and z^{25} all lie along the line $\theta = \frac{2\pi}{3}$ and start the loops of the spirals. Find the distances from the origin to the graphs of z^1, z^7, z^{13}, z^{19}, and z^{25}.
2; 128; 8192; 524,288; 33,554,432

14. Use either mathematical induction or DeMoivre's Theorem to prove that for all complex numbers z and all positive integers n, $|z^n| = |z|^n$. **See margin.**

Review

In 15 and 16, a polar equation is given. **a.** Sketch the graph of the equation. **b.** Classify the graph as a limaçon, rose curve, spiral of Archimedes, or logarithmic spiral. *(Lessons 8-4, 8-5)* **15a, 16a) See margin.**

15. $r = 3 \sin 4\theta$ **b) rose curve**

16. $r = 1 - \cos\theta$ **b) limaçon**

17. Prove that if z is any complex number, then $z - \bar{z}$ is an imaginary number. *(Lesson 8-1)* **Let $z = a + bi$. Then $\bar{z} = a - bi$ and $z - \bar{z} = a + bi - (a - bi) = a + bi - a + bi = 0 + 2bi$, which is an imaginary number.**

18. Graph the function $y = 3 \sin(3x + \pi)$ and identify its amplitude, period, and phase shift. *(Lesson 6-3)* **See margin.**

Additional Answers

14. Sample: By DeMoivre's Theorem, for $z = [r, \theta]$ with $r \geq 0$, $z^n = [r^n, n\theta]$, and $|z| = r$. So $|z^n| = |r^n| = r^n$, and $|z|^n = r^n$.
Sample: By mathematical induction, let $S(n)$: $|z^n| = |z|^n$. $S(1)$: $|z^1| = |z| = |z|^1$, so $S(1)$ is true. Assume $S(k)$: $|z^k| = |z|^k$. Then $|z^{k+1}| = |z^k \cdot z| = |z^k|\,|z| = |z|^k\,|z|^1 = |z|^{k+1}$. So $S(k) \Rightarrow S(k+1)$, and $S(n)$ is true for all integers n.

15. a.

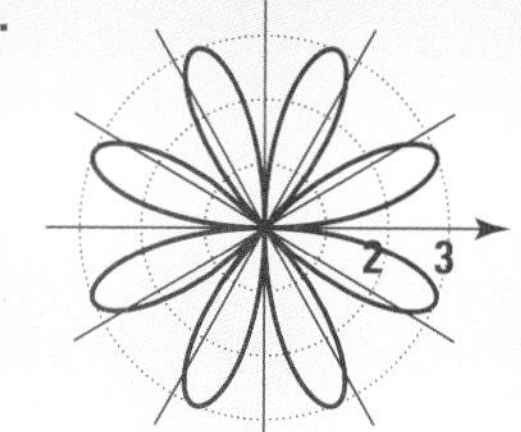

16. a.

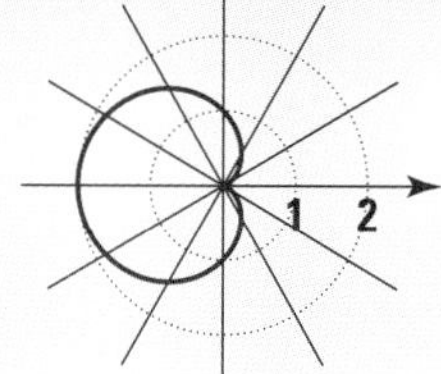

19. *Multiple choice.* The end behavior of $p(x) = 7x^5 - 4x^3 + 2x^2 - 5x + 9$ can be described as which of the following? *(Lesson 2-4)* b

(a) $\lim_{x\to-\infty} p(x) = -\infty$ and $\lim_{x\to\infty} p(x) = -\infty$

(b) $\lim_{x\to-\infty} p(x) = -\infty$ and $\lim_{x\to\infty} p(x) = \infty$

(c) $\lim_{x\to-\infty} p(x) = \infty$ and $\lim_{x\to\infty} p(x) = -\infty$

(d) $\lim_{x\to-\infty} p(x) = \infty$ and $\lim_{x\to\infty} p(x) = \infty$

20. *Multiple choice.* Determine the statement that is the correct negation of *If a person is going 15 miles per hour over the speed limit when stopped by the police, then the individual gets a ticket.* c

(a) *If a person is not going 15 miles per hour over the speed limit when stopped by the police, then the individual does not get a ticket.*

(b) *If a person is going 15 miles per hour over the speed limit when stopped by the police, then the individual does not get a ticket.*

(c) *There is a person who was going 15 miles per hour over the speed limit when stopped by the police and did not get a ticket.*

(d) *There is a person who was not going 15 miles per hour over the speed limit when stopped by the police and did not get a ticket.* *(Lesson 1-5)*

21. Solve each equation over the set of real numbers. *(Previous course)*

a. $x^3 = 13$ $\sqrt[3]{13}$ **b.** $x^3 = -13$ $-\sqrt[3]{13}$ **c.** $x^4 = 13$ $\sqrt[4]{13}, -\sqrt[4]{13}$ **d.** $x^4 = -13$ no real solution

Exploration

22. a. Graph the first 12 powers of $z = \frac{\sqrt{3}}{2} + \frac{i}{2}$. See left.

b. Describe the graphs of $z^{13}, z^{14}, \ldots, z^{24}$.

c. Graph z^{-1}, z^{-2}, and z^{-3}. Describe the pattern.

d. How are these results related to arithmetic mod 12? The exponents of terms that are equal are congruent to each other mod 12.

b) $z^{13}, z^{14}, \ldots, z^{24}$ will repeat the values of $z, z^2, \ldots, z^{12}$ in this way: $z = z^{13}, z^2 = z^{14}, \ldots, z^{12} = z^{24}$.

c) See graph for part a. $z^{-1} = z^{11}, z^{-2} = z^{10}, z^{-3} = z^9$

22a,c)

imaginary; real; z; z^2; z^3; z^4; z^5; z^6; z^7; z^8; $z^9 = z^{-3}$; $z^{10} = z^{-2}$; $z^{11} = z^{-1}$; z^{12}

Follow-up for Lesson 8-6

Practice

For more questions on SPUR Objectives, use **Lesson Master 8-6** (shown on pages 508–509).

Assessment

Written Communication Have students **work in pairs.** Have one partner compute and graph the powers in **Question 4** and the other partner do the same for **Question 5.** Then have students check each other's work. [Students find and graph powers of complex numbers.]

Extension

Discuss the fact that in the example given in the *Notes on Questions* to check **Question 14,** $a = 3$, $b = 4$, and $|z| = 5$. If $z^2 = c + di$, then $c = 7$, $d = 24$, and $|z^2| = 25$. Point out that 3, 4, and 5 are sides of a right triangle and so are 7, 24, and 25. These numbers are called Pythagorean triples because all three are integers. Then have students explore this question: Can powers of complex numbers be used to generate more Pythagorean triples? [They can; if *a*, *b*, and *c* are integer sides of a right triangle and $z = a + bi$, then for any *n*, if $z^n = c + di$, then *c*, *d*, and $|z^n|$ form a Pythagorean triple.] Ask students to find other Pythagorean triples by using this method.

Project Update Project 4, *Spirals,* on page 542, relates to the content of this lesson.

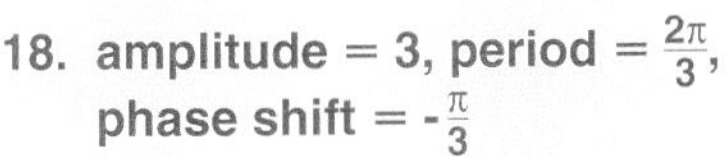

18. amplitude = 3, period = $\frac{2\pi}{3}$, phase shift = $-\frac{\pi}{3}$

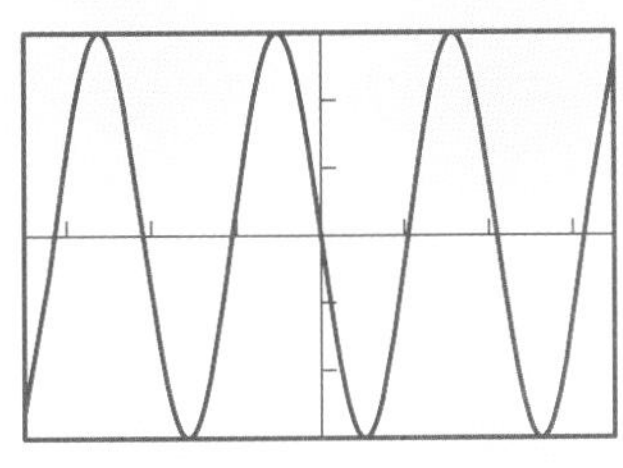

$-3.5 \le x \le 3.5$, *x*-scale = 1
$-3 \le y \le 3$, *y*-scale = 1

Setting Up Lesson 8-7

Discuss **Question 12** to remind students of the relationship between powers and roots: If $z^n = k$, then z is an nth root of k.

Lesson 8-7

Objectives

D Find roots of complex numbers.
K Use DeMoivre's Theorem to graph roots of complex numbers.

Resources

From the ***Teacher's Resource File***
- Lesson Master 8-7
- Answer Master 8-7
- Teaching Aids
  - 71 Warm-up
  - 82 Example 2 and the Geometric *n*th Roots Theorem
  - 83 *n*th Roots of Real Numbers

Additional Resources
- Visuals for Teachings 71, 82, 83

Teaching Lesson 8-7

Warm-up

Which of the following are 8th roots of 1?

1. 1 **2.** -1
3. i **4.** $-i$
5. $\frac{\sqrt{2}+i\sqrt{2}}{2}$ **6.** $\cos 60° + i \sin 60°$
7. $1 - i$ **8.** $[1, 225°]$

(1), (2), (3), (4), (5),and (8) are 8th roots of 1

LESSON

8-7 Roots of Complex Numbers

Examples of *n*th Roots of Complex Numbers

Roots of complex numbers are defined in the same way as roots of real numbers. For instance, since $(2 - 7i)^2 = -45 - 28i$, $2 - 7i$ is a square root of $-45 - 28i$. Since $(-1 + \sqrt{3}i)^9 = 512$, as you saw in the previous lesson, $-1 + \sqrt{3}i$ is a 9th root of 512. In general, if z and w are complex numbers and if $n \ge 2$ is an integer, then ***z* is an *n*th root of *w*** if and only if $z^n = w$. Although you may be accustomed to thinking of the *n*th roots of real numbers as rather complicated, the *n*th roots of complex numbers have a simple structure, and their geometry is exquisitely elegant.

Example 1

a. Find the cube roots of $27i$. **b.** Plot them in the complex plane.

Solution

a. Let $z = [s, \phi]$ represent a cube root of $27i$. By the definition of cube root, z must satisfy the equation

$$z^3 = 27i.$$

In polar form, this equation is

$$[s, \phi]^3 = \left[27, \tfrac{\pi}{2}\right].$$

So, by DeMoivre's Theorem,

$$[s^3, 3\phi] = \left[27, \tfrac{\pi}{2}\right].$$

This means that a complex number $z = [s, \phi]$ satisfies $z^3 = 27i$ if and only if

$$s^3 = 27 \quad \text{and} \quad 3\phi \equiv \tfrac{\pi}{2} \pmod{2\pi}.$$

Therefore, $s = \sqrt[3]{27} = 3$. Since 3ϕ and $\frac{\pi}{2}$ may differ by integral multiples of 2π,

$$3\phi = \tfrac{\pi}{2} + k \cdot 2\pi, \text{ where k is any integer.}$$

Solving for ϕ,

$$\phi = \tfrac{\pi}{6} + k \cdot \tfrac{2\pi}{3}, \text{ where k is any integer.}$$

Thus the cube roots of $27i$ have the polar form $\left[3, \frac{\pi}{6} + \frac{2\pi k}{3}\right]$, where k is any integer. Replacing k with 0, 1, and 2 gives the roots z_0, z_1, and z_2 as shown here in polar, trigonometric, and binomial forms.

$$k = 0: z_0 = \left[3, \tfrac{\pi}{6}\right] = 3\left(\cos \tfrac{\pi}{6} + i \sin \tfrac{\pi}{6}\right) = \tfrac{3\sqrt{3}}{2} + \tfrac{3}{2}i$$

$$k = 1: z_1 = \left[3, \tfrac{\pi}{6} + \tfrac{2\pi}{3}\right] = 3\left(\cos \tfrac{5\pi}{6} + i \sin \tfrac{5\pi}{6}\right) = -\tfrac{3\sqrt{3}}{2} + \tfrac{3}{2}i$$

$$k = 2: z_2 = \left[3, \tfrac{\pi}{6} + \tfrac{4\pi}{3}\right] = 3\left(\cos \tfrac{3\pi}{2} + i \sin \tfrac{3\pi}{2}\right) = -3i$$

Lesson 8-7 Overview

Broad Goals In this lesson, the algebra and geometry of *n*th roots of complex numbers are derived from DeMoivre's Theorem.

Perspective The algebra of *n*th roots is simple when complex numbers are written in polar form. One *n*th root of $[r, \theta]$ is $[r^{1/n}, \frac{\theta}{n}]$. The same numbers look more complicated in trigonometric form: $(r(\cos\theta + i \sin\theta))^{1/n} = r^{1/n}(\cos(\frac{\theta}{n}) + i \sin(\frac{\theta}{n}))$. But once a single *n*th root has been determined, repeatedly add $\frac{2\pi}{n}$ to the argument of this first *n*th root to obtain the other $n - 1$ *n*th roots. Geometrically, this guarantees that the graphs of the *n* *n*th roots of any nonzero complex number are the vertices of a regular *n*-gon centered at the origin. This is one of the most surprising and beautiful results in all of mathematics. It combines the arithmetic of complex numbers, the algebra of solving $z^n = k$, and the geometry of regular polygons.

In the set of real numbers, there are differences in how many *n*th roots a number has, depending on whether the number is positive or negative and whether *n* is odd or even. But, in the set of complex numbers, *n*th roots have an elegant and simple representation.This helps explain the situation with real numbers.

All other values of k yield numbers equal to z_0, z_1, or z_2. For instance, when $k = 3$,

$$z_3 = \left[3, \frac{\pi}{6} + \frac{6\pi}{3}\right] = 3\left(\cos\left(\frac{\pi}{6} + 2\pi\right) + i\sin\left(\frac{\pi}{6} + 2\pi\right)\right),$$

which, due to the periodicity of cosine and sine, is equal to z_0. Therefore, $27i$ has exactly 3 complex cube roots, z_0, z_1, and z_2.

b. These roots are plotted below.

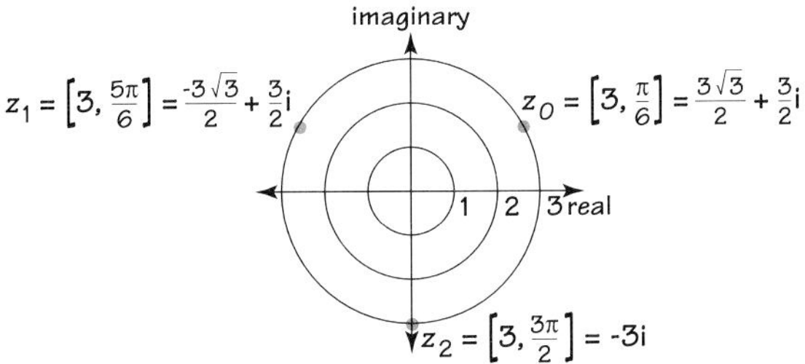

Check

If z_1 is a cube root, it must satisfy the equation $z^3 = 27i$. Rewrite $z_1 = -\frac{3\sqrt{3}}{2} + \frac{3}{2}i = -\frac{3}{2}(\sqrt{3} - i)$. Now cube z_1.

$$\begin{aligned}\left(-\tfrac{3}{2}(\sqrt{3} - i)\right)^3 &= \left(-\tfrac{3}{2}\right)^3(\sqrt{3} - i)^3 \\ &= -\tfrac{27}{8}(\sqrt{3} - i)(3 - 2\sqrt{3}i - 1) \\ &= -\tfrac{27}{8}(\sqrt{3} - i)(2 - 2\sqrt{3}i) \\ &= -\tfrac{27}{8} \cdot (-8i) \\ &= 27i\end{aligned}$$

Finding All nth Roots of a Complex Number

The procedure outlined in Example 1 can be used to find all nth roots of any complex number $[r, \theta]$ as follows. Let $z = [s, \phi]$ be an nth root of $[r, \theta]$. Then $z^n = [s^n, n\phi] = [r, \theta]$. Since the absolute values of these polar forms of z^n are equal, $s^n = r$, and so $s = \sqrt[n]{r}$. The arguments $n\phi$ and θ may differ by integral multiples of 2π, so

$$n\phi = \theta + k \cdot 2\pi, \text{ for } k \text{ an integer,}$$

or

$$\phi = \frac{\theta}{n} + k \cdot \frac{2\pi}{n}, \text{ for } k \text{ an integer.}$$

Thus one nth root of $[r, \theta]$ is $z = \left[\sqrt[n]{r}, \frac{\theta}{n}\right]$. The others are found by adding multiples of $\frac{2\pi}{n}$ to the argument. This proves the following theorem:

Complex nth Roots Theorem
(Polar Form) The n nth roots of $[r, \theta]$ are

$$\left[\sqrt[n]{r}, \frac{\theta}{n} + k \cdot \frac{2\pi}{n}\right], \text{ where } k = 0, 1, 2, \dots, n - 1.$$

(Trigonometric Form) The n nth roots of $r(\cos\theta + i\sin\theta)$ are

$$\sqrt[n]{r}\left(\cos\left(\frac{\theta}{n} + k \cdot \frac{2\pi}{n}\right) + i\sin\left(\frac{\theta}{n} + k \cdot \frac{2\pi}{n}\right)\right), \text{ where } k = 0, 1, 2, \dots, \text{ and } n - 1.$$

Notes on Reading

When approached using trigonometric form only, this material often causes students difficulty. However, this lesson is made easier by the use of polar form and by the large number of diagrams indicating the position of the roots as vertices of a regular polygon centered at the origin. Emphasize that the angles between consecutive nth roots are equal. Work through **Example 1** before doing the proof of the Complex nth Roots Theorem. Note how much easier **Example 2** is because the Complex nth Roots Theorem is used.

Make the following analogy between finding roots of complex numbers and real numbers. For real numbers, if you know r is a square root of a given number, then so is $-r$, because $r^2 = (-r)^2$. So you find one square root and use it to find the others. For complex numbers, the idea is to determine one of the nth roots $[r, \theta]$. Then the others are found by repeatedly adding $\frac{2\pi}{n}$ to the argument because $[r, \theta]^n = [r, \theta + \frac{2\pi}{n}]^n$. The Complex nth Roots Theorem should remind students of DeMoivre's Theorem. Write the two theorems next to each other in each form so that students can compare the theorems.

The Geometric nth Roots Theorem is certainly one of the great results of elementary mathematics. Ask students for the ideas it relates. (regular polygons; powers and roots of complex numbers; graphing)

Teaching Aid 82 shows the diagram for **Example 2** on page 516 and gives the statement of the Geometric nth Roots Theorem.

Error Alert Students might start with a correct solution $[r, \theta]$, but make errors in finding the other roots. Encourage them to express all the angles in degrees and check that each pair of consecutive roots are the same number of degrees apart, as done in **Example 2.**

Optional Activities

Technology You may want to show students a way to graph the nth roots of a complex number on a graphing calculator that has a parametric mode. Set the calculator to parametric mode. Enter $X = a\cos t$ and $Y = a\sin t$, where a is an nth root of r. (In **Example 1,** $a = 3$.) Set the viewing window so that the minimum value of t is the smallest positive argument in the solution set of roots. (In **Example 1,** tmin $= \frac{\pi}{6}$.) Set the maximum t value to $2\pi +$ minimum t value. Set the increments of t (tstep on some calculators) to $\frac{2\pi}{n}$). (In **Example 1,** tstep $= \frac{2\pi}{3}$.] Graphing in a "squared-off" window" is recommended. On some graphing calculators, an item in the zoom menu calibrates "square" graph paper. On some calculators, the points are connected, so that a regular n-gon is formed.

❶ Notice how beautifully the Geometric *n*th Roots Theorem explains why there are different numbers of real *n*th roots of a real number *x*, depending on whether *x* is positive or negative and *n* is odd or even. **Teaching Aid 83** shows the diagrams on page 517.

Additional Examples

1. **a.** Find the cube roots of 8 and plot them in the complex plane. **$[2, 0]$, $[2, \frac{2\pi}{3}]$, $[2, \frac{4\pi}{3}]$**

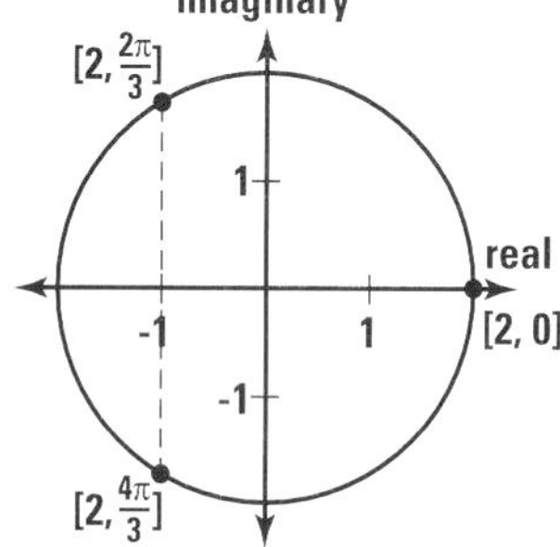

b. Find the cube roots of $4 + 4\sqrt{3}\,i$ and plot them in the complex plane.
$[2, \frac{\pi}{9}]$, $[2, \frac{7\pi}{9}]$, $[2, \frac{13\pi}{9}]$

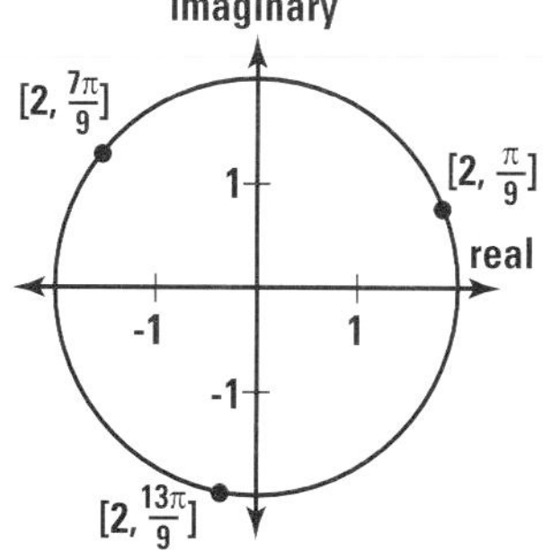

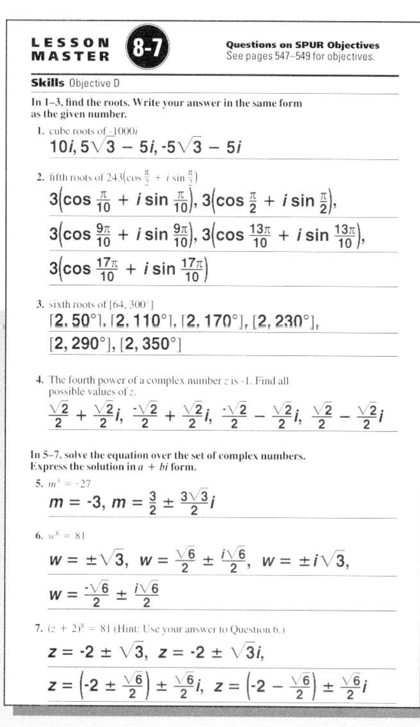

LESSON MASTER 8-7 **Questions on SPUR Objectives**
See pages 547–549 for objectives.

Skills Objective D

In 1–3, find the roots. Write your answer in the same form as the given number.

1. cube roots of $-1000i$
   $10i, 5\sqrt{3} - 5i, -5\sqrt{3} - 5i$
2. fifth roots of $243(\cos\frac{\pi}{2} + i\sin\frac{\pi}{2})$
   $3(\cos\frac{\pi}{10} + i\sin\frac{\pi}{10})$, $3(\cos\frac{\pi}{2} + i\sin\frac{\pi}{2})$, $3(\cos\frac{9\pi}{10} + i\sin\frac{9\pi}{10})$, $3(\cos\frac{13\pi}{10} + i\sin\frac{13\pi}{10})$, $3(\cos\frac{17\pi}{10} + i\sin\frac{17\pi}{10})$
3. sixth roots of $[64, 300°]$
   $[2, 50°]$, $[2, 110°]$, $[2, 170°]$, $[2, 230°]$, $[2, 290°]$, $[2, 350°]$
4. The fourth power of a complex number z is -1. Find all possible values of z.
   $\frac{\sqrt{2}}{2} + \frac{\sqrt{2}}{2}i$, $\frac{-\sqrt{2}}{2} + \frac{\sqrt{2}}{2}i$, $\frac{-\sqrt{2}}{2} - \frac{\sqrt{2}}{2}i$, $\frac{\sqrt{2}}{2} - \frac{\sqrt{2}}{2}i$

In 5–7, solve the equation over the set of complex numbers. Express the solution in $a + bi$ form.

5. $m^3 = -27$
   $m = -3$, $m = \frac{3}{2} \pm \frac{3\sqrt{3}}{2}i$
6. $w^8 = 81$
   $w = \pm\sqrt{3}$, $w = \frac{\sqrt{6}}{2} \pm \frac{i\sqrt{6}}{2}$, $w = \pm i\sqrt{3}$, $w = \frac{-\sqrt{6}}{2} \pm \frac{i\sqrt{6}}{2}$
7. $(z + 2)^8 = 81$ (Hint: Use your answer to Question 6.)
   $z = -2 \pm \sqrt{3}$, $z = -2 \pm \sqrt{3}i$, $z = \left(-2 \pm \frac{\sqrt{6}}{2}\right) \pm \frac{\sqrt{6}}{2}i$, $z = \left(-2 - \frac{\sqrt{6}}{2}\right) \pm \frac{\sqrt{6}}{2}i$

Example 2

Find the 5th roots of $16 + 16\sqrt{3}\,i$. Express the roots in both trigonometric and polar form, and graph them in the complex plane.

Solution

Let $[r, \theta] = 16 + 16\sqrt{3}\,i$. Then $r = \sqrt{16^2 + (16\sqrt{3})^2} = \sqrt{256 + 768} = 32$ and $\tan\theta = \frac{16\sqrt{3}}{16} = \sqrt{3}$, so $\theta = 60°$.

So $[r, \theta] = [32, 60°]$. Thus one 5th root is $\left[\sqrt[5]{32}, \frac{60°}{5}\right]$, which is $[2, 12°]$. In trigonometric form, this root is $2(\cos 12° + i\sin 12°)$.

The other four roots will also have an absolute value of 2 and will be spaced $\frac{360°}{n} = \frac{360°}{5} = 72°$ apart.

$$\begin{aligned}
k = 1&: [2, 84°] = 2(\cos 84° + i\sin 84°)\\
k = 2&: [2, 156°] = 2(\cos 156° + i\sin 156°)\\
k = 3&: [2, 228°] = 2(\cos 228° + i\sin 228°)\\
k = 4&: [2, 300°] = 2(\cos 300° + i\sin 300°)
\end{aligned}$$

Notice that if 72° is added once again to find one more root, $2(\cos 372° + i\sin 372°)$ would result, but this is the same as the first root, $2(\cos 12° + i\sin 12°)$.

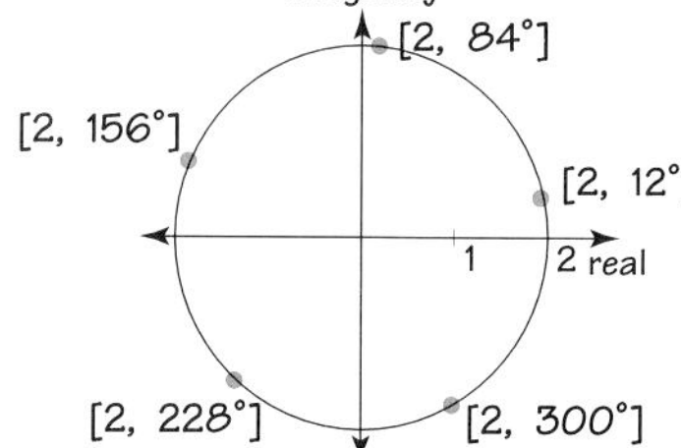

Graphing All *n* *n*th Roots of a Complex Number

Notice that the three cube roots from Example 1 lie on the circle with radius 3 centered at the origin, and z_0, z_1, and z_2 are spaced $\frac{2\pi}{3}$ radians apart on that circle. Thus, z_0, z_1, z_2 are the vertices of an equilateral triangle. In Example 2, the five 5th roots are the vertices of a regular pentagon centered at (0, 0). These examples are instances of the following gorgeous theorem.

Geometric *n*th Roots Theorem
When graphed in the complex plane, the *n*th roots of any nonzero complex number *z* are the vertices of a regular *n*-gon whose center is at (0, 0).

Proof
Refer to the Polar Form of the Complex *n*th Roots Theorem. Each succeeding value of *k* adds $\frac{2\pi}{n}$ to the argument while keeping the absolute value the same. This means that the *n*th roots of a number are all the same distance from the origin and are spaced $\frac{2\pi}{n}$ apart. Thus, the *n* roots determine congruent arcs and congruent chords on a circle.

Adapting to Individual Needs

Extra Help
You might want to explain how the discussion about the *n* *n*th roots of real numbers provides a quick way for finding these roots if at least one of the roots is real. Plot the real root, $\sqrt[n]{w}$, on the positive real axis (if w is positive) or on the negative real axis (if w is negative and n is odd). The other roots will have an absolute value of $\sqrt[n]{w}$ and will be spaced $\frac{360°}{n}$ apart. Then these points can be expressed in $a + bi$ form, if desired.

The n nth Roots of Real Numbers

1 Real numbers *are* complex numbers, so the Complex and Geometric nth Root Theorems can be applied to picture the nth roots of real numbers. In particular, these theorems explain the numbers of real nth roots of positive and negative numbers.

If w is a positive real number, then one of its nth roots is $\sqrt[n]{w}$, which lies on the positive part of the real axis. Since the other nth roots are vertices of a regular n-gon centered at the origin, there will be another vertex on the real axis only if n is even. This confirms that there are exactly two real nth roots of a positive number if n is even and exactly one real nth root if n is odd.

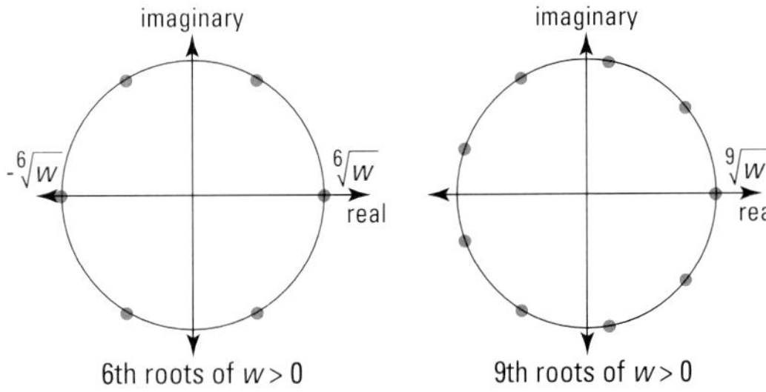

6th roots of $w > 0$ 9th roots of $w > 0$

If w is a negative real number, then $w = [-w, \pi]$ in polar form (note that $-w$ is a positive number), and its n complex nth roots are $\left[\sqrt[n]{-w}, \frac{\pi}{n} + \frac{2\pi k}{n}\right]$, where $k = 0, 1, 2, \dots,$ and $n - 1$. For the nth root to be real, its argument must be a multiple of π. The arguments of these nth roots equal $\pi\left(\frac{2k + 1}{n}\right)$, which is a multiple of π only if $n = 2k + 1$; that is, only if n is odd and $k = \frac{n - 1}{2}$. This confirms that there is no real nth root of a negative number when n is even and exactly one nth root of a negative number when n is odd.

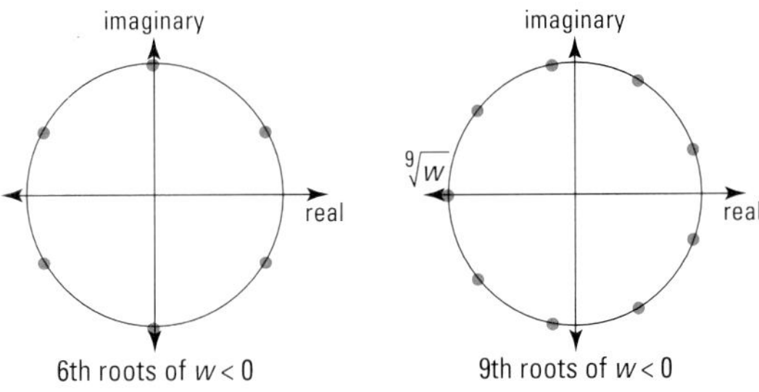

6th roots of $w < 0$ 9th roots of $w < 0$

QUESTIONS

Covering the Reading

1. Refer to Example 1. The cube roots are described by the polar coordinates $\left[3, \frac{\pi}{6} + \frac{2\pi k}{3}\right]$ for k an integer. Show that $k = 4$ gives one of the three roots found in the example.
   For $k = 4$, $\left[3, \frac{\pi}{6} + \frac{2\pi k}{3}\right] = \left[3, \frac{17\pi}{6}\right] = \left[3, \frac{5\pi}{6}\right]$, which is z_1.

2. Find the 6th roots of $32 + 32\sqrt{3}i$. Express the roots in both trigonometric and polar form, and graph them in the complex plane.
   $z_0 = [2, 10°] = 2(\cos 10° + i \sin 10°)$
   $z_1 = [2, 70°] = 2(\cos 70° + i \sin 70°)$
   $z_2 = [2, 130°] = 2(\cos 130° + i \sin 130°)$
   $z_3 = [2, 190°] = 2(\cos 190° + i \sin 190°)$
   $z_4 = [2, 250°] = 2(\cos 250° + i \sin 250°)$
   $z_5 = [2, 310°] = 2(\cos 310° + i \sin 310°)$

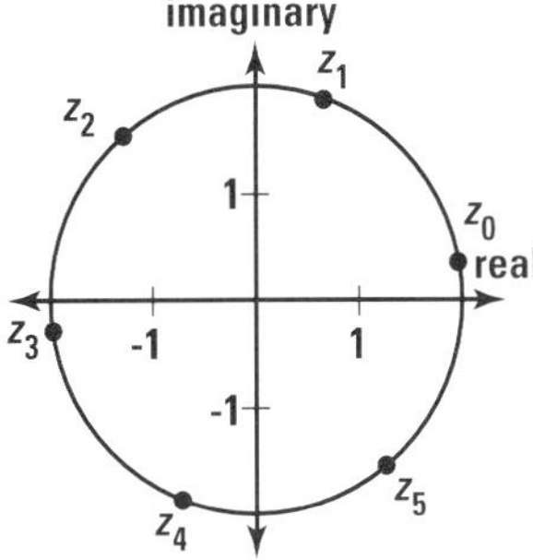

Adapting to Individual Needs

Challenge

Have students answer the following. Let T_n be the set of the nth roots of 1.

1. If a and b are in T_n, show that ab is in T_n also. $[(ab)^n = a^n b^n = 1 \cdot 1 = 1]$
2. If a is in T_n, show that $\frac{1}{a}$ is in T_n also. $\left[\left(\frac{1}{a}\right)^n = \frac{1}{a^n} = \frac{1}{1} = 1\right]$
3. If a is in T_n and $a \neq 1$, show that $1 + a + a^2 + \dots + a^{n-1} = 0$. [Using the Evaluation of an Infinite Geometric Series Theorem, $1 + a + \dots + a^{n-1} = \frac{1 - a^n}{1 - a} = \frac{1 - 1}{1 - a} = 0$]

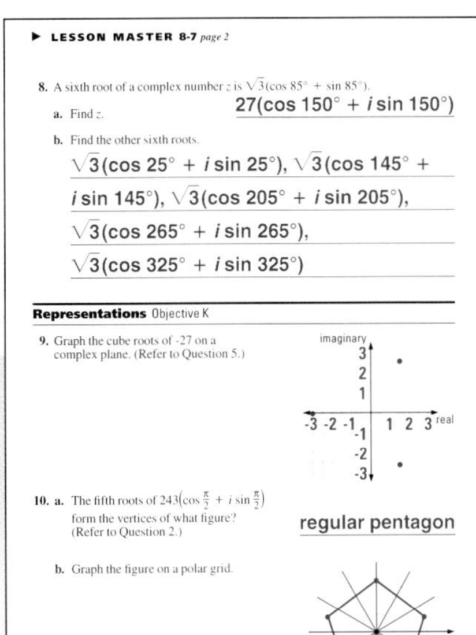

▶ **LESSON MASTER 8-7** *page 2*

8. A sixth root of a complex number z is $\sqrt{3}(\cos 85° + \sin 85°)$.
   a. Find z. $27(\cos 150° + i \sin 150°)$
   b. Find the other sixth roots. $\sqrt{3}(\cos 25° + i \sin 25°)$, $\sqrt{3}(\cos 145° + i \sin 145°)$, $\sqrt{3}(\cos 205° + i \sin 205°)$, $\sqrt{3}(\cos 265° + i \sin 265°)$, $\sqrt{3}(\cos 325° + i \sin 325°)$

Representations Objective K

9. Graph the cube roots of -27 on a complex plane. (Refer to Question 5.)

10. a. The fifth roots of $243\left(\cos \frac{\pi}{2} + i \sin \frac{\pi}{2}\right)$ form the vertices of what figure? (Refer to Question 2.) regular pentagon
    b. Graph the figure on a polar grid.

Notes on Questions

Questions 6–8, 12, 13 These questions anticipate the next two lessons and should be discussed.

Question 10 If the positive integer powers of $1 + i$ are graphed, then they lie on a spiral and (16, 0) is the 8th point on the spiral. The same is true of the 7 other 8th roots of 16.

Question 15 The general result is startling: the sum of the *n*th roots of any complex number is 0. (This is most easily proved by noting that, from the Factor Theorem, the sum of the zeros of the polynomial $x^n + a_{n-1}x^{n-1} + \ldots + a_1x + a_0$ is equal to $-a_{n-1}$. In the special case of the polynomial $x^n - z$, the *n* zeros are the *n*th roots of *z*, and $a_{n-1} = 0$.)

Question 16 This is a geometric sequence whose first term is 1 and whose common ratio is the nonreal number [.7, 80°].

Question 18 Here we have an example of the distributive property of conjugation over division.

Additional Answers

5. b.

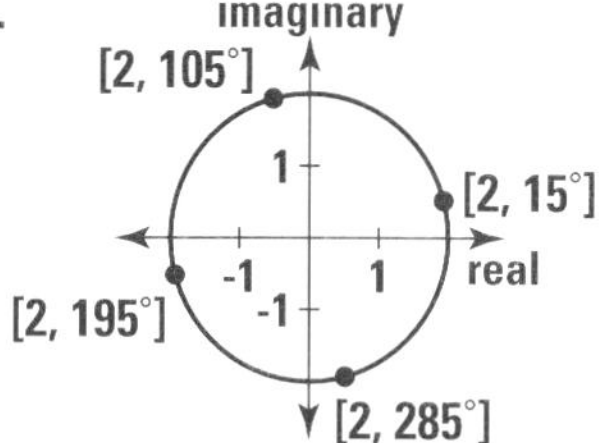

11. a.

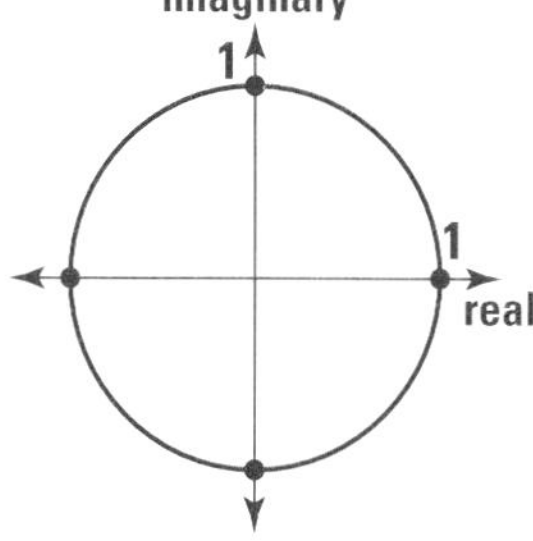

b.

imaginary

1 [1, 72°]

1

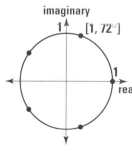

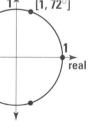

real

2)

imaginary

z_1, z_2, z_0, z_3, z_4, z_5

real

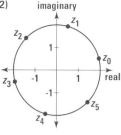

$z_0 \approx 1.93 + .52i$;
$z_1 \approx .52 + 1.93i$;
$z_2 = -\sqrt{2} + i\sqrt{2}$;
$z_3 \approx -1.93 - .52i$;
$z_4 \approx -.52 - 1.93i$;
$z_5 = \sqrt{2} - i\sqrt{2}$

3)

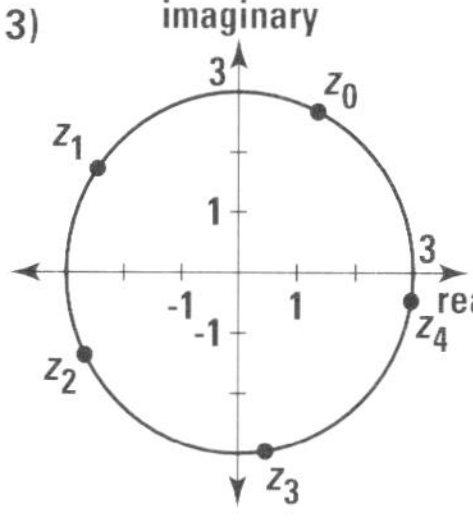

$z_0 =$
$3(\cos 63° + i \sin 63°)$
$z_1 =$
$3(\cos 135° + i \sin 135°)$
$z_2 =$
$3(\cos 207° + i \sin 207°)$
$z_3 =$
$3(\cos 279° + i \sin 279°)$
$z_4 =$
$3(\cos 351° + i \sin 351°)$

4) $[2, 228°]^5 =$
$[2^5, 5 \cdot 228°] =$
$[32, 1140°] =$
$[32, 60°] =$
$32(\cos 60° + i \sin 60°)$
$= 16 + 16\sqrt{3}i$

13b) $\frac{3\sqrt{2}}{2} \pm \frac{3\sqrt{2}}{2}i$, $-\frac{3\sqrt{2}}{2} \pm \frac{3\sqrt{2}}{2}i$

In 2 and 3, find and plot the roots in the complex plane. Write the roots in the same form as the given number.

2. the sixth roots of $64i$ See left.

3. the fifth roots of $z = 243[\cos(315°) + i \sin(315°)]$ See left.

4. Refer to Example 2. Show that [2, 228°] is a fifth root of $16 + 16\sqrt{3}\,i$ by raising the root to the fifth power. See left.

5. a. The fourth roots of $8 + 8\sqrt{3}\,i$ form the vertices of what figure?
   b. Find the fourth roots of this number and graph them in the complex plane. See margin.
   a) square

In 6–8, give the number of real and the number of nonreal solutions to the equation. (You do not have to solve the equation.)

6. $z^5 = 10$ 1 real, 4 nonreal

7. $z^9 = -4$ 1 real, 8 nonreal

8. $z^{164} = 1000$ 2 real, 162 nonreal

Applying the Mathematics

9. A cube root of a certain complex number is 9(cos 60° + *i* sin 60°). Find the complex number and its other cube roots.
   -729; -9, 9(cos 300° + *i* sin 300°)

10. a. $1 + i$ is an 8th root of what real number? 16
    b. What are its other 8th roots?
    $\sqrt{2}i$, $-1 + i$, $-\sqrt{2}$, $-1 - i$, $-\sqrt{2}i$, $1 - i$, $\sqrt{2}$

11. a. Graph the 4th roots of 1. See margin.
    b. Graph the 5th roots of 1. See margin.
    c. Describe the graph of the *n*th roots of 1. They are the vertices of a regular *n*-gon, with center at the origin and a vertex at (1, 0).

In 12 and 13, two equations are given. Solve each equation over the set of complex numbers. Express the solutions in $a + bi$ form and plot them in the complex plane. See margin for graphs.

12. a. $z^3 = 8$
    2, $-1 + \sqrt{3}i$, $-1 - \sqrt{3}i$
    b. $z^3 = -8$
    -2, $1 + \sqrt{3}i$, $1 - \sqrt{3}i$

13. a. $z^4 = 81$
    $z = \pm 3, \pm 3i$
    b. $z^4 = -81$
    See left.

14. If the center of the stop sign at the right is (0, 0) and the distance from a vertex of the sign to the center is 1 foot, then the vertices of the sign are the 8th roots of what number? -1

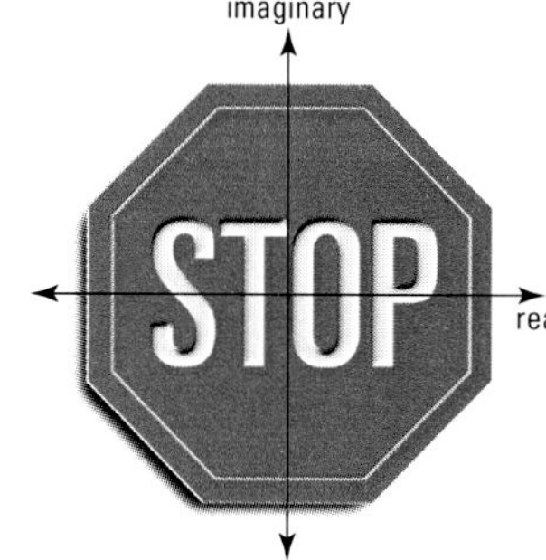

15. Show that the sum of the 3 cube roots of 8 is 0.
    The three cube roots of 8 are 2, $-1 + \sqrt{3}i$, and $-1 - \sqrt{3}i$. Their sum is $2 + (-1 + \sqrt{3}i) + (-1 - \sqrt{3}i) = 2 + (-2) = 0$

12. a.

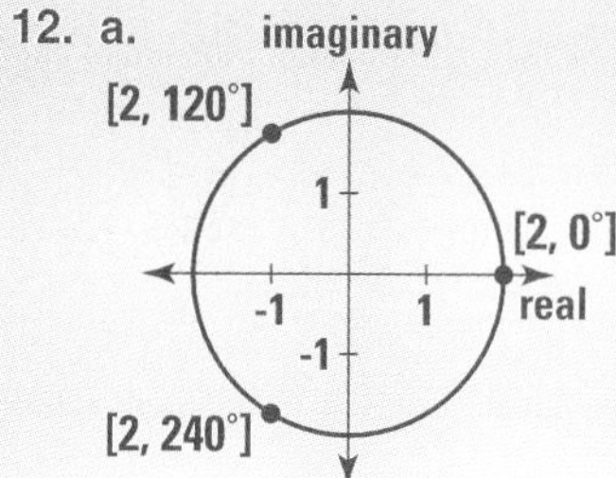

b.

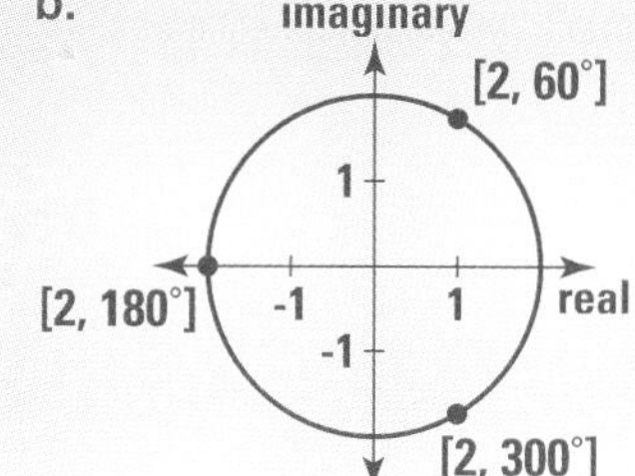

13. a.

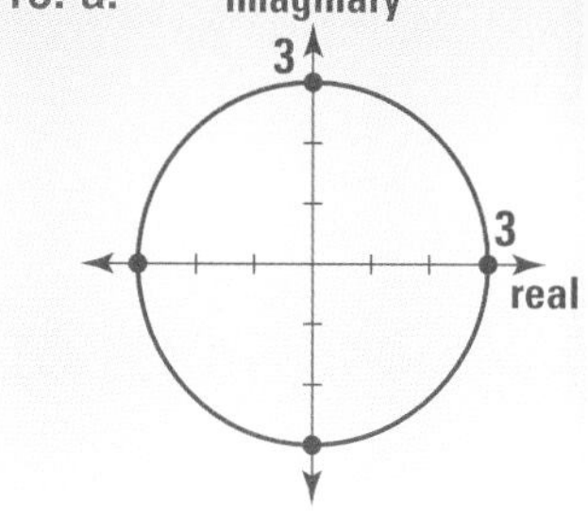

16a) [.7, 80°], $[(.7)^2, 160°]$, $[(.7)^3, 240°]$, $[(.7)^4, 320°]$, $[(.7)^5, 40°]$, $[(.7)^6, 120°]$, $[(.7)^7, 200°]$, $[(.7)^8, 280°]$

b)

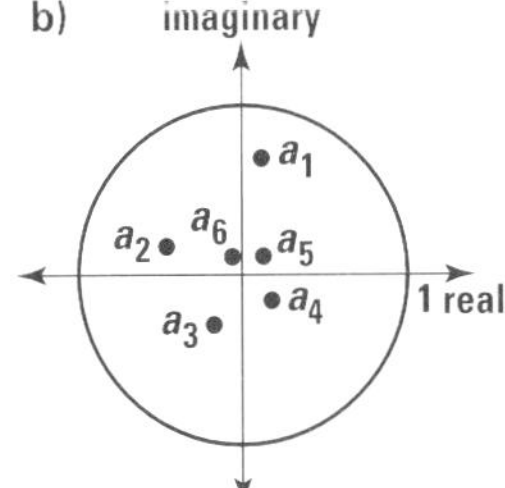

17)

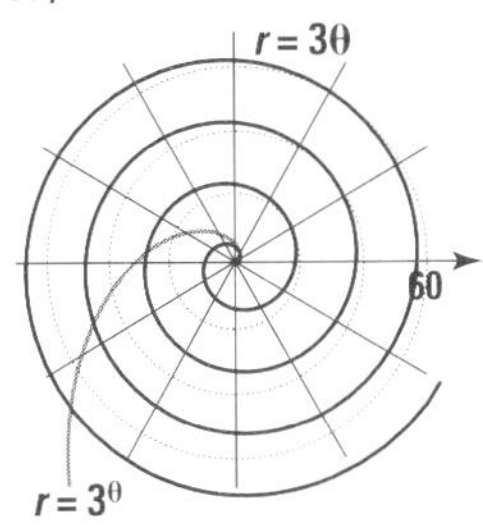

The graph of $r = 3\theta$ is a spiral of Archimedes, and that of $r = 3^\theta$ is a logarithmic spiral.

18) By definition of conjugate, $\bar{z} = 3 + 2i$ and $\bar{w} = -4 - i$. Therefore $\frac{\bar{z}}{\bar{w}} = \frac{3 + 2i}{-4 - i} \approx -.824 - .294i$. $\frac{z}{w} = \frac{3 - 2i}{-4 + i} \approx -.824 + .294i$, so $\overline{\left(\frac{z}{w}\right)} \approx -.824 - .294i$, which is equal to $\frac{\bar{z}}{\bar{w}}$.

Review

16. Define a sequence by $a_n = [.7, 80°]^n$.

a. Write the first eight terms in polar form. **See left.**

b. Graph the first six terms. **See left.**

c. What is $\lim\limits_{n \to \infty} a_n$? *(Lesson 8-6)* **0**

17. Sketch the polar graphs of the equations $r = 3\theta$ and $r = 3^\theta$ on the same polar grid, and identify their shapes. *(Lesson 8-5)* **See left.**

18. Let $z = 3 - 2i$ and $w = -4 + i$. Verify that $\frac{\bar{z}}{\bar{w}} = \overline{\left(\frac{z}{w}\right)}$. *(Lesson 8-1)* **See left.**

19. Consider the sequence defined recursively by

$$\begin{cases} a_1 = 3 \\ a_{k+1} = 2a_k - 1 \quad \text{for integers } k \geq 1. \end{cases}$$

a. Conjecture an explicit formula for the sequence. (Hint: It involves powers of 2.) **$a_n = 2^n + 1$, for all integers $n \geq 1$**

b. Use mathematical induction to prove your conjecture. *(Lessons 7-1, 7-3)* **See below.**

20. Consider the function f defined by

$$f(x) = \frac{6x^2 + 5x}{3x - 2}.$$

a. Find equations for all asymptotes. **$x = \frac{2}{3}$, $y = 2x + 3$**

b. Use limit notation to describe the end behavior of f and its behavior near any vertical asymptotes. *(Lessons 5-4, 5-5)* **See margin.**

21. Let $p(x) = x^3 + x^2 - 10x + 8$.

a. Given that $p(1) = 0$, name a factor of $p(x)$. **$x - 1$**

b. Given that $x + 4$ is a factor of $p(x)$, name a zero of $p(x)$. **-4**

c. At most, how many more zeros can $p(x)$ have? **1**

d. Suppose $p(x)$ is a factor of a polynomial $q(x)$. Name two zeros of $q(x)$. Justify your answer. *(Lessons 4-1, 4-4)* **1 and -4, by the Transitive Property of Polynomial Factors**

Exploration

22. Write a calculator or computer program that will determine the n nth roots of any complex number $a + bi$. **See margin.**

19b) $S(n)$: $a_n = 2^n + 1$. $S(1)$: $a_1 = 2^1 + 1 = 3$, so $S(1)$ is true. Assume $S(k)$: $a_k = 2^k + 1$. Then

$$\begin{aligned} a_{k+1} &= 2a_k - 1 \\ &= 2(2^k + 1) - 1 \\ &= 2^{k+1} + 2 - 1 \\ &= 2^{k+1} + 1 \end{aligned}$$

So $S(k) \Rightarrow S(k + 1)$. By mathematical induction, $S(n)$ is true for all positive integers n.

Follow-up for Lesson 8-7

Practice

For more questions on SPUR Objectives, use **Lesson Master 8-7** (shown on pages 516–517).

Assessment

Written Communication Have students **work in pairs.** Have each student give a number in $a + bi$ form. Then have students find and graph the five fifth roots of their partner's number, stating each root in $a + bi$ form. [Students find and graph roots of complex numbers.]

Extension

Ask students to give a question for each of the following answers. In all answers, the polygon has the origin as its center. You may wish to use the first answer and question as an example.

1. a regular hexagon in the complex plane with side 3, and with two vertices on the real axis. [What are the 6th roots of 729?]
2. a regular hexagon in the complex plane with side 3 and with two vertices on the imaginary axis. [What are the 6th roots of 729i?]
3. an equilateral triangle with side $2\sqrt{3}$ and one vertex on the negative imaginary axis. [What are the 3rd roots of 8i?]
4. a square with side $2\sqrt{2}$ with vertices only on the axes. [What are the 4th roots of 16?]

Students could also generate other "answers" to try to stump their classmates.

Project Update Project 4, *Spirals,* on page 542, relates to the content of this lesson.

b.

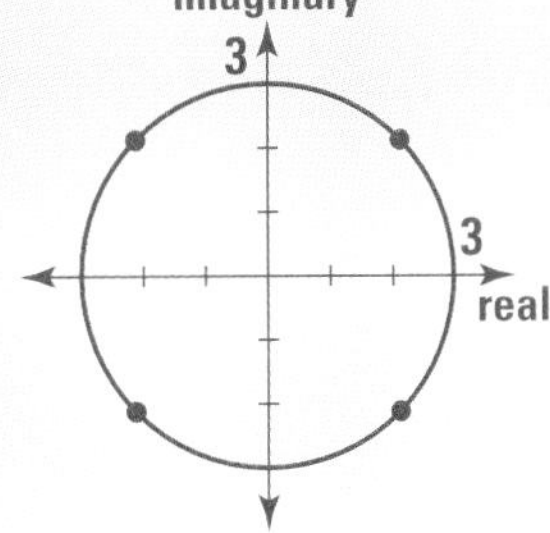

20\. b. $\lim\limits_{x \to -\infty} f(x) = -\infty$; $\lim\limits_{x \to \infty} f(x) = \infty$;

$\lim\limits_{x \to 2/3^+} f(x) = \infty$; $\lim\limits_{x \to 2/3^-} f(x) = -\infty$

22\. See Additional Answers at the back of this book.

Setting Up Lesson 8-8

Discuss **Questions 6–8** so that students see the relationship between the degree of the polynomial and the number of zeros it has.

Lesson 8-8

Objectives

E Find all zeros, and their multiplicities, of a given polynomial.

G Use the properties of polynomials to find or describe their zeros.

Resources

From the ***Teacher's Resource File***

- Lesson Master 8-8
- Answer Master 8-8
- Assessment Sourcebook: Quiz for Lessons 8-5 through 8-8
- Teaching Aid 72: Warm-up

Additional Resources

- Visual for Teaching Aid 72

Teaching Lesson 8-8

Warm-up

1. Find all solutions to the equation $(2x + 25)(x^2 + x + 6) = 0$.
-12.5, $-0.5 + 0.5i\sqrt{23}$, $-0.5 - 0.5i\sqrt{23}$
2. Find a 3rd degree polynomial equation that has the same solutions as the equation of Question 1.
Sample: $2x^3 + 27x^2 + 37x + 150 = 0$

Notes on Reading

This lesson focuses on the number of zeros of a polynomial function.

LESSON 8-8 The Number of Zeros of a Polynomial

Carl Friedrich Gauss

The Importance of Knowing the Number of Solutions

The number of solutions to an equation or inequality can be as important as the values of the solutions themselves. For instance, for a particular value of k, the number of nonnegative integer solutions (d, q) to $10d + 25q = k$ is the number of ways to make change of k cents using only dimes and quarters. When a quadratic equation is used to model the flight of a ball, the number of solutions to the equation can tell you how many times the ball reaches a certain height. If a ball reaches a height only once, then that must be the maximum height it reaches.

How Many Solutions Does $x^n = k$ Have?

Although real numbers can have only 0, 1, or 2 real nth roots, in the last lesson you saw that *every* nonzero complex number has n complex nth roots. Thus, when n is a positive integer and $k \neq 0$, determining the number of solutions to the equation $x^n = k$ is simpler in the set of complex numbers than it is in the set of real numbers. In the set of complex numbers, the equation $x^n = k$ always has n solutions.

How Many Zeros Does a Polynomial of Degree n Have?

You also saw in Lesson 4-4 that every polynomial of degree n has *at most* n zeros. In addition, it is easy to prove that certain polynomials have at least one zero.

❶ **Theorem**
Every polynomial of odd degree with real coefficients has at least one real zero.

Lesson 8-8 Overview

Broad Goals This lesson discusses the Fundamental Theorem of Algebra, that over the complex numbers, any polynomial of degree n has n zeros, counting its multiplicities. It also discusses how to find a polynomial from its zeros.

Perspective In Lesson 4-4 we used the remainder and factor theorems to prove that a polynomial of degree n has at most n zeros, and the equivalent fact that its graph may cross any given horizontal line at most n times. The major theorem in this lesson is the Fundamental Theorem of Algebra, which says that any polynomial of degree greater than or equal to 1 with complex coefficients has at least one complex zero. The Fundamental Theorem of Algebra is a generalization of the Complex nth Roots Theorem if we interpret the nth root of a number k as a solution to the polynomial equation $x^n - k = 0$, an equation of degree n.

❷ **Proof**
Recall that, when $p(x)$ is a polynomial of odd degree with real coefficients, the end behavior of the function p is such that as $x \to \infty$ and $x \to -\infty$, $p(x)$ approaches ∞ in one case and $-\infty$ in the other. Thus, because of the Intermediate Value Theorem, the graph of p must intersect the x-axis, and so $p(x)$ must have a real zero.

The above theorem cannot be extended to polynomials of even degree. Polynomials of even degree with real coefficients may not have any real zeros. An example is $x^2 + 7$.

However, in 1797, Gauss proved the following important generalization.

Fundamental Theorem of Algebra
If $p(x)$ is any polynomial of degree $n \geq 1$, with real or complex coefficients, then $p(x)$ has at least one complex zero.

Gauss' proof was based on geometric properties of the graphs of the real and imaginary parts of the equation

$$p(z) = 0$$

as $z = x + iy$ varies over the complex plane. He gave three other proofs of the theorem during his lifetime because he was searching for a proof that was entirely algebraic. To this day, all known proofs of the Fundamental Theorem of Algebra use geometry in some essential way, and all are beyond the scope of this course.

At the time Gauss proved this theorem, algorithms for solving polynomial equations of the 3rd and 4th degree were known, but it was not known whether there were similar algorithms to solve all equations of the 5th or any higher degree. Just as complex numbers were needed for solving quadratic, cubic, and quartic equations, some thought that perhaps new numbers, different from complex numbers, were needed for some equations of higher degree. Gauss's result implies that no other numbers are needed.

❸ Zeros with Multiplicity Greater than One

Sometimes the zeros of a polynomial $p(x)$ may be "repeated" in the following sense. For instance, the zeros of $p(x) = (x - 1)(x + 2)^5(x - 3)$ are 1, -2, and 3, but there is a sense in which the zero -2 occurs 5 times. The zero -2 is said to have *multiplicity* 5.

Definition
Suppose c is a zero of a polynomial $p(x)$ of degree at least 1. The largest positive integer m such that $(x - c)^m$ is a factor of $p(x)$ is called the **multiplicity** of the zero c of $p(x)$.

Zeros of multiplicity 1 are called **simple zeros** of $p(x)$.

❶ This theorem shows that every polynomial of *odd* degree with *real* coefficients has at least one *real* zero. The Fundamental Theorem of Algebra is much more general; it says that every polynomial of *any* degree ≥ 1 with complex coefficients has at least one zero. The price paid for this generality is that the zero may be nonreal.

Reading Mathematics As the preceding paragraph indicates, students must read this lesson very carefully. It is easy to overlook critical occurrences of the words real and complex. Understanding this paragraph will pave the way to understanding this lesson.

❷ Implicit in the proof of this theorem is the fact that polynomial functions are everywhere continuous. The sign of the coefficient of the lead term determines the end behavior of $p(x)$. A few graphs will help show why this must be true.

Each of the first two theorems has a limitation. For the first theorem, note that polynomials of even degree and real coefficients may have no real zeros: consider $p(x) = x^2 + 1$. (The zeros are i and $-i$.) For the Fundamental Theorem of Algebra, the polynomial must be of degree greater than or equal to one. A constant polynomial such as $f(x) = 4$ may have no zero. Again a graph will help.

❸ The concept of multiplicity builds on the idea (derived from the Factor Theorem) that a polynomial contains each of its zeros in the form of a linear factor. If the same linear factor appears more than once, then the number of times it appears is the multiplicity of the corresponding zero. Once students have this concept, they can easily show that the number of zeros that a polynomial has (counting multiplicities) is equal to its degree. You may wish to go through the proof of this theorem; it is a straightforward use of mathematical induction.

Optional Activities

Refer students to **Question 9.** Have them write a polynomial $q(x)$ that has 1 zero in the set of integers, 2 zeros in the set of rational numbers, 4 zeros in the set of real numbers, and 2 zeros in the set of imaginary numbers. [Sample: $q(x) = (x^2 + 16)(x^2 - 5)(x - 5)(5x + 1)$] Extend this activity by thinking of other combinations or by having students generate combinations of zeros and write appropriate polynomials.

Adapting to Individual Needs

Extra Help
Some students might not understand in the proof of the theorem on page 522 why $k \neq 0$ if $p(x)$ has degree zero and $p(x) = k$. Remind them that 0 is often called a polynomial with *no* degree.

Additional Examples

1. Find all zeros and their corresponding multiplicities for the polynomial $p(x) = x^5 - 2x^3 + x$. **Note that 0 is easily seen to be a zero, then factor the quadratic polynomial in x^2. Thus $p(x) = x(x - 1)^2(x + 1)^2$; -1 has multiplicity 2, 0 has multiplicity 1, and 1 has multiplicity 2.**
2. **a.** Give a polynomial of degree 4 which has zeros -1 (multiplicity 2), 2, and 0. **$p(x) = x(x - 2)(x + 1)^2 = x^4 - 3x^2 - 2x$, or any nonzero multiple of $p(x)$.**
   b. Give a polynomial of degree 4 which has zeros $2 + i$, $2 - i$, -1, and 1. **$p(x) = (x + 1)(x - 1)(x - 2 - i)(x - 2 + i) = x^4 - 4x^3 + 4x^2 + 4x - 5$**
   (Note that the reason the polynomial in Additional Example 2b has real coefficients is that the complex zeros are conjugates. This idea is discussed further in Lesson 8-9.)

Example 1

Find all zeros and their corresponding multiplicities for the polynomial $p(x) = x^4 + 4x^3 - 5x^2$.

Solution

The terms in the expression defining $p(x)$ have x^2 as their largest common factor.

$$p(x) = x^2 (x^2 + 4x - 5)$$

The remaining quadratic factor $x^2 + 4x - 5$ of $p(x)$ can be factored.

$$x^2 + 4x - 5 = (x - 1)(x + 5)$$

Therefore, a complete factorization of $p(x)$ is

$$p(x) = x^2 (x - 1)(x + 5).$$

Thus applying the Factor Theorem and the definition of multiplicity for zeros, $x = 0$ is a zero of multiplicity 2, while $x = 1$ and $x = -5$ are simple zeros of $p(x)$. Thus, although $p(x)$ has only three distinct zeros, it is said that $p(x)$ has four zeros, counting multiplicities.

In Example 1, the polynomial $p(x)$ of degree four has four zeros, counting multiplicities. In general, if multiplicities are counted, does a polynomial of degree $n \geq 1$ always have n zeros? The answer depends on the number system in which the zeros are allowed to exist. For instance, if only integer zeros are allowed, the polynomial $f(x) = 2x + 1$, which has degree 1, has no zeros. But if x can be any real number, then $f(x)$ has exactly one zero, $-\frac{1}{2}$. Similarly, the polynomial $h(x) = x^2 + 1$ has no real zeros but has exactly two complex zeros, i and $-i$. Is there a polynomial of degree $n \geq 1$ that has fewer than n complex zeros even after counting multiplicities? The answer to this question is no. The complex number system is large enough to provide n zeros for any polynomial of degree n, even those with complex coefficients.

Theorem
If $p(x)$ is any polynomial of degree n with real or complex coefficients, then $p(x)$ has exactly n real or complex zeros provided that each zero of multiplicity m is counted m times.

Proof
If $p(x)$ has degree zero, then it is of the form $p(x) = k$ with $k \neq 0$, and so it has no zero.
For polynomials of degree $n \geq 1$, the proof uses mathematical induction.

Let $S(n)$: *Every polynomial of degree n has exactly n complex zeros provided that each zero of multiplicity m is counted m times.*

$S(1)$ is true because $p(x) = ax + b$ has the one zero $-\frac{b}{a}$. (If $b = 0$, then 0 is the zero.)

Adapting to Individual Needs

Challenge
Have students answer the following.

1. Extend the results of **Question 25** from Lesson 8-1, to higher degree polynomial equations.
   [If $z_1, z_2, \ldots, z_n$ are all of the solutions of $a_nx^n + a_{n-1}x^{n-1} + \ldots + a_0 = 0$ (written repeatedly when multiplicities occur), then $z_1 \cdot z_2 \cdot \ldots \cdot z_n = (-1)^n\frac{a_0}{a_n}$ and $z_1 + z_2 + \ldots + z_n = \frac{-a_{n-1}}{a_n}$.]
2. Use the consequent of the if - then statement in part **1** to prove that the sum of the n nth roots of A is 0. [The nth roots of A are solutions to the equation $x^n - A = 0$. Therefore, their sum is $\frac{-a_{n-1}}{a_n} = \frac{0}{1} = 0$.]

Now we must show that for any positive integer k, $S(k)$ is true $\Rightarrow S(k+1)$ is true. Suppose $S(k)$ is true. That is, suppose every polynomial of degree k has exactly k complex zeros allowing for multiplicities. Now consider any polynomial $p(x)$ of degree $k + 1$. By the Fundamental Theorem of Algebra, $p(x)$ has a zero, call it z_1. Then, by the Factor Theorem, there exists a polynomial $q(x)$ such that

$$p(x) = (x - z_1)\,q(x).$$

Since the degree of $x - z_1$, is 1, the degree of $q(x)$ must be k by the Degree of a Product Theorem.

Furthermore, the zeros of $q(x)$ are zeros of $p(x)$. Since $q(x)$ is of degree k, by the inductive assumption it has k zeros. Thus $p(x)$ has at least $k + 1$ zeros: z_1 and the k zeros of $q(x)$. Since we know from Lesson 4-4 that $p(x)$ has no more than $k + 1$ zeros, $p(x)$ must have exactly $k + 1$ zeros. Thus $S(k) \Rightarrow S(k+1)$ for all k and so $S(n)$ is true for all positive integers n.

Finding a Polynomial from Its Zeros

By the Factor Theorem, if z_1 is a zero of $p(x)$, then $(x - z_1)$ is a factor of $p(x)$. Thus you can always write a formula for a polynomial if you know all its zeros.

Example 2

Give a polynomial of degree 3 which has the zeros 3, i, and -4.

Solution

Since a polynomial of degree 3 has at most 3 zeros, there are no other zeros. Let $p(x)$ be a polynomial with these zeros. Then $x - 3$, $x - i$, and $x + 4$ are factors of $p(x)$. Thus one possibility is that

$$p(x) = (x-3)(x-i)(x+4).$$

In standard form,

$$\begin{aligned} p(x) &= (x^2 - 3x - ix + 3i)(x + 4) \\ &= x^3 + (1 - i)x^2 + (-12 - i)x + 12i. \end{aligned}$$

All other possible polynomials are real or complex multiples of $p(x)$. For instance, another possible polynomial is $10p(x)$, or $10x^3 + (10 - 10i)x^2 + (-120 - 10i)x + 120i$.

Examination of Example 2 shows that the nonreal coefficients of $p(x)$ are caused by the fact that i is a zero of $p(x)$. If $p(x)$ had all real zeros, it would have all real coefficients.

QUESTIONS

Covering the Reading

1. **a.** Describe the end behavior of $p(x) = 8x^5 - 20x^4 + 3x - 1$.
   b. Explain why this end behavior forces $p(x)$ to have at least one real zero.
   a, b) See left.

1a) $\lim_{x \to -\infty} p(x) = -\infty$, and $\lim_{x \to \infty} p(x) = \infty$

b) Since $p(x) < 0$ for a small enough real number x, $p(x) > 0$ for a large enough real number x, and p is continuous, the Intermediate Value Theorem ensures that there exists a real number c such that $p(c) = 0$.

Notes on Questions

Question 1 Use an automatic grapher with domain set to $-5 \le x \le 5$ and range set to $-60 \le y \le 60$ to help students verify their conclusion. They may also practice their zooming in skills to estimate the zero.

LESSON MASTER 8-8

Questions on SPUR Objectives
See pages 547–549 for objectives.

Skills Objective E

In 1–3, a polynomial is given. a. Find all zeros of the polynomial. b. Give the multiplicities of the zeros.

1. $f(x) = (x+3)^5(2x-1)(x^2+1)$
   a. $-3, \frac{1}{2}, i, -i$ b. 5, 1, 1, 1
2. $g(t) = t^5 + 2t^3 - 3t$
   a. $0, 1, -1, \sqrt{3}i, -\sqrt{3}i$ b. 1, 1, 1, 1, 1
3. $h(x) = x^4 - 8x^3 + 20x^2 - 32x + 64$ given that $2i$ is a zero of $h(x)$.
   a. $2i, -2i, 4$ b. 1, 1, 2
4. Find a polynomial of degree 4 that has zeros 5, -5, i and $-i$.
   Sample: $f(x) = x^4 - 24x^2 - 25$

Properties Objective G

5. $p(x) = -2x^9 + 5x^6 + 7x^3 - 12$ has exactly __?__ complex zeros counting multiplicities. 9
6. A polynomial $f(x)$ has the following zeros: 3, 1, 0, $2i$, and $-2i$. The 3 and 0 each have multiplicity 2, and the other zeros have multiplicity 1.
   a. What is the degree of $f(x)$? 7
   b. Write a possible formula for $f(x)$ in factored form.
   Sample: $f(x) = (x-3)^2(x-1)(x^2)(x^2+4)$
7. An eighth-degree polynomial $q(x)$ has at least 2 simple zeros each with multiplicity 2.
   a. How many more zeros does $q(x)$ have, counting multiplicities? 4
   b. Write a possible formula for $f(x)$ in factored form.
   1 zero with multiplicity 4; 2 zeros with multiplicities 3 and 1; 2 zeros each with multiplicity 2; 3 zeros with multiplicities 2, 1 and 1; or 4 zeros each with multiplicity 1

Notes on Questions

Question 2 Remind students that all real numbers are complex numbers.

Question 5 Point out that the quadratic formula is valid for any quadratic polynomial—even one with nonreal coefficients—and should be used here.

Question 6 Students who expand the power should be admonished.

Question 8 There are infinitely many 5th degree polynomials with these zeros, but they are all multiples of each other.

Question 9 A diagram may prove to be a useful reminder and guide.

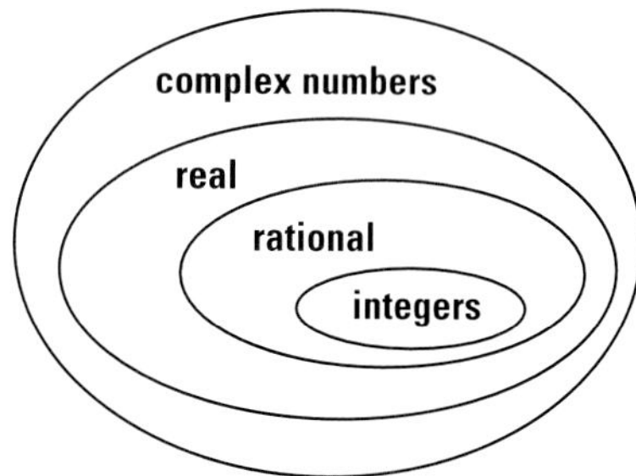

Question 12 Generalize **parts a and b.** The degree of the sum is the larger degree of $p(x)$ and $q(x)$. The degree of the product is the sum of the degrees of $p(x)$ and $q(x)$. In **part c,** ask students for an example where the number of zeros of the quotient is 5, 4, 3, 2, 1, and 0. [Begin with a polynomial $p(x)$ that has 5 distinct zeros. Every time a zero of $q(x)$ is a zero of $p(x)$, then there is one less zero in the quotient.]

Question 14 The equality of **parts c and d** $(\overline{z})^n = (\overline{z^n})$ will be used in proving the Conjugate Zeros Theorem of Lesson 8-9.

5) $i, -\frac{i}{2}$, both with multiplicity 1

7a) Sample: $p(x) = (x - 6)(x - 4i)x$

11) It has three more zeros. There can be three more simple zeros, or one zero with multiplicity 3, or one simple zero and one zero with multiplicity 2.

13b)

$z = [2, 135°]$, [2, 90°], [2, 45°], [2, 0°], [2, 180°], [2, 225°], [2, 270°], [2, 315°]

15) $(2 + i)^2 - 4(2 + i) + 5 = 4 + 4i - 1 - 8 - 4i + 5 = 0$; $(2 - i)^2 - 4(2 - i) + 5 = 4 - 4i - 1 - 8 + 4i + 5 = 0$

2. How many complex zeros, counting multiplicities, does the polynomial $f(x) = 3x^{11} - \frac{1}{2}x^4 + ix^2 - 2$ have? **11**

In 3–6, find all zeros and the corresponding multiplicities for the given polynomial.

3. $f(x) = x^6 - 4x^5 - 5x^4$ **0(multiplicity 4), -1, 5**

4. $g(y) = y - \frac{y^3}{6}$ **0, ± 6, all with multiplicity 1**

5. $q(t) = 2t^2 - it + 1$ **See left:**

6. $p(x) = (x^2 + 1)^2$ **$\pm i$, both with multiplicity 2**

7. a. Give a polynomial of degree 3 which has the zeros 6, $4i$, and 0. **See left.**

b. Give a second polynomial of degree 3 which has the zeros 6, $4i$, and 0. **Sample: $p(x) = 8x(x - 6)(x - 4i)$**

8. A 5th degree polynomial $p(x)$ has the simple zeros $1 + i$, $1 - i$, -1, and the zero 3 with multiplicity 2. Write a possible formula for $p(x)$ in factored form. **Sample: $p(x) = (x - 3)^2(x + 1)(x - (1 + i))(x - (1 - i))$**

Applying the Mathematics

9. How many zeros (counting multiplicities) does the polynomial $p(x) = (x^2 + 2)(x^2 - 2)(x + 2)^2(2x - 1)$ have in the given set of numbers?

a. integers **2** **b.** rational **3** **c.** real **5** **d.** complex **7**

10. Given $h(x) = x^4 - 6x^3 + 18x^2 - 32x + 24$, use the fact that 2 is a zero of $h(x)$ with multiplicity 2 to find all the zeros and their multiplicities. **2 (with multiplicity 2), $1 \pm \sqrt{5}i$**

11. A sixth degree polynomial has at least one simple zero and at least one zero of multiplicity 2. Give the possible multiplicities of the remaining zeros. **See left.**

12. If a polynomial $p(x)$ has 5 zeros and a polynomial $q(x)$ has 7 zeros (counting multiplicities), give the number of zeros of each.

a. $r(x)$, where $r(x) = p(x) + q(x)$ **7**

b. $s(x)$, where $s(x) = p(x)\,q(x)$ **12**

c. $t(x)$, where $t(x) = \frac{p(x)}{q(x)}$ **≤ 5**

Review

13. Suppose $z = -\sqrt{2} + \sqrt{2}\,i$ is an 8th root of w.

a. Find w. **256**

b. Find the other 8th roots of w (in polar form), and graph them on a polar grid. *(Lessons 8-6, 8-7)* **See left.**

14. Let $z = [r, \theta]$, where $r \geq 0$, and let n be a nonnegative integer. Give an expression in polar form for:

a. z^n **$[r^n, n\theta]$** **b.** $\overline{z}$ **$[r, -\theta]$** **c.** $(\overline{z})^n$ **$[r^n, -n\theta]$** **d.** $(\overline{z^n})$ **$[r^n, -n\theta]$**

e. Complete this sentence. Parts **c** and **d** show that, for any nonnegative integer n, the nth power of the conjugate of a complex number equals __?__. *(Lesson 8-6)* **the conjugate of the nth power of the complex number**

15. Show that $2 + i$ and $2 - i$ are both solutions to the equation $x^2 - 4x + 5 = 0$. *(Lesson 8-1)* **See left.**

16. Suppose $p(x)$ is a polynomial of odd degree and $\lim_{x \to \infty} p(x) = -\infty$. What is $\lim_{x \to -\infty} p(x)$? *(Lesson 2-4)* **$\infty$**

17b) $i^{4k} = 1$, $i^{4k+1} = i$, $i^{4k+2} = -1$, $i^{4k+3} = -i$

18b) $p(x) = 3x^4\left(1 - \frac{2}{3x} + \frac{1}{3x^3}\right)$

c) $\lim_{x \to -\infty} p(x) = \infty$, $\lim_{x \to \infty} p(x) = \infty$

17. **a.** Evaluate i^n for $n = 0, 1, 2, \ldots, 8$. **1, i, -1, $-i$, 1, i, -1, $-i$, 1**

b. Generalize the results of part **a** to write formulas for

$$i^{4k}, i^{4k+1}, i^{4k+2}, i^{4k+3}$$

for any nonnegative integer k. **See left.**

c. Use the result of part **b** to evaluate each of the following.

i. i^{59} **$-i$** **ii.** i^{18} **-1** **iii.** i^{60} *(Lesson 8-1)* **1**

18. Let $p(x)$ be the polynomial $p(x) = 3x^4 - 2x^3 + x$.

a. Find a polynomial of the form $f(x) = ax^n$ whose behavior is similar to that of $p(x)$ for large x. **$f(x) = 3x^4$**

b. Rewrite $p(x)$ to justify your claim in part **a**. **See left.**

c. Describe the end behavior of $p(x)$ using limit notation. *(Lesson 5-5)* **See left.**

19. The commands MOD and DIV in the computer language Pascal can be used to determine the results in the Quotient-Remainder Theorem. *(Lesson 4-2)*

n DIV *d* computes the integer quotient for $n \div d$.

n MOD *d* computes the integer remainder for $n \div d$.

a. Evaluate the following.

i. 157 DIV 11 **14** **ii.** 218 MOD 7 **1**

b. Write an expression in Pascal that gives the number of complete weeks in n days. ***n* DIV 7**

c. Carolyn's father is baking cookies and packaging them a dozen at a time. Assume that he bakes c cookies. If Carolyn gets all the leftovers, write an expression in Pascal that gives the number of cookies she gets. ***c* MOD 12**

20. Use the Intermediate Value Theorem to find an interval between two consecutive integers where the function f, defined by $f(t) = 12t^3 + 28t^2 - 173t - 252$, has a zero. *(Lesson 3-4)* **any one of: $-5 < x < -4$, $-2 < x < -1$, or $3 < x < 4$**

Exploration

21. Given the cubic polynomial $f(x) = x^3 + px^2 + qx + r$, let

$$A = \sqrt[3]{-\frac{(2p^3 - 9pq + 27r)}{54} + \sqrt{\frac{(2p^3 - 9pq + 27r)^2}{2916} + \frac{(3q - p^2)^3}{729}}}$$

and

$$B = \sqrt[3]{-\frac{(2p^3 - 9pq + 27r)}{54} - \sqrt{\frac{(2p^3 - 9pq + 27r)^2}{2916} + \frac{(3q - p^2)^3}{729}}}.$$

Cardano showed that the zeros of $f(x)$ are then

$$A + B - \frac{p}{3},$$

$$-\frac{A + B}{2} - \frac{p}{3} + \frac{A - B}{2}\sqrt{-3},$$

and

$$-\frac{A + B}{2} - \frac{p}{3} - \frac{A - B}{2}\sqrt{-3}.$$

Use these formulas to find the zeros of the polynomial

$$f(x) = x^3 + 2x^2 + 3x + 1.$$

$\approx -0.4302, -0.7849 \pm 1.307i$

22. Consider the five polynomials $p(x) = (x - 1)^m(x - 2)^n$, where m and n are positive integers such that $m + n = 6$. What do all these polynomials have in common? How do they differ? **See left.**

22) Sample: They all have 6 complex zeros. They each will have $x = 1$ with multiplicity m and $x = 2$ with multiplicity n. The end behavior of each function is the same: $\lim_{x \to -\infty} p(x) = \infty$, $\lim_{x \to \infty} p(x) = \infty$. The graphs differ in their "spread" depending on the choices for m and n.

Question 17b The general pattern is easily described with modular arithmetic: $i^x = i^y \Leftrightarrow x \equiv y \pmod 4$. Thus for all integers k, $i^{4k} = i^0$, $i^{4k+1} = i$, $i^{4k+2} = i^2$, and $i^{4k+3} = i^3$.

Question 21 Error Alert This example is difficult to carry out. Few people are able to work it through without errors. You might ask some student to program the formula into a computer.

Follow-up for Lesson 8-8

Practice

For more questions on SPUR Objectives, use **Lesson Master 8-8** (shown on page 523).

Assessment

Quiz A quiz covering Lessons 8-5 through 8-8 is provided in the Assessment Sourcebook.

Extension

This lesson discusses one of three "Fundamental" theorems in mathematics. Ask interested students to find out what the other two Fundamental theorems are, and who first proved them. [The Fundamental Theorem of Arithmetic appears to be first proven by Euclid. It states that any positive integer other than 1 can be written as a product of primes in one and only one way. The Fundamental Theorem of Calculus has been attributed to both Leibniz and Newton.

Setting Up Lesson 8-9

Discuss **Question 14.** Its result is used in Lesson 8-9.

Lesson 8-9

Objectives

E Find all zeros, and their multiplicities, of a given polynomial.
G Use the properties of polynomials to find or describe their zeros.

Resources

From the ***Teacher's Resource File***
- Lesson Master 8-9
- Answer Master 8-9
- Teaching Aids
  72 Warm-up
  84 Additional Examples
  85 Graphs and zeros of $p(x) = 4x^4 + 8x^3 - 3x^2 - 9x + c$

Additional Resources
- Visuals for Teaching Aids 72, 84, 85

Teaching Lesson 8-9

Warm-up

1. Find all solutions to the equation $x^3 + x^2 + x + 1 = 0$. $-1, i, -i$
2. Write a polynomial equation whose zeros are 1, -1, i, and $-i$. **Sample: $x^4 - 1 = 0$. Note that $x^4 - 1 = (x - 1)(x^3 + x^2 + x + 1)$, so the two questions are related. Solving this equation is Question 11 of this lesson.**

LESSON 8-9

Nonreal Zeros of Polynomials with Real Coefficients

❶ **Great Image.** *Polynomials contribute to the computer production of this Landsat image of the Great Lakes.*

Complex Zeros of Some Polynomials Come in Pairs

In the last lesson, we showed that every polynomial of degree n has exactly n zeros, if multiplicities are included. This lesson begins with a related question: If all the coefficients of the polynomial are real numbers, how many of these n zeros are real, how many are nonreal?

For example, the polynomial $p(x)$ of degree 2 defined by

$$p(x) = x^2 + 1$$

has no real zeros. It does, however, have two complex zeros, i and $-i$. In general, all polynomials *with real coefficients* satisfy the following important property.

> **Conjugate Zeros Theorem**
> Let $p(x)$ be a polynomial with real coefficients. If $z = a + bi$ is a zero of $p(x)$, then its complex conjugate $\bar{z} = a - bi$ is also a zero of $p(x)$.

This theorem is often nicely paraphrased as follows: *Complex zeros of a polynomial with real coefficients always occur in complex conjugate pairs.* Before we prove the theorem, we illustrate its use with the following example.

Example 1

Consider the polynomial $p(x)$ defined by $p(x) = x^4 + 2x^3 + 3x^2 + 2x + 2$.
a. Verify that i is a zero of $p(x)$.
b. Find the remaining zeros of $p(x)$ and their multiplicities.

Lesson 8-9 Overview

Broad Goals The real zeros of polynomials with real coefficients can be located with precision on the x-axis. This lesson examines the complex zeros of such polynomials. They are proved to occur in conjugate pairs, and an example is given that shows they change continuously as a coefficient of the polynomial changes continuously.

Perspective Showing the change in complex zeros as the coefficients of a polynomial change would be unreasonable without automatic graphers. But the notion that these zeros should be somehow related to each other is not at all unreasonable. Polynomials are continuous functions, and small changes in a coefficient means relatively small changes in the zeros. But these "relatively small changes" can be changes from real to nonreal zeros, or changes in the multiplicities of zeros. This is no different in concept from the small change in length of side that would change a square into a rectangle that is not a square.

Solution

a. Recall that $i^2 = -1$, $i^3 = -i$, and $i^4 = 1$. Consequently,

$$\begin{aligned} p(i) &= i^4 + 2i^3 + 3i^2 + 2i + 2 \\ &= 1 - 2i - 3 + 2i + 2 \\ &= 0. \end{aligned}$$

b. Because i is a zero of $p(x)$, it follows that $\bar{i} = -i$ is also a zero of $p(x)$ by the Conjugate Zeros Theorem. The Factor Theorem implies that $(x - i)$ and $(x + i)$ are factors of $p(x)$. Thus, $(x - i)(x + i) = x^2 + 1$ is a factor of $p(x)$. Divide $p(x)$ by $x^2 + 1$ to obtain the other factor.

$$\begin{array}{r|l} & x^2 + 2x + 2 \\ \hline x^2 + 1 & x^4 + 2x^3 + 3x^2 + 2x + 2 \\ & x^4 \quad\quad + x^2 \\ \hline & 2x^3 + 2x^2 + 2x + 2 \\ & 2x^3 \quad\quad + 2x \\ \hline & 2x^2 \quad\quad + 2 \\ & 2x^2 \quad\quad + 2 \\ \hline & 0 \end{array}$$

The remaining zeros of $p(x)$ are the zeros of the quotient polynomial

$$q(x) = x^2 + 2x + 2.$$

These can be found using the quadratic formula:

$$x = \frac{-2 \pm \sqrt{2^2 - 4 \cdot 2}}{2} = -1 \pm i.$$

Therefore, $p(x)$ has four simple zeros:

$$i, -i, -1 + i, \text{ and } -1 - i.$$

❷ Proving the Conjugate Zeros Theorem

The proof of the Conjugate Zeros Theorem relies on the following algebraic properties of complex conjugates (see Question 20 of Lesson 8-1, Question 19 of Lesson 8-2, and Question 14 of Lesson 8-6):
For all complex numbers z and w, and positive integers m,

(1) $\overline{z + w} = \bar{z} + \bar{w}$

(2) $\overline{z \cdot w} = \bar{z} \cdot \bar{w}$

(3) $(\overline{z^m}) = (\bar{z})^m$

(4) $z = \bar{z}$ if and only if z is a real number.

To prove the Conjugate Zeros Theorem, let

$$p(x) = a_n x^n + a_{n-1}x^{n-1} + \ldots + a_1 x + a_0,$$

where the a_i are all real numbers. We first show that

$$\overline{p(z)} = p(\bar{z})$$

for any complex number z. The argument is on page 528.

Notes on Reading

❶ **Science Connection** The Landsat, or Earth Resources Technology Satellites, were unmanned satellites launched from 1972 to 1978. They were used to take pictures of the earth so that such things as changes in ecology, pollution, the atmosphere, and ocean conditions could be studied.

Before the days of automatic graphers, it was not easy to see the real zeros of polynomials with real coefficients, though there are algebraic methods for determining bounds on them and there are algebraic ways to approximate them. Nowadays, it is relatively easy to determine the real zeros. This leads naturally to the question of seeing the complex zeros, the subject of this lesson.

The usefulness of the Conjugate Zeros Theorem is demonstrated by **Example 1** before the theorem is proved.

In **Example 1,** students could divide by $x - i$ first. The quotient is a polynomial of degree 3 with complex coefficients and a remainder of 0. Dividing this reduced polynomial by $x + i$ yields a quotient of $x^2 + 2x + 2$ and a remainder of 0. The Quadratic Formula can be used to find the remaining zeros, as shown in the example.

❷ Review the proof of the Conjugate Zeros Theorem with the class. The idea is simple. If p is a polynomial function *with real coefficients* and complex numbers z and w are conjugates, so are $p(z)$ and $p(w)$. Now any real number equals its conjugate, so if $p(z)$ is a real number, $p(w)$ is that same real number. In the proof, the real number is 0. The proof puts together simple properties to produce a powerful result. It is quite elegant.

Example 2 is straightforward and exhibits the ease with which a polynomial can be found with given zeros.

The solution to **Example 3d** states that the graph of p crosses the x-axis at its simple real zeros but is tangent to it at the real zero of multiplicity 2. A proof requires calculus, but here is the idea: Suppose that c is a simple real zero of a polynomial function p, so that $p(x) = q(x)(x - c)$ where $x - c$ is not a factor of the polynomial $q(x)$. Then, for values of x close enough to c, $q(x)$ remains close to some constant a so $p(x) \approx a(x - c)$. The graph of $y = a(x - c)$ is a straight line crossing the x-axis at $(c, 0)$, and the graph of p behaves roughly in the same way.

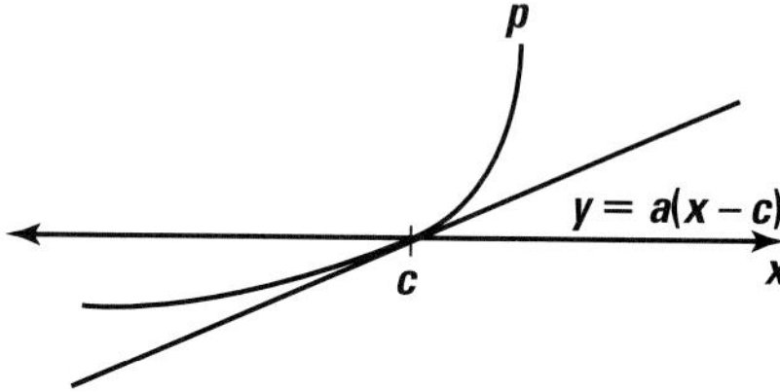

Now suppose that d is a real zero of p with multiplicity 2, so that $p(x) = r(x)(x - d)^2$, where $x - d$ is not a factor of $r(x)$. Then, for values of x close enough to d, $r(x)$ remains close to some constant b so $p(x) \approx b(x - d)^2$. The graph of $y = b(x - d)^2$ is a parabola tangent to the x-axis at its vertex, $(d, 0)$, and the graph of p behaves roughly in the same way.

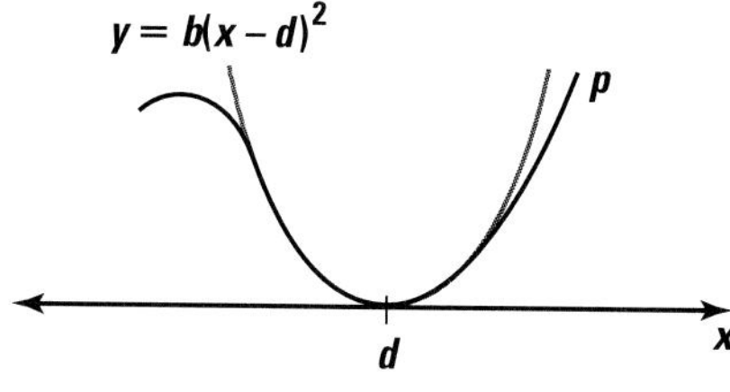

$$\begin{aligned}
\overline{p(z)} &= \overline{a_n z^n + a_{n-1} z^{n-1} + \ldots + a_1 z + a_0} \\
&= \overline{a_n z^n} + \overline{a_{n-1} z^{n-1}} + \ldots + \overline{a_1 z} + \overline{a_0} && \text{Property (1) applied repeatedly} \\
&= \overline{a_n}(\overline{z})^n + \overline{a_{n-1}}(\overline{z})^{n-1} + \ldots + \overline{a_1}(\overline{z}) + \overline{a_0} && \text{Properties (2) and (3)} \\
&= a_n(\overline{z})^n + a_{n-1}(\overline{z})^{n-1} + \ldots + a_1(\overline{z}) + a_0 && \text{Property (4)} \\
&= p(\overline{z})
\end{aligned}$$

Now it is easy to prove that complex zeros of polynomials with real coefficients occur in conjugate pairs. If z is a complex zero of p, then

$$0 = p(z).$$

Thus $\qquad \overline{0} = \overline{p(z)}.$

But $\overline{0} = 0$, so $\qquad 0 = \overline{p(z)} = p(\overline{z}).$

Therefore, $\overline{z}$ is also a zero of $p(x)$. This completes the proof of the Conjugate Zeros Theorem.

Example 2

Find the polynomial of smallest degree with real coefficients that has zeros 1, -2, and $-1 + i$, and write this polynomial in standard form.

Solution

Let $p(x)$ be such a polynomial. Since $p(x)$ has real coefficients and $-1 + i$ is a zero, $-1 - i$ must be a zero of $p(x)$. Therefore $p(x)$ must have 4 zeros, and must therefore have degree 4. By the Factor Theorem, a possible formula for $p(x)$ is

$$\begin{aligned}
p(x) &= (x - 1)(x + 2)[x - (-1 + i)][x - (-1 - i)] \\
&= (x - 1)(x + 2)(x + 1 - i)(x + 1 + i) \\
&= (x^2 + x - 2)(x^2 + 2x + 1 - i^2) \\
&= (x^2 + x - 2)(x^2 + 2x + 2) \\
&= x^4 + 3x^3 + 2x^2 - 2x - 4.
\end{aligned}$$

Obtaining Knowledge of Nonreal Zeros from Real Zeros

Real zeros of a polynomial $p(x)$ with real coefficients occur at points along the x-axis where the graph of

$$y = p(x)$$

crosses or touches the x-axis. The nonreal zeros of $p(x)$ do not appear on the x-axis because only real values of the variable are on the x-axis. However, using the Conjugate Zeros Theorem, information about the nonreal zeros can be inferred from knowledge of the real zeros.

Optional Activities

Writing Students may need some help organizing the techniques they have learned for finding zeros of polynomials. Have them write how they could find zeros for each of the following polynomials.

1. $x^n + c = 0$; c is a complex number [Use the Complex nth Roots Theorem.]
2. $ax^2 + bx + c = 0$; a, b, and c are complex [Use the Quadratic Formula.]
3. $ax^4 + bx^3 + cx^2 + dx + e = 0$; a, b, c, d, e are real [Locate real root(s) with an automatic grapher, divide, and use the Quadratic Formula. If there are no real roots, some of the complex roots must be "given;" others can be found through long division and through the Conjugate Zeros Theorem.]

Example 3

The curve pictured below is the graph of $y = p(x)$ for a polynomial $p(x)$ of degree 4 with real coefficients. The x-axis has been removed.

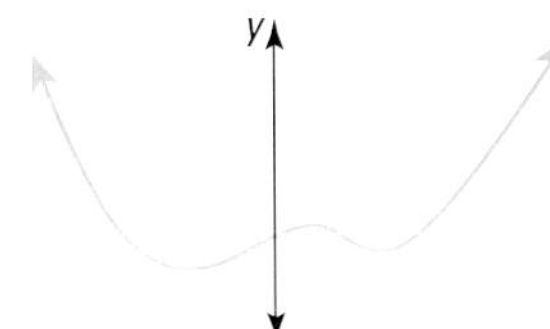

Reinsert the horizontal axis at a position that is consistent with the additional information provided about $p(x)$. Also, describe the nonreal zeros.

a. $p(x)$ has no real zeros.
b. $p(x)$ has one real zero.
c. $p(x)$ has exactly two real zeros and both are simple zeros.
d. $p(x)$ has two simple real zeros and one real zero of multiplicity 2.

Solution

a. Because p(x) has no real zeros, the graph of y = p(x) cannot intersect the x-axis. So the x-axis must lie below the graph. Since p(x) has degree 4, it must have 4 zeros. Because they are all nonreal and the coefficients of p(x) are real, they must be in complex conjugate pairs.

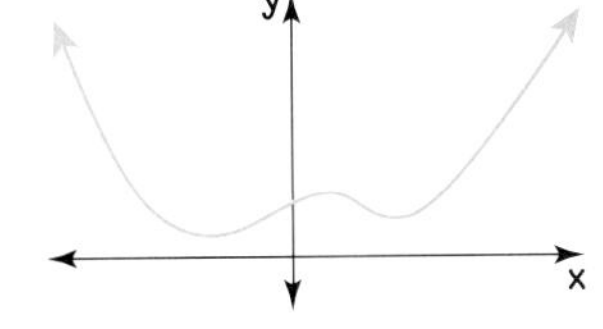

Therefore, there are either 2 pairs of conjugate zeros, each of multiplicity 1, or a single pair of conjugate zeros, each of multiplicity 2.

b. Since p(x) has one real zero, it intersects the x-axis at only one point. Because any nonreal zeros come in pairs, the real zero must have multiplicity 2 or 4, but if it had multiplicity 4, then $p(x) = (x - a)^4$, whose graph is a translation image of the graph of $y = x^4$. The graph is not that image, so we conclude that p(x) has one real zero of multiplicity 2 and a pair of conjugate nonreal zeros.

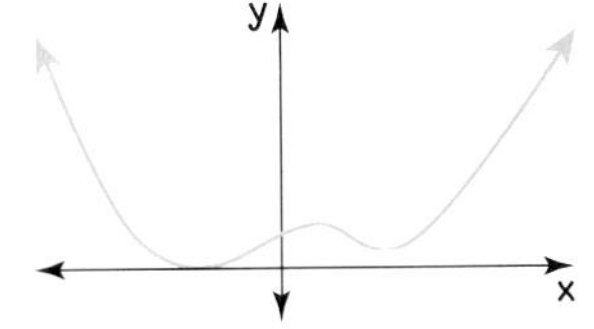

c. Because p(x) has only two real, simple zeros, the graph of y = p(x) crosses the x-axis exactly twice. The other 2 zeros of p(x) must be a complex conjugate pair.

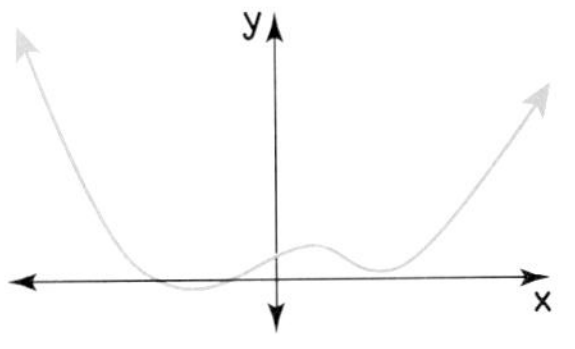

▶

In **Example 3** and elsewhere in the lesson, students are presented with graphs of polynomials of specified degree with real coefficients which have been drawn on coordinate planes without labeled axes. It should be noted that these graphs cannot be drawn arbitrarily. One cannot simply draw any curve with N relative extrema and claim it represents a polynomial of degree $N + 1$. In the graph of **Example 3,** for example, any four points will uniquely determine (up to a scale change) a 4th degree polynomial with real coefficients, but only if any four points on the graph give rise to the same polynomial can we say that the graph represents a polynomial with real coefficients of degree 4.

❸ Two important properties of polynomials are employed to provide a rough way of graphing nonreal zeros of real polynomial functions. The first is the fact that the zeros of a polynomial vary continuously as a function of the coefficients. The second property is the Conjugate Zeros Theorem. The first property implies that when the constant coefficient is increased by a tiny amount, the real zero of multiplicity 2 must change only slightly. It can no longer be real since the graph of the function no longer intersects the x-axis. Then the Conjugate Zeros Theorem implies that its conjugate must also be a zero. Thus the two zeros are symmetric about the real axis and are close to the old real zero.

LESSON MASTER 8-9 — **Questions on SPUR Objectives** See pages 547–549 for objectives.

Skills Objective E

1. Two of the zeros of the polynomial $p(x) = x^4 - 6x^3 + 11x^2 - 6x + 10$ are $3 - i$ and i. Find the remaining zeros of $p(x)$. **$3 + i, -i$**

2. If i is a zero of the polynomial $f(y) = 4y^4 - 8y^3 + 9y^2 - 8y + 5$, find the remaining zeros of p(y) **$i, 1 + \frac{i}{2}, 1 - \frac{i}{2}$**

3. If $1 - i$ and $4i$ are zeros of a fourth degree polynomial $q(x)$ with real coefficients, give a possible formula for $q(x)$.
Sample: $q(x) = x^4 - 2x^3 + 18x^2 - 32x + 32$

4. Find a polynomial $g(x)$ of smallest degree with real coefficients that has zeros $5 + i$ and 0.
Sample: $g(x) = x^3 - 10x^2 + 26x$

Properties Objective G

5. If $2i$ is a zero of $h(x) = x^2 - 4xi - 4$, is $-2i$ necessarily the other zero? Explain.
No; the Conjugates Zeros Theorem applies to polynomials with real coefficients.

6. Does there exist a polynomial $p(z)$ with real coefficients which has exactly three zeros: $5i$, $-5i$, and $3 + 2i$? Justify your answer.
No; the Conjugates Zeros Theorem, $3 - 2i$ must also be a zero.

7. What is the smallest possible degree of a polynomial $f(x)$ with real coefficients if $-2 - 2i$, $-1 + i$, and 6 are zeros of $f(x)$? **5**

8. Suppose $p(x)$ is a polynomial with real coefficients such that $p(x) = (x - 1 - 3i)q(x)$ where $q(x)$ is a polynomial. Give a factor of $q(x)$. **$x - 1 + 3i$**

9. Prove: If a polynomial with real coefficients has a nonreal zero z with multiplicity 2, then the degree of polynomial is at least 4.
By the Conjugates Zeros Theorem, $\bar{z}$ is also a zero with multiplicity 2. Since there are at least 2 zeros each with multiplicity 2, the degree must be at least 4.

Adapting to Individual Needs

Extra Help

If students are having difficulty, you might consider illustrating the family of polynomials p_c shown using *Mathematica* software. A *Mathematica* program will show the polynomial function's graph for different values of c along with a graph in the complex plane of corresponding zeros of $p_c(x)$. Seeing the pattern of zeros as c changes is quite remarkable and instructive.

❹ **Teaching Aid 85** shows this graph and the graph at the top of page 531.

Additional Examples

Additional Examples 1–3 are on **Teaching Aid 84.**

1. Let $p(x) = x^6 - 5x^5 + 10x^4 - 20x^3 + 24x^2$.
   a. Verify that $2i$ is a zero of $p(x)$. $\mathbf{p(2i) = (2i)^6 - 5(2i)^5 + 10(2i)^4 - 20(2i)^3 + 24(2i)^2 = -64 - 5(32i) + 160 + 160i - 96 = 0}$
   b. Find the remaining zeros of $p(x)$ and their multiplicities. **0, multiplicity 2; -2*i*, multiplicity 1; 2, multiplicity 1; 3, multiplicity 1**
2. Find a polynomial with real coefficients that has zeros -1, 3, and $2 + 3i$. $\mathbf{p(x) = (x + 1)(x - 3)(x - 2 - 3i)(x - 2 + 3i) = x^4 - 6x^3 + 18x^2 - 14x - 39}$
3. Suppose the curve below is the graph of $y = p(x)$ for a polynomial $p(x)$ of degree 5 with real coefficients. Insert the horizontal axis at a position consistent with the additional information provided about $p(x)$. Also, describe the nonreal zeros.

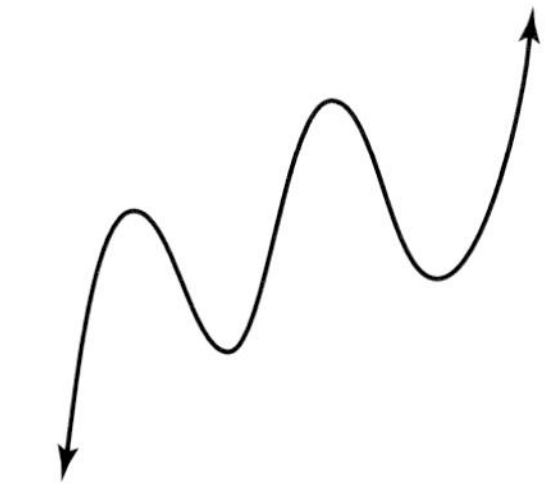

a. $p(x)$ has no real zeros. **Impossible**

b. $p(x)$ has exactly 1 real zero. **The other 4 reals are complex in conjugate pairs. Sample graph:**

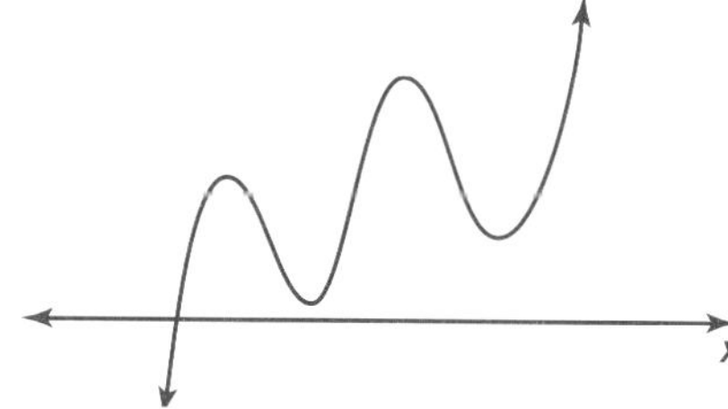

d. Since $p(x)$ has two simple real zeros and one real zero of multiplicity 2, the graph of $y = p(x)$ crosses the x-axis at two of the zeros, and just touches the x-axis at the third. Since $p(x)$ can have only 4 zeros counting multiplicities, it can have no nonreal zeros.

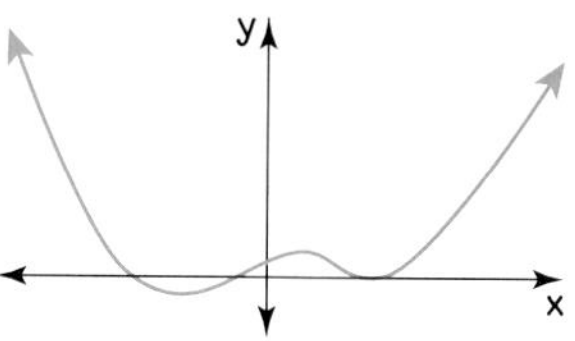

Graphs can show the effect of changes in a polynomial's constant coefficient on its complex zeros. It is a consequence of continuity that if the coefficients of $p(x)$ are changed only slightly, then the locations of the zeros of $p(x)$ change only slightly also. For example, if you vary the polynomial $p(x)$ by increasing its constant coefficient, the graph of p will slide up the y-axis without changing its shape. As this happens, its zeros change. For example, shown below are graphs of the six polynomial functions defined by

$$p_c(x) = 4x^4 + 8x^3 - 3x^2 - 9x + c$$

for c = -4, -2, 0, 2, 4, and 6, on the interval $-2 \le x \le 2$.

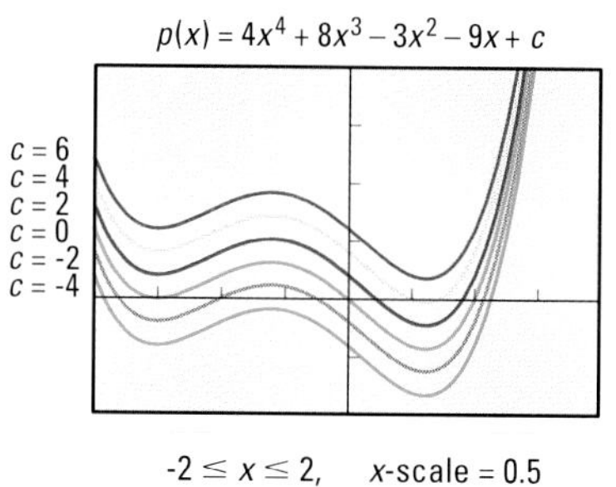

$-2 \le x \le 2$, x-scale = 0.5
$-10 \le y \le 20$, y-scale = 5

The lowest graph corresponds to $c = -4$ and the highest corresponds to $c = 6$, with the intermediate graphs increasing in height with the value of c. We know that each function has a total of 4 zeros. From their graphs, it appears that

- p_{-4} has two simple real zeros (and thus one pair of complex conjugate zeros),
- p_{-2} has four simple real zeros,
- p_0 has two simple real zeros and one real zero of multiplicity two (near -1.5),
- p_2 has two simple real zeros (and thus one pair of complex conjugate zeros),
- p_4 has two simple real zeros that are very close to each other (and two complex conjugate zeros),
- p_6 has no real zeros, so it must have two pairs of complex conjugate zeros.

Adapting to Individual Needs

Challenge

Let a be any complex number. Have students show that $(x - a)(x - \overline{a})$ is always a quadratic with real coefficients. $[(x - a)(x - \overline{a}) = x^2 - (a - \overline{a})x + a\overline{a})$. $a - \overline{a}$ and $a\overline{a}$ are always real, so the statement is true.]

The complex zeros of the $p_c(x)$ are displayed as dots in the complex plane below, with arrows to show how they move as the value of c increases.

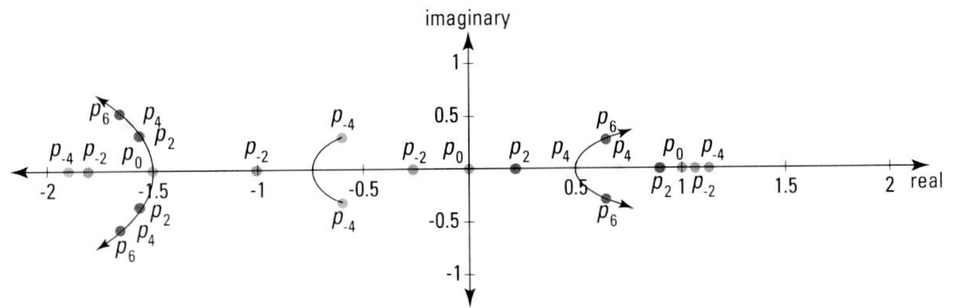

Read this graph by first finding the four zeros of p_{-4}. Notice that as c increases, two distinct real zeros merge into a real zero of multiplicity 2, and then split into complex conjugate zeros as c continues to increase. Automatic graphers have made it possible to track the movements of complex zeros more easily than ever before.

QUESTIONS

Covering the Reading

1. Suppose $p(x)$ is a polynomial with real coefficients such that $p(3 + 2i) = 4 - 7i$ and $p(2 - 3i) = 0$.
   a. Evaluate $p(3 - 2i)$. **$4 + 7i$**
   b. Evaluate $p(2 + 3i)$. **0**

2. Let $p(x) = x^2 + 3x - 2$.
   a. Find $p(4 + 7i)$. **$-23 + 77i$**
   b. Find $p(4 - 7i)$. **$-23 - 77i$**

3. Consider the polynomial $p(x) = x^2 + 4ix + 5$.
   a. Show that the zeros of $p(x)$ are i and $-5i$. **See left.**
   b. The zeros are not complex conjugates. Does this contradict the Conjugate Zeros Theorem? Why or why not?
   No, the coefficients of p are not all real numbers.

4. *True or false.* There is a polynomial with real coefficients which has exactly one complex nonreal zero. **False**

5. Two of the zeros of the polynomial $p(x) = x^4 - 9x^3 + 50x^2 - 49x + 41$ are $\frac{1 + i\sqrt{3}}{2}$ and $4 + 5i$. Find the remaining zeros of $p(x)$. **$\frac{1 - i\sqrt{3}}{2}$, $4 - 5i$**

6. One of the zeros of $p(x) = x^4 - 7x^2 + 4x + 20$ is $2 + i$. Find the remaining zeros. **$2 - i$ and -2 (with multiplicity 2)**

7. Find a polynomial of smallest degree with real coefficients that has zeros -3 and $2 - i$. **Sample: $p(x) = x^3 - x^2 - 7x + 15$**

In 8 and 9, trace the graph in Example 3.

8. Insert an x-axis so that $p(x)$ has four real simple zeros. **See left.**

9. Show a different position of the graph that also is an answer to Example 3 part **d**. **See left.**

3a) $p(i) = i^2 + 4i^2 + 5 = -1 - 4 + 5 = 0$; $p(-5i) = 25i^2 - 20i^2 + 5 = -25 + 20 + 5 = 0$.

8) Sample:

9) Sample:

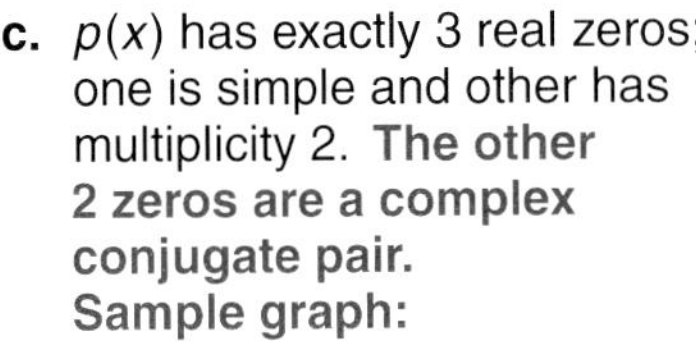
c. $p(x)$ has exactly 3 real zeros; one is simple and other has multiplicity 2. **The other 2 zeros are a complex conjugate pair.**
Sample graph:

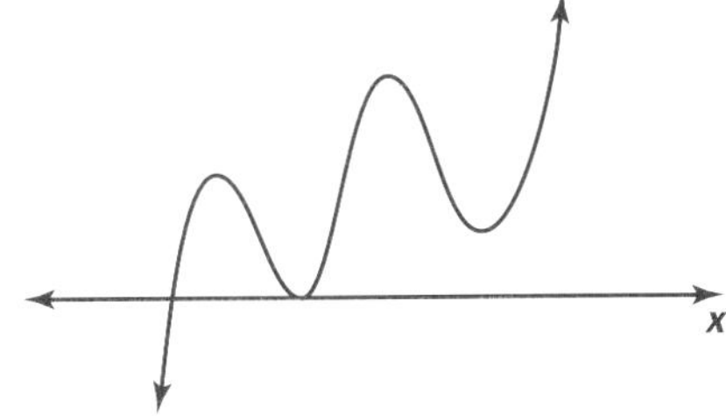

d. $p(x)$ has exactly 3 real zeros, all are simple zeros. **The other 2 zeros are a complex conjugate pair.**
Sample graph:

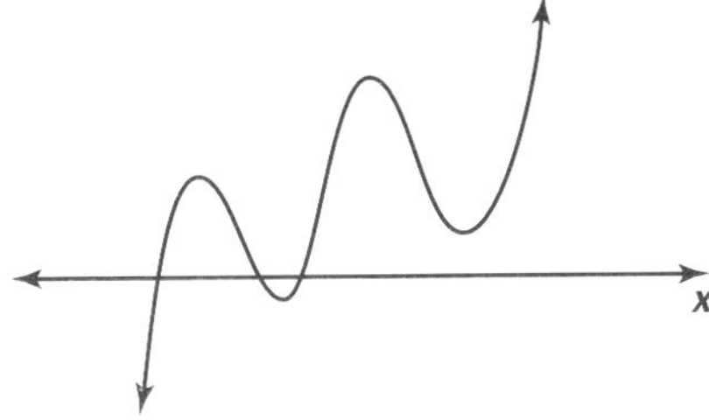

e. $p(x)$ has exactly 4 real, simple zeros. **Impossible**

f. $p(x)$ has 5 real, simple zeros. **There are no other zeros.**
Sample graph:

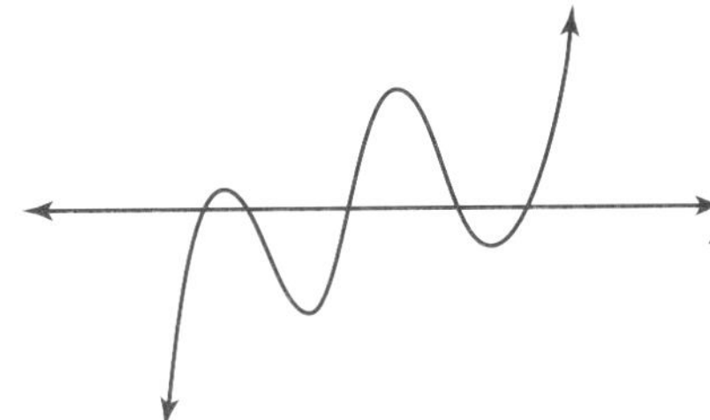

Notes on Questions

Questions 1–2 Utilize a generalization of the Conjugate Zeros Theorem found in the lesson but not stated explicitly as a theorem: Given complex nonreal numbers w and z, if $p(w) = z$, then $p(\overline{w}) = \overline{z}$.

Question 5 Students should be able to see that the Conjugate Zeros Theorem applies and that there are exactly four zeros.

Question 6 This question shows the power of the Factor Theorem, Conjugate Zeros Theorem, division of polynomials, and the Quadratic Formula when they work together.

Question 7 All the polynomials that work are nonzero multiples of the sample answer given.

Question 11 These zeros are the 4th roots of 1. It is easy to verify that their graphs are vertices of a square centered at the origin, confirming the Geometric *n*th Roots Theorem of the previous lesson. Also see the *Warm-Up* for this lesson.

Question 13 Remind students that for any constant $c \neq 0$, the zeros of $p(x)$ and $c \cdot p(x)$ are the same.

Question 16 Error Alert Students must read this question carefully. Those who assume incorrectly that the coefficients of $q(x)$ are reals may get results contradicting the given information; their 5th degree polynomial $p(x)$ will have more than 5 zeros.

Question 22 This question requires the use of a spreadsheet or computer program.

10a) There are four nonreal zeros: either two conjugate pairs (each zero of multiplicity 1), or one conjugate pair (each zero of multiplicity 2).
b) There is one pair of nonreal conjugate zeros, each of multiplicity 1.
c) There are no nonreal zeros.
d) There is one pair of nonreal conjugate zeros, each of multiplicity 1.

12b) If $p(x)$ does not have real coefficients, then $1 + 3i$ is not necessarily a zero of $p(x)$, and $p(x)$ may have degree 2.

17)

≈ [1.59, 1.65]

≈ [1.59, .08]

≈ [1.59, 3.22]

≈ [1.59, 4.79]

10. The curve at the right is the graph of a polynomial $p(x)$ of degree 5 with real coefficients, with the x-axis removed. For each of the following, sketch the graph and reinsert the horizontal axis so that the given condition is satisfied. Also, describe the nonreal zeros of $p(x)$. **See left.**

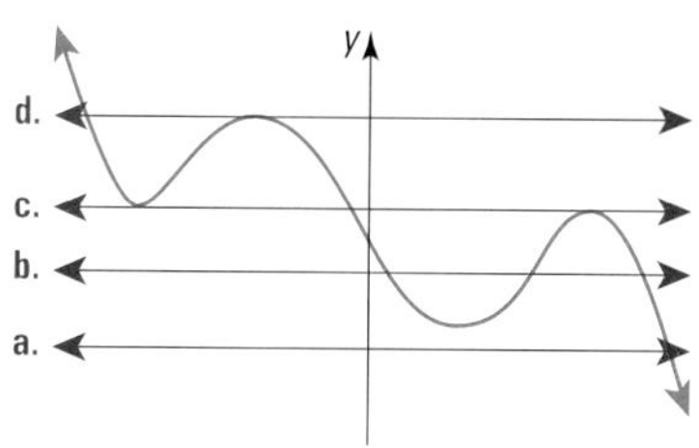

a. $p(x)$ has exactly one real, simple zero.
b. $p(x)$ has exactly three real, simple zeros.
c. $p(x)$ has exactly three real zeros, two of which have multiplicity two and one of which is a simple zero.
d. $p(x)$ has exactly two real zeros, one of multiplicity two and the other a simple zero.

Applying the Mathematics

11. Find all zeros of $p(x) = x^4 - 1$. **1, -1, *i*, -*i***

12. a. Find a polynomial $p(x)$, with real coefficients and of the lowest degree possible, that has the two zeros 2 and $1 - 3i$.
b. How does the answer to part **a** change if the requirement that $p(x)$ have real coefficients is dropped?
a) Sample: $p(x) = x^3 - 4x^2 + 14x - 20$ b) See left.

13. Find a polynomial of degree 3 with integer coefficients whose zeros include $\frac{1}{2}i$ and $\frac{2}{3}$. **Sample: $p(x) = 12x^3 - 8x^2 + 3x - 2$**

14. Consider the polynomials of the form $p(x) = x^2 + c$, where c is a real number.
a. For each value of c given below, indicate the zeros of $p(x)$ in the complex plane.
i. $c = -1$ **1, -1** **ii.** $c = 0$ **0** **iii.** $c = 1$ ***i*, -*i***
b. Imagine the graph of $p(x)$ sliding upwards as c varies from -1 to 1. Describe what happens to the location of the zeros of $p(x)$ as this occurs. **They get closer until they coincide at $c = 0$. Then they split apart in opposite directions along the imaginary axis.**

Review

15. Given that 1 is a zero of $p(x) = x^5 - x^4 + 6x^3 - 6x^2 + 9x - 9$, find all zeros of $p(x)$ and their multiplicities. *(Lesson 8-8)*
$\pm\sqrt{3}i$ (each with multiplicity 2), 1

16. Suppose $p(x)$ and $q(x)$ are polynomials, $p(x)$ has degree 5, and $p(x) = (x + 2)^2 q(x)$.
a. What is the degree of $q(x)$? **3**
b. If $3i$ is a zero of $q(x)$ with multiplicity 2, and -2 is a simple zero of $q(x)$, give all zeros of $p(x)$ and their multiplicities. *(Lesson 8-8)*
-2 (with multiplicity 3), 3*i* (with multiplicity 2)

17. Plot the solutions to $x^4 = 6 + 2i$ in the complex plane. *(Lesson 8-7)*
See left.

Additional Answers

22. **For $c = -5$, the zeros are about -2.50, 2.34, and $.08 \pm .93i$. As c increases, the real zeros move toward the origin and the nonreal zeros move toward each other until they merge at about .11 (a zero of multiplicity 2) when $c \approx -.05$; at that time, the other zeros are -2.33 and 2.13 . As c increases, the zero at .11 splits into two real zeros which move apart along the real axis, while the other**

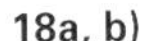

18a, b)

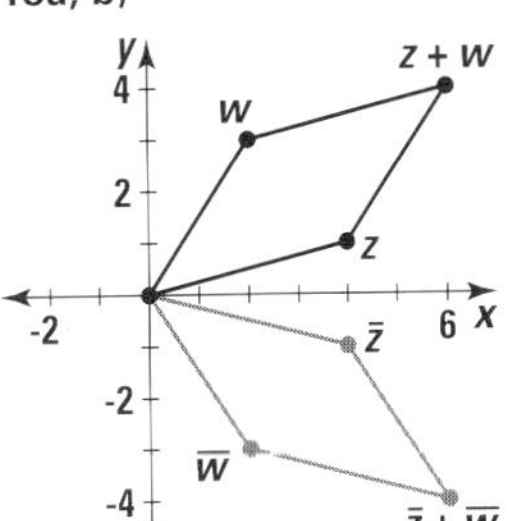

18. Let $z = 4 + i$ and $w = 2 + 3i$.

a. Sketch a graph which verifies the Geometric Addition Theorem for $z + w$. **See left.**

b. On the same set of axes, also graph $\bar{z}$, $\bar{w}$, and $\bar{z} + \bar{w}$. **See left.**

c. Explain how your diagram illustrates the property that $\bar{z} + \bar{w} = \overline{z + w}$. *(Lessons 8-1, 8-3)* **$\bar{z} + \bar{w}$ is the reflection image of $z + w$ over the real axis, so $\bar{z} + \bar{w} = \overline{z + w}$.**

19. Let $p(t) = 2t^3 - 3t^2 + 4$.

a. Use the Remainder Theorem to find $p\left(-\frac{1}{2}\right)$. **3**

b. Find $q(t)$ so that $p(t) = q(t)\left(t + \frac{1}{2}\right) + p\left(-\frac{1}{2}\right)$. *(Lesson 4-3)* **$2t^2 - 4t + 2$**

20. Write the logical expression associated with the following network. *(Lesson 1-4)* **not ((p and q) or r)**

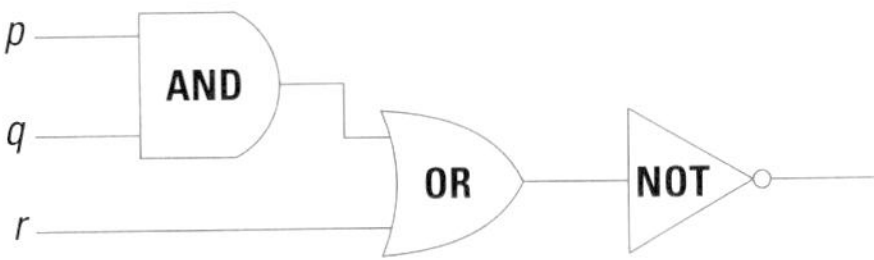

Exploration

21. a. Use the technique of Question 14 with an automatic grapher to study the zeros of $p(x) = x^4 - 4x^2 + c$ for $c = -5$, $c = 0$, and $c = 3$.

b. Continue the analysis of the polynomial for $c > 3$. Good values to try are $c = 4$ and $c = \frac{25}{4}$. For $c = \frac{25}{4}$, one of the zeros is $\frac{3 + i}{2}$.

a,b) See below.

22. The polynomial
$$p(x) = x^4 - 5x^2 + x + c$$
has a graph similar to the one displayed in Example 3. Use technology to find the zeros of $p(x)$ for various values of c between -5 and 5. Then use the idea discussed at the end of the lesson to graph the zeros of $p(x)$ for these values of c. **See margin.**

21a) For $c = -5$, the zeros are $\pm\sqrt{5}$, $\pm i$; for $c = 0$, the zeros are 0, ± 2; for $c = 3$, the zeros are $\pm\sqrt{3}$, ± 1. As c slides from -5 to 0, its two real zeros move closer to the origin, and its two imaginary zeros converge at the origin. As c then slides from 0 to 3, the polynomial has 4 real zeros.

b) For $c = 4$, the zeros are $\pm\sqrt{2}$; for $c = \frac{25}{4}$, the zeros are $\frac{3 \pm i}{2}$. As c slides from 3 to 4, its positive zeros converge to $\sqrt{2}$, and its negative zeros converge to $-\sqrt{2}$. As c slides from 4 to $\frac{25}{4}$, its four complex zeros converge to two complex zeros.

Follow-up for Lesson 8-9

Practice

For more questions on SPUR Objectives, use **Lesson Master 8-9** (shown on page 529).

Assessment

Oral Communication Have students explain their work for **Question 10.** [Students describe the zeros of a polynomial and their graphs.]

Extension

Cooperative Learning If a polynomial $p(x)$ of degree > 1 has real coefficients, then you can always find values of c such that $p_c(x) = p(x) + c$ has nonreal zeros. By adjusting the values of c, you can see what happens to those zeros, as was done in the lesson. If your class acquires the material of this lesson easily, then have the class **work in groups** and have each group examine a polynomial $p(x)$, find values of c for which there are nonreal zeros of $p_c(x)$, and show how those nonreal zeros change as c changes.

real zeros continue moving toward the origin. When $c \approx 4.69$, the two largest zeros merge into 1.53, then split into complex conjugates.

c	approximate zeros
-5	-2.50, .08 − .93i, .08 + .93i, 2.34
-1	-2.36, .10 − .39i, .10 + .39i, 2.17
-.05	-2.33, .11, .11, 2.13
0	-2.32, 0.00, .20, 2.12
4.5	-2.11, -.93, 1.37, 1.67
4.69	-2.10, -.96, 1.53, 1.53
5	-2.08, -1.00, 1.54 − .19i, 1.54 + .19i

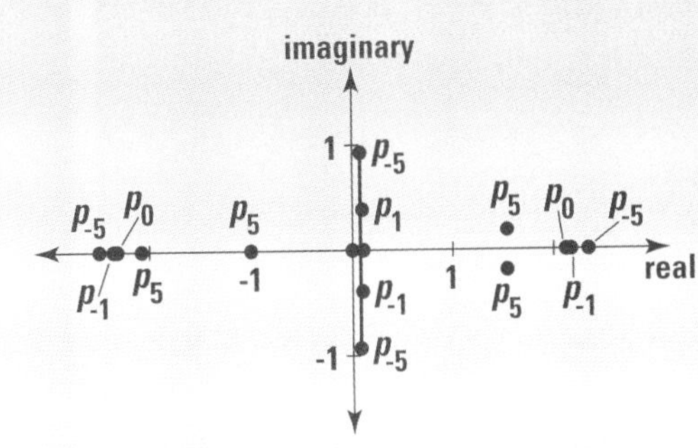

Lesson 8-10

Objectives
There are no SPUR Objectives for any reading lesson.

Resources
From the ***Teacher's Resource File***
- Answer Master 8-10
- Teaching Aids
  72 Warm-up
  86 Orbits of [1, 18°] and [1, $\frac{1}{3}$ radian] when $f(z) = z^2$.

Additional Resources
- Visuals for Teaching Aids 72, 86

Teaching Lesson 8-10

Warm-up
Enter 3 into your calculator set to radians. Repeatedly press the sine key, writing down the values you get rounded to the nearest thousandth.

1. Give a recursive definition for the sequence you are creating. **$a_0 = 3$; $a_{n+1} = \sin a_n$**
2. Conjecture the limit of the nth term of this sequence as $n \to \infty$. **0**

LESSON

8-10 Discrete Dynamical Systems

Chaos. *Research into discrete dynamical systems has improved the mathematical models used for weather forecasting.* *See page 538.*

Examples of Discrete Dynamical Systems

Some interesting things can happen when you enter a number in your calculator and then press one of the function keys repeatedly. For example, enter the number 2 and then press the square root key, $\boxed{\sqrt{x}}$, 9 times. (On some calculators, this will produce an error message. You may need to use $\boxed{\sqrt{x}}$ $\boxed{=}$ to take the square root of the previous result.) The following sequence of numbers will be displayed (rounded to three decimal places): 2.000, 1.414, 1.189, 1.091, 1.044, 1.022, 1.011, 1.005, 1.003, 1.001. These numbers are approximations to the first ten terms of the sequence defined recursively by

$$\begin{cases} x_0 = 2 \\ x_{k+1} = \sqrt{x_k} \quad \text{for integers } k \geq 0. \end{cases}$$

As k gets larger and larger, the corresponding x_k values appear to get closer and closer to 1; that is, apparently,

$$\lim_{k \to \infty} x_k = 1.$$

❶ Begin again with the number 2 but this time use the cosine function key, $\boxed{\cos}$, with your calculator set for radian measure. The following numbers will be displayed, again rounded to three decimal places:

2.000, -.416, .915, .610, .820, .683, .776, .714, .756, .728.

These are approximations to the first ten terms of the sequence defined recursively by

$$\begin{cases} y_0 = 2 \\ y_{k+1} = \cos y_k \quad \text{for integers } k \geq 0. \end{cases}$$

Lesson 8-10 Overview

Broad Goals This reading lesson introduces discrete dynamical systems.

Perspective This material involves a variety of concepts that the students have seen before, but in an interesting new context. A discrete dynamical system is a set S and a function f that maps S into itself. We then follow a particular member s of S, and look at $f(s)$, $f(f(s))$, $f(f(f(s)))$, etc. This sequence of values is called an *orbit*.

A dynamical system in which the orbits of nearby points behave quite differently from one another is said to exhibit *chaos*. The study of such systems is only in its infancy, having begun in this century, and the name *chaos* has appeared only in the past two decades as descriptive of certain types of behavior in these systems.

Among the most interesting of discrete dynamical systems are those in which S is the set of complex numbers. A particularly simple system is found when S consists of those numbers whose graphs are on the unit circle and f is the squaring function. That system is discussed in some detail.

The numbers y_k seem to be "settling down" on some number between .7 and .8 as k gets larger and larger, but the exact value of this limit is much less obvious.

Finally, if you again begin with the number 2 but use the squaring function, x^2, the following numbers (again rounded) are displayed: 2, 4, 16, 256, 65536, $4.295 \cdot 10^9$, $1.8447 \cdot 10^{19}$, $3.4028 \cdot 10^{38}$, $1.1579 \cdot 10^{77}$, overflow. These numbers are values or estimates of the first ten terms of the sequence defined by

$$\begin{cases} z_0 = 2 \\ z_{k+1} = z_k^2 \quad \text{for integers } k \geq 0. \end{cases}$$

This is a sequence whose terms increase without bound as k gets larger and larger.

The preceding calculator examples are illustrations of *discrete dynamical systems*. A **discrete dynamical system** is a set D together with a function

$$f: D \to D$$

from D into itself. For example, in the square root sequence given earlier, the set D is the set of all nonnegative real numbers. The function f is defined for all x in D by

$$f(x) = \sqrt{x}.$$

Because $\sqrt{x} \geq 0$ for all $x \geq 0$, f is a function from D into itself.

❷ Orbits in a Discrete Dynamical System

The sequence 2.000, 1.414, 1.189, 1.091, . . . is called the *orbit with initial point* 2 for the system with $x_{k+1} = \sqrt{x_k}$. Here is a general definition.

Definition

Let a set D and a function f: $D \to D$ constitute a discrete dynamical system. The sequence $a_0, a_1, a_2, \ldots$ defined by

$$\begin{cases} a_0 = d \\ a_{k+1} = f(a_k) \quad \text{for integers } k \geq 0 \end{cases}$$

is the **orbit with initial point *d*,** written ***O*(*d*)**.

One of the fundamental problems concerning discrete dynamical systems is to determine how the orbit $O(d)$ varies with the initial point d. In the case of the discrete dynamical system given by the square root function on the set D of nonnegative real numbers, all orbits with nonzero initial points are sequences with limits equal to 1.

However, not all orbits in dynamical systems have limits. For instance, let f be the function from the reals to the reals defined by

$$f(x) = \frac{1}{1 - x}.$$

Notes on Reading

❶ In first entering 2 and then repeatedly pressing the cos key until the value stabilizes, students should realize that they are using their calculator and recursion to solve $\cos(x) = x$ for its one real zero. They may wish to use an automatic grapher to check their solution.

❷ It is critical that students understand the definition of *orbit*. Because $O(d)$ uses function notation, they may think that it represents a single number. Stress that $O(d)$ is a *sequence*, a sequence of values that begins with d, the sequence d, $f(d)$, $f(f(d))$, $f(f(f(d)))$, ...

Optional Activities

Activity 1 Writing After students complete the lesson, you might have them write a paragraph explaining why some orbits contain a finite number of distinct points and others an infinite number of distinct points, giving an example of each.

Activity 2 Cooperative Learning To emphasize Lorenz' discovery of how small changes in the initial conditions can create large changes in the results, you might have students **work in groups** to make up and tell stories in which the initial condition varies only slightly from a normal routine. For example, let's say a person pushed the snooze button one extra time one morning and so was about seven minutes late getting into the car. Because she was a little late, she didn't get a parking place at the health club. Because she didn't get a parking place, she had to circle the block. Because she had to circle the block, she didn't have enough time to work out. Because she didn't have enough time to work out, she started running her errands. Because she was late in getting to the grocery store, she had to wait in a long line. Because she had to wait in a long line, she ended up being the hundredth person at the store and was awarded free groceries for a month.

The orbit with initial point $\frac{3}{4}$ is the sequence obtained as follows.

$$a_0 = \frac{3}{4}$$
$$a_1 = f(a_0) = f\left(\frac{3}{4}\right) = \frac{1}{1-\frac{3}{4}} = 4$$
$$a_2 = f(a_1) = f(4) = \frac{1}{1-4} = -\frac{1}{3}$$
$$a_3 = f(a_2) = f\left(-\frac{1}{3}\right) = \frac{1}{1+\frac{1}{3}} = \frac{3}{4}$$
$$a_4 = f(a_3) = f\left(\frac{3}{4}\right) = \frac{1}{1-\frac{3}{4}} = 4$$

Notice that $a_4 = a_1$, so the orbit begins to repeat. This orbit is periodic. Its *period*, the number of terms from one appearance of a term to its next appearance, is 3. The values of the orbit do not approach a limit. You can verify that this would happen with any initial points other than 0 and 1.

Orbits in the Iterated Squaring Function with Real Numbers

The orbits of the squaring function on the set of nonnegative real numbers are more complicated. Their behavior depends on the initial point d. If $d > 1$, the orbit $O(d)$ is a sequence whose terms increase without bound. For instance, $O(2) = 2, 4, 16, 256, 65536, 4294967296, \ldots$. If $0 \le d < 1$, the orbit with initial point d has limit equal to zero. $O(.5) = .5, .25, .0625, .0039063, .0000153, 2.3283 \cdot 10^{-10}, \ldots$, which seems to approach 0 very rapidly. If $d = 1$, the orbit with initial point d is a constant sequence with each term equal to 1.

The orbits of the squaring function are extremely sensitive to changes in the initial point d near $d = 1$. If the initial point d is just a little less than 1, the orbit changes from a constant sequence whose terms all equal 1 to a sequence with limit equal to zero. If the initial point is changed from 1 to a number a little larger than 1, the orbit changes from a constant sequence whose terms all equal 1 to a sequence whose terms increase without bound. For example, the 15th term of the orbit $O(1.001)$ is approximately 1.29397×10^7.

Orbits in the Iterated Squaring Function with Complex Numbers

Now consider the squaring function defined over a domain of complex numbers, in particular, the domain D of all points of the unit circle. Each z in D has absolute value equal to 1. Therefore, $z = [1, \theta]$ for some θ, and $f(z) = [1, \theta]^2 = [1, 2\theta]$ because squaring a complex number doubles its argument.

Adapting to Individual Needs

Extra Help

With some students you might wish to approach these examples using a computer. Here is a sample program for generating the orbits. Here A is the argument of the initial point on the unit circle (in radians), N is the number of points you want, and the function is the squaring function.

```
INPUT A, N
LET PI = 3.14159265
FOR K = 1 TO N
        PRINT COS(A),SIN(A)
        IF A > 2*PI THEN A = A – 2*PI
        LET A = A^2
NEXT K
```

Start with the values in the lesson, A = 18° = .34159265 radians and then with A = .33333333 radians to see the difference in behavior. If you can graph the coordinates, the students are given a visual representation of what is going on. The computer instructions for graphing differ too much from machine to machine for us to give them here. You should be aware that round-off error will eventually cause difficulties in the output, both numerical and graphical.

Suppose $d = [1, 18°]$. Then the orbit is given by the sequence

$$\begin{aligned} a_0 &= d &&= [1, 18°] \\ a_1 &= f([1, 18°]) &&= [1, 36°] \\ a_2 &= f([1, 36°]) &&= [1, 72°] \\ a_3 &= f([1, 72°]) &&= [1, 144°] \\ a_4 &= f([1, 144°]) &&= [1, 288°] \\ a_5 &= f([1, 288°]) &&= [1, 576°] = [1, 216°] \\ a_6 &= f([1, 216°]) &&= [1, 432°] = [1, 72°]. \end{aligned}$$

Note that $a_6 = a_2$. It follows that

$$\begin{aligned} a_7 &= f(a_6) = f(a_2) = a_3 \\ a_8 &= f(a_7) = f(a_3) = a_4 \end{aligned}$$

and so on. Therefore, the orbit $O(d)$ is periodic, with period 4:

$$O(d) = [1, 18°], [1, 36°], [1, 72°], [1, 144°], [1, 288°], [1, 216°], \ldots$$

and then the last four of these numbers are repeated over and over. The six different points in the orbit are plotted below. The directed arcs in the diagram describe the order of points in the orbit of d.

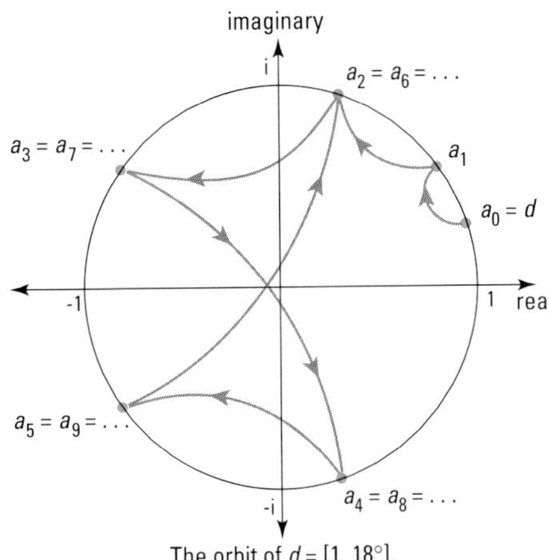

The orbit of $d = [1, 18°]$.

The orbit with $d = [1, 18°]$ consists of only finitely many different points because the argument θ of the complex number is a rational multiple of one revolution; that is,

$$18° = \frac{1}{20}(360°).$$

For any other complex number d on the unit circle whose argument is a rational multiple of 360° or 2π, the orbit with initial point d eventually repeats the same points, and therefore consists of only a finite number of distinct points.

However, if the argument of d is not a rational multiple of 2π, then the orbit is not periodic; it consists of infinitely many distinct points which have no limit. For instance, let

$$d = \left[1, \tfrac{1}{3} \text{ radian}\right].$$

Like other sequences, orbits may have a single limiting value as in the square root example that begins the lesson. They may be periodic, as is the case with the system with the function $f(x) = \frac{1}{1 - x}$ immediately following the definition and the example on page 537. That example, also shown on **Teaching Aid 86,** uses complex numbers in polar form. The initial point on the unit circle (for the dynamical system f: $D \rightarrow D$ where $f(z) = z^2$ and D is the unit circle) is chosen so that the argument is a rational multiple of 360°. The orbit will be periodic for any initial point with this characteristic.

When a small change in the value of d produces dramatic changes in $O(d)$, as shown on page 538, it is said that the system is exhibiting *chaotic* behavior. In this example, an initial point is chosen with an argument in radian measure that is not a rational multiple of 2π.

The final discussion of chaos is important in emphasizing that mathematics is a continually developing subject. At this point it is not known whether chaos will develop into a subject of great importance, but it is certainly a very interesting subject.

Literature Connection Students interested in reading more on this subject will enjoy and benefit from the book *Chaos: Making a New Science,* by James Gleick. This book was a best-seller in the nation in 1989. It is mentioned in the Projects.

Adapting to Individual Needs

Challenge

Have students answer the following.

1. Describe a function f for which the period of every point in its domain is 1. [$f(x) = x$]
2. Let $f(x) = \frac{1}{x}$. What is the period of any point (other than 1) in the domain of f? [2] Why? [$f(x)$ is self-inverse.] Give formulas for other functions f with period 1 for all points in their domain (except for those values for which $f(x) = x$). [Any self-inverse function such as f: $x \rightarrow -x$. A less obvious f has $f(x) = \frac{x}{x - 1}$.]

Since each squaring doubles the argument, the terms of the orbit are $\left[1, \frac{1}{3}\right], \left[1, \frac{2}{3}\right], \left[1, \frac{4}{3}\right], \left[1, \frac{8}{3}\right], \left[1, \frac{16}{3}\right], \ldots$. Hence, an explicit formula for the sequence is

$$a_n = \left[1, \frac{2^n}{3}\right] \text{ for integers } n \geq 0.$$

The following proof by contradiction shows that no two terms of the orbit are equal. Suppose that n and m were distinct positive integers with $a_n = a_m$. Then the arguments of a_n and a_m would differ by a multiple of 2π. That is, there would be an integer k such that

$$\frac{2^n}{3} = \frac{2^m}{3} + 2\pi k.$$

Solving this equation for π,

$$\pi = \frac{1}{2k}\left(\frac{2^n}{3} - \frac{2^m}{3}\right).$$

Because the right side of the preceding equation is a rational number and π is irrational, this last statement is false. We have reached a contradiction. Consequently, all terms of the orbit of d are distinct complex numbers. The graphs below show the first 50 terms (on the left) and the first 250 terms (on the right) of the orbit.

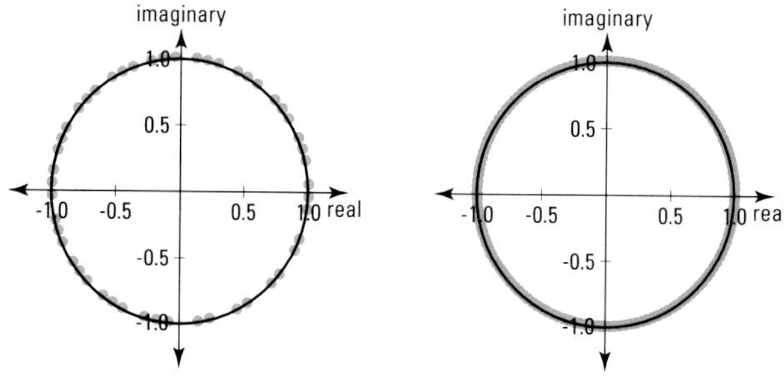

It can be proved that when the argument of d is not a rational multiple of 2π, the points in the orbit $O(d)$ with no period are *dense* on the unit circle in the sense that any arc of this circle, no matter how short, contains infinitely many points of the orbit! For any initial point with an argument that *is* a rational multiple of 2π, a small change in the initial point can give an argument that is an irrational multiple of 2π, resulting in a dense orbit. For any initial point with an argument that is an irrational multiple of 2π, a small change in the initial point can give an argument that is a rational multiple of 2π, resulting in an orbit with a finite number of points. In this way, for any initial point on the unit circle, the orbit is extremely sensitive to small changes from the initial point. Mathematicians refer to the type of behavior exhibited by the orbits in this example as **chaos**.

These ideas are relatively new. Analysis of discrete dynamical systems began only in the early 1960s with mathematical models for weather forecasting. As you know, predicting the weather is tricky business. The complicated interaction of temperature, moisture conditions, air pressures

538

When frost is predicted, citrus farmers coat their produce with water. The coating then freezes instead of the produce.

and winds frequently confounds and frustrates professional meteorologists as well as people who are planning a picnic or raising a garden. However, interest in predicting the weather goes far beyond curiosity, picnics and gardens. If we could predict the weather with some degree of accuracy over reasonable lengths of time, we could save lives lost in severe storms, vastly improve farm economy through better planning, and facilitate travel and communication.

The development of high speed, large memory digital computers that began in the 1950s gave scientists of that day strong reason to hope that the problem of predicting weather could finally be solved in a way that would be quite adequate for most practical purposes. After all, they already knew the most important variables affecting the weather and they could apply the laws of physics to obtain equations relating these variables. Thus, they had the tools necessary to construct a reasonable realistic mathematical model for the weather system. To be sure, such a model would involve many variables and very complicated equations, but a computer large enough and fast enough to analyze the model seemed only a few years away.

Preliminary work on a computer model of the weather system was already underway at the Massachusetts Institute of Technology in 1960. There, the meteorologist Edward Lorenz used a vacuum tube digital computer to analyze a rather crude mathematical model of the weather system. He varied the model until he identified twelve equations relating temperature, atmospheric pressure, and wind velocity that seemed to reflect the essential features of the real weather patterns that he had studied for many years. Lorenz entered initial weather data and the computer printed out a row of numbers once each minute that corresponded to the successive one-day forecasts of this mathematical model.

However, one day in 1961, Lorenz accidently discovered a feature of his model that had profound consequences not only for weather forecasting but also for the study of other complex systems in economics, physics, chemistry, and mathematics. In attempting to repeat part of a computer run, he reentered the data, but used approximations to three decimal places instead of the six decimal place values used previously. He expected the use of these approximations to have little noticeable effect on the results of the run. At first, the output for the two runs matched closely, as expected. But then they began to deviate from one another more and more until the two predictions were radically different.

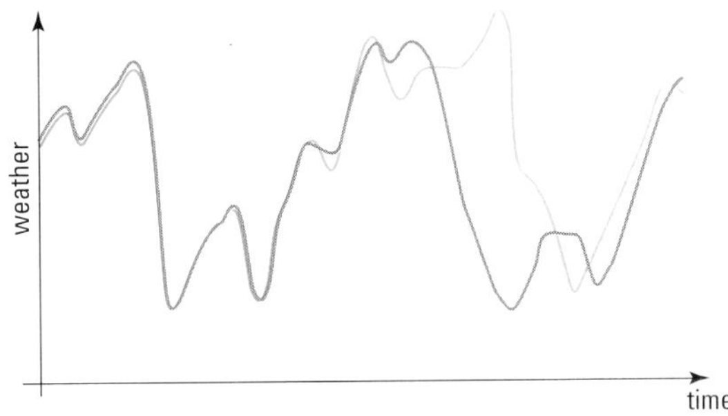

Notes on Questions

Question 1 Before starting, some students may conjecture that the limit of the sequence of values is 0, but doing the question will change their opinion. With a sufficient number of iterations, the calculator will indeed display the number 1. Ask why this is the case.

Question 5 Error Alert This question is deceptive in that the argument 1 radian would seem to divide anything including 2π; but it does not because there is no rational number q such that $2\pi = 1q$. This is a hard question and should be related to **Example 4.**

Questions 7–8 Graphically, a fixed point of f is a value of x where the graph of $y = f(x)$ intersects the line $y = x$.

Question 18 If students need a hint, you might say: "Since m is an odd integer, $\exists$ k such that $m =$ __?__ " and see if this helps.

Question 19 Project 7 gives students additional opportunities to explore the function $f(z) = z^2 + c$.

Edward Lorenz

After careful consideration, Lorenz realized that the differences in the outputs of the two runs were not due to a computer error, but rather that they revealed a disturbing intrinsic property of his mathematical model: *small differences in the initial conditions for the system could result in radically different predictions.*

In this lesson, you have observed a similar phenomenon for discrete dynamical systems. Small changes in the initial point on the unit circle can result in radically different orbits generated by the squaring function. The chaotic behavior that Lorenz observed in his weather model indicates that unpredictability may be an intrinsic characteristic of our weather system rather than an annoying result of the simplifying assumptions that underlie any mathematical model of it. Many other phenomena, such as chemical reactions, the flow of fluids, the flow of highway traffic, economic growth, and the beating of the heart, also exhibit chaotic behavior. The field of dynamical systems is in its infancy and may provide the key to understanding these diverse phenomena.

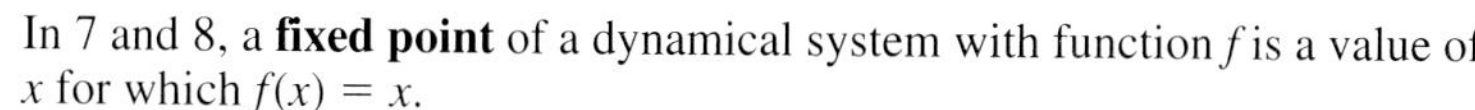

QUESTIONS

Covering the Reading

1. Enter .5 in your calculator and press the square root button, $\sqrt{x}$, repeatedly. Describe what happens and make a conjecture. **To 4 digits, the sequence is .5000, .7071, .8409, .9170, . . . It approaches 1.**
2. Compute the orbit of $d = -\frac{1}{2}$ for the dynamical system defined by D = set of real numbers, and $f(x) = \frac{1}{1-x}$. **$-\frac{1}{2}, \frac{2}{3}, 3, -\frac{1}{2}, \frac{2}{3}, 3$**
3. Compute the first four terms in the orbit of $d = 7$ for the dynamical system defined by D = set of nonnegative real numbers, and $f(x) = x^2$. **7; 49; 2401; 5,764,801**

In 4 and 5, consider the dynamical system defined by D = unit circle in the complex plane, and $f(z) = z^2$. **4, 5) See left for graphs.**

4)

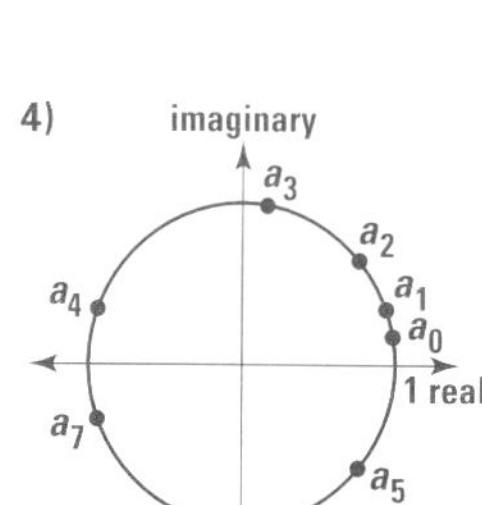

5)

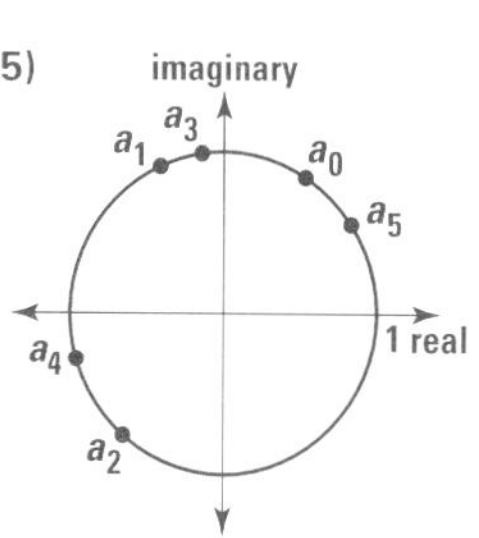

4. Compute and graph the orbit of [1, 10°]. **[1, 10°], [1, 20°], [1, 40°], [1, 80°], [1, 160°], [1, 320°], [1, 280°], [1, 200°], [1, 40°], [1, 80°], . . .**
5. Compute and graph the first six terms of the orbit of [1, 1 radian]. **[1, 1], [1, 2], [1, 4], [1, 8], [1, 16], [1, 32]**
6. In this lesson, we observed that if you enter the number 2 in your calculator and repeatedly press the cosine function button, the numbers displayed by your calculator seem to be approaching some number x between .7 and .8.
   a. Assuming that these numbers do converge to some number x, explain why it must be true that $\cos x = x$. **See margin.**
   b. Use part **a** to compute x to three decimal places. **0.739**

In 7 and 8, a **fixed point** of a dynamical system with function f is a value of x for which $f(x) = x$.

7. Find all fixed points for the function f when $f(x) = x^2$. **1, 0**
8. Prove that, in the dynamical system in Question 2, the period of every number is no more than 3. **See margin.**

Additional Answers

6. a. Let a_k be the kth number obtained (by pressing the cosine key k times). Then a_k is approaching x for larger and larger k. But $a_k = \cos a_{k-1}$, and $\cos a_{k-1}$ approaches $\cos x$ since the cosine function is continuous. Therefore, $x = \cos x$.

8. For all $x \neq 1$, let $a_0 = x$. Then $a_1 = \frac{1}{1-x}$. If $x \neq 0$, $a_2 = \frac{1}{1-\frac{1}{1-x}} = \frac{1-x}{1-x-1} = \frac{1-x}{-x} = \frac{x-1}{x}$, and $a_3 = \frac{1}{1-\frac{x-1}{x}} = \frac{x}{x-(x-1)} = \frac{x}{1} = x$. So $a_3 = a_0$, hence the period is 3.

14. b. $(zw)^5 = [6, 110°]^5 = [6^5, 5 \cdot 110°] = [7776, 550°]$
$z^5 \cdot w^5 = [243, 200°] \cdot [32, 350°] = [(243)(32), 200° + 350°] = [7776, 550°]$.
So $(zw)^5 = z^5 \cdot w^5$.

9. Suppose that f is the function defined for all real numbers x by $f(x) = \sin x$ and that D is the set of all real numbers x between $-\pi$ and π.
   a. Find a fixed point of this system. 0
   b. Are there any others? No

10)
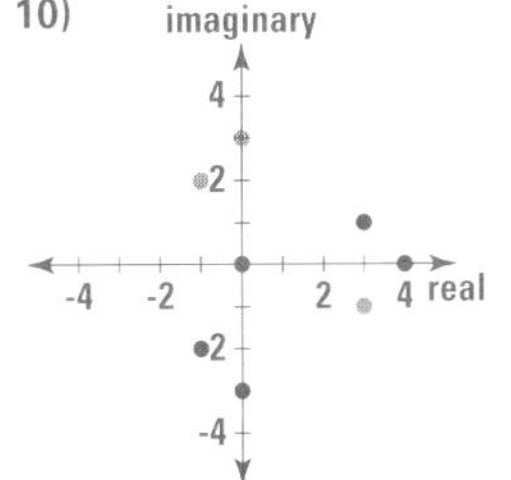

Extension

Project Update Project 3, *Exploring Chaos*, and Project 7, *Creating Fractals*, on pages 542–543, relate to the content of this lesson.

Review

10. The graph at the right shows five of the zeros of a polynomial of degree 8 with real coefficients. Copy and complete the graph so it shows all of the zeros. *(Lessons 8-1, 8-9)* See left.

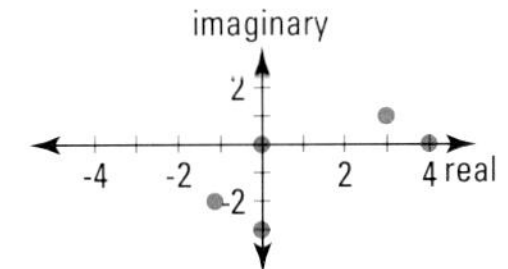

11. Write a formula for a fourth degree polynomial with real coefficients whose zeros include 0, $1 - 2i$, and 2. *(Lesson 8-9)*
    Sample: $P(x) = x^4 - 4x^3 + 9x^2 - 10x$
12. Find all zeros and their multiplicities for the polynomial $p(x) = (x + 2)^2(x^4 - 2x^2 - 8)$. *(Lesson 8-8)* -2 (with multiplicity 3), $2, \pm\sqrt{2}i$
13. Find the fourth roots of $16\left(\cos\frac{4\pi}{5} + i\sin\frac{4\pi}{5}\right)$ and graph the roots in a complex plane. *(Lesson 8-7)* See left.

13) $z_0 = 2\left(\cos\frac{\pi}{5} + i\sin\frac{\pi}{5}\right)$, $z_1 = 2\left(\cos\frac{7\pi}{10} + i\sin\frac{7\pi}{10}\right)$, $z_2 = 2\left(\cos\frac{6\pi}{5} + i\sin\frac{6\pi}{5}\right)$, $z_3 = 2\left(\cos\frac{17\pi}{10} + i\sin\frac{17\pi}{10}\right)$

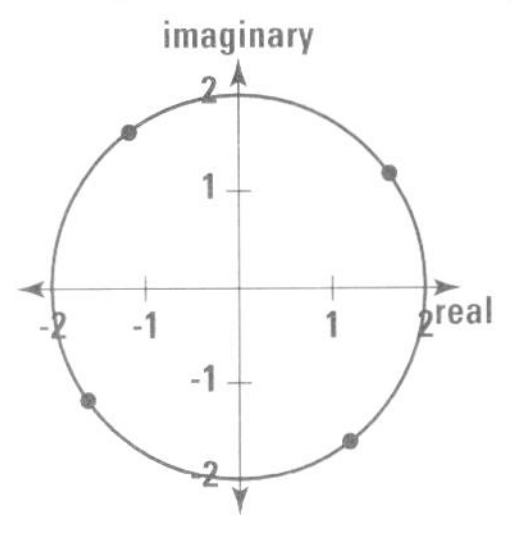

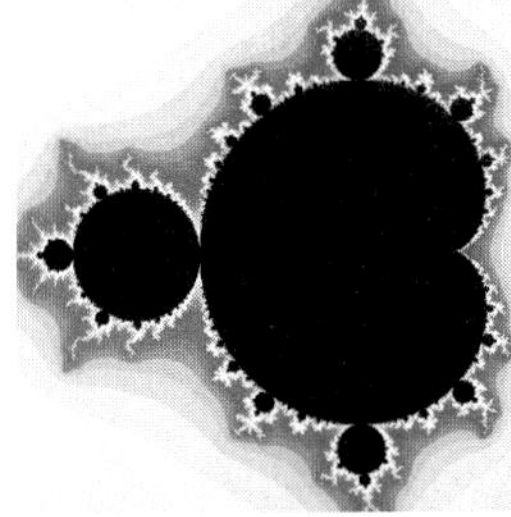

14. Let $z = [3, 40°]$ and $w = [2, 70°]$.
    a. Find a polar representation for each number. Samples are given.
       i. zw [6, 110°] ii. z^5 [243, 200°] iii. w^5 [32, 350°]
    b. Use your answers to part **a** to confirm that $(zw)^5 = z^5 \cdot w^5$. *(Lessons 8-3, 8-6)* See margin.
15. a. Sketch the polar graph of the equation $r = 1 + 2\cos\theta$. See margin.
    b. Give equations for any lines of symmetry of the graph. *(Lessons 8-4, 8-5)* $\theta = 0°$
16. Find a recursive definition for the sequence with explicit formula $t_n = 5 - 4n$ for integers $n \geq 1$. *(Lesson 7-1)* See margin.
17. The period T (in seconds) of a pendulum is given by $T = 2\pi\sqrt{\frac{\ell}{g}}$, where ℓ is the length of the pendulum (in feet) and g is the gravitational acceleration (32 ft/sec^2). Find the length of a pendulum whose period is 12 seconds. *(Lesson 3-3)* $\frac{1152}{\pi^2} \approx 116.7$ feet
18. Prove: *If m is any odd integer, then $m^2 + m - 3$ is an odd integer.* *(Lesson 1-8)* See margin.

Exploration

19. If c is a fixed complex number and f is the function defined for all complex numbers z by $f(z) = z^2 + c$, then use what you know about the geometry of addition and multiplication to explain how the point $f(z)$ can be located from the point z in the complex plane. (Note: This function is used to define the Mandelbrot set, which is important for the study of fractals.)
    $f(z)$ is constructed by squaring the absolute value of the complex number z and doubling its argument to obtain z^2. The point is translated by adding c to give $f(z)$.

In this graph, points colored black are members of the Mandelbrot set.

15. a.

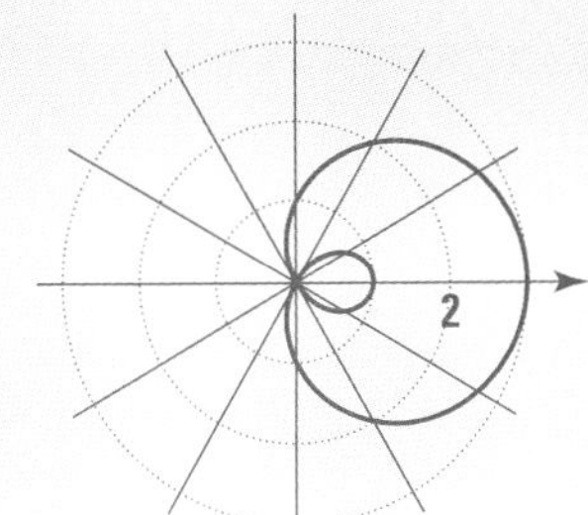

16. $\begin{cases} t_1 = 1, \\ t_{n+1} = t_n - 4 \text{ for } n \geq 1 \end{cases}$

18. If m is odd, then $m = 2k + 1$ for some integer k.
$m^2 + m - 3 = (2k + 1)^2(2k + 1) - 3 =$
$(4k^2 + 4k + 1) + (2k + 1) - 3 =$
$(4k^2 + 6k - 2) + 1 =$
$2(2k^2 + 3k - 1) + 1$
Since $(2k^2 + 3k - 1)$ is an integer, $m^2 + m - 3$ is an odd integer by definition.
$\therefore$ If m is any odd integer, then $m^2 + m - 3$ is an odd integer.

Chapter 8 Projects

The projects relate chiefly to the content of the lessons of this chapter as follows:

Project	Lesson(s)
1	8-4, 8-5
2	8-2
3	8-10
4	8-5, 8-6, 8-7
5	8-1, 8-3
6	8-1
7	8-10
8	8-1, 8-3

1 Polar Equations for Conic Sections This is a standard topic in analytic geometry courses. Though such courses have almost vanished, students may find analytic geometry texts in libraries.

2 Three-Dimensional "Polar" Coordinates Students interested in geography or astronomy may be particularly interested in these coordinate systems.

3 Exploring Chaos Some of the beginnings of the history of the study of chaos are given in Lesson 8-10.

4 Spirals This is the least mathematical of all the projects suggested here. You may wish to have students superimpose polar coordinate systems on the spirals and determine whether the natural curve seems to be a spiral of Archimedes, a logarithmic spiral, or neither of these.

PROJECTS 8 CHAPTER EIGHT

A project presents an opportunity for you to extend your knowledge of a topic related to the material of this chapter. You should allow more time for a project than you do for a typical homework question.

1 Polar Equations for Conic Sections

The conic sections have polar equations. Write a report describing these equations and the role played by the eccentricity of the conic. Use analytic geometry, calculus, or trigonometry books as aids in your research.

2 Three-Dimensional "Polar" Coordinates

There are coordinate systems which extend the idea of polar coordinates to three dimensions. Find out about and describe at least two of these systems. (Books on mapmaking are one source.)

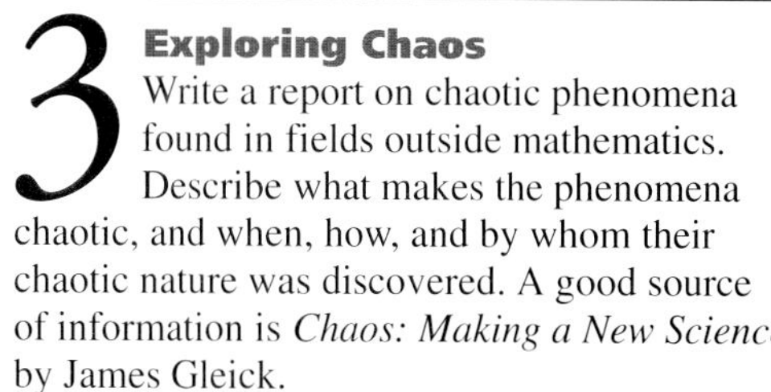

3 Exploring Chaos

Write a report on chaotic phenomena found in fields outside mathematics. Describe what makes the phenomena chaotic, and when, how, and by whom their chaotic nature was discovered. A good source of information is *Chaos: Making a New Science*, by James Gleick.

4 Spirals

Spirals occur frequently in nature. Visit a library. Copy pictures of chambered nautiluses, sun flowers, and other natural objects to show your class, and explain their mathematical properties.

5 Matrix Representations of Complex Numbers

Four representations of complex numbers are in this chapter: binomial, rectangular, polar, and trigonometric. Show that a fifth representation, the matrix $a + bi = \begin{bmatrix} a & -b \\ b & a \end{bmatrix}$ satisfies the following properties of the complex numbers.

a. Rules for complex addition and multiplication hold.
b. The modulus of $a + bi$ is the determinant of its matrix.
c. The multiplicative inverse of a complex number is the inverse of this matrix.
d. The matrix form has special matrices which correspond to 1 (the multiplicative identity) and 0 (the additive identity).
e. The argument of a complex number is related to its matrix representation.

6 Quaternions

The Irish mathematician William Rowan Hamilton attempted to reconcile the diverse phenomena of eighteenth century physics with a new mathematical system he called *quaternions*. This system extended the ordered pair concept to ordered four-tuples. Find out how he defined addition and multiplication, and what the relationships among his "quaternionic units" are.

Possible responses

1. **The general equation for all conic sections in polar coordinates is $p = \frac{eq}{1 + e\cos\theta}$ where e is the eccentricity: $e = 1$ (parabola), $e < 1$ (ellipse), and $e > 1$ (hyperbola). The focus is at the pole, and the directrix perpendicular to the polar axis is at a distance q from the pole. For any curve which is the focus of a point which moves so that the ratio of its distance from a fixed point to its distance from a fixed line is constant, the ratio is the *eccentricity* of the curve, the fixed point is the *focus*, and the fixed line is the *directrix*.**
2. **Sample: (1) Cylindrical Coordinates A point in space may be described in a similar manner to rectangular coordinates. Keep the third, z, coordinate, but replace the first two (x and y) coordinates with their polar equivalents. Hence a cylindrical coordinate is (r, θ, z), as shown.**

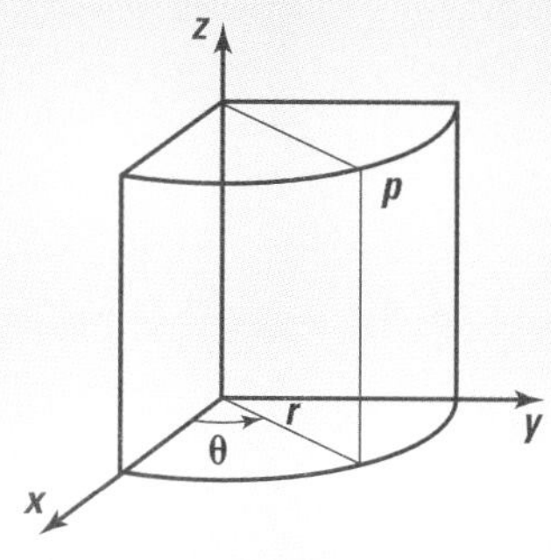

7 Creating Fractals

Let c be a complex number and consider the dynamical system defined by D = set of complex numbers, and $f(z) = z^2 + c$.

a. Write a computer program which will input values for c and d and print out the first several terms in the orbit $O(d)$ while also graphing them.

b. Select a few values for c, and for each one, use your program to investigate $O(d)$ for different values of d. Values of c and d with $|c| < 2$ and $|d| < 2$ work the best. Describe the behavior of the orbits you get. Some good values to try for c are $c = 0$, $-.4 + .2i$, $-.12 + .74i$, $-.39054 - .58679i$, -1.25, $.32 + .043i$, and $-.11 + .67i$.

c. The program below inputs a value of c, then tests values of d to determine whether the terms of $O(d)$ attain an arbitrarily large distance from the origin. If not, the point d is plotted white on the screen.

```
10  NC = 319
20  NR = 199
30  LR = -1.5
40  LI = -1.5
50  UR = 1.5
60  UI = 1.5
70  INPUT "ENTER C AS ORDERED PAIR:";CR,CI
80  SCREEN 1
90  FOR DR = LR TO UR STEP (UR-LR)/NC
100    FOR DI = LI TO UI STEP (UI-LI)/NR
110       K = 0
120       ZR = DR
130       ZI = DI
140          K = K + 1
150          TEMP = ZR*ZR−ZI*ZI+CR
160          ZI = 2*ZR*ZI+CI
170          ZR = TEMP
180          DS = ZR*ZR+ZI*ZI
190          IF DS<100 AND K<30 THEN GOTO 140
200       IF DS<100 THEN PSET
          ((DR-LR)/(UR-LR)*NC,(UI-DI)/(UI-LI)*NR)
210    NEXT DI
220 NEXT DR
230 END
```

Note that lines 10 and 20 assume that pixels are numbered from 0 to 319 from left to right and from 0 to 199 from top to bottom. Lines 30 through 60 set the viewing window so the lower left is $-1.5 - 1.5i$ and the upper right is $1.5 + 1.5i$. Line 80 sets the screen to graphics mode, and line 200 plots points. These lines may have to be modified for your particular computer and for the window you want. The program will plot a white region corresponding to the points d for which the first 30 terms of $O(d)$ stay within 10 units of the origin. The edge of the white region is called the **Julia set** of the function $f(z) = z^2 + c$.

Run the program to see the Julia sets for some of the values of c you investigated in part **b**. Also try $c = i$, $-.194 + .6557i$, and $.11031 - .67037i$. Note that in Interpreted BASIC, the program can take a long time to run.

d. Find out what the Mandelbrot set is, and write a program to draw it. Some good resources are *The Beauty of Fractals*, by Heinz-Otto Peitgen and Peter H. Richter, and *Chaos, Fractals, and Dynamics*, by Robert L. Devaney.

8 Applications of Complex Numbers

Report on one of the following applications of complex numbers.

a. acoustics
b. electricity
c. higher mathematics, such as differential equations

5 Matrix Representations of Complex Numbers This project is straightforward but subtle. If students do not know where to begin, suggest that they put the properties of complex numbers in $a + bi$ form in one column, and the same property as it would look for matrices in a second column. Then the only task is to verify that the matrix property as stated is correct. Notice that, as in the rectangular coordinate representation (a, b) of a complex number, both a and b are real numbers.

6 Quaternions Many books in higher algebra discuss quaternions.

7 Creating Fractals There is software that will create fractals. One example is *Exploring Fractals on the Macintosh* by Brent Wahl.

8 Applications of Complex Numbers This project requires going into physics or higher mathematics texts and can involve a substantial amount of mathematics.

When r is fixed and z and θ vary, a cylinder is formed. When z is fixed and r and θ vary, a plane parallel to the xy-plane is formed. When θ is fixed and z and r vary, a plane containing the z-axis is formed. The intersection of these surfaces defines the point $P(r, \theta, z)$. To convert from cylindrical to rectangular coordinates:

$x = r\cos\theta$
$y = r\sin\theta$
$z = z$

(2) Spherical Coordinates
The position of a point P in space may be assigned coordinates by its radius vector, r (the distance from P to a fixed origin) and two angles—θ (colatitude angle) which is the angle made by a vector from the origin to point P with the polar or z-axis, and ϕ (longitude) which is the angle between the θ plane and a fixed plane through the polar axis (the initial meridian plane—here, the $x - z$ plane).

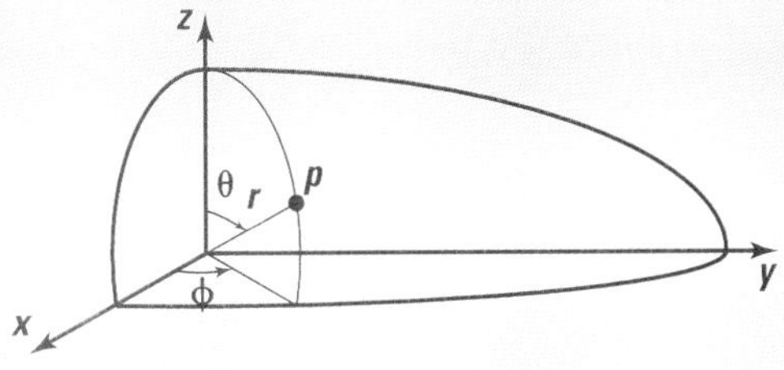

(Responses continue on page 544.)

Summary

The Summary gives an overview of the entire chapter and provides an opportunity for students to consider the material as a whole. Thus, the Summary can be used to help students relate and unify the concepts presented in the chapter.

Additional Responses, page 542

3. **Students' reports may contain some of the following main topics:**
   a. **chaotic phenomena in**
      i. **weather (Edward Lorenz)**
      ii. **wildlife populations (Robert May)**
      iii. **astronomy (Michael Henon)**
      iv. **earthquakes**
      v. **clouds**
      vi. **physiology (blood vessels, bronchial tubes)**
   b. **the great red spot of Jupiter**
   c. **the work of Benoit Mandelbrot**
   d. **the work of Michael Burnsley**
4. **Answers will vary. One good source of information on spirals in nature is *Patterns in Nature* by Peter S. Stevens.**
5. a. **Addition holds:**

$$\begin{bmatrix} a & -b \\ b & a \end{bmatrix} + \begin{bmatrix} c & -d \\ d & c \end{bmatrix} =$$

$$\begin{bmatrix} a+c & -(b+d) \\ b+d & a+c \end{bmatrix}$$

$(a + bi) + (c + di) =$
$(a + c) + (b + d)i$

Multiplication holds:

$$\begin{bmatrix} a & -b \\ b & a \end{bmatrix} \bullet \begin{bmatrix} c & -d \\ d & c \end{bmatrix} =$$

$$\begin{bmatrix} ac - bd & -ad - bc \\ bc + ad & -bd + ac \end{bmatrix} =$$

$$\begin{bmatrix} ac - bd & -(ad + bc) \\ ad + bc & ac - bd \end{bmatrix} =$$

$(a + bi) \bullet (c + di)$
$= ac - bd + adi + bci$
$= (ac - bd) + (ad + bc)i$

b. **det** $\left(\begin{bmatrix} a & -b \\ b & a \end{bmatrix}\right) = a^2 + b^2$, **and the modulus of $a + bi$ is $\sqrt{a^2 + b^2}$. Hence, the modulus of $a + bi$ is the square root of the determinant of its matrix.**

SUMMARY

Complex numbers are numbers which can be written in the form $a + bi$, where a and b are real numbers and $i^2 = -1$. With normal polynomial addition and multiplication they form a field.

Four forms of writing complex numbers are discussed in this chapter: the binomial form $a + bi$, rectangular form (a, b), polar form $[r, \theta]$, and trigonometric form $r(\cos\theta + i\sin\theta)$. They are related by the equations $r = \sqrt{a^2 + b^2}$, $a = r\cos\theta$, and $b = r\sin\theta$. The graph of a complex number in the complex plane is shown here.

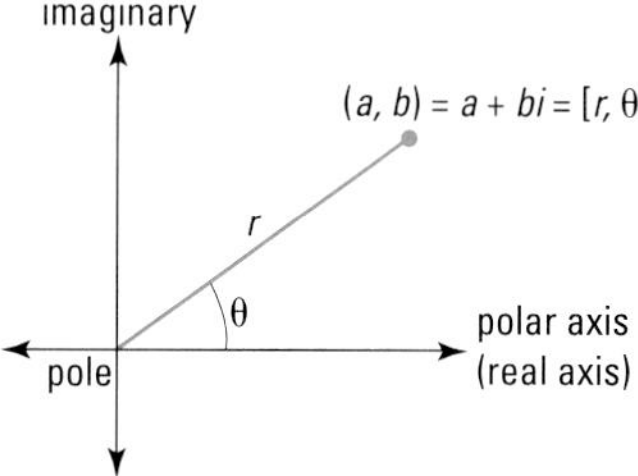

Adding $w = (a, b)$ to z applies the translation $(x, y) \rightarrow (x + a, y + b)$ to z. The graphs in the complex plane of w, 0, z, and $z + w$ are consecutive vertices of a parallelogram. Multiplying z by $w = [s, \phi]$ applies to z a composite of a size change of magnitude s and a rotation of ϕ about the pole. If $z = [r, \theta]$ and $w = [s, \phi]$, then $zw = [rs, \theta + \phi]$.

The polar equation $r = f(\theta)$ can be graphed on a polar grid by finding sets of ordered pairs $[r, \theta]$ that satisfy the equation. A second method involves plotting the rectangular graph of $r = f(\theta)$, then using the height of the graph at various angles θ to make the polar graph. The height becomes the distance from the pole at the angle θ.

Polar graphs are often quite beautiful. Here are some equations and the names of their graphs (a is a nonzero real number, n is a positive integer, and $\sin\theta$ can be replaced by $\cos\theta$.)

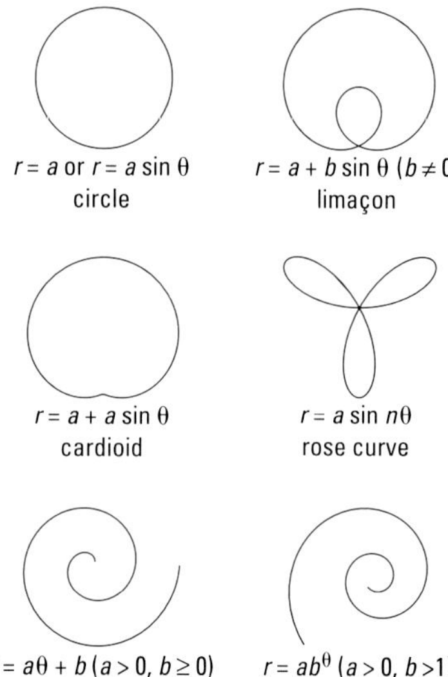

Polar form is most convenient for stating DeMoivre's Theorem: If $z = [r, \theta]$, then $z^n = [r^n, n\theta]$. When graphed in the complex plane, if $z \neq 0$ and $|z| \neq 1$, then the powers of z lie on a logarithmic spiral. From DeMoivre's Theorem, one can prove that the nth roots of a nonzero number z are given by $\left[\sqrt[n]{r}, \frac{\theta}{n} + k \cdot \frac{2\pi}{n}\right]$ for $k = 0, 1, 2, \ldots, n - 1$. When graphed in the complex plane, the nth roots of z form the vertices of a regular n-gon centered at (0, 0).

The Fundamental Theorem of Algebra states that every polynomial $p(x)$ of degree at least 1, over the set of complex numbers, has at least one zero in the set of complex numbers. The number of zeros it has is equal to its degree, provided that multiplicities are counted. In the case that all coefficients of $p(x)$ are real, whenever a nonreal number is a zero of $p(x)$, so is its conjugate.

Discrete dynamical systems is an area of mathematics which has only been developed since the 1960s. It may lead to a better understanding of many different phenomena, including weather forecasting.

c. **The additive inverse of** $\begin{bmatrix} a & -b \\ b & a \end{bmatrix}$ **is** $\begin{bmatrix} -a & b \\ b & a \end{bmatrix}$, **which is the matrix for $-a - bi$, the additive inverse of $a + bi$. The multiplicative inverse of**

$$\begin{bmatrix} a & -b \\ b & a \end{bmatrix} \text{ is } \begin{bmatrix} \frac{a}{a^2+b^2} & \frac{b}{a^2+b^2} \\ \frac{-b}{a^2+b^2} & \frac{a}{a^2+b^2} \end{bmatrix},$$

which is the matrix for $\frac{a - bi}{a^2 + b^2}$, and

$$(a + bi)\frac{a - bi}{a^2 + b^2} = \frac{a^2 - b^2 i^2}{a^2 + b^2} = \frac{a^2 + b^2}{a^2 + b^2} = 1.$$

Hence, the multiplicative inverse of a complex number is the multiplicative inverse of its matrix.

CHAPTER EIGHT

VOCABULARY

Below are the most important terms and phrases for this chapter. You should be able to give a general description and a specific example of each and a precise definition for those marked with an asterisk (*).

Lesson 8-1
* imaginary number
* imaginary unit, *i*
* complex number, real part, imaginary part
* equality of complex numbers
* addition, multiplication of complex numbers
field properties
field of complex numbers
* complex conjugates
complex plane
real axis
imaginary axis
voltage
current
impedance
circuits connected in series

Lesson 8-2
pole
polar axis
polar coordinates, $[r, \theta]$
polar grid
Polar-Rectangular Conversion Theorem

Lesson 8-3
Geometric Addition Theorem
* absolute value, modulus, $|z|$
polar form of a complex number
* argument of a complex number
trigonometric form of a complex number
Geometric Multiplication Theorem

Lesson 8-4
limaçon
cardioid

Lesson 8-5
rose curve, leaves, petals
spiral of Archimedes
logarithmic spiral

Lesson 8-6
DeMoivre's Theorem

Lesson 8-7
* *n*th root of a complex number
Complex *n*th Roots Theorem
Geometric *n*th Roots Theorem

Lesson 8-8
Fundamental Theorem of Algebra
* multiplicity of a zero
* simple zero

Lesson 8-9
Conjugate Zeros Theorem

d. The multiplicative identity matrix is $\begin{bmatrix}1 & 0\\0 & 1\end{bmatrix}$, because $\begin{bmatrix}1 & 0\\0 & 1\end{bmatrix}\begin{bmatrix}a & -b\\b & a\end{bmatrix} = \begin{bmatrix}a & -b\\b & a\end{bmatrix}$. The additive identity matrix is $\begin{bmatrix}0 & 0\\0 & 0\end{bmatrix}$, because $\begin{bmatrix}0 & 0\\0 & 0\end{bmatrix} + \begin{bmatrix}a & -b\\b & a\end{bmatrix} = \begin{bmatrix}a & -b\\b & a\end{bmatrix}$.

e. The argument of $a + bi$ is $\tan^{-1}\frac{b}{a}$ or $\sin^{-1}\frac{b}{\sqrt{a^2+b^2}}$. For the matrix with determinant $d = a^2 + b^2$, the argument is $\sin^{-1}\frac{b}{\sqrt{d}}$ or $\cos^{-1}\frac{a}{\sqrt{d}}$.

Vocabulary

Terms, symbols, and properties are listed by lesson to provide a checklist of concepts a student must know. Emphasize to students that they should read the vocabulary list carefully before starting the Progress Self-Test. If students do not understand the meaning of a term, they should refer back to the indicated lesson.

6. Quaternion numbers are numbers of the form $x = x_0 + x_1 i + x_2 j + x_3 k$, where x_0, x_1, x_2, and x_3 are real numbers. The following relationships hold among the quaternionic units: $i^2 = j^2 = k^2 = -1$, and $ij = jk = ki = -ji = -kj = -ik = -1$. Addition is defined as $x + y = (y_0 + x_0) + (y_1 + x_1)i + (y_2 + x_2)j + (y_3 + x_3)k$. Scalar multiplication is defined as $cx = cx_0 + cx_1 i + cx_2 j + cx_3 k$. Multiplication is defined as $xy = (x_0y_0 - x_1y_1 - x_3y_1 - x_1y_2 + x_3y_2 + x_1y_3 - x_2y_3 - x_3y_3) + (x_1y_0 + x_0y_1)i + (x_2y_0 + x_0y_2)j + (x_3y_0 + x_0y_3)k$.
7. See Additional Answers at the back of this book.
8. Sample (for part a, acoustics): use of complex numbers to represent the pressure of waves and the impedance. For example $p = \frac{A}{r}e^{j(\omega t - kr)}$, where p is pressure, A is the Amplitude Factor, r is the radial distance, ω is the regular frequency, j is the imaginary unit, t is time, and k is the wavelength constant.
   Sample (for part b, electricity): Students' reports may include the following main points:
   a. use of letter $j = \sqrt{-1}$ instead of i in expressing complex numbers
   b. use of complex numbers to represent current, voltage, and
   c. use of Euler's identity to deal with certain time functions
   Sample (for part c, differential equations):
   a. use of Euler's formula to determine roots of characteristic equation
   b. the occurence of roots of differential equations is often as complex conjugates

Progress Self-Test

For the development of mathematical competence, feedback and correction, along with the opportunity to practice, are necessary. The Progress Self-Test provides the opportunity for feedback and correction; the Chapter Review provides additional opportunities and practice. We cannot overemphasize the importance of these end-of-chapter materials. It is at this point that the material "gels" for many students, allowing them to solidify skills and understanding. In general, student performance should be markedly improved after these pages.

Assign the Progress Self-Test as a one-night assignment. Worked-out solutions for all questions are in the Selected Answers section of the student book. Encourage students to take the Progress Self-Test honestly, grade themselves, and then be prepared to discuss the test in class.

Advise students to pay special attention to those Chapter Review questions (pages 547–548) that correspond to questions missed on the Progress Self-Test.

Additional Answers

6. a. $z^1 = 2(\cos\frac{\pi}{3} + i\sin\frac{\pi}{3})$
$z^2 = 4(\cos\frac{2\pi}{3} + i\sin\frac{2\pi}{3})$
$z^3 = 8(\cos\pi + i\sin\pi)$
$z^4 = 16(\cos\frac{4\pi}{3} + i\sin\frac{4\pi}{3})$

b.

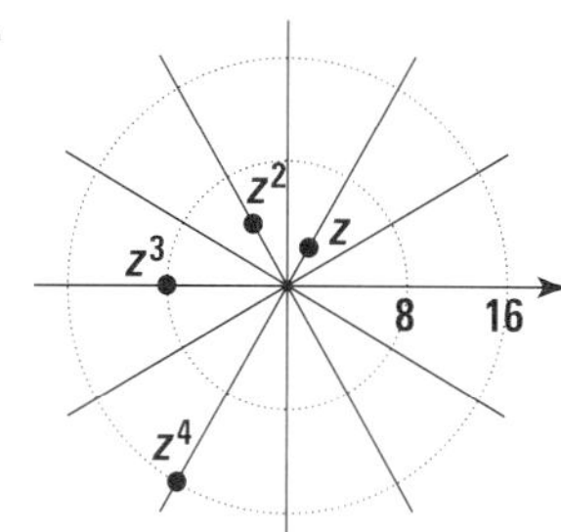

c. farther

CHAPTER EIGHT

PROGRESS SELF-TEST

Take this test as you would take a test in class. Then check the test yourself using the solutions at the back of the book.

1. Let $z = 8 - 5i$ and $w = -2 + 3i$. Calculate the following. **See below.**
a. $z - w$ **b.** zw **c.** $\frac{z}{w}$ **d.** $\overline{w}$

2. Express $\left[8, \frac{5\pi}{6}\right]$ using rectangular coordinates. **$(-4\sqrt{3}, 4)$**

3. Let $z = 4\sqrt{3} - 4i$.
a. Write z in rectangular coordinate form.
b. Find the absolute value of z.
c. Find the argument θ of z if $0 \le \theta < 2\pi$.
d. Write z in polar form. **a–d) See below.**

4. Suppose a voltage of $-3 - 8i$ volts across an AC circuit gives rise to a current of 6 amps. Use Ohm's Law $I = \frac{V}{Z}$ to find the impedance of the circuit. **$-\frac{1}{2} - \frac{4}{3}i$ ohms**

5. Illustrate the multiplication of $z = 10(\cos 25° + i\sin 25°)$ by $w = \frac{1}{2}(\cos 35° + i\sin 35°)$ with a diagram that verifies the Geometric Multiplication Theorem.

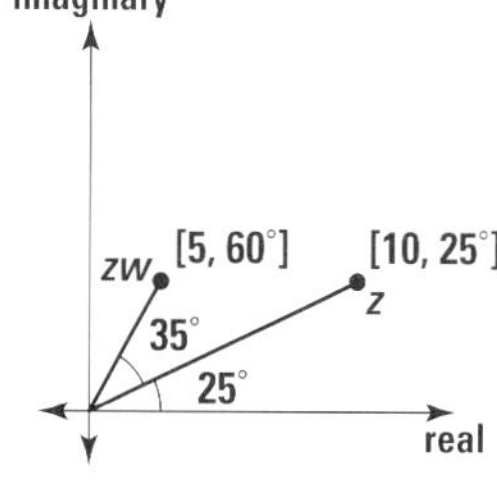

1a) $10 - 8i$ **b)** $-1 + 34i$
c) $-\frac{31}{13} - \frac{14}{13}i$ **d)** $-2 - 3i$

3a) $(4\sqrt{3}, -4)$ **b)** 8
c) $\frac{11\pi}{6}$ **d)** $\left[8, \frac{11\pi}{6}\right]$

6, 7, 11) See margin.

6. Let $z = 2\left(\cos\frac{\pi}{3} + i\sin\frac{\pi}{3}\right)$.
a. Calculate z^1, z^2, z^3, and z^4.
b. Graph them in the complex plane.
c. Are the numbers in the sequence getting closer to or farther away from 0?

7. a. Calculate the fifth roots of $243i$.
b. Plot them in the complex plane.

8. Find all zeros and their multiplicities for the polynomial $p(x) = (x^4 - 81)(x^2 + 6x + 9)$.

9. Let $z = a + bi$.
a. Find a formula for $\overline{z^2}$.
b. Find a formula for $(\overline{z})^2$.
c. Use parts **a** and **b** to show that $\left(\overline{z^2}\right) = (\overline{z})^2$ $\forall$ complex numbers z.

10. Suppose $p(x)$ is a fifth degree polynomial with real coefficients which has zeros 2, $5i$, and $1 - i$.
a. Find all other zeros of $p(x)$. **$-5i$, $1 + i$**
b. Write a possible formula for $p(x)$ in factored form. **See below.**

11. Sketch the polar graph of the equation $r = 2 + 2\sin\theta$.

12. a. Sketch the polar graph of the equation $r = 3\cos 4\theta$. **See below.**
b. Identify the type of curve you get. **eight-leafed rose curve**

a)

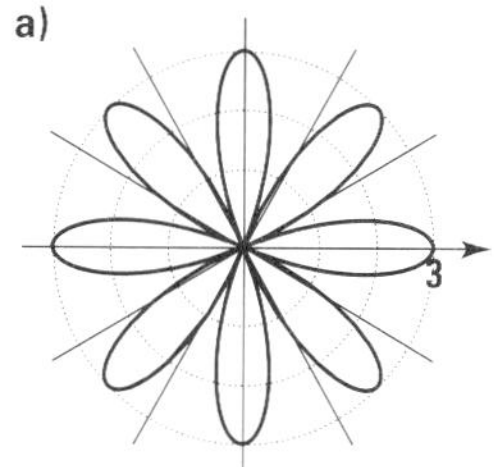

8) -3 (with multiplicity 3), 3, $\pm 3i$

9a) $a^2 - b^2 + 2abi$ **b)** $a^2 - b^2 - 2abi$
c) $\overline{z^2} = \overline{a^2 - b^2 + 2abi} = a^2 - b^2 - 2abi = (\overline{z})^2$

10b) $p(x) = (x - 2)(x - 5i)(x + 5i)(x - 1 - i)\cdot(x - 1 + i)$

7. a. [3, 18°], [3, 90°], [3, 162°], [3, 234°], [3, 306°]

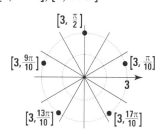

b.

$[3, \frac{\pi}{2}]$ $[3, \frac{9\pi}{10}]$ $[3, \frac{\pi}{10}]$ 3 $[3, \frac{13\pi}{10}]$ $[3, \frac{17\pi}{10}]$

11.

3

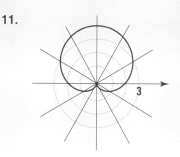

CHAPTER REVIEW

Questions on SPUR Objectives

SPUR stands for **S**kills, **P**roperties, **U**ses, and **R**epresentations. The Chapter Review questions are grouped according to the SPUR Objectives for this chapter.

SKILLS DEAL WITH THE PROCEDURES USED TO GET ANSWERS.

Objective A: *Express complex numbers in binomial, rectangular, polar and trigonometric form.* *(Lessons 8-1, 8-3)*

In 1–6, the complex number is written in either binomial, rectangular, polar, or trigonometric form. Write it in the other three forms. **See margin.**

1. $6\sqrt{3} - 6i$ **2.** $8\left(\cos\frac{7\pi}{4} + i\sin\frac{7\pi}{4}\right)$

3. $[2.5, 35°]$ **4.** -4 **5.** $-7 + 5i$ **6.** $\left[-\frac{1}{2}, \frac{5\pi}{2}\right]$

7. Find the absolute value and argument θ for the complex number $-24 + 7i$, given that $0° \le \theta < 360°$. $|-24 + 7i| = 25$, $\theta \approx 163.7°$

8. Given that $[r, \theta]$ is the imaginary number $0 + bi$ with $b > 0$, find r and θ, if θ is restricted to the interval $0 \le \theta < 2\pi$. $r = b$, $\theta = \frac{\pi}{2}$

9. Suppose $P = \left[-4, \frac{3\pi}{2}\right]$. a) Sample: $\left[4, \frac{\pi}{2}\right]$

a. Give polar coordinates for P with $r \ne -4$.

b. Give polar coordinates for P with $r > 0$ and $\theta < 0$. Sample: $\left[4, -\frac{3\pi}{2}\right]$

c. Give the general form of the polar coordinates for P with $r > 0$. $\left[4, \frac{\pi}{2} + 2n\pi\right]$, n an integer

Objective B: *Perform operations with complex numbers.* *(Lessons 8-1, 8-3)*

In 10 and 11, rewrite each expression in binomial form.

10. $\sqrt{-48}$ $4\sqrt{3}i$ **11.** $\frac{4 - \sqrt{-12}}{6}$ $\frac{2}{3} - \frac{\sqrt{3}}{3}i$

12. Express the solutions to $x^2 = -80$ using i notation. $\pm 4\sqrt{5}i$

In 13–16, perform the indicated operation and write the result in $a + bi$ form. **13, 14) See right.**

13. $(7 + 3i) + (8 - 6i)$ **14.** $(4 - 9i)^2$

15. $\frac{3 - 5i}{10 + 2i}$ $\frac{5}{26} - \frac{7}{13}i$ **16.** $(10 + 3i)(8 - 4i)$ $92 - 16i$

125

17. Find the product of $2 + 11i$ and its conjugate.

18. Express in $a + bi$ notation: $(3 + 9i)(4 - i) - \frac{8 + 2i}{1 + i}$. $16 + 36i$

19. Evaluate i^9. i

In 20 and 21, find $z \cdot w$ and express the result in the same form as that of the given numbers.

20. $z = [10, 150°]$, $w = [2, 40°]$ $[20, 190°]$

21. $z = \sqrt{3}(\cos 50° + i\sin 50°)$, $w = \sqrt{7}(\cos 12° + i\sin 12°)$

22. Find z so that $z \cdot [3, 80°] = [24, 300°]$. $[8, 220°]$ 21) $\sqrt{21}(\cos 62° + i\sin 62°)$

Objective C: *Convert between polar and rectangular representations of points.* *(Lesson 8-2)*

23. Suppose $P = \left[1, \frac{\pi}{3}\right]$ and $Q = \left[-1, \frac{2\pi}{3}\right]$.

a. Determine rectangular coordinates for P and Q. **See below.**

b. *True or false.* P and Q are reflection images of each other over the polar axis. **True**

In 24 and 25, give one pair of polar coordinates for the (x, y) pair. **24) Sample:** $\approx [\sqrt{85}, 130.6°]$

24. $(-6, 7)$ **25.** $(\sqrt{3}, -1)$ Sample: $\left[2, \frac{11\pi}{6}\right]$

26. If $P = \left[r, \frac{5\pi}{6}\right] = (x, 2)$, solve for r and x. $r = 4$, $x = -2\sqrt{3}$

Objective D: *Find powers and roots of complex numbers.* *(Lessons 8-6, 8-7)*

27. Express $\left[1.7, \frac{\pi}{3}\right]^6$ in $a + bi$ form. $\approx 24.1 + 0i$

28. Find $(-1 + 3i)^4$. $28 + 96i$

13) $15 - 3i$ 14) $-65 - 72i$

23a) $P = \left(\frac{1}{2}, \frac{\sqrt{3}}{2}\right)$, $Q = \left(\frac{1}{2}, -\frac{\sqrt{3}}{2}\right)$

Chapter 8 Review

Resources

From the ***Teacher's Resource File***

- Answer Master for Chapter 8 Review
- Assessment Sourcebook: Chapter 8 Test, Forms A–D Chapter 8 Test, Cumulative Form

Additional Resources

- TestWorks CD-ROM

The main objectives for the chapter are organized in the Chapter Review under the four types of understanding this book promotes—Skills, Properties, Uses, and Representations.

Whereas end-of-chapter material may be considered optional in some texts, in UCSMP *Precalculus and Discrete Mathematics* we have selected these objectives and questions with the expectation that they will be covered. Students should be able to answer these questions with about 85% accuracy after studying the chapter.

You may assign these questions over a single night to help students prepare for a test the next day, or you may assign the questions over a two-day period. If you work the questions over two days, then we recommend assigning the *evens* for homework the first night so that students get feedback in class the next day, then assigning the *odds* the night before the test, because answers are provided to the odd-numbered questions.

It is effective to ask students which questions they still do not understand and use the day or days as a total class discussion of the material which the class finds most difficult.

Additional Answers

1. $(6\sqrt{3}, -6)$, $\left[12, \frac{11\pi}{6}\right]$, $12\left(\cos\frac{11\pi}{6} + i\sin\frac{11\pi}{6}\right)$
2. $4\sqrt{2} - 4\sqrt{2}i$, $(4\sqrt{2}, -4\sqrt{2})$, $\left[8, \frac{7\pi}{4}\right]$
3. $2.5\cos 35° + 2.5i\sin 35°$, $(2.5\cos 35°, 2.5\sin 35°)$, $2.5(\cos 35° + i\sin 35°)$
4. $(-4, 0)$, $[4, \pi]$, $4(\cos\pi + i\sin\pi)$
5. $(-7, 5)$, $\approx [\sqrt{74}, 144°]$, $\approx \sqrt{74}(\cos 144° + i\sin 144°)$
6. $-\frac{1}{2}i$, $\left(0, -\frac{1}{2}\right)$, $\frac{1}{2}\left(\cos\frac{3\pi}{2} + i\sin\frac{3\pi}{2}\right)$

Assessment

Evaluation The Assessment Sourcebook provides five forms of the Chapter 8 Test. Forms A and B present parallel versions in a short-answer format. Forms C and D offer performance assessment. The fifth test is Chapter 8 Test, Cumulative Form. About 50% of this test covers Chapter 8, 25% of it covers Chapter 7, and 25% of it covers earlier chapters.

For information on grading, see *General Teaching Suggestions: Grading* in the *Professional Sourcebook,* which begins on page T20 in the Teacher's Edition.

Feedback After students have taken the test for Chapter 8 and you have scored the results, return the tests to students for discussion. Class discussion of the questions that caused trouble for the most students can be very effective in identifying and clarifying misunderstandings. You might want to have them write down the items they missed and work, either in groups or at home, to correct them. It is important for students to receive feedback on every chapter test, and we recommend that students see and correct their mistakes before proceeding too far into the next chapter.

Additional Answers

29. $[4, \frac{\pi}{6}], [4, \frac{5\pi}{6}], [4, \frac{3\pi}{2}]$
30. $3(\cos(\frac{\pi}{36} + \frac{\pi n}{3}) + i\sin(\frac{\pi}{36} + \frac{\pi n}{3}))$ for $n = 0, 1, 2, 3, 4, 5$
31. $2\cos\frac{\pi n}{5} + 2i\sin\frac{\pi n}{5}$; $n = 0, 1, 2, \ldots, 9$
33. b. $(r(\cos\theta + i\sin\theta))^n = r^n(\cos n\theta + i\sin n\theta)$
35. zeros: 0, 3, (both with multiplicity 2)
36. zeros: ± 3, $\pm 2i$ (all with multiplicity 1)
39. $z - w = -1 + 3i$, so $\overline{z - w} = -1 - 3i$. $\overline{z} - \overline{w} = (3 - 2i) - (4 + i) = -1 - 3i$. So $\overline{z - w} = \overline{z} - \overline{w}$.
40. $z(v + w) = (3 + 2i) \cdot (3 + 2i) = 5 + 12i$, and $zv + zw = (-9 + 7i) + (14 + 5i) = 5 + 12i$, so $z(v + w) = zv + zw$.
41. If $z = 0 + bi$ and $w = 0 + di$, then $zw = bdi^2 = -bd = -bd + 0i$, which is a real number.
42. $z = r\cos\theta + (r\sin\theta)i$ and $w = r\cos(-\theta) + (r\sin(-\theta))i = r\cos\theta - (r\sin\theta)i$. So z and w are complex conjugates.

CHAPTER EIGHT

In 29–31, find the indicated roots of the given number. Express the roots in the same form as the given number. **See margin.**

29. cube roots of $\left[64, \frac{\pi}{2}\right]$

30. sixth roots of $729\left(\cos\frac{\pi}{6} + i\sin\frac{\pi}{6}\right)$

31. tenth roots of 1024

32. One cube root of z is $\frac{5\sqrt{2}}{2} + \frac{5\sqrt{2}}{2}i$.

a. Write z in $a + bi$ form. $-\frac{125\sqrt{2}}{2} + \frac{125\sqrt{2}}{2}i$

b. Write the other two cube roots of z in polar form. **See below.**

33. a. According to DeMoivre's Theorem, $[r, \theta]^n = \underline{\ ?\ }$. $[r^n, n\theta]$

b. Restate DeMoivre's Theorem in trigonometric form. **See margin.**

34. If $3(\cos 30° + i\sin 30°)$ is the fifth root of w, write w in polar form. $243(\cos 150° + i\sin 150°) = [243, 150°]$

Objective E: *Find all zeros, and their multiplicities, of a given polynomial.* *(Lessons 8-8, 8-9)*

In 35 and 36, find all zeros and the corresponding multiplicities for the given polynomial.

35. $p(x) = x^4 - 6x^3 + 9x^2$ **See margin.**

36. $p(x) = x^4 - 5x^2 - 36$ **See margin.**

37. If $1 - i$ is a zero of $p(x) = x^3 + x^2 - 4x + 6$, find the remaining zeros. $1 + i$, -3

38. a. Find all zeros and their multiplicities for the polynomial $p(x) = 4x^2 - 4xi - 1$.

b. Does the answer to part **a** contradict the Conjugate Zeros Theorem? Explain why or why not. **No. This theorem does not apply if the coefficients of the polynomial are not all real numbers.**

a) $\frac{i}{2}$ with multiplicity 2

PROPERTIES DEAL WITH THE PRINCIPLES BEHIND THE MATHEMATICS.

39–43b) See margin.

Objective F: *Prove or verify properties of complex numbers.* *(Lessons 8-1, 8-3, 8-6)*

In 39 and 40, let $z = 3 + 2i$, $v = -1 + 3i$, and $w = 4 - i$.

39. Verify that $\overline{z - w} = \overline{z} - \overline{w}$.

40. Verify that $z(v + w) = zv + zw$.

41. Prove that if z and w are imaginary numbers, then zw is a real number.

42. Let $z = [r, \theta]$ and $w = [r, -\theta]$. Show that z and w are complex conjugates by writing them in $a + bi$ form.

43. Let $z = [r, \theta]$ and let n and m be positive integers.

a. Use DeMoivre's Theorem to write z^n, z^m, and z^{n+m} in polar form.

b. Use the answers to part **a** to show that $z^n \cdot z^m = z^{n+m}$.

32b) $\left[5, \frac{11\pi}{12}\right], \left[5, \frac{19\pi}{12}\right]$

46) $5 - 2i$

47) $p(x)$ has real coefficients, so the conjugate of $2i$ would have to be a zero. But $p(x)$ has degree 3 and so cannot have 4 zeros.

48bi) cannot be determined

46, 47, 48bi) See left below.

Objective G: *Use the properties of polynomials to find or describe their zeros.* *(Lessons 8-8, 8-9)*

44. According to the Fundamental Theorem of Algebra, $p(x) = 5x^7 - 9x^4 + 2ix^3 - 6$ has exactly $\underline{\ ?\ }$ complex zeros. **7**

45. *True or false.* Every polynomial of odd degree $n \geq 1$ with real coefficients has at least one real zero. **True**

46. If $5 + 2i$ is a zero of a polynomial $q(x)$ with real coefficients, then $\underline{\ ?\ }$ must also be a zero.

47. Without doing any computation, explain why 3, -2, and $2i$ cannot all be zeros of the polynomial $p(x) = -3x^3 + 9x^2 - 12x + 36$.

48. Suppose that $q(x)$ is a fourth degree polynomial with real coefficients, $q(4) = 0$, $q(4i) = 0$, and $q(3 - i) = 1 + 2i$.

a. Counting multiplicities, how many real zeros and how many nonreal zeros does $q(x)$ have? **2 real, 2 nonreal**

b. Find each value.

i. $q(-4)$ ii. $q(-4i)$ **0** iii. $q(3 + i)$ **$1 - 2i$**

49. Suppose $p(x)$ and $q(x)$ are polynomials such that $p(x) = (x - z)q(x)$ and z is a zero of $q(x)$. Then what do you know about the multiplicity of z as a zero of $p(x)$? **Its multiplicity is at least 2.**

43. a. $z^n = [r^n, n\theta]$; $z^m = [r^m, m\theta]$; $z^{n+m} = [r^{n+m}, (n + m)\theta]$
b. $z^n \cdot z^m = [r^n, n\theta] \cdot [r^m, m\theta] = [r^n \cdot r^m, n\theta + m\theta] = [r^{n+m}, (n + m)\theta] = z^{n+m}$

53. a.–d.

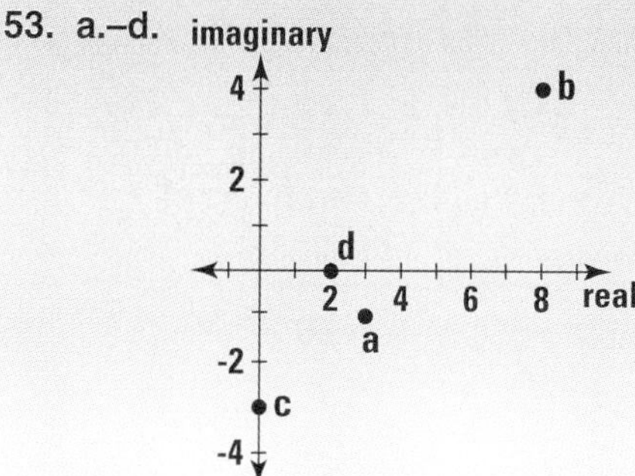

CHAPTER EIGHT

USES DEAL WITH APPLICATIONS OF MATHEMATICS IN REAL SITUATIONS.

Objective H: *Use complex numbers to solve AC circuit problems.* *(Lesson 8-1)*

50. Two AC circuits are connected in series. If the voltage across one is $-2 + 5i$ and the voltage across another is $3 - 8i$, find the total voltage. **$1 - 3i$ volts**

51. The voltage across an AC circuit is $8 - 14i$ volts, and the impedance is $4 + 2i$ ohms. Find the current. **$\frac{1}{5} - \frac{18}{5}i$ amps**

52. The current in an AC circuit is 5 amps and the impedance is $-3 + 8i$ ohms. Find the voltage. **$-15 + 40i$ volts**

REPRESENTATIONS DEAL WITH PICTURES, GRAPHS, OR OBJECTS THAT ILLUSTRATE CONCEPTS.

Objective I: *Graph complex numbers and verify the Geometric Addition and Geometric Multiplication Theorems.* *(Lessons 8-1, 8-2, 8-3)*

53. Graph the complex numbers on the same complex plane. **See margin.**

a. $3 - i$ **b.** $8 + 4i$ **c.** $-3i$ **d.** 2

54. Graph the complex numbers on the same polar grid. **See margin.**

a. $\left[4, \frac{5\pi}{6}\right]$ **b.** $[-2, 20°]$

c. $3.7(\cos 115° + i \sin 115°)$

d. $3\left(\cos \frac{11\pi}{4} + i \sin \frac{11\pi}{4}\right)$ **e.** $\left[\frac{5}{2}, \pi\right]$

55. *True or false.* The complex numbers represented by $P = \left[1, \frac{\pi}{3}\right]$ and $Q = \left[-1, \frac{2\pi}{3}\right]$ are complex conjugates. **True**

56. Let $A = 0 + 0i$, $B = 2 - 6i$, $C = 5 + i$, and $D = B + C$. **b) See margin.**

a. What figure does $ABDC$ form in the complex plane? **a parallelogram**

b. Prove the result in part **a**.

57. Illustrate the multiplication of $z = 4(\cos 70° + i \sin 70°)$ by $w = 5(\cos 20° + i \sin 20°)$ with a diagram showing the appropriate size change and rotation. **See margin.**

58. a. Graph $\triangle FLY$ in the complex plane when $F = -2 + 3i$, $L = -i$, and $Y = 4 + 2i$.

b. Multiply each vertex by $z = -1 - i$ and graph the result as $\triangle F'L'Y'$.

c. Find the ratio of similitude of $\triangle F'L'Y'$ to $\triangle FLY$ and relate the result to the Geometric Multiplication Theorem.

d. How does the argument of F' compare to the argument of F? Explain your answer. Use the Geometric Multiplication Theorem. **See margin.**

59. Verify the Geometric Addition Theorem for the complex numbers $z = 1 + 4i$ and $w = 2 - 5i$. **See margin.**

Objective J: *Sketch graphs of polar equations.* *(Lessons 8-4, 8-5)*

In 60–62, sketch the graph of the polar equation by using a table of values. **See margin.**

60. $r = 6 \cos \theta$ **61.** $r = \frac{2}{\theta}$ **62.** $r \cos \theta = 5$

In 63 and 64, sketch the rectangular graph of the given equation. Then use the rectangular graph to sketch the polar graph. Identify the type of curve that results. **See margin for graphs.**

63. $r = 5 \cos 4\theta$, $0 \le \theta \le 2\pi$ **8-leafed rose curve**

64. $r = 2 + 3 \cos \theta$, $0 \le \theta \le 2\pi$ **limaçon**

65. Sketch the graphs of $r = 4^{\theta}$ and $r = 4 + \theta$ on the same polar grid. Identify the type of curve represented by each graph. **See margin.**

Objective K: *Use DeMoivre's Theorem to graph powers and roots of complex numbers.* *(Lessons 8-6, 8-7)* **66–69) See margin.**

66. a. Graph z^1, z^2, z^3, z^4, and z^5 when $z = 1 - i$.

b. Are the numbers in the sequence getting closer to or farther away from 0?

67. a. Graph w^1, w^2, w^3, and w^4 when $w = [.5, 40°]$.

b. Are the numbers in the sequence getting closer to or farther away from 0?

68. a. The graphs of the fifth roots of $\left[32, \frac{5\pi}{4}\right]$ are the vertices of what figure?

b. Plot the fifth roots of $\left[32, \frac{5\pi}{4}\right]$ in a complex plane.

69. Graph the sixth roots of 1 in a complex plane.

58. a.,b.

imaginary
4
F
Y
L'
-2
L
4
real
F'
-4
Y'

c. $FY = \sqrt{37}$, $LY = 5$, $FL = \sqrt{20}$, $F'Y' = \sqrt{74}$, $L'Y' = \sqrt{50}$, $F'L' = \sqrt{40}$. So $\frac{F'Y'}{FY} = \frac{\sqrt{74}}{\sqrt{37}} = \sqrt{2}$, $\frac{L'Y'}{LY} = \frac{\sqrt{50}}{5} = \sqrt{2}$, and $\frac{F'L'}{FL} = \frac{\sqrt{40}}{\sqrt{20}} = \sqrt{2}$. The ratio of similitude is $\sqrt{2}$. In polar form, $z = \left[\sqrt{2}, \frac{5\pi}{4}\right]$ and so all distances are multiplied by $\sqrt{2}$.

d. The argument of F' ($\approx 348.7°$) is 225° greater than the argument of F ($\approx 123.7°$). $(-2 + 3i) \cdot (-1 - i) = [\sqrt{13}, 123.7°] \cdot [\sqrt{2}, 225°] = [\sqrt{26}, 348.7°]$ or applying a size change of $\sqrt{2}$ and a rotation of 225° to F to obtain F'.

59. $z + w = 3 - i$; vertices: $A = (0, 0)$, $B = (2, -5)$, $C = (3, -1)$, $D = (1, 4)$;

slope of $\overline{AB}$ is $\frac{-5 - 0}{2 - 0} = -\frac{5}{2}$,

slope of $\overline{AD} = \frac{4 - 0}{1 - 0} = 4$,

slope of $\overline{DC} = \frac{4 - (-1)}{1 - 3} = -\frac{5}{2}$,

slope of $\overline{BC} = \frac{-5 - (-1)}{2 - 3} = 4$

Since the slopes of opposite sides are equal, $ABCD$ is a parallelogram.

60.–69. See Additional Answers at the back of this book.

54. a.–e.

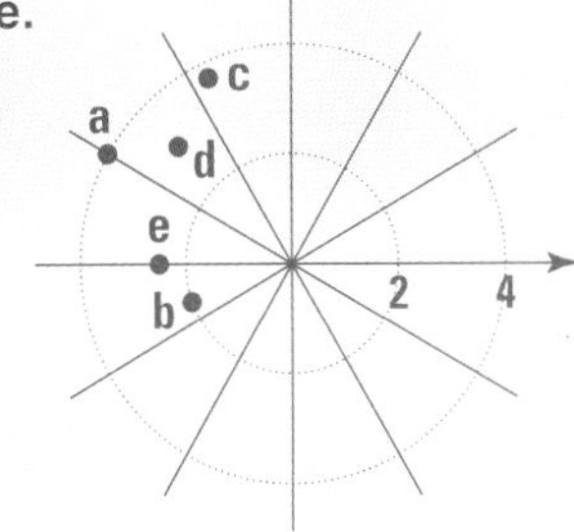

56. b. $D = B + C = 7 - 5i$

slope of $\overline{CA}$ is $\frac{1 - 0}{5 - 0} = \frac{1}{5}$;

slope of $\overline{CD} = \frac{-5 - 1}{7 - 5} = -3$;

slope of $\overline{DB} = \frac{-5 - (-6)}{7 - 2} = \frac{1}{5}$;

slope of $\overline{AB} = \frac{-6 - 0}{2 - 0} = -3$

Both pairs of opposite sides are parallel, so $ABDC$ is a parallelogram.

57.

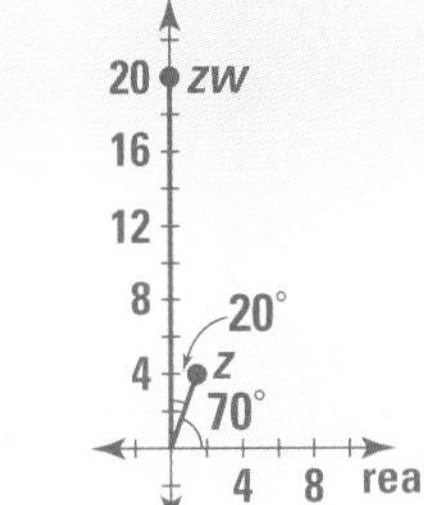

Chapter 9 Planner

Adapting to Individual Needs

The student text is written for the vast majority of students. The chart at the right suggests two pacing plans to accommodate the needs of your students. Students in the Full Course should complete the entire text by the end of the year. Students in the Minimal Course will spend more time when there are quizzes and more time on the Chapter Review. Therefore, these students may not complete all of the chapters in the text.

Options are also presented to meet the needs of a variety of teaching and learning styles. For each lesson, the Teacher's Edition provides a section entitled *Adapting to Individual Needs.* This section regularly includes **Optional Activities, Challenge** problems, **English Language Development** suggestions, and suggestions for providing **Extra Help.** The Teacher's Edition also frequently includes an **Error Alert,** an **Extension,** and an **Assessment** alternative. The options available in Chapter 9 are summarized in the chart below.

Chapter 9 Pacing Chart

Day	Full Course	Minimal Course
1	9-1	9-1
2	9-2	9-2
3	9-3	9-3
4	Quiz*; 9-4	Quiz*; begin 9-4.
5	9-5	Finish 9-4.
6	9-6	9-5
7	Self-Test	9-6
8	Review	Self-Test
9	Test*	Review
10	Comprehensive Test*	Review
11		Test*
12		Comprehensive Test*

*in the Teacher's Resource File

In the Teacher's Edition...

Lesson	Optional Activities	Extra Help	Challenge	English Language Development	Error Alert	Extension	Cooperative Learning	Ongoing Assessment
9-1	●	●	●		●	●	●	Written
9-2	●	●	●		●	●	●	Written
9-3	●	●	●		●	●		Quiz
9-4	●	●	●		●	●		Written
9-5	●	●	●		●	●		Oral
9-6	●	●	●		●	●		

In the Additional Resources...

	In the Teacher's Resource File							
Lesson	Lesson Masters	Teaching Aids*	Answer Masters	Technology Sourcebook	Assessment Sourcebook	Visual Aids**	Technology	Explorations Software
9-1	9-1	87, 89, 90, 91	9-1			87, 89, 90, 91, AM		9-1
9-2	9-2	87, 92, 93, 94, 95	9-2	Calc 13		87, 92, 93, 94, 95, AM		9-2
In-class Activity		96	9-3			96, AM		
9-3	9-3	87, 97, 98, 99	9-3		Quiz	87, 97, 98, 99, AM		
9-4	9-4	88, 100	9-4			88, 100, AM		
9-5	9-5	88, 101	9-5			88, 101, AM		9-5
9-6		88, 102	9-6			88, 102, AM		
End of chapter					Tests			

*Teaching Aids are pictured on pages 550C and 550D.

**Visual Aids provide transparencies for all Teaching Aids and all Answer Masters.

Also available is the Study Skills Handbook which includes study-skill tips related to reading, note-taking, and comprehension.

Integrating Strands and Applications

	9-1	9-2	9-3	9-4	9-5	9-6
Mathematical Connections						
Number Sense	●	●			●	
Algebra	●	●	●		●	●
Logic and Reasoning	●	●			●	●
Statistics/Data Analysis	●			●		
Patterns and Functions	●	●	●		●	●
Discrete Mathematics				●		●
Interdisciplinary and Other Connections						
Music		●				
Science	●	●	●	●	●	●
Social Studies	●	●		●	●	●
Technology	●	●	●		●	
Consumer	●		●		●	
Sports		●	●	●		

Teaching and Assessing the Chapter Objectives

				In the Teacher's Resource File		
Chapter 9 Objectives (Organized into the SPUR catetgories—Skills, Properties, Uses, and Representations)	**Lessons**	**Progress Self-Test Questions**	**Chapter Review Questions**	**Chapter Test, Forms A and B**	**Chapter Test, Forms C**	**Chapter Test, Forms D**
Skills						
A: Compute average rates of change in functions.	9-1	3	1–3		1	✓
B: Use the definition of derivative to compute derivatives.	9-2, 9-3	5	4–8		2	
Properties						
C: Use derivatives to identify properties of functions.	9-5	9	9–13			
Uses						
D: Find rates of change in real situations.	9-1, 9-2, 9-3, 9-4	2	14–16			✓
E: Use derivatives to find the velocity and acceleration of a moving object.	9-2, 9-3, 9-4	8	17–19		3	
F: Use derivatives to solve optimization problems.	9-5	8	20–21			✓
Representations						
G: Relate average rate of change to secant lines of graphs of functions.	9-1	1	22–23		1	
H: Estimate derivatives by finding slopes of tangent lines.	9-2, 9-3	4	24–27		2	
I: Determine properties of derivatives from the graph of a function.	9-5	6, 7	28–29		4	✓

Assessment Sourcebook
Quiz for Lessons 9-1 through 9-3
Chapter 9 Test, Forms A–D
Chapter 9 Test, Cumulative Form
Comprehensive Test, Chapters 1–9

TestWorks CD-ROM

Teaching Aids

TEACHING AID 87

Warm-up
Lesson 9-1

In Houston, on March 1, the sun sets at 6:20 P.M. On April 1, the sun sets at 6:40 P.M. By how many minutes per day does sunset get later during the month of March?

Warm-up
Lesson 9-2

Suppose $g(x) = 5x^2 - 12x$. Calculate each of the following.

1. $g(x + \Delta x)$
2. $g(x + \Delta x) - g(x)$
3. $\frac{g(x + \Delta x) - g(x)}{\Delta x}$
4. $\lim_{\Delta x \to 0} \frac{g(x + \Delta x) - g(x)}{\Delta x}$

Warm-up
Lesson 9-3

Work with the same classmate you were paired with for the In-class Activity on page 568 in the Student Edition. Fill in the chart below with the values you found from Parts 3 and 4 of the activity. Then plot the points of the function f'.

x	$f(x) = \sin x$	$f'(x)$

TEACHING AID 88

Warm-up
Lesson 9-4

Listed here are the highest Dow-Jones stock averages for each year from 1962 to 1982. In which year was the highest rate of change per year of the yearly rate of change?

1962	726.01	1969	968.85	1976	1014.79
1963	767.21	1970	842.00	1977	999.75
1964	891.71	1971	950.82	1978	907.74
1965	969.26	1972	1036.27	1979	897.61
1966	995.15	1973	1051.70	1980	1000.17
1967	943.08	1974	891.66	1981	1024.05
1968	985.21	1975	881.81	1982	1070.55

(Source: *The World Almanac and Book of Facts* 1998, p. 127)

Warm-up
Lesson 9-5

1. Consider the quadratic function q with $q(x) = 9x^2 - 27x + 12$.
   a. Use the Derivative of a Quadratic Function formula to determine a formula for q'.
   b. For what values of x is $q'(x) > 0$?
   c. Graph q. From the graph of q, for what values of x is q an increasing function?
   d. Compare your answers to parts b and c.

Warm-up
Lesson 9-6

Estimate the slope of the tangent to the graph of $y = e^x$ at the point $(3, e^3)$ by calculating the slope determined by the points $(3, e^3)$ and $(3 + k, e^{3+k})$, where k is very close to zero.

TEACHING AID 89
Lesson 9-1

Length of Day Table and Graph

Length of day (in minutes) on first day of month at 50° north latitude

Date	Day of year	Length
January 1	1	490
February 1	32	560
March 1	60	659
April 1	91	775
May 1	121	882
June 1	152	964
July 1	182	977
August 1	213	913
September 1	244	809
October 1	274	698
November 1	305	587
December 1	335	504

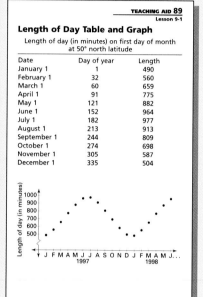

Length of day (in minutes): 500, 600, 700, 800, 900, 1000

J F M A M J J A S O N D J F M A M J . . .
1997 1998

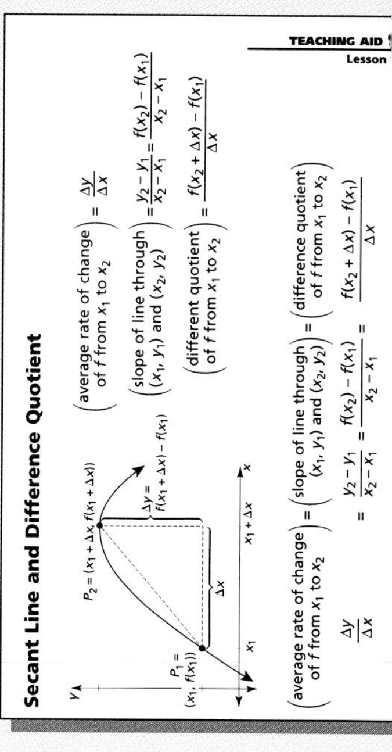

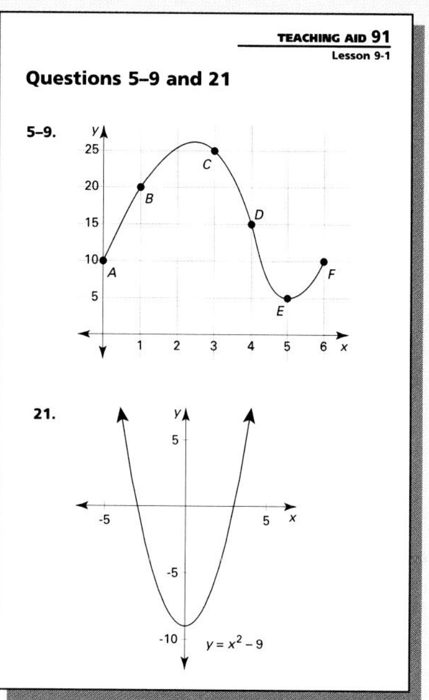

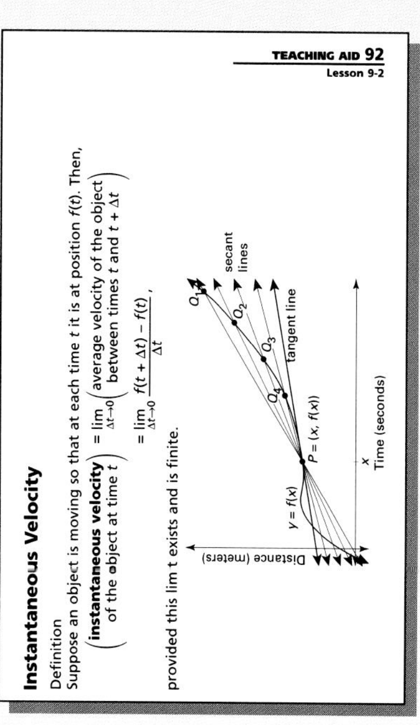

TEACHING AID 92
Lesson 9-2
Instantaneous Velocity
Definition
Suppose an object is moving so that at each time t it is at position f(t). Then,
provided this lim t exists and is finite.
secant lines
tangent line
Distance (meters)
Time (seconds)

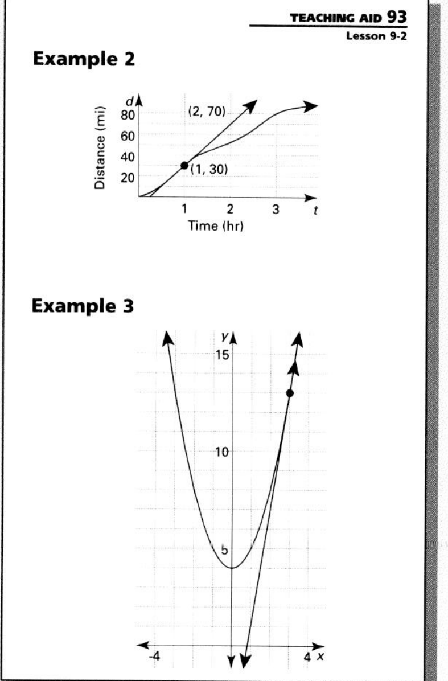

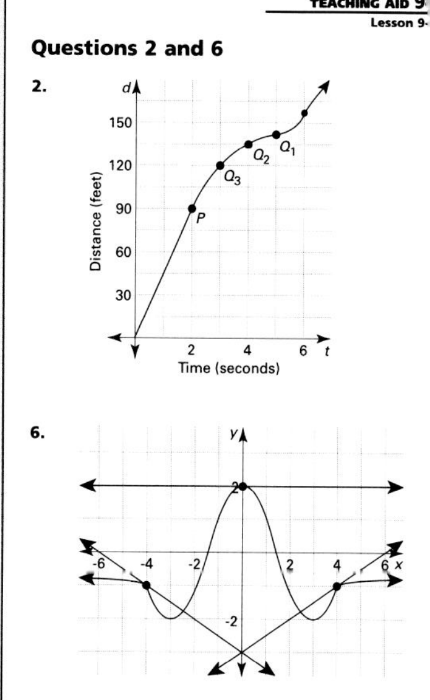

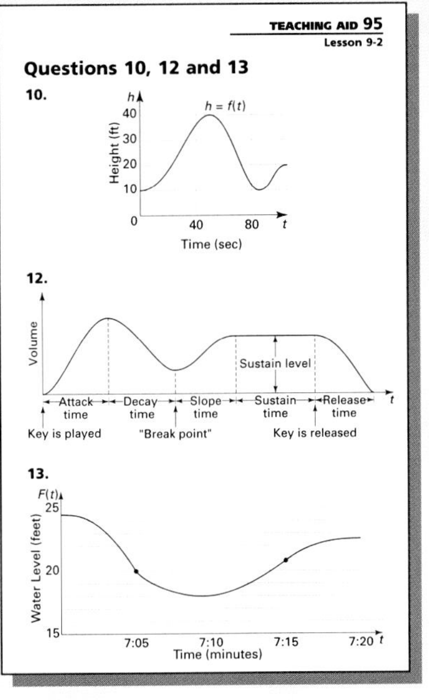

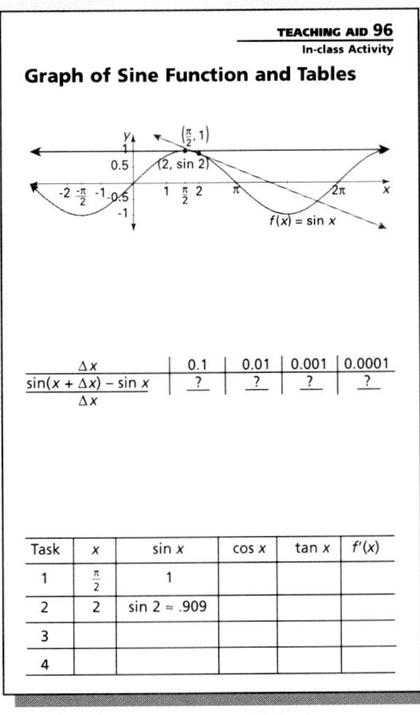

Δx	0.1	0.01	0.001	0.0001
$\frac{\sin(x + \Delta x) - \sin x}{\Delta x}$	?	?	?	?

Task	x	sin x	cos x	tan x	$f'(x)$
1	$\frac{\pi}{2}$	1			
2	2	sin 2 ≈ .909			
3					
4					

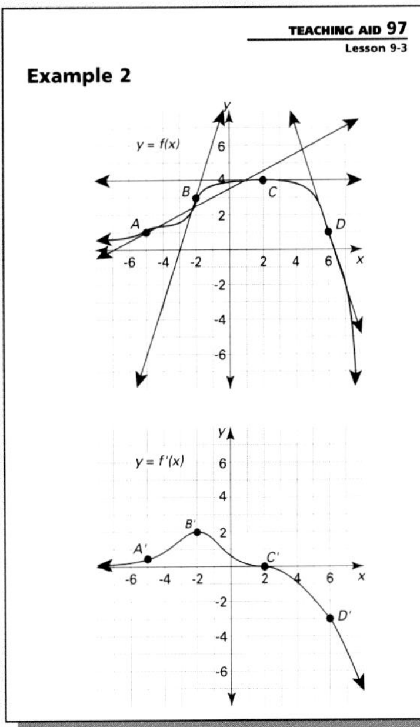

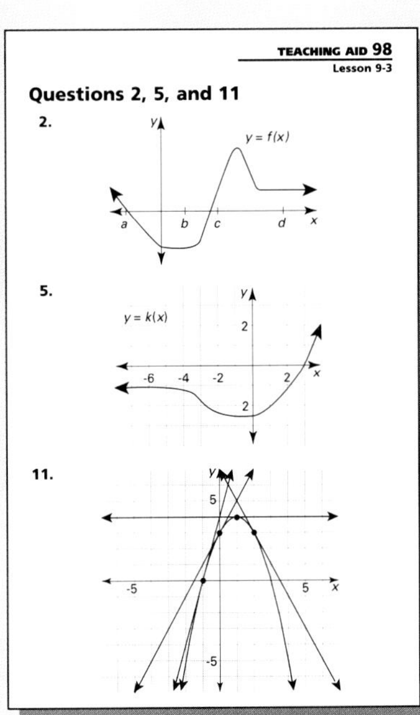

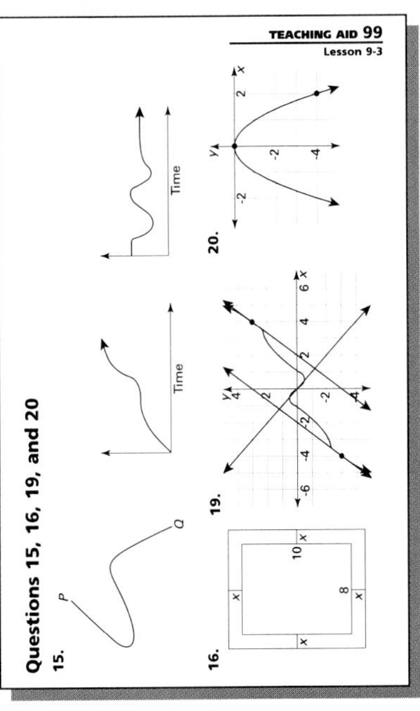

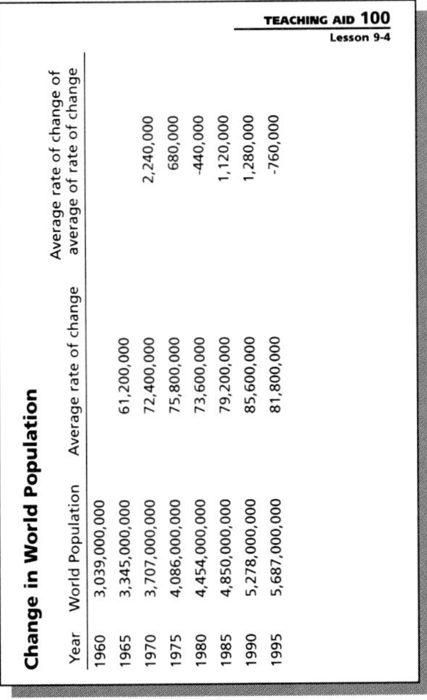

Change in World Population

Year	World Population	Average rate of change	Average rate of change of average of rate of change
1960	3,039,000,000		
1965	3,345,000,000	61,200,000	
1970	3,707,000,000	72,400,000	2,240,000
1975	4,086,000,000	75,800,000	680,000
1980	4,454,000,000	73,600,000	-440,000
1985	4,850,000,000	79,200,000	1,120,000
1990	5,278,000,000	85,600,000	1,280,000
1995	5,687,000,000	81,800,000	-760,000

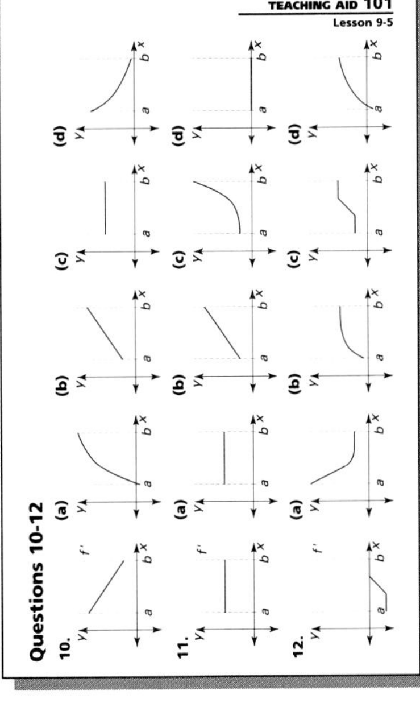

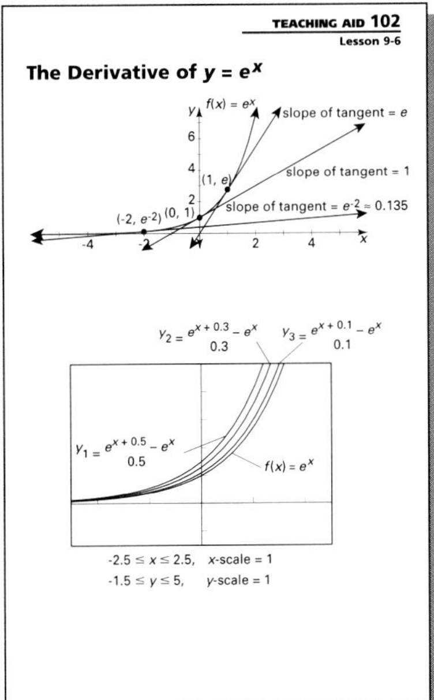

Chapter Opener

Pacing

All lessons in this chapter are designed to be covered in one day. At the end of the chapter, you should plan to spend 1 day to review the Progress Self-Test, 1–2 days for the Chapter Review, and 1 day for a test. You may wish to spend a day on projects, and possibly a day is needed for quizzes and the In-class Activity. This chapter should therefore take 9–12 days. Spending more than
13 days on this chapter is not recommended; there is opportunity to review ideas in later chapters.

Using Pages 550–551

Four statements involving rates of change are given; many more could be found. Newton's Law of Cooling is related to the derivative of a function, discussed in Lesson 9-3. The biological law more specifically relates to the derivative of an exponential function, to be dealt with in Lesson 9-6. The last two laws deal with rates of rates, namely accelerations and decelerations, an idea dealt with in Lesson 9-4.

CHAPTER 9

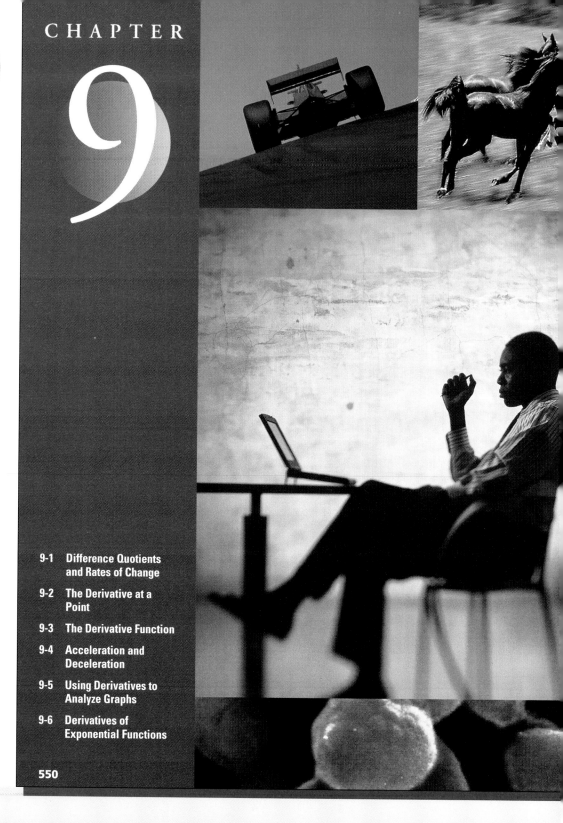

Chapter 9 Overview

The purpose of the chapter is to help students become comfortable with the idea of the derivative as studied in calculus. We do not want students to learn a multitude of cookbook formulas for finding the derivative. Hence, shortcut formulas for finding the derivative are omitted, except the formula for finding the derivative of a quadratic.

In our first pilots, some teachers skipped this chapter, saying that their students "would get it next year in calculus." That is exactly why this chapter is here! This chapter has consistently received the highest ratings of any chapter in the book. The approach taken is intuitive rather than formal, and the material is relatively easy for most students. This takes some of the fear and mystery out of calculus. Evidence supports the fact that students who have been introduced to the ideas of calculus do better in that course.

The first three lessons lead to the study of the first derivative. In Lesson 9-1, rates of change are reviewed and tied to the difference quotient. These ideas are extended in Lesson 9-2 to finding the limit of the difference quotient as $\Delta x \to 0$. The second lesson also introduces the term *derivative,* but all derivatives are computed only at a particular point. Lesson 9-3 culminates the study of the first derivative by treating it as a function.

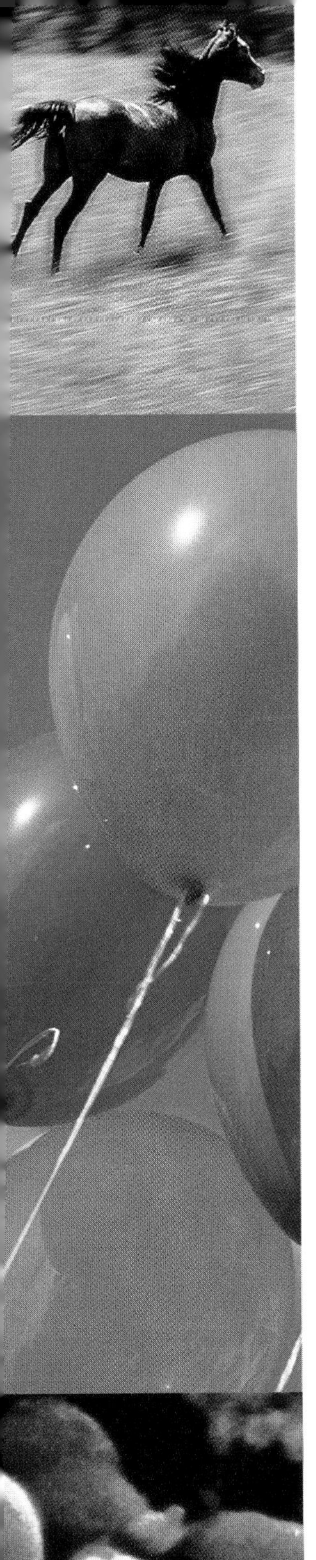

The Derivative in Calculus

Algebra can be briefly described as the study of variables and their properties. Geometry can be described as the study of visual patterns. Calculus is often divided into two parts: differential calculus and integral calculus. This chapter concentrates on **differential calculus**, which can be briefly described as *the study of rates of change in continuous functions*. The ideas in differential calculus help to determine whether functions are increasing or decreasing and how fast they are doing so.

Statements about rates of change appear in a variety of places.

In physics: The rate of change of the temperature of a body with respect to time is proportional to the difference between the temperature of the body and that of its surroundings. (Newton's Law of Cooling)

In biology: Under ideal growth conditions, the rate of growth of a colony of bacteria is proportional to the number of bacteria.

In business: As the number of items to be produced increases, the cost of producing each item tends to decrease, but the rate of decrease diminishes.

In the news: "The decrease in the unemployment rate for June was the smallest decrease this year."

Calculus is so important that it is required of all college students majoring in the sciences, engineering, or economics, and in many business schools. Differential calculus provides the mathematical tool to describe rates of change precisely and compute them efficiently. That tool is the *derivative*. This chapter focuses on the meaning, interpretation, and significance of the derivative. In Chapter 13, you can see some ideas of integral calculus.

Photo Connections

This photo collage makes real-world connections to the content of the chapter: the derivative in calculus.

Race Car: Two concepts relating to auto racing are velocity and acceleration. Both these topics are discussed throughout this chapter.

Horses: The concept of optimization is discussed in Lesson 9-5. Given an amount of fencing for an enclosure, such as a horse corral, this concept can be used to determine the maximum area that can be enclosed.

Laptop Computer: The use of laptop computers has increased dramatically in recent years. **Question 15** in Lesson 9-1 shows how the sales of laptop computers can be related to rate of change.

Balloons: **Example 4** on page 564 examines the instantaneous rate of change of the volume of a spherical balloon when the radius is increasing at a steady rate.

Bacteria: The population growth of many types of bacteria can be modeled by exponential functions. Derivatives of exponential functions are discussed in Lesson 9-6.

Chapter 9 Projects

At this time, you might want to have students look over the projects on page 592.

Lesson 9-4 introduces the second derivative in the context of acceleration and deceleration. Again there is an emphasis on rate of change, but this time it is on the rate of change of a rate.

Lesson 9-5 uses derivatives to find maximum and minimum points of graphs. Lesson 9-6 considers derivatives of exponential functions, important functions in the solution of differential equations.

If you have access to software such as The Math Exploration Toolkit or the Calculus Toolkit, you may want to utilize it frequently throughout this chapter. In whole-class activities with some form of large-scale monitor or overhead projection device, you might graph a number of secant lines and give students a visual display of the mathematical ideas. If you do not have either one of these pieces of software, you may still be able to accomplish the same results by using your automatic grapher to graph a function and several lines on the same coordinate system.

You might begin the chapter by asking students what they know about calculus, what they have heard, and what they expect. If they seem fearful, remind them that most things people don't know seem hard, but once they are learned, they seem quite a bit easier.

Lesson 9-1

Objectives

A Compute average rates of change in functions.

D Find rates of change in real situations.

G Relate average rate of change to secant lines of graphs of functions.

Resources

From the ***Teacher's Resource File***

- Lesson Master 9-1
- Answer Master 9-1
- Teaching Aids
  - 87 Warm-up
  - 89 Length of Day Table and Graph
  - 90 Secant Line and Difference Quotient
  - 91 Questions 5–9 and 21

Additional Resources

- Visuals for Teaching Aids 87, 89, 90, 91
- Exploration 9-1

Teaching Lesson 9-1

Warm-up

In Houston, on March 1, the sun sets at 6:20 P.M. On April 1, the sun sets at 6:40 P.M. By how many minutes per day does sunset get later during the month of March?

$\frac{20}{31}$, or about $\frac{2}{3}$ minutes per day; note that this is a rate of change, a slope

LESSON

9-1 *Difference Quotients and Rates of Change*

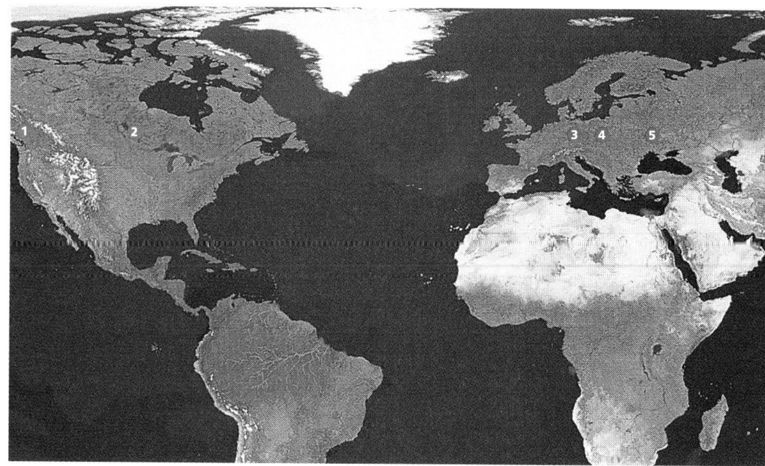

1. Vancouver 2. Winnipeg 3. Frankfurt 4. Prague 5. Kiev

This lesson reviews some ideas about change and introduces terms and notation that are needed to make them precise.

Average Rates of Change

Consider the following example of rate of change familiar to everyone except those who live on the equator. All through the year the length of a day from sunrise to sunset changes. Here is a table of lengths of days in 1997 for places at 50° north latitude, the latitude of Vancouver and Winnipeg in Canada; Frankfurt, Germany; Prague, the capital of the Czech Republic; and Kiev, the capital of Ukraine. Days are numbered beginning with January 1, 1997.

Length of day (in minutes) on first day of month at 50° north latitude

Date	Jan 1	Feb 1	Mar 1	Apr 1	May 1	Jun 1	Jul 1	Aug 1	Sep 1	Oct 1	Nov 1	Dec 1
Day of year	1	32	60	91	121	152	182	213	244	274	305	335
Length	490	560	659	775	882	964	977	913	809	698	587	504

Let $f(x)$ be the length of day x. Then f is periodic with period one year, because each year the lengths of days are about the same. The graph of f has much the same appearance as a sine curve.

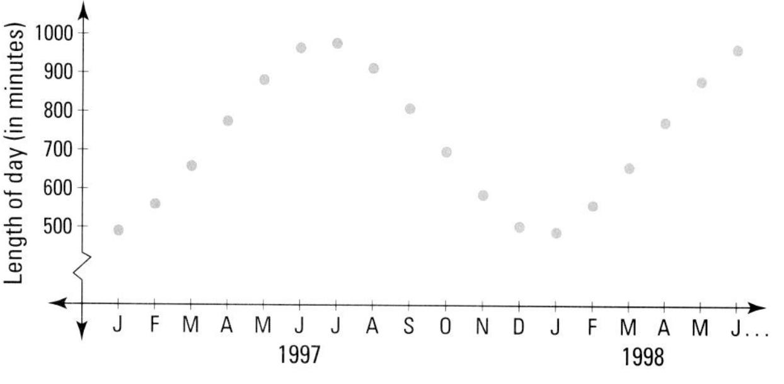

Lesson 9-1 Overview

Broad Goals The purpose of this lesson is to show that average rate of change, average velocity, slope, and difference quotient are different aspects of the same idea and involve the same calculations.

Perspective Students have seen the basic ideas of calculus before: for the derivative, that idea is *rate of change*. This idea is covered in the previous UCSMP courses *Advanced Algebra* and *Functions, Statistics, and Trigonometry*.

Throughout this lesson there is an emphasis on helping students connect *rate of change* to *slope* and to the *difference quotient*. The lesson opens with a discrete function that maps the number of a day of a year to the length of the day at 50° N latitude. The utility of this situation is that everyone knows that the length of day changes, getting longer in summer and shorter in winter (in the Northern Hemisphere), but most people are generally unaware of how fast it changes.

That rate of change is what is basic for the derivative.

Geometrically, the average rate of change in length of day from one time of year to another is the slope of the line containing these points of the function.

The other situation considered in this lesson is the classic example of the height of a projectile over time. The rate of change in

From the graph, you can see that the length of a day does not change evenly. In March and April the length is increasing rapidly, but in June the length is increasing slowly to its peak. In September and October the length is decreasing rapidly, but the decrease slows in December.

To discuss these changes, some new notation is useful. Change is found by subtraction; the change in days from day x_1 to day x_2 is $x_2 - x_1$. This difference is called $\mathbf{\Delta x}$, read "delta x." (Δ is the upper case Greek letter Delta, which corresponds to *D*, the first letter in *Difference*.) The change in length of day from $f(x_1)$ to $f(x_2)$ is called $\mathbf{\Delta y}$, read "delta y." That is, $\Delta y = f(x_2) - f(x_1) = y_2 - y_1$. For instance, from April 1st (day 91) to May 1st (day 121), $\Delta x = 121 - 91 = 30$ days, and $\Delta y = 882 - 775 = 107$ minutes.

The *average rate of change* is found by dividing the changes. To find how fast the length of day has been changing from April 1st to May 1st, divide $\Delta y = 107$ minutes by $\Delta x = 30$ days to get

$$\frac{\Delta y}{\Delta x} = \frac{107}{30}\frac{\text{minutes}}{\text{day}} \approx 3.6\,\frac{\text{minutes}}{\text{day}}.$$

This means that, in April, each day is about 3.6 minutes longer than the previous day, on the average. You should recognize that the average rate of change is the slope of the line through (91, 775) and (121, 882). In fact, if $y = f(x)$, then

$$\frac{\Delta y}{\Delta x} = \frac{y_2 - y_1}{x_2 - x_1} = \frac{f(x_2) - f(x_1)}{x_2 - x_1}.$$

Definition
Let f be a function defined at x_1 and x_2, with $x_1 \neq x_2$. The **average rate of change** of a function f from x_1 to x_2 is the slope of the line through $(x_1, f(x_1))$ and $(x_2, f(x_2))$.

$$m_{sec} = \frac{f(x_2) - f(x_1)}{x_2 - x_1} = \frac{\Delta y}{\Delta x}$$

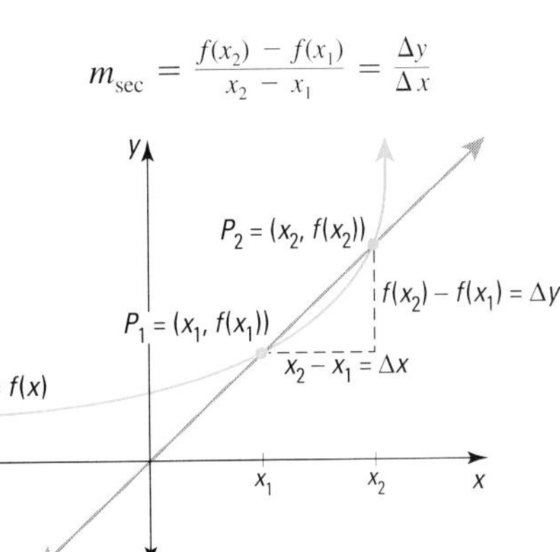

Secant Lines-of-Graphs

The length-of-day function is a discrete function, but the definition applies to all real functions. The figure at the left shows the graph of a continuous function f, along with two distinct points on its graph: $P_1 = (x_1, f(x_1))$ and $P_2 = (x_2, f(x_2))$. Recall that in geometry a **secant line to a circle** is a line that intersects the circle at two distinct points. Similarly, when a function is continuous, a line passing through two distinct points on the graph of the function is called a **secant line for the graph of the function**. Thus, the average rate of change of the function f from x_1 to x_2 equals the slope m_{sec} of the secant line through P_1 and P_2.

Notes on Reading

When many different terms are associated with an idea, it is usually because the idea arose in a variety of different contexts. Yet this same quality can cause confusion with students learning the idea for the first time. This is true for the major idea of this lesson, which has three names: (1) *average rate of change,* (2) *slope,* and (3) *difference quotient.* The term that is used depends on the situation:

1. *Average rate of change* conveys the application of the idea. Average velocity is just a special case.
2. *Slope* relates most easily to the graph, to the geometry. When the function is a continuous function, we are referring specifically here to the slope of a secant line to the curve that is its graph.
3. *Difference quotient* refers to the particular algebraic way of rewriting the idea that is useful in calculus. Point out the summary of this information on page 593.

Be sure to include appropriate units of measurement along with the numerical value of the average rate of change and for the slope. Attention to the language and notation here will pay off throughout the chapter.

Also point out the utility of the idea. Did students know that the length of day changes more in March and September than it does in June and December? **Teaching Aid 89** is given with the graphs and table for easy reference.

this situation is the average velocity of the projectile. This example is utilized to introduce the difference quotient because it involves a continuous function, and so the denominator of the quotient can be made as small as one wishes.

Optional Activities

Activity 1 Technology Connection
Materials: *Explorations* software

You may use *Exploration 9-1, Average Rate of Change,* to introduce the difference quotient. You can choose a function and designate two points on its graph. The display shows the two points, the secant line joining them, and the change in x and y. The algebraic computation for the difference quotient is shown next to the graph.

Activity 2 Have students generalize their answers to **Question 14**. That is, what is the value of the difference quotient for any line, $f(x) = mx + b$? [The difference quotient is:

$$\frac{f(x + \Delta x) - f(x)}{\Delta x} = \frac{m(x + \Delta x) + b - (mx + b)}{\Delta x} = \frac{mx + m\Delta x + b - mx - b}{\Delta x} = \frac{m\Delta x}{\Delta x} = m.]$$

Example 1 relates velocity to the average rate of change of directed distance with respect to time. This connection is important here because we begin Lesson 9-2 on the derivative at a point with a discussion of instantaneous velocity. Help students see that the unit for rate of change, in this case $\frac{\text{feet}}{\text{sec}}$, is an appropriate unit for velocity.

Relate the calculated velocities to their respective secant lines. The average velocity 0 from $t = 20$ to $t = 30$ bears special mention. Point out that the graph is of time versus height, not that of the path of the projectile.

❶ Carefully go through the substitutions that cause the familiar $\frac{y_2 - y_1}{x_2 - x_1}$ formula to be transformed into the unfamiliar $\frac{f(x_1 + \Delta x) - f(x_1)}{\Delta x}$. First substitute $f(x)$ for y in each case; then let $x_2 = x_1 + \Delta x$. The equality of the various expressions and their graphical interpretations is found on **Teaching Aid 90.**

Example 2 on page 556, reviews the necessary manipulative skills prior to finding the derivative. Here we just want students to evaluate the difference quotient over the interval t to $t + \Delta t$. In the next lesson we will take this same computation and find the limit as $\Delta t \to 0$. Help students see that the formula derived in **Example 2** can be used to evaluate the average rate of change when t and Δt are known. This is done in **Example 3** and foreshadows Lesson 9-3 in which the derivative is treated as a function.

Atlantis, lifting off for the 44th shuttle flight, is propelled by a booster rocket.

Example 1

A projectile is propelled into the air from ground level with an initial velocity of 800 ft/sec. If Earth's gravity is considered to be constant, its height (in feet) after t seconds is given by the function $h(t) = 800t - 16t^2$. This function is graphed below for $0 \le t \le 40$. Several secant lines are also drawn. Find the average rate of change of height with respect to time over the following intervals.

a. $10 \le t \le 20$ **b.** $20 \le t \le 30$ **c.** $30 \le t \le 40$

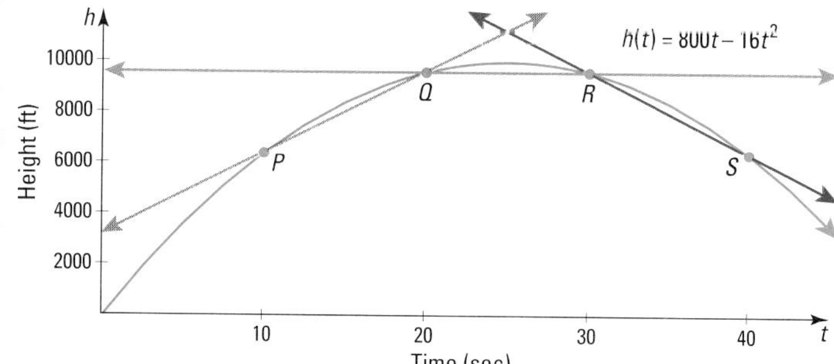

Solution

In this example, the function is called h (for height) instead of f and the independent variable is called t (for time) instead of x. The average rate of change of height with respect to time over the interval $t_1 \le t \le t_2$ is $\frac{h(t_2) - h(t_1)}{t_2 - t_1}$.

a. At $t_1 = 10$, $h(t_1) = 800(10) - 16(10)^2 = 6400$.
At $t_2 = 20$, $h(t_2) = 800(20) - 16(20)^2 = 9600$.
Thus, the average rate of change is
slope of $\overleftrightarrow{PQ} = \frac{h(t_2) - h(t_1)}{t_2 - t_1} = \frac{9600 - 6400}{20 - 10} = 320$ ft/sec.

b. At $t_1 = 20$, $h(t_1) = 9600$, and at $t_2 = 30$,
$h(t_2) = 800(30) - 16(30)^2 = 9600$.
Thus, the average rate of change is
slope of $\overleftrightarrow{QR} = \frac{9600 - 9600}{30 - 20} = 0$ ft/sec.
Since $\overleftrightarrow{QR}$ has slope 0, it is horizontal.

c. At $t_1 = 30$, $h(t_1) = 9600$, and at $t_2 = 40$, $h(t_2) = 6400$.
Thus, the average rate of change is
slope of $\overleftrightarrow{RS} = \frac{6400 - 9600}{40 - 30} = -320$ ft/sec.

Average Velocity

The rate of change of an object's directed distance from a fixed point (or the position of an object on a line) over a time interval is called its **average velocity** over that interval. The results of Example 1 thus calculate average velocities of the projectile. Comparing parts **a** and **c** shows that the projectile travels the same distance during both 10-second intervals: 3200 feet. However, from $t = 10$ to $t = 20$ it travels in a positive direction (up), so its average

Adapting to Individual Needs

Extra Help

In problems like **Example 1,** some students have trouble directly evaluating $\frac{h(t_2) - h(t_1)}{t_2 - t_1}$. Be sure to follow the text's method of explicitly calculating $h(t_2)$ and $h(t_1)$ and then substituting these values into the expression for slope.

velocity is positive (320 ft/sec). From $t = 30$ to $t = 40$ it travels in a negative direction (down), so its average velocity is negative (-320 ft/sec).

What does the average velocity of zero in part **b** mean? It does not mean that the projectile is stopped in midair, like a cartoon character, for 10 seconds. It simply means that the projectile's *average* velocity from $t = 20$ to $t = 30$ is 0 because its height is the same at both times. In actuality, in this time interval the projectile first moves up and then back down.

What Is the Difference Quotient?

The concept of average rate of change is an important one in mathematics. When many average rates of change are to be calculated for a particular function f, it helps to have a general formula. One such formula is

$$\begin{pmatrix}\text{the average rate of change}\\ \text{in } f \text{ from } x_1 \text{ to } x_2\end{pmatrix} = \frac{f(x_2) - f(x_1)}{x_2 - x_1}.$$

❶ This formula can be rewritten in terms of x_1, Δx, and f.

Begin with $\begin{pmatrix}\text{the average rate of change}\\ \text{in } f \text{ from } x_1 \text{ to } x_2\end{pmatrix} = \frac{\Delta y}{\Delta x} = \frac{f(x_2) - f(x_1)}{x_2 - x_1}.$

Since $x_2 - x_1 = \Delta x$, add x_1 to both sides to obtain $x_2 = x_1 + \Delta x$ and so $f(x_2) = f(x_1 + \Delta x)$. The denominator is Δx. Substituting for $f(x_2)$ in the numerator,

$$\begin{pmatrix}\text{the average rate of change}\\ \text{in } f \text{ from } x_1 \text{ to } x_2\end{pmatrix} = \frac{\Delta y}{\Delta x} = \frac{f(x_1 + \Delta x) - f(x_1)}{\Delta x}.$$

The quantity $\frac{f(x_1 + \Delta x) - f(x_1)}{\Delta x}$ is called the **difference quotient** of f over the interval from x_1 to $(x_1 + \Delta x)$.

The difference quotient is illustrated in the diagram below. In traveling from P_1 to P_2, the x-coordinate changes by Δx and the y-coordinate by $\Delta y = f(x_1 + \Delta x) - f(x_1)$.

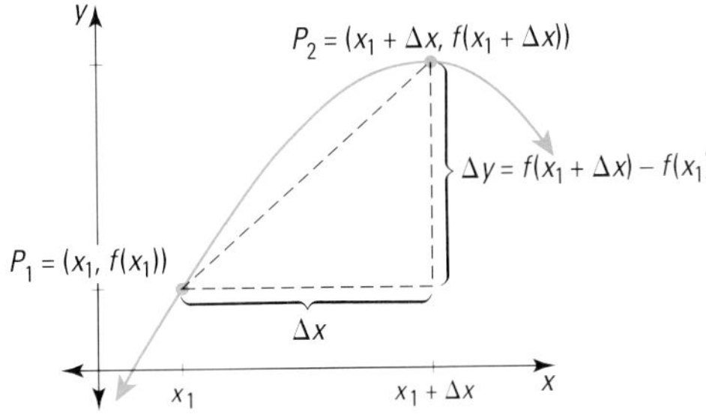

Thus when $x_2 = x_1 + \Delta x$ and $y = f(x)$,

$$\begin{pmatrix}\text{the average rate of change}\\ \text{in } f \text{ from } x_1 \text{ to } x_2\end{pmatrix} = \begin{pmatrix}\text{slope of line through}\\ (x_1, y_1) \text{ and } (x_2, y_2)\end{pmatrix} = \begin{pmatrix}\text{difference quotient}\\ \text{of } f \text{ from } x_1 \text{ to } x_2\end{pmatrix}$$

$$\frac{\Delta y}{\Delta x} = \frac{y_2 - y_1}{x_2 - x_1} = \frac{f(x_2) - f(x_1)}{x_2 - x_1} = \frac{f(x_1 + \Delta x) - f(x_1)}{\Delta x}$$

Furthermore, if y is the directed distance of an object at time x, then these quotients give the average velocity of the object over the interval from x_1 to x_2.

Error Alert In problems like **Example 2,** many students incorrectly evaluate expressions of the form $\frac{h(t + \Delta t) - h(t)}{\Delta t}$. For their benefit, ask students what simpler expressions are needed to evaluate the given expression. They should respond with $h(t + \Delta t)$ and $h(t)$. On the board write $h(t) = 800t - 16t^2$ and circle it. Then write $h(t + \Delta t) = 800(t + \Delta t) - 16(t + \Delta t)^2$, reminding students that each t in $h(t)$ is replaced by $t + \Delta t$ for $h(t + \Delta t)$. Expand and simplify the expression for $h(t + \Delta t)$ completely and circle it with a different color chalk. Then write $\frac{h(t + \Delta t) - h(t)}{\Delta t}$ and, using different colors of chalk for the two components of the numerator, replace $h(t + \Delta t)$ and $h(t)$ by their circled expansions, and proceed to simplify. Immediately after this, invite students to evaluate $\frac{h(t + \Delta t) - h(t)}{\Delta t}$ for another $h(t)$. Students may appreciate being reminded that the denominator Δt comes from $(t + \Delta t) - t$.

LESSON MASTER 9-1

Questions on SPUR Objectives
See pages 596–599 for objectives.

Skills Objective A

1. Find the average rate of change in $q(x) = x^2 + 12$ from $x = -1$ to $x = 4$. **3**
2. Find the average rate of change in $g(n) = 3n^3 - n^2 + 6$ over the interval $-2 \le n \le 2$. **12**
3. Let $f(x) = 2x^2 + 3x$. Find the average rate of change in f over the given interval.
   a. From x to $x + \Delta x$ **$4x + 3 + 2\Delta x$**
   b. From 2 to 2.1 **11.2**
   c. From 2 to 2.01 **11.02**

Uses Objective D

4. A stone is thrown upward from a height of 2 meters with an initial velocity of 8 meters per second. If only the effect of gravity is considered, then the stone's height in meters after t seconds is given by the equation $h(t) = -4.9t^2 + 8t + 2$.
   a. Find a formula for the average velocity from $t = 1$ to $t = 1 + \Delta t$. **$-1.8 - 4.9\Delta t$ m/sec**
   b. Use your answer in part a to find the average from $t = 1$ to $t = 3\frac{1}{2}$. **-14.05 m/sec**

Representations Objective G

5. Refer to the graph of g at the right. Find the average rate of change in g over each interval.
   a. C to E **5**
   b. $0 \le x \le 35$ **$\frac{2}{7}$**

   Over what interval does the average rate of change in g have the given value?
   c. 0 **B to D**
   d. $-\frac{3}{2}$ **A to C**
6. Suppose $P = (3, 7)$ and $Q = (9, a)$ are points on the graph of the function h. If the average rate of change in h from $x = 3$ to $x = 9$ is $-\frac{5}{3}$, find a. **$a = -3$**

Adapting to Individual Needs

Challenge

Have students research a recent almanac for data concerning the U.S. budget.

1. Collect data for the annual U.S. budget debt for the most recent 10 years and make the indicated calculations involving the year, the debt that year, and the rate of change from that year to the most recent year.
2. Calculate the average rate of change, both in dollars and percentage, for the 10-year period.
3. Perform the same analysis on the annual U.S. budget deficit.
4. Describe your observations and conclusions.
[Exact answers will vary with the set of years chosen.]

Note that the length-of-day example is discrete, so Δx cannot be smaller than 1. But in **Examples 2–3,** the function is continuous, so Δx can be as small as we wish. This will help prepare students for Lesson 9-2.

Additional Examples

1. A projectile propelled straight up leaves the ground at a velocity of 960 feet per second. Find the average rate of change of the height of the projectile with respect to time over the given intervals. Assume the height at time t is given by $h(t) = 960t - 16t^2$.
   a. $10 \le t \le 20$ 480 ft/sec
   b. $20 \le t \le 30$ 160 ft/sec
   c. $30 \le t \le 40$ -160 ft/sec
   d. $25 \le t \le 35$ 0 ft/sec
2. Refer to the function h with $h(t) = 960t - 16t^2$ in Additional Example 1. Find a formula for the difference quotient giving the average rate of change of h for the interval from t to $t + \Delta t$.
   $\frac{h(t + \Delta t) - h(t)}{\Delta t} = 960 - 32t - 16\Delta t$
3. Use the formula from Additional Example 2 to find the projectile's average velocity from t to $t + \Delta t$ for $t = 5$ and
   a. $\Delta t = 1$. 784 ft/sec
   b. $\Delta t = .5$. 792 ft/sec
   c. $\Delta t = .1$. 798.4 ft/sec

Example 2

Refer to the function h defined in Example 1. Find a formula for the difference quotient giving the average rate of change of h for the interval from t to $t + \Delta t$.

Solution

In this case, t plays the role of x_1, and Δt the role of Δx in the difference quotient. The computation is tedious but straightforward.

$$\begin{pmatrix}\text{average rate of change} \\ \text{of h from t to t + }\Delta t\end{pmatrix} = \frac{h(t + \Delta t) - h(t)}{\Delta t}$$

$$= \frac{[800(t + \Delta t) - 16(t + \Delta t)^2] - [800t - 16t^2]}{\Delta t}$$

$$= \frac{[800t + 800\Delta t - 16(t^2 + 2t\Delta t + (\Delta t)^2)] - [800t - 16t^2]}{\Delta t}$$

$$= \frac{800t + 800\Delta t - 16t^2 - 32t\Delta t - 16(\Delta t)^2 - 800t + 16t^2}{\Delta t}$$

$$= \frac{800\Delta t - 32t\Delta t - 16(\Delta t)^2}{\Delta t}$$

$$= 800 - 32t - 16\Delta t$$

In calculating average rates of change, continuous functions differ from discrete functions in a fundamental way. For any continuous function, the value of Δx (or, in the case of Example 2, Δt) can be made as close to zero as you wish.

Example 3

Use the formula from Example 2 to find the projectile's average velocity from t to $t + \Delta t$ for $t = 5$ and the indicated value of Δt.

a. $\Delta t = 1$ (that is, from 5 to 6 seconds)
b. $\Delta t = .5$ (that is, from 5 to 5.5 seconds)
c. $\Delta t = -.1$ (that is, from 4.9 to 5 seconds)

Solution

From Example 2, the average velocity equals the difference quotient, $800 - 32t - 16\Delta t$.

a. For $t = 5$ and $\Delta t = 1$, the average velocity is $800 - 32(5) - 16(1) = 624$ ft/sec.
b. For $t = 5$ and $\Delta t = .5$, the average velocity is $800 - 32(5) - 16(.5) = 632$ ft/sec.
c. For $t = 5$ and $\Delta t = -.1$, the average velocity is $800 - 32(5) - 16(-.1) = 641.6$ ft/sec.

In Example 3, you can see that the average velocity gets closer and closer to 640 ft/sec as Δt gets closer and closer to 0. This limit idea is studied further in the next lesson.

QUESTIONS

Covering the Reading

In 1 and 2, consider the length-of-day data given at the beginning of this lesson.

1. Find the average rate of change in the length of day from August 1st to September 1st. $\approx$ -3.35 minutes/day

2. From February 1st to March 1st, on the average, each day is __?__ minutes __?__ than the previous day. 3.5; longer

3. Finish this sentence. The slope of the secant line through $(x_1, f(x_1))$ and $(x_1 + \Delta x,$ __?__ $)$ equals the average rate of change of f from __?__ to __?__.
$f(x_1 + \Delta x)$; x_1; $x_1 + \Delta x$

4. If $y = f(x)$, give three expressions equal to $\frac{\Delta y}{\Delta x}$. See left.

4) $\frac{y_2 - y_1}{x_2 - x_1}$, $\frac{f(x_2) - f(x_1)}{x_2 - x_1}$, $\frac{f(x_1 + \Delta x) - f(x_1)}{\Delta x}$

In 5–9, refer to the function graphed below.

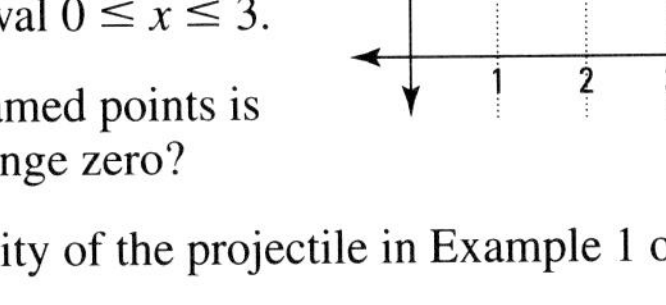

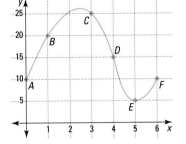

5. In going from B to C, find Δx and Δy. $\Delta x = 2$, $\Delta y = 5$

6. Between which two named points is $\Delta y = -10$? C to D or D to E

7. Find the average rate of change of the function from D to F. -2.5

8. Find the average rate of change of the function over the interval $0 \le x \le 3$. 5

9. Between which two named points is the average rate of change zero? A and F

10. Find the average velocity of the projectile in Example 1 over the indicated time interval.
   a. 10 sec to 11 sec 464 ft/sec
   b. 10 sec to 10.3 sec 475.2 ft/sec
   c. 9.99 sec to 10 sec 480.16 ft/sec

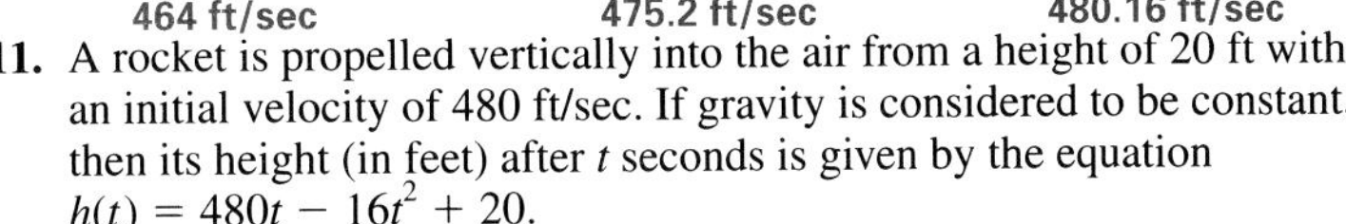

11. A rocket is propelled vertically into the air from a height of 20 ft with an initial velocity of 480 ft/sec. If gravity is considered to be constant, then its height (in feet) after t seconds is given by the equation $h(t) = 480t - 16t^2 + 20$.
   a. Sketch a graph of height vs. time. See left.
   b. Find the average velocity from $t = 4$ to $t = 12$. Include appropriate units with your answer. 224 ft/sec
   c. Find a formula for the average velocity from $t = 4$ to $t = 4 + \Delta t$. $352 - 16\Delta t$ ft/sec

11a)

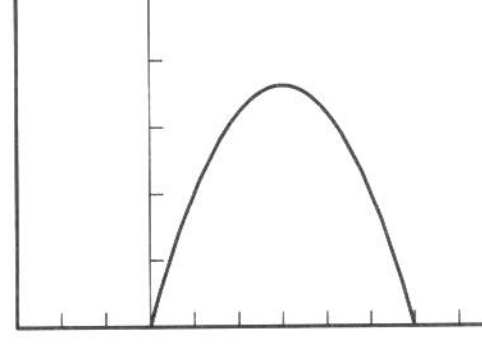

$-15 \le x \le 40$, x-scale = 5
$0 \le y \le 5000$, y-scale = 1000

Applying the Mathematics

12. Suppose P and Q are two points on the curve $y = x^2 - x + 2$. If the x-coordinate of P is 1 and the x-coordinate of Q is 4, find the slope of the secant line $\overleftrightarrow{PQ}$. 4

13. Determine the average rate of change of the function f defined by $f(x) = x^2$ over the interval $-1 \le x \le 2$. 1

Notes on Questions

Questions 1–2 Geography Connection The length-of-day data given at the beginning of the lesson applies only to locations at 50° north latitude. For locations nearer to the North Pole, the lengths of days vary even more. At 60° north latitude, the longest day is 18 hours 30 minutes. At the North Pole itself, the sun never sets for six months and then never rises for six months.

Questions 5–9 Teaching Aid 91 has the graph for these questions.

Cooperative Learning As an extension of these questions, students may learn from and enjoy the following activity. Draw a graph (as below) and ask students to make up a story of an automobile trip consistent with this graph.

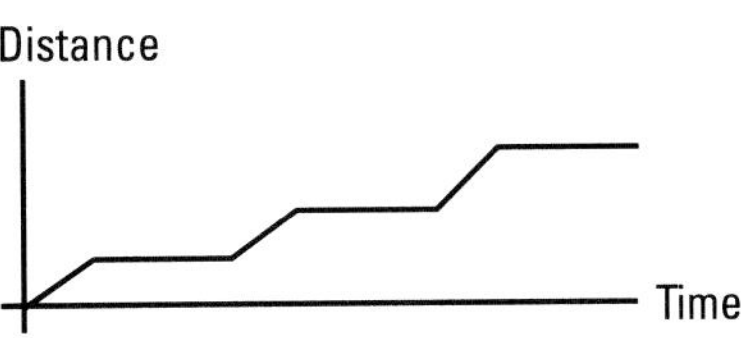

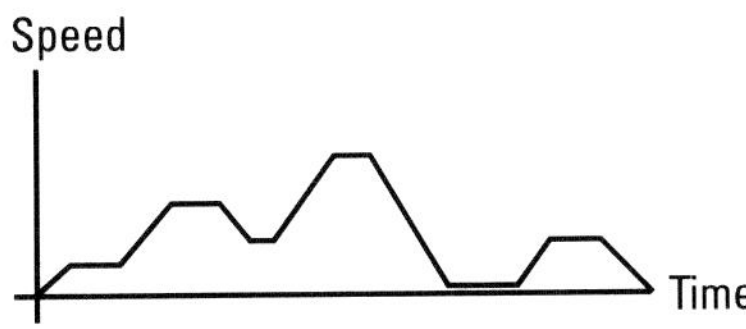

Ask students to interpret positive, negative, and zero slopes on these graphs. Given one of these graphs, you may ask students to sketch the other. Students could go into groups to make up stories.

Notes on Questions

Question 16 This is an important question to discuss in class. Students need to relate the various statements in **part b** to the different parts of the difference quotient. For those statements that could be either true or false, have students give you a particular situation that makes the statement true and a particular situation that makes the statement false. Of course, the situations must be in agreement with the data given in the problem.

Question 17 You can use this problem to introduce Lesson 9-2.

Question 21 This graph is on **Teaching Aid 91.**

Question 22 Every constant in the formula should be explained. The 250 is half the difference (in minutes) between the shortest and longest days. The 733 is the average length of a day (in minutes). (It is slightly more than 12 hours because the sun has width.) The $\frac{2\pi}{365}$ is the period. The 80 is the phase shift to get the function to have its maximum at June 21. The data for **part b** can be found in some almanacs, which contain this information for latitudes that are multiples of 10°.

14. a. Calculate the difference quotient, $\frac{f(x + \Delta x) - f(x)}{\Delta x}$, for the function f defined by $f(x) = \frac{1}{2}x - 5$. $\frac{1}{2}$

b. Give a geometric interpretation for your answer to part **a**. The slope of the line through any two points on the graph of f is always $\frac{1}{2}$.

15. Tina has a job selling laptop computers. Her weekly salary is $300 plus a $25 commission for each computer that she sells after the first 5.

a. Construct a table of values and a graph with number of computers as the independent variable and salary as the dependent variable. Assume Tina sells at most 10 computers. See margin.

b. If the number of computers she sells increases from 5 to 8, what is her average salary increase per computer sold? Include appropriate units with your answer. $25/computer

c. If the number of computers she sells increases from 3 to 7, what is her average salary increase per computer sold? Include appropriate units with your answer. $12.50/computer

16. A meteorologist records temperatures at half-hour intervals from the beginning to the end of the shift. At the end of the shift, the meteorologist reports that the average rate of change of temperature with respect to time over the entire shift is .4°F/hr, and that the actual change in temperature over the same time period is 3°F.

a. If the shift began at 6:00 A.M., at what time did it end? 1:30 P.M.

b. With regard to the above situation, determine whether each of the following statements must be *true*, must be *false*, or could be either *true* or *false*. i, ii, iii could be true or false; iv is true; v is false

i. Over the entire shift, the temperature steadily increased.

ii. A linear model with a slope of .4 is an accurate model for the data.

iii. The temperature never decreased during the shift.

iv. The temperature at the end of the shift was higher than the temperature at the beginning.

v. If a continuous curve is drawn through the data points, then the slope of the secant line determined by the temperatures at the beginning and end of the shift will be negative.

17. In Example 3, the average velocity $800 - 32(5) - 16(\Delta t) = 640 - 16(\Delta t)$ was computed for smaller and smaller values of Δt.

a. Find the value of $640 - 16(\Delta t)$ when $\Delta t = .001$. 639.984 ft/sec

b. What is $\lim_{\Delta t \to 0} (640 - 16\Delta t)$? 640 ft/sec

c. If t is fixed, what is $\lim_{\Delta t \to 0} (800 - 32t - 16\Delta t)$? $800 - 32t$ ft/sec

Review

18. Solve $\sin x > \frac{1}{2}$ over the interval $0 \le x \le \frac{\pi}{2}$. *(Lesson 6-8)* $\frac{\pi}{6} < x \le \frac{\pi}{2}$

19. Assume $x \neq 0$, $x \neq \frac{1}{3}$, or $x \neq -\frac{1}{3}$. Write the following expression as a simple fraction. *(Lesson 5-2)*

$$\frac{\frac{3}{x} - \frac{1}{3}}{\frac{1}{x^2} - 9} \quad \frac{9x - x^2}{3 - 27x^2}$$

Additional Answers

15. a.

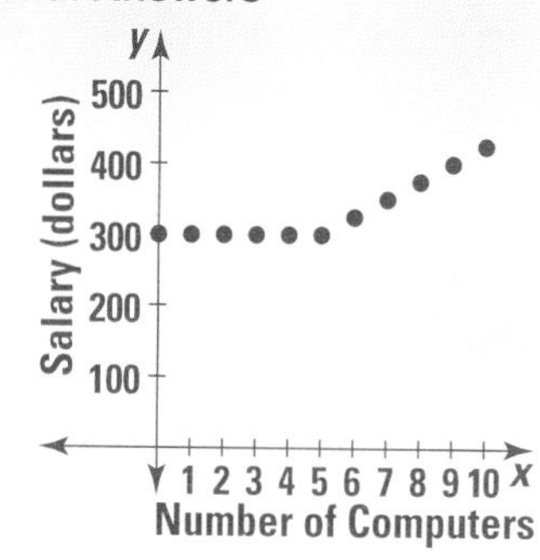

n	S	n	S
0	300	6	325
1	300	7	350
2	300	8	375
3	300	9	400
4	300	10	425
5	300		

20. *Multiple choice.* If $\sqrt{3}$ is a zero of a polynomial $p(x)$, then which of the following is true? c
   (a) $\sqrt{3}$ is a factor of $p(x)$.
   (b) $x + \sqrt{3}$ is a factor of $p(x)$.
   (c) $x - \sqrt{3}$ is a factor of $p(x)$.
   (d) $p(-\sqrt{3}) = 0$. *(Lesson 4-4)*

21. Refer to the graph of the function f with $y = f(x) = x^2 - 9$ at the right.
   a. For what values of x is $y > 0$?
   b. For what values of x is $y < 0$?
   c. What are the zeros of the function?
   d. What is the range of the function?
   (Lessons 2-1, 2-2, 3-3, 3-7)

   a) $x > 3$ or $x < -3$
   b) $-3 < x < 3$
   c) -3; 3
   d) $\{y: y \geq -9\}$

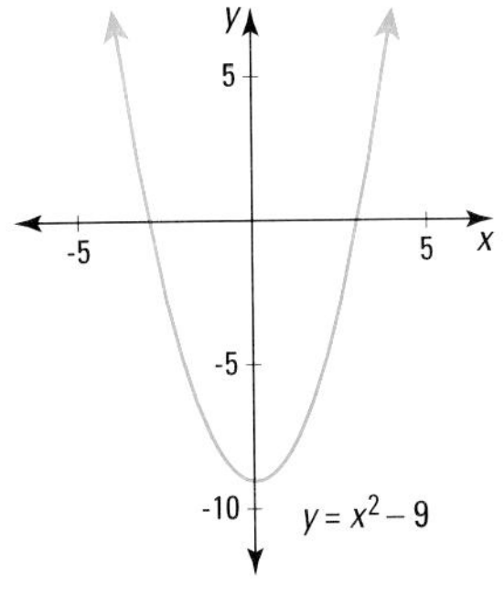

Exploration

22a) $f(1) \approx 488.5$; that is very close to the actual value of 490.
b) $f(305) \approx 566$; that is 21 minutes less than the actual value.
c) For the shortest day, December 21, $x = 355$, and for the longest day, June 21, $x = 172$. $f(355) \approx 483$ minutes and $f(172) \approx 983$ minutes.
d) Answers will vary depending on the students' latitude.

22. The values of the length-of-day function in this lesson can be approximated by using the formula See left.

$$f(x) = 250 \sin\left(\frac{2\pi}{365}(x - 80)\right) + 733.$$

   a. How close to the data is the value given by $f(x)$ for January 1st?
   b. How close to the data is the value given by $f(x)$ for November 1st?
   c. Use this formula to approximate the lengths of the longest and shortest days of the year at latitude 50°N.
   d. Find data for the lengths of days where you live, and search for a sine function that approximates these values.

Follow-up for Lesson 9-1

Practice
For more questions on SPUR Objectives, use **Lesson Master 9-1** (shown on page 555).

Assessment
Written Communication Have students repeat **Question 10,** this time choosing three other progressively smaller time intervals, different from those in the text, that "zero in" on a particular time. Ask them to predict the average velocity at that time as Δt gets closer and closer to 0. [Students compute rates of change in real situations.]

Extension
Science Connection The opening example on the length of day may surprise students in that the data fit a sine curve. You might have students call the weather bureau to get even more detailed data for an entire year. A large plot could be made on paper for a bulletin board. As a project, students might compare these data with those for a city near the Arctic Circle and a city near the equator, giving the information in tabular and graphical form, and estimating the length of day by a formula such as that found in **Question 22.**

Project Update Project 4, *Here Comes the Sun,* on page 592, relates to the content of this lesson.

Setting Up Lesson 9-2
Be certain to discuss **Question 17.** This is important background for Lesson 9-2.

Lesson 9-2

Objectives

B Use the definition of derivative to compute derivatives.
D Find rates of change in real situations.
E Use derivatives to find the velocity and acceleration of a moving object.
H Estimate derivatives by finding slopes of tangent lines.

Resources

From the ***Teacher's Resource File***
- Lesson Master 9-2
- Answer Master 9-2
- Teaching Aids
  87 Warm-up
  92 Definition and Graph of Instantaneous Velocity
  93 Examples 2 and 3
  94 Questions 2 and 6
  95 Questions 10, 12, and 13
- Technology Sourcebook
  Calculator Master 13

Additional Resources
- Visuals for Teaching Aids 87, 92, 93, 94, 95
- Exploration 9-2

Teaching Lesson 9-2

Warm-up

Suppose $g(x) = 5x^2 - 12x$.
Calculate each of the following.
1. $g(x + \Delta x)$ $5x^2 + 10x\Delta x + 5(\Delta x)^2 - 12x - 12\Delta x$
2. $g(x + \Delta x) - g(x)$
   $10x\Delta x + 5(\Delta x)^2 - 12\Delta x$

LESSON

9-2 The Derivative at a Point

How Fast? *The velocity of a ball at a given point can be estimated by dividing the distance between successive images of the ball near that point by the time interval between the strobes.*

Calculating Instantaneous Velocity

Consider again the motion of the projectile in the examples of Lesson 9-1. After t seconds the projectile is $h(t) = 800t - 16t^2$ feet above ground level. It follows that between times $t = 0$ and $t = 40$ seconds the projectile's average velocity is $\frac{h(40) - h(0)}{40 - 0} = 160$ ft/sec. But is this how fast the projectile is moving at each moment of its flight? No. At the moment of its launch it has its maximum velocity, and it climbs more and more slowly until it reaches a maximum height. Then it begins to fall back to Earth, dropping faster and faster, its velocity decreasing from zero through negative values, until it hits Earth.

To determine the velocity of the projectile at a particular instant of time, say exactly 5 seconds after it is launched, you could approximate the answer by computing the projectile's average velocity over the interval from 5 to 6 seconds after launch. You could obtain a more accurate approximation by computing the average velocity over the interval from 5 to 5.5 seconds or even from 4.9 to 5 seconds after launch. In Example 3 of Lesson 9-1 these were found to be 624 ft/sec, 632 ft/sec, and 641.6 ft/sec, respectively. You can imagine that this process of calculating average velocities over smaller and smaller time intervals could be continued forever. The numbers obtained would come closer and closer to the projectile's velocity at exactly 5 seconds after launch. For this reason, we define the term *instantaneous velocity* to mean the limit approached by these numbers as the lengths of the time intervals approach zero.

Lesson 9-2 Overview

Broad Goals This lesson builds on the last lesson to develop the idea of instantaneous rate of change, instantaneous velocity, and the derivative of a function at a point.

Perspective The projectile situation of the previous lesson is examined in some detail. Now the limit of the difference quotient is taken as the denominator approaches 0. What was average velocity becomes (in the limit) the instantaneous velocity. What was the slope of a secant line to the graph of the function becomes (in the limit) the slope of the line tangent to the graph at a particular point. That slope is the derivative of the function at the point.

A variety of examples of the derivative are given. From a graph of the distance of a car from a starting point over a period of time, students are asked to draw tangents to estimate the slope. From a formula for a quadratic function, the derivative can be calculated from its definition. Students are also asked to compute the instantaneous rate of change of the volume of a sphere in relation to its radius.

Definition

Suppose an object is moving so that at each time t it is at position $f(t)$. Then,

$$\begin{pmatrix}\text{instantaneous velocity}\\ \text{of the object at time } t\end{pmatrix} = \lim_{\Delta t \to 0}\begin{pmatrix}\text{average velocity of the object}\\ \text{between times } t \text{ and } t+\Delta t\end{pmatrix} = \lim_{\Delta t \to 0}\frac{f(t+\Delta t)-f(t)}{\Delta t},$$

provided this limit exists and is finite.

Example 1

For the projectile from Example 1 of Lesson 9-1 what is the instantaneous velocity at time $t = 5$ seconds?

Solution

Use the definition of instantaneous velocity with $t = 5$.

$$\begin{pmatrix}\text{instantaneous velocity}\\ \text{at time } t=5\end{pmatrix} = \lim_{\Delta t \to 0}\begin{pmatrix}\text{average velocity between}\\ \text{times } t=5 \text{ and } t=5+\Delta t\end{pmatrix}$$
$$= \lim_{\Delta t \to 0}\frac{f(5+\Delta t)-f(5)}{\Delta t}$$
$$= \lim_{\Delta t \to 0}(800 - 32 \cdot 5 - 16\Delta t) \quad \text{from Example 2 of Lesson 9-1}$$
$$= \lim_{\Delta t \to 0}(640 - 16\Delta t)$$
$$= 640 \text{ ft/sec}$$

Picturing Instantaneous Velocity

Just as the idea of average velocity has a geometric interpretation in terms of slopes of secant lines, the idea of instantaneous velocity also has a geometric interpretation. Let $f(x)$ be the distance, from some reference point, of a moving object at time x seconds, and consider the graph of f. Take an interval of time from x seconds to $x + \Delta x$ seconds. Then

$$\begin{pmatrix}\text{average velocity from}\\ \text{time } x \text{ to time } x+\Delta x\end{pmatrix} = \frac{f(x+\Delta x)-f(x)}{\Delta x} = \begin{pmatrix}\text{the slope of the secant line though the}\\ \text{points } (x, f(x)) \text{ and } (x+\Delta x, f(x+\Delta x))\end{pmatrix}.$$

Now imagine computing average velocities for smaller and smaller values of Δx. Each of the average velocities equals the slope of a secant line through $P = (x, f(x))$ and a second point $Q = (x + \Delta x, f(x + \Delta x))$ on the graph of f, where Q gets closer and closer to P. For instance, the drawing on page 562 shows a sequence of secant lines through P and points Q_1, Q_2, Q_3, and Q_4 that get closer and closer to P. If the graph of f is the kind of smooth curve shown in the drawing, then the secant lines will come closer and closer to a line that just skims the graph at the point P. This line is defined to be the **tangent line** to the graph at P. The slopes of the secant lines get closer and closer to the slope of this tangent line.

3. $\frac{g(x+\Delta x)-g(x)}{\Delta x}$ $\mathbf{10x + 5\Delta x - 12}$
4. $\lim_{\Delta x \to 0}\frac{g(x+\Delta x)-g(x)}{\Delta x}$ $\mathbf{10x - 12}$

Notes on Reading

Reading Mathematics There is a lot of reading in this lesson, and you should try to have students summarize what they have read. They should recall the three key terms of the last lesson and note that each has a corresponding term in this lesson.

1. Average rate of change becomes *instantaneous rate of change*. As a special case, average velocity becomes instantaneous velocity.
2. The slope of the secant line to the graph of a continuous function becomes the *slope of the tangent line to that graph*.
3. The difference quotient becomes the *derivative*.

And when does all this happen? [When we take the limit as $x_2 \to x_1$, or equivalently, as $\Delta x \to 0$.]

You may want to begin discussing the lesson by referring back to **Example 3** from Lesson 9-1. Have the students evaluate the average velocity from t to $t + \Delta t$ for $t = 5$ and successively smaller values of Δt, namely $\Delta t = .01, .001, .0001$, and $.00001$. Or begin with **Question 17** of Lesson 9-1, as such computations provide a concrete basis for the results obtained in **Example 1** of the current lesson. You may also use a spreadsheet or short program to do this.

You might ask your students what kind of velocity (average or instantaneous) is displayed by a car's speedometer. [Instantaneous] Compare this to the velocity calculated after completing a 200-mile car trip in 3 hours and 46 minutes. [Average] Note that **Teaching Aid 92** gives the definition and graph of instantaneous velocity.

Optional Activities

Activity 1 Technology Connection
Materials: Explorations software

Students may use *Exploration 9-2, Instantaneous Velocity,* as an alternative to **Example 1.** Students choose an initial velocity for a projectile launched from ground level. A graph shows the height function with respect to time. Students can observe changes in the tangent line and the instantaneous velocity at a point on the graph.

Activity 2 Another intuitive way to understand **Question 11** is to ask students to draw the tangent line to the graph at $x = 0$. They should see that there are many possible lines (with many different slopes) that can be drawn, passing only through the origin. Since no unique tangent line can be drawn to the graph at the origin, a tangent line, and therefore its slope, does not exist there. Therefore, $A'(0)$ does not exist.

Activity 3 Technology Connection You might wish to assign *Technology Sourcebook, Calculator Master 11.* In this activity, students use the programming and graphing features of a graphics calculator to determine the slopes of secant lines and tangent lines at specific points on a function.
They observe trends in the equations for the secant line near a point as Δx approaches zero.

If you have the appropriate software, graph the function f from **Example 1.** Then try to graph a line that is tangent to the curve when $t = 5$. Then graph several secant lines joining point P to other points Q on the curve. Make sure that you choose points Q that get closer and closer to point P. Help students see that the secant lines get closer and closer to the tangent line. The tangent line should have a slope that is very close to the value of the derivative at point P. The accuracy of the results depend on how accurately you estimated the tangent line.

❶ In the definition of derivative, point out that f' is called the derivative function because it is "derived from" function f. Mention that $f'(x)$ is read as "f prime of x." Insist that students learn this definition. You may wish to mention that some calculus texts refer to it as Df and others as $\frac{dy}{dx}$.

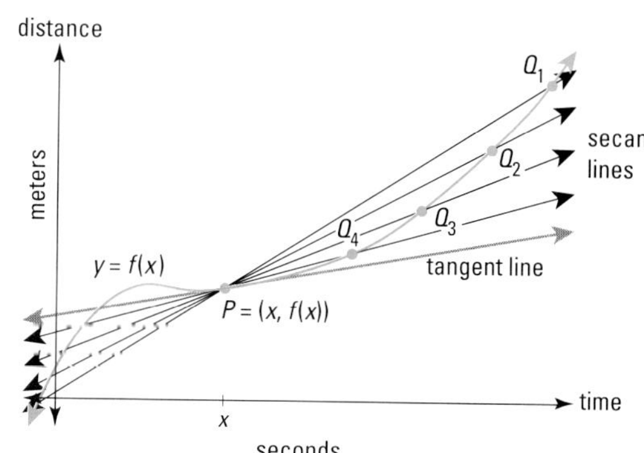

$$\begin{aligned}\begin{pmatrix}\text{the slope of the tangent}\\ \text{line at } (x, f(x))\end{pmatrix} &= \lim_{\Delta x \to 0}\begin{pmatrix}\text{the slope of the secant line through}\\ (x, f(x)) \text{ and } (x + \Delta x, f(x + \Delta x))\end{pmatrix}\\ &= \lim_{\Delta x \to 0}\frac{f(x + \Delta x) - f(x)}{\Delta x}\\ &= \lim_{\Delta x \to 0}(\text{average velocity from time } x \text{ to } x + \Delta x)\\ &= \text{instantaneous velocity at time } x\end{aligned}$$

So instantaneous velocity can be interpreted geometrically as the slope of a tangent line. Lines tangent to circles intersect them at exactly one point. But for other curves, a tangent line at P may intersect the curve at a second point different from P, as in the above graph, in which there is a second point of intersection to the left of P. That does not affect the instantaneous velocity at P.

Example 2

The graph at the right shows the distance d (in miles) of a car from its starting point t hours after it begins a trip. Estimate the instantaneous velocity of the car at time $t = 1$ hour by sketching the tangent line to the graph at $t = 1$ and finding an approximate value for its slope.

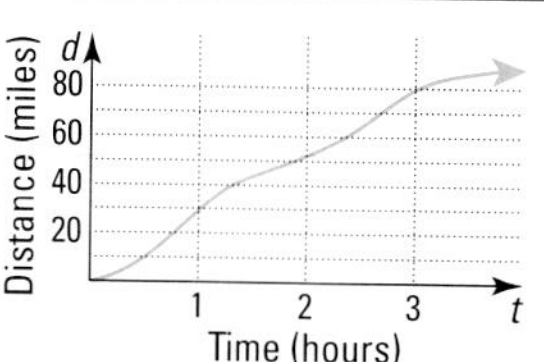

Solution

From the graph, you can see that after one hour of travel, the car is 30 miles from its starting point. Sketch the tangent line at the point (1, 30) by drawing a line which is on one side of the curve near that point. It appears that this line also contains the point (2, 70). Therefore, the slope of the line is approximately

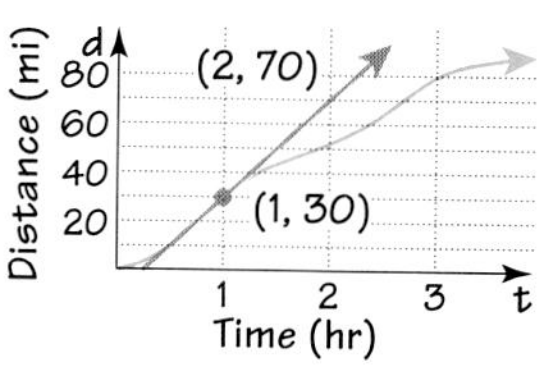

$$\frac{(70 - 30)\text{ miles}}{(2 - 1)\text{ hours}} = 40 \text{ mph}.$$

It follows that the instantaneous velocity of the car at time $t = 1$ hour is approximately 40 mph.

LESSON MASTER 9-2 **Questions on SPUR Objectives** See pages 596–599 for objectives.

Skills Objective B

In 1–3, find the derivative of the function at the given value of x.

1. $f(x) = 3x^2 + 4$; $x = 2$ — 12
2. $g(x) = -12x + 8$; $x = .5$ — -12
3. $h(x) = 22$; $x = 7$ — 0
4. Let $f(x) = -2x^2 + x - 3$
   a. Compute $f'(0)$. — 1
   b. Compute $f'(3)$. — -11

Uses Objective D

5. The typical number of mosquitoes $m(r)$ in hundreds of thousands in a certain county during the month of June is approximated by $m(r) = 8r - r^2$, where r is the average total rainfall for the month in inches.
   a. Find the derivative of m when $r = 2$. — 4
   b. What does your answer to part a mean?
   At a rainfall of 2 inches, the mosquito population is increasing at the rate of 400,000 mosquitoes per inch of rain.

Uses Objective E

6. The height h in feet of a small rocket t seconds after launch is approximated by $h(t) = 320t - 16t^2$.
   a. Find the instantaneous velocity at time $t = 5$. — 160 ft/sec
   b. Find the instantaneous velocity at time $t = 14$. — -128 ft/sec
   c. Find the instantaneous velocity at time $t = 10$. — 0 ft/sec
   d. At what time does the rocket reach its maximum height? — at $t = 10$ sec

Adapting to Individual Needs

Extra Help

Cooperative Learning Some students may have difficulty sketching accurate tangents. For problems requiring such sketches, you might want to have students **work in small groups.** Have each member of the group sketch the pertinent tangent and calculate its slope. Then have the group use the average of the slopes to estimate the corresponding instantaneous velocity.

The Derivative of a Function at a Point

In the discussion above, the quantity

$$\lim_{\Delta x \to 0} \frac{f(x + \Delta x) - f(x)}{\Delta x}$$

appears both in the definition of instantaneous velocity and in the definition of slope of a tangent line. This remarkable quantity arises naturally in many other settings, and so it has been given a special name. It is called the *derivative of f at x*.

1 **Definition**

The **derivative of a real function *f* at *x***, denoted ***f*′(*x*)**, is given by:

$$f'(x) = \lim_{\Delta x \to 0} \frac{f(x + \Delta x) - f(x)}{\Delta x},$$

provided this limit exists and is finite.

The definition asserts that a derivative is a limit of difference quotients. With discrete functions, for any value of x, values of Δx can be found so that $x + \Delta x$ is between two domain values and $f(x + \Delta x)$ is consequently not defined, so there is no limit. Thus discrete functions do not have derivatives. A function must be continuous and its graph must be "smooth" at a point to have a derivative at the point. It can be shown that all polynomial, exponential, logarithmic, and trigonometric functions defined on the real numbers have derivatives at every point.

Example 3

Let f be the function with $f(x) = x^2 + 4$ for all real numbers x. Find $f'(3)$, the derivative of f at $x = 3$.

Solution

Use the definition of derivative with $x = 3$.

$$f'(3) = \lim_{\Delta x \to 0} \frac{f(3 + \Delta x) - f(3)}{\Delta x} \quad \text{definition of derivative}$$

$$= \lim_{\Delta x \to 0} \frac{((3 + \Delta x)^2 + 4) - (3^2 + 4)}{\Delta x} \quad \text{definition of } f$$

$$= \lim_{\Delta x \to 0} \frac{(9 + 6(\Delta x) + (\Delta x)^2 + 4) - (9 + 4)}{\Delta x} \quad \text{expanding the binomial square}$$

$$= \lim_{\Delta x \to 0} \frac{6(\Delta x) + (\Delta x)^2}{\Delta x}$$

$$= \lim_{\Delta x \to 0} (6 + \Delta x)$$

$$= 6$$

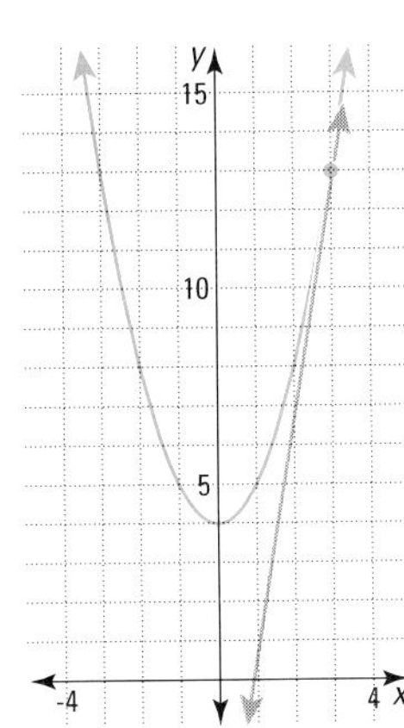

Check

Sketch the tangent line to the graph of $y = f(x)$ at the point $(3, f(3))$. The slope of this line seems approximately equal to 6.

Students should understand the derivative in three ways: algebraically from its definition; geometrically as the slope of a tangent line; and in an applied manner as instantaneous rate of change. These are the P, R, and U of SPUR. Calculating the derivative comes under S and completes the basic understandings.

Example 1 emphasizes the application. **Example 3** emphasizes the calculation. The visual relationship of the derivative to the slope of the tangent line is the idea that is behind **Example 2. Example 4** combines an application and the skill of calculation.

The graphs in **Examples 2–3** are given on **Teaching Aid 93.**

Error Alert Some students might incorrectly think that the slope of the tangent only approximates the instantaneous velocity. Explain that while a rough sketch is, in fact, virtually always imprecise, the slope of the theoretical tangent line is precisely the instantaneous velocity at the point of tangency.

Adapting to Individual Needs

Challenge

Have students answer these questions.

1. Find the equation of the secant line for the U.S. debt data collected in Lesson 9-1. Let x be the year, where $x = 0$ is the first year of the study and $x = 9$ is the tenth year, and let $y =$ the debt in billions of dollars.
   a. Find the derivative of this function at each year.
   b. What do you observe?
2. Use an automatic grapher to find the linear regression line (line of best fit) for this same data.
   a. Find the derivative of this function at each year.
   b. What do you observe?
3. Perform the same analysis for the deficit data.

[Exact answers will vary with the set of years chosen.]

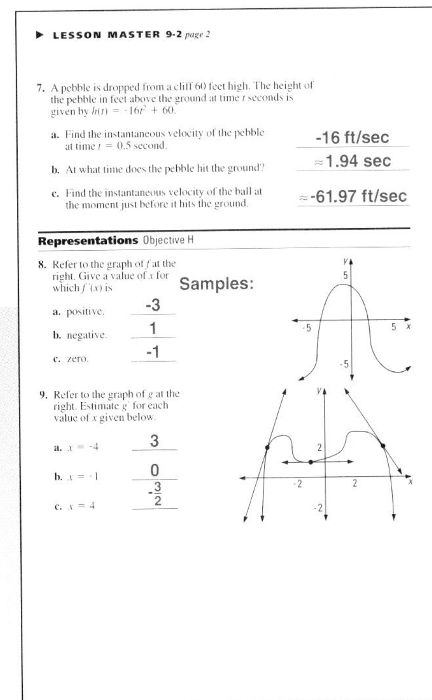

▶ **LESSON MASTER 9-2** *page 2*

7. A pebble is dropped from a cliff 60 feet high. The height of the pebble in feet above the ground at time t seconds is given by $h(t) = -16t^2 + 60$.
   a. Find the instantaneous velocity of the pebble at time $t = 0.5$ second. **-16 ft/sec**
   b. At what time does the pebble hit the ground? **≈1.94 sec**
   c. Find the instantaneous velocity of the ball at the moment just before it hits the ground. **≈-61.97 ft/sec**

Representations Objective H

8. Refer to the graph of f at the right. Give a value of x for which $f'(x)$ is **Samples:**
   a. positive. **-3**
   b. negative. **1**
   c. zero. **-1**
9. Refer to the graph of g at the right. Estimate g' for each value of x given below.
   a. $x = -4$ **3**
   b. $x = -1$ **0**
   c. $x = 4$ **$-\frac{3}{2}$**

Some students may ask if the work of **Example 3** can be generalized to an instantaneous velocity formula, as was done in **Example 2** of Lesson 9-1 for average velocity. The answer, of course, is yes. The derivative function is the topic of Lesson 9-3. These students may simply replace occurrences of 3 with x in the work of **Example 3** and take the limit as $\Delta x \to 0$ as the final step. This is akin to what they are asked to do in the *Warm-up* on page 560.

Additional Examples

1. In Additional Example 3 of Lesson 9-1, the average velocity of the projectile from time t to time $t + \Delta t$ was given by $\frac{h(t+\Delta t) - h(t)}{\Delta t} = 960 - 32t - 16\Delta t.$ What is the instantaneous velocity at time $t = 30$ seconds? **0 ft/sec; the projectile must be at its peak then; going neither up nor down**
2. Repeat **Example 2** of this lesson when $t = 3$ hours. **A tangent to the graph at (3, 80) seems to go through (1, 50). Thus the instantaneous velocity is about 15 mph.**
3. **a.** Using $f(x) = x^2 + 4$ again, calculate $f'(-3)$, $f'(-2)$, $f'(-1)$, $f'(0)$, $f'(1)$, $f'(2)$, and $f'(3)$.

x	-3	-2	-1	0	1	2	3
$f'(x)$	-6	-4	-2	0	2	4	6

b. Conjecture something about the function f'. **It seems that $f'(x) = 2x$. Also, for all values of x considered here, $f'(-x) = -f'(x)$, so f' may be an odd function.**

Instantaneous Rates of Change Are Derivatives

Velocity is only one of many kinds of rates of change. It applies when x represents time and $y = f(x)$ represents the position of an object in one dimension such as height or distance. If x and y are any quantities related by an equation $y = f(x)$, then, for a particular value of x, the **instantaneous rate of change of f at x** is defined to be the derivative of f at x. This means,

$$\left(\begin{array}{c}\text{instantaneous rate of}\\ \text{change of } f \text{ at } x\end{array}\right) = f'(x) = \lim_{\Delta x \to 0} \frac{f(x + \Delta x) - f(x)}{\Delta x}.$$

When there is no confusion, the instantaneous rate of change or instantaneous velocity is sometimes referred to as the rate of change or velocity *at* x.

Imagine a spherical balloon being blown up so that the radius is increasing at a steady rate. Example 4 asks for the instantaneous rate of change in the sphere's volume. You need to use the formula for the cube of a binomial: $(x + y)^3 = x^3 + 3x^2y + 3xy^2 + y^3$.

Example 4

Recall that the volume V of a sphere with radius r is given by $V(r) = \frac{4}{3}\pi r^3$.

a. Compute $V'(1)$, the instantaneous rate of change of V at $r = 1$.
b. Compute $V'(2)$, the instantaneous rate of change of V at $r = 2$.

Solution

a. From the definition of instantaneous rate of change,

$$\begin{aligned} V'(1) &= \lim_{\Delta x \to 0} \frac{V(1 + \Delta x) - V(1)}{\Delta x} \\ &= \lim_{\Delta x \to 0} \frac{\frac{4}{3}\pi(1 + \Delta x)^3 - \frac{4}{3}\pi}{\Delta x} \\ &= \lim_{\Delta x \to 0} \frac{\frac{4}{3}\pi(1 + 3\Delta x + 3(\Delta x)^2 + (\Delta x)^3) - \frac{4}{3}\pi}{\Delta x} \\ &= \lim_{\Delta x \to 0} \frac{\frac{4}{3}\pi(3\Delta x + 3(\Delta x)^2 + (\Delta x)^3)}{\Delta x} \\ &= \lim_{\Delta x \to 0} \frac{4}{3}\pi(3 + 3\Delta x + (\Delta x)^2) \\ &= \lim_{\Delta x \to 0} \frac{4\pi(3)}{3} = 4\pi. \end{aligned}$$

b. Similarly, $V'(2) = \lim_{\Delta x \to 0} \frac{\frac{4}{3}\pi(2 + \Delta x)^3 - \frac{4}{3}\pi \cdot 8}{\Delta x}$.

Activity

Do the algebra to obtain $V'(2) = 16\pi$. **See Question 9 on page 565.**

Physically, Example 4 can be interpreted as follows: If you want to blow up a balloon so that its radius increases steadily, you will need to put in 4 times as much air when the radius is 2 units as you will at the instant when the radius is 1 unit.

564

Additional Answers, page 565

3. a. $y = -\frac{5}{2}x - 2$

b.

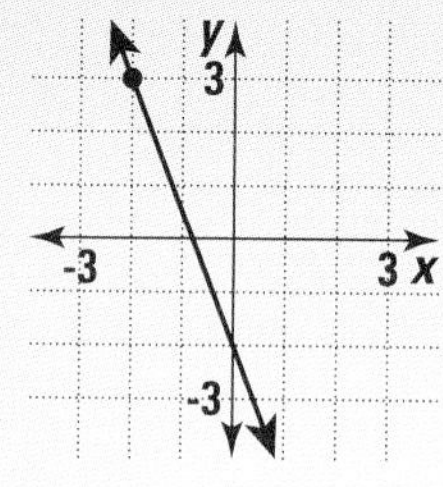

c. Sample:

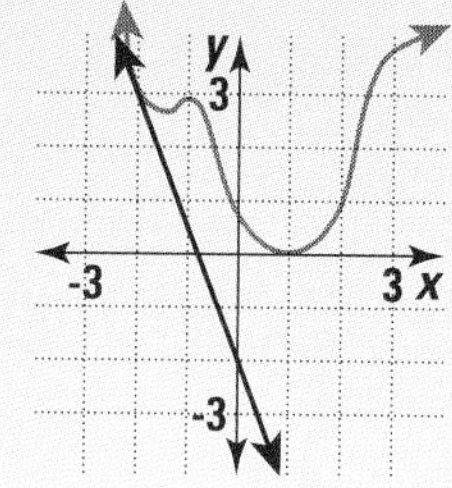

8. a., b.

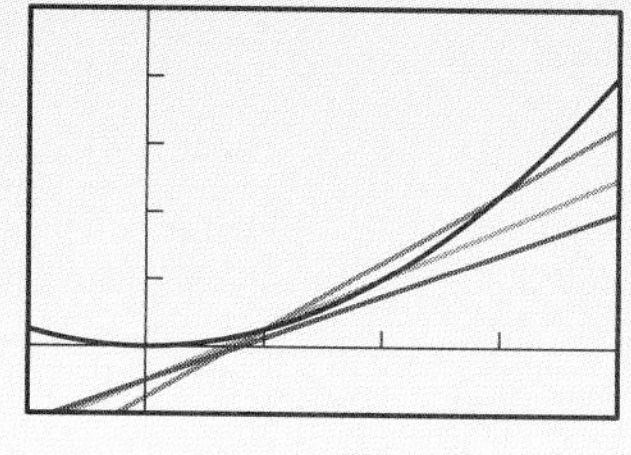

$-1 \le x \le 4$, x-scale = 1
$-2 \le y \le 10$, y-scale = 2

2a) Samples: 17.5 ft/sec, 22.5 ft/sec, 30 ft/sec

b) Slope $\approx$ 40 ft/sec

c) Sample: 40 ft/sec

4) The derivative of a real function f at a point x is $\lim\limits_{\Delta x \to 0} \frac{f(x + \Delta x) - f(x)}{\Delta x}$, provided this limit exists and is finite.

6a) $g'(-4) = -\frac{1}{2}$, $g'(0) = 0$, $g'(4) = \frac{1}{2}$

b) at $x = -4$, $y = -\frac{1}{2}x - 3$; at $x = 0$, $y = 2$; at $x = 4$, $y = \frac{1}{2}x - 3$

7) For a discrete function, you cannot find values of x so that $\Delta x \to 0$.

QUESTIONS

Covering the Reading

1. For the projectile in Example 1, the average velocity between times $t = 10$ and $t = 10 + \Delta t$ is $480 - 16\Delta t$ ft/sec. Find the instantaneous velocity at time $t = 10$ seconds. **480 ft/sec**

2. Use the graph at the right, which shows the distance traveled by a driver going through a turn. **See left.**
   a. Estimate the slopes of the secant lines $\overleftrightarrow{PQ_1}$, $\overleftrightarrow{PQ_2}$, and $\overleftrightarrow{PQ_3}$. (Include units with your answer.)
   b. Trace the graph and sketch the tangent line to the curve at P. Find the slope of the line you drew. (Include units with your answer.)
   c. Estimate the instantaneous velocity of the driver at $t = 2$ seconds.

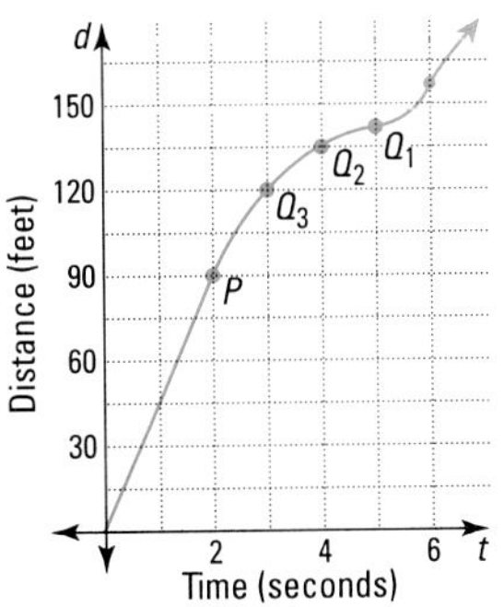

3. a. Find an equation for the line ℓ through the point (-2, 3) with slope $\frac{-5}{2}$.
   b. Graph ℓ.
   c. Graph a function that has ℓ as a tangent line at $x = -2$.

See margin.

4. Give the definition of a derivative at a point. **See left.**

5. *True or false.* Suppose a function f has a derivative at every point. Then the slope of the tangent line to the graph of f at x is $f'(x)$. **True**

6. The figure at the right shows the graph of an even function g.
   a. Find approximate values for the derivatives of g at $x = -4$, $x = 0$, and $x = 4$.
   b. Write the equations of the tangent lines to the graph at $x = -4$, $x = 0$, and $x = 4$.

See left.

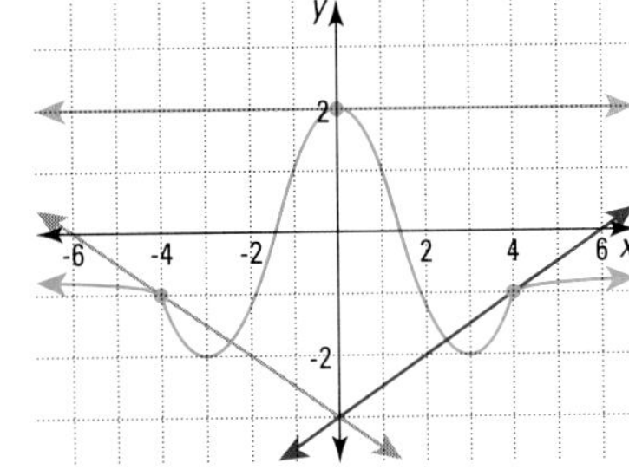

7. Explain why discrete functions do not have derivatives. **See left.**

8. Let $f(x) = .5x^2$. **See margin.**
   a. Graph f for $0 \le x \le 4$.
   b. Sketch secants through $(1, f(1))$ and $(1 + \Delta x, f(1 + \Delta x))$ for $\Delta x = 2$, 1, and 0.5.
   c. Find the slopes of the three secants in part **b**.
   d. Use the definition of the derivative of f at x to find the slope of the tangent to f at $x = 1$ algebraically.
   e. Sketch the tangent to f at $x = 1$.

9. Fill in the algebraic steps missing in Example 4, part **b**. **See margin.**

4. The volume of a cube with side s is given by the formula $V(s) = s^3$. Calculate $V'(2)$ and $V'(4)$ and interpret your answers.
$V'(2) = 12$; $V'(4) = 48$; The instantaneous rate of change of the volume of a continuously expanding cube when the side has length 4 is 4 times that when the side has length 2.

Notes on Questions

Questions 2, 6, 10, 12, and 13 These questions are important for understanding the geometry of the derivative. Be flexible on the answers, as accuracy depends on how well the tangent lines are drawn. The graphs for these questions can be found on **Teaching Aids 94 and 95.**

c. 2, 1.5, 1.25
d. 1
e.

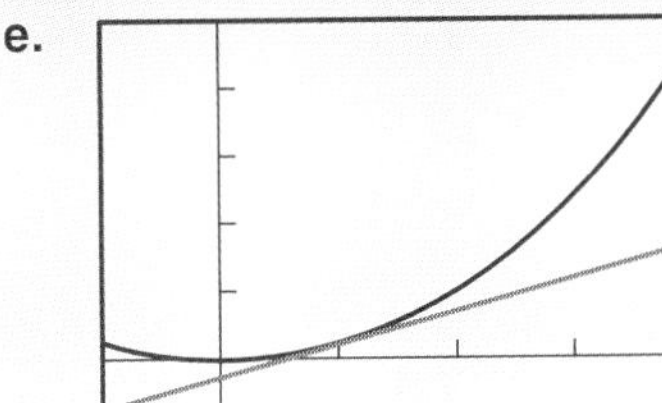

$-1 \le x \le 4$, x-scale $= 1$
$-2 \le y \le 10$, y-scale $= 2$

9. $$V'(2) = \lim_{\Delta x \to 0} \frac{V(2 + \Delta x) - V(2)}{\Delta x}$$
$$= \lim_{\Delta x \to 0} \frac{\frac{4}{3}\pi(2 + \Delta x)^3 - \frac{4}{3}\pi(2)^3}{\Delta x}$$
$$= \lim_{\Delta x \to 0} \frac{\frac{4}{3}\pi(8 + 12\Delta x + 6(\Delta x)^2 + (\Delta x)^3) - \frac{4}{3}\pi(8)}{\Delta x}$$
$$= \lim_{\Delta x \to 0} \frac{\frac{4}{3}\pi(12\Delta x + 6(\Delta x)^2 + (\Delta x)^3)}{\Delta x}$$
$$= \lim_{\Delta x \to 0} \frac{4}{3}\pi(12 + 6\Delta x + (\Delta x)^2) = 16\pi$$

Notes on Questions

Questions 10, 12, and 13 The reason calculus is required in so many areas is that the derivative has meaning in a variety of situations. Here we have water level in a reservoir, a roller coaster, and sounds in music. In this lesson the derivative was applied to a projectile and in the last lesson the opening example was the length of day. It is difficult to imagine five more diverse examples. Yet, these situations have in common that they change over time, and what the derivative does is to give a mathematical way of dealing with that change.

Question 11 We say that the absolute value function does not have a derivative at $x = 0$.

Question 12 History Connection The physicist Robert A. Moog and the inventor Donald Buchla independently developed the first commercially successful synthesizers in the 1960s.

Question 14 The rate of change for a linear function is constant and equals its slope.

Question 15 The average rate of change here means the amount that the measure of the angle increases as the number of sides increases. This amount gets smaller as n gets larger. There is no meaning to the instantaneous rate of change for this situation because the function is discrete.

Questions 22–24 Here are three more situations in which the derivative has meaning, in case students thought **Questions 10, 12, and 13** exhaust the variety.

11c) $A'(0)$ is $\lim\limits_{\Delta x \to 0} \frac{A(0 + \Delta x) - A(0)}{\Delta x}$; **This limit does not exist because it has different values when approaching zero from the right and from the left.**

13a) $f'(7{:}05) \approx -\frac{9}{7} \approx -1.3$ **ft/min;** $f'(7{:}15) \approx 1$ **ft/min**

b) At 7:05, the water level is falling at about 1.3 ft/min; at 7:15, the water level is rising at about 1 ft/min.

Applying the Mathematics

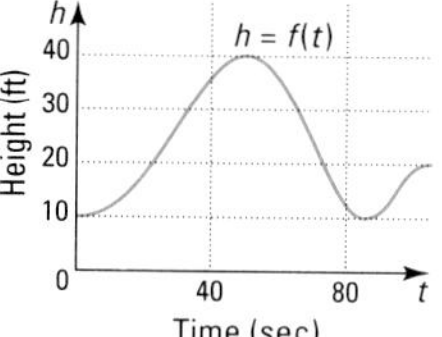

10. Let h be the height (in feet) of a car on a roller coaster t seconds after a ride begins and suppose t and h are related by the equation $h = f(t)$. A graph of f is shown at the left. By drawing tangents, approximate the instantaneous rate of change of height with respect to time at $t = 30$ seconds, $t = 60$ seconds, and $t = 100$ seconds. At which of these times is the height of the roller coaster changing the fastest? **See margin.**

11. Consider the absolute value function A with $A(x) = |x|$.

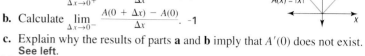

$A(x) = |x|$

   a. Calculate $\lim\limits_{\Delta x \to 0^+} \frac{A(0 + \Delta x) - A(0)}{\Delta x}$. **1**

   b. Calculate $\lim\limits_{\Delta x \to 0^-} \frac{A(0 + \Delta x) - A(0)}{\Delta x}$. **-1**

   c. Explain why the results of parts **a** and **b** imply that $A'(0)$ does not exist. **See left.**

12. Many musical synthesizers allow the user to control the *envelope* of created sounds. The envelope determines the volume of the tone from the time that a key is first played until the time the tone dies out. The graph below shows the envelope for a typical sound. **See margin.**

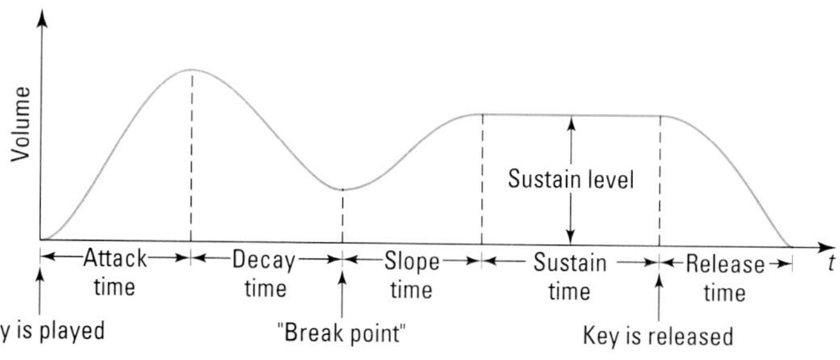

   a. Describe two different times at which the derivative of volume with respect to time is:
      i. positive ii. negative iii. zero

   b. Describe what you would hear when the derivative is:
      i. positive ii. negative iii. zero

13. The water level $f(t)$ in a reservoir at various times t is graphed below.

   a. Estimate the derivative of f at 7:05 and at 7:15. **See left.**

   b. What does the derivative mean in each case? **See left.**

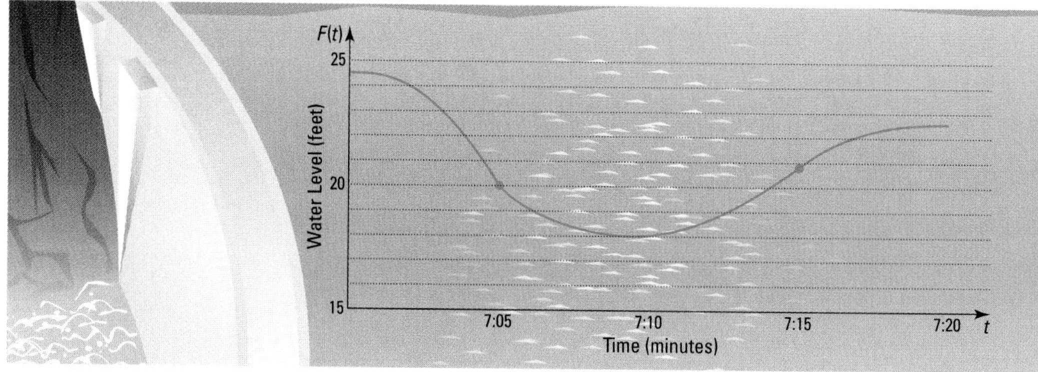

Additional Answers

10. $h'(30) \approx 1$ ft/sec; $h'(60) \approx -.7$ ft/sec; $h'(100) \approx \frac{1}{2}$ ft/sec; at $t = 30$.

12. a. i. During the attack and slope times
   ii. During the decay and release times
   iii. Sample: at the break point and during the sustain time

   b. i. Sound getting louder
   ii. Sound getting softer
   iii. Constant volume

16. Let S be the sequence defined by $S_n = 2n^2 + 1$, $\forall$ positive integers n. Show that S satisfies the recursive definition: $T_1 = 3$; $T_{k+1} = T_k + 4k + 2$, $\forall$ integers $k \geq 1$. $S_1 = 2 \cdot 1^2 + 1 = 3$; so S has the same initial condition as T. For all n,

$$\begin{aligned} S_{n+1} &= 2(n+1)^2 + 1 \\ &= 2(n^2 + 2n + 1) + 1 \\ &= 2n^2 + 4n + 2 + 1 \\ &= (2n^2 + 1) + 4n + 2 \\ &= S_n + 4n + 2. \end{aligned}$$

So, S satisfies the same recurrence relation as T. Since in this relation S_{n+1} is defined in terms of S_n by the Recursion Principle, they are the same sequence.

22. a. Degrees Fahrenheit/minute

   b. The oven is
      i. heating up slowly.
      ii. heating up quickly.
      iii. cooling off.
      iv. maintaining a constant temperature.

Review

14b) The average rate of change is the slope of the secant line through $x = 2$ and $x = 2 + \Delta x$, but f is a line. Hence, the slope of the secant line is the slope of f.

15a) $f(n) = \frac{180(n-2)}{n}$

14. Given the function f with $f(x) = 3x - 4$.
  a. Calculate the average rate of change of the function from $x = 2$ to $x = 2 + \Delta x$. **3**
  b. Interpret your answer to part **a** in terms of slopes of secant lines from $x = 2$ to $x = 2 + \Delta x$. *(Lesson 9-1)* **See left.**

15. Recall that the sum of the interior angles of an n-gon is $180(n - 2)$. Let $f(n)$ be the measure of *one* angle of a regular n-gon.
  a. Write a formula for $f(n)$ in terms of n. **See left.**
  b. Find $f(20)$ and $f(24)$. **$f(20) = 162$, $f(24) = 165$**
  c. What is the average rate of change of f from $n = 20$ to $n = 24$? *(Lesson 9-1)* **$\frac{3}{4}$**

16. Prove that the explicit formula

$$a_n = 2n^2 + 1 \qquad \forall \text{ positive integers } n$$

and the recursive formula

$$\begin{cases} a_1 = 3 \\ a_{k+1} = a_k + 4k + 2 \end{cases} \qquad \forall \text{ integers } k \geq 1$$

define the same sequence. *(Lessons 7-1, 7-3)* **See margin.**

In 17–21, evaluate without using a calculator. *(Lessons 2-6, 2-9, 6-2, 6-7)*

17. $\sin \frac{7\pi}{6}$ **-0.5**

18. $\cos^2 \frac{5\pi}{12} + \sin^2 \frac{5\pi}{12}$ **1**

19. $\tan^{-1}\sqrt{3}$ **$\frac{\pi}{3}$**

20. $\log_2 \frac{1}{16}$ **-4**

21. $\ln e^{\pi}$ **π**

Exploration

Naim Suleymanoglu, from Turkey, three-time Olympic gold-medal winner

In 22–24, imagine a function describing the situation. **See margin.**
  a. Give a reasonable unit for the derivative.
  b. Describe when the derivative would be each of the following.
    i. small and positive
    ii. large and positive
    iii. negative
    iv. zero

22. baking (temperature of oven over time)

23. weightlifting (height of bar over time)

24. jogging (distance over time)

Follow-up for Lesson 9-2

Practice

For more questions on SPUR Objectives, use **Lesson Master 9-2** (shown on pages 562–563).

Assessment

Written Communication Have students **work in pairs.** Ask each student to make up a problem like **Example 3.** Have students solve their partner's problems and provide a check like the one given for the example. [Students use the definition of derivative to compute derivatives and estimate derivatives by finding slopes of tangent lines.]

Extension

Have students come up with other functions besides the absolute value function in **Question 11** that fail to have a derivative at a specific point or points. [Samples: step functions fail to have derivatives at the end-points of each segment; $f(x) \Rightarrow \sqrt{x}$ does not have a derivative at $x = 0$; $g(x) \Rightarrow \frac{1}{x-1}$ does not have a derivative at $x = 1$.]

Project Update Project 2, *The History of Calculus,* on page 592, relates to the content of this lesson.

23. a. inches/second
  b. i. When the bar is being slowly lifted
    ii. During rapid lifting of the bar
    iii. When the bar is being lowered
    iv. When the bar is being held steady, or while it is on the floor

24. a. feet/second
  b. i. When the jogger is moving slowly
    ii. When the jogger is running at top speed
    iii. Never
    iv. When the jogger stops or runs in place

Setting Up Lesson 9-3

Do the In-class Activity on page 568.

In-class Activity

Resources

From the ***Teacher's Resource File***

- Teaching Aid 96: Graph of the Sine Function and Tables
- Answer Master 9-3

Additional Resources

- Visual for Teaching Aid 96

In this activity, students use successive approximation to estimate the derivative of the sine function at $x = 2$, $x = \frac{\pi}{2}$, and two other values of x of their own choosing. The results of the activity are applied at the very beginning of Lesson 9-3, where it is noted that the data from the activity suggest that the value of the derivative of the sine function at x is the value of $\cos x$.

Cooperative Learning We encourage students to work on this activity in pairs, so that each student can check their partner's work.

Introducing Lesson 9-3

The Derivative Function

IN-CLASS

ACTIVITY

Here is a graph of the sine function f defined by $f(x) = \sin x$.

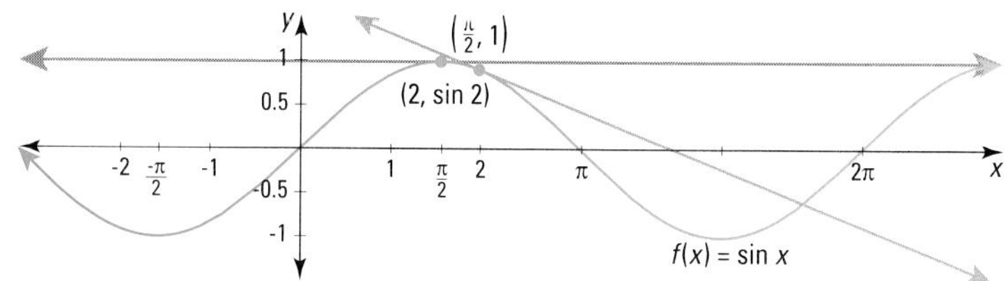

1 What is the value of the derivative of f at $x = \frac{\pi}{2}$? **0**

2 Consider the point at $x = 2$.

a. Is the derivative positive, negative, or zero? **negative**

b. To determine the slope more accurately, calculate the derivative of f at $x = 2$. By definition,

$$f'(2) = \lim_{\Delta x \to 0} \frac{\sin(2 + \Delta x) - \sin 2}{\Delta x}.$$

To estimate this limit, evaluate the difference quotient for some small values of Δx. Make certain your calculator is set to radian mode.

$\Delta x = 0.1$ $\quad \frac{\sin(2 + 0.1) - \sin 2}{0.1} = \underline{?}$ **-.461**

$\Delta x = 0.01$ $\quad \frac{\sin(2 + 0.01) - \sin 2}{0.01} = \underline{?}$ **-.421**

$\Delta x = 0.001$ $\quad \frac{\sin(2 + 0.001) - \sin 2}{0.001} = \underline{?}$ **-.417**

$\Delta x = 0.0001$ $\quad \frac{\sin(2 + 0.0001) - \sin 2}{0.0001} = \underline{?}$ **-.416**

c. Estimate $f'(2)$. **≈ -.416**

3 Repeat part **2b** with a value of x between 0 and $\frac{\pi}{2}$. Fill in the table. Then estimate $f'(x)$ for your value of x. **See margin.**

Δx	0.1	0.01	0.001	0.0001
$\frac{\sin(x + \Delta x) - \sin x}{\Delta x}$	?	?	?	?

4 Estimate $f'(x)$ for another value of x. Record your results. Complete the table, examine for interesting results, and summarize. **See margin.**

Task	x	$\sin x$	$\cos x$	$\tan x$	$f'(x)$
1	$\frac{\pi}{2}$	1			
2	2	$\sin 2 \approx .909$			
3					
4					

568

Additional Answers

3. Sample: $x = \frac{\pi}{3}$
   a. .456
   b. .496
   c. .500
   d. .500
   e. $\frac{1}{2}$
4. See table at the right. The values in the columns for $\cos x$ and $f'(x)$ are either identical or approximately the same.

Sample:

Task	x	$\sin x$	$\cos x$	$\tan x$	$f'(x)$
1	$\frac{\pi}{2}$	1	0	undef.	0
2	2	≈ .909	≈ -.416	≈ -2.19	≈ -.416
3	$\frac{\pi}{3}$	$\frac{\sqrt{3}}{2}$	$\frac{1}{2}$	$\sqrt{3}$	$\frac{1}{2}$
4	$\frac{\pi}{4}$	$\frac{\sqrt{2}}{2}$	$\frac{\sqrt{2}}{2}$	1	$\frac{\sqrt{2}}{2}$

LESSON

9-3

The Derivative Function

A cannonball is another example of a projectile whose path can be modeled by a quadratic equation. See Example 1.

Determining Values of a Derivative Function

Examine again the graph of the sine function $f(x) = \sin x$. This time look at the values of the derivative at various points.

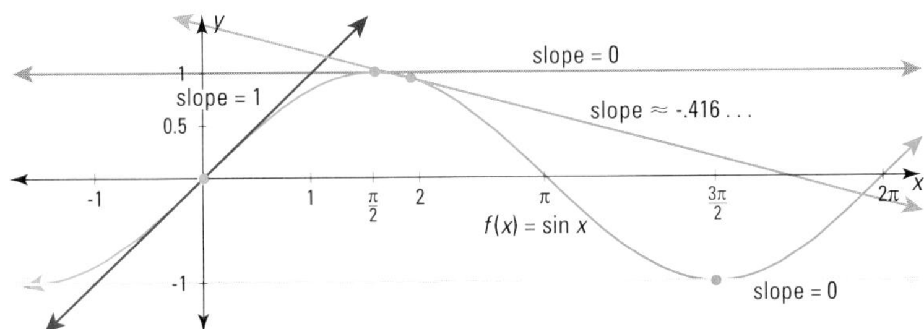

At $x = \frac{\pi}{2}$, the value of the derivative is 0.
At $x = 0$, the value of the derivative is 1.
At $x = 2$, the value of the derivative is about -.416, which is very near cos 2.
At $x = \frac{3\pi}{2}$, the value of the derivative is 0, which equals $\cos \frac{3\pi}{2}$.

In fact, the slopes of tangents to the graph of $f(x) = \sin x$ are positive when $0 \le x < \frac{\pi}{2}$, when the cosine function is positive. The slopes are negative when $\frac{\pi}{2} < x < \frac{3\pi}{2}$, when the cosine function is negative. In the In-class Activity on page 568, your estimate to the derivative of the sine function at any number x should have been close to $\cos x$. The cosine function is the *derivative* of the sine function.

Some calculator and computer programs show this graphically. On page 570 are graphs of four functions. The blue curve is the cosine function. The

Lesson 9-3

Objectives

B Use the definition of derivative to compute derivatives.
D Find rates of change in real situations.
E Use derivatives to find the velocity and acceleration of a moving object.
H Estimate derivatives by finding slopes of tangent lines.

Resources

From the ***Teacher's Resource File***
- Lesson Master 9-3
- Answer Master 9-3
- Assessment Sourcebook: Quiz for Lessons 9-1 through 9-3
- Teaching Aids
  87 Warm-up
  97 Example 2
  98 Questions 2, 5, and 11
  99 Questions 15, 16, 19, and 20

Additional Resources
- Visuals for Teaching Aids 87, 97, 98, 99

Teaching Lesson 9-3

Warm-up

Work with the same classmate you were paired with for the *In-class Activity* on page 568. Fill in the chart below with the values you found from **parts 3 and 4** of the activity. Then plot the points of the function f'. **Sample:**

x	$f(x) = \sin x$	$f'(x)$
$\frac{\pi}{2}$	1	0
2	≈ .909	≈ -.416
$\frac{\pi}{3}$	$\frac{\sqrt{3}}{2}$	$\frac{1}{2}$
$\frac{\pi}{4}$	$\frac{\sqrt{2}}{2}$	$\frac{\sqrt{2}}{2}$

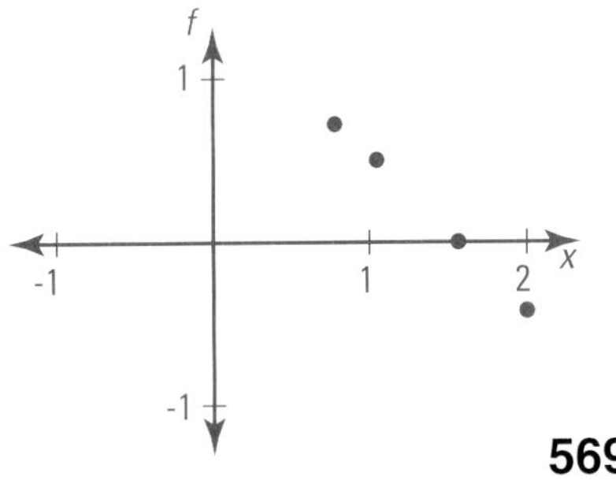

Lesson 9-3 Overview

Broad Goals In the last lesson, students computed the derivative at a particular point. This lesson expands on that idea by computing the derivative at every point of the function. This leads to the consideration of the derivative as a function itself.

Perspective Examples from the previous lesson are extended here. The derivative of the projectile height function, its velocity function, is shown to be a linear function.

This is generalized to obtain a general formula for the derivative of a quadratic function. The derivative of the volume function for a sphere is found to be the surface area function.

Notes on Reading

Stress to students that no new computations are involved in this lesson. In Lesson 9-2 the limit of the difference quotient was computed for *a particular value* of x. In this lesson, the limit of the difference quotient will be obtained for *any value* of x.

The result at the beginning of this lesson, that the derivative of the sine is the cosine, can be quite surprising to students. We do not have the tools at the present time to provide a proof. Indeed, the proof is better left to a calculus course. Instead, we present this result as simply a statement of fact. You can make this fact more convincing with the *Warm-up* on page 569. Confirm what was found by using an automatic grapher to display $y = \sin x$ and $y = \cos x$ on one screen. Then discuss the slope of the lines tangent to $y = \sin x$ at many points in the interval $0 \le x < 2\pi$. Relate each slope to the corresponding point on the curve $y = \cos x$.

❶ The four functions shown on page 570 give a graphic display of the cosine function as the limit of the difference quotients of the sine function. Some automatic graphers have the capability of showing such displays. In general, to approximate the derivative of a function f, enter a new function $g(x) = \frac{f(x + \Delta x) - f(x)}{\Delta x}$, where Δx is some very small number, say 0.001. (We use larger

LESSON MASTER 9-3 **Questions on SPUR Objectives** See pages 596–599 for objectives.

Skills Objective B

In 1–4, find the derivative of the function whose formula is given.

1. $f(y) = 7y^2$ — 14x
2. $g(x) = 7x^2 - 3x$ — 14x − 3
3. $p(v) = -4.5v$ — -4.5
4. $q(x) = 94$ — 0

Uses Objective D

5. If \$800 is invested at an interest rate of 7.5% compounded continuously, the amount in the account after t years is $A(t) = 800e^{0.075t}$ dollars. The derivative of A is $A' = 60e^{0.075t}$.
   a. Find the amount in the account after 5 years. — ≈ \$1163.99
   b. Find $A'(5)$. — ≈ \$87.30
   c. What does your answer to part b mean? — At 5 years, the balance is increasing at a rate of about \$87.30 per year.

6. A certain flashlight is pointed directly at a wall. The area A in square inches of the illuminated area is $A(d) = \pi d^2 + 2\pi d + \pi$ where d is the flashlight's distance in inches from the wall.
   a. Find the illuminated area at $d = 3$ inches. — $16\pi \approx 50.27$ in²
   b. Find the derivative of $A(d)$. — $2\pi d + 2\pi$
   c. Find the instantaneous rate of change of the illuminated area when $d = 3$ inches. — $8\pi \approx 25.13$ in²/in.
   d. Find the illuminated area at $d = 6$ inches. — $49\pi \approx 153.94$ in²
   e. Calculate $A'(6)$. — $14\pi \approx 43.98$ in²/in.
   f. What does your answer to part e mean? — The instantaneous rate of change of the illuminated area when the flashlight is 6 inches from the wall is $14\pi \frac{\text{in}^2}{\text{in.}}$

other three curves are functions defined by the difference quotients for the sine function

$$f_{\Delta x}(x) = \frac{\sin(x + \Delta x) - \sin x}{\Delta x},$$

when $\Delta x = 1$, $\Delta x = 0.5$, and $\Delta x = 0.1$. You can see that the limit of $f_{\Delta x}$ as $\Delta x \to 0$ seems to be the cosine function. That is, for all x, the exact value of the derivative of the sine function at x is $\cos x$.

❶

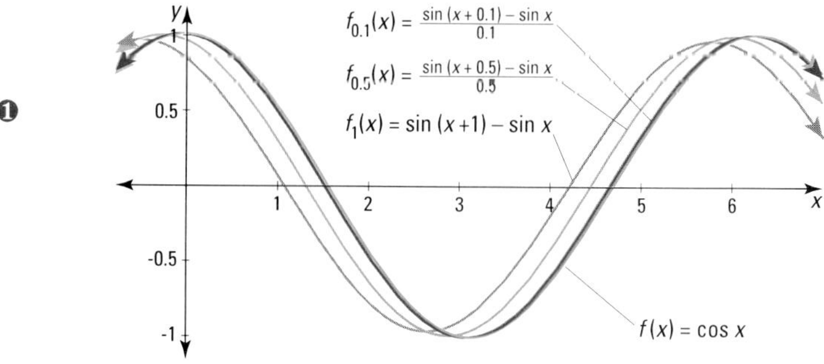

> **Definition**
> Suppose that f is a function that has a derivative $f'(x)$ at each point x in the domain of f. Then the function $f': x \to f'(x)$ for all x in the domain of f is called the **derivative function of f.**

Velocity as a Derivative Function

For the projectile discussed in Lessons 9-1 and 9-2, the derivative at each time is the (instantaneous) velocity of the projectile at that time. So the derivative function is a velocity function. Example 1 shows how to obtain a formula for this velocity.

Example 1

Suppose the height (in feet) of a projectile t seconds after launch is given by $h(t) = 800t - 16t^2$. Find a formula for its velocity t seconds after launch.

Solution

The velocity at each time t is the instantaneous rate of change of the position function h at t. This is the limit of the difference quotient as the change in t, Δt, approaches 0. In other words, it is the derivative of the position function.

$$h'(t) = \text{velocity at time } t = \lim_{\Delta t \to 0} \frac{h(t + \Delta t) - h(t)}{\Delta t}$$

$$= \lim_{\Delta t \to 0} (800 - 32t - 16\Delta t) \quad \text{from Lesson 9-1, Example 2}$$

$$= (800 - 32t)\ \frac{\text{ft}}{\text{sec}}$$

For example, after 30 seconds the velocity is $800 - 32 \cdot 30 = -160\ \frac{\text{ft}}{\text{sec}}$, which means that the projectile is moving downward at a speed of $160\ \frac{\text{ft}}{\text{sec}}$. This is about 110 miles per hour.

Optional Activities

✎ **Writing** Have students graph the height function h and the velocity function v in **Question 3.** Then have them write a paragraph explaining how they can use the graph to check that $v(t)$ is the derivative of $h(t)$. [Sample: When $0 < t < 18.75$, the values of $v(t)$ are positive, indicating positive slopes of the tangent lines to the graph of $h(t)$ for these time values. As t approaches 18.75 from the right, the positive values decrease, which indicates that the rate of change of height with respect to time is decreasing (though still positive.) At $t = 18.75$, $v(t) = 0$, indicating a horizontal tangent line to the graph of h, which corresponds to the maximum height value. For $t > 18.75$, the values of $v(t)$ are negative, indicating negative slopes of the tangent lines to the graph of h for these time values.]

Graphing a Derivative Function

Given a graph of a function f, you can make a rough sketch of its derivative function f' as follows. Imagine moving from left to right along the graph of f. For each value of x, draw or imagine the tangent line to the graph at the point $(x, f(x))$. Estimate its slope $f'(x)$, and plot the point $(x, f'(x))$ on the graph of f'. Example 2 shows how this is done.

Example 2

A function f is graphed below. Use the graph of f to estimate $f'(x)$ when $x = -5, -2, 2,$ and 6. Use this information to sketch a graph of f' for values of x between -5 and 6.

Solution

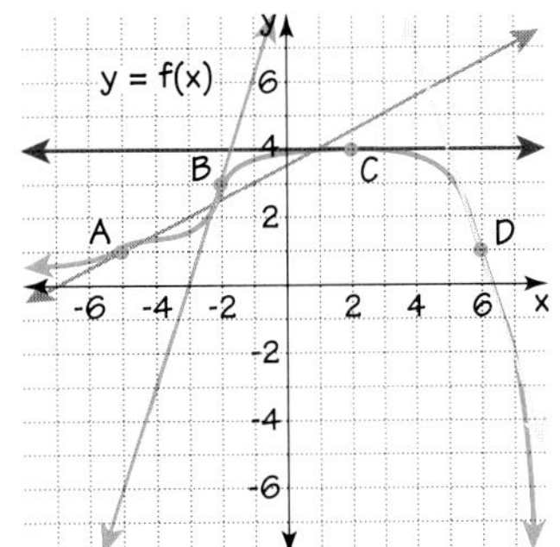

Draw tangent lines to the graph of f at the indicated values of x. At the point $A = (-5, f(-5))$, the tangent line has slope about $\frac{1}{2}$. So $f'(-5) \approx \frac{1}{2}$ and the point $A' = \left(-5, \frac{1}{2}\right)$ is on the graph of f'.

The slope of the tangent at the point $B = (-2, f(-2))$ is about 2. Therefore $f'(-2) = 2$, and $B' = (-2, 2)$ is on the graph of f'. Between $x = -5$ and $x = -2$ the graph of f rises more and more steeply, indicating that the graph of f' increases from $\frac{1}{2}$ to 2.

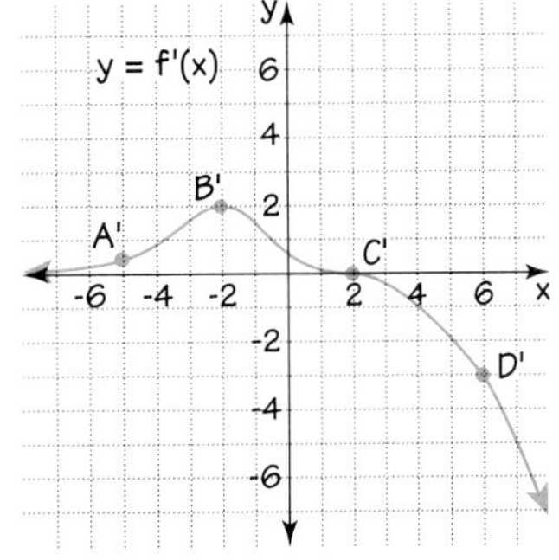

At $C = (2, f(2))$ the tangent is horizontal, with slope 0. Therefore $f'(2) = 0$ and $C' = (2, 0)$ is on the graph of f'. Since the graph of f flattens out rapidly between $x = -2$ and $x = 2$, the graph of f' decreases quickly to 0 at $x = 2$.

At $D = (6, f(6))$ the slope of the tangent line is about -3. Therefore $f'(6) = -3$ and $D' = (6, -3)$ is on the graph of f'. The graph of f decreases more and more steeply as x moves from left to right between $x = 2$ and $x = 6$. Therefore between $x = 2$ and $x = 6$ the graph of f' decreases from 0 to -3.

Finding a Formula for the Derivative of a Quadratic Function

In general, it is not always easy as it was in Example 1 to find a formula for the derivative of a function. However, there are calculator and computer programs which calculate derivatives, and some time is spent in most calculus classes calculating derivatives. In Example 1, the derivative of the quadratic function $h(t) = 800t - 16t^2$ was calculated. The ideas used in that calculation can be applied to any quadratic function.

values of Δx so that the graphs can be distinguished.) For most well-behaved functions, g is a very good approximation to f'.

Make the connection between the instantaneous rate of change function of **Example 1** in this lesson and the average rate of change function of **Example 2** in Lesson 9-1. All we have done here is to take the limit as $\Delta t \to 0$.

Example 2 is extremely important and continues to emphasize the geometric interpretation of the derivative. You will probably need to discuss this example in detail in class. **Teaching Aid 97** shows the graphs for this example. After discussing the proof of the theorem on the derivative of a quadratic, you may want to do another example like that of **Example 2** but starting with a quadratic function. Show that the type of analysis done in **Example 2** leads to the graph of a straight line as required by the theorem.

Ask students to translate the graph of $y = f(x)$ in **Example 2** either upward or downward (vertically only). How does the graph of the derivative of the translated function compare to that of the original? This exercise should help students see that the constant term in a function is not reflected in the derivative.

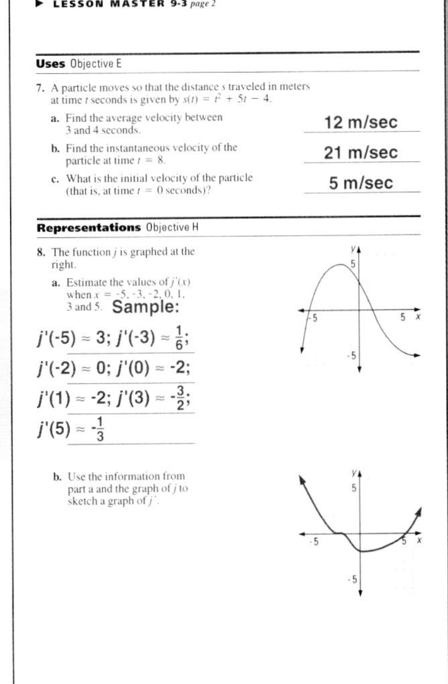

▶ **LESSON MASTER 9-3** *page 2*

Uses Objective E

7. A particle moves so that the distance s traveled in meters at time t seconds is given by $s(t) = t^2 + 5t - 4$.
   a. Find the average velocity between 3 and 4 seconds. **12 m/sec**
   b. Find the instantaneous velocity of the particle at time $t = 8$. **21 m/sec**
   c. What is the initial velocity of the particle (that is, at time $t = 0$ seconds)? **5 m/sec**

Representations Objective H

8. The function j is graphed at the right.
   a. Estimate the values of $j'(x)$ when $x = -5, -3, -2, 0, 1,$ 3 and 5. **Sample:**
   $j'(-5) \approx 3$; $j'(-3) \approx \frac{1}{6}$; $j'(-2) \approx 0$; $j'(0) \approx -2$; $j'(1) \approx -2$; $j'(3) \approx -\frac{3}{2}$; $j'(5) \approx -\frac{1}{3}$
   b. Use the information from part a and the graph of j to sketch a graph of j'.

Adapting to Individual Needs

Extra Help

In doing a problem like **Example 2,** it is useful to have the graph of f' directly below that of f (as in the text). Alternately, graph f' on the same coordinate system as f, using a different color for each function.

❷ Many students have already seen the conclusion of the Derivative of a Quadratic Function Theorem in another form in a previous course. They may have been taught that the vertex of the graph of $y = ax^2 + bx + c$ has first coordinate $x = -\frac{b}{2a}$. If we set $2ax + b = 0$ and solve for x, we obtain the same result. This is done in Lesson 9-5.

❸ Emphasize to students that when questions ask for the derivative to be found by using the definition, they must take the limit of the difference quotient. If no specific instructions are given, then they may feel free to use the theorems for the derivative of a constant, linear, or quadratic function.

Example 3 of this lesson continues **Example 4** of the previous lesson. Students may be surprised that the derivative of the volume formula is the surface area formula. This is not coincidence, as indicated in the paragraph before the *Questions* on page 573. In general the derivative of a volume formula for a class of similar figures (all spheres are similar) is a multiple of the surface area formula for that class.

Additional Examples

1. Suppose that the height (in feet) of a projectile t seconds after launch is given by $h(t) = 100 + 960t - 16t^2$. Find a formula for its velocity t seconds after launch. **$h'(t) = 960 - 32t$ ft/sec (From this we can see that its initial velocity was 960 ft/sec. The decrease in velocity over time is 32 ft/sec, which is due to gravity, as we will see in the next lesson. In general, if $h(t) = h_0 + v_0t - 16t^2$, then $h'(t) = v_0 - 32t$ ft/sec, and so h_0 = initial height and v_0 = initial velocity.)**

❷ **Theorem (Derivative of a Quadratic Function)**
If $f(x) = ax^2 + bx + c$, where a, b, and c are real numbers and $a \neq 0$, then $f'(x) = 2ax + b$ for all real numbers x.

Proof
Apply the definition of derivative at each point x.

$$f'(x) = \lim_{\Delta x \to 0} \frac{f(x + \Delta x) - f(x)}{\Delta x}$$

$$= \lim_{\Delta x \to 0} \frac{a(x + \Delta x)^2 + b(x + \Delta x) + c - (ax^2 + bx + c)}{\Delta x}$$ Substitute for $f(x)$.

$$= \lim_{\Delta x \to 0} \frac{a(x^2 + 2x\Delta x + (\Delta x)^2) + bx + b\Delta x + c - ax^2 - bx - c}{\Delta x}$$ Expand and distribute.

$$= \lim_{\Delta x \to 0} \frac{ax^2 + 2ax\Delta x + a(\Delta x)^2 + bx + b\Delta x + c - ax^2 - bx - c}{\Delta x}$$ Combine like terms.

$$= \lim_{\Delta x \to 0} \frac{2ax\Delta x + a(\Delta x)^2 + b\Delta x}{\Delta x}$$ Δx is a factor of each term in the numerator.

$$= \lim_{\Delta x \to 0} (2ax + a\Delta x + b)$$

$$= 2ax + b$$ Take the limit.

For the function $h(t) = 800t - 16t^2$ in Example 1, $a = -16$, $b = 800$, and $c = 0$. The above theorem states that the derivative function is $h'(t) = 2at + b = -32t + 800$, exactly what was found in Example 1.

The formula for finding the derivative of a quadratic function can be applied to linear functions ($a = 0$ and $b \neq 0$) and to constant functions ($a = 0$ and $b = 0$) since the proof above does not depend on the values of a, b, or c. For example, the derivative of $f(x) = 0x^2 + 3x + 2$ is $f'(x) = 2 \cdot 0 \cdot x + 3 = 3$, and the derivative of $g(x) = 5 = 0x^2 + 0x + 5$ is $g'(x) = 0x + 0 = 0$. These results agree with the slopes of these functions.

Theorems
(Derivative of a Linear Function) If $f(x) = mx + b$, then $f'(x) = m$.
(Derivative of a Constant Function) If $\forall x$, $f(x) = k$, then $f'(x) = 0$.

The next example generalizes Example 4 of the previous lesson.

Example 3

The volume $V(r)$ and the surface area of a sphere of radius r are given by the formulas $V(r) = \frac{4}{3}\pi r^3$ and $S(r) = 4\pi r^2$. Verify that $V'(r) = S(r)$ for all r.

▶

Adapting to Individual Needs

Challenge

1. Ask students which function below could be the derivative of the other? [$f = g'$]

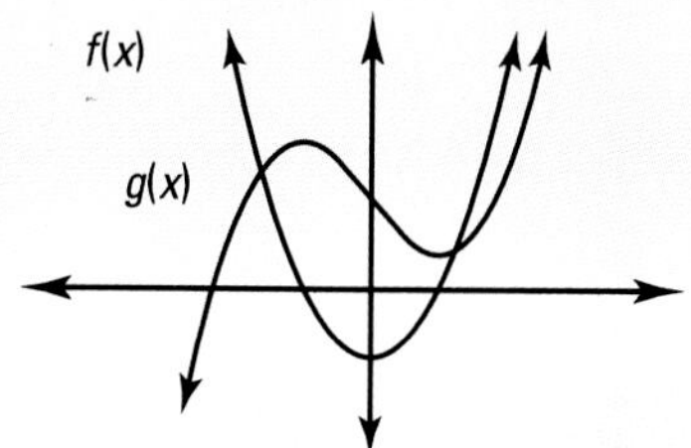

2. Pose this problem:
Let $y = f(x)$ and $g(x) = f(x) + C$ for all x.
Prove: For all x, $f'(x) = g'(x)$. [For all x,

$$g'(x) = \lim_{\Delta x \to 0} \frac{g(x + \Delta x) - g(x)}{\Delta x}$$

$$= \lim_{\Delta x \to 0} \frac{f(x + \Delta x) + C - (f(x) + C)}{\Delta x}$$

$$= \lim_{\Delta x \to 0} \frac{f(x + \Delta x) - f(x)}{\Delta x} = f'(x).]$$

Solution

From the definition of the derivative,

$$V'(r) = \lim_{\Delta r \to 0} \frac{V(r + \Delta r) - V(r)}{\Delta r}$$
$$= \lim_{\Delta r \to 0} \frac{\frac{4}{3}\pi(r + \Delta r)^3 - \frac{4}{3}\pi r^3}{\Delta r} \text{ for all r.}$$

Now there is only algebra to do, just as in Example 4 of Lesson 9-2. You should do the work to find that

$$V'(r) = 4\pi r^2.$$

Since $S(r) = 4\pi r^2$ for all r, $V'(r) = S(r)$.

Example 3 verifies that the instantaneous rate of change of the volume of a sphere at a given radius exactly equals its surface area for that radius. That is, as the radius increases (or decreases), you can think of the volume changing by the addition (or peeling away) of very thin layers of surface area.

QUESTIONS

Covering the Reading

1. a. For $0 \le x \le 2\pi$, when is the slope of the tangent to the graph of $f(x) = \sin x$ positive?
   b. For $0 \le x \le 2\pi$, when is the cosine function positive?
   See margin.

2. Refer to the graph of the function f at the left. Indicate whether the value of f' for the given value of x is positive, negative or zero.
   a. a **negative** b. b **zero**
   c. c **positive** d. d **zero**

3. If the projectile in Example 1 is propelled upward with an initial velocity of 600 ft/sec, then its height is given by $h(t) = 600t - 16t^2$.
   a. Find the velocity function. $\mathbf{v(t) = h'(t) = 600 - 32t}$
   b. What is the projectile's velocity at 6 seconds? **408 ft/sec**

4. a. Estimate $\lim_{\Delta x \to 0} \frac{\sin(3 + \Delta x) - \sin 3}{\Delta x}$ to three decimal places by using very small positive values of Δx. $\mathbf{\approx -.990}$
   b. According to what is said in this lesson, the answer to part **a** should be very close to what value of which trigonometric function?
   cos 3 ≈ -.98999

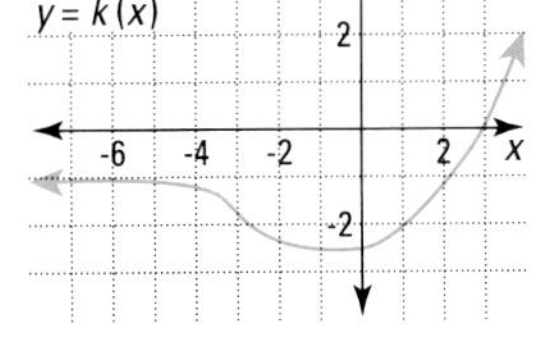

5. The function k is graphed at the left. Estimate the values of k' when $x = -6, -3, -1$, and 2, and use this information to sketch a graph of k'.
   See margin.

In 6 and 7, an equation describing a function is given. **a.** Use the definition of derivative to find the derivative of the function. **b.** Check your answer to part **a** using the theorem for the derivative of a quadratic function. **See margin.**

6. $f(x) = 3x + 1$ 7. $g(x) = 5x^2 + 2x$

In 8 and 9, find the derivative of the given function.

8. $f(x) = -6x + 4$ $\mathbf{f'(x) = -6}$ 9. $f(t) = 7$ $\mathbf{f'(t) = 0}$

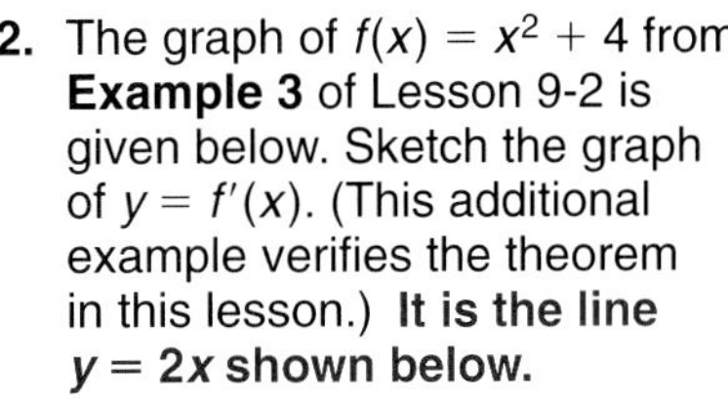

2. The graph of $f(x) = x^2 + 4$ from **Example 3** of Lesson 9-2 is given below. Sketch the graph of $y = f'(x)$. (This additional example verifies the theorem in this lesson.) **It is the line $y = 2x$ shown below.**

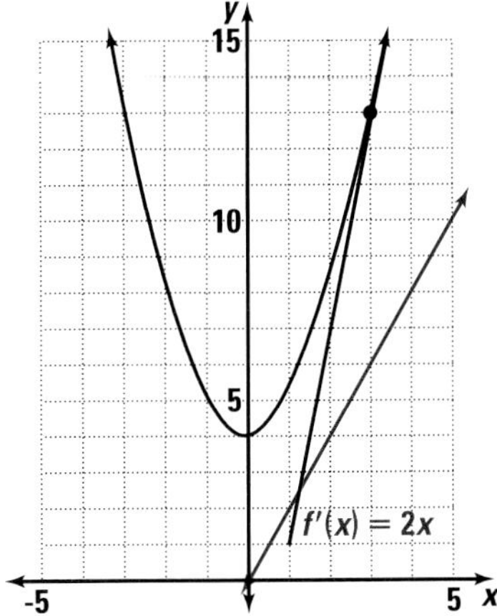

Notes on Questions

Question 1 The idea is to see that the two parts are asking the same question using different language.

Questions 2, 5, and 11 These help students connect the derivative to its geometric interpretation. Make sure that students understand these questions. **Teaching Aid 98** is provided with these graphs.

Question 4b Error Alert If students have difficulty here, remind them that the quantity in **part b** is the derivative of the sine function at $x = 3$.

Additional Answers, page 573

1. a. $0 \le x < \frac{\pi}{2}, \frac{3\pi}{2} < x \le 2\pi$
   b. $0 \le x < \frac{\pi}{2}, \frac{3\pi}{2} < x \le 2\pi$

5. $k'(-6) = 0$, $k'(-3) \approx -1$, $k'(-1) \approx -\frac{1}{10}$, $k'(2) \approx 1$. See graph at the right.

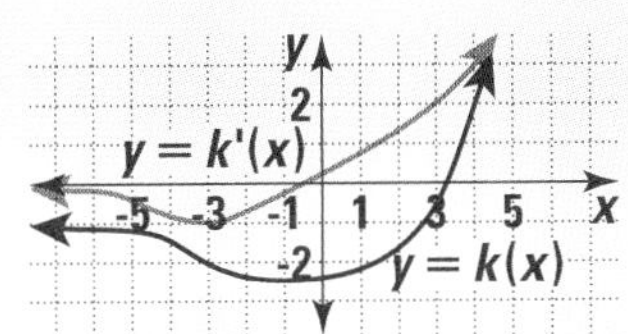

6. a. $f'(x) = \lim_{\Delta x \to 0} \frac{3(x + \Delta x) - 3x}{\Delta x} = \lim_{\Delta x \to 0} \frac{3\Delta x}{\Delta x} = 3$
   b. $f(x) = 0x^2 + 3x + 1$, so $f'(x) = 2 \cdot 0x + 3 = 3$.

7. a. $g'(x) = \lim_{\Delta x \to 0} \frac{5(x + \Delta x)^2 + 2(x + \Delta x) - (5x^2 + 2x)}{\Delta x} = \lim_{\Delta x \to 0} \frac{10x\Delta x + 5(\Delta x)^2 + 2\Delta x}{\Delta x} = \lim_{\Delta x \to 0} (10x + 5\Delta x + 2) = 10x + 2$
   b. $g(x) = 5x^2 + 2x + 0$, so $g'(x) = 10x + 2$.

Notes on Questions

Question 12 Knowledge of the binomial theorem helps here.

Questions 15, 16, 19, and 20 The illustrations for these questions are provided on **Teaching Aid 99.**

Question 16 The unit of $A'(x)$ is square inches per inch. Here it does not pay to reduce units. The unit square feet per foot is found in the *Extension* for this lesson.

Question 23 You may wish to discuss this question in detail. In a few places in the next few lessons we give the derivative of a cubic function because we do not expect students to memorize the formula that the derivative of $f: x \to x^3$ is $f': x \to 3x^2$. If the result from this question is assumed known, then those "givens" can be explained. Still, we discourage memorizing a general formula at this time.

10c)

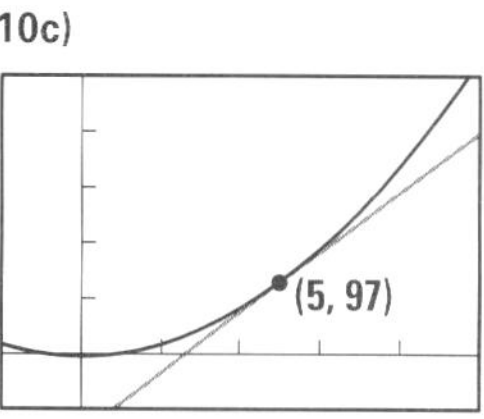

$-2 \le x \le 10$, x-scale = 2
$-75 \le y \le 375$, y-scale = 75

10. a. If $g(x) = 4x^2 - 3$, find $g'(x)$. **$g'(x) = 8x$**

b. What is the value of $g'(5)$? **40**

c. Use an automatic grapher to graph g. Check your answer to part **b** by estimating the slope of the tangent line to the graph of g at the point $(5, g(5))$. **See left.**

11. At the right is a graph of $f(x) = -x^2 + 2x + 3$. Some tangent lines to the graph are shown.

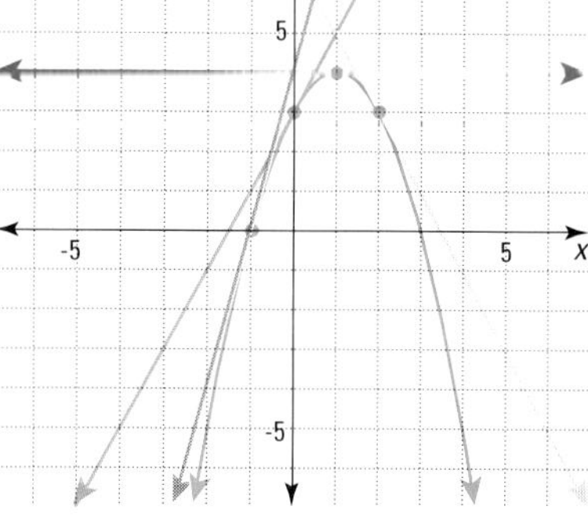

a. Use the graph to fill in approximate values for the table below. **4, 2, 0, -2**

x	$f'(x)$
-1	
0	
1	
2	

b. Find the derivative of f using the theorem for the derivative of a quadratic function. **$f'(x) = -2x + 2$**

c. Check your answers to part **a** by evaluating this derivative at the four values of x given in part **a**. **$f'(-1) = 4$, $f'(0) = 2$, $f'(1) = 0$, $f'(2) = -2$**

12. Supply the missing algebraic steps in Example 3. **See margin.**

Applying the Mathematics

13) ***f* and *g* are almost identical.**

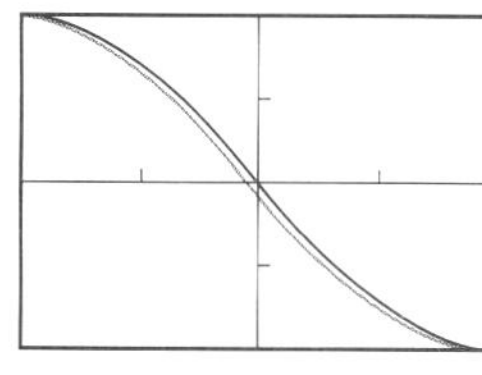

$-\frac{\pi}{2} \le x \le \frac{\pi}{2}$, x-scale = $\frac{\pi}{4}$
$-1 \le y \le 1$, y-scale = 0.5

13. Plot $f(x) = \frac{\cos(x + 0.1) - \cos x}{0.1}$ and $g(x) = -\sin x$ on the same screen. Make a conjecture based on the results. **See left.**

14. a. Let $f(x) = x^2 - 2$ and $g(x) = x^2 + 1$. Use the first theorem of this lesson to find f' and g'.

b. On the same set of axes, sketch graphs of f and g. Choose three values of x and draw tangent lines to each graph at those three points.

c. The functions f and g differ by a constant. How are their derivatives related? Explain why this relationship holds.

See margin.

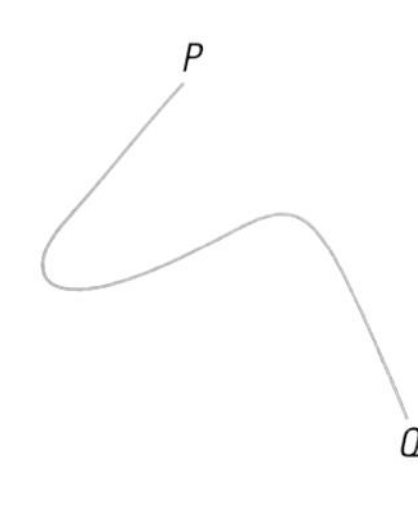

15. The diagram at the left shows part of a race track. A driver travels at top speed in the straight parts but must slow down in the turns.

a. If the driver goes from point P to point Q, which of the graphs below is the better description of distance as a function of time? **i**

(i)

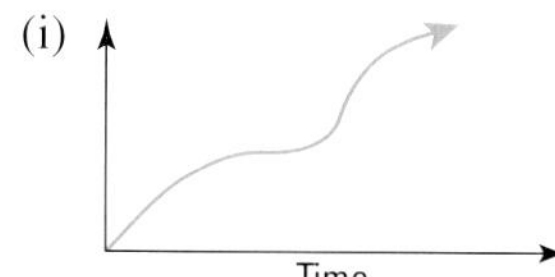

(ii)

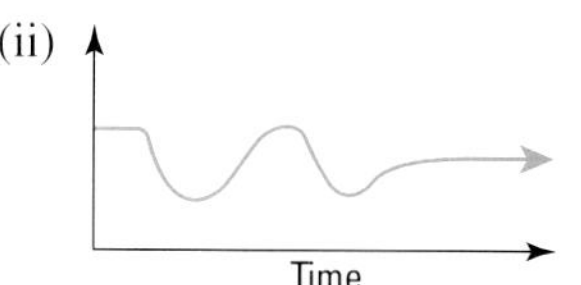

b. What does the graph you did not choose describe? **Velocity as a function of time**

Additional Answers

12. $V'(r)$

$$= \lim_{\Delta r \to 0} \frac{\frac{4}{3}\pi(r + \Delta r)^3 - \frac{4}{3}\pi r^3}{\Delta r}$$

$$= \lim_{\Delta r \to 0} \frac{\frac{4}{3}\pi(r^3 + 3r^2\Delta r + 3r(\Delta r)^2 + (\Delta r)^3) - \frac{4}{3}\pi r^3}{\Delta r}$$

$$= \lim_{\Delta r \to 0} \frac{4}{3}\pi(3r^2 + 3r\Delta r + (\Delta r)^2) = 4\pi r^2$$

14. a. $f'(x) = 2x$, $g'(x) = 2x$

b. See graph at the right. Shows tangents at $x = -1$, 0, and 1.

c. $f'(x) = g'(x)$ for all x. The derivative of a constant is zero, so if $h(x) = x^2 + c$, then $h'(x) = 2x + 0 = 2x$ for any real number c.

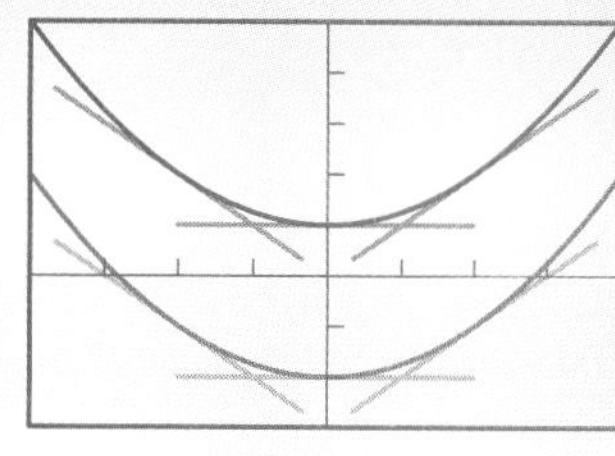

$-2 \le x \le 2$, x-scale = 0.5
$-3 \le y \le 5$, y-scale = 1

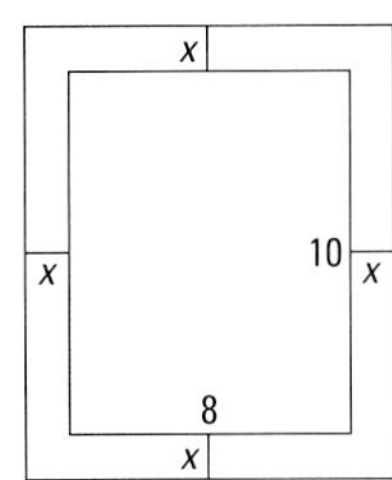

16. A flyer is to be made by putting a white border of width x inches around an 8″ by 10″ photograph, as shown at the left. The area of the border is $A(x) = 4x^2 + 36x$ square inches.
   a. Find the instantaneous rate of change of A with respect to x when $x = 2$ inches. **$A'(2) = 52$ square inches per inch**
   b. What is the meaning of the number you get? **See margin.**

17. For what values of x is the derivative of $f(x) = -3x^2 - 18x + 7$ positive? **$x < -3$**

Review

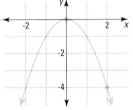

18. *True or false.* The instantaneous rate of change of a function f at the point $(x, f(x))$ is the slope of the tangent line at that point. *(Lesson 9-2)* **True**

19. At the left is graphed $g: x \to -x^2$. Find the average rate of change of g from $x = 0$ to $x = 2$. *(Lesson 9-1)* **-2**

20. The function f is graphed at the right, along with tangent lines at $x = -4$, $x = 0$, and $x = 4$.
   a. Based on the symmetry of the graph, what kind of function is f? **See left.**
   b. Estimate the derivative at each value of x.
   i. $x = -4$ **i) $\approx \frac{3}{2}$**
   ii. $x = 0$ **≈ -1**
   iii. $x = 4$ *(Lessons 2-4, 9-2)* **$\approx \frac{3}{2}$**

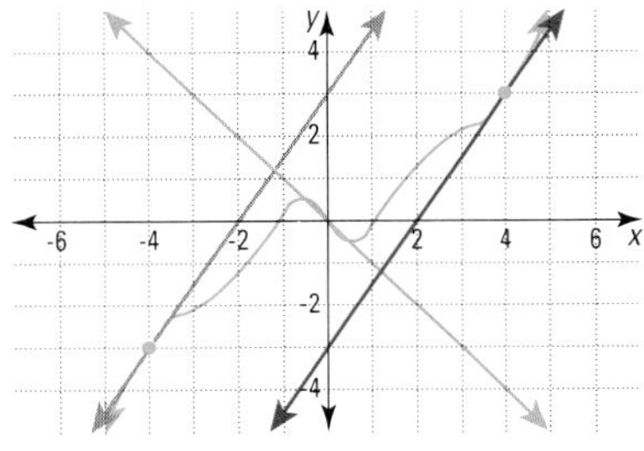

20a) an odd function; that is, $f(-x) = -f(x)$

21. Snell's Law describes the behavior of light when it travels from one medium into another. It states that $n_1 \sin \theta_1 = n_2 \sin \theta_2$, where n_1 and n_2 are the indexes of refraction for the first and second mediums, and θ_1 and θ_2 are the angles from the vertical at which the light hits the boundary between the mediums. Suppose light in air (index of refraction = 1.0) traveling at an angle of 60° with the vertical enters a diamond (index of refraction = 2.42). In the diamond, what angle will the light ray make with the vertical? *(Lessons 6-7, 6-8)* **$\approx 21°$**

22. Describe the end behavior of the function g with $g(x) = \frac{2x^2 - 2x - 1}{x - 2}$. *(Lesson 5-5)* **As $x \to -\infty$, $g(x) \to -\infty$; as $x \to \infty$, $g(x) \to \infty$.**

Exploration

23. Obtain information about the derivative function for the function f defined by $f(x) = x^3$ in these different ways.
   a. by using the difference quotient to approximate values of f'
   b. by using the definition of derivative
   c. by using an automatic grapher and carefully obtaining slopes of tangents
   a–c) If $f(x) = x^3$; then $f'(x) = 3x^2$.

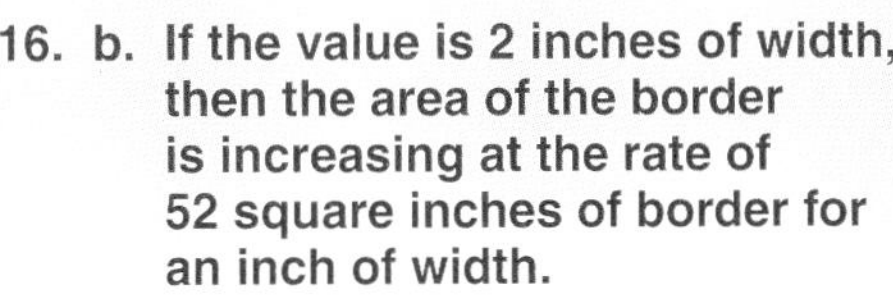

16. b. If the value is 2 inches of width, then the area of the border is increasing at the rate of 52 square inches of border for an inch of width.

Practice

For more questions on SPUR Objectives, use **Lesson Master 9-3** (shown on pages 570–571).

Assessment

Quiz A quiz covering Lessons 9-1 through 9-3 is provided in the *Assessment Sourcebook.*

Extension

A rectangular region adjacent to a building is to be enclosed with 120 feet of fencing. The area of the region is given by $A(w) = 120w - 2w^2$. Calculate the instantaneous rate of change of this function when $w = 20$ feet. What is the meaning of the number that you get?

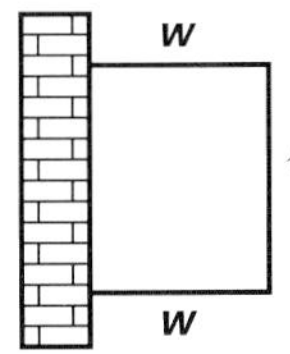

[$A'(20) = 40$ square feet per foot. This means that when the width is 20, then a small increase in width will produce a small square unit increase of 40 times the numerical amount in area.]

Project Update Project 1, *Newton's Method for Finding Zeros of Equations,* Project 2, *The History of Calculus,* and Project 3, *Smooth vs. Non-Smooth Curves,* on page 592, relate to the content of this lesson.

Lesson 9-4

Objectives

D Find rates of change in real situations.

E Use derivatives to find the velocity and acceleration of a moving object.

Resources

From the ***Teacher's Resource File***

- Lesson Master 9-4
- Answer Master 9-4
- Teaching Aids
  - 88 Warm-up
  - 100 Changes in World Population

Additional Resources

- Visuals for Teaching Aids 88, 100

Teaching Lesson 9-4

Warm-up

Listed here are the highest Dow-Jones stock averages for each year from 1962 to 1982. In which consecutive years was the highest rate of change per year of the yearly rate of change? **1975–76**

1962	726.01	1973	1051.70
1963	767.21	1974	891.66
1964	891.71	1975	881.81
1965	969.26	1976	1014.79
1966	995.15	1977	999.75
1967	943.08	1978	907.74
1968	985.21	1979	897.61
1969	968.85	1980	1000.17
1970	842.00	1981	1024.05
1971	950.82	1982	1070.55
1972	1036.27		

(Source: *The World Almanac and Book of Facts 1998*)

LESSON

9-4

Acceleration and Deceleration

What a Drag. *A drag chute decelerates the space shuttle Discovery as it lands at the Kennedy Space Center Shuttle Landing Facility. Its deployment causes an abrupt change in the shuttle's instantaneous velocity.*

A Discrete Example of Acceleration and Deceleration

Below are estimates of the world population in recent years, from the International Data Base of the United States Bureau of the Census. In the right column are average rates of change of population per year between the successive values in the middle column. For instance, the average rate of change of population between 1975 and 1980 is calculated as

$$\frac{4{,}454{,}000{,}000 - 4{,}086{,}000{,}000}{1980 - 1975} = 73{,}600{,}000\ \frac{\text{people}}{\text{year}}.$$

Year	World Population	Average rate of change during previous 5 years $\left(\frac{\text{people}}{\text{year}}\right)$
1960	3,039,000,000	
1965	3,345,000,000	61,200,000
1970	3,707,000,000	72,400,000
1975	4,086,000,000	75,800,000
1980	4,454,000,000	73,600,000
1985	4,850,000,000	79,200,000
1990	5,278,000,000	85,600,000
1995	5,687,000,000	81,800,000

The world population has not been constant. Because the population is growing, the average rates of change are positive. The rate of change has also not been constant. For most of the time periods, the rate of change has been growing. It is said that the growth is *accelerating*. **Acceleration** is the rate of change of a rate. The acceleration is calculated in the rightmost column on page 577. The unit of the right column is $\frac{\text{people}}{\text{year}}$ per year. For instance, the number 680,000 means that in the years from 1970 to 1975, the amount of

576

Lesson 9-4 Overview

Broad Goals The goal of this lesson is to discuss the second derivative, the derivative of a derivative, and to tie this in with the concepts of acceleration and deceleration.

Perspective Again the first example is discrete, this time with population growth. The rate of change of the rate of change of the population yields an acceleration or deceleration of population growth.

Again the continuous example is the projectile height function. Now there can be instantaneous acceleration, and for the projectile function the instantaneous acceleration is shown to be constant and equal to the acceleration due to gravity.

Optional Activities

Have students refer to the diagram below to answer the questions at the right:

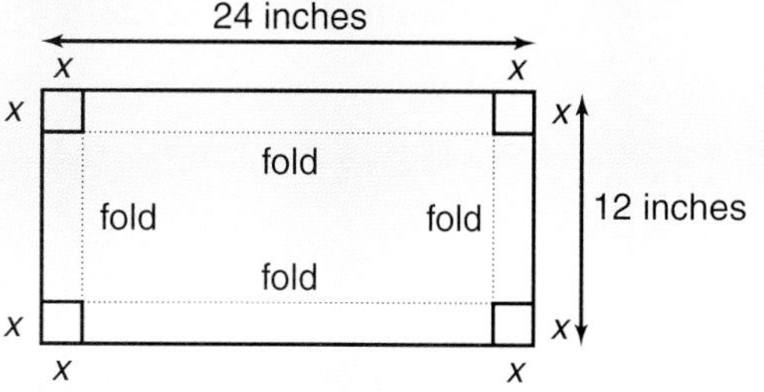

population increase per year itself increased by about 680,000 each year. It was calculated using the average rate of change numbers for 1970 and 1975.

$$\frac{75{,}800{,}000\ \frac{\text{people}}{\text{year}} - 72{,}400{,}000\ \frac{\text{people}}{\text{year}}}{(1975 - 1970)\text{ years}} = 680{,}000\ \frac{\frac{\text{people}}{\text{year}}}{\text{year}}$$

Year	World Population	Average rate of change	Average rate of change of average of rate of change
1960	3,039,000,000		
1965	3,345,000,000	61,200,000	
1970	3,707,000,000	72,400,000	2,240,000
1975	4,086,000,000	75,800,000	680,000
1980	4,454,000,000	73,600,000	-440,000
1985	4,850,000,000	79,200,000	1,120,000
1990	5,278,000,000	85,600,000	1,280,000
1995	5,687,000,000	81,800,000	-760,000

From 1975 to 1980, the population change per year lessened. It had been 75,800,000 people per year from 1970 to 1975; it became 73,600,000 people per year from 1975 to 1980. It is said that the population increase *decelerated*. When acceleration is negative, it is called **deceleration**.

You are, of course, familiar with the terms acceleration and deceleration as they pertain to buses or cars. These words have a similar meaning to that in the population growth example above. A car accelerates when its velocity (rate of change of position) increases. That is, the rate of change of velocity is what is called acceleration. For instance, if a car goes from 20 mph to 60 mph in 5 seconds, then its average acceleration—its average rate of change of velocity—is $\frac{40 \text{ mph}}{5 \text{ sec}}$ or 8 mph per second. A car is said to decelerate when its velocity decreases.

However, there is a difference between the world population and car acceleration examples. Population data are discrete whereas the positions of a car are thought of as being continuous. So the instantaneous acceleration for population cannot be defined, but instantaneous acceleration for the motion of an object can be defined.

Instantaneous Acceleration

The **instantaneous acceleration** $a(t)$ of a projectile or other object at time t is defined to be the instantaneous rate of change of its velocity with respect to time at time t. To compute it, take the derivative of the velocity function v at t:

$$a(t) = v'(t) = \lim_{\Delta t \to 0} \frac{v(t + \Delta t) - v(t)}{\Delta t}.$$

The units for acceleration are $\frac{\text{ft/sec}}{\text{sec}}$, the same as the units of the difference quotient $\frac{v(t + \Delta t) - v(t)}{\Delta t}$. This is written as feet per second per second or $\frac{\text{ft}}{\text{sec}^2}$.

In 1975–76, the Dow-Jones stock average increased by 143 points per year more than it had increased the previous year, the largest acceleration in growth of the average in this time period. (Note: Old data has purposely been used here because, in recent years, the changes have been so great that any one could tell when the change was greatest. This data also illustrates that there was a 20-year period in which the Dow-Jones average did not change that much. This may come as a surprise to some students.)

Notes on Reading

This lesson applies the ideas of the first three lessons to the first derivative itself. The discussion on page 577 shows that there is meaning for taking the rate of change of a rate of change. **Teaching Aid 100** shows the changes in world population.

Students may be familiar with the ideas of acceleration and with the fact that acceleration tells how fast the velocity is changing. Thus, it is natural that the acceleration is just the derivative of the velocity. This discussion provides a natural lead-in to acceleration as being the second derivative of distance from a starting point.

You might extend the graph-sketching activities of the first three lessons in this chapter. Give students a time versus distance graph of a car trip. Ask them to sketch plausible corresponding velocity and acceleration graphs. How is a slowdown in velocity reflected in the acceleration graph?

1. Find a formula $V(x)$ for the volume of a box in terms of x. [$V(x) = 4x^3 - 72x^2 + 288x$]
2. Given that $V'(x) = 12x^2 - 144x + 288$, find a formula for the acceleration of volume as a function of x. [$V''(x) = 24x - 144$]
3. What is the rate of change of volume expansion at $x = 1$? [$V''(1) = -120$ in^3 per in^2]
4. What is the "acceleration" at $x = 5$? What does this negative acceleration imply? [$V''(5) = -24$ in^3 per in^2; the volume is decreasing at a slower rate.]

Adapting to Individual Needs

Extra Help

Emphasize that we can speak of *average acceleration* whether the function is continuous or discrete; but we can only speak of *instantaneous acceleration* for a continuous function with first and second derivatives.

The **Example** finishes off the explanation for how the height of a projectile is modeled by a quadratic polynomial. Here we see that the coefficient of the square term is half of the acceleration.

Additional Examples

1. a. Suppose a projectile has height $h(t) = 960t - 16t^2$. Find the acceleration $a(t)$ of the projectile at any time t. **$a(t) = -32$ ft/sec^2**
   b. Determine the acceleration of the projectile at time $t = 4$ seconds. **$a(4) = -32$ ft/sec^2; These answers could be expected since the only force acting on the projectile is gravity.**
2. When an object moves so that its position at time t seconds is given by $s(t) = \frac{2}{3}t^3 - 8t^2 + 5t + 7$ m/sec, then the velocity of the object is given by $v(t) = 2t^2 - 16t + 5$.
   a. Find a formula for the acceleration of the object. **$a(t) = 4t - 16$**
   b. At time $t = 1$ minute, is the object speeding up or slowing down? **Speeding up**

Notes on Questions

Questions 5–6 Error Alert Be sure students understand the distinction between these two statements. The statement in **Question 6** is false because an object could have negative velocity but its acceleration could be positive; for instance, if an object was coming down to earth at a slower and slower pace.

Example

a. Find the instantaneous acceleration $a(t)$ of a projectile whose position at time t is given by $h(t) = 800t - 16t^2$.
b. Determine the instantaneous acceleration of the projectile at $t = 20$ sec.

Solution

a. By definition, the acceleration $a(t)$ is the derivative of the velocity function.
Since $v(t) = 800 - 32t$, From Lesson 9-3, Example 1
then $v'(t) = -32$. Derivative of a Linear Function Theorem
$\therefore$ for all t, $a(t) = -32 \frac{ft}{sec^2}$.

b. Since $a(t) = -32$ for *all* values of t, the acceleration at t = 20 sec is $-32 \frac{ft}{sec^2}$.

Acceleration and Derivatives

In general, position, velocity, and acceleration are related as follows:

acceleration = derivative of velocity
acceleration = derivative of (derivative of position).

Another way to state the relationship between position and acceleration is to say the following:

Let $s(t)$ represent the position of an object at time t. Then instantaneous velocity at time $t = v(t) = s'(t)$, and instantaneous acceleration at time $t = a(t) = v'(t) = (s')'(t)$.

Because acceleration is a derivative of a derivative, acceleration is said to be the *second derivative* of position with respect to time, written $a(t) = s''(t)$.

Given an arbitrary function f, the derivative function f' of f is called the **first derivative** of f. The **second derivative** of f is the derivative of the first derivative and is denoted f''.

The functions h, v, and a of the Example are graphed below.

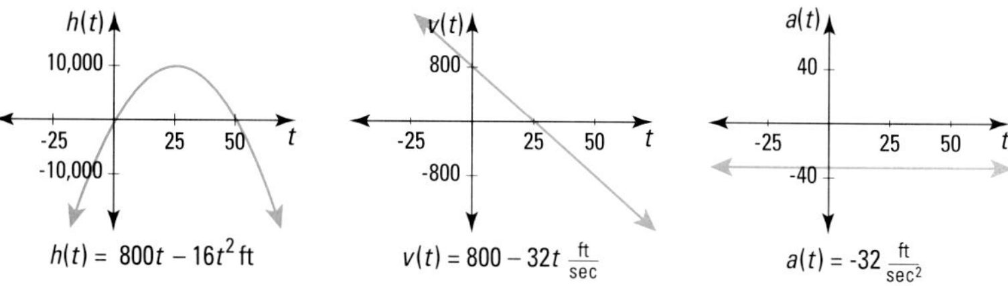

The equation $h(t) = 800t - 16t^2$ is of the form $h(t) = v_0t - \frac{1}{2}gt^2$, the equation for the height of a projectile at time t if v_0 is the initial velocity and g is the acceleration due to gravity. You can see that v_0 is, in fact, the value of the first derivative $v(t)$ when $t = 0$, and g is -32 ft/sec^2, the second derivative of $v(t)$ for all t. This is the constant acceleration due to the gravity of Earth. When the acceleration is constant, people usually do not speak of the *instantaneous acceleration at time t*, but simply *the acceleration*.

Adapting to Individual Needs

Challenge

Pose this problem: The height, in feet after t seconds, of a ball dropped from an initial height of 144 feet is $h(t) = -16t^2 + 144$.

1. How long does it take the ball to hit the ground? [3 seconds]
2. What is the ball's velocity at the time of impact? [-96 ft/sec]
3. What is the ball's average velocity? [-32 ft/sec]
4. At what time and height is the ball traveling at that velocity? [1 sec; 128 ft]

Additional Answers

1. **61,200,000 is the average rate of change in world population for the years 1960 to 1965. It is found by taking one-fifth of the difference between the 1965 and 1960 populations.**

10.

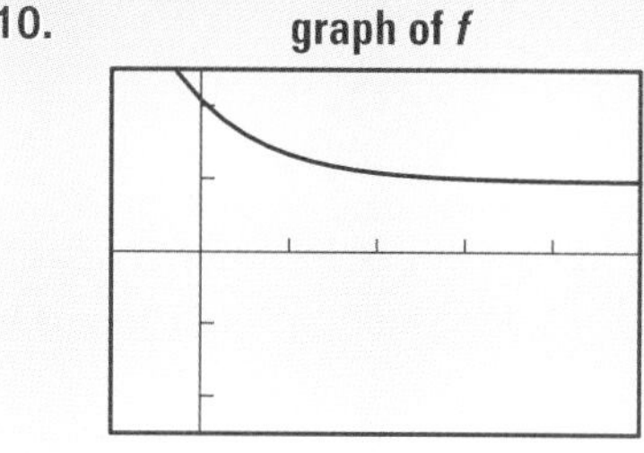

$-2 \le x \le 10$, x-scale = 2
$-180 \le y \le 180$, y-scale = 80

QUESTIONS

Covering the Reading

In 1–3, use the world population data in this lesson.

1. What does the number 61,200,000 in the third column mean, and how was it calculated? **See margin.**

2. What is the average rate of change of the average rate of change of population from 1975 to 1980? **-440,000 $\frac{\text{people}}{\text{year}}$ per year**

3. If the average acceleration of the world population had remained the same from 1990 to 1995 as it was from 1985 to 1990, what would the population have been in 1995? **5,363,600,000 people**

4. A car went from 0 to 60 mph in 6 seconds. What was its average acceleration during this time interval? **10 mph/sec**

5. *True or false.* If the acceleration of a moving object is negative, then its velocity is decreasing. **True**

6. *True or false.* If the velocity of a moving object is negative, then the acceleration of the object is negative. **False**

7. a. Is the height of the projectile in the Example increasing or is it decreasing at time $t = 3$ seconds? **increasing**
   b. Is its velocity increasing or is it decreasing at this time? **decreasing**
   c. Is its acceleration increasing or is it decreasing at this time? **Neither; it is always -32 ft/sec^2**

8. Let $s(t) = 10 + 15t - 4.9t^2$ be the height (in meters) of an object at time t.
   a. Find the velocity $v(t)$ at time t. **$v(t) = s'(t) = 15 - 9.8t$ m/sec**
   b. Find the acceleration $a(t)$ at time t. **$a(t) = v'(t) = s''(t) = -9.8$ m/sec^2**

Applying the Mathematics

In 9 and 10, a hot object is placed on a table to cool. The temperature (in degrees Fahrenheit) of the object after x minutes is given by

$$f(x) = 80e^{-0.555x} + 70.$$

9. What units should be used to measure the second derivative of f? **See left.**

9) **$\frac{\text{degree Fahrenheit}}{\text{min}}$ per minute or degrees Fahrenheit/min^2**

10. For this function, the first derivative is $f'(x) = -44.4e^{-0.555x}$ and the second derivative of f is $f''(x) = 24.642e^{-0.555x}$. Use an automatic grapher to graph f, f', and f'' over the interval $0 \le x \le 10$. (Use a separate set of axes for each function.) **See margin.**
   a. How fast is the rate of cooling changing at time $t = 2$ minutes?
   b. How fast is the temperature changing at time $t = 2$ minutes?
   c. At what time during the first 10 minutes is the rate of cooling changing the fastest?
   d. At what time during the first 10 minutes is the rate of cooling changing the slowest?

Questions 9–10 These questions preview Lesson 9-6, where exponential functions are discussed. At this time you might just note that exponential functions have the property that their derivatives are exponential with the same base.

(Notes on Questions continue on page 580.)

Follow-up for Lesson 9-4

Practice

For more questions on SPUR Objectives, use **Lesson Master 9-4** (shown below).

Assessment

Written Communication Give students the general equation $h(t) = \frac{1}{2}gt^2 + v_0t + h_0$ for the height h at time t of a projectile, where g is the constant acceleration due to the gravity of Earth (-32 ft/sec^2 or 9.8 m/sec^2), v_0 is the initial velocity, and h_0 is the initial height. Have each student make up and solve a problem like **Question 8.** [Students use derivatives to find the velocity and acceleration of a moving object.]

(Follow-up continues on page 580.)

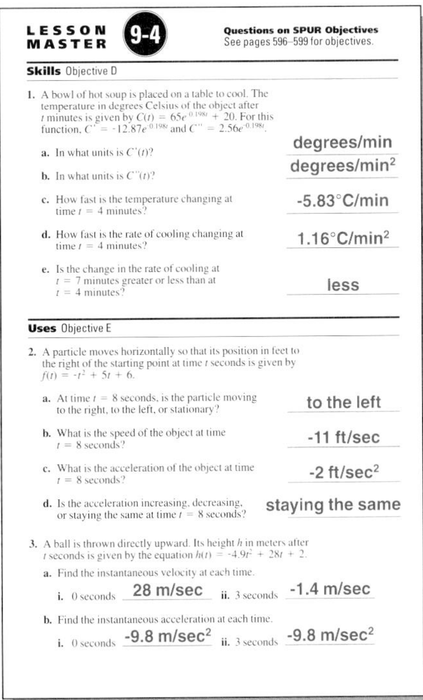

LESSON MASTER 9-4 **Questions on SPUR Objectives** See pages 596–599 for objectives.

Skills Objective D

1. A bowl of hot soup is placed on a table to cool. The temperature in degrees Celsius of the object after t minutes is given by $C(t) = 65e^{-0.198t} + 20$. For this function, $C' = -12.87e^{-0.198t}$ and $C'' = 2.56e^{-0.198t}$.
   a. In what units is $C'(t)$? **degrees/min**
   b. In what units is $C''(t)$? **degrees/min^2**
   c. How fast is the temperature changing at time $t = 4$ minutes? **-5.83°C/min**
   d. How fast is the rate of cooling changing at time $t = 4$ minutes? **1.16°C/min^2**
   e. Is the change in the rate of cooling at $t = 7$ minutes greater or less than at $t = 4$ minutes? **less**

Uses Objective E

2. A particle moves horizontally so that its position in feet to the right of the starting point at time t seconds is given by $f(t) = -t^2 + 5t + 6$.
   a. At time $t = 8$ seconds, is the particle moving to the right, to the left, or stationary? **to the left**
   b. What is the speed of the object at time $t = 8$ seconds? **-11 ft/sec**
   c. What is the acceleration of the object at time $t = 8$ seconds? **-2 ft/sec^2**
   d. Is the acceleration increasing, decreasing, or staying the same at time $t = 8$ seconds? **staying the same**

3. A ball is thrown directly upward. Its height h in meters after t seconds is given by the equation $h(t) = -4.9t^2 + 28t + 2$.
   a. Find the instantaneous velocity at each time.
      i. 0 seconds **28 m/sec** ii. 3 seconds **-1.4 m/sec**
   b. Find the instantaneous acceleration at each time.
      i. 0 seconds **-9.8 m/sec^2** ii. 3 seconds **-9.8 m/sec^2**

10. (continued)

graph of f'

$-2 \le x \le 10$, x-scale = 2
$-50 \le y \le 10$, y-scale = 20

graph of f''

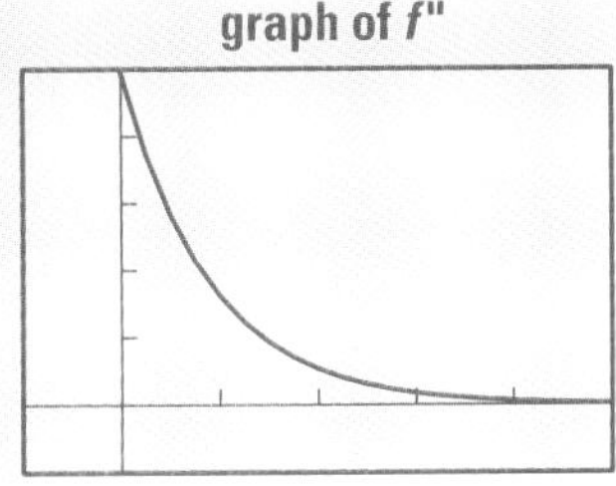

$-2 \le x \le 10$, x-scale = 2
$-5 \le y \le 25$, y-scale = 5

a. ≈ 8.12 degrees/min
b. ≈ -14.63 degrees/min^2
c. at the beginning; $t = 0$
d. at the end; $t = 10$

Extension

Have interested students research the populations for a number of the European countries since about 1975 and discuss the implications of this on the world population. [Thirteen of the European countries have a zero growth rate, meaning that births and deaths are in equilibrium.]

Project Update Project 2, *The History of Calculus,* on page 592, relates to the content of this lesson.

Notes on Questions

Question 12 This question again requires students to graph the first derivative by investigating the graph of the function. You might do this problem in class.

Questions 13 and 17 This surprising result, that for positive x the derivative of the log function is the reciprocal function, deserves some explanation. Take choice I of **Question 17** and draw tangents to the graph at various points. It is obvious that when x is near zero, the slope of the tangent is quite large, and that this slope decreases to near zero as x becomes large. This suggests a graph like that of $y = \frac{1}{x}$.

11. Refer to the world population data in this lesson. If the acceleration of the world population remained the same from 1995 to 2025 as it was from 1990 to 1995, what would the population be in 2025? **7,742,000,000**

Review

12. A function f is graphed at the left along with some tangents to the graph. Estimate $f'(x)$ at the three points shown and sketch a graph of f'. *(Lesson 9-3)* **See left.**

12) $f'(1) \approx -2$, $f'(4) \approx 1$
$f'(6) \approx \frac{1}{2}$

13. The derivative of $g(x) = \ln x$ is $g'(x) = \frac{1}{x}$ for all $x > 0$. What is the slope of the tangent line to the graph of g at the point $(2, g(2))$? *(Lesson 9-3)* $\frac{1}{2}$

14. Prove that 3 is a factor of $n^3 + 2n$ for all positive integers n. *(Lesson 7-4)* **See margin.**

15. Prove the identity $\sin^2 x = \frac{1 - \cos 2x}{2}$. (Hint: Begin with an identity for $\cos 2x$.) *(Lessons 6-2, 6-6)* **See margin.**

16. Let $f: x \to \frac{x^3 - 2x^2 - x + 2}{x^2 + x - 2}$ be a real function. *(Lessons 2-1, 5-4, 5-5)*
- **a.** What is the domain of f? **all real numbers except $x = -2$ or $x = 1$**
- **b.** Use an automatic grapher to graph f. Classify the discontinuities of f as removable or essential. **See margin.**
- **c.** Write equations for any horizontal or vertical asymptotes. **$x = -2$**

17. Match each graph with the appropriate function.

I. 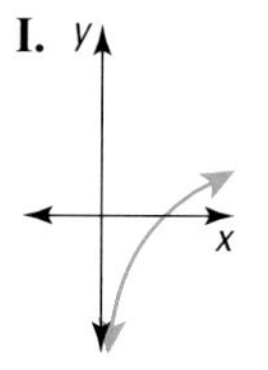

II. 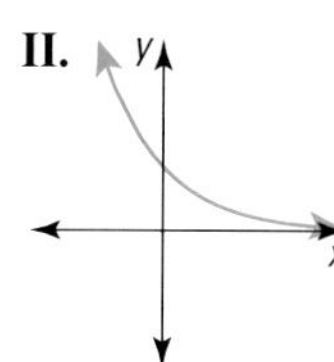

III. 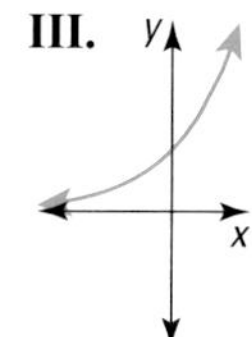

IV. 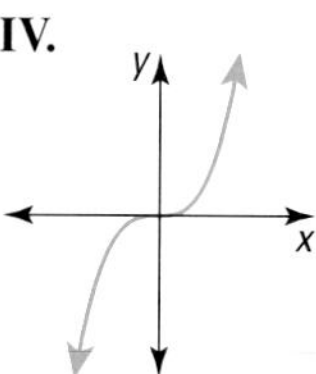

a. $y = e^x$ **III** **b.** $y = x^3$ **IV** 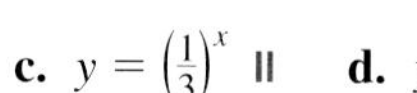 **c.** $y = \left(\frac{1}{3}\right)^x$ **II** **d.** $y = \ln x$ **I**
(Previous course, Lessons 2-7, 2-9)

The Force of Gravity

Exploration

18. What do the following mean? **See margin.**
- **a.** an acceleration in housing starts (real estate)
- **b.** a deceleration in unemployment (labor)
- **c.** the acceleration principle (economics)
- **d.** the acceleration due to gravity (physics)

19. Look on the Internet for a recent estimate of what the world population will be in 2025.
- **a.** Does this estimate assume that the average rate of change in world population will increase?
- **b.** Does it assume that the change in world population is accelerating or decelerating?

Answers will vary.

Additional Answers

14. $S(1) = 1^3 + 2(1) = 3$ has 3 as a factor so $S(1)$ is true. Assume $S(k) = k^3 + 2k$ has a factor of 3. Then $S(k + 1) = k^3 + 3k^2 + 3k + 1 + 2k + 2 = (k^3 + 2k) + (3k^2 + 3k + 3)$. $k^3 + 2k$ has a factor of 3 and $3k^2 + 3k + 3 = 3(k^2 + k + 1)$ so it has a factor of 3. Thus, $S(k) \Rightarrow S(k + 1)$ and by Mathematical Induction $n^3 + 2n$ has a factor of 3 for all integers n.

15. $\cos 2x = \cos^2 x - \sin^2 x$
$\cos 2x = (1 - \sin^2 x) - \sin^2 x$ Pythagorean Identity
$\cos 2x = 1 - 2\sin^2 x$ Addition
$2\sin^2 x = 1 - \cos 2x$
$\sin^2 x = \frac{1 - \cos 2x}{2}$

16. b. Removable discontinuity at $x = 1$, essential discontinuity at $x = -2$

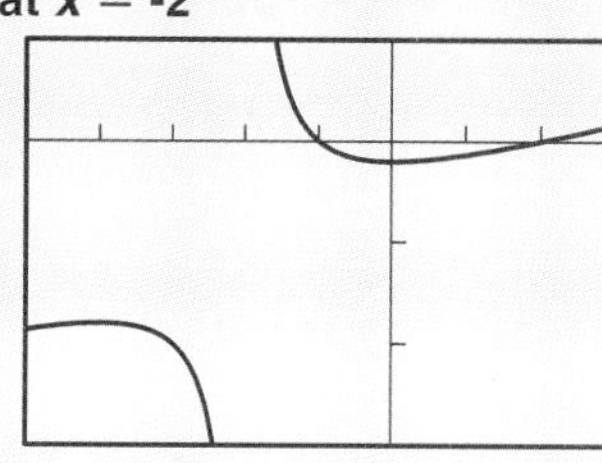

$-5 \le x \le 3$, x-scale $= 1$
$-15 \le y \le 5$, y-scale $= 5$

18. Sample:
- a. There were more houses begun (to be built) in the current period than in the previous period.
- b. The unemployment level started dropping more slowly.
- c. The principle that an increase in the demand will create a greater demand for capital goods.
- d. Two bodies attract each other and that force causes them to come together at an ever-increasing velocity.

LESSON

9-5

Using Derivatives to Analyze Graphs

Using Derivatives to Determine Where a Function Is Increasing or Decreasing

In Lesson 9-3 it was stated that the derivative of the sine function is the cosine function. Now compare the graphs of these functions in a new way. When the value of the cosine function (in blue) is positive, as it is between $x = -\frac{\pi}{2}$ and $x = \frac{\pi}{2}$, the sine function (in orange) is increasing. When the value of the cosine function is negative, as it is between $x = \frac{\pi}{2}$ and $x = \frac{3\pi}{2}$, the sine function is decreasing.

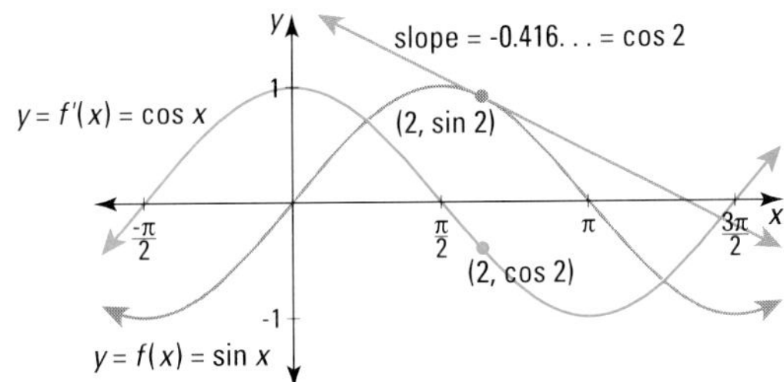

This is because the values of the derivative function are the slopes of lines tangent to the graph of the function. When the slopes of tangents to the graph of a function are positive, the function is increasing. When the slopes of tangents to the graph of a function are negative, the function is decreasing.

These important facts are summarized in the theorem below.

> **Theorem**
> Suppose f is a function whose derivative function f' exists for all x in the interval $a < x < b$.
>
> (1) If $f'(x) > 0 \; \forall \; x$ in the interval $a < x < b$, then f is increasing on the interval.
> (2) If $f'(x) < 0 \; \forall \; x$ in the interval $a < x < b$, then f is decreasing on the interval.

Lesson 9-5

Objectives

C Use derivatives to identify properties of functions.
F Use derivatives to solve optimization problems.
I Determine properties of derivatives from the graph of a function.

Resources

From the ***Teacher's Resource File***
- Lesson Master 9-5
- Answer Master 9-5
- Teaching Aids
  - 88 Warm-up
  - 101 Questions 10–12

Additional Resources
- Visuals for Teaching Aids 88, 101
- Exploration 9-5

Warm-up

Consider the quadratic function q with $q(x) = 9x^2 - 27x + 12$.

1. Use the Derivative of a Quadratic Function formula to determine a formula for q'. **$q'(x) = 18x - 27$**
2. For what values of x is $q'(x) > 0$? **$x > 1.5$**
3. Graph q. From the graph of q, for what values of x is q an increasing function? **The graph is a parabola with minimum point at (1.5, 8.25); q is increasing for values of x larger than 1.5.**
4. Compare your answers from parts **2** and **3** above. **The value of x for which q is increasing are those values for which the derivative is positive.**

Notes on Reading

In the previous lessons, students have learned that there is meaning to the value of the derivative, and they may have already been aware of the theorem on this page. The second use of the derivative found on page 582 is an outgrowth of this first use, namely to find points of relative maxima or minima.

Lesson 9-5 Overview

Broad Goals This lesson brings together and extends the geometric ideas about the derivative that have been discussed in earlier lessons and the definitions of increasing and decreasing functions from Lesson 2-3. The key ideas are: a function whose derivative exists on an interval is (1) increasing on that interval if the derivative is positive, (2) decreasing on that interval if the derivative is negative, and (3) either has a relative minimum or maximum or "flattens out" where the derivative is zero.

Perspective The key ideas are not proved but induced visually from what is known about derivatives as slopes of tangents to curves. From these ideas, the coordinates of the vertex of the graph of a quadratic function can be deduced. This is a result students have seen before, but it provides a nice completion to the projectile example that have been used throughout the chapter.

You might wish to continue the projectile idea. Suppose you toss a ball into the air. Then it is going up (positive velocity, positive derivative) at first and going down (negative velocity, negative derivative) later. The velocity function is continuous, so there is an intermediate value at which the velocity is zero. At that point, the ball is neither going up nor down; it is at its maximum height.

❶ The discussion about relative maxima/minima and the derivative provides an opportunity for reviewing logic from Chapter 1. The relationship is: *If a function has a relative maximum or relative minimum value at a point and the derivative exists at that point, then the derivative at that point is zero.*

But the graphs point out the fact that the converse is not true. Even if the derivative is zero at a point, there may not be a relative maximum or minimum value at that point. You might say that zeros of first derivatives are merely candidates to be x-coordinates of relative minimum or maximum points.

For **Example 1,** use an automatic grapher to display the graphs of $y = f(x)$ and $y = f'(x)$ simultaneously. Point out how zeros and positive or negative intervals of $y = f'(x)$ are related to the graph of $y = f(x)$.

Example 1

Prove that $f(x) = x^3 - 6x^2 + 9x - 5$ is decreasing on the interval $1 < x < 3$ using the theorem on page 581 and the fact that $f'(x) = 3x^2 - 12x + 9$.

Solution

It would be very difficult to prove that f is decreasing on $1 < x < 3$ by the methods of Lesson 2-3. But, if the theorem on page 581 is used, then it is only necessary to show that $f'(x) < 0$ for all x in the interval $1 < x < 3$. This can be done using the Test-Point Method. Note that f' is continuous and $f'(x) = 3(x^2 - 4x + 3) = 3(x - 3)(x - 1)$. Therefore $f'(1) = 0$ and $f'(3) = 0$ and 1 and 3 are consecutive zeros. A convenient test point is $x = 2$. Since $f'(2) = 3(2)^2 - 12(2) + 9 = -3$, it follows that $f'(x) < 0$ for all x in the interval $1 < x < 3$. Therefore, by the above theorem, f is decreasing on $1 < x < 3$.

❶ Using Derivatives to Find Maxima or Minima

What if the value of the derivative at a particular point is zero? Then the situation is more complex. The point may be a relative maximum or minimum (as in the graph at the left) or the point may indicate where the graph is flat or momentarily "flattens out" (as in the graph at the right).

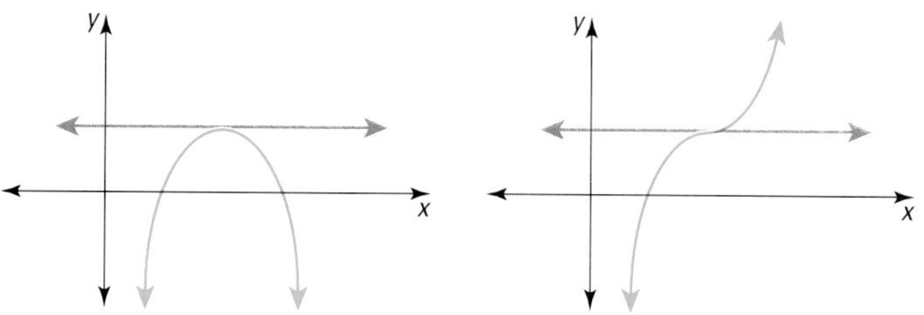

Certainly, if there is a relative maximum or minimum point, and the graph of the function is smooth, then the derivative will be zero. This fact can be used to give an elegant proof, using calculus, of a result that you may have seen before.

❷ **Vertex of a Parabola Theorem**

Let a, b, and c be real numbers with $a \neq 0$. Then the parabola that is the graph of $f(x) = ax^2 + bx + c$ has its vertex at the point where $x = -\frac{b}{2a}$.

Proof

The vertex is at the point where the derivative of f is zero.

Since $f'(x) = 2ax + b$,

the vertex is at the point where

$$0 = 2ax + b.$$

Thus $x = -\frac{b}{2a}$.

Optional Activities

Activity 1 Technology Connection
Materials: Explorations software

Students may use *Exploration 9-5, Functions and Derivative Functions,* as an alternative to **Example 1.** Students can choose different functions from a list or enter their own. The program has a table of values and graphs of the function and its derivative. Areas of increasing and decreasing values for the function are indicated with background colors.

Activity 2 You might ask students to generalize **Questions 10–11.** That is, if f' is a straight non-vertical line, what are possible graphs for f? [If f' is a horizontal line, $f' = a$, $a > 0$, then f is an oblique line with a positive slope. If f' is a horizontal line, $f' = b$, $b < 0$, then f is an oblique line with a negative slope. If f' is an oblique line with a positive slope, then f is parabola that opens upward. If f' is an oblique line with a negative slope, then f is a parabola that opens downward.]

Adapting to Individual Needs

Extra Help

In **Example 3,** some forgetful students may think that if the amount of fencing is fixed, then the area is also fixed. A table of lengths, widths, and corresponding areas will quickly dispel that belief. Symmetry of areas around the maximum is also worth seeing again.

Example 2

What is the maximum height reached by our favorite projectile, the one whose height at time t is given by $h(t) = 800t - 16t^2$?

Solution

Use the Vertex of a Parabola Theorem. When $h(t) = 800t - 16t^2$, $a = -16$ and $b = 800$. So the maximum height occurs at time $t = -\frac{b}{2a} = -\frac{800}{-32} = 25$ seconds. That height is $h(25)$, so substitute $t = 25$ into the formula for $h(t)$.

$$h(25) = 800 \cdot 25 - 16 \cdot 25^2 = 10{,}000$$

The projectile thus reaches a maximum height of 10,000 feet.

The next example illustrates the use of the preceding theorem to solve what is called an **optimization problem**—one in which the value of one variable is sought to obtain the most optimal, or desirable, value of another.

Example 3

A rectangular region adjacent to a building is to be enclosed with 120 feet of fencing. What should the dimensions of the region be in order to maximize the enclosed area?

Solution

In this case, the variable to be optimized is the area of the region. The area is a function of length and width, which are to be chosen. However, since the fencing is limited to 120 feet, choosing one dimension, say the width w, forces a choice for the other, the length $\ell = 120 - 2w$. Thus, the area can be described as a function of the width:

$$\begin{aligned} A(w) &= \ell w \\ &= (120 - 2w)w \\ &= 120w - 2w^2. \end{aligned}$$

Notice that the graph of A is a parabola which opens downward, so that A has a maximum at its vertex. Thus, the maximum area is obtained when the width is chosen to correspond to this vertex; that is, when

$$w = -\frac{b}{2a} = \frac{-120}{2(-2)} = 30.$$

Then $\ell = 120 - 2(30) = 60.$

Thus the optimal dimensions of the region are 30 ft x 60 ft. The maximum area is 1800 sq ft.

Check

Try increasing or decreasing the width just a little and calculating the area. If $w = 30.1$, then $\ell = 59.8$ and $A = 1799.98$ sq ft. If $w = 29.9$, then $\ell = 60.2$ and again $A = 1799.98$. Since $1799.98 < 1800$, this checks that the value $w = 30$ yields a relative maximum.

❷ The Vertex of a Parabola Theorem should not be new to students. In fact, they may have proved this result algebraically in an earlier course. Now, however, they can use the tools of calculus to provide a sophisticated proof of the vertex relationship. Remind students that $f'(x) = 2ax + b$ was the conclusion of the Derivative of a Quadratic Function Theorem in Lesson 9-3.

Error Alert In **Example 2,** some students must be reminded that while the zero of $h'(t)$ provides the time at which the maximum height is reached, the height itself is calculated using $h(t)$.

Example 3 applies calculus tools to solve a type of problem that was solved by means of an automatic grapher in Chapter 2. Help students see the value of different problem-solving techniques and when one technique might be used over another.

Students sometimes think that optimization problems are all either obvious or contrived. You might point out that they often use an optimization problem when studying for tests. Students wish to optimize their total score. But there is a cost involved; students must study. So most students study long enough to get a good score but not so long that they cannot do their other obligations or have fun.

Adapting to Individual Needs

Challenge

Let $f(x) = x^3 + x + 2$. Have students answer the following questions.

1. Find $f'(x)$. [$3x^2 + 1$]
2. Write an equation for the tangent line to the graph of f at (2, 12). [$y = 13x - 14$]
3. Use a graph to verify your result.
4. Give the intervals of increasing and decreasing. [Always increasing]
5. Explain why the graph of f has no relative maximum or minimum points. [At no point does the function change from increasing to decreasing.]

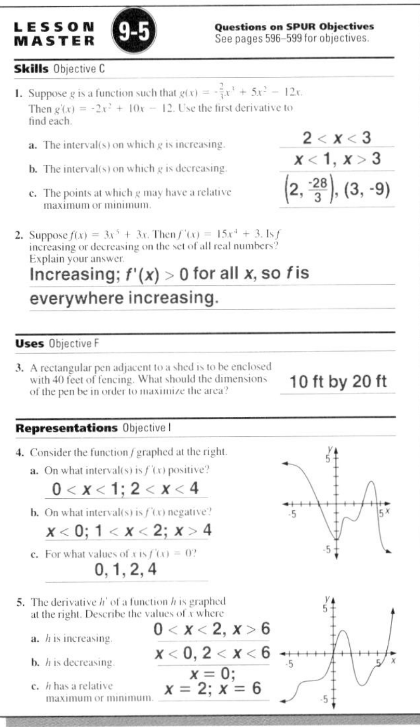

LESSON MASTER 9-5 **Questions on SPUR Objectives** See pages 596–599 for objectives.

Skills Objective C

1. Suppose g is a function such that $g(x) = -\frac{2}{3}x^3 + 5x^2 - 12x$. Then $g'(x) = -2x^2 + 10x - 12$. Use the first derivative to find each.
   a. The interval(s) on which g is increasing. $2 < x < 3$
   b. The interval(s) on which g is decreasing. $x < 1, x > 3$
   c. The points at which g may have a relative maximum or minimum. $\left(2, \frac{-28}{3}\right), (3, -9)$

2. Suppose $f(x) = 3x^5 + 3x$. Then $f'(x) = 15x^4 + 3$. Is f increasing or decreasing on the set of all real numbers? Explain your answer.
   Increasing; $f'(x) > 0$ for all x, so f is everywhere increasing.

Uses Objective F

3. A rectangular pen adjacent to a shed is to be enclosed with 40 feet of fencing. What should the dimensions of the pen be in order to maximize the area? 10 ft by 20 ft

Representations Objective I

4. Consider the function f graphed at the right.
   a. On what interval(s) is $f'(x)$ positive? $0 < x < 1; 2 < x < 4$
   b. On what interval(s) is $f'(x)$ negative? $x < 0; 1 < x < 2; x > 4$
   c. For what values of x is $f'(x) = 0$? 0, 1, 2, 4

5. The derivative h' of a function h is graphed at the right. Describe the values of x where
   a. h is increasing. $0 < x < 2, x > 6$
   b. h is decreasing. $x < 0, 2 < x < 6$
   c. h has a relative maximum or minimum. $x = 0; x = 2; x = 6$

Additional Examples

1. Given that $f(x) = \frac{1}{3}x^3 - x^2 - 8x + 12$ and that $f'(x) = x^2 - 2x - 8$, determine the intervals where f is increasing and the intervals where f is decreasing. **f increases on $(-\infty, -2)$ or $(4, \infty)$; f decreases on $[-2, 4]$. An automatic grapher can easily verify this solution. Set $-6 \le x \le 10$ and $-50 \le y \le 50$ for a good view.**
2. Using the height function from Additional Example 1 of Lesson 9-1, $h(t) = 960t - 16t^2$, what is the maximum height reached by a projectile propelled straight up. **14,400 feet, which is approximately 2.73 miles**
3. In **Example 3** of this lesson, suppose that the rectangular region adjacent to the building is to be enclosed and divided into 3 separate dog runs using the 120 feet of fencing. What dimensions will result in a region of total maximum area?

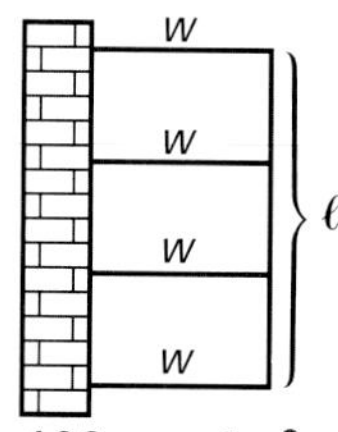

$A(w) = 120w - 4w^2$, so $A'(w) = 120 - 8w$. The maximum area is achieved if $w = 15$ and $\ell = 60$. This area is 900 square feet.

4b) $h'(n\pi) = 0$ for all integers n

8d) $\left(-1, \frac{20}{3}\right)$, $(3, -4)$

e)

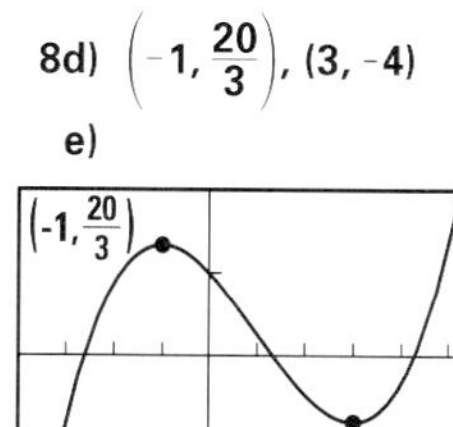

$-4 \le x \le 6$, x-scale = 1
$-10 \le y \le 10$, y-scale = 5

QUESTIONS

Covering the Reading

1. The derivative g' of a function g is graphed at the right.
   a. On what intervals is g increasing?
   b. On what intervals is g decreasing? **$-2 < x < 1$**

   a) $x < -2$ or $x > 1$

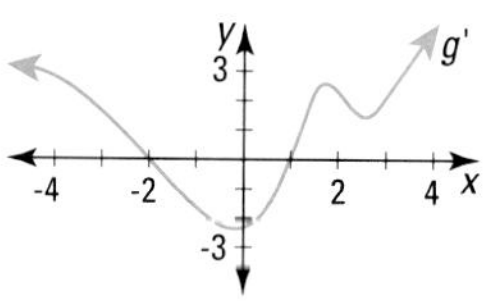

2. Use the derivative to determine the largest intervals on which $f(x) = -2x^2 + 3x + 1$ is increasing and on which it is decreasing. **See margin.**
3. Use the fact that if $f(x) = -x^3 + 3x^2 - 3x$, then $f'(x) = -3x^2 + 6x - 3$.
   a. Graph f and f'. **See margin.**
   b. For what values of x does the graph of f' lie below the x-axis? What does this tell you about f? **all values except $x = 1$; $f(x)$ is everywhere decreasing except at $x = 1$**
   c. Find $f'(1)$. **0**
   d. Does f have a relative maximum or have a relative minimum at $x = 1$? Explain your choice. **See margin.**
4. a. Find all x such that $h(x) = \cos x$ has a relative maximum or relative minimum at x. **$x = n\pi$ for all integers n.**
   b. What does your answer to part **a** tell you about h'? **See left.**
5. If $f(x) = 2x^3 - x^2 + 1$, then $f'(x) = 6x^2 - 2x$. Is f increasing or decreasing on the interval $0 < x < \frac{1}{3}$? **decreasing**
6. A rock is thrown upwards so that its height (in feet) t seconds after being thrown is given by $h(t) = -16t^2 + 30t + 10$. What is the maximum height that it achieves? **≈ 24 ft**
7. Let P be a positive real number. Find the dimensions of the rectangle of maximum area that has perimeter P. **$l = w = \frac{P}{4}$**

Applying the Mathematics

8. Use the fact that if $f(x) = \frac{1}{3}x^3 - x^2 - 3x + 5$, then $f'(x) = x^2 - 2x - 3$.
   a. Compute f''. **$f''(x) = 2x - 2$**
   b. Determine the intervals on which f is increasing. **$x < -1$ or $x > 3$**
   c. Determine the intervals on which f is decreasing. **$-1 < x < 3$**
   d. Use f' to find possible relative minima and maxima. **See left.**
   e. Check your answers to parts **b–d** above by plotting the function using an automatic grapher. **See left.**
9. On a certain interval, as one travels along the graph of $y = f(x)$ from left to right, the slopes of the tangents to the curve are increasing. Must the function be increasing on the interval? Explain your answer. **See margin.**

Additional Answers

2. Increasing: $x < \frac{3}{4}$; decreasing: $x > \frac{3}{4}$
3. a. See the graph at the right.
   d. No; as the graph shows, $f(x)$ merely "flattens out" at $x = 1$.

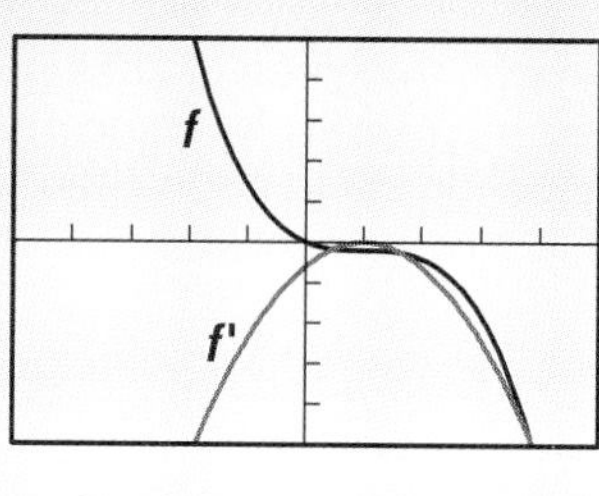

$-5 \le x \le 5$, x-scale = 1
$-25 \le y \le 25$, y-scale = 5

9. No; for example, consider the function $y = x^2$ graphed at the right. As x goes from -4 to -3 to -2 to -1 to 0, $f'(x)$ goes from -8 to -6 to -4 to -2 to 0. Those slopes are increasing, but the function is decreasing.

In 10–12, the graph of f' is given. *Multiple choice.* Tell which of the other graphs could be f. **10) a 11) b 12) a**

0. 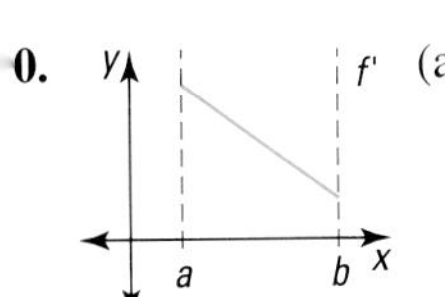 (a) 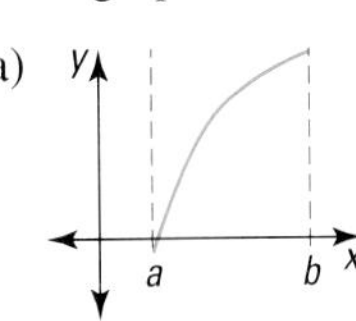 (b) 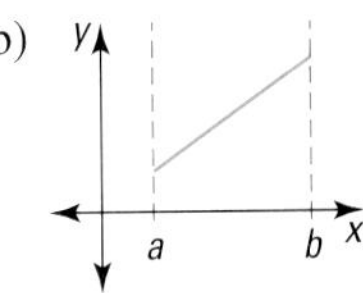 (c) 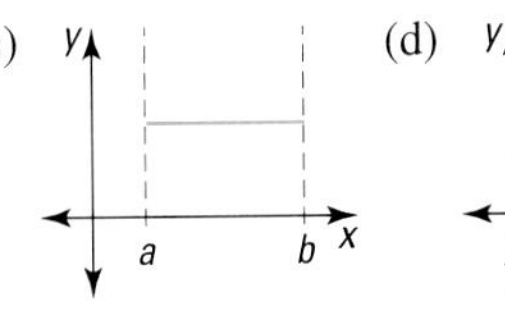 (d) 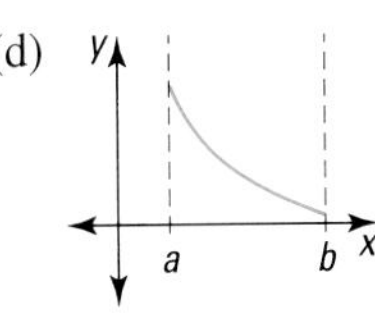

1. 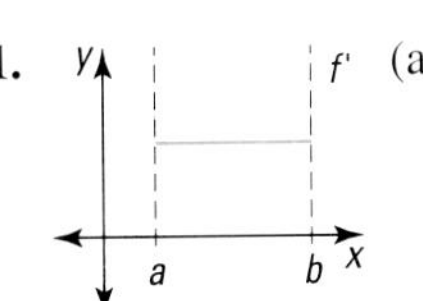 (a) 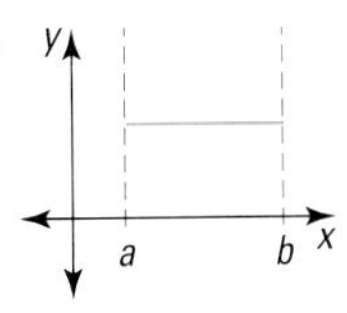 (b) 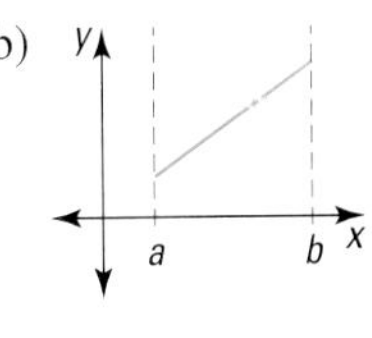 (c) 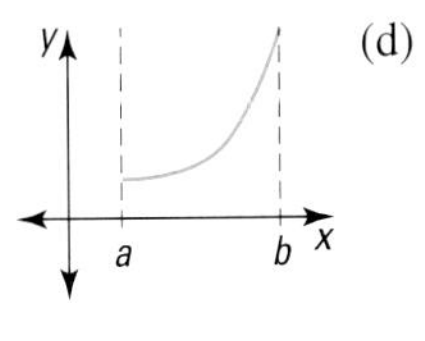 (d) 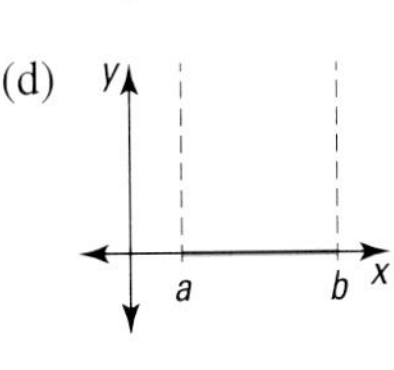

2. 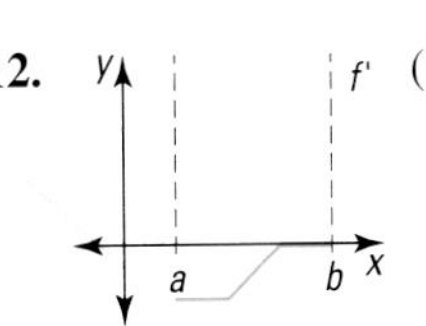 (a) 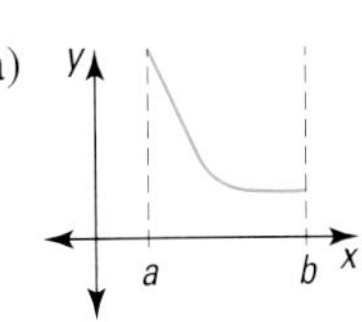 (b) 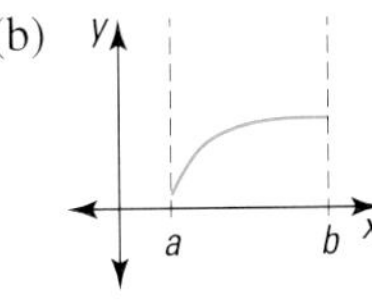 (c) 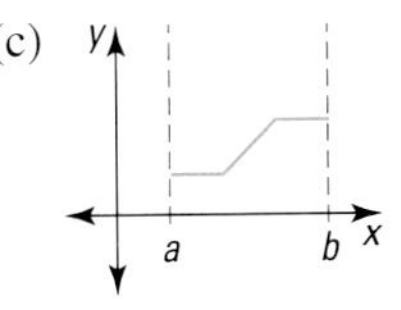 (d) 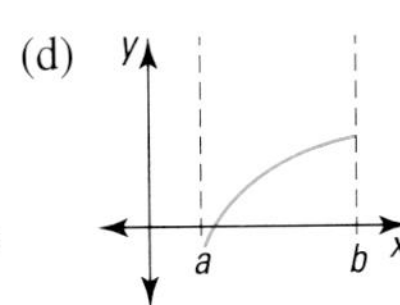

Review

13a) The curve is increasing from April to July and from October to December.

Jan Apr July Oct

b) i) True ii) False iii) True iv) False

13. The table below gives the average price of a certain stock each month throughout a particular year. **See left.**

month	Jan	Feb	Mar	Apr	May	Jun	Jul	Aug	Sep	Oct	Nov	Dec
price ($)	22	20	19	18.5	19	20.5	23	22.5	21.5	20	22	22.5

Draw a scatterplot of price vs. month. Sketch a curve to fit the data.

a. Determine where the curve is increasing.

b. Determine whether each statement is *true or false*.

i. The average price of the stock rose from April to July.

ii. The average price of the stock fell from October to December.

iii. The pace at which the average price of the stock fell increased from July to October.

iv. The pace at which the average price of the stock rose decreased from April to July. *(Lesson 9-4)*

14. A particle moves so that its position (in feet) after t seconds is given by $f(t) = 2t^2 + 3t - 1$. **a) $v(3) = 15$ ft/sec**

a. Find the instantaneous velocity of the particle at time $t = 3$ seconds.

b. What is the acceleration at $t = 3$ seconds? *(Lessons 9-3, 9-4)*
$a(3) = 4$ ft/sec^2

15. Let $f(x) = e^{-x^2}$. The derivative function of f is $f'(x) = -2xe^{-x^2}$. Find the slope of the tangent line to the graph of f at the point $(1, f(1))$. *(Lessons 9-2, 9-3)* **$f'(1) = -2e^{-1} \approx -.74$**

Notes on Questions

Question 3 If you discussed the Exploration **Question 23** of Lesson 9-3, then you can explain how $f'(x)$ is found from $f(x)$ without having to go through the calculation. Even if you did not do that question, you should discuss this question. It relates the sign of the derivative to whether the function is increasing or decreasing and also relates the derivative to maximum/minimum values.

Questions 10–12 These questions reinforce the geometric interpretation of the derivative. You may want to consider doing one of these problems in class before students do the other two for homework. **Teaching Aid 101** is provided to ease explanation.

9. continued

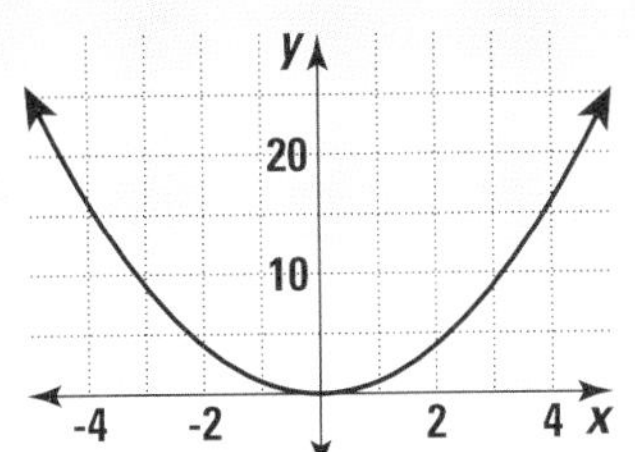

Follow-up for Lesson 9-5

Practice

For more questions on SPUR Objectives, use **Lesson Master 9-5** (shown on page 583).

Assessment

Oral Communication Have students explain how they arrived at their answers for **Questions 10–12.** [Students use the graph of the derivative of a function to describe the behavior of the function.]

Extension

Social Studies Connection Give students an example of an optimization problem in the area of economics: Suppose a manufacturer can sell x items per week at a price $P(x) = 200 - 0.01x$ cents, and that it costs $f(x) = 50x + 20000$ cents to produce the x items. What number of items should be produced to obtain maximum profits? [The total revenue per week on x items is $xP(x) = 200x - 0.01x^2$. The manufacturer's profit T is revenue minus cost: $T(x) = xP(x) - f(x) = 200x - 0.01x^2 - (50x + 20000) = -0.01x^2 + 150x - 20000$. $T'(x) = -.02x + 150$; $T'(x) = 0$ when $x = 7500$. This x-value must yield a maximum because $T(x)$ is a parabola opening downward. Thus the maximum profit occurs when 7500 items are produced. The selling price is $1.25.]

Project Update Project 2, *The History of Calculus,* on page 592, relates to the content of this lesson.

17b)

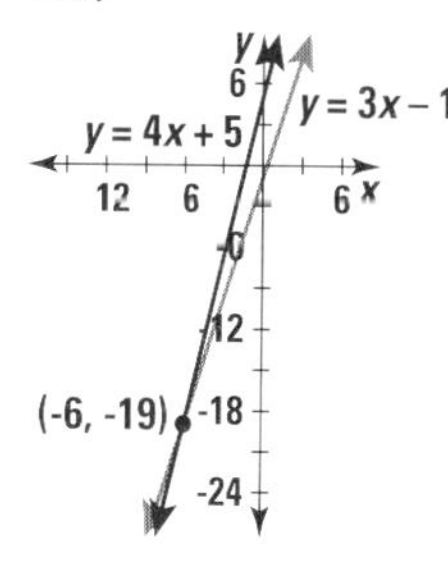

21a) Sample: $f(x) = x^3$ is increasing on the set of reals, but at $x = 0$, $f'(x) = 0$.
b) Sample: $f(x) = -x^3$ is decreasing on the set of reals, but at $x = 0$, $f'(x) = 0$.

16. Let $g(x) = 3x^2 + 1$ for all real numbers x. Use the difference quotient to write an expression for the average rate of change of g over the interval from -1 to $-1 + \Delta x$. Use this expression to find the average rate of change of g over the interval [-1, -0.9]. *(Lesson 9-1)* **$-6 + 3\Delta x$; -5.7**

17. a. Give the measure, to the nearest degree, of the acute angle between the lines with equations $y = 3x - 1$ and $y = 4x + 5$. **≈ 4°**

b. Graph the lines by hand and measure the angle to check your answer to part **a.** *(Lesson 6-5)* **See left.**

18. Let f and g be described by $f(x) = e^x$ and $g(x) = \ln x$.

a. Find a formula for $h(x)$ if the graph of h is the image of the graph of f under $T_{2,3}$. **$h(x) = e^{x-2} + 3$**

b. Find a formula for $k(x)$ if the graph of k is the image of the graph of g under $T_{3,2}$. **$k(x) = \ln(x - 3) + 2$**

c. Find a formula for $h \circ k$. *(Lessons 3-2, 3-8)* **$h \circ k(x) = x, x \geq 3$**

19. What is the probability that at least one head will appear in two tosses of a fair coin? *(Previous course)* **.75**

20. Fill in the blank.

a. 6! = __?__ · 5! **6**

b. 8! = 8 · __?__ **7!**

c. $n! = n \cdot$ __?__ for any positive integer n. *(Previous course)* **$(n - 1)!$**

Exploration

21. In this lesson you learned a theorem which told you how to get information about a graph by using derivatives. The converse of each part of this theorem is false. Find counterexamples as explained below to show this. **See left.**

a. Find a function f that is increasing on an interval but whose derivative is not positive on the interval.

b. Find a function f that is decreasing on an interval but whose derivative is not negative on the interval.

586

LESSON

9-6

Derivatives of Exponential Functions

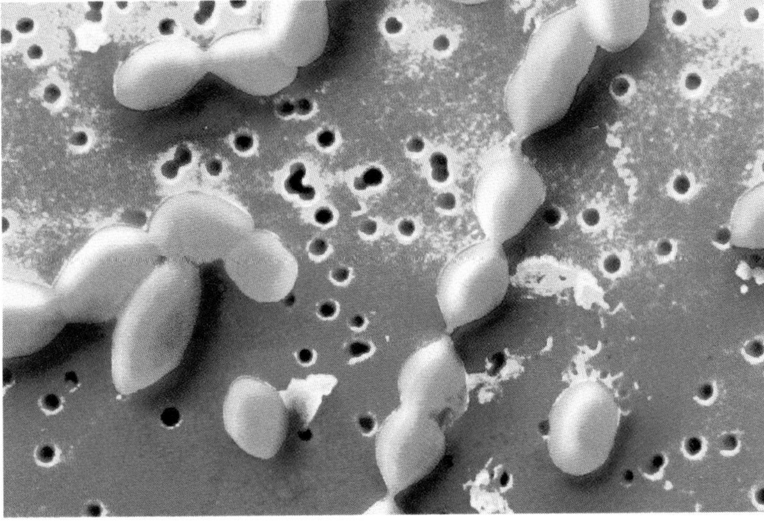

The population growth of these pneumococcus (pneumonia) bacteria is modeled by an exponential function.

In this chapter, you have encountered derivatives of a few familiar functions. For each of these functions f, the function f' which maps x onto the instantaneous rate of change of f at x is another familiar function. Here is a quick summary.

Function f	Derivative f'	Location
sine	cosine	Lesson 9-3
quadratic	linear	Lesson 9-3
linear	constant	Lesson 9-3
constant	0	Lesson 9-3
cubic	quadratic	Questions in Lessons 9-3, 9-5
natural log	reciprocal	Question 13 in Lesson 9-4

The Derivative of $f(x) = ab^x$

Now consider exponential functions, those functions f of the form $f(x) = ab^x$ for all x, with $a > 0$, $b > 0$, and $b \neq 1$. From Lesson 2-7, recall that these functions model many growth situations. For instance, if a population of bacteria begins with 5 bacteria and doubles every 3 hours, then $f(x) = 5 \cdot 2^{x/3}$ gives the population after x hours.

For a fixed Δx, an exponential function increases or decreases by an amount proportional to the value of the function. For instance, in the bacteria situation above, at 3 hours, there are 10 bacteria and they will increase by 10 in the next three hours. At 6 hours there are 20 bacteria and they will increase by 20 in the next three hours.

If the growth (or decay) is continuous, then the instantaneous rate of change at a point is also proportional to the value of the function at that point. This can be seen on page 588.

Lesson 9-6

Objectives

There are no SPUR objectives for any reading lesson.

Resources

From the ***Teacher's Resource File***

- Answer Master 9-6
- Teaching Aids
  88 Warm-up
  102 The Derivative of $y = e^x$

Additional Resources

- Visuals for Teaching Aids 88, 102

Teaching Lesson 9-6

Warm-up

Estimate the slope of the tangent to the graph of $y = e^x$ at the point $(3, e^3)$ by calculating the slope determined by the points $(3, e^3)$ and $(3 + k, e^{3+k})$, where k is very close to zero. **Sample: when $k = 0.01$, the slope ≈ 20.**

Notes on Reading

Is there anything after calculus? Most students are unaware of what that might be. This lesson provides a glimpse of one part of mathematics that follows calculus in the analysis stream, a required course for all engineers and most physical scientists, namely differential equations. A differential equation is an equation that involves the derivatives of an unknown function.

Lesson 9-6 Overview

Broad Goals In this lesson, the functions f of the form $f(x) = ab^x$ are considered and shown to have derivative f', where for all x, $f'(x) = (\ln b)f(x) = a(\ln b)b^x$.

Perspective The informal approach taken in this chapter has allowed a variety of functions to be considered, including sine, log, and some polynomial functions. Perhaps surprising is the fact that the derivatives of these familiar functions are also familiar functions. Now, in this lesson, exponential functions are considered and found to have derivatives that are also exponential functions. This means that the function f grows at a rate proportional to its values and that all of its derivatives are multiples of itself. Because f satisfies the differential equation $f' = kf$, exponential functions are fundamental in solving a variety of kinds of these equations.

The simplest differential equations are those that ask for the function given its derivative, the antiderivative. Integrals solve those equations. The next simplest are those in which the rate of change of a function is proportional to the values of the function, that is, equations of the form $f'(x) = kf(x)$. The solutions to those equations are exponential functions, the same exponential functions that students have seen before.

This lesson relates those prior experiences to derivatives by considering a bacteria growth situation, and informally generalizing from it the conclusion that the rate of change of the function at a given value of x is a fixed multiple of the function evaluated at that x.

Teaching Aid 102 is provided to illustrate the derivative of $y = e^x$.

Error Alert Some students may be confused about finding the instantaneous rate of change in connection with the bacteria example, a situation that suggests increases in discrete increments. Explain that we are looking at a model for the bacteria situation given by $f(x) = 5 \cdot 2^{x/3}$, a continuous function that is useful for approximating growth.

Take the opportunity to point out the marvelous properties of the number e. Students have seen it in the formula $P = e^{rt}$ with continuous compounding, as the base for natural logarithms, as a sum of an infinite series $1 + \frac{1}{1!} + \frac{1}{2!} + \frac{1}{3!} + \dots$, in the equation $e^{i\pi} = -1$ in connection with complex numbers, and now as the base of the function $y = e^x$ so fundamental to solving differential equations.

Begin with $\quad f'(x) = \lim\limits_{\Delta x \to 0} \dfrac{f(x + \Delta x) - f(x)}{\Delta x}.$

Substitute $\quad = \lim\limits_{\Delta x \to 0} \dfrac{ab^{x+\Delta x} - ab^x}{\Delta x}$

$$= \lim_{\Delta x \to 0} \frac{ab^x(b^{\Delta x} - 1)}{\Delta x}.$$

Since ab^x is independent of Δx, it can be factored out of the limit.

$$= \left(\lim_{\Delta x \to 0} \frac{b^{\Delta x} - 1}{\Delta x}\right) ab^x$$

It can be proved that for $b > 0$ and $b \neq 1$, the limit in the parentheses above exists and equals $\ln b$. While a proof is beyond the scope of this book, a few calculations for small values of Δx shows that this is plausible. For example, examine the values below for $b = 2$.

Δx	$\frac{2^{\Delta x} - 1}{\Delta x}$
.1	0.7177
.01	0.6956
.001	0.6934
.0001	0.6932

Since $\ln 2 = 0.693147\ldots$, these values support the conclusion that $\lim\limits_{\Delta x \to 0} \frac{2^{\Delta x} - 1}{\Delta x} = \ln 2$. Then, when

$$f(x) = a \cdot 2^x,$$
$$f'(x) = \left(\lim_{\Delta x \to 0} \frac{2^{\Delta x} - 1}{\Delta x}\right) \cdot a \cdot 2^x = (\ln 2)\, a \cdot 2^x = (\ln 2)\, f(x).$$

In general, when $f(x) = ab^x$, then

$$f'(x) = (\ln b)\, f(x).$$

That is, the derivative of an exponential function is the product of the natural log of the base and the original exponential function.

The Derivative of $y = e^x$

Since $\ln b$ is a constant, every exponential function thus possesses the property that its instantaneous rate of change is proportional to its value. Moreover, when $b = e$, $\ln b = \ln e = 1$. Consequently, the exponential function with base e, the function f defined by $f(x) = e^x$, equals its derivative $f'(x)$ for all real numbers x. That is, the instantaneous rate of change of this function at any point equals the value of the function at that point. Geometrically, at each point (a, e^a) on the graph of the function $f(x) = e^x$ the slope of the tangent $f'(a)$ equals e^a.

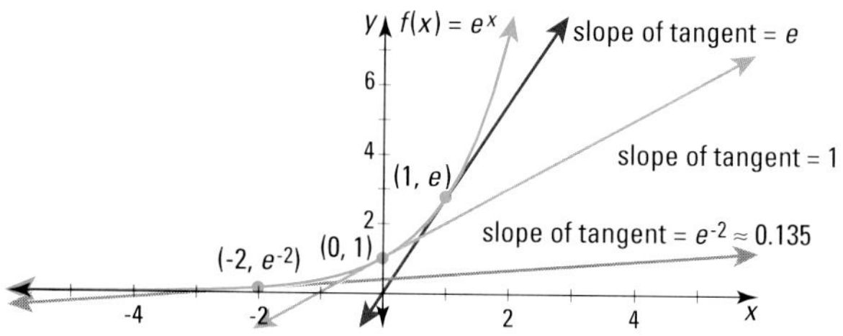

Optional Activities

For the function in **Question 1** that is used to model a bacteria population in the lesson, ask students to determine how much greater the values of the f' will be compared with f. [$f'(x) = 5(\ln 2)\, 2^{x/3} / 3 \approx 1.16 \cdot 2^{x/3}$. The values of f' will be about .23 times greater than the values of f.]

This can be confirmed by examining the graphs of functions of the form

$$f_{\Delta x}(x) = \frac{e^{x+\Delta x} - e^x}{\Delta x}$$

for values of Δx approaching zero. In general,

$$\lim_{\Delta x \to 0} f_{\Delta x}(x) = f'(x)$$

and the graphs at the right for $\Delta x = 0.5$, 0.3, and 0.1, along with $f(x) = e^x$ itself, suggest that

$$f'(x) = e^x.$$

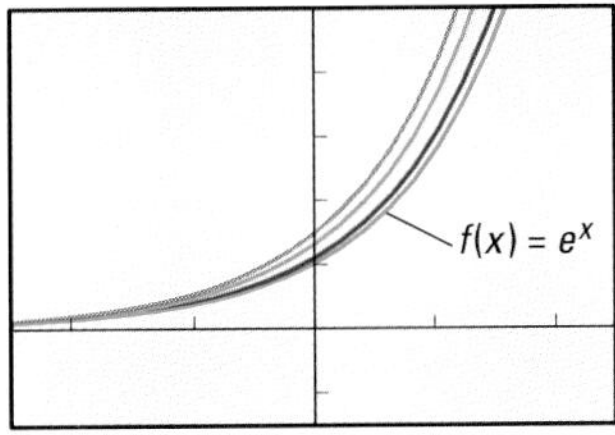

$-2.5 \le x \le 2.5$, x-scale = 1
$-1.5 \le y \le 5$, y-scale = 1

Since the exponential function with base e equals its first derivative, its first derivative also equals its second derivative. The significance of this property is that if a situation is modeled by the exponential function $f(x) = e^x$, then the velocity and acceleration for that situation are also modeled by that same equation.

The importance of derivatives, such as those at the beginning of this lesson, is that many physical laws are statements involving quantities, rates of change of those quantities (for instance, velocity), and rates of change of rates of change of those quantities (for instance, acceleration due to gravity). These laws, then, can be succinctly stated in terms of a function and its first and second derivatives.

Given such a property, to determine exactly what function or functions might model this kind of situation, one has to solve an equation involving functions and their derivatives. Finding derivatives is called **differentiation**, and such an equation is called a **differential equation**. Exponential functions with base e uniquely satisfy the simplest differential equation $f' = f$ and are fundamental in solving other, more complicated, differential equations. Differential equations are often used in the study of the physical world, enough so that almost all college programs of study for engineering and physical science require a course in differential equations, often taken just after calculus.

QUESTIONS

Covering the Reading

1a) $f(4) \approx 12.6$; there are about 13 bacteria at 4 hours.
b) $f(6) - f(3) = 20 - 10 = 10$; $f(3) - f(0) = 10 - 5 = 5$; so $f(6) - f(3)$ is double $f(3) - f(0)$.

1. Consider the function $f(x) = 5 \cdot 2^{x/3}$ used in this lesson to model a bacteria population. **See left.**
   a. Estimate $f(4)$ and tell what it signifies.
   b. Show that $f(6) - f(3)$ is double $f(3) - f(0)$.

2. a. Name four points on the graph of $f: x \to e^x$.
   b. Give the slopes of the tangent to the graph at each of the points you name in part **a**. **1, e, e^2, e^3**

   a) Sample: (0,1), (1, e), (2, e^2), (3, e^3)

Adapting to Individual Needs

Extra Help

Most students benefit from relating the derivative to real-world situations. Hence, you might apply the concepts of the lesson to find $f'(x)$ for the function $f(x) = 5 \cdot 2^{x/3}$, used to model bacteria growth. First rewrite the function to clearly identify b, as follows:

$f(x) = 5 \cdot (2^{1/3})^x$. Then $b = 2^{1/3}$, and

$$\begin{aligned} f'(x) &= (\ln b)\, f(x) = \ln 2^{1/3} \cdot 5 \cdot 2^{x/3} \\ &= \tfrac{1}{3} \cdot \ln 2 \cdot 5 \cdot 2^{x/3} \\ &\approx \tfrac{1}{3} \cdot \ln 2 \cdot 5 \cdot (2^{1/3})^x \\ &\approx 1.155 \cdot 1.260^x. \end{aligned}$$

Discuss what this means for the bacteria situation. For example, $f'(5) \approx 1.155 \cdot 1.260^5 \approx 3.7$. So at 5 hours, the bacteria count is increasing at the rate of about 3.7 bacteria per hour. Similarly, $f'(10) \approx 1.155 \cdot 1.260^{10} \approx 11.6$. So at 10 hours, the bacteria count is increasing at the rate of about 11.6 bacteria per hour.

Notes on Questions

Question 4 Some students may skip this question because they think the derivation is long. Remind students that not all proofs are long.

Question 5 Like many questions throughout this chapter, this question would be inconceivable without an automatic grapher.

Question 13 Geography Connection The Petronas Towers in Kuala Lumpur, Malaysia, were completed in 1996. They are 1483 feet tall, making them slightly taller than the Sears Tower.

Additional Answers

4. Given $f(x) = ab^x \Rightarrow f'(x) = (\ln b)f(x)$, let $a = 1$ and $b = e$. Then, $f(x) = 1 \cdot e^x \Rightarrow f'(x) = (\ln e)f(x)$. Hence, $f(x) = e^x \Rightarrow f'(x) = f(x)$.

5. g': $x \rightarrow (\ln 3)3^x$

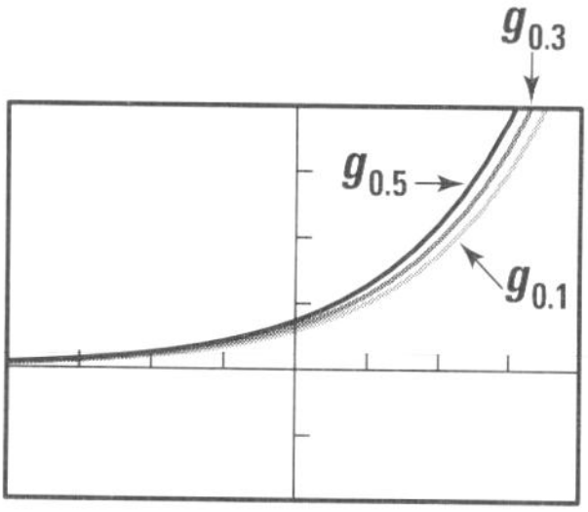

$-2 \le x \le 2$, x-scale $= 0.5$
$-4 \le y \le 8$, y-scale $= 2$

8. c. Sample:

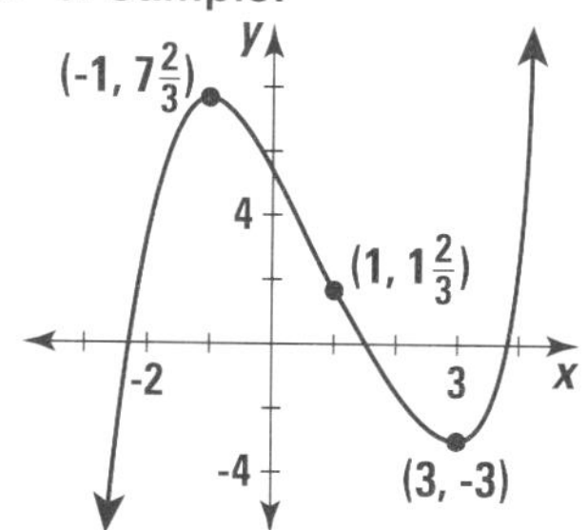

9. b. The car is decelerating more rapidly during the first four seconds of braking than during the last six seconds.

3a) ≈ 7.77, ≈ 7.43, ≈ 7.39

10a) $t = 0$, 1, and 2 seconds
b) vertical; over the zero mark
c) $t = \frac{1}{2}$ and $\frac{3}{2}$ seconds
d) at the extremes
e) $t = 0$, 1, and 2 seconds
f) vertical; over the zero mark

3. a. Calculate $\frac{e^{2+\Delta x} - e^2}{\Delta x}$ for $\Delta x = 0.1, 0.01$, and 0.001. **See left.**

b. What is $\lim\limits_{\Delta x \to 0} \frac{e^{2+\Delta x} - e^2}{\Delta x}$? $e^2 \approx 7.389$

4. Assuming that $f(x) = ab^x \Rightarrow f'(x) = (\ln b)f(x)$ for all $b > 0$, $b \ne 1$, prove that $f(x) = e^x \Rightarrow f'(x) = f(x)$. **See margin.**

5. Graph the function $g_{\Delta x}$ defined by $g_{\Delta x}(x) = \frac{3^{x+\Delta x} - 3^x}{\Delta x}$, for $\Delta x = 0.5$, $\Delta x = 0.3$, and $\Delta x = 0.1$. What function is $\lim\limits_{\Delta x \to 0} g_{\Delta x}$? **See margin.**

6. Write Newton's Law of Cooling (from page 551) as a differential equation, letting f be the function mapping time onto the temperature of a body and a_0 be the temperature of the surroundings.
$f'(t) = k(f(t) - a_0)$

Review

7. Suppose an object's velocity at time t seconds is given by $v(t) = -2t^2 + 3t$. At what times is the object's velocity increasing? *(Lesson 9-5)*
$t < 3/4$ sec

8. A function f possesses the following characteristics:

The graph of f contains $\left(-1, 7\frac{2}{3}\right)$, $\left(1, 1\frac{2}{3}\right)$, and $(3, -3)$,
$f'(x) > 0$ on the intervals $x < -1$ and $x > 3$, and
$f'(x) < 0$ on the interval $-1 < x < 3$.

a. On which interval(s) is f increasing? $x < -1$ and $x > 3$
b. On which interval(s) is f decreasing? $-1 < x < 3$
c. Sketch a possible graph of f. *(Lesson 9-5)* **See margin.**

9. Suppose that at the instant the driver of a car applies the brakes, the car is traveling at 55 mph. After 4 seconds, it is traveling at 25 mph, and 10 seconds after applying the brakes, it comes to a complete stop.

a. Find the average acceleration of the car over each of the two time intervals. -7.5 mph/sec, ≈ -4.2 mph/sec
b. Compare the answers to part **a**. Interpret your comparison in terms of the motion of the car. *(Lesson 9-4)* **See margin.**

10. The horizontal distance (in cm) from a vertical plumb line of a swinging ball at time t seconds is given by $s(t) = 5 \sin \pi t$, its velocity by $v(t) = 5\pi \cos \pi t$, and its acceleration by $a(t) = -5\pi^2 \sin \pi t$. Consider only values of t in the interval $0 \le t \le 2$. *(Lessons 9-3, 9-4)*

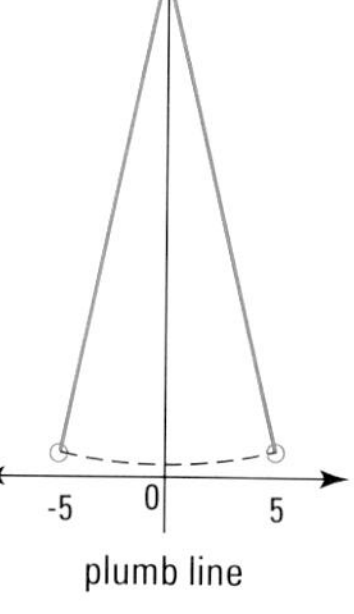

a. At what times is the ball moving the fastest?
b. Where is the ball at these times?
c. At what times is the velocity changing the most?
d. Where is the ball at these times?
e. At what times is the velocity changing the least?
f. Where is the ball at the times of part **e**?

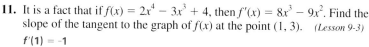

See left.

11. It is a fact that if $f(x) = 2x^4 - 3x^3 + 4$, then $f'(x) = 8x^3 - 9x^2$. Find the slope of the tangent to the graph of $f(x)$ at the point $(1, 3)$. *(Lesson 9-3)*
$f'(1) = -1$

590

12. At what point of the graph of $g(x) = 2x^2 + 6x - 4$ is the tangent line to the graph horizontal? *(Lesson 9-3)* **(-1.5, -8.5)**

13. If a penny is dropped from the top of the Sears Tower, which is 1454 feet tall, then ignoring air resistance, its height (in feet) after t seconds is given by $h(t) = 1454 - 16t^2$. *(Lesson 9-2)*
    a. When does it hit the ground? **at about $t = 9.53$ seconds**
    b. How fast is it falling at the instant it hits the ground? **about 305 ft/sec**
    c. Convert your answer in part **b** to miles per hour. **about 208 mph**

14. Let $f(x) = -3x^2 - x$.
    a. Find a formula for the slope of the secant line through the points $(2, f(2))$ and $(2 + \Delta x, f(2 + \Delta x))$. **$m = -13 - 3\Delta x$**
    b. Use the answer to part **a** to find the slope of the tangent line to the graph of f at $x = 2$. *(Lessons 9-1, 9-2)* **-13**

15. The vertices of the polygon shown here are the nth roots of z. What are n and z? *(Lesson 8-7)* **$n = 5$; $z = 32i$**

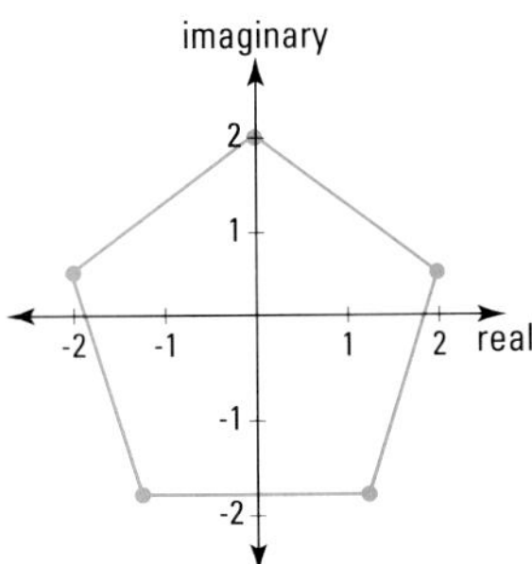

16) Sample:

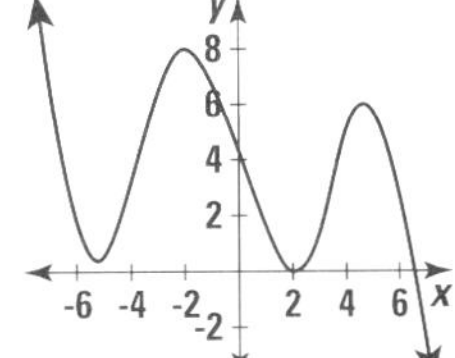

16. Sketch the graph of a fifth degree polynomial function whose leading coefficient is negative, and which has one real zero of multiplicity 2 and one simple real zero. *(Lessons 5-5, 8-8)* **See left.**

17. Write the base 2 representations of 8, 16, and 24. *(Lesson 4-6)*
    1000, 10000, 11000

Exploration

18. Find the value of b so that the exponential function f with $f(x) = b^x$ satisfies the differential equation $f' = 2f$. (That is, the slope of the tangent at each point of the graph of f is double the value of the function.) **$b = e^2$**

19. Find a physical law, not mentioned in this chapter, that can be described using a differential equation.
    Sample: Kirchoff's law for circuits: $E(t) = LI' + RI$ where E is a voltage source, L is an indoctance, R is a resistance, and I is current.

Follow-up for Lesson 9-6

Extension

You might have students verify the following relationship: $g'(x) = \frac{1}{f'(g(x))}$ if $g(x)$ and $f(x)$ are inverses. when

1. $f(x) = \ln x$ (and so $g(x) = e^x$).
2. $f(x) = 3x + 5$. (Find $g(x)$ before proceeding.)

Adapting to Individual Needs

Challenge

Have students answer the following questions.

1. Let $f(x) = e^{ax}$. Prove that $f'(x) = a \cdot e^{ax}$. [$f(x) = e^{ax} = (e^a)^x$. So $f'(x) = \ln(e^a) \cdot (e^a)^x = a \cdot e^{ax}$.]
2. How many solutions does the following differential equation $f'(x) = 2$ have? [infinite number] What are they? [$f(x) = 2x + C$, where C is any real number.]
3. Graph $f(x) = \ln x$ and $g(x) = \frac{1}{x}$ on $(0, \infty)$.
    a. Which one could be the derivative of the other? [$f'(x) = g(x)$]
    b. Test this result by looking at tangent lines at various points. [The tangent line for $f(x)$ at $x = c$ has a slope of $\frac{1}{c}$.]

Chapter 9 Projects

The projects relate to the content of the lessons of this chapter as follows:

Project	Lesson(s)
1	9-3
2	9-2, 9-3, 9-4, 9-5
3	9-3
4	9-1

1 Newton's Method for Finding Zeros of Equations Newton's Method can be programmed so that the x-intercept at each step is recorded. The strength of the method is that polynomials and many other curves become straighter and straighter as one zooms in on any point, so the accuracy of each approximation is far better than the previous.

2 The History of Calculus Virtually any book on the history of mathematics or encyclopedia will have much about these mathematicians.

3 Smooth vs. Non-Smooth Curves This straightforward project is accessible to most students.

4 Here Comes the Sun This project extends an idea exhibited in Lesson 9-1. You might wish to have students put the data on a poster and use more than 12 points for a year. A smooth curve can be drawn easily if one point a week, 52 for the year, is used.

A project presents an opportunity for you to extend your knowledge of a topic related to the material of this chapter. You should allow more time for a project than you do for a typical homework question.

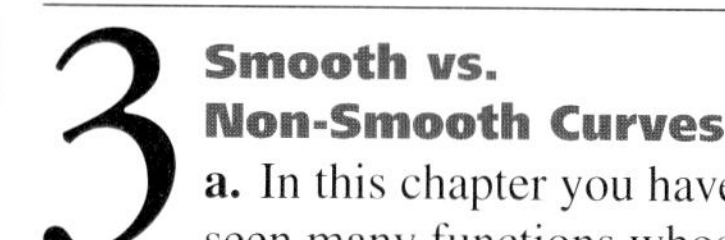

1 Newton's Method for Finding Zeros of Equations

Newton's Method is another technique that can be used to approximate the zeros of an equation. The technique uses equations of tangent lines to the curve at various points. Refer to the graph of f above. Let x_1 be the first approximation to the zero r. Construct the tangent line to the graph at $(x_1, f(x_1))$. Because its slope is $f'(x_1)$, an equation for this line is

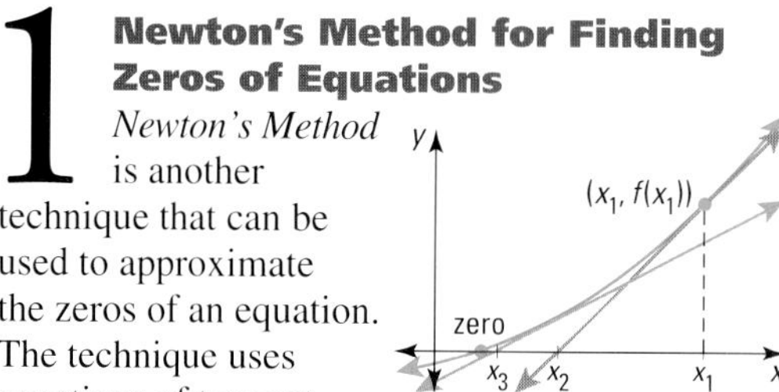

$$y - f(x_1) = f'(x_1)(x - x_1).$$

The x-intercept of this line is x_2, which becomes the next approximation to the zero.

a. Find a formula for x_2.

b. Draw the tangent to the graph at $(x_2, f(x_2))$ and write the equation of this tangent line.

c. Find the x-intercept, x_3, of the tangent line in part **b**. This becomes the next approximation to the zero.

d. Generalize the process described above to find a formula for the $(n + 1)$st approximation.

e. Apply the above technique to approximate a zero to $f(x) = 2x^3 + 3x^2 + 1$. (The derivative of f is $f'(x) = 6x^2 + 6x$.) Compare your results using *Newton's Method* to an approximation found by using some other technique that you know.

2 The History of Calculus

Isaac Newton and Gottfried Leibniz are generally credited as the co-inventors of calculus. Write a report on the particular contributions that each of these mathematicians made.

3 Smooth vs. Non-Smooth Curves

a. In this chapter you have seen many functions whose derivatives exist.

i. Choose at least 5 of these functions and graph them using an automatic grapher.

ii. Locate any relative maximum or relative minimum points for the function.

iii. Evaluate the derivative at these relative minimum or relative maximum points.

iv. Choose any one of the relative maximum or relative minimum points. Repeatedly zoom in on the function at that location. What appears to happen to the graph?

v. Relate your result in part **iv** to your knowledge of the derivative and its value in part **iii**.

b. Not all functions have a derivative at every value in the domain of the function. For instance, $f(x) = |x - 2| + 3$ has a minimum point at (2, 3) but the derivative does not exist there. Repeatedly zoom in on this part of the function. Compare your result to part **iv** above.

c. Generalize your results from parts **a** and **b**.

4 Here Comes the Sun

Use an almanac or some other source to find the time of sunrise where you live for the first day of each month of the year.

a. Graph your data and draw a smooth curve which approximates it. What kind of curve do you get? Find a formula for the function you have graphed.

b. Find the average rate of change in time of sunrise from month to month. Graph this data and try to find the formula for a function that fits this data.

c. When is the time of sunrise changing fastest? When is it changing slowest?

d. Compare your answers to parts **a–c** with the results of the analysis performed on the length-of-day function in this chapter.

Possible Responses

1. a. Let $x = x_2$ and $y = 0$ in the equation for the tangent line, $y - f(x_1) = f'(x_1)(x - x_1)$. So $0 - f(x_1) = f'(x_1)(x_2 - x_1)$, $x_2 - x_1 = \frac{-f(x_1)}{f'(x_1)}$, $x_2 = x_1 - \frac{f(x_1)}{f'(x_1)}$.

   b. The equation of the tangent line is $y - f(x_2) = f'(x_2)(x - x_2)$.

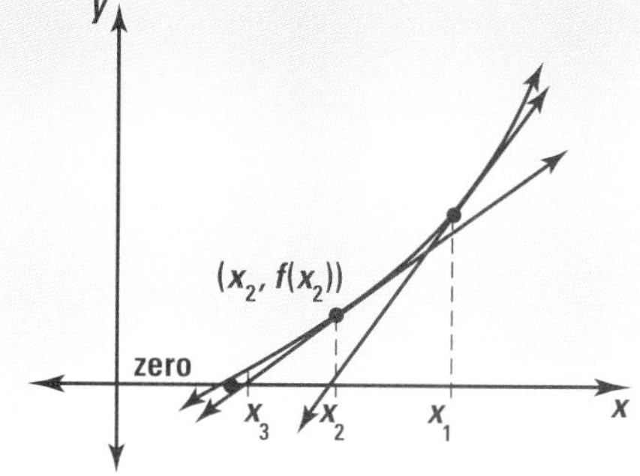

   c. Similarly to part a, x_3 is found to be $x_2 - \frac{f(x_2)}{f'(x_2)}$.

   d. $x_{n+1} = x_n - \frac{(f(x_n)}{f'(x_n)}$

   e. $f(x) = 2x^3 + 3x^2 + 1$, and $f'(x) = 6x^2 + 6x$. Arbitrarily, let $x_1 = -2$.

SUMMARY

The purpose of this chapter is to introduce the fundamental ideas of differential calculus, the branch of calculus concerned with rates of change.

The average rate of change of a function f over the interval from x_1 to x_2 equals the slope of the secant line through $(x_1, f(x_1))$ and $(x_2, f(x_2))$. If $x_2 - x_1 = \Delta x$, then the average rate of change is

$$\frac{\Delta y}{\Delta x} = \frac{y_2 - y_1}{x_2 - x_1} = \frac{f(x_2) - f(x_1)}{x_2 - x_1} = \frac{f(x_1 + \Delta x) - f(x_1)}{\Delta x}.$$

This last expression is called a difference quotient.

When f is a function giving the position of an object along a line relative to a starting point, then the average rate of change of f over an interval is the average velocity over that interval.

The limit as $\Delta x \to 0$ of the average rate of change or difference quotient is the derivative of the function f at x_1. Geometrically, this number is the limit of the slope of the secant line as $x_2 \to x_1$, and is the slope of the line tangent to the curve at the point (x_1, y_1). If f is a function giving the position of an object, then the derivative at a point is the instantaneous velocity at that point.

At the top of the next column the left column contains quantities which can be calculated for all functions, including discrete functions. The corresponding limits in the right column can only be calculated if the derivative exists.

change between two points	limit as one point approaches the other
average rate of change	instantaneous rate of change
slope of secant	slope of tangent
difference quotient	derivative

Given a function f, the function mapping each number x to the derivative of f at x is the derivative function f'. A function is increasing on an interval when its derivative is positive at all points on that interval. A function is decreasing on an interval when its derivative is negative on that interval. When a smooth function has a relative maximum or minimum at a point, its derivative is zero at that point.

Acceleration is the rate of change of a rate of change. It is found by calculating the derivative of a derivative, or second derivative. If a function is a position function, then acceleration is given by the derivative of the velocity function. Negative acceleration is known as deceleration.

Exponential functions possess the property that their derivatives are proportional to their values. Further, when the base is e, the derivative is equal to the function itself. This fact makes exponential functions particularly useful in modeling phenomena in the sciences.

VOCABULARY

Below are the most important terms and phrases for this chapter. You should be able to give a general description and a specific example of each and a precise definition for those marked with an asterisk (*).

Lesson 9-1
differential calculus
* Δx, Δy
* average rate of change
secant line to a circle
secant line for the graph of a function
* average velocity
* difference quotient

Lesson 9-2
* instantaneous velocity
tangent line to the graph of a function
* derivative of a function at a point
instantaneous rate of change of f at x

Lesson 9-3
* derivative of a function f, f'
Derivative of a Quadratic Function Theorem

Lesson 9-4
* acceleration
* deceleration
instantaneous acceleration
* first derivative, second derivative

Lesson 9-5
Vertex of a Parabola Theorem
optimization problem

Summary

The Summary gives an overview of the entire chapter and provides an opportunity for students to consider the material as a whole. Thus, the Summary can be used to help students relate and unify the concepts presented in the chapter.

Vocabulary

Terms, symbols, and properties are listed by lesson to provide a checklist of concepts a student must know. Emphasize to students that they should read the vocabulary list carefully before starting the Progress Self-Test. If students do not understand the meaning of a term, they should refer back to the indicated lesson.

n	$f(x_n)$	$f'(x_n)$	$x_{n+1} = x_n - \frac{f(x_n)}{f'(x_n)}$
1	-3	12	-1.7
2	0.53125	7.875	≈ -1.68
3	-0.016064	6.8544	≈ -1.68

The Intermediate Value Theorem allows us to use the Bisection Method (found in Chapter 3) to estimate the roots.

For example, it may be observed from a graph, that $x = -2$ and $x = -1$.

Step	Interval to check	Value of endpoints	Midpoint	Value at midpoint
1	(-2, -1)	(-3, + 2)	-1.5	+1
2	(-2, -1.5)	(-3, +1)	-1.75	-0.53
3	(-1.75, -1.5)	(-0.53, +1)	-1.625	+0.339
4	(-1.75, -1.625)	(-0.53, +0.339)	-1.6875	-0.68
5	(-1.6875, -1.625)	(-0.68, +0.339)	-1.6563	+0.143
6	(-1.6875, -1.6563)	(-0.68, +0.143)	-1.6719	+0.039
7	(-1.6875, -1.6719)	(-0.68, +0.039)	-1.6797	-0.014
8	(-1.6797, -1.6719)	(-0.014, +0.039)	-1.6758	+0.013
9	(-1.6797, -1.6758)	(-0.014, +0.013)		

To two decimal places, the zero is at $x = -1.68$. It took the Bisection Method 8 steps to find the zero to two decimal places; it took Newton's Method only 3.

(Responses continue on page 594.)

Progress Self-Test

For the development of mathematical competence, feedback and correction, along with the opportunity to practice, are necessary. The Progress Self-Test provides the opportunity for feedback and correction; the Chapter Review provides additional opportunities and practice. We cannot overemphasize the importance of these end-of-chapter materials. It is at this point that the material "gels" for many students, allowing them to solidify skills and understanding. In general, student performance should be markedly improved after these pages.

Additional Responses, page 592

2. Students' reports may include some of the following main points:
   Newton:
   i. Devised corpuscular theory of light
   ii. Verified laws of gravitation
   iii. Justified Kepler's laws of planetary motion
   iv. Wrote *Method of Fluxions* which contained differential calculus, differential equations which allowed him to find maxima, minima, tangents to curves, points of inflection, convexity and concavity of curves, and Newton's method for approximating the values of real roots of an algebraic or transcendental numerical equation
   v. Wrote *Arithmetica Universalis* which contained many important results about the theory of equations: imaginary roots of real polynomials must occur in conjugate pairs; rules for finding an upper polynomial; an extension of Descartes' rule of signs to give limits on the number of imaginary roots of a real polynomial; and formulas expressing the sum of nth powers of the roots of a polynomial in terms of the coefficients of the polynomial

CHAPTER NINE

PROGRESS SELF-TEST

Take this test as you would take a test in class. Then check the test yourself using the solutions at the back of the book.

1. The function f is graphed below.
   a. Find the average rate of change in f from $x = -4$ to $x = -2$. **-3/2**
   b. Find the average rate of change in f from $x = -2$ to $x = 2$. **3/4**
   c. Find an interval over which the average rate of change in f is $-\frac{1}{2}$. **Sample: $x = 0$ to $x = 2$**
   d. Find an interval over which the average rate of change in f is 0. **Samples: $x = -4$ to $x = -1$, $x = -1$ to $x = 2$, $x = -4$ to $x = 2$**

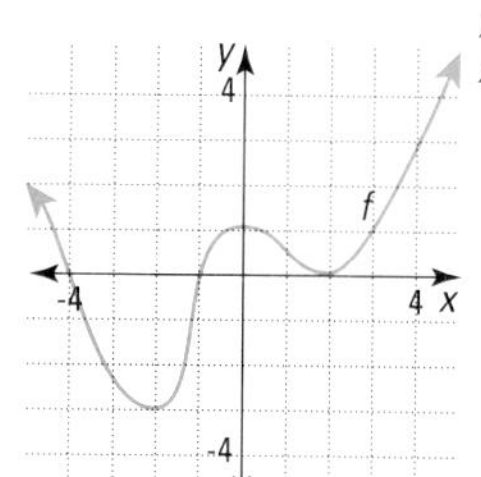

2. The table below shows the percent of the U.S. labor force in farm-related occupations every ten years from 1940 to 1990.
   a. Find the average rate of change in the given interval.
      i. from 1940 to 1950 **-.58% per year**
      ii. from 1980 to 1990 **-.03% per year**
   b. Does the average rate of change appear to be dropping faster or slower as time goes on? **b) slower**
   c. Is the acceleration positive or negative? **positive**

year	% of labor force in farm occupations
1940	17.4
1950	11.6
1960	6.1
1970	3.6
1980	2.7
1990	2.4

3a) $16 + 4\Delta x$ b) 16.4

3. Let f be defined by $f(x) = 4x^2 - 3$.
   a. Find a formula for the average rate of change of f from 2 to $2 + \Delta x$.
   b. Use your answer to part **a** to find the average rate of change of f from 2 to 2.1.
4. The function g is graphed below, along with two tangent lines. Estimate each value.
   a. $g'(-3)$ b. $g'(1)$ **2/3**

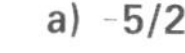

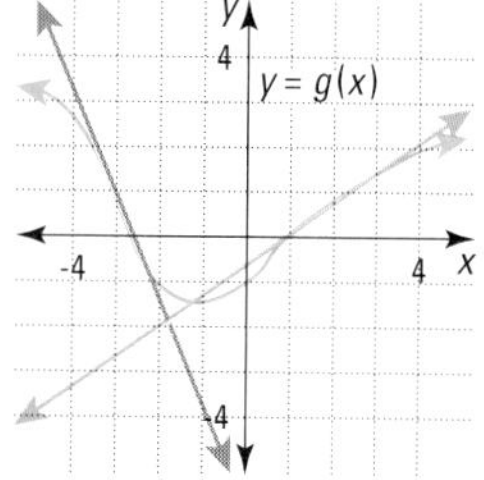

four-row cotton stripper

Project 2, continued
Liebniz:
i. Developed *characteristica generalis,* a universal language, using mathematical and symbolic logic created from formal rules that would obviate the need for thinking (e.g., logical addition, multiplication, negation, null class, and class inclusion)
ii. Independently from Newton created calculus and introduced the $\int$ integral notation
iii. Introduced the theory of determinants
iv. Generalized binomial theorem to the multinomial theorem

3. a. i. Sample:
$y_1(x) = x^2 + 4$
$y_2(x) = x^2 - x + 2$
$y_3(x) = x^3$
$y_4(x) = \sin x$
$y_5(x) = \frac{1}{2}x - 5$

CHAPTER NINE

5. Let $h(x) = -2x^2 + x$.

a. Find a formula for h'. **$h'(x) = -4x + 1$**

b. Find the slope of the line tangent to the graph of h at $x = 3$. **-11**

6. *Multiple choice.* The graph of f is shown below.

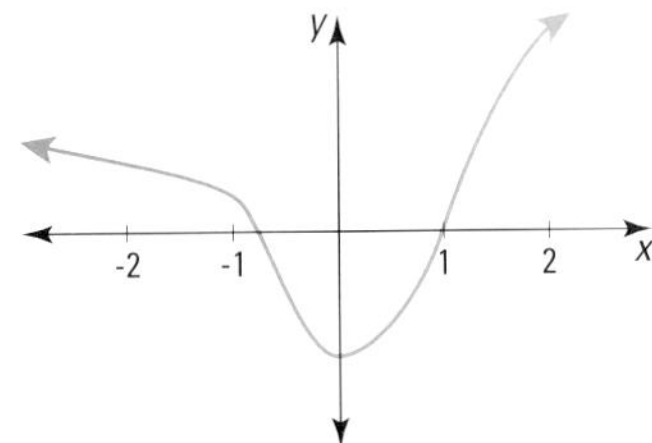

Which of the graphs below could be the graph of f'?

(a)

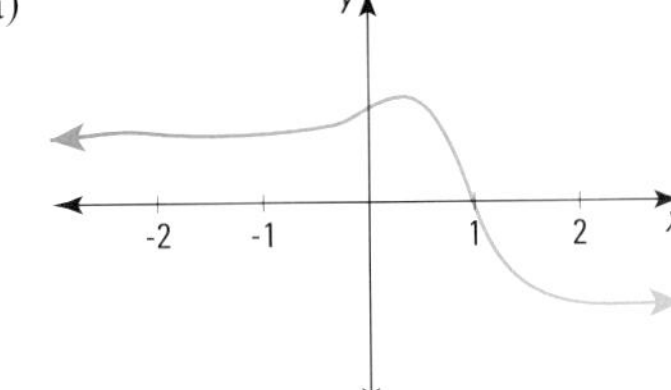

(b)

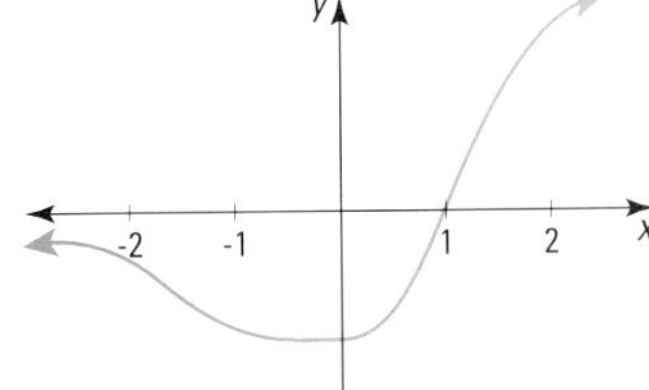

(c)

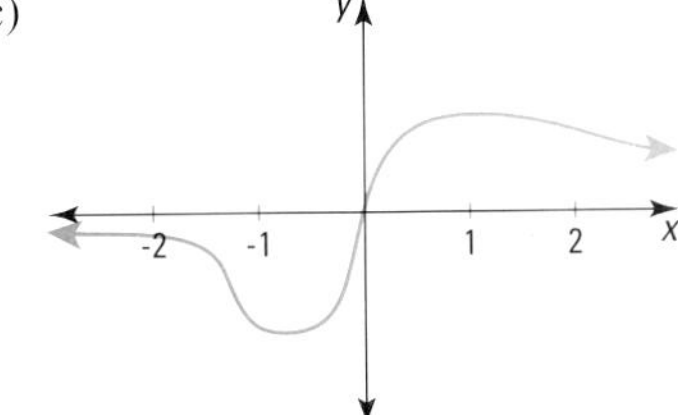

7. Copy the graph of the function k below and sketch tangent lines at $x = -1$, $x = 0$, $x = 1$, and $x = 2$. Is $k''(x)$ positive or negative on the interval $-1 < x < 2$? **See below.**

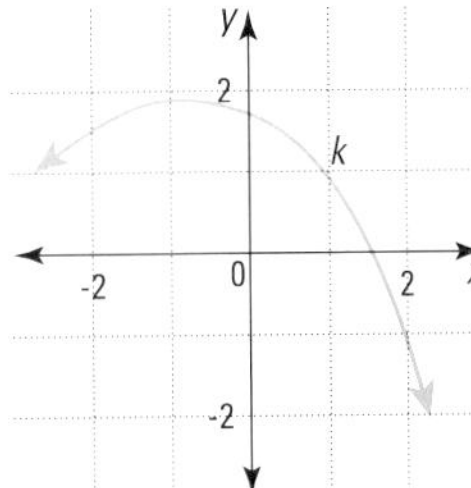

8. A ball is thrown so that its height (in feet) after t seconds is given by $h(t) = -16t^2 + 64t + 50$.

a. Find the instantaneous velocity of the ball 1 second after it is thrown. **32 ft/sec**

b. Find the acceleration of the ball 1 second after it is thrown. What is the physical meaning of your answer? **See below.**

c. Find the maximum height reached by the ball. **114 ft** **d) 0 ft/sec**

d. What is the instantaneous velocity of the ball when it reaches its maximum height?

9. Given that $f(x) = e^{-x^2}$, then $f'(x) = -2xe^{-x^2}$. Find the interval(s) on which f is increasing and those on which f is decreasing. (Use the fact that $e^{-x^2} > 0$ for all x.) **f is increasing when $x < 0$. f is decreasing when $x > 0$.**

7) negative

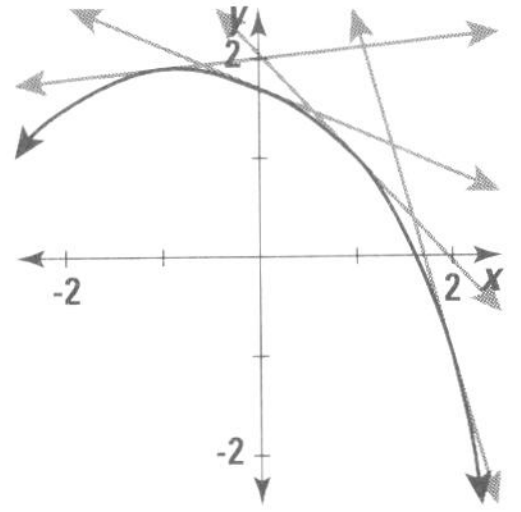

8b) -32 ft/sec^2; acceleration due to gravity.

Assign the Progress Self-Test as a one-night assignment. Worked-out *solutions* for all questions are in the Selected Answers section of the student book. Encourage students to take the Progress Self-Test honestly, grade themselves, and then be prepared to discuss the test in class.

Advise students to pay special attention to those Chapter Review questions (pages 596–599) that correspond to questions missed on the Progress Self-Test.

Project 3a, continued

iii. $y_4'(x) = \cos x$ and $\cos(\frac{\pi}{2} + 2n\pi) = 0$ for n an integer.
$y_1'(x) = 2x$, and $2 \cdot 0 = 0$.
$y_2'(x) = 2x - 1$, and $(2)\frac{1}{2} - 1 = 1 - 1 = 0$.
$y_4'(x) = \cos x$ and $\cos(-\frac{\pi}{2} + 2n\pi) = 0$ for n an integer.

iv. The graph looks more and more like a horizontal line.

v. The derivative at a point is the slope of the tangent line to the function at that point. Since the derivatives were zero at each minimum and maximum point as shown in part iii, we would expect the tangent line at each maximum or minimum point to have a slope of zero (i.e., be a horizontal line). Zooming in on a section of the graph causes its image to appear more and more like the tangent at that point.

3. b. The graph of f remains V-shaped when zooming in on its minimum point (2, 3), while the graphs in part a. (iv) got closer and closer to a horizontal line.

3. c. If when zooming in on a portion of a graph, the graph does not approach a line, then the derivative does not exist at that point. If however, it does approach a line, the derivative is equal to the slope of that line; if such a line is horizontal, then the derivative of the function is zero at that point.

(Responses continue on page 598.)

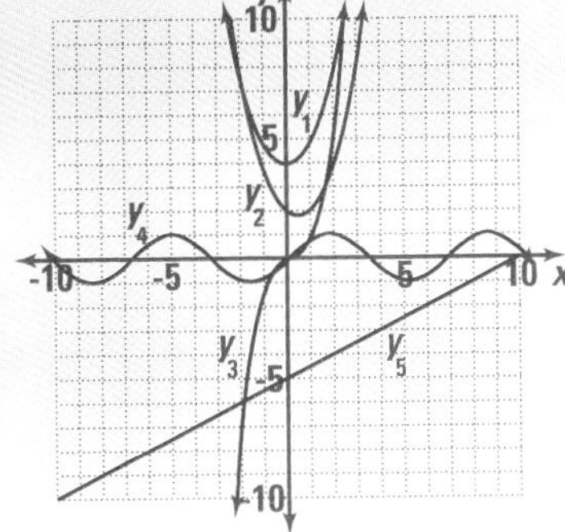

ii. relative maxima: for y_4: which occurs at $x = \frac{\pi}{2} + 2\pi n$ for n an integer
relative minima: for y_1: 4 which occurs at $x = 0$; for y_2: $\frac{7}{4}$ which occurs at $x = \frac{1}{2}$; for y_4: -1 which occurs at $x = -\frac{\pi}{2} + 2\pi n$ for n an integer

Chapter 9 Review

Resources

From the ***Teacher's Resource File***

- Answer Master for Chapter 9 Review
- Assessment Sourcebook: Chapter 9 Test, Forms A–D Chapter 9 Test, Cumulative Form Comprehensive Test, Chapters 1–9

Additional Resources

- TestWorks CD-ROM

The main objectives for the chapter are organized in the Chapter Review under the four types of understanding this book promotes—Skills, Properties, Uses, and Representations.

Whereas end-of-chapter material may be considered optional in some texts, in UCSMP *Precalculus and Discrete Mathematics* we have selected these objectives and questions with the expectation that they will be covered. Students should be able to answer these questions with about 85% accuracy after studying the chapter.

You may assign these questions over a single night to help students prepare for a test the next day, or you may assign the questions over a two-day period. If you work the questions over two days, then we recommend assigning the *evens* for homework the first night so that students get feedback in class the next day, then assigning the *odds* the night before the test, because answers are provided to the odd-numbered questions.

CHAPTER REVIEW

Questions on SPUR Objectives

SPUR stands for **S**kills, **P**roperties, **U**ses, and **R**epresentations. The Chapter Review questions are grouped according to the SPUR Objectives for this chapter.

SKILLS DEAL WITH THE PROCEDURES USED TO GET ANSWERS.

Objective A: *Compute average rates of change in functions.* *(Lesson 9-1)*

1. Find the average rate of change in $f(x) = 3x^2 + 1$ from $x = -1$ to $x = 4$. **9**
2. Let g be the function defined by $g(x) = x^3$.
   a. Calculate the average rate of change in g from 1 to $1 + \Delta x$. **$3 + 3\Delta x + (\Delta x)^2$**
   b. Use your answer to part **a** to find the average rate of change in g on the indicated interval. **i) 3.31 ii) 3.0301**
      i. from 1 to 1.1 ii. from 1 to 1.01
3. Let $k(t) = -2t^2 + 5t$.
   a. Find the average rate of change in k from t to $t + \Delta t$. **$-4t + 5 - 2\Delta t$**
   b. Use your answer to part **a** to find the average rate of change of k from 2 to 2.5. **-4**

Objective B: *Use the definition of derivative to compute derivatives.* *(Lessons 9-2, 9-3)*

4. Let f be the function defined by $f(x) = 2x^2$ $\forall$ real numbers x. Use the definition of derivative to compute $f'(1)$ and $f'(-1)$. **$f'(1) = 4$, $f'(-1) = -4$**
5. Given that $f(x) = -x^2 + x + 1$ for all real numbers x, find a formula for the instantaneous rate of change of f at x. **$f'(x) = -2x + 1$**

In 6–8, find the derivative of the function whose formula is given.

6. $f(x) = 2x$ **$f'(x) = 2$**
7. $g(x) = -3x^2$ **$g'(x) = -6x$**
8. $k(x) = -3x^2 + 2x$ **$k'(x) = -6x + 2$**

PROPERTIES DEAL WITH THE PRINCIPLES BEHIND THE MATHEMATICS.

Objective C: *Use derivatives to identify properties of functions.* *(Lesson 9-5)*

9. *True or false.* If the derivative of a function is 0 at a point, then the function has a relative minimum or maximum at that point. **False**
10. Let $f(x) = x + e^{-2x}$ for all real numbers x. The first derivative of f is $f'(x) = 1 - 2e^{-2x}$ and the second derivative is $f''(x) = 4e^{-2x}$. Is f increasing, decreasing, or neither on the interval $1 < x < 2$? **increasing**
11. Use the fact that the derivative of $f(x) = x^3 + 3x + 2$ is $f'(x) = 3x^2 + 3$ to prove that f is increasing on the set of all real numbers. **See margin.**
12. Suppose for a function f, $f''(x) < 0$ $\forall$ x in the interval $1 < x < 4$. Are the slopes of tangents to the graph of f increasing or decreasing on $1 < x < 4$? **decreasing**
13. If $f(x) = x^3 - 1.5x^2 - 18x$, then $f'(x) = 3x^2 - 3x - 18$. **See margin.**
    a. Use the first derivative to find
       i. the interval(s) on which f is increasing,
       ii. the interval(s) on which f is decreasing,
       iii. the points at which f may have a relative maximum or minimum.
    b. Check your answers with an automatic grapher.

Additional Answers

11. $f'(x) = 3x^2 + 3$. Since $x^2 \geq 0$ for all real x, $f'(x) = 3x^2 + 3 > 0$ for all real numbers. Since the derivative is positive, the slopes of the tangents to the curve are all positive, and the function is increasing for all real numbers.
13. a. i. $x < -2$ or $x > 3$
    ii. $-2 < x < 3$
    iii. $x = -2$ or $x = 3$

b.

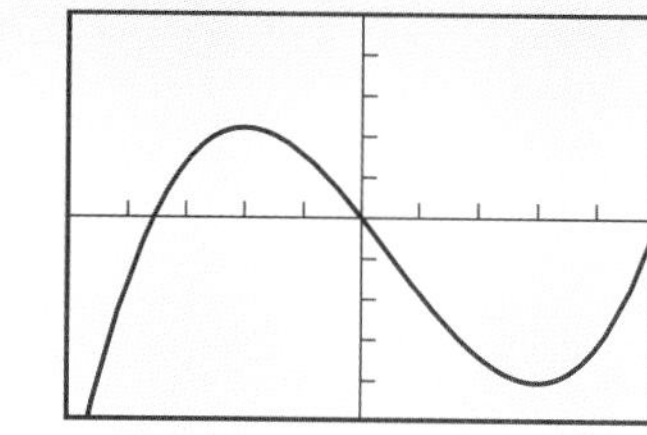

$-5 \leq x \leq 5$, x-scale $= 1$
$-50 \leq y \leq 50$, y-scale $= 10$

USES DEAL WITH APPLICATIONS OF MATHEMATICS IN REAL SITUATIONS.

14, 15, 16a, 16b, 18) See margin.

Objective D: *Find rates of change in real situations.* *(Lessons 9-1, 9-2, 9-3, 9-4)*

14. Suppose a 4-oz potato takes 5 minutes to bake in a microwave oven, a 6-oz potato takes 7 minutes to bake, 10 oz of potatoes take 10 minutes, and 16 oz of potatoes take 14 minutes. **See margin.**

a. Find the average rate of change in baking time with respect to potato weight from 4 oz to 6 oz. What is the meaning of your answer in terms of baking time?

b. Find the average rate of change from 10 oz to 16 oz.

c. Compare your answers to parts **a** and **b** in terms of baking time.

d. Assume the average rate of change from 16 oz to 20 oz is the same as that from 10 oz to 16 oz. How long would it take to bake 20 oz of potatoes?

15. The table below gives the number of stocks traded on the New York Stock Exchange (NYSE) for the years 1980–1996.

a. Make a scatterplot of the number of stocks traded (in billions) versus year after 1980. Sketch a reasonable curve to fit the data.

b. On the interval from 1983 to 1987, is the rate of change of stocks traded per year increasing, decreasing, or constant?

c. During what year does it appear that the number of stocks traded changed fastest?

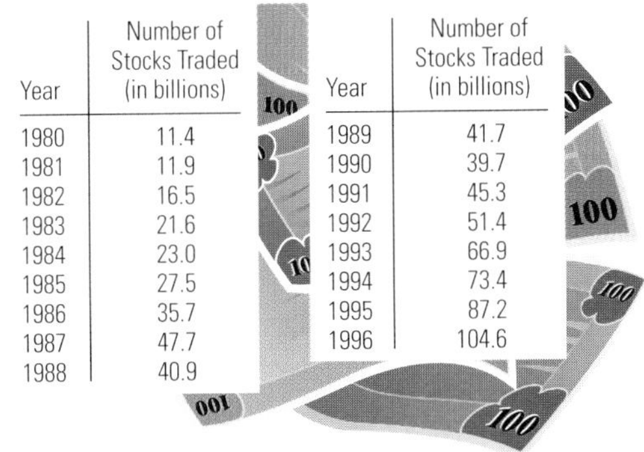

Year	Number of Stocks Traded (in billions)	Year	Number of Stocks Traded (in billions)
1980	11.4	1989	41.7
1981	11.9	1990	39.7
1982	16.5	1991	45.3
1983	21.6	1992	51.4
1984	23.0	1993	66.9
1985	27.5	1994	73.4
1986	35.7	1995	87.2
1987	47.7	1996	104.6
1988	40.9		

16. Radon gas is an odorless radioactive gas emitted naturally from Earth. If 500 grams of radon is initially present, then the amount remaining after t days is $A(t) = 500e^{-0.182t}$ grams. The derivative of A is $A'(t) = -91e^{-0.182t}$ and the second derivative is $A''(t) = 16.562e^{-0.182t}$.

a. What units are appropriate for measuring $A'(t)$ and $A''(t)$?

b. Find $A'(7)$ and tell what it means.

c. Is the radon decaying faster after 5 days or after 7 days? **5 days**

Objective E: *Use derivatives to find the velocity and acceleration of a moving object.* *(Lessons 9-2, 9-3, 9-4)* **17d) -80 ft/sec**

17. A ball is dropped from a 100-foot tower. The height (in feet) of the ball above the ground at time t seconds is given by $h(t) = -16t^2 + 100$.

a. What is the instantaneous velocity of the ball at time $t = 2$ seconds? **-64 ft/sec**

b. What is the acceleration of the ball at time $t = 2$ seconds? **-32 ft/sec²** **c) 2.5 sec**

c. At what time t does the ball hit the ground?

d. What is the instantaneous velocity of the ball at the moment it hits the ground?

18. Below is the graph of the distance of a subway car from the beginning of its route over time.

a. Estimate the velocity of the subway car at each time.

i. $t = 2$ **ii.** $t = 5$ **iii.** $t = 8$ **iv.** $t = 12$

b. What is happening to the subway car at $t = 5$ and $t = 12$?

c. Sketch a rough graph of the subway car's velocity.

d. When is the subway car's acceleration positive? When is it negative?

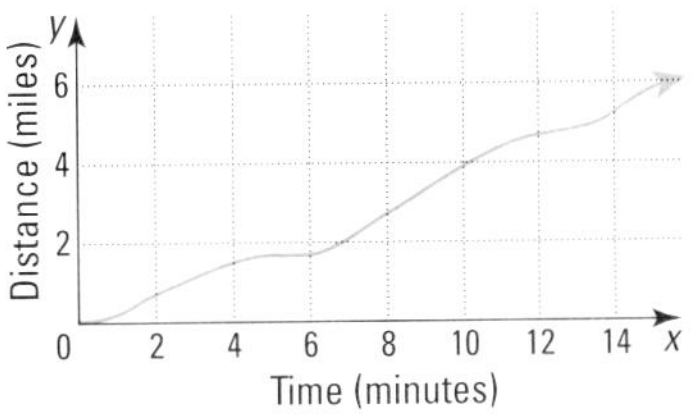

It is effective to ask students which questions they still do not understand and use the day or days as a total class discussion of the material which the class finds most difficult.

Assessment

Evaluation The Assessment Sourcebook provides six forms of the Chapter 9 Test. Forms A and B present parallel versions in a short-answer format. Forms C and D offer performance assessment. The fifth test is Chapter 9 Test, Cumulative Form. About 50% of this test covers Chapter 9, 25% of it covers Chapter 8, and 25% of it covers earlier chapters. In addition to these tests, Comprehensive Test Chapters 1–9 gives roughly equal attention to all chapters covered thus far.

15. a.

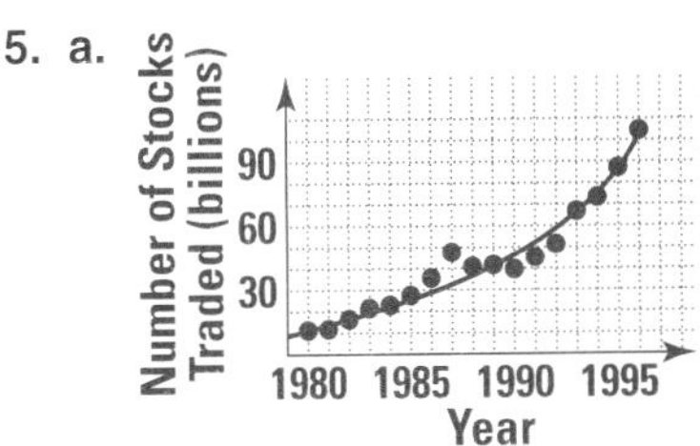

b. increasing

c. 1986–1987

16. a. $A'(t)$: grams/day; $A''(t)$: g/day²

b. ≈ -25.5 grams/day; at 7 days, the amount of radon present is decreasing by about 25.5 grams/day.

18. a. i. 1 mi/min **ii.** 0 mi/min **iii.** 1 mi/min **iv.** 0 mi/min

b. It is stationary.

c.

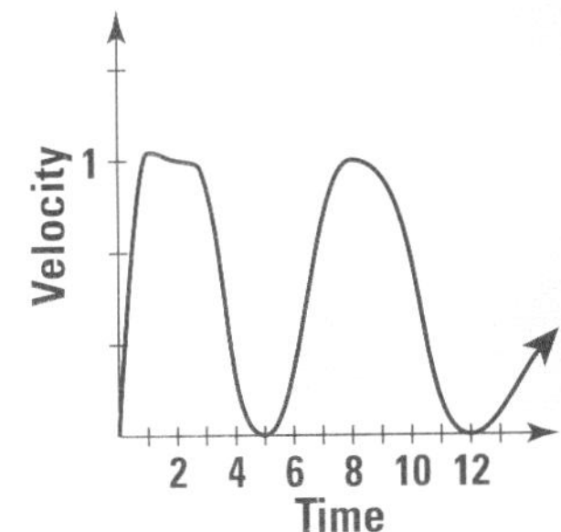

d. positive: $0 < x < 2$, $5 < x < 8$; negative: $2 < x < 5$, $8 < x < 12$

14. a. 1 min/oz; an extra minute of cooking time is required for every additional ounce of potatoes.

b. $\frac{2}{3}$ min/oz; as weight increases, the rate of change of baking time needed decreases for every additional ounce of potatoes.

c. Potatoes weighing between 10 and 16 ounces need less cooking time per ounce than potatoes weighing between 4 and 6 ounces.

d. $16\frac{2}{3}$ minutes

For information on grading, see *General Teaching Suggestions: Grading* in the *Professional Sourcebook*, which begins on page T20 in the Teacher's Edition.

Feedback After students have taken the test for Chapter 9 and you have scored the results, return the tests to students for discussion. Class discussion of the questions that caused trouble for the most students can be very effective in identifying and clarifying misunderstandings. You might want to have them write down the items they missed and work, either in groups or at home, to correct them. It is important for students to receive feedback on every chapter test, and we recommend that students see and correct their mistakes before proceeding too far into the next chapter.

Additional Responses, page 592
Project 4
4. a. Sample:

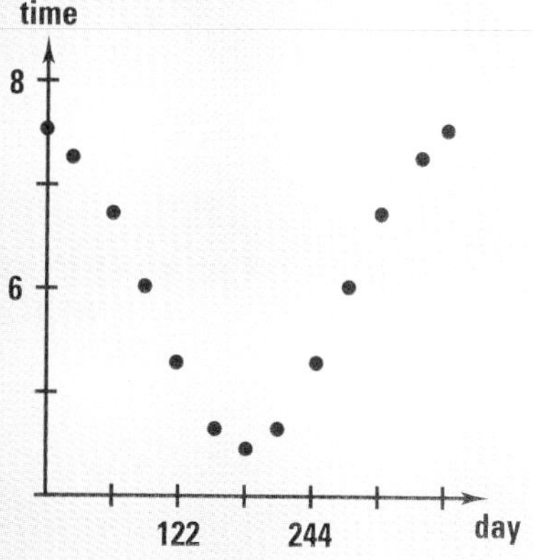

The graph appears to be a cosine curve.
$y = 6 + 1.5\cos(\frac{2\pi}{365}x)$,
where y is the time of number of days.

CHAPTER NINE

19. A particle moves horizontally so that its position (in meters) to the right of its starting point at time t seconds is given by $f(t) = -3t^2 + 13t + 16$.

a. At time $t = 2$ seconds, is the particle moving to the left, to the right or stationary?

b. Is the particle speeding up or slowing down at time $t = 2$ seconds? **slowing down**

a) to the right

Objective F: *Use derivatives to solve optimization problems.* (Lesson 9-5)

20. An object is thrown upwards so that its height (in feet) t seconds after being thrown is given by $h(t) = -16t^2 + 50t + 80$. What is the maximum height it reaches? **$a \approx$ 119 ft**

21. A triangular platform is to be built in the corner formed by two walls as shown below. The 4-meter outer edge of the platform forms an angle of θ with one of the walls. The area of the platform is to be maximized.

a. Use trigonometry to show that the area can be written as a function of θ:
$A(\theta) = 8 \sin\theta \cos\theta$
$= 4 \sin 2\theta$.

b. Using the fact that $A'(\theta) = 8 \cos 2\theta$, find θ in the interval $0 < \theta < \frac{\pi}{2}$ so that $A(\theta)$ is maximized.
$\theta = \frac{\pi}{4}$

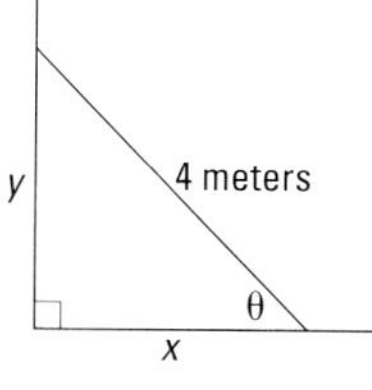

a) See below.

REPRESENTATIONS DEAL WITH PICTURES, GRAPHS, OR OBJECTS THAT ILLUSTRATE CONCEPTS.

Objective G: *Relate average rate of change to secant lines of graphs of functions.* (Lesson 9-1)

22. Refer to the graph of f below.

a. What is the average rate of change in f from $x = -4$ to $x = -1$? **-1/3**

b. What is the average rate of change in f from $x = -1$ to $x = 1$? **3/2**

c. With two of the five indicated points as endpoints, over what interval is the average rate of change in f zero? **x = 1 to x = 5**

d. Over what interval is the average rate of change $\frac{2}{5}$? **Sample: x = -4 to x = 1**

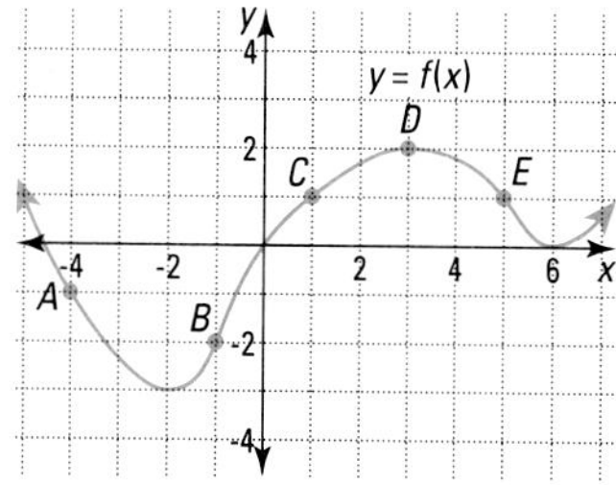

23. Suppose that U and V are points on the graph of the function g, and that $U = (-1, y)$ and $V = (5, -7)$. If the average rate of change in g from $x = -1$ to $x = 5$ is $-\frac{2}{3}$, find y. **-3**

Objective H: *Estimate derivatives by finding slopes of tangent lines.* (Lessons 9-2, 9-3)

24. Refer to the graph of f below. Estimate $f'(x)$ for the given value of x.

a. $x = -2$ **3** **b.** $x = 1$ **0** **c.** $x = 5$ **-1**

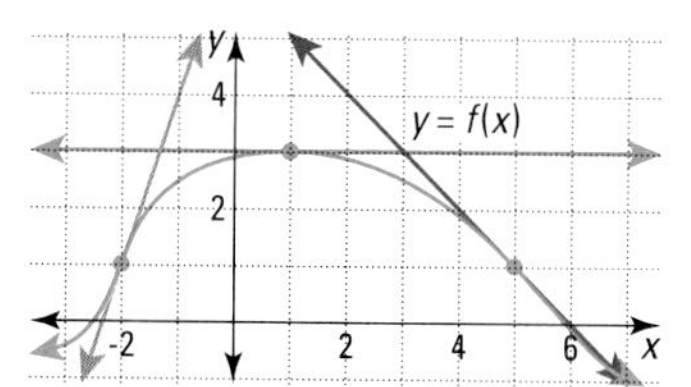

21a) $A(\theta) = \frac{1}{2}xy = \frac{1}{2}(4 \cos\theta)(4 \sin\theta) = 8 \sin\theta \cos\theta = 4(2 \sin\theta \cos\theta) = 4 \sin 2\theta$

4. b. Let $f(x) = 6 + 1.5\cos(\frac{2\pi}{365}x)$.

Month	First Day	Last Day	Average Rate of Change $\frac{f(\text{last day}) - f(\text{first day})}{\text{last day} - \text{first day}}$
Jan	0	31	-0.0068
Feb	31	59	-0.0179
Mar	59	90	-0.0245
Apr	90	120	-0.0247
May	120	151	-0.0213
Jun	151	181	-0.0043

Month	First Day	Last Day	Average Rate of Change $\frac{f(\text{last day}) - f(\text{first day})}{\text{last day} - \text{first day}}$
Jul	181	212	0.0061
Aug	212	343	0.0177
Sep	343	273	0.0247
Oct	273	304	0.0248
Nov	304	334	0.018
Dec	334	365	0.0067

25. Refer to the graph of g below.
  a. Estimate the values of $g'(-4)$, $g'(-2)$, $g'(0)$, $g'(3)$, and $g'(5)$. **See margin.**
  b. Sketch a graph of g' over the interval $-6 \le x \le 6$. **See margin.**

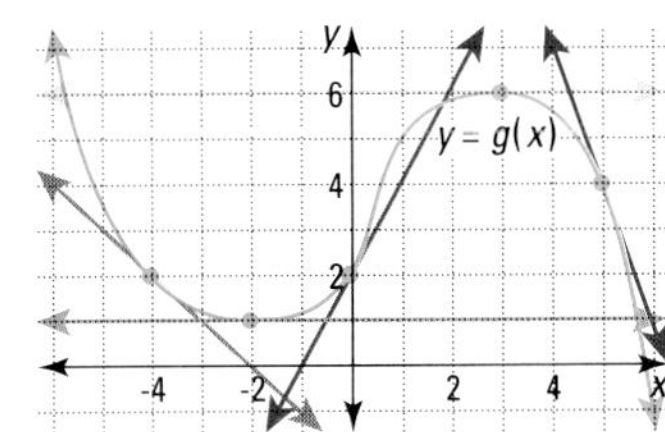

26. *Multiple choice.* The graph of f' is shown below. Which of the graphs below could be the graph of f? **a**

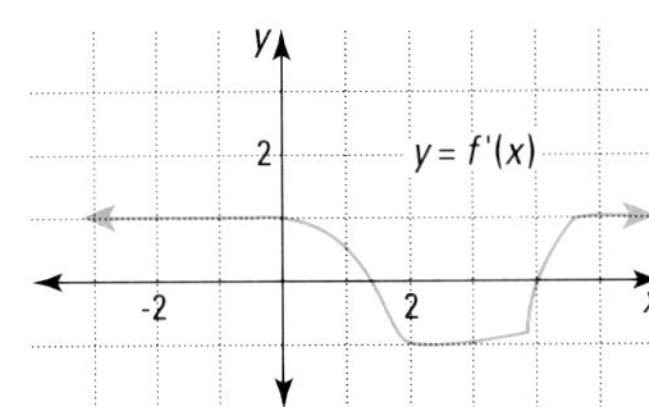

(a)

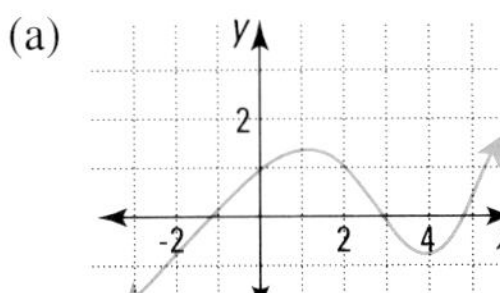

(b)

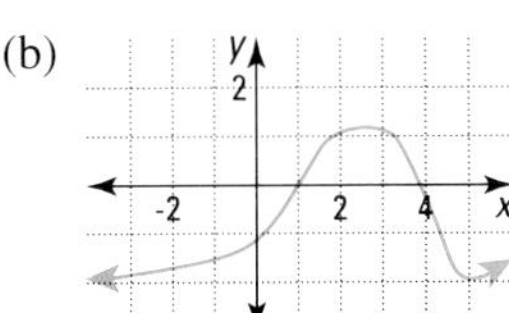

(c)

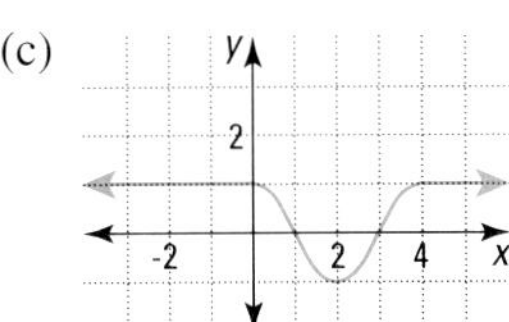

27. Sketch the graph of a function f such that $f'(0) = 1, f'(2) = 1, f'(3) = 2$.
See margin.

Objective I: *Determine properties of derivatives from the graph of a function.* (Lesson 9-5)

28. Refer to the graph of f below.
  a. On what interval(s) is the derivative of f positive? $-1 < x < 3$
  b. On what interval(s) is the derivative of f negative? $x < -1, x > 3$
  c. Where is the derivative equal to 0? $x = -1, x = 3$
  d. Estimate $f'(0), f'(3)$, and $f'(6)$. **See below.**
  e. Is $f''(x)$ positive or negative on the interval $0 \le x \le 7$? **negative**

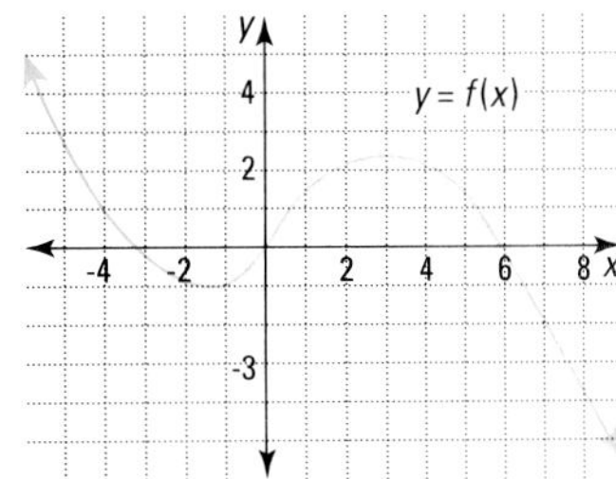

29. Use the graph of g' shown below.
  a. Estimate the intervals on which g is increasing and the intervals on which g is decreasing.
  b. Where may g have a relative minimum or maximum? $x = -3, x = 1$
  c. Estimate the intervals on which g'' is positive and the intervals on which g'' is negative.

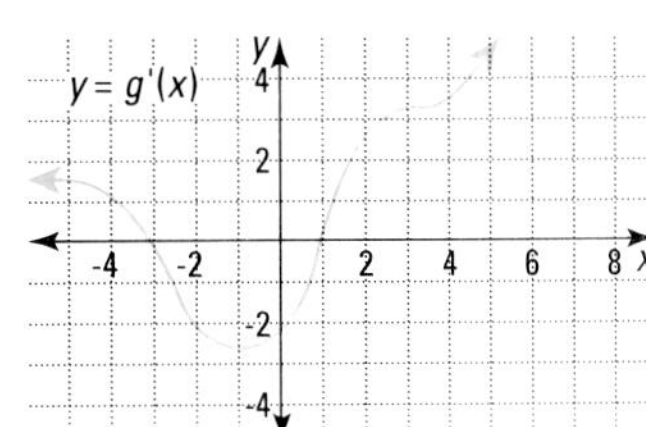

a) increasing: $x < -3$, $x > 1$; decreasing: $-3 < x < 1$
c) positive: $x > -1$; negative: $x < -1$

28d) $f'(0) \approx 1.5$, $f'(3) \approx 0$, $f'(6) \approx -2$

Additional Answers

25. a. $g'(-4) = -1$, $g'(-2) = 0$, $g'(0) = 2$, $g'(3) = 0$, $g'(5) = -3$
  b.

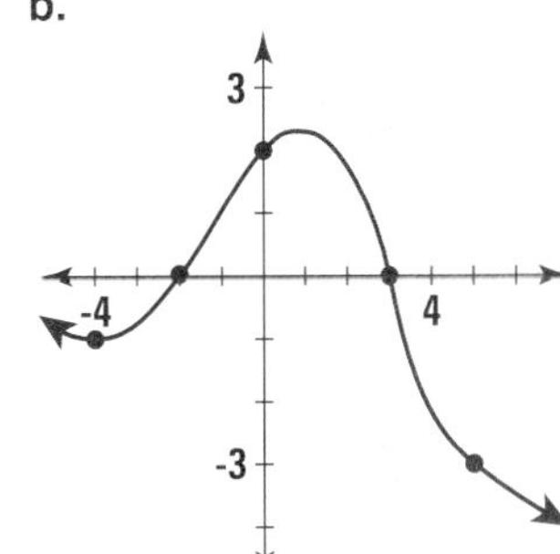

27. **Sample:**

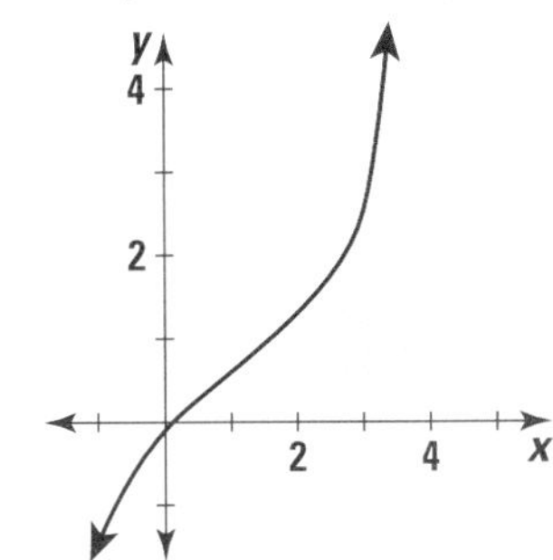

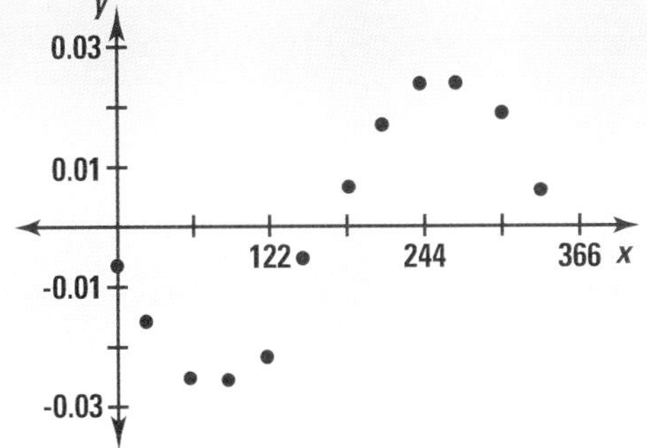

A formula that fits these data is $y = -0.025 \sin(\frac{2\pi}{365}x)$.

c. The fastest change is March to April and September to October. The slowest change is June to July and December to January.

d. The time of sunrise is later when the length of the day is shorter, and the time of sunrise is earlier when the length of the day is longer. When the rate of change in time of sunrises is the slowest: (1) June to July, the length of the day is longest; and (2) December to January, the length of the day is shortest.

Adapting to Individual Needs

The student text is written for the vast majority of students. The chart at the right suggests two pacing plans to accommodate the needs of your students. Students in the Full Course should complete the entire text by the end of the year. Students in the Minimal Course will spend more time when there are quizzes and more time on the Chapter Review. Therefore, these students may not complete all of the chapters in the text.

Options are also presented to meet the needs of a variety of teaching and learning styles. For each lesson, the Teacher's Edition provides a section entitled *Adapting to Individual Needs.* This section regularly includes **Optional Activities, Challenge** problems, **English Language Development** suggestions, and suggestions for providing **Extra Help.** The Teacher's Edition also frequently includes an **Error Alert,** an **Extension,** and an **Assessment** alternative. The options available in Chapter 10 are summarized in the chart below.

Chapter 10 Pacing Chart

Day	Full Course	Minimal Course
1	10-1	10-1
2	10-2	10-2
3	10-3	10-3
4	Quiz*; 10-4	Quiz*; begin 10-4.
5	10-5	Finish 10-4.
6	10-6	10-5
7	Quiz*; 10-7	10-6
8	10-8	Quiz*; begin 10-7.
9	Self-Test	Finish10-7.
10	Review	10-8
11	Test*	Self-Test
12		Review
13		Review
14		Test*

*in the Teacher's Resource File

In the Teacher's Edition...

Lesson	Optional Activities	Extra Help	Challenge	English Language Development	Error Alert	Extension	Cooperative Learning	Ongoing Assessment
10-1	●	●	●		●	●		Oral
10-2	●	●	●	●	●	●	●	Written
10-3	●	●	●		●	●		Quiz
10-4	●	●	●		●	●	●	Written
10-5	●	●	●		●	●		Oral
10-6	●	●	●		●	●		Quiz
10-7	●	●			●	●	●	Written
10-8	●	●	●		●	●		

In the Additional Resources...

	In the Teacher's Resource File							
Lesson	Lesson Masters	Teaching Aids*	Answer Masters	Technology Sourcebook	Assessment Sourcebook	Visual Aids**	Technology	Explorations Software
10-1	10-1	103	10-1			103, AM		
10-2	10-2	103, 106	10-2	Calc 14		103, 106, AM		
10-3	10-3	103	10-3		Quiz	103, AM		
10-4	10-4	104	10-4			104, AM		10-4
10-5	10-5	104, 107, 108	10-5			104,107,108,AM		10-5
10-6	10-6	104, 109	10-6	Calc 15	Quiz	104, 109, AM		10-6
In-class Activity			10-7					10-7
10-7	10-7	105	10-7			105, AM		
10-8		105	10-8			105, AM		
End of chapter					Tests			

*Teaching Aids are pictured on pages 600C.

**Visual Aids provide transparencies for all Teaching Aids and all Answer Masters.

Also available is the Study Skills Handbook which includes study-skill tips related to reading, note-taking, and comprehension.

Integrating Strands and Applications

	10-1	10-2	10-3	10-4	10-5	10-6	10-7	10-8
Mathematical Connections								
Number Sense	●	●	●	●	●	●	●	●
Algebra		●	●	●	●	●	●	●
Logic and Reasoning	●	●	●	●	●	●	●	●
Probability	●	●	●	●	●	●	●	●
Patterns and Functions	●	●	●	●	●	●	●	●
Discrete Mathematics	●	●	●	●	●	●	●	●
Interdisciplinary and Other Connections								
Science			●					
Social Studies	●	●		●				
Multicultural		●	●	●	●	●		
Technology		●	●	●	●	●	●	
Career		●	●					
Consumer	●	●		●	●	●		●
Sports	●	●	●	●	●		●	

Teaching and Assessing the Chapter Objectives

				In the Teacher's Resource File		
Chapter 10 Objectives (Organized into the SPUR catetgories—Skills, Properties, Uses, and Representations)	**Lessons**	**Progress Self-Test Questions**	**Chapter Review Questions**	**Chapter Test, Forms A and B**	**Chapter Test, Forms**	
					C	**D**
Skills						
A: Describe the essential features of counting problems.	10-1	1, 2	1–5			
B: Evaluate expressions indicating permutations or combinations.	10-3, 10-4	6, 7	6–10		2	
C: Apply the Binomial Theorem to expand binomials or find specific terms.	10-5	11	11–14		5	
Properties						
D: Use properties of permutations and combinations to prove identities.	10-3, 10-4	15	15–17			
E: Apply the Binomial Theorem to deduce properties of sets.	10-6	13	18–19			
Uses						
F: Use the Multiplication Counting Principle and permutations to solve counting problems.	10-2, 10-3	4, 5, 8, 9	20–28		3	
G: Use combinations and the Binomial Theorem to solve counting problems.	10-4,10-6, 10-7	1, 2, 10, 14	29–35		3	✓
H: Find binomial probabilities in realistic situations.	10-6	12, 16	36–37		4	
Representations						
I: Use a possibility tree to determine the number of outcomes in a given situation.	10-2	3	38–40		1	✓

Assessment Sourcebook
Quiz for Lessons 10-1 through 10-3
Quiz for Lessons 10-4 through 10-6
Chapter 10 Test, Forms A–D
Chapter 10 Test, Cumulative Form

TestWorks CD-ROM

Teaching Aids

TEACHING AID 103

Warm-up
Lesson 10-1

Consider the symbols *A*, *B*, and *C*.

1. Write all sets of 3 symbols from *A*, *B*, *C*, without repetition.
2. Write all collections of 3 symbols from *A*, *B*, *C*, with repetition.
3. Write all strings of 3 symbols from *A*, *B*, *C*, without repetition.
4. Write all strings of 3 symbols from *A*, *B*, *C*, with repetition.

Warm-up
Lesson 10-2

Two teams *A* and *B* play each other until one of them loses twice.

1. Draw a tree diagram with all possibilities of this situation and indicate who wins with each possibility.
2. If the teams are evenly matched and team *A* loses the first game, what is the probability that it will win the match?

Warm-up
Lesson 10-3

Take a permutation of *k* of the four letters *a*, *e*, *s*, and *t*. For each value of *k* from 1 to 4, what is the probability that your permutation is a word in the English language?

TEACHING AID 104

Warm-up
Lesson 10-4

Consider all the subsets of the set {1, 2, 3, 4, 5}.

1. How many subsets have only even numbers as elements?
2. How many subsets have only odd numbers as elements?
3. How many subsets have both even numbers and odd numbers as elements?
4. How many subsets have neither even numbers nor odd numbers as elements?

Warm-up
Lesson 10-5

1. Expand $(3x - y)^4$.
2. Verify your answer to Question 1 by substituting 2 for *x* and 6 for *y*.

Warm-up
Lesson 10-6

Given that about 51% of the babies born in the United States are boys, and assuming that births of boys and girls are independent, what is the probability that in a family of three children, the eldest is a boy, the second is a girl, and the third is a boy?

TEACHING AID 105

Warm-up
Lesson 10-7

Work with a partner to compare your answers to the questions in the In-class Activity on page 639 in the Student Edition.

Warm-up
Lesson 10-8

1. According to the work in Lesson 10-7, how many terms are in the expansion of $(x + y + z)^4$?
2. $(x + y + z)^2 = x^2 + y^2 + z^2 + 2xy + 2xz + 2yz$. Square this six-term polynomial to obtain the full expansion of $(x + y + z)^4$.

TEACHING AID 106
Lesson 10-2

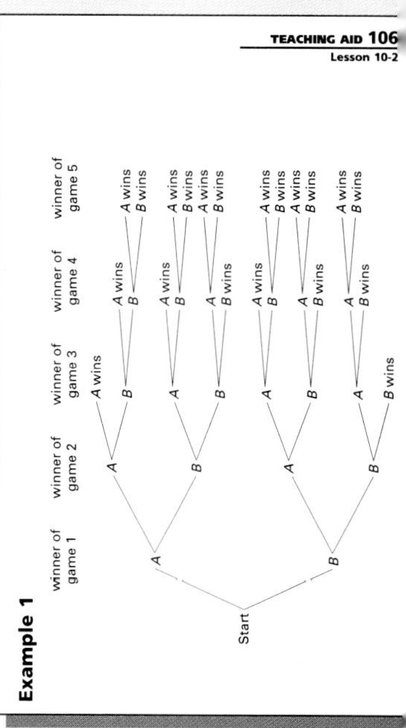

TEACHING AID 107
Lesson 10-5

Page Head

row 0 → 1
row 1 → 1 1
row 2 → 1 2 1
row 3 → 1 3 3 1
row 4 → 1 4 6 4 1
row 5 → 1 5 10 10 5 1
row 6 → 1 6 15 20 15 6 1
row 7 → 1 7 21 35 35 21 7 1
row 8 → 1 8 28 56 70 56 28 8 1
row 9 → 1 9 36 84 126 126 84 36 9 1
row 10 → 1 10 45 120 210 252 210 120 45 10 1

TEACHING AID 108
Lesson 10-5

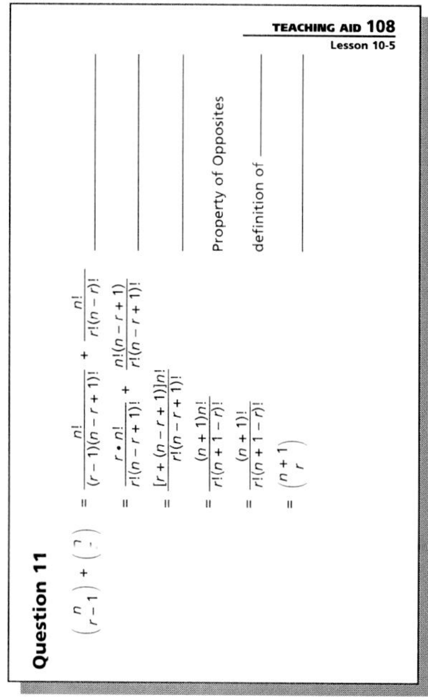

TEACHING AID 109
Lesson 10-6

Pascal's Triangle as a Triangle of Combinations

$\binom{0}{0}$

$\binom{1}{0}$ $\binom{1}{1}$

$\binom{2}{0}$ $\binom{2}{1}$ $\binom{2}{2}$

$\binom{3}{0}$ $\binom{3}{1}$ $\binom{3}{2}$ $\binom{3}{3}$

$\binom{4}{0}$ $\binom{4}{1}$ $\binom{4}{2}$ $\binom{4}{3}$ $\binom{4}{4}$

...

1

1 1

1 2 1

1 3 3 1

1 4 6 4 1

...

Chapter Opener

Pacing

All lessons in this chapter are designed to be covered in one day. At the end of the chapter, you should plan to spend 1 day to review the Progress Self-Test, 1–2 days for the Chapter Review, and 1 day for a test. You may wish to spend a day on projects, and possibly a day is needed for quizzes and the In-class Activity. This chapter should therefore take 11–14 days. Spending more than 15 days on this chapter is not recommended; there is ample opportunity to review ideas in later chapters.

Using Pages 600–601

To determine how much of this content your students have had (or remember), you might ask whether they can answer any of the questions on this page now. Problem 1 is the easiest; some students study this counting problem even before algebra. Problem 2 involves permutations; Problem 3 applies combinations; and Problem 4 uses both combinations and the Multiplication Counting Principle. Problem 5 is unlikely to have been studied by any students. All of these problems are examined in the next lesson; 4 of them in the reading and 1 in the questions. All five problems are solved in the chapter.

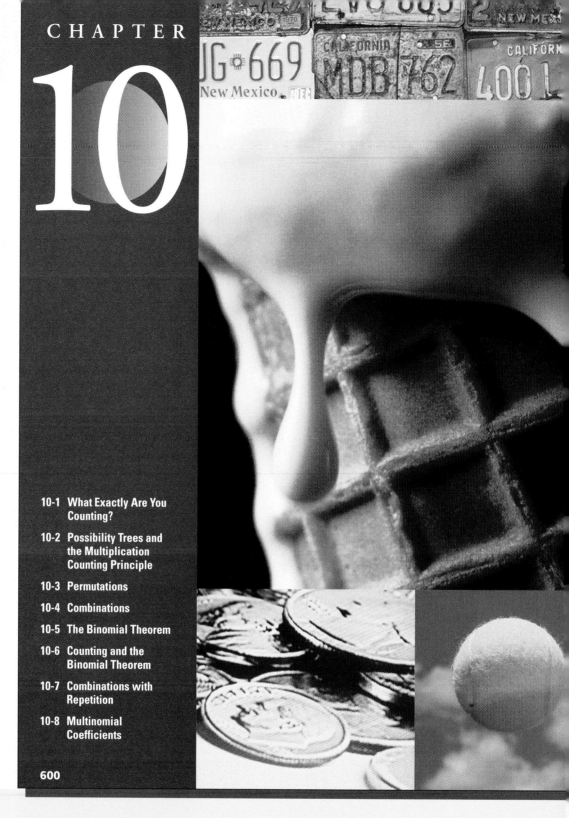

CHAPTER 10

Chapter 10 Overview

We would expect that most students taking UCSMP *Precalculus and Discrete Mathematics* have studied permutations and combinations and have seen the binomial theorem before. In previous UCSMP courses, the material of Lessons 10-2 through 10-6 is covered in some detail. In particular, in UCSMP *Functions, Statistics, and Trigonometry*, it is covered over a span of two chapters and mastery is expected.

Thus, when we were planning this book, we at first debated whether to include this content. The debate did not take long, however, because several arguments sufficiently strong for inclusion were given. They are: (1) This content is very important in all of mathematics and deserves to be seen twice. (2) Combinatorics is an important part of discrete mathematics and belongs in a course that gives strong attention to that subject. (3) Counting problems are tricky; almost all students can benefit from a second exposure. (4) In previous courses, many of the major theorems were stated but not proved, but here, with mathematical induction, they can all be proved.

Once we wrote this chapter, we found two other benefits to our decision. (5) By assuming prior familiarity, we are able to organize the chapter in a more cohesive manner because we do not have to spend

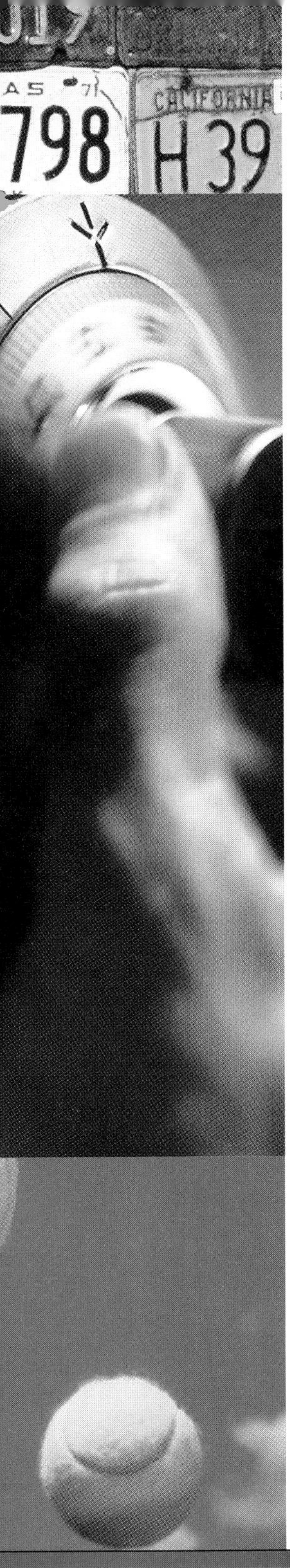

COMBINATORICS

Counting is a simple, everyday task. But there are many counting problems for which sophisticated counting procedures are needed. Here are some examples.

Problem 1: The automobile license plates for a certain state list two letters followed by four digits from 0 to 9, inclusive. How many different license plates are possible?

Problem 2: A bridal party consists of 4 bridesmaids, 4 ushers, the bride, and the groom. In how many ways can the bridal party be arranged in a row for portraits if the bride and groom always stand together?

Problem 3: A play in the Lotto game in the Illinois State Lottery consists of choosing a set of six different numbers from among the integers from 1 to 48, inclusive. What are the odds of winning?

Problem 4: A ski club has 80 members, 50 men and 30 women. A planning committee consisting of 5 men and 3 women is to be selected. How many different committees are possible?

Problem 5: Among the integers from 1000 to 9999 (inclusive), how many have at least one digit which is a 7 or a 5?

These and other types of counting problems are studied in a branch of mathematics called *combinatorics.* **Combinatorics** is the science of counting. The theorems of combinatorics can be deduced from simple principles, and help solve the above problems and many others.

Photo Connections

The photo collage makes real-world connections to the content of the chapter: combinatorics.

License Plates: Finding the number of different license plates a state can offer is one type of counting problem covered in this chapter.

Ice Cream: A two-dip ice cream cone with vanilla ice cream on top of strawberry ice cream represents the same combination as a cone with strawberry ice cream on top of vanilla ice cream. Combinations are discussed in Lesson 10-4.

Combination Lock: Order must be considered when determining the number of different possible lock combinations. Despite its name, these are permutation problems.

Coins: The Binomial Theorem indicates the number of different ways of obtaining a certain number of heads (or tails) when *n* coins are tossed. This topic is discussed in Lesson 10-6.

Tennis Balls: Possible outcomes relating to various types of sports events are discussed in Lesson 10-2.

Chapter 10 Projects

At this time, you might want to have students look over the projects on pages 649–650.

as much time reviewing prior ideas. (6) We can take the counting ideas further than is customarily done at this level. In particular, we are able to consider combinations with repetition and multinomial coefficients. The problems in the chapter opener represent the span of problems to be discussed in this chapter. Lesson 10-1 is designed to help students focus on the essential features of a counting problem, prior to studying techniques actually needed for problem solution.

Lessons 10-2, 10-3, and 10-4 cover the standard counting problems requiring the Multiplication Counting Principle, permutations, or combinations. Then there are two lessons covering the Binomial Theorem. In Lesson 10-5, the Binomial Theorem is used to expand binomials raised to any positive integer power. In Lesson 10-6, the Binomial Theorem is related to counting problems and probability.

Lesson 10-7 discusses combinations which allow repetitions, a topic not found in most schoolbooks but one which naturally completes the range of problems considered here. Lesson 10-8 connects permutations and combinations with the coefficients of $(a_1 + a_2 + \ldots + a_k)^n$, thus completing the connection between counting problems and powers of polynomials.

Lesson 10-1

Objectives

A Describe the essential features of counting problems.

Resources

From the ***Teacher's Resource File***

- Lesson Master 10-1
- Answer Master 10-1
- Teaching Aid 103: Warm-up

Additional Resources

- Visual for Teaching Aid 103

Teaching Lesson 10-1

Warm-up

Consider the symbols *A, B,* and *C.*

1. Write all sets of 3 symbols from *A, B, C,* without repetition.
   {A, B, C}
2. Write all collections of 3 symbols from *A, B, C,* with repetition.
   ***{A, A, A}, {A, A, B}, {A, A, C}, {A, B, B}, {A, B, C}, {A, C, C}, {B, B, B}, {B, B, C}, {B, C, C}, {C, C, C}* (The braces do not indicate sets.)**
3. Write all strings of 3 symbols from *A, B, C,* without repetition.
   ABC, ACB, BAC, BCA, CAB, CBA
4. Write all strings of 3 symbols from *A, B, C,* with repetition.
   AAA, AAB, AAC, ABA, ABB, ABC, ACA, ACB, ACC, BAA, BAB, BAC, BBA, BBB, BBC, BCA, BCB, BCC, CAA, CAB, CAC, CBA, CBB, CBC, CCA, CCB, CCC

LESSON

10-1 What Exactly Are You Counting?

How many skeins? *To count the number of skeins of yarn, you might separate the skeins by color, by location, or some other feature.*

The Essential Features of a Counting Problem

The key to solving many counting problems is to identify the *essential mathematical features* of the items being counted. If you can recognize these features, you can reformulate the problem in a way that makes it easier to solve and that is free of unimportant details.

How do you determine the essential features of a counting problem? Generally, the items to be counted are written down as symbols. You must determine whether the order of the symbols is important, and you must also consider whether symbols can be repeated. One way to think about the essential features is to determine in which cell of the following diagram the problem would fit.

❶

	repetition of symbols allowed	repetition of symbols not allowed
ordered symbols		
unordered symbols		

The focus of this lesson is to analyze some problems to determine the cell in which the problems belong. Later lessons of the chapter focus on techniques for actually solving the problems.

Lesson 10-1 Overview

Broad Goals The goal of this lesson is to have students distinguish between counting problems that involve repetitions and those that do not, and counting problems in which order is important from those in which order does not matter.

Perspective Many texts begin a discussion of combinatorics with permutations and combinations. After students have studied both types of problems, the two are mixed together and students are expected to determine which require the use of permutations and which require the use of combinations. We have chosen to begin the study of combinatorics somewhat differently. By having students focus first on the essential features of a problem—whether repetitions are allowed and whether order is important—we hope to avoid some of the confusion that typically occurs when students learn techniques first and only later try to remember when to apply them.

The four types of problems are covered in the following places: symbols ordered, repetition allowed (corollary of the multiplication counting principle, Lesson 10-2); symbols ordered, repetition not allowed (permutations, Lesson 10-3); symbols unordered, repetition allowed (combinations with repetition, Lesson 10-7); symbols

Example 1

Identify the essential features of the items to be counted in Problem 1 on page 601.

The automobile license plates for a certain state list two letters followed by four digits from 0 to 9, inclusive. How many different license plates are possible?

Solution

In this state, a license number consists of six symbols. The first two symbols can be any of the 26 letters in the alphabet and the last four symbols can be any of the 10 digits from 0 through 9.

Two license numbers such as those shown at the left are different even though both use the same six symbols. Thus, for a license plate the order of the six symbols is important. Repetition is allowed because a letter or digit can be used more than once in a license number. **So this is a problem about ordered symbols with repetition of symbols allowed.**

❷ Ordered Symbols with Repetition

When the symbols in a problem must be ordered, it is common to refer to the ordered list of symbols as a **string**. Then the license plate problem can be reformulated in the following way:

> Count the number of strings of six symbols in which the first two symbols are selected from the 26 letters of the alphabet (with repetition allowed) and the last four symbols are selected from the digits 0 through 9 (with repetition allowed).

The license plate problem can be solved by using the Multiplication Counting Principle. This principle is discussed in the next lesson.

Example 2

Identify the essential features of the items to be counted in Problem 3 on page 601.

A play in the Lotto game in the Illinois State lottery consists of choosing six numbers from among the integers from 1 to 48, inclusive. What are the odds of winning?

Solution

To know the odds, you must know how many different choices are possible. The order in which the six numbers are selected is unimportant and the six numbers selected must all be different. Consequently, **a play in the Lotto game is a problem involving unordered symbols with no repetitions allowed.**

Notes on Reading

❶ This box illustrates the four major types of counting problems to be discussed in this chapter. In this lesson, students essentially determine to which cell a given problem belongs. During the course of the chapter, students will learn the techniques needed to solve problems in any of the four cells. The appropriate techniques for each cell are indicated in the chapter summary on page 651.

Error Alert Remind students that whether or not the word "inclusive" is explicitly stated, the numbers "from a to b" include a and b. Students will encounter this in situations throughout the chapter. You might want to review that "between a and b" suggests that a and b are not included.

❷ It is important that students associate the use of the word *string* with the concept of an ordered list of symbols. Hence, when we use string in the text or in the answers, it is understood that order is important, whether or not it is explicitly stated.

Example 1 belongs in the upper left cell; **Examples 2–3** in the lower right cell; **Example 4** in the lower left cell.

Though students may know techniques for solving some of these problems from earlier study, it is important to avoid discussing the actual solution of these problems at this point. The *Exploration* on page 606 allows students to display this knowledge. For those students who have not had previous exposure to combinatorics, such discussion can be confusing and make the content appear harder than necessary.

We also strongly discourage you from introducing the words *permutation* and *combination* at this time. If students have studied these ideas before, let them feel good when they encounter them again in the lessons. If they are not familiar with these words, early introduction will cause them to focus on terminology rather than on the essential characteristics of the problem.

unordered, repetition not allowed (combinations, Lesson 10-4).

To clarify the distinction, we use the word *string* to refer to an ordered set of symbols; the unordered counterpart is the traditional word *set*.

Optional Activities

Activity 1 Social Studies Connection
Many states now have various lottery games. Hence, if your state has such a lottery, a natural extension of **Example 2** is to answer the question again for your state for a number of the lottery games. Later in the chapter, you can actually determine the number of possible plays in each game.

Additional Examples

In 1–4, determine whether the symbols are ordered or unordered and whether repetition is allowed or not allowed.

1. The number of strings of 4 letters that can be made from the letters of CONQUEST
   Ordered symbols, no repetition
2. The number of subsets of 4 letters that can be formed from the letters of CONQUEST
   Unordered symbols, no repetition
3. The number of different 3-scooped ice-cream cones that can be made if 31 flavors are available **Ordered symbols with repetition**
4. The number of different orders of 3 one-scoop ice-cream cones that can be made if 31 flavors are available **Unordered symbols with repetition**

Notes on Questions

Question 2 Contrast the word *string* with the word *set*, which refers to an unordered collection.

Questions 3–9 Do not discuss the actual answers to the questions asked; focus only on the essential features. Otherwise, the arithmetic gets in the way of the concepts. If students wish to show you that they can answer some of the questions, have them do it on their homework papers as part of **Question 23.**

Question 11 You might use this question as a lead-in to the next lesson; it is easy and its solution should be known to many students.

(Notes on Questions continue on page 606.)

Unordered Symbols Without Repetition

When the symbols in a problem are unordered, with no repetitions allowed, the unordered list of symbols is referred to as a **set**.

Sets of six numbers selected without repetition from among the integers from 1 through 48 are the same as 6-element subsets of the set {1, 2, 3, . . . , 47, 48}. Thus, the Lotto problem can also be stated as:

How many different 6-element subsets are there of the set of all integers from 1 through 48?

The committee problem (Problem 4) stated in the chapter opener is similar in some essential ways to the Lotto problem but it has an important new ingredient.

Example 3

Reformulate the following problem by using the language of sets and subsets.

A ski club has 80 members, 50 men and 30 women. A planning committee consisting of 5 men and 3 women is to be selected. How many different committees are possible?

Solution

The order in which the persons on the planning committee are selected or listed does not change the composition of the committee. Also, no person can be selected more than once for a given committee. Consequently, you can think of a committee as a subset of 5 men of the set of 50 male club members, together with a subset of 3 women of the set of 30 female members. Therefore, the committee problem can be reformulated as follows:

How many ways is it possible to choose a 5-element subset of a set of 50 elements and a 3-element subset of a set of 30 elements?

Counting the "male" and "female" subcommittees of the committee is essentially the same counting problem as the Lotto problem. The essential features of this part of the problem can be explained in terms of the diagram at the beginning of the lesson. The new ingredient is that these two subcommittees are put together to form a committee. This feature requires taking a step beyond the diagram.

Example 4

Describe the essential features of the items to be counted in the following problem.

At a school fair, a $1 ticket at the fishing pool allows the participant to choose three prizes from four bags, each of which contains a different type of prize. Any combination of selections is acceptable: all selections can be made from the same bag, two can be made from one bag and one from a different bag, or all three can be made from different bags. How many different selections are possible?

Optional Activities

Activity 2 You can use part of this activity after students have completed the corresponding Question. Ask students to describe the essential features of each problem with the following changes.
Question 3: The lock is a dial with 39 numbers and in a combination the same number cannot be dialed twice [ordered, no repetition]
Question 4: You are looking for the number of integers with two identical digits [ordered, repetition]
Question 5: You are grouping the letters of STRING in sets of three [unordered, no repetition]
Question 6: There are 13 people nominated for three prizes, and one person can win more than one prize [unordered, repetition]
Question 7: The same person can fill two different offices [ordered, repetition]
Question 8: You are grouping digits into sets of four [unordered, no repetition]
Question 9: A trick-or-treater cannot take two pieces of candy from the same bowl [unordered, no repetition.]

Solution

Let the four bags be labeled *a*, *b*, *c*, and *d*. Selection of prizes can be thought of as choosing 3 of these labels, with repetition allowed. The order of the selection is unimportant. For instance, a selection of *abb* is equivalent to selections of *bab* or *bba*. So **this problem is one of counting unordered symbols when repetition is allowed.** A general technique for handling such problems is discussed in Lesson 10-7.

QUESTIONS

Covering the Reading

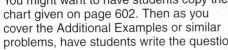

1) determining whether or not the order of symbols counts and whether or not repetition of symbols is allowed

1. What is meant by finding the *essential features* of a counting problem? See left.
2. Define *string*. A string is an ordered list of symbols.

In 3–9, describe the essential features of each problem. That is, decide whether the symbols are ordered or unordered and whether repetition of symbols is allowed. (You do not have to compute the solutions to these problems.)

3. A combination lock has four dial wheels with the digits from 0 through 9 on each wheel. How many different lock combinations are possible? Ordered symbols; repetition is allowed.
4. How many integers from 100 to 999, inclusive, have three different digits? Ordered symbols; repetition is not allowed.
5. How many different code words can be constructed from the letters in the word STRING? Ordered symbols; repetition is not allowed.
6. There are 13 applicants to fill three sales positions in different departments of a large department store. In how many different ways can these openings be filled? Ordered symbols; repetition is not allowed.
7. A club with 50 members has the following officers: president, vice-president, treasurer, and secretary. If all members of the club are eligible for all offices, how many different slates of officers are possible? Ordered symbols; repetition is not allowed.
8. How many different four-digit house numbers can be constructed from the six brass numerals 1, 2, 3, 4, 5, 6? Ordered symbols; repetition is not allowed.
9. At her son's birthday party, Mrs. May allows children to choose 4 toys from 5 bowls set on a table. If there is only one kind of toy in each bowl and no bowl contains the same kind of toy as another bowl, how many different selections are possible? Unordered symbols; repetition is allowed.

Applying the Mathematics

10. Identify the essential features of Problem 2 on page 601. Ordered symbols; repetition is not allowed.
11. A school club is conducting an election of officers. There are 3 candidates for president, 2 for vice-president, and 3 for secretary-treasurer. Identify the essential features of the problem of counting the number of different ways a ballot can be completed. Offices are unordered, and repetition is not allowed.

Follow-up for Lesson 10-1

Practice

For more questions on SPUR Objectives, use **Lesson Master 10-1** (shown below).

Assessment

Oral Communication Have students describe the difference between a *string* and a *set* and make up a counting problem involving each term. [Students show understanding of whether a set or string is involved in a counting problem.]

Extension

Project Update Project 1, *Integer Partitions,* and Project 6, *Scheduling Problems,* on pages 649–650, relate to the content of this lesson.

Adapting to Individual Needs

Extra Help

You might want to have students copy the chart given on page 602. Then as you cover the Additional Examples or similar problems, have students write the question number in the appropriate box. You might want to ask students to generate other problems and find their location in the chart.

Challenge

Have students determine the number of scores possible in the following situation.

A test has 10 questions. Each correct answer is given 2 points. Wrong answers cause a deduction of $\frac{1}{2}$ point, while there is no penalty for leaving a question blank. [45]

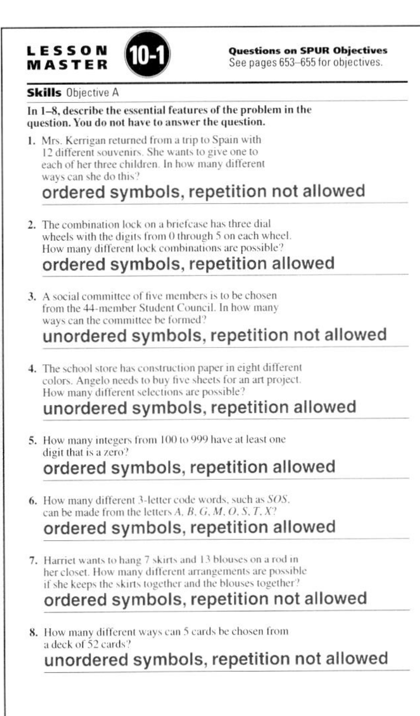

LESSON MASTER 10-1 **Questions on SPUR Objectives** See pages 653–655 for objectives.

Skills Objective A

In 1–8, describe the essential features of the problem in the question. You do not have to answer the question.

1. Mrs. Kerrigan returned from a trip to Spain with 12 different souvenirs. She wants to give one to each of her three children. In how many different ways can she do this?
ordered symbols, repetition not allowed
2. The combination lock on a briefcase has three dial wheels with the digits from 0 through 5 on each wheel. How many different lock combinations are possible?
ordered symbols, repetition allowed
3. A social committee of five members is to be chosen from the 44-member Student Council. In how many ways can the committee be formed?
unordered symbols, repetition not allowed
4. The school store has construction paper in eight different colors. Angelo needs to buy five sheets for an art project. How many different selections are possible?
unordered symbols, repetition allowed
5. How many integers from 100 to 999 have at least one digit that is a zero?
ordered symbols, repetition allowed
6. How many different 3-letter code words, such as *SOS*, can be made from the letters *A, B, G, M, O, S, T, X*?
ordered symbols, repetition allowed
7. Harriet wants to hang 7 skirts and 13 blouses on a rod in her closet. How many different arrangements are possible if she keeps the skirts together and the blouses together?
ordered symbols, repetition not allowed
8. How many different ways can 5 cards be chosen from a deck of 52 cards?
unordered symbols, repetition not allowed

Notes on Questions

Question 12 This is a problem that later can be solved using combinations.

Question 13 This kind of problem is discussed in Lesson 10-8.

Question 17 Here is a counting problem different from those in this chapter—one answered essentially by division.

Questions 19–20 The negation to **Question 19** should be true; the negation to **Question 20** should be false.

Additional Answers

14. c. $r = \sqrt{\cos\theta}$, $r = -\sqrt{\cos\theta}$,

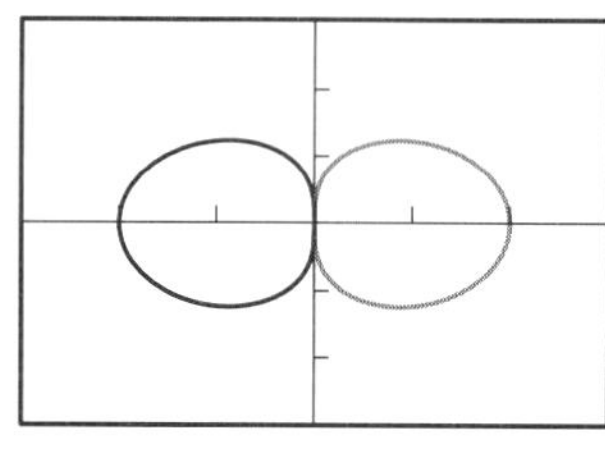

$0 \le \theta \le 2\pi$, θ-step $= \frac{\pi}{6}$
$-1.5 \le x \le 1.5$, x-scale $= 0.5$
$-1.5 \le y \le 1.5$, y-scale $= 0.5$

d. Transform the polar equation into a rectangular equation:

$r = \pm\sqrt{\cos\theta}$

$\sqrt{x^2 + y^2} = \pm\sqrt{\dfrac{x}{\sqrt{x^2 + y^2}}}$

$x^2 + y^2 = \dfrac{x}{\sqrt{x^2 + y^2}}$

$x = \pm(x^2 + y^2)^{3/2}$

which is not standard form for an ellipse.

12a) samples:

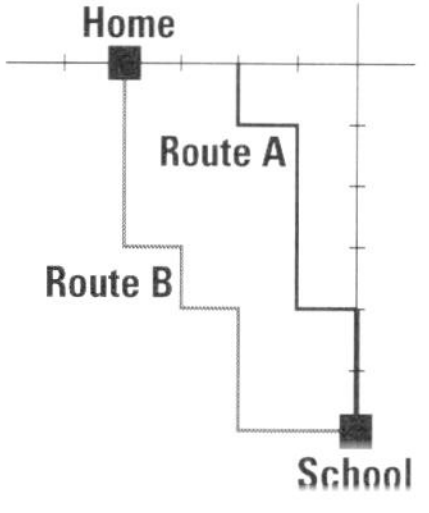

b) for the samples in part a: SSSESESSEE, EESESSSESS

14a) Because the cosine function has period 2π, any interval of length 2π contains all possible values of the function.

b) $\frac{\pi}{2} < \theta < \frac{3\pi}{2}$

12. Suppose a home is 6 blocks north and 4 blocks west of your school.

a. Draw two different street routes 10 blocks long that you can follow from the home to your school. **a, b) See left.**

b. Describe the two street routes in part **a** as strings of 10 symbols selected from the letters S (South one block) and E (East one block).

c. Identify the essential features of the problem of counting all street routes from the home to your school.
Ordered symbols; repetition is allowed.

13. Suppose that three different coins—a nickel, a dime, and a quarter—are to be placed in three different cups in a collection of 9 different cups. Identify the essential features of the problem of counting the number of different ways of distributing the three coins among the 9 cups.
Ordered symbols; repetition is not allowed.

Review

14. Consider the polar equation $r^2 = \cos\theta$. **a, b) See left.**

a. Explain why the complete polar graph of this equation can be obtained by plotting it on the interval $0 \le \theta \le 2\pi$.

b. For what values of θ in the range $0 \le \theta \le 2\pi$ is r undefined?

c. Use an automatic grapher to plot the graphs of $r = \sqrt{\cos\theta}$ and $r = -\sqrt{\cos\theta}$ for those values of θ for which r is defined. **See margin.**

d. The graph resembles the union of two ellipses. Explain why the two curves are not ellipses. *(Lesson 8-4)* **See margin.**

15. Use an automatic grapher to conjecture whether the equation below is an identity. If it is an identity, prove it. If not, give a counterexample.

$$(\tan\theta)(\sin\theta + \cot\theta\cos\theta) = \sec\theta \quad \textit{(Lessons 6-1, 6-2)}$$

See margin.

16. *Multiple choice.* If 3 is a zero of a polynomial p, then which is true? **c**

(a) 3 is a factor of p. (b) $x + 3$ is a factor of p.
(c) $x - 3$ is a factor of p. (d) $p(-3) = 0$ *(Lesson 4-4)*

17. a. How many positive integers less than 1000 are divisible by 7? **142**

b. How many positive integers less than an integer n are divisible by d? (Hint: Use the greatest integer function.) *(Lessons 3-5, 4-1)* $\left\lfloor \frac{n}{d} \right\rfloor$

18. Determine the interval(s) over which the function f graphed at the left is decreasing. *(Lesson 2-3)* $x < -1$, $x > 0$

In 19 and 20, write the negation of each statement. *(Lesson 1-2)*

19. *For all positive integers n, n is prime.* **∃ a positive integer n that is not prime.**

20. *There exist positive integers n and m such that nm = 11.* **∀ positive integers n and m, $nm \ne 11$.**

In 21 and 22, expand each product. *(Previous course)*

21. $(x + y)^2$
$x^2 + 2xy + y^2$

22. $(2x - y)^3$
$8x^3 - 12x^2y + 6xy^2 - y^3$

Exploration

23. Pick one of the problems from Questions 3–9 in this lesson, and try to determine the actual solution to the problem. **(3) 10,000; (4) 648; (5) 720; (6) 1716; (7) 5,527,200; (8) 360; (9) 625**

15.

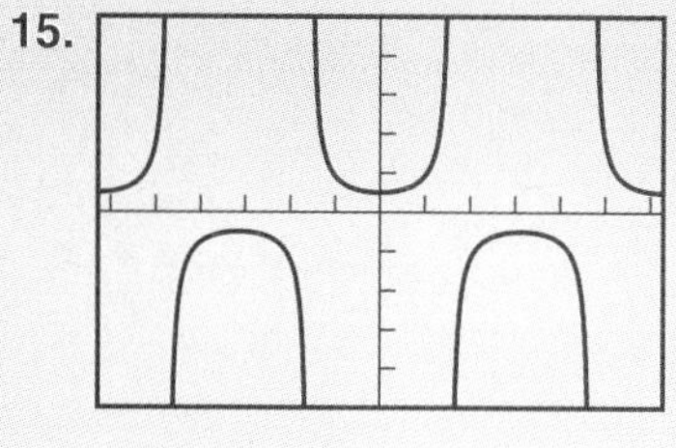

$-2\pi \le x \le 2\pi$, x-scale $= 1$
$-10 \le y \le 10$, y-scale $= 2$

$$\begin{aligned} \text{left side} &= (\tan\theta)(\sin\theta + \cot\theta\cos\theta) \\ &= \frac{\sin\theta}{\cos\theta}\left(\sin\theta + \frac{\cos\theta\cos\theta}{\sin\theta}\right) \\ &= \frac{\sin\theta}{\cos\theta}\left(\frac{\sin^2\theta + \cos^2\theta}{\sin\theta}\right) \\ &= \frac{\sin\theta}{\cos\theta}\left(\frac{1}{\sin\theta}\right) \\ &= \frac{1}{\cos\theta} \\ &= \sec\theta \\ &= \text{right side} \end{aligned}$$

Setting Up Lesson 10-2

Question 12 can be answered by forming a tree. You might wish to do that in anticipation of Lesson 10-2.

LESSON

10-2

Possibility Trees and the Multiplication Counting Principle

An ice try. *Some sports, such as hockey, feature a championship series which is won by the team which wins n of 2n − 1 games. All possible outcomes can be shown on a tree. See Example 1.*

Examples of Possibility Trees

Many counting problems can be solved by taking advantage of the fact that the items to be counted can be selected or constructed through a succession of steps. For example, a string $s_1, s_2, s_3, \ldots, s_k$ of k symbols can be constructed by the following succession of k steps.

Step 1: Select the first element, s_1.
Step 2: Select the second element, s_2.
Step 3: Select the third element, s_3.
⋮
Step $k-1$: Select the $(k-1)$st element, s_{k-1}.
Step k: Select the kth element, s_k.

Example 1

In some competitions between two players or teams, the first to win three games wins the competition. Describe the possible outcomes of such a competition as a succession of steps.

Solution

Call the players *A* and *B*. By the time five games have been played, either *A* or *B* must have won three games. Thus this competition is a succession of 3 to 5 games. The possible outcomes of the competition are the sequences of wins and losses shown in the diagram on page 608. ▸

Lesson 10-2

Objectives

F Use the Multiplication Counting Principle to solve counting problems.

I Use a possibility tree to determine the number of outcomes in a given situation.

Resources

From the ***Teacher's Resource File***
- Lesson Master 10-2
- Answer Master 10-2
- Teaching Aids
  103 Warm-up
  106 Example 1
- Technology Sourcebook
  Calculator Master 14

Additional Resources
- Visuals for Teaching Aids 103, 106

Teaching Lesson 10-2

Warm-up

Two teams *A* and *B* play each other until one of them loses twice.

1. Draw a tree diagram with all possibilities of this situation and indicate who wins with each possibility.

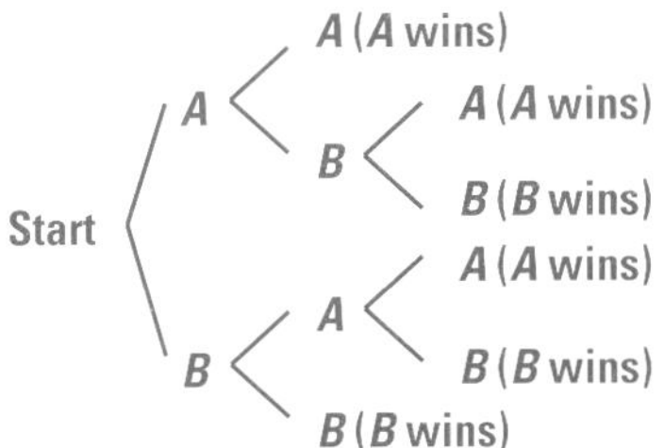

2. If the teams are evenly matched and team *A* loses the first game, what is the probability that team *A* will win the match? $\frac{1}{3}$

Lesson 10-2 Overview

Broad Goals This lesson emphasizes two types of problems—those that can be solved by constructing possibility trees and those that can be solved by using the Multiplication Counting Principle.

Perspective The Multiplication Counting Principle is found in four previous UCSMP texts. The treatment here is more formal in three ways: the outline of a proof by induction is left for students to complete; there is a more formal subscript statement of the principle; and the language of strings is used. A corollary of this principle is that n^r is the number of r-symbol strings that can be made from a set of n symbols.

The fact that we use a "set" of n symbols here means that the symbols themselves have no repetition. In Lesson 10-8 we consider the situation where the original collection of symbols contains repetitions.

Notes on Reading

Although we use possibility trees to lead to the Multiplication Counting Principle, students need to understand that not all tree problems can be solved by applying the principle. The problem of **Example 1** on page 607 is one such example.

❶ **Error Alert** Because the branches of the tree of **Example 1** are of different lengths, some students may have trouble reading the tree to determine the total number of outcomes. Use **Teaching Aid 106** to trace out the different outcomes. Students need to see that each time a branch terminates, there is one outcome. You might have students write out the sequence of team wins for each branch of the tree, similar to that done with the code words for the tree in **Example 2.**

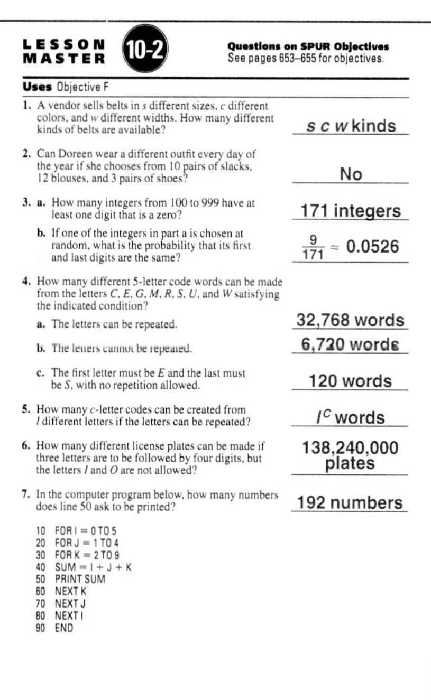

LESSON MASTER 10-2 **Questions on SPUR Objectives** See pages 653–655 for objectives.

Uses Objective F

1. A vendor sells belts in s different sizes, c different colors, and w different widths. How many different kinds of belts are available? $s\,c\,w$ kinds
2. Can Doreen wear a different outfit every day of the year if she chooses from 10 pairs of slacks, 12 blouses, and 3 pairs of shoes? No
3. a. How many integers from 100 to 999 have at least one digit that is a zero? 171 integers
   b. If one of the integers in part a is chosen at random, what is the probability that its first and last digits are the same? $\frac{9}{171} \approx 0.0526$
4. How many different 5-letter code words can be made from the letters C, E, G, M, R, S, U, and W satisfying the indicated condition?
   a. The letters can be repeated. 32,768 words
   b. The letters cannot be repeated. 6,720 words
   c. The first letter must be E and the last must be S, with no repetition allowed. 120 words
5. How many c-letter codes can be created from l different letters if the letters can be repeated? l^c words
6. How many different license plates can be made if three letters are to be followed by four digits, but the letters I and O are not allowed? 138,240,000 plates
7. In the computer program below, how many numbers does line 50 ask to be printed? 192 numbers

```
10 FOR I = 0 TO 5
20 FOR J = 1 TO 4
30 FOR K = 2 TO 9
40 SUM = I + J + K
50 PRINT SUM
60 NEXT K
70 NEXT J
80 NEXT I
90 END
```

❶

winner of game 1 | winner of game 2 | winner of game 3 | winner of game 4 | winner of game 5

Start
A – A – A wins
A – A – B – A wins
A – A – B – B – A wins
A – A – B – B – B wins
A – B – A – A wins
A – B – A – B – A wins
A – B – A – B – B wins
A – B – B – A – A wins
A – B – B – A – B wins
A – B – B – B wins
B – A – A – A wins
B – A – A – B – A wins
B – A – A – B – B wins
B – A – B – A – A wins
B – A – B – A – B wins
B – A – B – B wins
B – B – A – A – A wins
B – B – A – A – B wins
B – B – A – B wins
B – B – B wins

Because there are 20 ways to get "wins," the diagram shows that there are 20 possible outcomes for this competition. Each outcome is represented by a path from the point marked "Start" to a point where either A or B wins the competition. Two outcomes require 3 games, 6 require 4 games, and 12 require 5 games.

The diagram used in Example 1 to display the possible outcomes of the competition is called a **possibility tree**. Each game in each outcome of the competition is represented by a **branch point** or **node** of the tree; the first node is labeled "Start." A node corresponds to a step in which several choices or results are possible. The ends of the branches are called **leaves**. The number of possible outcomes of the playoff series, 20, is equal to the number of leaves in the possibility tree for the competition.

A possibility tree can be used to count strings if the number of strings is not too large.

Example 2

Use a possibility tree to count the number of different two-letter code words that can be constructed from the letters A, B, and C if repetition of letters is not allowed.

Solution

There are three branches leaving the start node, representing the selection of the first letter. However, because repetition of letters is not allowed, the possibility tree has only two branches leaving each of those nodes, representing selection of the second letter.

Optional Activities

Activity 1 Technology Connection
In *Technology Sourcebook, Calculator Master 14,* students use a programmable calculator to simulate random guessing of security codes. Then they examine the relationship between the number of codes possible and the average number of guesses needed to "crack" the code.

Activity 2 After assigning and discussing **Question 23,** you might have students **work in groups** to invent one problem for each of Lessons 10-2 through 10-7 and then use these problems as review for the chapter.

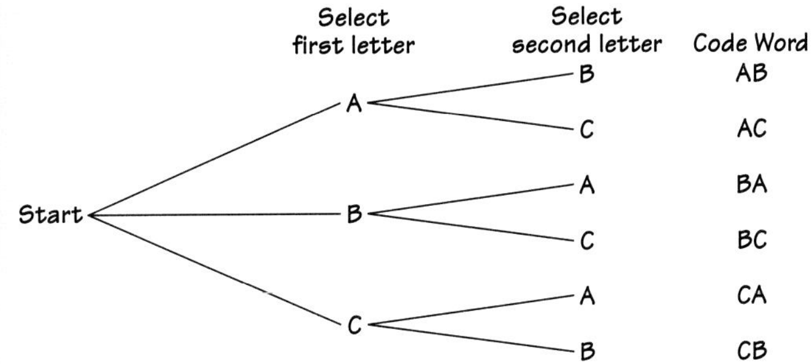

There are six leaves on this possibility tree, and so **there are six possible code words if repetition is not allowed.**

The Multiplication Counting Principle

In the possibility tree of Example 2, in each step the same number of branches lead from each node. The number of leaves in such a possibility tree is the product of the numbers of branches leaving the nodes for each step of the tree. For instance, in Example 2, there are 3 branches to indicate selection of the first letter and 2 branches leaving each of those branches to indicate selection of the second letter. So the total number of leaves in the tree is $3 \cdot 2 = 6$.

This special feature of certain possibility trees illustrates the following general Multiplication Counting Principle, which you may have encountered, without proof, in previous courses.

The Multiplication Counting Principle
Suppose that strings result from a procedure which consists of k successive steps and that:

the 1st step can be done in n_1 ways,
the 2nd step can be done in n_2 ways,
⋮
and the kth step can be done in n_k ways.

Then the number of strings is

$$n_1 \cdot n_2 \cdot \ldots \cdot n_k.$$

A proof of the Multiplication Counting Principle using mathematical induction is outlined in Question 15. The following example illustrates how this principle can be used to solve the license plate problem on page 601.

Adapting to Individual Needs

Extra Help
In **Example 5** we assume that students are familiar with the following Addition Counting Principle: The number of elements in the union of two disjoint sets is the sum of the elements in each one of them. Symbolically, $A \cup B = \varnothing \Rightarrow N(A \cup B) = N(A) + N(B)$. Some students might benefit from a review of the Addition Counting Principle.

English Language Development
You might want to point out that the word *complement* means "to fill out" or "complete." Both the use of the word with respect to angles and with respect to sets are variants of this meaning. (The word "compliment" meaning "to praise" has a different derivation.)

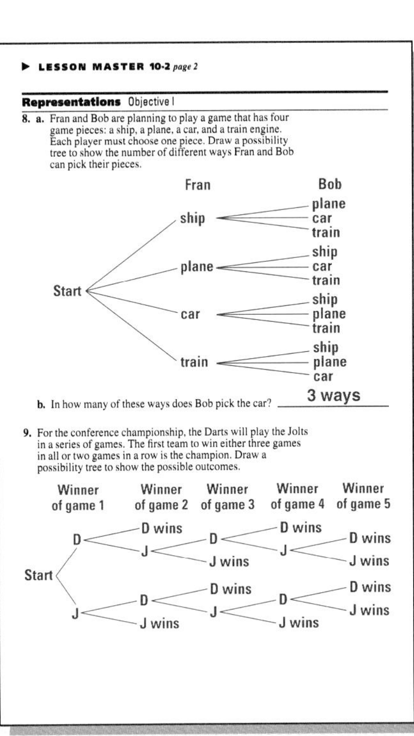
► LESSON MASTER 10-2 *page 2*

Representations Objective I

8. a. Fran and Bob are planning to play a game that has four game pieces: a ship, a plane, a car, and a train engine. Each player must choose one piece. Draw a possibility tree to show the number of different ways Fran and Bob can pick their pieces.

b. In how many of these ways does Bob pick the car? 3 ways

9. For the conference championship, the Darts will play the Jolts in a series of games. The first team to win either three games in all or two games in a row is the champion. Draw a possibility tree to show the possible outcomes.

Examples 3–4 tie in naturally to Project 4 on page 650, *License Plate Numbers*. If students consider the population of their state and the number of license plate identifications found in these two problems, they may wonder how the Department of Motor Vehicles comes up with enough license plate identifications for all the registered vehicles in the state. This could lead to an interesting project for a single student or for a group of students.

The solution of **Example 5** applies a De Morgan Law with negations on both sides, namely: *p or q ≡ not((not p) and (not q))*. The complexity of this application of that Law signals the possibility that students may be confused as they read it.

Additional Examples

1. a. Describe the possible outcomes of a competition in which the first team to win two games wins the series. (This is sometimes called "best 2 of 3.") **Call the competitors *A* and *B*. The possibilities are *A-A*, *A-B-A*, *A-B-B*, *B-B*, *B-A-A*, and *B-A-B*. Using a tree:**

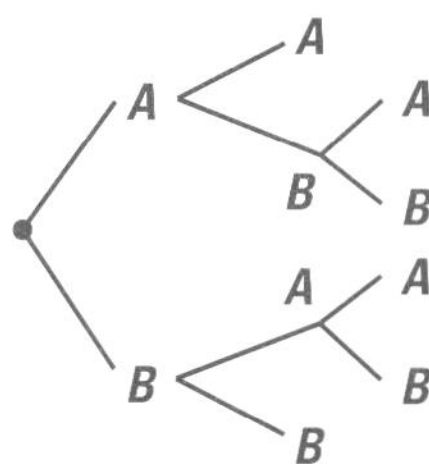

b. The outcome for Additional Example 1a is the same as the possible outcomes of a competition in which the first team to lose two games loses the competition (as in the *Warm-up* on page 607). Why is this so? **If one team wins two games, then the other team loses two games.**

Example 3

Compute the number of different 6-symbol license plate identifications that are possible if the first two symbols can be any of the 26 letters of the alphabet and the last four symbols can be any of the digits from 0 to 9, inclusive.

Solution

Think of constructing a 6-symbol license plate identification as a process of selecting six symbols, one at a time from left to right. There are 26 possible selections for each of the first two symbols because there are 26 letters of the alphabet. There are 10 possible selections for each of the last four symbols because there are 10 digits from 0 to 9. Therefore, by the Multiplication Counting Principle, there are

26 ·	26 ·	10 ·	10 ·	10 ·	10 = 6,760,000
1st letter	2nd letter	1st digit	2nd digit	3rd digit	4th digit

different possible license plate identifications.

In Illinois, for an extra fee, car owners have the option of creating their own strings of digits or letters on a variety of backgrounds. The woman in the photo is operating a machine that stamps a plate.

How Many Strings with Repetition Are There?

The answer to Example 3 could be written $26^2 \cdot 10^4$, where 26^2 is the number of two-letter strings with repetition and 10^4 is the number of four-digit strings with repetition. These are instances of the following corollary to the Multiplication Counting Principle.

Theorem
If repetition is allowed, the number of r-symbol strings that can be made from a set of n symbols is n^r.

Proof
Each symbol in the string can be selected in n ways. There are r selections to be made. Thus the number of strings is $\underbrace{n \cdot n \cdot \ldots \cdot n}_{r \text{ factors}} = n^r$.

Example 4

Suppose that the license plate problem is modified by requiring that no symbol in the license plate be repeated. Count the total number of different license plates that are possible in this case.

Adapting to Individual Needs

Challenge

Have students suppose that 4 students are selected from their high school class at random to be class officers. The first person to be selected is President, the second one is Vice President, the third is Secretary, and the fourth is Treasurer. Tell students to let n represent the number of students in their class and answer these questions.

1. How many different results are possible? $[n(n-1)(n-2)(n-3)]$
2. How many of these results would have you as an officer? $[n(n-1)(n-2)(n-3) - (n-1)(n-2)(n-3)(n-4)]$

Solution

Because no repetition is allowed, the number of letters and digits that can be selected is reduced by one each time a selection is made. Therefore, there are

26	·	25	·	10	·	9	·	8	·	7
1st letter		2nd letter		1st digit		2nd digit		3rd digit		4th digit

or 3,276,000 different license plates with no symbol repeated.

Counting Strings by Using the Complement

Sometimes it is rather complicated to count the items of a set which possess a particular property. In such cases it may be more efficient to count the items in the **complement** of the set, that is, to count the items in the set which do *not* have the given property.

Example 5

Among the integers from 1000 through 9999, how many have at least one digit which is a 5 or a 7?

Solution

The set S of all integers from 1000 through 9999 consists of all strings $d_1d_2d_3d_4$ of 4 digits in which repetition is allowed. Note that d_1 must be one of the digits from 1 through 9, while d_2, d_3, and d_4 can be any of the digits from 0 through 9. By the Multiplication Counting Principle, the set S contains 9000 integers.

The given problem asks you to count the integers in S which have one, two, three, or four digits of 5 or 7. But it is simpler to count those integers in S that do not contain a 5 and do not contain a 7.

$$\begin{pmatrix}\text{number of integers}\\\text{containing a 5 or 7}\end{pmatrix} = 9000 - \begin{pmatrix}\text{number of integers not containing}\\\text{a 5 and not containing a 7}\end{pmatrix}$$

Now the integers not containing a 5 and not containing a 7 are strings of 4 digits where the first digit can be any of 1, 2, 3, 4, 6, 8, 9 and the other digits can be any of 0, 1, 2, 3, 4, 6, 8, 9. So the number of integers satisfying this condition is $7 \cdot 8 \cdot 8 \cdot 8 = 3584$. Thus the number of integers containing a 5 or a 7 is $9000 - 3584 = 5416$.

2)

Select first letter	Select second letter	Code Word
A	A	AA
	B	AB
	C	AC
B	A	BA
	B	BB
	C	BC
C	A	CA
	B	CB
	C	CC

QUESTIONS

Covering the Reading

1. Refer to Example 1. How many possible outcomes are there if Team A wins the first two games? **4**

2. Modify the possibility tree in Example 2 to find the number of possible code words which can be formed if the letters can be repeated. **See left. 9 possible code words**

2. Use a possibility tree to count the number of ways to arrange the numbers 1, 2, 4, and 5 so that no number is next to a number that is one larger than it.

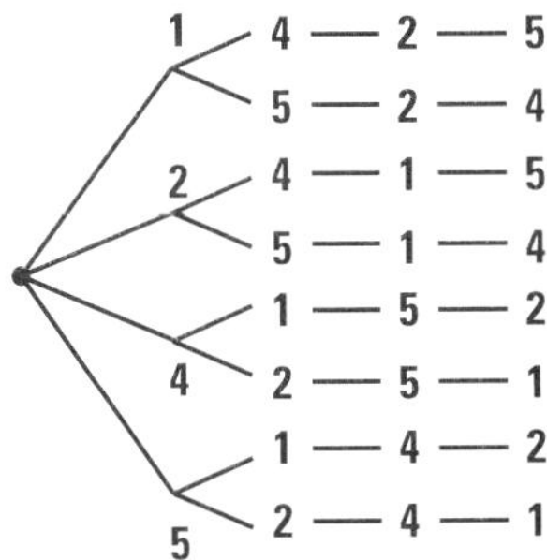

3. A business wants a seven-digit phone number that ends 00. If there are three exchanges (first three numbers) that are available to this business, how many phone numbers ending in 00 are available? **There are ten choices for each of the remaining digits, so there are 300 numbers in all.**

4. How many 7-digit phone numbers have no repeated digits? Assume that all numbers are possible. **604,800**

5. Among the 3-digit integers, how many have at least one digit that is a 2 or a 4? **452**

Notes on Questions

Question 3 Emphasize that the major reason for drawing a possibility tree is to exhibit the possibilities, not just to count them. To count them without listing, one could use the Multiplication Counting Principle.

Sports Connection The long-distance foot race called the marathon was first held at the 1896 Olympic Games held in Athens. The race was called a "marathon" after a coastal area in Greece, where, in 490 B.C., a runner ran the 25 miles from Marathon to Athens to announce the Athenian victory over the Persians. In 1924, the length of the marathon was standardized at 26 miles 385 yards. This was the distance of the race during the 1908 Olympic Games held in London—that race started at Windsor Castle and ended at the royal box in the Olympic stadium.

Question 4 If the chairs are in a row, then they are distinguishable (left, center, right). If the chairs are in a circle, they are in some sense indistinguishable; then there are only two possibilities.

Question 10 This kind of lock is also used for some security systems. It is felt that no one who did not know the combination would be willing to go through 10,000 combinations. You might mention that the word "combination" as used here is different from the word "combination" that will be used later in this chapter. In fact, this common daily use of the word is a mathematical "permutation!"

Germany's Uta Pippig winning the New York City marathon in 1993

3. Each runner in a marathon receives a T-shirt as a souvenir. The T-shirts are available in three colors: white, blue, and red; and four sizes: S, M, L, and XL. Draw and label a possibility tree to count the number of different T-shirts that are available. **See margin. 12 different shirts**

4. Use a possibility tree to count the number of different ways that Luis, Van, and Charisse can be seated in a row of three chairs. **See margin. 6 different seatings**

5. In the World Series for baseball, the first team to win four games wins the series. Suppose that the 2099 World Series is played between the Atlanta Braves and the Toronto Blue Jays and that the Braves win the first three games. Use a possibility tree to count the number of different ways that the series can be completed. **See margin. 5 ways to complete the series**

6. How many different four-digit numbers can be constructed from the digits 1, 2, 3, 4, 5, 6 under the given condition?

a. Repetition of digits is not allowed. **360**

b. Repetition is allowed. **1296**

7. A grocery store carries n brands of liquid dish soap. Each brand offers four different sized bottles—small, medium, large, and economy—and each is available as either lemon-scented or pine-scented. How many different types of liquid dish soap bottles are available at the store? $\mathbf{8n}$

8. Explain why it would not be easy to use a possibility tree to solve the license plate problem in Example 4. **It would be impractical to represent all 3,276,000 possible outcomes.**

9. How many of the integers from 1000 through 9999 have at least one digit which is an 8? **3168**

Applying the Mathematics

10. a. A bicycle combination lock has four dial wheels with the digits from 0 through 9 on each wheel. How many different possible combinations are there for this type of lock? **10,000**

b. Generalize part **a** if there are w dial wheels and d symbols on each wheel. d^w

11. There are 13 applicants to fill three sales positions in different departments of a large department store. In how many different ways can these openings be filled? **1716**

12. A computer program includes the following nested loop:

```
100 FOR I = 1 TO 7
200   FOR J = 1 TO 12
300     B(I) = B(I) – C(I, J) * B(J)
400   NEXT J
500 NEXT I
```

How many times is line 300 executed when the program is run? **84**

Additional Answers

3. Select color Select size

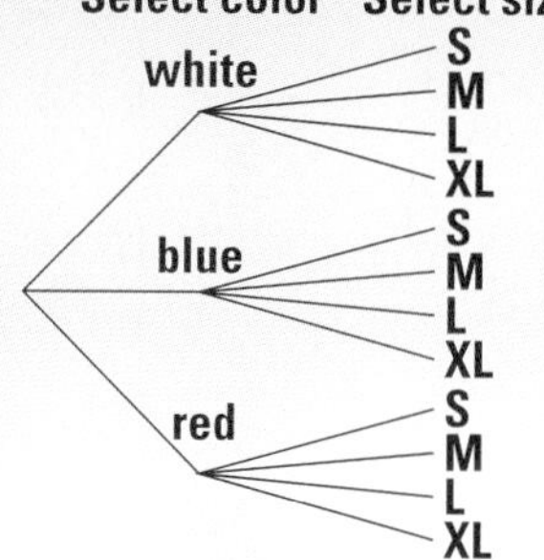

4.

Chair 1	Chair 2	Chair 3
Luis	Charisse	Van
	Van	Charisse
Van	Charisse	Luis
	Luis	Charisse
Charisse	Van	Luis
	Luis	Van

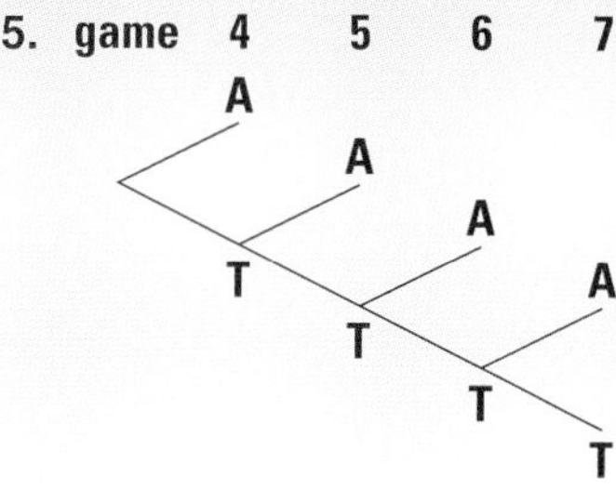

13. a. Among the integers from 200 through 999, how many have at least one digit which is a 4, 5, or 6? **555**
    b. If an integer from 200 through 999 is chosen at random, what is the probability that all three digits are 4s, 5s, or 6s? **≈ 0.00375**

14. a. If A is a set with n elements, use the Multiplication Counting Principle to prove that there are 2^n different subsets of A (counting the empty set and A itself as subsets of A). (Hint: Think of constructing subsets of A as follows: Arrange the elements of A in some order as a list. Then make n successive decisions, Yes or No, for the question: Do you put this element on the list in the subset?) **See left.**
    b. Consider the excerpt from a cereal box reproduced here. How many combinations of fruits are possible? **15**

So many kinds of fruit, the possibilities are endless....

Delicious apples.
Sweet pineapples.
Chewy apricots.
Plump raisins.

So many kinds of fruit, it gives you a different fruit taste in every bite.

Try some and see.

    c. What does the empty set represent in the situation of part **b**?
    a spoonful of cereal (and milk); no fruit

15. Take the following as an axiom: *If one step can be done in m ways and a second step can be done in n ways, then the two steps can be done in mn ways.* Use this axiom and the Principle of Mathematical Induction to prove the Multiplication Counting Principle. (Hint: If each item in the set to be counted is described by $k + 1$ successive steps, think of the first k steps as a single step.) **See left.**

Review

In 16 and 17, identify the essential features of the problem. You do not have to do the counting. *(Lesson 10-1)*

16. Each question on a 20-question multiple-choice test has five options. Determine the number of ways of answering the test.
    Ordered symbols; repetition is allowed.

17. A buffet table is divided into four sections. The first section contains a choice of salad, soup, or fruit plate. The second section contains peas, carrots, green beans, and two types of potatoes. The third section contains chicken, roast beef, pork chops, and fish. The last section contains five different desserts. If all the items within each section are arranged in a row, determine the number of different arrangements of items.
    Ordered symbols; repetition is not allowed.

14a) There are two choices for each element: include in the subset, or don't include it. Since there are n elements, by the Multiplication Counting Principle, there are n factors of 2, or 2^n subsets.

15) $S(1)$ is true because the number of ways the first step can be done is n_1. Assume $S(k)$, the number of ways to do the first k steps, is $n_1 \cdot n_2 \cdot \ldots \cdot n_k$. Let m be the number of ways to do the first k steps and let n represent the number of ways to do the $(k + 1)$st step. Then by the inductive hypothesis, $m = n_1 \cdot n_2 \cdot \ldots \cdot n_k$ and $n = n_{k+1}$, so $mn = n_1 \cdot n_2 \cdot \ldots \cdot n_k \cdot n_{k+1}$. So $S(k + 1)$, the number of ways to do the $(k + 1)$st steps, is $n_1 \cdot n_2 \cdot \ldots \cdot n_k + n_{k+1}$. Thus $S(n)$ is true for all n.

Question 11 If the positions were indistinguishable, then the number of ways would be 286. (Divide 1716 by 3.) This question can be used to lead in to the next lesson.

Question 12 This context is found in *Functions, Statistics, and Trigonometry.* It will be very easy for students who had studied it in that book.

Follow-up for Lesson 10-2

Practice

For more questions on SPUR Objectives, use **Lesson Master 10-2** (shown on pages 608–609).

Assessment

Written Communication Have students **work in pairs.** Ask each student to make up a license plate problem, different from the ones in the text. One student should allow repeating symbols in the problem. The other student should not. Have students solve their partner's problem and discuss the solutions. [Students use the Multiplication Counting Principle to solve counting problems.]

Extension

Project Update Project 4, *License Plate Numbers,* and Project 6, *Scheduling Problems,* on page 650, relate to the content of this lesson.

19d) $\frac{n}{2}(n + 1) - \frac{m}{2}(m - 1)$

18. Use the difference quotient to prove that for any linear function $f(x) = mx + b$, the average rate of change of f from x to $x + \Delta x$ is m. *(Lesson 9-1)* **See below.**

19. Use the formula $\sum_{i=1}^{n} i = \frac{n(n+1)}{2}$ to find the following.

a. $1 + 2 + 3 + \ldots + 70$ **2485**

b. $\sum_{i=1}^{200} i - \sum_{i=1}^{100} i$ **15,050**

c. the sum of all 4-digit positive integers **49,495,500**

d. the sum of all the integers from m to n *(Lesson 7-2)* **See left.**

20. Write the *product* of all positive integers from m to n as a quotient of two factorials. *(Previous course)* $\frac{n!}{(m-1)!}$

In 21 and 22, solve without using a calculator. *(Lessons 2-9, 3-2)*

21. $3^x = 9^{4x+3}$ $-\frac{6}{7}$

22. $\log_5 y + \log_5 3 = 4$ $\frac{625}{3}$

Exploration

23. Invent a problem, different from the ones in this lesson, which requires the Multiplication Counting Principle for its solution. **Answers will vary.**

18) $$\frac{\Delta y}{\Delta x} = \frac{f(x + \Delta x) - f(x)}{\Delta x} = \frac{m(x + \Delta x) + b - (mx + b)}{\Delta x} = \frac{mx + m\Delta x + b - mx - b}{\Delta x} = \frac{m\Delta x}{\Delta x} = m$$

Setting Up Lesson 10-3

You can use **Question 11** to introduce the idea of permutations. Call the 13 people *A, B, C, D, E, F, G, H, I, J, K, L, M.* As a permutation problem, we want the number of strings of 3 symbols from the 13.

LESSON

10-3

Permutations

Fred and Angela's Wedding. *There are 3,628,800 ways to order ten people in a line. Instead of trying them all, there are often restrictions which limit the possibilities. See Question 12.*

What Is a Permutation?

The word *math* is a string consisting of the four letters *m, a, t,* and *h* in which repetition does not occur. Other strings without repetition of these four letters are listed below, but none of them is a word in the English language.

amht *tamh* *atmh* *htma*

All of these strings are examples of *permutations*.

Definition
A **permutation** of the symbols $a_1, a_2, \ldots, a_n$ is a string of all these symbols without repetition.

For example,

1 2 3 3 1 2 2 3 1

are three different permutations of the numbers 1, 2, and 3.

Counting Permutations by Using Possibility Trees

You could use a possibility tree to list all of the permutations of the four letters *m, a, t, h*. On page 616, part of that tree is shown.

Lesson 10-3

Objectives

B Evaluate expressions indicating permutations.
D Use properties of permutations to prove identities.
F Use the Multiplication Counting Principle and permutations to solve counting problems.

Resources

From the ***Teacher's Resource File***
- Lesson Master 10-3
- Answer Master 10-3
- Assessment Sourcebook: Quiz for Lessons 10-1 through 10-3
- Teaching Aid 103: Warm-up

Additional Resources
- Visual for Teaching Aid 103

Teaching Lesson 10-3

Warm-up

Take a permutation of *k* of the four letters *a, e, s,* and *t*. For each value of *k* from 1 to 4, what is the probability that your permutation is a word in the English language? **When $k = 1$, there are 4 permutations, and one, a, is a word, so the probability is .25. When $k = 2$, there are 12 permutations, and ae, as, at, et, and ta are words (many may not be considered words by students but they are in the *Merriam Webster Collegiate Dictionary*, Tenth Edition), so the probability is $\frac{5}{12}$. (Note: the word "es" is in some dictionaries.) When $k = 3$, there are 24 permutations, and ate, eat, eta, sat, sea, set, tas, and tea are words, so the probability is $\frac{1}{3}$. (Note: the words "sae" and "tae" are in some dictionaries.) When $k = 4$, there are 4! permutations, and east, eats, etas, sate, seat, seta, and teas are words, so the probability is $\frac{7}{24}$. (Note: the word "ates" is in some dictionaries.)**

Lesson 10-3 Overview

Broad Goals This lesson covers the familiar formula $P(n, r) = \frac{n!}{(n-r)!}$ for the number of permutations of length *r* from *n* different symbols, and its special case $P(n, n) = n!$.

Perspective A permutation is a string of length *r* from a collection of *n* symbols without repeating any of the collection. The most common symbols for the number of such permutations for a fixed *n* and *r* are $_nP_r$ and $P(n, r)$. We use the latter; it is easier to type, overtly exhibits this number as a function of two variables, and shows the key letters in the order they are read: "Permutations of *n* things *r* at a time."

Notes on Reading

In this lesson, we consider only permutations of *n distinct* objects. In Lesson 10-8, students learn about the number of permutations of *n* objects when two or more of those objects are the same.

❶ We assume students are so familiar with the factorial symbol (!) that they do not even need review on it. Test our assumption. Before beginning this lesson, ask students for the value of 3! [6], then 4! [24], then 5! [120], then 6! [720], then 2! [2], then 1! [1]. Make certain that students can find the factorial key on their calculators.

Emphasize the connection between the Permutation Theorem and the Multiplication Counting Principle. The Multiplication Counting Principle, together with mathematical induction, provides the proof of the Permutation Theorem. In fact, you may want to do **Question 14,** which asks for the proof, as part of the class discussion.

The situation of **Example 1** contains a slight variant of the standard permutation problem. The three girls must be treated as a single symbol for the purposes of obtaining the number of permutations of 7 objects (6 boys and 1 set of girls). The potential for error occurs when students fail to realize that the three girls, treated previously as a single object, can themselves be permuted. The final solution requires the product of the number of permutations of seven objects with the number of permutations of girls. After discussing **Example 1** you might want to discuss **Question 3** to help students focus on the differences involved when these 10 people are arranged with no restrictions versus when restrictions are involved.

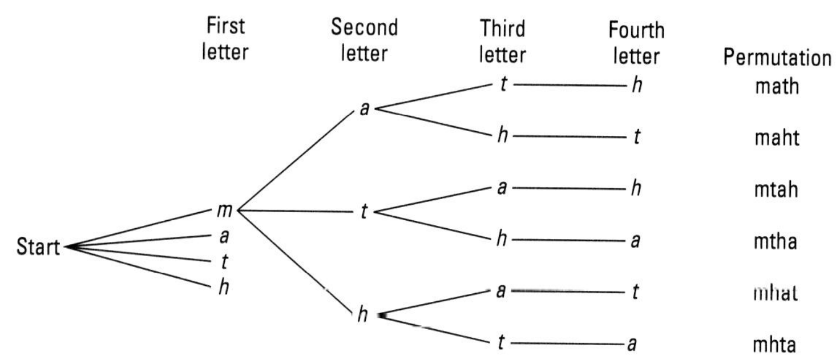

If completed, this possibility tree would be quite large. However, you can count the number of permutations of these four letters without listing them

Counting Permutations by Using the Multiplication Counting Principle

Any one of the four letters can be selected as the first letter. Any of the three remaining letters can be chosen as the second letter. Two letters remain available as the third choice and only one letter remains for the fourth position. Therefore, by the Multiplication Counting Principle, there are

❶ $$4 \cdot 3 \cdot 2 \cdot 1 = 4! = 24$$

different permutations of these four letters.

Here are the 24 permutations of the letters *m, a, t,* and *h* systematically listed. (Do you see the system?)

math	amth	tmah	hmat
maht	amht	tmha	hmta
mtah	atmh	tamh	hamt
mtha	athm	tahm	hatm
mhat	ahmt	thma	htma
mhta	ahtm	tham	htam

Notice that all of the permutations in a given column begin with the same first letter. The permutations in the column are obtained by following the first letter with all possible permutations of the remaining three letters. This recursive nature of permutations along with mathematical induction can be used to prove the following result. In Question 14 you are asked to supply a proof.

> **Permutation Theorem**
> There are $n!$ permutations of n different elements.

For example, there are $5! = 5 \cdot 4 \cdot 3 \cdot 2 \cdot 1 = 120$ permutations of the letters *a, b, c, d,* and *e.*

Optional Activities

Ask students if the answers to **Question 11** would be the same if only even digits were considered. [No; the integers must be between 1000 and 9999, the first digit may not be 0. Therefore, 4 • 4 • 3 • 2 = 96 integers have all different even digits, while 500 have even digits with possible repetitions.] To extend the question, ask students how many integers are combinations of even and odd digits, with repetition allowed. [9000 − (625 + 500) = 7875.]

Example 1

In how many ways can 6 boys and 3 girls be arranged in a row if the three girls must always stand next to each other?

Solution

You can think of arranging the boys and girls in the row as a two-step process.

Step 1: Select an arrangement for the boys and reserve a space for the girls' part of the row.

Step 2: Select an arrangement for the girls within their part of the row.

You can think of the girls' part of the row as a single unit G that is to be arranged with the six boys $B_1, B_2, B_3, B_4, B_5, B_6$ to complete the row. An arrangement of $\{G, B_1, B_2, B_3, B_4, B_5, B_6\}$ is a string of ordered symbols without repetition; it is a permutation, so **there are 7! arrangements of the boys with a space for the girls.** The arrangement of the three girls in their part of the row is also a string without repetition; thus **there are 3! different ways to arrange the girls.** Therefore, by the Multiplication Counting Principle, **there are**

$$7! \cdot 3! = 30{,}240$$

different ways to arrange the boys and girls in a row with the girls next to one another.

Counting Permutations of Symbols from a Larger Set of Symbols

Suppose you wanted to make four-letter strings from the letters in the word *logarithm*. There are nine letters to choose from, so the first letter can be chosen in 9 ways. Because no letter can be used more than once, the second letter can be chosen in only 8 ways, the third in 7 ways, and the fourth in 6 ways. Hence, by the Multiplication Counting Principle, there are

$$9 \cdot 8 \cdot 7 \cdot 6 = 3024$$

different four-letter strings using the letters in *logarithm* only once. These strings are called *permutations of 9 elements taken 4 at a time.*

Definition

Let $S = \{a_1, a_2, \ldots, a_n\}$. A **permutation of the n elements of S taken r at a time** is a string of r of the elements of S without repetition.

Both the symbols $P(n, r)$ and ${}_nP_r$ are used to denote the number of permutations of n elements taken r at a time. From the *logarithm* example above, we showed that $P(9, 4) = {}_9P_4 = 9 \cdot 8 \cdot 7 \cdot 6 = 3024$.

There is a way to express $P(9, 4)$ as a quotient of factorials. Using this method,

$$P(9, 4) = 9 \cdot 8 \cdot 7 \cdot 6 = \frac{9 \cdot 8 \cdot 7 \cdot 6 \cdot 5!}{5!} = \frac{9!}{5!} = \frac{9!}{(9-4)!}$$

Similarly, $P(12, 2) = \dfrac{12 \cdot 11 \cdot 10!}{10!} = \dfrac{12!}{(12-2)!}$ and

$P(100, 13) = \dfrac{100!}{87!} = \dfrac{100!}{(100-13)!}$.

Students who have studied from *Functions, Statistics, and Trigonometry* most probably used ${}_nP_r$ notation rather than $P(n, r)$. Refer to the Perspectives for this and the next lesson to inform students regarding why we made this selection here. (We use different notations in different books so that students are familiar with the variety of symbols for these ideas, and so that they are less likely to be confused when they see a new symbol.)

Adapting to Individual Needs

Extra Help

Some students might not understand that order is crucial to the concept of permutations. Emphasize that a permutation is a *string*. Illustrate the importance of order as you discuss **Example 2.** Explain that we are not merely counting how many different *sets* of three trophy winners can be chosen from the eight competitors. (This will be considered in the next lesson.) Instead, we want to count *strings* in order to distinguish who places first, who places second, and who places third. Hence, a permutation such as *Fred* (1st place), *Mia* (2nd place), *Lucy* (3rd place) is different from the permutation *Mia* (1st place), *Fred* (2nd place), *Lucy* (3rd place).

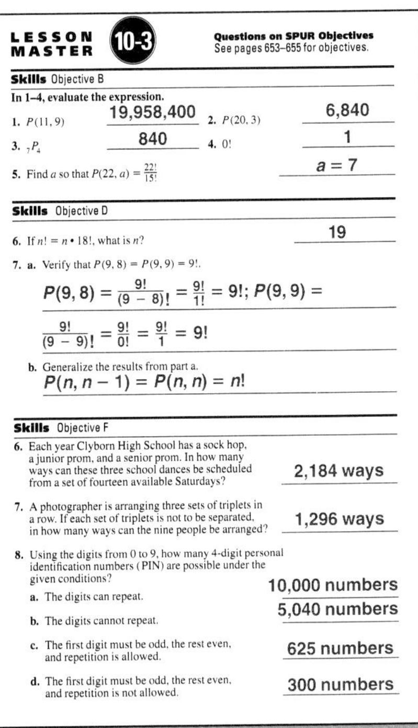

LESSON MASTER 10-3 — Questions on SPUR Objectives. See pages 653–655 for objectives.

Skills Objective B

In 1–4, evaluate the expression.

1. $P(11, 9)$ — 19,958,400
2. $P(20, 3)$ — 6,840
3. ${}_7P_4$ — 840
4. $0!$ — 1
5. Find a so that $P(22, a) = \frac{22!}{15!}$ — $a = 7$

Skills Objective D

6. If $n! = n \cdot 18!$, what is n? — 19
7. a. Verify that $P(9, 8) = P(9, 9) = 9!$.
   $P(9, 8) = \frac{9!}{(9-8)!} = \frac{9!}{1!} = 9!$; $P(9, 9) = \frac{9!}{(9-9)!} = \frac{9!}{0!} = \frac{9!}{1} = 9!$
   b. Generalize the results from part a.
   $P(n, n-1) = P(n, n) = n!$

Skills Objective F

6. Each year Clyborn High School has a sock hop, a junior prom, and a senior prom. In how many ways can these three school dances be scheduled from a set of fourteen available Saturdays? — 2,184 ways
7. A photographer is arranging three sets of triplets in a row. If each set of triplets is not to be separated, in how many ways can the nine people be arranged? — 1,296 ways
8. Using the digits from 0 to 9, how many 4-digit personal identification numbers (PIN) are possible under the given conditions?
   a. The digits can repeat. — 10,000 numbers
   b. The digits cannot repeat. — 5,040 numbers
   c. The first digit must be odd, the rest even, and repetition is allowed. — 625 numbers
   d. The first digit must be odd, the rest even, and repetition is not allowed. — 300 numbers

In **Example 2,** help students see that $\frac{8!}{5!} = \frac{8 \cdot 7 \cdot 6 \cdot 5 \cdot 4 \cdot 3 \cdot 2 \cdot 1}{5 \cdot 4 \cdot 3 \cdot 2 \cdot 1} =$ $8 \cdot 7 \cdot 6$ by dividing out common factors. Hence, it is not necessary to evaluate 8! on the calculator and then divide it by 5!. While division of these factorials could be done on calculators because the numbers are small, when the numbers get above 69, many calculators can no longer handle factorial computations even in scientific notation. Consequently, being able to simplify the computation before resorting to technology is important. The technique of simplifying such expressions can be discussed in this lesson and also in the next lesson on combinations.

Additional Examples

1. Four boy-girl couples go together to a dance.
   a. If the pair in each couple stands next to each other for a picture, in how many ways an the 8 people be arranged? $4! \cdot 2^4 = 384$
   b. If the pair in each couple stands next to each other and boys and girls alternate, in how many ways can the 8 people be arranged? $2 \cdot 4! = 48$
2. In a 1990 contest of a mathematics organization, 3 of the 6 people with the best scores came from the same school. The contest rules specified that, if there were ties, 3 winners would be selected at random. It turned out that the three winners all came from this school. What was the probability of this occurring? $\frac{3!3!}{6!} = .05$

The reasoning in the computation on page 617 and mathematical induction can be used to prove the following theorem.

$P(n, r)$ Calculation Theorem
The number $P(n, r)$ of permutations of n elements taken r at a time is given by

$$P(n, r) = \frac{n!}{(n - r)!}.$$

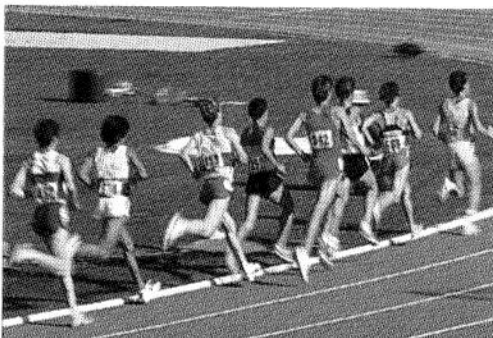

Example 2

There are 8 competitors in the final heat for the 800-meter race in a track meet. A large, a medium, and a small trophy will be awarded to the first-, second-, and third-place finishers. How many different ways can these trophies be awarded?

Solution 1

The number of different ways to award the trophies equals the number of different ways that a first-, a second-, and a third-place finisher can be chosen from among the 8 competitors. This is the same as the number of 3-symbol strings that can be taken from a set of 8 symbols without repetition. Therefore, there are $P(8, 3)$ different ways to award the three trophies.

$$P(8, 3) = \frac{8!}{(8 - 3)!} = \frac{8!}{5!} = 8 \cdot 7 \cdot 6 = 336$$

Solution 2

Use the Multiplication Counting Principle. There are 8 ways to select the first-place finisher, 7 ways to select the second-place finisher, and 6 ways to select the third-place finisher. Therefore, there are $8 \cdot 7 \cdot 6 = 336$ different ways to award the trophies.

Notice that if $r = n$ in the formula for $P(n, r)$, then

$$P(n, n) = \frac{n!}{(n - n)!} = \frac{n!}{0!}.$$

Because the Permutation Theorem states that there are $n!$ permutations of n different things, it follows that

$$n! = \frac{n!}{0!}.$$

This is one reason why 0! is defined to equal 1.

1a)

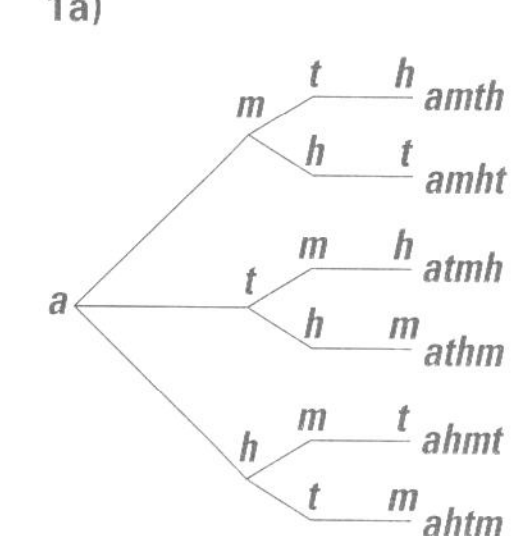

QUESTIONS

Covering the Reading

1. Refer to the possibility tree at the beginning of the lesson.
   a. Complete the portion of the tree whose first letter is a. See left.
   b. Do you get the six permutations in the second column of the list on page 616? Yes

Adapting to Individual Needs

Challenge

Have students answer the following question: 12 different numbers are the elements of a 3×4 matrix. How many different matrices are possible? $[6 \cdot 12! = 2,874,009,600]$

2. How many 6-digit numbers with all digits different can be constructed from the numbers 1, 2, 3, 4, 5, and 6? **720**

3. In Example 1, the number of different ways to arrange 6 boys and 3 girls in a row with the girls next to one another was computed. Find the number of different ways to arrange the 6 boys and 3 girls in a row under each condition.
   a. The boys and girls can stand anywhere in the row. **362,880**
   b. The boys must all stand next to each other. **17,280**
   c. The boys must all stand next to each other and the girls must stand next to each other. **8640**

4. How many six-letter strings can be made by using letters of the word *logarithm* no more than once? **60,480**

In 5 and 6, evaluate the expression.

5. $P(7, 3)$ **210**

6. $P(9, 9)$ **362,880**

7. How many 3-digit numbers with different digits can be constructed from the numbers 0, 2, 4, 6, and 8? **48**

Applying the Mathematics

8. Find n so that $P(18, n) = \frac{18!}{15!}$. $n = 3$

9a) $P(10, 9) = \frac{10!}{(10-9)!} = \frac{10!}{1!} = \frac{10!}{1} = \frac{10!}{0!} = \frac{10!}{(10-10)!} = P(10, 10)$

9. a. Use the $P(n, r)$ Calculation Theorem to verify that $P(10, 9) = P(10, 10)$.
   b. Generalize part **a**. $\forall$ **integers** $n \geq 2$, $P(n, n-1) = P(n, n)$
   a) See left.

10. A combination for a padlock consists of three numbers from 0 to 35.
    a. How many combinations are possible? **46,656**
    b. How many combinations consist of three different numbers? **42,840**

11. Consider those integers from 1000 to 9999 which have only odd digits.
    a. How many of these have all different digits? **120**
    b. How many have odd digits with possible digit repetitions? **625**

12. A bridal party consists of 4 bridesmaids, 4 ushers, and the bride and groom. In how many ways can the bridal party be arranged for portraits if the bride and groom always stand together? **725,760**

13. Five boys and five girls are to give speeches in a contest. If boys and girls alternate, how many arrangements of speakers are possible? **28,800**

14. Use mathematical induction and the Multiplication Counting Principle to prove the Permutation Theorem. (Hint: Each permutation of n elements can be constructed by selecting the first term and then following it by some permutation of the remaining $n - 1$ elements.) **See margin.**

15. a. Show that $(n-2)! = (n-2) \cdot (n-3)!$. **See below.**
    b. Solve for n: $P(n, 3) = 5 \cdot P(n, 2)$. $n = 7$

    a) $(n-2)! = (n-2)(n-3)(n-4)(n-5) \ldots (2)(1) =$
    $(n-2)[(n-3)(n-4)(n-5) \ldots (2)(1)] = (n-2)(n-3)!$

Notes on Questions

Question 3 Error Alert Do not underestimate the trickiness of these sorts of questions. Even very experienced and able mathematicians get tripped up on them. Advise students to proceed slowly and carefully, writing down instances of each type to make the possibilities clear. You might call the boys $B1$, $B2$, $B3$, $B4$, $B5$, and $B6$, and call the girls $G1$, $G2$, and $G3$.

Question 4 As a possible follow-up question, ask students if there are more six-letter strings from the letters or seven-letter strings of the word *logarithm*. [Seven-letter strings] Are there more 8-letter strings than 7-letter strings? [Yes.] Are there more 9-letter strings than 8-letter strings? [No, they are equal.] Ask students to generalize these results. [If $n > r > s$, then $P(n, r) > P(n, s)$, but $P(n, n-1) = P(n, n)$. The same is not true for combinations.] **Question 9** considers the case when $r = n - 1$.

Question 13 The incorrect answer 14,400 may arise from forgetting that either a boy or a girl can start.

Additional Answers

14. For $n = 1$, the number of possible permutations is $1 = 1! = n!$ Assume the theorem is true for $n = k$. That is, there are $k!$ permutations of k different elements. Consider $n = k + 1$. There are $k!$ permutations of the first k elements by the inductive hypothesis. Then there are $k + 1$ places to insert the $(k + 1)$st element into any of these permutations. So by the Multiplication Counting Theorem, there are $k!\,(k + 1) = (k + 1)!$ permutations. Hence, by mathematical induction, the Permutation Theorem is true.

Notes on Questions

Question 16 These are what is known as *circular permutations.* In general, the number of circular permutations of n objects is $(n - 1)!$

Question 17 The sample answer given can be found by using the $P(n, r)$ Calculation Theorem. There is another answer: $n = 12$, $r = 8$.

16. Lin, Olivia, Aisha, Fred, and Helen are to be seated at a circular table. Two arrangements of these five people around the table are regarded as the *same seating arrangement* if and only if one is a rotation image of the other. That is, the two arrangements place the people in the same order around the table, even if the people sit in different chairs in the two seatings. The two seatings below are assumed to be the same.

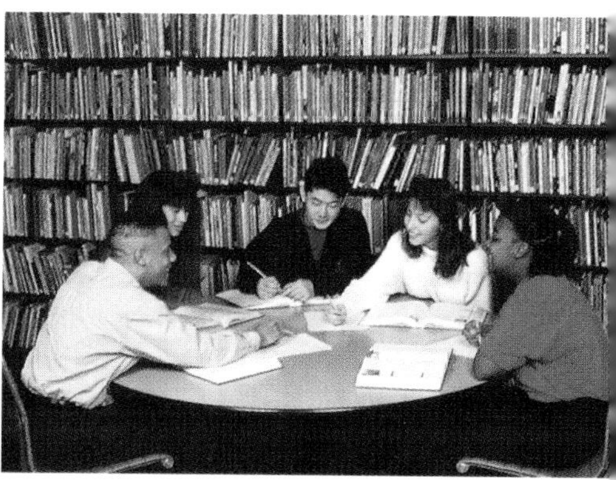

How many different *seating arrangements* are possible? (Hint: Because only the *order* of people around the table and not the particular chair occupied by a person matters when counting seating arrangements, you can count all possible seating arrangements by selecting a particular chair for one of the people, say Lin, and then counting the number of ways that the remaining 4 people can be arranged in the other chairs.) **24**

17. Find positive integers n and r such that $P(11, 6) \cdot P(5, 3) = P(n, r)$.
Sample: $n = 11$, $r = 9$

Review

18. Suppose that a computer program contains the following lines of code.

```
100 FOR I = 0 TO 11
110   FOR J = 1 TO 4
120     FOR K = 1 TO 10
130       PRINT I + J + K
140     NEXT K
150   NEXT J
160 NEXT I
```

How many lines of output are produced by this code? *(Lesson 10-2)*
480

19)

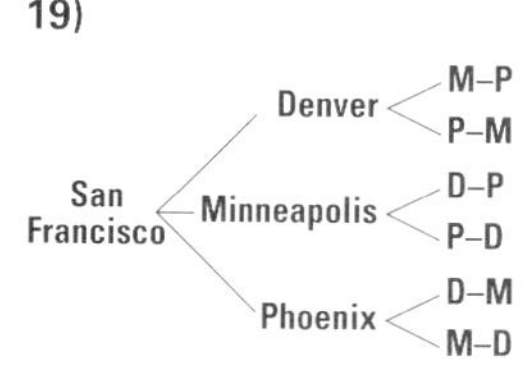

19. A salesperson must leave company headquarters in San Francisco to visit Denver, Minneapolis, and Phoenix once each. Draw a possibility tree illustrating the number of different sales trips which are possible. What is this number? *(Lesson 10-2)* **See left. 6 trips**

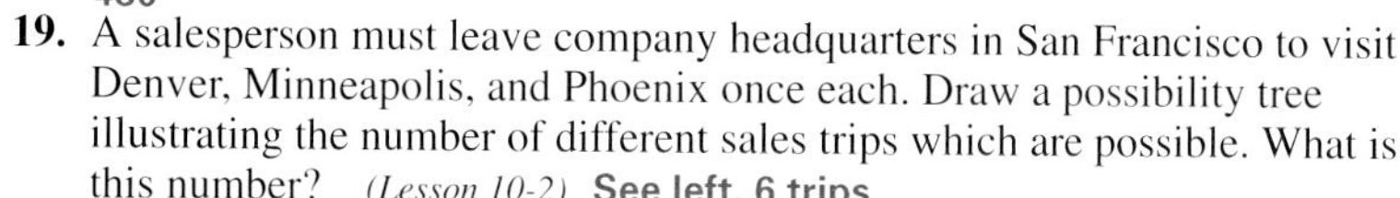

20. Rewrite in $a + bi$ form: $\frac{3 - 6i}{2 + 5i}$. *(Lesson 8-1)* $-\frac{24}{29} - \frac{27}{29}i$

21. The lens equation

$$\frac{1}{p} + \frac{1}{q} = \frac{1}{f}$$

relates the object distance p, the image distance q, and the focal length f when a lens is used to concentrate or disperse light (as on a screen or photographic film). If an object is 20 cm away from a lens with a focal length of 8 cm, how far is the image from the lens? *(Lesson 5-8)* **$\frac{40}{3}$ cm**

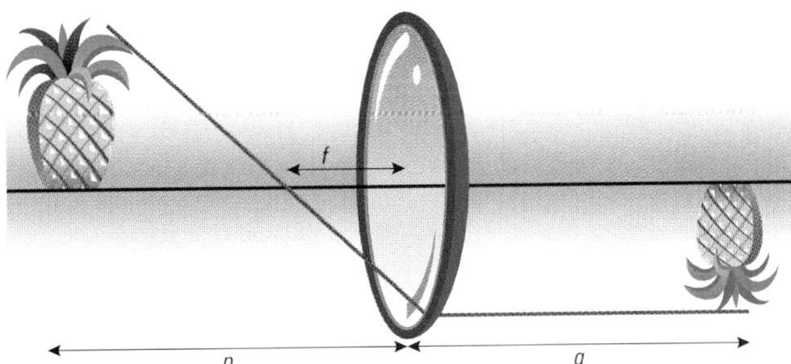

22. Find a formula for a polynomial function of lowest degree whose graph could be that shown below. *(Lesson 4-4)* **$f(x) = 2x^3 + 14x^2 - 12x - 144$**

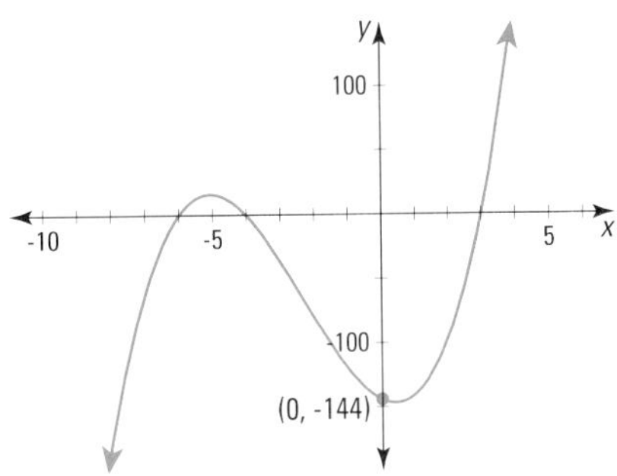

23. Describe the transformation that maps the graph of $y = \ln x$ onto the graph of $y = 2 \ln (x + 1) + 7$. *(Lesson 3-8)* **$(x, y) \rightarrow (x - 1, 2(y + 7))$**

Exploration

24. Choose a professional sport with more than one league or division, and determine the number of ways in which the final team standings could occur. How many of these would have your favorite team or teams in first place? **Answers will vary.**

Practice

For more questions on SPUR Objectives, use **Lesson Master 10-3** (shown on page 617).

Assessment

Quiz A quiz covering Lessons 10-1 through 10-3 is provided in the *Assessment Sourcebook.*

Extension

Ask students to consider these probability questions. The numbers 1, 2, ... , n are arranged in random order. Find the probability of each of the following events.

1. The digits 1 and 2 appear next to each other $\left[\frac{(n-1)!2!}{n!} = \frac{2}{n}\right]$
2. The digits 1, 2, and 3 appear next to each other $\left[\frac{(n-2)!3!}{n!} = \frac{6}{n(n-1)}\right]$
3. How would your answers to Questions 1–2 above change if the digits in each question had to be in increasing order? $\left[\frac{1}{n}, \frac{1}{n(n-1)}\right]$

Project Update Project 4, *License Plate Numbers,* on page 650, relates to the content of this lesson.

Setting Up Lesson 10-4

Use **Question 10** to point out that the word *combination* in the next lesson has a different meaning than the word has in this question. You should ask how many students have studied combinations before.

Lesson 10-4

Objectives

B Evaluate expressions indicating combinations.
D Use properties of combinations to prove identities.
G Use combinations to solve counting problems.

Resources

From the ***Teacher's Resource File***

- Lesson Master 10-4
- Answer Master 10-4
- Teaching Aid 104: Warm-up

Additional Resources

- Visual for Teaching Aid 104
- Exploration 10-4

Teaching Lesson 10-4

Warm-up

Consider all the subsets of the set {1, 2, 3, 4, 5}.

1. How many subsets have only even numbers as elements? **3**
2. How many subsets have only odd numbers as elements? **7**
3. How many subsets have both even numbers and odd numbers as elements? **21**
4. How many subsets have neither even numbers nor odd numbers as elements? **1, the null set ∅**

(Note: The sum of the answers to the four questions is 32, or 2^5.)

LESSON

10-4 *Combinations*

What Is a Combination?

In the Lotto game in the Illinois State Lottery, a player chooses a set of 6 different numbers from among the integers from 1 to 48, inclusive. The order in which the numbers are selected is unimportant; only the resulting set of 6 different numbers matters.

Example 2 of Lesson 10-1 pointed out that each play in the Lotto game can be thought of in either of the following two ways:

1. Choosing 6 numbers without repetition from among the integers from 1 to 48, inclusive.
2. Choosing a 6-element subset from the 48-element set {1, 2, 3, 4, . . . , 46, 47, 48}.

Each choice is called a *combination* of 48 elements taken 6 at a time.

> **Definition**
> Let $S = \{a_1, a_2, \dots, a_n\}$. A **combination of n elements of S taken r at a time** is an r-element subset of S, or equivalently, an unordered set without repetition of r of these elements.

The symbols $\boldsymbol{C(n, r)}$, ${}_nC_r$, or $\binom{n}{r}$ are all commonly used to denote the number of combinations of n elements taken r at a time. $C(n, r)$, read "n choose r," is used to emphasize that C is a (discrete) function of the two variables n and r, and to emphasize that $C(n, r)$ is related to $P(n, r)$. The number of choices in the Lotto game described above is thus written $C(48, 6)$, ${}_{48}C_6$, or $\binom{48}{6}$.

❶ How Do Permutations and Combinations Differ?

The difference between permutations and combinations of n elements taken r at a time is that permutations are ordered and combinations are unordered. For example,

312 451 123 145 231 345

are all different permutations of the 5 numbers 1, 2, 3, 4, 5 taken 3 at a time. However, 312, 123, and 231 represent the *same* combination of the 5 numbers taken 3 at a time, as do 451 and 145.

Lesson 10-4 Overview

Broad Goals In this lesson, the familiar computation formula $C(n, r) = \frac{n!}{r!(n-r)!}$ for the number of combinations of r elements from a set of n elements and some of its special cases are derived.

Perspective A combination is a set of length r from a collection of n symbols without repeating any of the collection. There are three common symbols for the number of such combinations for a fixed n and r: ${}_nC_r$, $C(n, r)$, and $\binom{n}{r}$. We use the middle of these for the same reasons given for the corresponding permutation symbol. However, we also use the last of these because it is the most common symbol used by mathematicians; in expressions with more than one of these symbols, it is the shortest to write and, consequently, the clearest.

Optional Activities

Activity 1 Technology Connection
Materials: Explorations software

Students may use *Exploration 10-4, Permutations and Combinations,* to explore these counting methods. The activity demonstrates the number of permutations and combinations for a configuration that the student chooses. The program displays a sample set of permutations and one combination from the same sample set.

In general, it is possible to relate the number $P(n, r)$ of permutations of n elements taken r at a time to the number $C(n, r)$ of combinations of n elements taken r at a time. Consider the set $\{a, b, c, d, e\}$. The combinations of these 5 elements taken 3 at a time are listed below. (We write *abc* for $\{a, b, c\}$, and so on.)

abc	*acd*	*bcd*	*cde*
abd	*ace*	*bce*	
abe	*ade*	*bde*	

Observe that each combination contains 3 different, or distinct, letters. For each combination, there are 3! permutations of its letters. Hence, the total number of permutations of 5 elements taken 3 at a time is

$$P(5, 3) = 3!\ C(5, 3).$$

A Formula for $C(n, r)$

This argument can be generalized. There are $C(n, r)$ ways of choosing r elements from n. Then there are $r!$ ways of arranging each of the r-element sets. Therefore, the total number of permutations of n elements taken r at a time is found by the Multiplication Counting Principle to be

$$P(n, r) = r!\ C(n, r).$$

Solving for $C(n, r)$ and using $P(n, r) = \frac{n!}{(n-r)!}$ yields the following formula, useful for computation.

> **$C(n, r)$ Calculation Theorem**
> The number $C(n, r)$ of combinations of n elements taken r at a time is given by
> $$C(n, r) = \frac{n!}{r!(n-r)!}.$$

Evaluating $C(n, r)$

Some calculators have keys for computing $C(n, r)$ and $P(n, r)$. You should check to see if your calculator has this capability.

The next example shows how to calculate $C(n, r)$ when you have no calculator.

Example 1

Evaluate $C(8, 3)$.

Solution

Let $n = 8$ and $r = 5$ in the formula for $C(n, r)$.

$C(8, 3) = \frac{8!}{3!(8-3)!} = \frac{8!}{3!\,5!}$. To compute this, rewrite the numerator:

$\frac{8 \cdot 7 \cdot 6 \cdot 5!}{3!\,5!} = \frac{8 \cdot 7 \cdot 6}{3 \cdot 2} = 56.$

Notes on Reading

Multicultural Connection There are many Biblical references to using "lots" to settle disputes or to divide property. Lotteries in Europe appeared in the 15th Century. Today lotteries are used to finance public projects and programs, and can be found just about everywhere in the world, except in India and China. In Australia, for example, lottery money was used to finance the Sydney Opera House.

❶ It is important that students understand the relationship between combinations and permutations because of the connection between the computational formulas for these two quantities. Students need to see that each combination of r elements can itself be permuted in $r!$ ways. This leads to the $C(n, r)$ Calculation Theorem.

All three examples in this lesson once again discuss the simplification of factorial expressions. Emphasize that cancellations can simplify the work immensely before resorting to the use of technology.

Error Alert Some students may be surprised and perhaps confused by the generalization that $C(n, r) = C(n, n-r)$. Use $C(8, 5)$ to explain that for every 5-element subset of the 8-element set there is a corresponding "leftover" 3-element subset.

Activity 2 Social Studies Connection Most states now have lotteries. If your state has a lottery, now may be the time to bring a discussion of it into your classroom. Students can determine the number of possible different tickets for the games administered by the lottery commission. Some of these may involve combinations, and some may allow repetitions of numbers so that the Multiplication Counting Principle is the technique used to determine the number of outcomes.

Activity 3 In conjunction with **Question 9,** you may want to have students give a verbal and an algebraic proof that $C(n, 1) = C(n, n-1) = n$. [If subsets of one element are taken from n objects, there are n possibilities. Similarly, if subsets of all elements except one are taken from n objects, there are n possibilities. Algebraically, $C(n, 1) = \frac{n!}{1!(n-1)!} = C(n, n-1) = \frac{n!}{(n-1)!1!} = n$.]

Activity 4 Cooperative Learning You might have students **work in groups** and generalize the claim in **Question 15b.** [The product of any r consecutive integers is divisible by $r!$.] Then have students prove their generalization. [$C(n, r) = \frac{n!}{r!(n-r)!} = \frac{n(n-1)(n-2)\ldots(n-(r-1))}{r!}$; the numerator is the product of r consecutive integers, divisible by $r!$ since the quotient is an integer.]

Students should not have any difficulty understanding the discussion of probability in **Example 2.** Here $N(X)$ is the number of elements in S and $P(X)$ is the probability that X occurs. The definition being applied is the familiar one: If E is an event in a sample space S with $N(S)$ equally likely outcomes, then $P(E) = \frac{N(E)}{N(S)}$.

In **Example 3,** newer calculators are able to exhibit the answer without using scientific notation.

Have students distinguish between the situation of **Example 3** in this lesson and **Example 1** on page 617 of the previous lesson (picturing boys and girls). Although they are quite similar and involve taking products of two computations, the essential difference is that the order of the people is unimportant here in **Example 3,** but was important in **Example 1.** Hence, **Example 3** relates to combinations while **Example 1** relates to permutations.

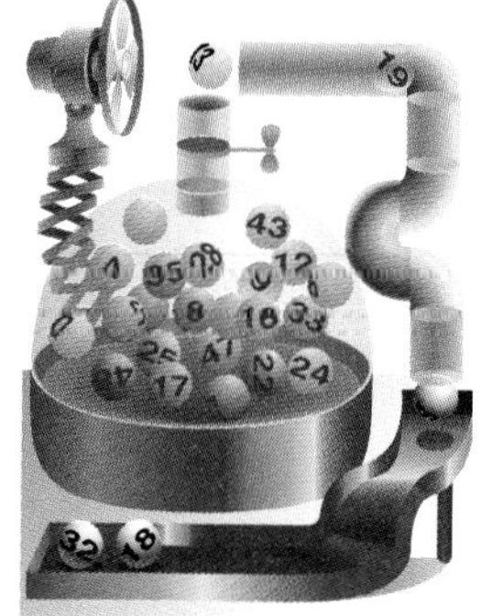

Example 2 and its check show two ways to determine combinations if the factorials are too large to be calculated directly.

Example 2

What is the probability of winning the Lotto game of the Illinois State Lottery in a single play?

Solution

A play in the Lotto game consists of choosing six different numbers from among the integers from 1 to 48, inclusive. Thus, the number of different ways of playing Lotto is equal to the number of combinations of these 48 integers taken 6 at a time; that is, it is equal to $C(48, 6)$. By the $C(n, r)$ Calculation Theorem, $C(48, 6) = \frac{48!}{6!42!}$. A calculator gives the value 12,271,512. Assuming the combinations occur randomly, the probability of winning is $\frac{1}{12,271,512}$, or about 0.000000081.

Check

$$\frac{48!}{6!42!} = \frac{48 \cdot 47 \cdot 46 \cdot 45 \cdot 44 \cdot 43}{6 \cdot 5 \cdot 4 \cdot 3 \cdot 2 \cdot 1} = 12,271,512.$$

The probability of picking the winning numbers on one play of Lotto is not very encouraging news for Lotto players, even when the jackpot reaches 30 million dollars (as it sometimes does)! Although the Lotto game provides smaller prizes to players who match four or five of the winning numbers, it and other state lottery games are usually designed to return only about half of the receipts to the players in prize money. The other receipts go to advertise and conduct the game, and pay for projects funded by the state.

Some Properties of Combinations

Notice that $C(8, 5) = \frac{8!}{5!(8-5)!} = \frac{8!}{5!\,3!} = \frac{8!}{(8-3)!\,3!}$, which equals $C(8, 3)$. Thus the number of ways of choosing 5 elements from 8 equals the number of ways of choosing 3 elements from 8. The generalization of this fact is one of the basic properties of combinations. Two basic properties are listed below, each given in two notations.

Theorem (Basic Properties of Combinations)
For all n and r for which $C(n, r)$ is defined:

$C(n, r)$ notation	$\binom{n}{r}$ notation
a. $C(n, r) = C(n, n - r)$	$\binom{n}{r} = \binom{n}{n-r}$;
b. $C(n, n) = C(n, 0) = 1$	$\binom{n}{n} = \binom{n}{0} = 1.$

Adapting to Individual Needs

Extra Help

If you want to use cards to generate combination problems (see **Question 16**), you may need to spend some time carefully explaining a deck of cards to students. We have found that students are not as familiar with cards today as students were in previous years.

Challenge

Have students answer the following questions.

1. Find out how many members are on your school board and how many members are required to have a quorum. In how many ways can that quorum be reached? [A committee of n which requires at least r to make a quorum, can have a quorum in $C(n, r) + C(n, r + 1) + \ldots + C(n, n)$ ways.]
2. A football team has 3 quarterbacks, 6 halfbacks, 4 fullbacks, and 18 linemen. How many different teams can be picked using 1 quarterback, 2 half-backs, 1 fullback, and 7 linemen? [5,728,320]
3. Six students are selected at random from your math class and put in descending order according to social security numbers. How many different arrangements are possible? Does

Proof

a. Here is an algebraic proof, relying on the $C(n, r)$ Calculation Theorem.

$$C(n, n-r) = \frac{n!}{(n-r)!(n-[n-r])!} \quad C(n, r) \text{ Calculation Theorem}$$
$$= \frac{n!}{(n-r)!\,r!} \quad \text{because } n - [n-r] = r$$
$$= C(n, r) \quad C(n, r) \text{ Calculation Theorem}$$

A verbal proof can also be given, relying on the definition of $C(n, r)$. Each time you choose an r-element subset from a set of n elements, you leave behind the complementary subset of $n - r$ elements. Therefore, each combination of n elements taken r at a time corresponds to a combination of n elements taken $n - r$ at a time, making $C(n, r) = C(n, n - r)$.

b. Algebraic and verbal proofs are left to you as Question 9.

Problem 4 from the beginning of this chapter can be solved by identifying two combinations and then applying the Multiplication Counting Principle.

Example 3

A ski club has 80 members, 50 men and 30 women. A planning committee consisting of 5 men and 3 women is to be selected. How many different committees are possible?

Solution

Select the men and women separately. The 5 men can be selected in $\binom{50}{5}$ ways. The 3 women can be selected in $\binom{30}{3}$ ways. According to the Multiplication Counting Principle, the two selections can be made in $\binom{50}{5} \cdot \binom{30}{3}$ ways.

$$\binom{50}{5} \cdot \binom{30}{3} = \frac{50!}{5!\,45!} \cdot \frac{30!}{3!\,27!}$$

Using the factorial or $C(n, r)$ key on a calculator, you may get the answer displayed in scientific notation.

$$\approx 8.6022 \times 10^9$$

To keep the answer from being displayed in scientific notation, some paper and pencil work may be necessary.

$$\frac{50!}{5!\,45!} \cdot \frac{30!}{3!\,27!} = \frac{50 \cdot 49 \cdot 48 \cdot 47 \cdot 46 \cdot 45!}{5 \cdot 4 \cdot 3 \cdot 2 \cdot 1 \cdot 45!} \cdot \frac{30 \cdot 29 \cdot 28 \cdot 27!}{3 \cdot 2 \cdot 1 \cdot 27!}$$
$$= \frac{50 \cdot 49 \cdot 48 \cdot 47 \cdot 46 \cdot 30 \cdot 29 \cdot 28}{5 \cdot 4 \cdot 3 \cdot 2 \cdot 3 \cdot 2}$$

Since the result is an integer, there are always common factors in the numerator and denominator.

$$= \frac{\overset{10}{50} \cdot 49 \cdot \overset{\overset{4}{12}}{48} \cdot 47 \cdot \overset{23}{46} \cdot \overset{10}{30} \cdot 29 \cdot \overset{14}{28}}{5 \cdot 4 \cdot 3 \cdot 2 \cdot 3 \cdot 2}$$
$$= 10 \cdot 49 \cdot 4 \cdot 47 \cdot 23 \cdot 10 \cdot 29 \cdot 14$$

Hold off the multiplications by 10 until the end. Do the rest with a calculator.

$$= 8{,}602{,}165{,}600$$

Thus, there are 8,602,165,600 different planning committees possible.

this question use combinations or permutations? [$C(n, 6) \cdot 6!$, where n is the size of the class; combination then permutation]

Additional Examples

1. Evaluate $\binom{12}{5}$. **792**
2. To play one "Little Lotto" game, the player selects 5 different numbers from the integers from 1 to 35. The player wins if these numbers match the 5 numbers chosen randomly by some process. What is the probability of winning this game? **$\frac{1}{324632}$, or about .000003 (about 3 in a million)**
3. A test is to cover two chapters, one with 10 lessons, the other with 8 lessons. You have time to study only 5 lessons, so you decide to pick 3 from the longer chapter and 2 from the shorter chapter. How many different combinations of lessons could you choose? **3360**

LESSON MASTER 10-4 Questions on SPUR Objectives See pages 653–655 for objectives.

Skills Objective B

In 1–4, evaluate the expression.

1. $C(15, 6)$ 5,005
2. $C(9, 9)$ 1
3. ${}_{10}C_5$ 252
4. $\binom{7}{3}$ 35
5. Find a and b so that $C(a, 5) = \frac{11!}{6!5!}$. $a = 11, b = 6$
6. Find j and k so that $C(6, 4) \cdot 4! = P(j, k)$. $j = 6, k = 4$

Skills Objective D

7. Show that $C(n, r) \cdot r! = P(n, r)$.
$C(n, r) \cdot r! = \frac{n!}{r!(n-r)!} \cdot r! = \frac{n!}{(n-r)!} = P(n, r)$
8. a. Verify that $C(10, 3) = C(10, 7)$.
$C(10, 3) = \frac{10!}{3!7!} = 120$; $C(10, 7) = \frac{10!}{7!3!} = 120$
b. Generalize the results from part a.
$C(n, r) = C(n, n - r)$

Skills Objective G

9. The high school band has been rehearsing seven pieces. The band director needs to select two of them for an audition tape. In how many ways can this choice be made? 21 ways
10. At a family party, 18 people need to be seated at two tables, a table for eight and a table for ten. In how many ways can the table assignments be made? 43,758 ways
11. Rigio's deluxe pizza offers any three toppings from a choice of nine. Armando's deluxe pizza allows any four toppings from a choice of eight. Which pizzeria offers the greater number of different possible deluxe pizzas? Rigio's
12. Lorna needs to pack 5 blouses and 4 pairs of slacks for a vacation. She has 14 blouses and 8 pairs of slacks to choose from. In how many different ways can she choose her clothes for the trip? 140,140 ways

Notes on Questions

Question 1 Ask for an example of two similar problems, one requiring permutations and one requiring combinations.

Question 2 This is an important question. Students may see any of these notations in some future course or on a test.

Question 12 The generalization is a theorem in Lesson 10-6.

Question 13 Of course, most of these "words" are not words in an English or any other language dictionary.

Question 16 All the pertinent information about cards needed to solve this problem is contained in the statement of the question. In general, the closer that r is to $\frac{n}{2}$, the larger $C(n, r)$ is. Thus, from a 52-card deck, the number of 50-card hands is smaller than either of these. From a 12-card deck, the number of 5-card hands equals the number of 7-card hands. Project 2, *Card Game Odds,* on page 649 has students explore a variety of situations with cards and various card hands.

Questions 20 and 23 These questions review ideas that are applied in the next lesson. Be sure to discuss them.

Question 21b The result is an interesting difference of two squares identity. Ask students if they can derive a similar identity involving cosines. [$\cos(\alpha + \beta)\cos(\alpha - \beta) = \cos^2\alpha\cos^2\beta - \sin^2\alpha\sin^2\beta$]

Question 24 History Connection The first ice-cream cones appeared at the 1904 World's Fair in St. Louis. Ernest Hamwi, a recent immigrant from Syria, sold *Zalabia,* a thin waffle served with sugar. His booth was next to a very popular one selling ice cream, and, when the ice-cream vendor ran out of dishes, Mr. Hamwi rolled his waffles in the shape of a cones so they could be used to hold the ice cream. Ice cream cones became a big hit, and soon afterwards. Mr. Hamwi founded the Missouri Cone Company.

1) A combination of elements of a set S is an unordered subset without repetition allowed. A permutation is a subset of S which is ordered.

2a) $C(n, r)$, $\binom{n}{r}$, ${}_nC_r$

b) $C(n, r) = \frac{n!}{r!(n-r)!}$

$\binom{n}{r} = \frac{n!}{r!(n-r)!}$

${}_nC_r = \frac{n!}{r!(n-r)!}$

9a) $C(n, n) = \frac{n!}{n!(n-n)!} = \frac{n!}{n!\,0!} = \frac{n!}{n! \cdot 1} = 1$

14a)i) $10 \cdot 9 \cdot 8 \cdot 7 = 5040 = (24)(210) = (4!)(210)$

ii) $33 \cdot 32 \cdot 31 \cdot 30 = 982{,}080 = (24)(40{,}920) = (4!)(40{,}920)$

iii) $97 \cdot 96 \cdot 95 \cdot 94 = 83{,}156{,}160 = (24)(3{,}464{,}840) = (4!)(3{,}464{,}840)$

Questions

Covering the Reading

1. Describe the difference between permutations and combinations. **See left.**

2. **a.** Give three different notations for the combinations of n elements taken r at a time. **See left.**
   b. Write the $C(n, r)$ Calculation Theorem in each of these notations. **See left.**

3. **a.** List all possible 4-element combinations of the set $\{a, b, c, d, e\}$.
   b. There are several possible permutations of the letters in each combination in part **a**. How many? **24**
   c. Use the results from parts **a** and **b** to determine $P(5, 4)$. **120**
   a) *abcd, abce, abde, acde, bcde*

In 4–6, evaluate the expressions.

4. $C(7, 3)$ **35**
5. ${}_{12}C_5$ **792**
6. $\binom{100}{3}$ **161,700**

7. The Fantastic 5 lottery in the state of Idaho requires a player to choose 5 different numbers from 1 to 32, inclusive.
   a. How many different plays are possible in Fantastic 5? **201,376**
   b. Determine the probability of winning Fantastic 5 with one play. **≈ .00000497**

8. If $\binom{15}{8} = \binom{15}{x}$ and $x \neq 8$, what is the value of x? **7**

9. **a.** Give an algebraic proof that $C(n, n) = 1$. **See left.**
   b. Give a verbal proof that $C(n, n) = 1$.
   If there are n objects, there is only one way to choose all n of them.

10. A ski club has 40 members, 25 men and 15 women. A planning committee consisting of 3 men and 2 women is to be selected. How many different committees are possible? **241,500**

Applying the Mathematics

11. A test consists of 12 questions. Each student is required to choose 10 of these questions to answer and to omit the remaining 2 questions. How many different subsets of questions could be chosen? **66**

12. **a.** Evaluate $\binom{4}{0} + \binom{4}{1} + \binom{4}{2} + \binom{4}{3} + \binom{4}{4}$. **16**
   b. Evaluate $\binom{5}{0} + \binom{5}{1} + \binom{5}{2} + \binom{5}{3} + \binom{5}{4} + \binom{5}{5}$. **32**
   c. Conjecture the value of $\binom{6}{0} + \binom{6}{1} + \binom{6}{2} + \binom{6}{3} + \binom{6}{4} + \binom{6}{5} + \binom{6}{6}$. **64**

13. There are 5 vowels and 21 consonants in the English alphabet. How many different 7-letter "words" can be formed that contain 4 different consonants and 3 different vowels? **301,644,000**

14. **a.** Verify that each of the following products of four consecutive integers is divisible by 4!. **See left.**
   i. $10 \cdot 9 \cdot 8 \cdot 7$ **ii.** $33 \cdot 32 \cdot 31 \cdot 30$ **iii.** $97 \cdot 96 \cdot 95 \cdot 94$
   b. Use the formula for $C(n, 4)$ to write an elegant proof that the product of any four consecutive positive integers is divisible by 4!. **See margin.**

Additional Answers

14. b. $C(n, 4) = \frac{n!}{4!(n-4)!} = \frac{n(n-1)(n-2)(n-3)}{4!}$, **and $C(n, 4)$ is an integer. So, the product of any 4 consecutive integers n, $n-1$, $n-2$, and $n-3$ is divisible by 4!.**

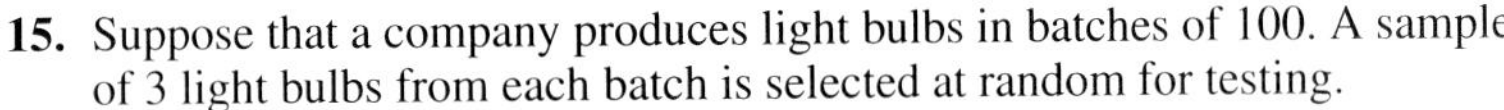

15. Suppose that a company produces light bulbs in batches of 100. A sample of 3 light bulbs from each batch is selected at random for testing.
    a. How many different test samples can be selected? **161,700**
    b. Suppose that there are 2 defective light bulbs in a certain batch. How many of the possible test samples will not contain either of the two defective bulbs? **152,096**

16. In some varieties of poker, a poker hand consists of 5 cards selected from a 52-card deck. In other varieties, a poker hand has 7 cards. Which is greater, the number of different 7-card hands or the number of different 5 card hands? **the number of different 7-card hands**

Review

17. Consider the letters in the word *English*.
    a. How many permutations of these letters are there? **7! = 5040**
    b. How many different five-letter strings are there using these letters if the letters can be used at most once? **2520**
    c. How many different five-letter strings are there if letters can be used more than once? *(Lessons 10-2, 10-3)* **16,807**

18. There are 50 contestants in a talent competition. Prizes will be awarded for first, second, and third place. How many different possibilities are there for the top three finishers? *(Lessons 10-2, 10-3)* **117,600**

19. Sketch the graph of a function whose derivative at -1 is -2 and whose derivative at 5 is 0.5. *(Lesson 9-2)* **See left.**

19) Sample:

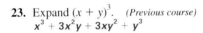

20. Write $\sum_{j=0}^{4} a_j x^{4-j} y^j$ in expanded form. *(Lesson 7-2)*
    $a_0x^4 + a_1x^3y + a_2x^2y^2 + a_3xy^3 + a_4y^4$

21. a. Prove that $\sin(\alpha + \beta)\sin(\alpha - \beta) = \sin^2\alpha\cos^2\beta - \cos^2\alpha\sin^2\beta$.
    b. Add and subtract $\sin^2\alpha\sin^2\beta$ from the right side of the identity above and use the Pythagorean Identity to simplify the result. *(Lesson 6-5)*
    a, b) See margin.

22. Write the contrapositive of the following statement:
    If his pants are not blue, then his coat is not green.
    If his coat is green, then his pants are blue. *(Lesson 1-5)*

23. Expand $(x + y)^3$. *(Previous course)*
    $x^3 + 3x^2y + 3xy^2 + y^3$

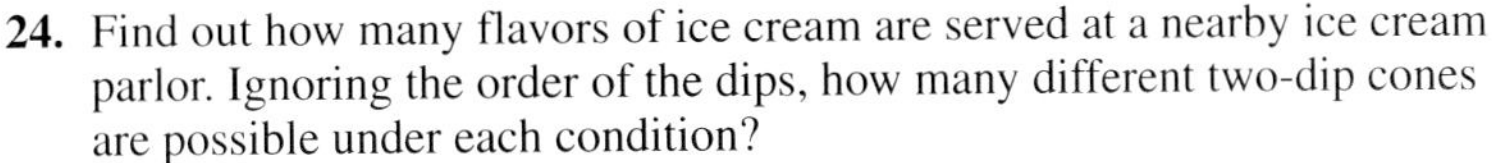

Exploration

24. Find out how many flavors of ice cream are served at a nearby ice cream parlor. Ignoring the order of the dips, how many different two-dip cones are possible under each condition?
    a. Both dips can be the same.
    b. Both dips must be different.
    Sample: Suppose there are 31 flavors.
    a) $\frac{31}{2}(1 + 31) = 496$ b) $\frac{30}{2}(1 + 30) = 465$

Follow-up for Lesson 10-4

Practice

For more questions on SPUR Objectives, use **Lesson Master 10-4** (shown on page 625).

Assessment

Written Communication Ask students to **work in pairs.** Have students make up lottery rules of their own. Then have them write a problem like **Example 2** for their lottery, solve it independently, and compare results. [Students use combinations to solve counting problems.]

Extension

Ask students to consider this probability question: Each of the fifty states has two senators and a committee of fifty senators is chosen at random.

1. What is the probability that a given state is represented? [P(a given state is represented) = 1 − P(the state is NOT represented). There are $C(100, 50)$ ways to choose a committee and $C(98, 50)$ ways a given state would not be included. Therefore, $1 - \frac{C(98, 50)}{C(100, 50)} = 1 - .24747\ldots = .752525\ldots$. So a given state will be represented about 75% of the time.]
2. What is the probability that all states are represented? [There are 2^{50} ways to choose a senator from each state, so $\frac{2^{50}}{C(100, 50)} \approx 1.12 \cdot 10^{-14}$, which is very small!]

Project Update Project 2, *Card Game Odds,* on page 649 relates to the content of this lesson.

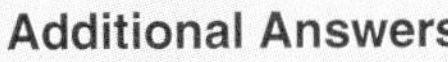

Additional Answers

21. a. $\sin(\alpha + \beta)\sin(\alpha - \beta)$
$= (\sin\alpha\cos\beta + \sin\beta\cos\alpha) \cdot (\sin\alpha\cos\beta - \sin\beta\cos\alpha)$
$= \sin^2\alpha\cos^2\beta - \sin\alpha\sin\beta\cos\beta\cos\alpha + \sin\alpha\sin\beta\cos\alpha\cos\beta - \sin^2\beta\cos^2\alpha$
$= \sin^2\alpha\cos^2\beta - \sin^2\beta\cos^2\alpha$
$= \sin^2\alpha\cos^2\beta - \cos^2\alpha\sin^2\beta$

b. $\sin^2\alpha\cos^2\beta - \cos^2\alpha\sin^2\beta$
$= \sin^2\alpha\cos^2\beta + \sin^2\alpha\sin^2\beta - \sin^2\alpha\sin^2\beta - \cos^2\alpha\sin^2\beta$
$= \sin^2\alpha(\cos^2\beta + \sin^2\beta) - \sin^2\beta(\sin^2\alpha + \cos^2\alpha)$
$= \sin^2\alpha - \sin^2\beta$

Setting Up Lesson 10-5

Discuss both **Questions 20 and 23.** Be certain that students are comfortable with the answers to each one.

Lesson 10-5

Objectives

C Apply the Binomial Theorem to expand binomials or find specific terms.

Resources

From the ***Teacher's Resource File***
- Lesson Master 10-5
- Answer Master 10-5
- Teaching Aids
  104 Warm-up
  107 Pascal's Triangle
  108 Question 11

Additional Resources
- Visuals for Teaching Aids 104, 107, 108
- Exploration 10-5

Teaching Lesson 10-5

Warm-up

1. Expand $(3x - y)^4$. $81x^4 - 108x^3y + 54x^2y^2 - 12xy^3 + y^4$
2. Verify your answer to Question 1 by substituting 2 for x and 6 for y. **The given expression and the expanded result each have the value 0 when $x = 2$ and $y = 6$.**

LESSON

10-5 The Binomial Theorem

Pascal's Triangle

Consider the expansion of the binomial powers shown below.

$$(x + y)^0 = 1$$
$$(x + y)^1 = 1x + 1y$$
$$(x + y)^2 = 1x^2 + 2xy + 1y^2$$
$$(x + y)^3 = 1x^3 + 3x^2y + 3xy^2 + 1y^3$$
$$(x + y)^4 = 1x^4 + 4x^3y + 6x^2y^2 + 4xy^3 + 1y^4$$
$$(x + y)^5 = 1x^5 + 5x^4y + 10x^3y^2 + 10x^2y^3 + 5xy^4 + 1y^5$$

In earlier courses you may have learned that the coefficients of these powers can be arranged in the following array, known as **Pascal's triangle**, after the French mathematician and philosopher Blaise Pascal (1623–1662). The elements of the array are called **binomial coefficients**.

❶

	Row
1	0
1 1	1
1 2 1	2
1 3 3 1	3
1 4 6 4 1	4
1 5 10 10 5 1	5
⋮	⋮

Note that the first and last elements in each row are 1 and all other elements can be obtained as the sum of the two elements immediately above it to the left and right. (See Question 11.) For example, 10 in the 5th row is the sum of 6 and 4 in the 4th row. This gives a recursive way of constructing the triangle.

Example 1

a. Find row 6 of Pascal's triangle.
b. Write $(a + b)^6$ in expanded form.

Solution

a. The sum of adjacent terms in row 5 determine the "inside" five elements of row 6.

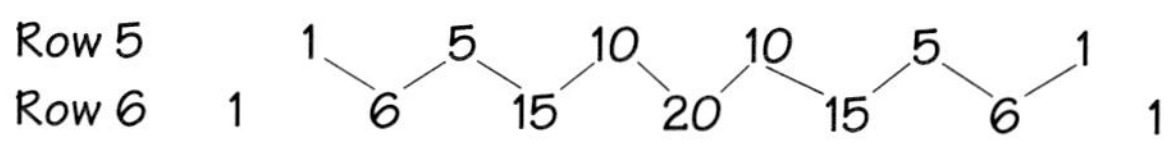

The lines indicate the elements in row 5 which are added to obtain the element in row 6.

Lesson 10-5 Overview

Broad Goals This lesson gives students experience in expanding powers of binomials, using combinatorial and arithmetic ways of remembering and deducing properties of these powers.

Perspective The Binomial Theorem, that $(x + y)^n = \sum_{k=0}^{n} \binom{n}{k} x^{n-k} y^k$, shows that the coefficients of the nth power of the binomial $x + y$ are the combinations $\binom{n}{k}$. When these combinations are written in order for increasing values of n, the array of positive integers known as Pascal's triangle appears. Thus there are algebraic, combinatorial, and arithmetic ways of determining the binomial coefficients.

Many symbol manipulators have an "expand" function. If a product of two or more polynomials or a power of a polynomial is entered, this function will write the product in expanded form. We encourage you to show students how such a symbol manipulator works. It solidifies the terminology of "expand" and "expanded form," provides students with a way of checking their work, and enables explorations that would be difficult without the terminology.

b. The elements of row 6 are the seven coefficients in the expansion of $(a+b)^6$. The sum of the exponents in each term is 6. Also, the powers of a begin at a^6 and decrease to a^0, while the powers of b begin at b^0 and increase to b^6. Thus,

$$(a+b)^6 = a^6 + 6a^5b + 15a^4b^2 + 20a^3b^3 + 15a^2b^4 + 6ab^5 + b^6.$$

Expanding $(x + y)^n$

Pascal's triangle gives a recursive method for generating the powers of $x + y$, because to find the numbers in row k of the triangle, you must first find the numbers in row $k - 1$. But if you wanted to expand $(x + y)^{30}$, it is inefficient to construct 30 rows of Pascal's triangle. However, there is an explicit formula for $(x + y)^n$ which is quite elegant and is obtained by counting techniques.

To develop the formula for $(x + y)^n$, first consider a special case, $(x + y)^8$. By definition,

$$(x + y)^8 = (x + y)(x + y)(x + y)(x + y)(x + y)(x + y)(x + y)(x + y).$$

Each term in the expansion of $(x + y)^8$ is found by choosing an x or y from each of the 8 binomials $(x + y)$. These eight xs and ys are multiplied. So each term is of the form x^ay^b, where $a + b = 8$ and a and b are integers from 0 to 8. Thus, when like terms are combined,

$$(x+y)^8 = \underline{\ ?\ }x^8 + \underline{\ ?\ }x^7y + \underline{\ ?\ }x^6y^2 + \underline{\ ?\ }x^5y^3 + \underline{\ ?\ }x^4y^4 + \underline{\ ?\ }x^3y^5 + \underline{\ ?\ }x^2y^6 + \underline{\ ?\ }xy^7 + \underline{\ ?\ }y^8,$$

where each coefficient of x^ay^b is the number of different ways xs and ys are chosen to obtain x^ay^b. There is only one way to obtain x^8: when all the choices are xs. So the coefficient of x^8 is 1. The choices which contribute to the x^7y term have 1 y chosen from the 8 binomials $(x + y)$. There are $\binom{8}{1} = 8$ ways to do that.

So the coefficient of x^7y is 8. The choices which contribute to the x^6y^2 term have 2 ys chosen from the 8 binomials $(x + y)$. There are $\binom{8}{2} = 28$ ways of choosing 2 objects from 8, so the coefficient of x^6y^2 is 28. Continuing this process gives

$$(x+y)^8 = \binom{8}{0}x^8 + \binom{8}{1}x^7y + \binom{8}{2}x^6y^2 + \binom{8}{3}x^5y^3 + \binom{8}{4}x^4y^4 + \binom{8}{5}x^3y^5 + \binom{8}{6}x^2y^6 + \binom{8}{7}xy^7 + \binom{8}{8}y^8$$
$$= x^8 + 8x^7y + 28x^6y^2 + 56x^5y^3 + 70x^4y^4 + 56x^3y^5 + 28x^2y^6 + 8xy^7 + y^8.$$

This sum can be written more concisely with summation notation.

$$(x+y)^8 = \sum_{k=0}^{8} \binom{8}{k} x^{8-k}y^k$$

The general formula for $(x + y)^n$ is known as the Binomial Theorem. Omar Khayyam, perhaps the greatest mathematician of the 12th century, knew of it. In 1676, Isaac Newton generalized the Binomial Theorem to apply to any rational power of $(x + y)$. That result is beyond the scope of this book.

The Binomial Theorem is stated on the next page. Its proof is elegant and generalizes the example of $(x + y)^8$.

Notes on Reading

This is the first of two lessons on the Binomial Theorem. In this first lesson, students are expected to use the theorem to expand a binomial to any positive integer power or to find a specific term of such an expansion without actually computing the entire expansion. Consequently, this is a very skill-oriented lesson. The applications of the theorem are contained in the next lesson. By separating the computation from the applications we are able to keep the lessons to a reasonable length.

Students who have had UCSMP *Functions, Statistics, and Trigonometry* will have covered this material in more depth than is given here in two lessons. They may have studied binomial probabilities and then normal distributions as the limit of the binomial distributions.

❶ You might point out that Pascal's triangle can be considered as a *two-dimensional sequence,* for it involves two variables and its representation goes in two directions. The process used in **Example 1** uses the recurrence relation for this sequence found in **Question 11.** An explicit formula for the sequence is given by the Binomial Theorem. You can use **Teaching Aid 107** with 10 rows of the triangle to help students see the patterns in it.

Optional Activities

Activity 1 Technology Connection
Materials: *Explorations* software

Students may use *Exploration 10-5, Binomial Expansion,* as an alternative to **Examples 2–3.** The activity demonstrates the relationship between Pascal's Triangle and the Binomial Theorem. Students can choose a row and term in that row, then observe the expansion for that binomial.

Activity 2 Once students are familiar with the computations in this lesson, you might show them how to create the nth row of Pascal's Triangle on their graphing calculator. Have them choose a particular value for n, say $n = 8$. Have them enter $y = C(8, x)$ into the function menu on their graphing calculators. On some calculators, they will enter $y = 8\ nCr\ X$ into their [Y =] menu. When they look at a table for the function, with tables values starting at zero and increasing by 1, they will see the 8th row of Pascal's Triangle. Have them notice and explain the value of the function for $x = -1$. [Error or undefined; taking subsets of -1 elements from a group of 8 objects makes no sense.] Have them notice and explain the values of the function for $x \geq 9$. [0; there are zero ways to take subsets containing 9 or more elements from a group of 8 objects.] Point out that changing the value of n will produce any row that is desired.

❷ **Error Alert** Be careful to note that $\binom{n}{r}$ is the rth term in the nth row only if the counting of both rows and terms begins with 0. That is, the top row is the 0th row, as indicated on page 628, and the outside left diagonal of 1s is considered the 0th diagonal. In **Example 3,** the counting begins with the more traditional 1. Because of this potential confusion, it is easier to first write the exponents for the term, and then write the coefficient which agrees with them, as is done in **Example 3.**

Additional Examples

1. a. Write down the terms of row 9 of Pascal's triangle. **1 9 36 84 126 126 84 36 9 1**
   b. Write $(a + b)^9$ in expanded form. $\mathbf{a^9 + 9a^8b + 36a^7b^2 + 84a^6b^3 + 126a^5b^4 + 126a^4b^5 + 84a^3b^6 + 36a^2b^7 + 9ab^8 + b^9}$
2. Give the coefficient of x^6y^5 in the expansion of $(x + y)^{11}$. **462**
3. Give the 4th term in the expansion of $(2b - 4a^2)^7$. $\mathbf{\binom{7}{3}(2b)^4(-4a^2)^3 = -35840b^4a^6}$

The Binomial Theorem
For all positive integers n and numbers x and y,

$$(x + y)^n = \binom{n}{0}x^n + \binom{n}{1}x^{n-1}y + \binom{n}{2}x^{n-2}y^2 + \ldots + \binom{n}{k}x^{n-k}y^k + \ldots + \binom{n}{n-1}xy^{n-1} + \binom{n}{n}y^n = \sum_{k=0}^{n}\binom{n}{k}x^{n-k}y^k.$$

Proof
By definition,

$$(x + y)^n = \underbrace{(x + y)(x + y)(x + y)\ldots(x + y)}_{n \text{ factors}}.$$

Each term in the expansion is of the form x^ay^b where a and b are nonnegative integers with $a + b = n$, and one of x or y is selected from each of the n factors $(x + y)$. The term $x^{n-k}y^k$ is obtained by choosing y from any k of the n factors. Consequently, because there are $\binom{n}{k}$ ways of selecting k items from a set of n items, the coefficient of the term $x^{n-k}y^k$ in the expansion of $(x + y)^n$ is $\binom{n}{k}$.

❷ Using the Binomial Theorem To Find Terms in a Binomial Expansion

The Binomial Theorem shows that all of the coefficients in the expansion of $(x + y)^n$ are combinations of the form $\binom{n}{k}$, which means that Pascal's triangle is an array of combinations. Thus either Pascal's triangle or the Binomial Theorem can be used to obtain any term in a binomial expansion.

Example 2

Give the coefficient of $x^{22}y^8$ in the expansion of $(x + y)^{30}$.

Solution

The coefficients in the expansion of $(x + y)^{30}$ are in the 30th row of Pascal's triangle, so we use the Binomial Theorem. From the Binomial Theorem, the expansion of $(x + y)^{30}$ has 31 terms, each of the form $\binom{30}{k}x^{30-k}y^k$. The term with $k = 8$ is

$$\binom{30}{8}x^{30-8}y^8 = \binom{30}{8}x^{22}y^8.$$

So the coefficient is $\binom{30}{8} = \frac{30!}{8!22!} = 5852925.$

It is customary to write the binomial expansion of $(x + y)^n$ with the exponents of x in decreasing order, as done above. Then $\binom{n}{0}x^n$ is the 1st term, $\binom{n}{1}x^{n-1}y$ is the 2nd term, $\binom{n}{2}x^{n-2}y^2$ is the 3rd term, and, in general, $\binom{n}{k}x^{n-k}y^k$ is the $(k + 1)$st term.

Adapting to Individual Needs

Extra Help
If some students are confused in **Example 2** by the fact that $(x + y)^{30}$ has 31 terms, refer them to the expansions of binomial powers at the opening of the lesson. Have them note that, in general, $(x + y)^n$ has $n + 1$ terms, just as there are $n + 1$ elements in the nth row of Pascal's triangle. Show how this agrees with the Binomial Theorem. There are $n + 1$ terms in the expansion because there are $n + 1$ integers k from 0 to n.

Example 3

Find the eighth term in the expansion of $(3p - 2)^{15}$.

Solution

Think of finding the eighth term of $(x + y)^n$, where $n = 15$.

$(x + y)^{15} = \sum_{k=0}^{15} \binom{15}{k} x^{n-k} y^k$. Here $x = 3p$, $y = -2$, and the eighth term occurs when $k = 7$. So the eighth term is

$$\binom{15}{7}(3p)^{15-7}(-2)^7 = \frac{15!}{7!8!}(6561p^8)(-128)$$
$$= -5{,}404{,}164{,}480p^8.$$

Pascal investigated many of the properties of the binomial coefficients, and in fact invented mathematical induction in order to prove some of them! You will examine some of these properties in the Questions and in the next lesson.

QUESTIONS

Covering the Reading

1. Refer to Example 1.
   a. Use row 6 of Pascal's triangle to find row 7. **1, 7, 21, 35, 35, 21, 7, 1**
   b. Expand $(a + b)^7$. c. Expand $(a - b)^7$. **See left.**
   $a^7 + 7a^6b + 21a^5b^2 + 35a^4b^3 + 35a^3b^4 + 21a^2b^5 + 7ab^6 + b^7$
2. What combination will yield the coefficient of the term $x^{20}y^{10}$ in the expansion of $(x + y)^{30}$? $\binom{30}{10}$
3. Write out the Binomial Theorem for the case $n = 9$. **See margin.**
4. a. Expand $(2a + b)^6$. **See left.**
   b. Verify that the sum of the coefficients is a power of 3.
   $64 + 192 + 240 + 160 + 60 + 12 + 1 = 729 = 3^6$
5. Find the fourth term of $(s + 5r)^{15}$. **$56875s^{12}r^3$**
6. Find the tenth term of $(2x - 3y)^{13}$. **$-225{,}173{,}520x^4y^9$**

Applying the Mathematics

7. Use the Binomial Theorem to find each.
   a. the 4th power of the complex number $1 + i$ **-4**
   b. the 8th power of the complex number $1 + i$ **16**
8. Without computing the entire expansion of $(2a + b)^{25}$, find the coefficient of the term that has a^{12} as a factor. **$\approx 2.13 \times 10^{10}$**
9. Write $\sum_{k=0}^{7}\left[\binom{7}{k}x^{7-k}2^k\right]$ as the power of a binomial. **$(x + 2)^7$**
10. For all positive integers n, $\binom{n}{n} = 1$. How is this fact related to the makeup of Pascal's triangle?
    The outside right diagonal (the last term in each row) is 1.

1c) $a^7 - 7a^6b + 21a^5b^2 - 35a^4b^3 + 35a^3b^4 - 21a^2b^5 + 7ab^6 - b^7$

4a) $64a^6 + 192a^5b + 240a^4b^2 + 160a^3b^3 + 60a^2b^4 + 12ab^5 + b^6$

Blaise Pascal (1623–1662)

Notes on Questions

Question 4b Prove this result for any power of $2a + b$ by letting $a = 1$ and $b = 1$. This proof will pave the way for the proof of the first theorem of the next lesson.

Questions 5–6 Again, here, the leftmost term is called the 1st term.

Question 7 Students can check their results by rewriting $1 + i$ as $[\sqrt{2}, 45°]$ and using DeMoivre's Theorem.

Question 9 Error Alert If students do not understand the question, have them write out the summation, first letting $k = 0$, then $k = 1$, then $k = 2$, and so on. Then the answer becomes rather evident.

Additional Answers

3. $(x + y)^9 = \sum_{k=0}^{n}\binom{9}{k}x^{9-k}y^k =$
$\binom{9}{0}x^9 + \binom{9}{1}x^8y + \binom{9}{2}x^7y^2 + \binom{9}{3}x^6y^3 + \binom{9}{4}x^5y^4 + \binom{9}{5}x^4y^5 + \binom{9}{6}x^3y^6 + \binom{9}{7}x^2y^7 + \binom{9}{8}xy^8 + \binom{9}{9}y^9$

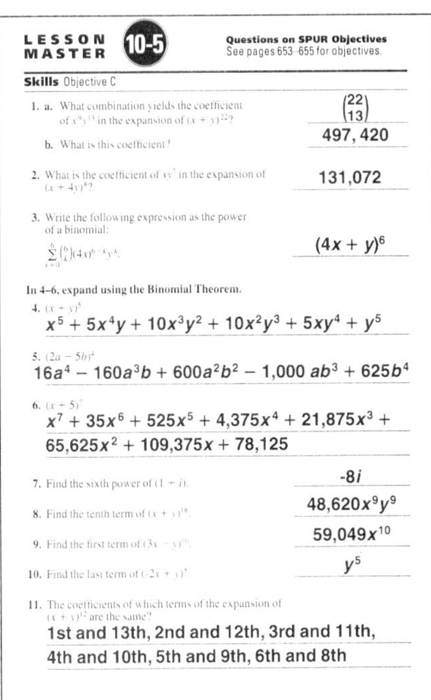

LESSON MASTER 10-5 — **Questions on SPUR Objectives** See pages 653–655 for objectives.

Skills Objective C

1. a. What combination yields the coefficient of x^9y^{13} in the expansion of $(x + y)^{22}$? $\binom{22}{13}$
   b. What is this coefficient? **497, 420**
2. What is the coefficient of xy^7 in the expansion of $(x + 4y)^8$? **131,072**
3. Write the following expression as the power of a binomial: $\sum_{k=0}^{6}\binom{6}{k}(4x)^{6-k}y^k$. **$(4x + y)^6$**

In 4–6, expand using the Binomial Theorem.

4. $(x + y)^5$
   $x^5 + 5x^4y + 10x^3y^2 + 10x^2y^3 + 5xy^4 + y^5$
5. $(2a - 5b)^4$
   $16a^4 - 160a^3b + 600a^2b^2 - 1{,}000\,ab^3 + 625b^4$
6. $(x + 5)^7$
   $x^7 + 35x^6 + 525x^5 + 4{,}375x^4 + 21{,}875x^3 + 65{,}625x^2 + 109{,}375x + 78{,}125$
7. Find the sixth power of $(1 + i)$. **$-8i$**
8. Find the tenth term of $(x + y)^{18}$. **$48{,}620x^9y^9$**
9. Find the first term of $(3x - y)^{10}$. **$59{,}049x^{10}$**
10. Find the last term of $(-2x + y)^5$. **y^5**
11. The coefficients of which terms of the expansion of $(x + y)^{12}$ are the same?
    1st and 13th, 2nd and 12th, 3rd and 11th, 4th and 10th, 5th and 9th, 6th and 8th

Adapting to Individual Needs

Challenge

The Binomial Theorem can be used to estimate powers of numbers just a little larger than 1, the kinds of numbers that often appear in expressions of compound interest. For instance, $1.06^2 = (1 + .06)^2 = 1 + 2(.06) + (.06)^2 = 1.1236$. The last term does not change anything in the hundredth place. Students could explore other powers of similar numbers, noting how many terms of the binomial expansion are needed to get accuracy to the nearest hundredth or thousandth.

Notes on Questions

Question 11 Go over this proof in class. The proof is provided on **Teaching Aid 108.**

Question 17 Some calculators give 1.08972864 E10 as the answer. Since 1.08972864 E10 = $1.08972864 \cdot 10^{10}$, and the answer is divisible by 100, the answer can be written in base 10 rather easily: 10,897,286,400.

Follow-up for Lesson 10-5

Practice

For more questions on SPUR Objectives, use **Lesson Master 10-5** (shown on page 631).

Assessment

Oral Communication Have students explain how they arrived at their answer for **Question 4, 5, or 6.** [Students show their understanding of applying the Binomial Theorem to find a specific term in the expansion of a binomial.]

Extension

Project Update Project 3, *Extending Pascal's Triangle,* on page 649, relates to the content of this lesson.

11a) ${}_nC_r$ Calculation Theorem
b) forming a least common denominator
c) addition of fractions and Distributive Property
d) $(n + 1)!$
e) ${}_nC_r$ Calculation Theorem

12) $\binom{n}{r}$ is the coefficient of $x^{n-4}y^r$ in the expansion of $(x + y)^n$. But $(x + y)^n = (y + x)^n$, so $\binom{n}{r}$ is also the coefficient of $y^{n-r}x^r = x^{n-(n-r)}y^{n-r}$, which is $\binom{n}{n-1}$. So $\binom{n}{r} = \binom{n}{n-1}$.

18d)

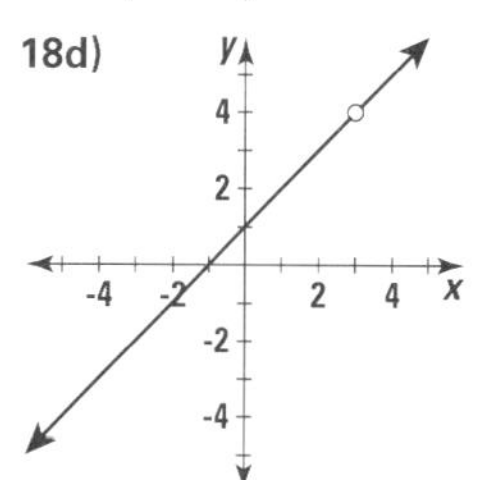

11. The fact that each "interior" entry in Pascal's triangle is the sum of the two entries immediately above it can be expressed as the identity $\binom{n}{r-1} + \binom{n}{r} = \binom{n+1}{r}$ for all positive integers n and r with $r \le n$. Fill in the missing reasons in the following proof of this identity.

$$\binom{n}{r-1} + \binom{n}{r} = \frac{n!}{(r-1)!(n-r+1)!} + \frac{n!}{r!(n-r)!} \quad \text{\underline{a.}}$$
$$= \frac{r \cdot n!}{r!(n-r+1)!} + \frac{n!(n-r+1)}{r!(n-r+1)!} \quad \text{\underline{b.}}$$
$$= \frac{[r + (n-r+1)]n!}{r!(n-r+1)!} \quad \text{\underline{c.}}$$
$$= \frac{(n+1)n!}{r!(n+1-r)!} \quad \text{Property of Opposites}$$
$$= \frac{(n+1)!}{r!(n+1-r)!} \quad \text{definition of \underline{d.}}$$
$$= \binom{n+1}{r} \quad \text{\underline{e.}}$$

a–e) See left.

12. Use the Binomial Theorem to explain why $\binom{n}{r} = \binom{n}{n-r}$. (Hint: Begin "$\binom{n}{r}$ is the coefficient of . . .") See left.

Review

In 13–15, evaluate the given expression. *(Lessons 10-3, 10-4)*

13. $C(9, 4)$ 126
14. $\binom{11}{6}$ 462
15. $P(93, 4)$ 70,073,640

16. A pizza place offers the following toppings: pepperoni, sausage, onions, green peppers, and mushrooms.
    a. How many different kinds of pizzas with three toppings can be ordered? 10
    b. How many different kinds with any number of toppings (between none and all five) can be ordered? *(Lessons 10-2, 10-4)* 32

17. Consider the following problem: How many 10-person batting orders can be formed from a softball team's 15-person roster?
    a. State its essential features.
    b. Solve the problem. *(Lessons 10-1, 10-3)* $\approx 1.0897 \times 10^{10}$

    a) Ordered symbols; repetition is not allowed.

18. Let f be the real function defined by $f(x) = \frac{x^2 - 2x - 3}{x - 3}$.
    a. Determine the values of x at which f is undefined. $x = 3$
    b. Classify any discontinuities as essential or removable. removable
    c. Find equations of any vertical asymptotes. none
    d. Sketch a graph of f. *(Lessons 5-4, 5-5)* See left.

19. *Multiple choice.* When does $\lim_{x \to -\infty} b^x = \infty$? c
    (a) $b > 1$ (b) $b = 1$ (c) $0 < b < 1$ (d) $b < 0$ *(Lesson 2-7)*

Exploration

20. Find the sum of the squares of the elements in the first few rows of Pascal's triangle. Find a pattern to predict the exact value of the sum of the squares of the elements in the 12th row. See margin.

Additional Answers

20.

row	sum of squares of elements
0	1
1	2
2	6
3	20

The sum of the squares for row n seems to be the middle element of row $2n$. So the sum of squares of the elements of the 12th row would be the middle element of row 24.

$\binom{24}{12} = 2{,}704{,}156$

Setting Up Lesson 10-6

Go over **Question 2** or the *Warm-up* so that students see numerical verification of the symbolic algebra of the Binomial Theorem. Numerical substitution is used at the beginning of Lesson 10-6 to prove the Sum of Binomial Coefficients Theorem.

LESSON

10-6 *Counting and the Binomial Theorem*

❶ Because of the Binomial Theorem, Pascal's triangle can be considered as a triangle of combinations.

$$\begin{array}{ccccccccc} & & & & \binom{0}{0} & & & & \\ & & & \binom{1}{0} & & \binom{1}{1} & & & \\ & & \binom{2}{0} & & \binom{2}{1} & & \binom{2}{2} & & \\ & \binom{3}{0} & & \binom{3}{1} & & \binom{3}{2} & & \binom{3}{3} & \\ \binom{4}{0} & & \binom{4}{1} & & \binom{4}{2} & & \binom{4}{3} & & \binom{4}{4} \\ & & & & \vdots & & & & \end{array} \qquad \begin{array}{ccccccccc} & & & & 1 & & & & \\ & & & 1 & & 1 & & & \\ & & 1 & & 2 & & 1 & & \\ & 1 & & 3 & & 3 & & 1 & \\ 1 & & 4 & & 6 & & 4 & & 1 \\ & & & & \vdots & & & & \end{array}$$

This explains why the entries in Pascal's triangle are sometimes called binomial coefficients.

Notice that the sum of the elements in the third row of Pascal's triangle is 2^3 and the sum of the elements in the fourth row is 2^4. These facts are generalized in the following theorem.

Sum of Binomial Coefficients Theorem
∀ integers $n \ge 0$,

$$\binom{n}{0} + \binom{n}{1} + \binom{n}{2} + \ldots + \binom{n}{k} + \ldots + \binom{n}{n} = 2^n.$$

That is,

$$\sum_{k=0}^{n} \binom{n}{k} = 2^n.$$

❷ **Proof**
The proof is elegant. From the Binomial Theorem, for all numbers x and y and integers $n \ge 1$,

$$(x + y)^n = \sum_{k=0}^{n} \binom{n}{k} x^{n-k} y^k.$$

Since the Binomial Theorem is true for all numbers x and y, it is true when $x = 1$ and $y = 1$.

Thus $$(1 + 1)^n = \sum_{k=0}^{n} \binom{n}{k} 1^{n-k} 1^k.$$

So $$2^n = \sum_{k=0}^{n} \binom{n}{k}$$

The case when $n = 0$ is left for you to prove as Question 6.

The above theorem can be interpreted as a property of combinatorics. Let S be a set with n elements. Each subset of S has k elements, where $0 \le k \le n$.

Lesson 10-6

Objectives

E Apply the Binomial Theorem to deduce properties of sets.
G Use the Binomial Theorem to solve counting problems.
H Find binomial probabilities in realistic situations.

Resources

From the ***Teacher's Resource File***
- Lesson Master 10-6
- Answer Master 10-6
- Assessment Sourcebook: Quiz on Lessons 10-4 through 10-6
- Teaching Aids
  104 Warm-up
  109 Pascal's Triangle as a Triangle of Combinations
- Technology Sourcebook Calculator Master 15

Additional Resources
- Visuals for Teaching Aids 104, 109
- Exploration 10-6

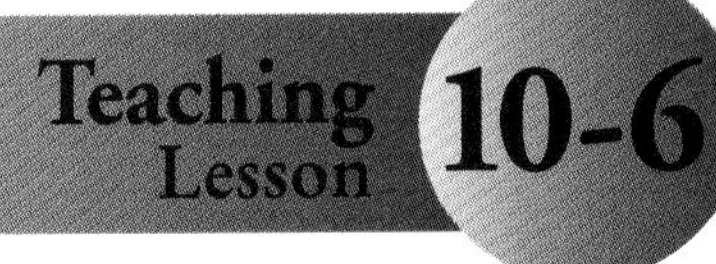

Warm-up

Given that about 51% of the babies born in the United States are boys, and assuming that births of boys and girls are independent, what is the probability that in a family of three children, the eldest is a boy, the second is a girl, and the third is a boy? **.51 • .49 • .51 = .127449 ≈ .13**

Notes on Reading

❶ Pascal's triangle as a triangle of combinations is shown on **Teaching Aid 109.**

❷ In **Question 14** of Lesson 10-2, students proved that there are 2^n subsets of a set with n elements.

Lesson 10-6 Overview

Broad Goals This lesson deals with applications to counting and probability.

Perspective Suppose an experiment has two outcomes, success or failure, with a probability p of success. Then the probability of failure is $1 - p$. Then, if there are n repetitions (trials) of this experiment, from the Multiplication Counting Principle, there are 2^n permutations of successes and failures. Of these, $\binom{n}{k}$ have k successes, and so the probability of k successes in n trials is $\frac{\binom{n}{k}}{2^n} p^k (1 - p)^{n-k}$. This lesson develops the mathematics of binomial experiments which is covered extensively in Chapter 10 of UCSMP *Functions, Statistics, and Trigonometry.* This material should be review for students who studied from that book.

Here is another proof of the same result that ties in with Pascal's triangle and binomial coefficients.

The situation of **Examples 1–2** are known as *binomial experiments.* In a binomial experiment:

1. There are a series of n independent trials or experiments. Independence in the trials simply means that the outcome of one trial is not affected by the outcome of any other trail.
2. Each trial has two outcomes.
3. The probability of each of the two outcomes remains constant from trial to trial.

Example 1 illustrates the fact that the binomial coefficient gives the number of ways that a given situation can occur in a series of n trials. In this calculation only the binomial coefficient is needed and the actual terms of the binomial are not important.

Consumer Connection The situation in **Example 3,** on page 636, is, in theory, not precisely a binomial experiment, though it is often assumed to be so, because the total number of light bulbs produced is finite. Thus, if the probability of finding a first defective bulb is truly 1%, then after one has found a defective bulb, the probability that the next bulb is defective is slightly less (because you have already found one of the 1% of bulbs that is defective). The distribution is thus an example of a hypergeometric distribution. However, because the number of bulbs is large, the binomial probabilities are very close to the hypergeometric probabilities.

Because $\binom{n}{k}$ is the number of different subsets of S with k elements, it follows that the total number of different subsets of S is also given by

$$\underbrace{\binom{n}{0}}_{\text{0-element subsets}} + \underbrace{\binom{n}{1}}_{\text{1-element subsets}} + \ldots + \underbrace{\binom{n}{k}}_{k\text{-element subsets}} + \ldots + \underbrace{\binom{n}{n}}_{n\text{-element subsets}}.$$

Also, by the argument of Question 14 of Lesson 10-2, S has a total of 2^n subsets. So the Sum of Binomial Coefficients Theorem reflects the number of subsets of a set. This fact provides an alternate approach to solving certain counting problems.

Example 1

Suppose a coin is tossed 4 times. How many arrangements of *H*s and *T*s are possible?

Solution 1

The following arrangements of *H*s and *T*s are possible.

HHHH	HTHH	THHH	TTHH
HHHT	HTHT	THHT	TTHT
HHTH	HTTH	THTH	TTTH
HHTT	HTTT	THTT	TTTT

There are a total of 16 arrangements.

Solution 2

To calculate the number of arrangements without listing them, apply the theorem in Lesson 10-2 to the number of 4-symbol strings that can be made from 2 symbols with repetition, which gives 2^4 as the number.

Solution 3

Reformulate the problem in terms of subsets. A particular arrangement of *H*s and *T*s can be identified by indicating which of the tosses are *H*s. For instance, the arrangement *HTTH* can be indicated as {1, 4}, the arrangement *HHHT* as {1, 2, 3}, and the arrangement *TTTT* as the null set { }. Each arrangement corresponds to a different subset of {1, 2, 3, 4}, and the total number of arrangements is the total number of subsets of {1, 2, 3, 4}, which is 2^4.

Since the number of elements in a subset of {1, 2, 3, 4} corresponds to the number of *H*s in an arrangement, and the number of k-element subsets is $\binom{4}{k}$, the number of ways of obtaining k heads is given by an element in the 4th row of Pascal's triangle.

0 heads can occur in 1 way.	{1,2,3,4} has 1 subset with 0 elements.
1 head can occur in 4 ways.	{1,2,3,4} has 4 subsets with 1 element.
2 heads can occur in 6 ways.	{1,2,3,4} has 6 subsets with 2 elements.
3 heads can occur in 4 ways.	{1,2,3,4} has 4 subsets with 3 elements.
4 heads can occur in 1 way.	{1,2,3,4} has 1 subset with 4 elements.

Optional Activities

Activity 1 Technology Connection
Materials: *Explorations* software

Students may use *Exploration 10-6, Binomial Probability,* as an alternative to **Example 3.** By choosing the number of trials, and the probability of defective results, students can use a table to find the binomial probability of a chosen result. Randomly generated items allow students to compare the theoretical probability with the experimental results.

Activity 2 Writing After discussing **Question 10,** ask students to write an explanation of why it is necessary to return each ball to the box before drawing the next ball and how the problem would change if the balls are not replaced. [If the balls are not replaced, then the probability of picking a red ball changes as the balls are picked: the probability of picking a red ball next time decreases if a red ball is picked and increases if a white ball is picked. Therefore, the trials are not independent and binomial probabilities cannot be used.]

Tossing a coin repeatedly is an example of an experiment that involves a series of *trials*, each of which has two possible outcomes. In such an experiment, the Binomial Theorem indicates the number of different ways that a particular event can happen. For example, in the series of n coin tosses, suppose the event is obtaining exactly k tails (and therefore $n - k$ heads). The number of ways the event can happen is the same as $\binom{n}{k}$, the number of ways to choose k tails from a total of n tosses. But $\binom{n}{k}$ is also the coefficient of the term $H^{n-k}T^k$ in the expansion of $(H + T)^n$. Notice that in this term, the exponent of T is k, the number of tails desired, and the exponent of H is $n - k$, the number of heads desired. Thus, if a coin is tossed n times, expanding $(H + T)^n$ gives a list of terms $\binom{n}{k}H^{n-k}T^k$, the coefficients of which are the number of ways to obtain $n - k$ heads and k tails.

Example 2

A coin is flipped six times. How many of the possible sequences of heads and tails have at least three tails?

Solution

Following the ideas in the discussion above, look at the terms in the expansion of $(H + T)^6$.

$$(H+T)^6 = \binom{6}{0}H^6 + \binom{6}{1}H^5T + \binom{6}{2}H^4T^2 + \binom{6}{3}H^3T^3 + \binom{6}{4}H^2T^4 + \binom{6}{5}HT^5 + \binom{6}{6}T^6$$

At least 3 tails means 3, 4, 5, or 6 tails. Therefore, the total number of ways to obtain at least 3 tails is the same as the sum of the coefficients of H^3T^3, H^2T^4, HT^5, and T^6:

$$\binom{6}{3} + \binom{6}{4} + \binom{6}{5} + \binom{6}{6} = 20 + 15 + 6 + 1 = 42.$$

Suppose that an unfair coin is used in the series of coin tosses above, so that the probability of obtaining a head from a single toss is $h = .7$ (and thus the probability of a tail is $t = .3$). Suppose further that you wish to find the probability that in n tosses, you will obtain exactly k tails (and $n - k$ heads). Since each toss is independent of the others, the probability of obtaining a particular sequence consisting of k tails and $n - k$ heads is $h^{n-k}t^k = (.7)^{n-k}(.3)^k$. Since there are $\binom{n}{k}$ such sequences, the total probability is $\binom{n}{k}h^{n-k}t^k$, which is one term of the expansion of $(h + t)^n$. For example, the probability of obtaining exactly 2 tails out of 6 tosses of the unfair coin is

$$\binom{6}{2}(.7)^{6-2}(.3)^2 = \frac{6!}{2!4!}(.7)^4(.3)^2 \approx .324.$$

When $h + t = 1$, we call $\binom{n}{k}h^{n-k}t^k$ a **binomial probability**. An important application of binomial probabilities is in the calculation of probabilities involving samples taken from a larger population.

As in **Example 1,** the binomial coefficient in **Example 2** still gives the number of ways that the given situation can occur in n trials. But in **Example 3,** because the probability of the event is desired, the actual terms of the binomial are also of interest. The terms of the binomial are simply the probabilities of the two outcomes, in this case, the probability of being acceptable and the probability of being defective. Students need to realize that $(.99)^9(.01)^3$ gives the probability of getting 9 good bulbs and 3 defective ones. (The *Warm-up* is designed to get at this idea.) This result must still be multiplied by the binomial coefficient which gives the number of ways in 12 trials that 9 good and 3 defective bulbs might be found.

It may be useful to have students write a few of the different sequences that describe the situation in **Example 3a.** Here are three of the possible ways to obtain 3 defective bulbs in 12 trials:

GGGGDGGDGGDG
DDDGGGGGGGGG
GDGGDGGGGGGD

By writing out a few of the different ways to obtain the desired result, students may see the need for multiplying the probabilities by the binomial coefficient.

LESSON MASTER 10-6

Questions on SPUR Objectives
See pages 653–655 for objectives.

Properties Objective E

1. What combination yields the number of 5-element subsets that can be formed from a set with 9 elements? $\binom{9}{5}$

2. How is ${}_{10}C_7 + {}_{10}C_8 + {}_{10}C_9 + {}_{10}C_{10}$ related to the number of subsets that can be formed from a set?
It gives the number of subsets containing at least 7 elements that can be formed from a 10-element set.

Uses Objective G

3. In how many ways is it possible to obtain at least three heads in 11 tosses of a coin? 1,981 ways

4. In how many ways is it possible to obtain at least six tails in eight tosses of a coin? 37 ways

5. A pizzeria offers ten different pizza toppings. In how many different ways can a pizza be topped if at least one topping is used? 1,023 ways

Uses Objective H

6. A long multiple-choice text is designed so that each of the choices, A, B, C, and D, is the correct answer 25% of the time. A computer randomly assigns the correct answer to A, B, C, and D in each question. What is the probability that in the first ten questions A is the correct answer for five questions? ≈ 0.058

7. In a board game, a player must roll a 1 or a 2 on a die to attain a bonus. In five rolls of a fair die, what is the probability that the player will roll a 1 or a 2 at least once? ≈ 0.868

8. A cereal manufacturer has packaged a small toy in 8% of its boxes of cereal. Assuming that the boxes are randomly distributed to the stores, what is the probability that a purchase of four boxes will result in
   a. exactly four toys? ≈ 0.00004
   b. no toys? ≈ 0.7164
   c. at least one toy? ≈ 0.2836
   d. at least two toys? ≈ 0.0344

Activity 3 Technology Connection
You might wish to assign *Technology Sourcebook, Calculator Master 15.* In this activity, students use the programming features of a graphics calculator to simulate the tossing of a fair coin. Students collect data on the number of heads per tosses for a single experiment and then on the number of heads observed out of 6 tosses for multiple experiments. Then students are asked to calculate the binomial probabilities and compare them with their experimental results.

Additional Examples

1. In how many ways can a team win at least 10 of its first 15 games? **4944**
2. A team has in the past won about 60% of its games. Taking this percentage as the probability that the team will win any game it plays, what is the probability that the team will win at least 10 of its first 15 games? $\sum_{k=10}^{15}\binom{15}{k}(.6)^k(.4)^{15-k} \approx .403$, **or about 40%**

Notes on Questions

Question 2 It is important to go over this question to ensure that students understand the basic idea underlying the lesson.

Question 7 Ask for other situations that are equivalent to this one. (Samples: getting a disease if it is expected that 60% of people will get it; shooting baskets with a 60% probability of making one.)

Question 12 It is significant that de Méré's intuition was not accurate in this situation despite the fact that he was a professional gambler. It is a good example of the role of mathematics in clarifying situations that are not well-understood.

(Notes on Questions continue on page 638.)

Example 3

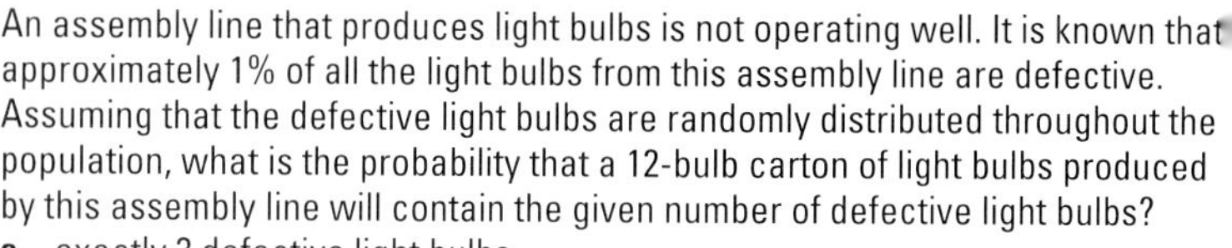

An assembly line that produces light bulbs is not operating well. It is known that approximately 1% of all the light bulbs from this assembly line are defective. Assuming that the defective light bulbs are randomly distributed throughout the population, what is the probability that a 12-bulb carton of light bulbs produced by this assembly line will contain the given number of defective light bulbs?

a. exactly 3 defective light bulbs

b. more than one defective light bulb

Solution

Think of the 12-bulb carton as a series of 12 trials, each of which consists of selecting a light bulb. A trial has two possible outcomes—selecting a good bulb or selecting a defective bulb. These trials are independent, that is, whether one bulb is good or defective does not depend on whether another bulb is good or defective. Let g and d represent the probabilities of a bulb being good or defective, respectively. Here $g = .99$ and $d = .01$. Expand $(g + d)^{12}$.

$$(g + d)^{12} = \sum_{k=0}^{12}\binom{12}{k}g^{12-k}d^k$$

The probability that k bulbs in the carton are defective and $12 - k$ are good is given by the term $\binom{12}{k}g^{12-k}d^k$.

a. The probability that a 12-bulb carton will contain exactly 3 defective light bulbs is given by the term with $k = 3$.

$$\binom{12}{3}g^{12-3}d^3 = \binom{12}{3}(.99)^9(.01)^3 = \frac{12!}{3!9!}(.99)^9(.01)^3 \approx .000201$$

b. The probability that a 12-bulb carton will contain more than one defective light bulb is equal to 1 minus the probability of containing 0 or 1 defective light bulbs.

$$1 - \left(\binom{12}{0}g^{12-0}d^0 + \binom{12}{1}g^{12-1}d^1\right)$$
$$= 1 - \left(\binom{12}{0}(.99)^{12} + \binom{12}{1}(.99)^{11}(.01)^1\right)$$
$$\approx .00617$$

The reciprocal of .000201 is about 4975; the reciprocal of .00617 is about 162. So about 1 in 5000 cartons will have 3 defective bulbs, and about 1 in 160 will have more than one defective bulb.

QUESTIONS

Covering the Reading

1. **a.** How many subsets are there of {1, 2, 3, 4}? **16**
   b. List them. **See left.**

1b) {1, 2, 3, 4}, {1}, {2}, {3}, {4}, { }, {1, 2}, {1, 3}, {1, 4}, {2, 3}, {2, 4}, {3, 4}, {1, 2, 3}, {1, 2, 4}, {1, 3, 4}, {2, 3, 4}

2. Compute the number of subsets of an 8-element set that contain the given number of elements.
   a. exactly 3 elements **56**
   b. 3 or fewer elements **93**

3. Refer to Example 3. What is the probability that the carton contains exactly 2 defective light bulbs? $\approx$ **.00597**

Adapting to Individual Needs

Extra Help

Before you discuss the solution to **Example 3b,** some students might benefit from a review of the following basic properties of probability.

(1) If A and B are mutually exclusive events in the same finite sample space, then the $P(A \text{ or } B) = P(A) + P(B)$.

(2) If C is any event, then $P(\text{not } C) = 1 - P(C)$.

Now the solution in **Example 3b** can be explained by letting A = "the carton contains 0 defective bulbs," B = "the carton contains exactly 1 defective bulb," and C = "the carton contains more than 1 defective bulb."

In 4 and 5, a coin is flipped five times.

4. How many of the possible sequences of heads and tails have the given number of heads?
a. 0 1 **b.** 1 5 **c.** 2 10 **d.** 3 10 **e.** 4 5 **f.** 5 1

5. How many sequences of heads and tails are possible altogether? 32

6. Prove the Sum of Binomial Coefficients Theorem for the case when $n = 0$. See left.

6) If $n = 0$, then $2^0 = 1$ and $\sum_{k=0}^{0} \binom{0}{k} = \binom{0}{0} = \frac{0!}{0!\,0!} = 1$, so $\sum_{k=0}^{n} \binom{n}{k} = 2^n$ for $n = 0$.

7. Suppose a coin is weighted so that the probability of heads is .6. If the coin is tossed 10 times, give the probability of obtaining each.

a. 10 heads $\approx$ .0060 **b.** 9 heads $\approx$ .0403 **c.** 8 heads $\approx$ .1209 **d.** 7 heads $\approx$ .2150

8. Evaluate $\sum_{k=0}^{6} \binom{6}{k}$ without writing the terms and computing them. 64

Applying the Mathematics

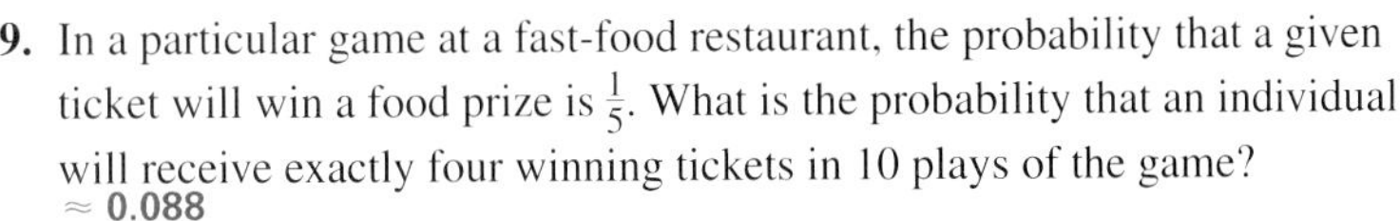

9. In a particular game at a fast-food restaurant, the probability that a given ticket will win a food prize is $\frac{1}{5}$. What is the probability that an individual will receive exactly four winning tickets in 10 plays of the game? $\approx$ 0.088

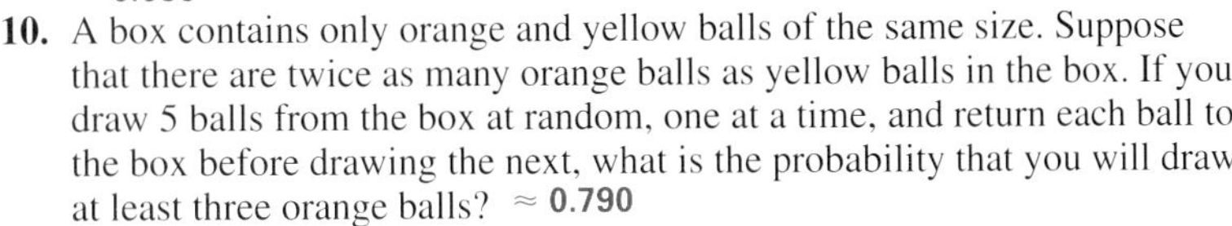

10. A box contains only orange and yellow balls of the same size. Suppose that there are twice as many orange balls as yellow balls in the box. If you draw 5 balls from the box at random, one at a time, and return each ball to the box before drawing the next, what is the probability that you will draw at least three orange balls? $\approx$ 0.790

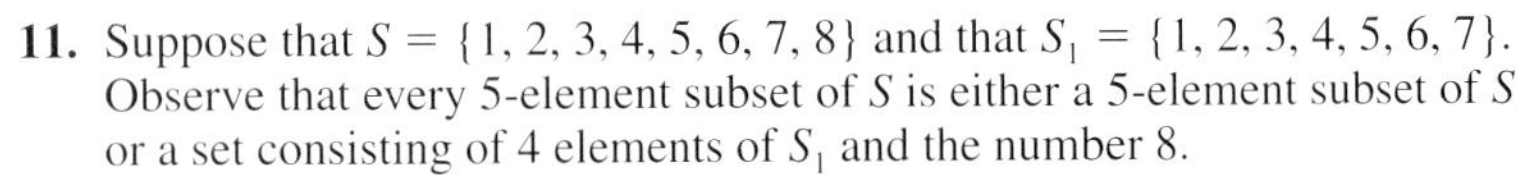

11. Suppose that $S = \{1, 2, 3, 4, 5, 6, 7, 8\}$ and that $S_1 = \{1, 2, 3, 4, 5, 6, 7\}$. Observe that every 5-element subset of S is either a 5-element subset of S_1 or a set consisting of 4 elements of S_1 and the number 8.

a. Use this observation to explain why $\binom{7}{5} + \binom{7}{4} = \binom{8}{5}$. See left.

b. Prove the identity $\binom{n}{r-1} + \binom{n}{r} = \binom{n+1}{r}$, for all positive integers n and r with $r \le n$, by interpreting both sides of the identity in terms of counting r-element subsets of certain sets. See left.

11a) The number of 5-element subsets of S_1 plus the number of 4-element subsets of S_1 is the number of 5-element subsets of S.

b) Let S be a set of $n + 1$ elements and let S_1 be a set of n of these elements. Then every r-element subset of S is either an r-element subset of S_1 or an $(r - 1)$-element subset of S_1 along with the leftover element not in S_1. So $\binom{n+1}{r} = \binom{n}{r} + \binom{n}{r-1}$.

12. Historians of mathematics usually give 1654 as the year in which the branch of mathematics called probability theory was born. That was the year in which a professional gambler, the Chevalier de Méré, posed several problems involving dice games to Pascal. One of the problems that de Méré discussed with Pascal was the following: Which is more likely to occur, (1) at least one 1 in a single roll of 4 dice, or (2) at least one pair of 1s in 24 rolls of two dice? Based on his experience as a gambler, de Méré believed that these outcomes were equally likely.

a. Think of a single roll of 4 dice as 4 successive rolls of a single die. Also, regard a roll of a single die as "good" if it comes up 1 and "defective" if it does not come up 1. Use the method of Example 3**b** to compute the probability of getting at least one 1 in a single roll of 4 dice.

b. Find the probability of rolling a pair of 1s in a single roll of a pair of dice. $\approx$ .0278

c. Compute the probability that out of 24 rolls of a pair of dice, at least one roll will result in a pair of 1s. $\approx$ .4914

d. Was de Méré's belief correct? No

a) $\approx$ .5177

Follow-up for Lesson 10-6

Practice

For more questions on SPUR Objectives, use **Lesson Master 10-6** (shown on page 635).

Assessment

Quiz A quiz covering Lessons 10-4 through 10-6 is provided in the *Assessment Sourcebook.*

Extension

Refer students to **Question 10.** Ask them to compute the probability of drawing at least three orange balls if the probability of drawing an orange ball is changed from $\frac{2}{3}$ to the following.

1. $\frac{1}{6}$ [$\approx$ 0.0355]
2. $\frac{1}{4}$ [$\approx$ 0.10312]
3. $\frac{1}{3}$ [$\approx$ 0.20988]
4. $\frac{1}{2}$ [0.5]
5. $\frac{3}{4}$ [$\approx$ 0.89648]
6. p [$6p^5 - 15p^4 + 10p^3$]

Project Update Project 3, *Extending Pascal's Triangle,* and Project 5, *Simulated Sampling,* on pages 649–650, relate to the content of this lesson.

Adapting to Individual Needs

Challenge

Have students answer the following.

1. Write a program for your calculator that will calculate the binomial probability when you input the number of trials, the number of successes, and the probability of success. [Answers may vary.]
2. How many times must a fair coin be tossed so that the probability of getting at least 2 heads is .9 or better? [7]
3. A batch of n items is known to contain r defectives. If a sample of k items is selected at random, find the probability that the sample has exactly 2 defectives. [$C(k, 2)\left(\frac{r}{m}\right)^2\left(1 - \left(\frac{r}{m}\right)\right)^{k-2}$]

Notes on Questions

Question 13 Relate this proof, which involves raising $(1 + -1)$ to the nth power, to the proof of the Sum of Binomial Coefficients Theorem, and to **Question 4** on page 631 of the previous lesson.

Question 14 Error Alert Some students will answer 32, forgetting that one of the subsets is the null set containing no letter.

Question 15 Ask students how they checked their result. Many will not have done so, and so this provides an opportunity to review substitution as a means of checking.

Question 16 Some calculators can only give estimates; others will give the exact answer 1,294,365,618.

Question 17 This ad, with the phrase, "Do the math" in the largest type, was repeated many times in Chicago area newspapers, indicating that someone felt that the result was particularly appealing.

Additional Answers

20.

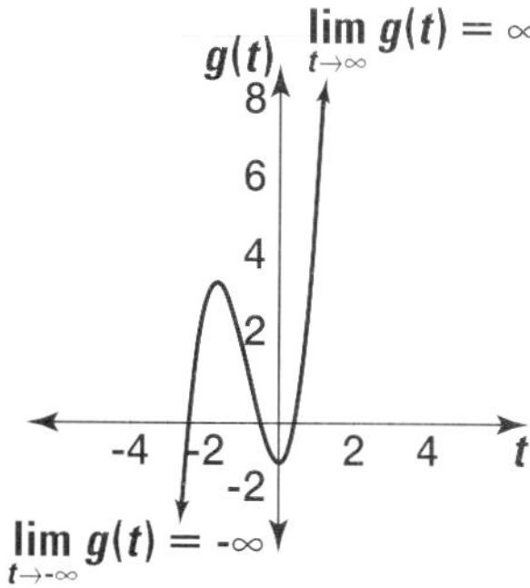

13) The expression $\binom{n}{0} - \binom{n}{1} + \binom{n}{2} - \binom{n}{3} + \ldots \pm \binom{n}{n}$ represents the coefficients of the expansion of $(x - y)^n$. Letting $x = y = 1$, we obtain $(x - y)^n = (1 - 1)^n = 0$, so the sum of the coefficients must be zero.

13. Prove that for each positive integer n,

$$\underbrace{\binom{n}{0} - \binom{n}{1} + \binom{n}{2} - \binom{n}{3} + \ldots + (-1)^n\binom{n}{n}}_{\text{positive and negative terms alternate}} = 0.$$

(Hint: Use the proof of the Sum of Binomial Coefficients Theorem as a guide.) **See left.**

14. On a certain test, a student may answer A, B, C, D, or E, or any combination of these choices. How many different answers are possible, assuming that each answer must include at least one letter? **31**

Review

15. Expand $(2a - b)^7$. *(Lesson 10-5)* $\mathbf{128a^7 - 448a^6b + 672a^5b^2 - 560a^4b^3 + 280a^3b^4 - 84a^2b^5 + 14ab^6 - b^7}$

16. The student body of a small high school consists of 52 tenth-graders, 47 eleventh-graders, and 43 twelfth-graders. A committee consisting of two representatives from each grade is to be formed. How many possible committees are there? *(Lessons 10-3, 10-4)* $\mathbf{1.2944 \times 10^9}$

17. A furniture store had an advertisement with the following lure:

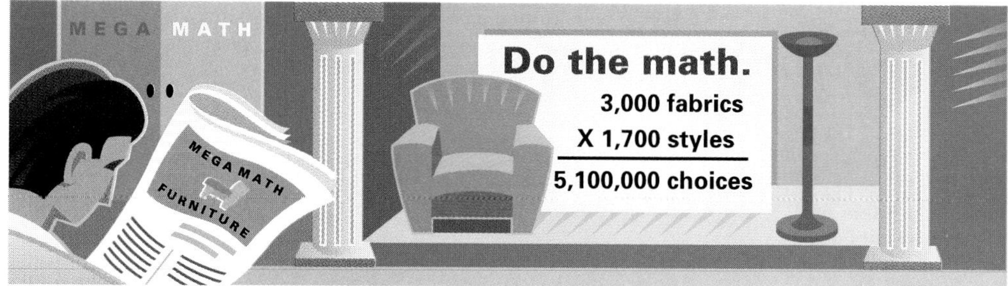

What must be true about the mixing of styles and fabrics in order for the store's mathematics to be correct? *(Lesson 10-2)* **Each style is available in 3000 fabrics.**

18. Let $f(x) = x^3 - 3x^2$. Use the fact that $f'(x) = 3x^2 - 6x$ to find the interval(s) on which f is increasing. *(Lesson 9-5)* **when $x < 0$ or $x > 2$**

19. a. Sketch the polar graph of the equation $r = 2 \sin 4\theta$. **See left.**

b. Identify the resulting curve. **eight-leafed rose curve**

c. Identify all lines and points of symmetry. *(Lesson 8-5)* **See left.**

20. Describe the end behavior of the polynomial function $g(t) = 2t^3 + 5t^2 - 1$ pictorially and in limit notation. *(Lesson 5-5)* **See margin.**

19a)

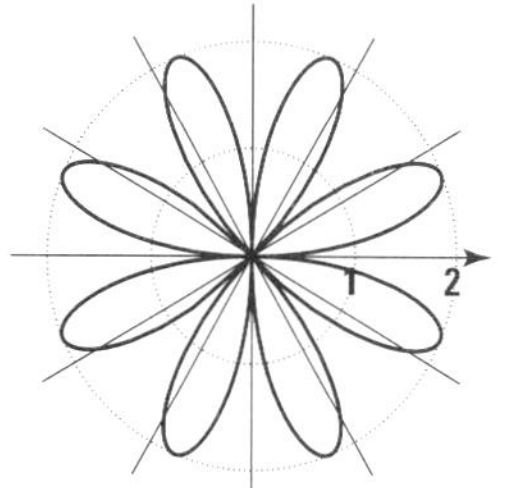

c) point symmetry; line symmetry with respect to $\theta = \frac{\pi}{8}, \frac{\pi}{4}, \frac{3\pi}{8}, \frac{\pi}{2}, \frac{5\pi}{8}, \frac{3\pi}{4}, \frac{7\pi}{8}, \pi$

Exploration

21. Conduct an experiment to test the theoretical results obtained in Question 12. How well do your results agree with theory? **Answers may vary.**

Setting Up Lesson 10-7

Do the In-class Activity on page 639.

Introducing Lesson 10-7

Expanding Powers of Trinomials

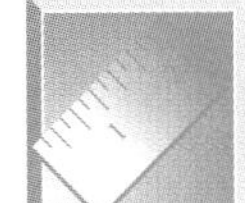

IN-CLASS ACTIVITY

A symbol manipulator is very helpful for this activity.

1–5) See margin.

1 **a.** By hand, expand $(x + y + z)^2$. Verify your result by letting $x = 2$, $y = 3$, and $z = 5$.
b. How many terms are in the expansion?

2 **a.** Consider three boxes labeled x, y, and z.

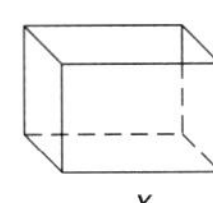

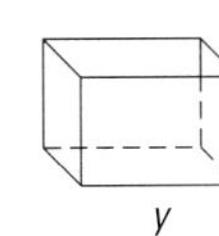

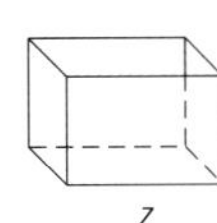

Identify the ways in which 2 identical balls can be placed in these three boxes. (Suggestion: Label a way "xz" if 1 ball is placed in x and 1 ball is placed in z. Label a way "y^2" if both balls are placed in y, and so on.)
b. In how many ways can the 2 balls be placed in these three boxes?
c. Explain why the way xz needs to be counted twice in the calculation for part **b**.
d. How are the ways in part 2**a** related to the expansion in part 1**a**?

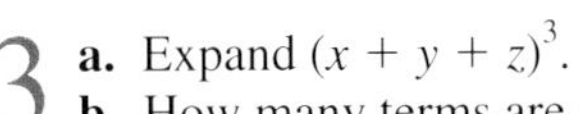

3 **a.** Expand $(x + y + z)^3$.
b. How many terms are in the expansion?
c. Use the expansion to identify all the ways in which 3 identical balls can be placed in three boxes x, y, and z.

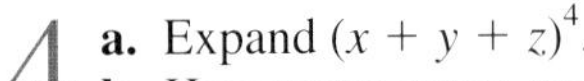

4 **a.** Expand $(x + y + z)^4$.
b. How many terms are in the expansion?
c. Use the expansion to identify the number of ways in which, given 4 identical balls, 2 can be placed in x and 2 in y.

5 **a.** Use the results of parts 1**a**, 3**a**, and 4**a** to conjecture about the number of terms in the expansion of $(x + y + z)^n$.
b. Check your conjecture for some value of n greater than 4.
c. How many terms are in the expansion of $(x + y + z)^{13}$?

In-class Activity

Resources

From the ***Teacher's Resource File***
- Answer Master 10-7

This activity sets up Lessons 10-7 and 10-8 with a counting situation.

Each term in the expansion of $(x + y)^n$ is of the form $C(n, r)x^ry^{n-r}$ and corresponds to a choice of the number r from the numbers 0 through n. Consider two boxes marked x and y in which n identical balls are placed. The number of terms tells us the number of different results. There are $n + 1$ terms. The coefficient $C(n, r)$ tells us how many ways each term can be achieved—the number of combinations.

Now each term is of the form $M(n, a_1, a_2)x^{a_1}y^{a_2}z^{n-a_1-a_2}$. Each term is the number of different ways of distributing a_1 balls in box x, a_2 balls in box y, and the remainder in box z. The number of terms is the number of different results. In Lesson 10-7, each different result is called a *combination with repetition,* or a *collection with repetition. The multinomial coefficient* $M(n, a_1, a_2)$ tells us in how many ways each term can be achieved.

It might be useful to identify each part of this activity with the number of collections with repetition, or with the multinomial coefficient. **Parts 2a, 3b, 4b, and 5a** ask for the number of terms in the expansion, so they are about combinations with repetition. **Parts 2b–d, 3c, and 4c** ask for the ways in which the terms can be achieved, so they are about multinomial coefficients.

Additional Answers

1. a. $(x + y + z)^2 = x^2 + 2xy + 2xz + y^2 + 2yz + z^2$.
If $x = 2$, $y = 3$, and $z = 5$:
$(2 + 3 + 5)^2 = (10)^2 = 100$;
$(2)^2 + 2(2)(3) + 2(2)(5) + (3)^2 + 2(3)(5) + (5)^2 = 100$
b. 6
2. a. $x^2, xy, xz, y^2, yz, z^2$
b. $x^2 + 2xy + 2xz + y^2 + 2yz + z^2 =$ 9 ways
c. Ball$_1$ in box x and ball$_2$ in box z or ball$_1$ in box z and ball$_2$ in box x
d. They are the variable parts of the expansion.
3. a. $x^3 + 3x^2y + 3x^2z + 3xy^2 + 6xyz + 3xz^2 + y^3 + 3y^2z + 3yz^2 + z^3$
b. 10
c. Same as part a
4. a. $x^4 + 4x^3y + 4x^3z + 6x^2y^2 + 12x^2yz + 6x^2z^2 + 4xy^3 + 12xy^2z + 12xyz^2 + 4xz^3 + y^4 + 4y^3z + 6y^2z^2 + 4yz^3 + z^4$
b. 15
c. 6
5. a. $\binom{n+2}{n}$
b. Sample: $(x + y + z)^6$ has $\binom{8}{6} = 28$ terms
c. 105

Lesson 10-7

Objectives

G Use combinations and the Binomial Theorem to solve counting problems.

Resources

From the ***Teacher's Resource File***

- Lesson Master 10-7
- Answer Master 10-7
- Teaching Aid 105 Warm-up

Additional Resources

- Visual for Teaching Aid 105
- Exploration 10-7

Teaching Lesson 10-7

Warm-up

Have students work with a partner to compare their answers to the questions in the In-class Activity on page 639.

Notes on Reading

❶ Because a set does not allow repeated elements, we use the term *collection with repetition* to refer to an ordered group of objects with repetition allowed. The collections on the middle of this page are denoted in alphabetical order but need not be so: *xyxz* refers to the same collection as *xxyz*. We also call them *combinations with repetition.*

LESSON 10-7 Combinations with Repetition

The following problems are related to the In-class Activity on the preceding page.

Problem 1: How many terms are there in the expansion of $(x + y + z)^{13}$?

Problem 2: Find the number of strings of 3 nonnegative integers whose sum is 13. (Two such strings are 3, 5, 5 and 9, 0, 4.)

While these two problems appear to be quite different, they happen to be equivalent. The appropriate counting technique can be developed by again using the Binomial Theorem.

Consider Problem 1. A term in the expansion of $(x + y + z)^{13}$ is obtained by selecting one of x or y or z from each of the 13 factors in $(x + y + z)^{13}$,

$$(x + y + z)(x + y + z)(x + y + z) \cdot \ldots \cdot (x + y + z),$$

and then taking their product. The order in which the *x*s, *y*s, and *z*s are selected is not important and the same letter can be selected more than once. A *collection* is like a combination with repetition. The order of the symbols makes no difference and the symbols can be repeated. So *abb* is the same collection as *bab*.

Therefore, each term in the expansion of $(x + y + z)^{13}$ corresponds to a collection of 13 letters selected from the three letters, x, y, z, *with repetition* allowed. Here are some examples.

❶

Term of $(x + y + z)^{13}$	Corresponding Collection
x^2yz^{10}	*xxyzzzzzzzzzz*
y^8z^5	*yyyyyyyyzzzzz*

Thus, counting the terms in the expansion of $(x + y + z)^{13}$ is equivalent to counting the number of collections of 13 letters selected from 3 letters with repetition.

Note that the variable part of each term in the expansion of $(x + y + z)^{13}$ is of the form $x^m y^n z^p$, where m, n, and p are nonnegative integers and $m + n + p = 13$. Therefore, the problem of finding the number of terms in the expansion of $(x + y + z)^{13}$ is also equivalent to the problem of finding the number of strings of 3 nonnegative integers which add to 13.

Still another problem equivalent to these is the following. Think of the exponent 13 as thirteen identical balls. Think of each variable x, y, and z as a box. Each distribution of all thirteen balls in the three boxes can be thought of as a term in the expansion of $(x + y + z)^{13}$. For instance, in the distribution pictured at the top of the next page, 3 balls are placed in box x, 5 in box y, and 5 in box z.

Lesson 10-7 Overview

Broad Goals This lesson provides the techniques for completing the last cell of the box introduced in the first lesson, situations involving the counting of sets of unordered symbols with repetition allowed.

Perspective The number of combinations of k elements that can be constructed from a set of n elements with repetition allowed is $\binom{k+n-1}{k}$, or equivalently, $\binom{k+n-1}{n-1}$. This kind of counting problem determines the number of terms in the expansion of a polynomial of n terms to the kth power, the number of strings of n nonnegative integers whose sum is k, and the number of ways of distributing k balls into n boxes. This lesson develops and applies the mathematics of these sorts of problems.

Optional Activities

Activity 1 Technology Connection
Materials: *Explorations* software

Students may use *Exploration 10-7, Combinations with Repetitions,* as an alternative to Problem 1 at the beginning of this lesson. Students can choose the number of terms and the power for a polynomial expansion. Sample combinations with repetition are shown as graphical examples and the formula for calculating the total number of terms is developed on the screen.

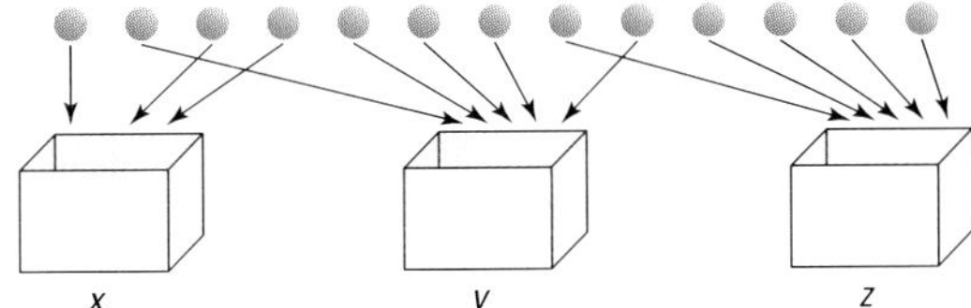

Therefore this distribution corresponds to the term $x^3y^5z^5$. Because the balls are identical, any distribution which places 3 balls in box x, 5 in box y, and 5 in box z also represents the term $x^3y^5z^5$. Therefore, the number of terms in the expansion of $(x + y + z)^{13}$ is the same as the number of ways of distributing 13 identical balls in 3 different boxes.

❷ The essential feature of the balls-in-boxes distribution is that only the number of balls to be placed in each box is important. The order in which the balls are placed is not important. A distribution of 13 balls in three different boxes can therefore be described by the following two steps.

Step 1: Decide how many balls are in the first box.
Step 2: Decide how many balls are in the second box.

The remaining balls must be in the third box.

The number of ways of carrying out these steps can be represented as follows. Let a "❍" represent each ball and arrange 13 of them in a row. Insert separators, represented by blanks, between the balls in box 1 and box 2 and between the balls in box 2 and box 3. Thus

❍❍❍❍ _ ❍❍❍❍❍ _ ❍❍❍❍

Step 1: insert separator — Step 2: insert separator

means placing 4 balls in box x, 5 in box y, and 4 balls in box z.

Thus there are 15 positions, 13 to be filled by a ball and 2 to remain blank. (The blanks can go on the ends; for example, starting with both blanks means box z gets all 13 balls.) So there are $\binom{15}{13}$ ways of taking 15 positions and choosing 13 to be filled with a ❍. So there are $\binom{15}{13}$ ways of placing 13 balls in 3 boxes. Think of 15 as $13 + 3 - 1$.

The preceding argument can be generalized as follows. To place r balls in n boxes, think of r positions for balls and $n - 1$ positions for blanks. The number of possible ways to place these balls is $\binom{r + (n-1)}{n}$.

Think of the three boxes in the preceding example as an n-element set, where $n = 3$. Think of the number of balls in each box as the number of times each box is selected. Then each different distribution of the 13 balls among the three boxes represents one r-element collection ($r = 13$) constructed from the n-element set. Thus the number of 13-element collections that can be constructed from a 3-element set is equal to $\binom{15}{13} = \binom{13 + (3-1)}{13} = \binom{r + (n-1)}{r}$, the number of ways 13 balls can be distributed among 3 boxes. This argument generalizes to be a proof of the theorem on page 642.

❷ This discussion is important in providing an understanding of the theorem that follows. Students need to see that if r objects are to be distributed among n boxes then decisions are only made for $n - 1$ boxes. The decision for the nth box is then determined because all r objects must be distributed. So $n - 1$ can be considered as the number of separators between the boxes, which can be represented as blanks. Hence, there are a total of $r + (n - 1)$ positions and r of these are to be taken. The number of ways this situation can occur is the combination given in the theorem.

Notice that because repetitions are allowed, r can be larger than n. In particular, in the situation of $(x + y + z)^{13}$, r = the number of balls = 13 and n = the number of boxes = 3.
Emphasize the equivalence of the following four problems:

1. the number of collections of r elements that can be constructed from a set of n elements with repetition allowed,
2. the number of terms in the expansion of a polynomial of n terms to the rth power,
3. the number of strings of n nonnegative integers whose sum is r, and
4. the number of ways of distributing r balls into n boxes.

The student who understands why these problems are equivalent has a deep understanding of this lesson. With this in mind, ask for the balls in boxes equivalent to Problems 1 and 2 that open this lesson. (How many ways can 13 balls be put into 3 boxes?) Then ask for the rewording of these in the language of the theorem. (How many 13-element collections can be constructed from a set of 3 elements with repetition allowed?)

Activity 2 Writing Have students formulate **Questions 13, 14, and 16** into all four equivalent types of problems discussed in the lesson. Often students will find that reformulation into one (or more) of the ways will make the most "sense" to them as they work these types of problems. [**Question 13:** the number of collections of 12 elements from a set of 5; the number of terms in the expansion of $(a + b + c + d + e)^{12}$; the number of strings of 5 nonnegative integers whose sum is 12; the number of ways of distributing 12 balls into 5 boxes.
Question 14: the number of collections of 3 elements from a set of 4; the number of terms in the expansion $(a + b + c + d)^3$; the number of strings of 4 nonnegative integers whose sum is 3; the number of ways of distributing 3 balls into 4 boxes.
Question 16: the number of collections of 4 elements from a set of 6; the number of elements in the expansion $(a + b + c + d + e + f)^4$; the number of strings of 6 nonnegative integers whose sum is 4; the number of ways of distributing 4 balls into 6 boxes.]

The most difficult aspect of this lesson for students is likely to be differentiating problems requiring the theorem and problems requiring the $C(n, r)$ Calculation Theorem from Lesson 10-4. Remind students that with typical combinations we do not allow repetition of symbols while in the balls and boxes interpretation we do. Thus, if the context of the application allows for repetition of elements, then the techniques of the current lesson may be required.

It is very useful to have a symbol manipulator in this lesson so that students can verify or see verified the number of terms in each expansion without you having to write them out.

Additional Examples

1. How many terms are in the expansion of $(a + b + c + d)^{12}$? $\binom{15}{12} = 455$; **think of four boxes denoted by *a*, *b*, *c*, *d*, and putting 12 balls into them**
2. In how many ways can 6 students new to a school be added to the numbers currently in 5 homerooms? $\binom{10}{6} = 210$; **think of the students as balls and the homerooms as boxes**

Theorem
Suppose that n and r are positive integers. The number of r-element collections with repetitions allowed that can be constructed from a set with n elements is given by

$$\binom{r + (n - 1)}{r}.$$

The expression $\binom{r + (n - 1)}{r}$ also gives the number of terms in the expansion of $(x_1 + \ldots + x_n)^r$. So, the expansion of $(x + y + z)^{13}$ has $\binom{13 + (3 - 1)}{13} = \binom{15}{13} = \frac{15 \cdot 14}{2} = 105$ terms.

Although the various representations used above are equivalent, usually one of them is more convenient or natural to use in a given application. The following problem illustrates a situation in which the balls-in-boxes model seems most appropriate.

Example

How many integers from 0 to 9999 have the property that the sum of their digits is 8? (Two of these integers are 125 and 7001.)

Solution

Every integer between 0 and 9999 can be expressed as a string of four digits from 0 through 9. Think of the positions in these strings of four digits as four boxes. Think of the digit d as d identical balls. For example, the digit 3 corresponds to 3 balls and the digit 7 corresponds to 7 balls. With this interpretation, every integer from 0 to 9999 whose digits add up to 8 corresponds to a distribution of 8 identical balls in 4 boxes. For example,

Integer with Digit Sum = 8	Distribution of 8 Balls in 4 Boxes
1 2 5	0, 1, 2, 5 balls
7 0 0 1	7, 0, 0, 1 balls

Therefore, according to the theorem, **the number of integers from 0 to 9999 whose digit sum is 8 is**

$$\binom{8 + 4 - 1}{8} = \binom{11}{8} = \frac{11 \cdot 10 \cdot 9}{3 \cdot 2} = 165.$$

You can use both the collections-with-repetitions model and the balls-in-boxes model to solve a variety of counting problems, as you will see in the Questions.

You have now encountered all four types of problems mentioned in the chart in Lesson 10-1: permutations (order matters) with or without repetition, and combinations (order does not matter) with or without repetition.

Adapting to Individual Needs

Extra Help

You might want to apply the discussion on page 639 to an expansion with which students are already familiar, such as $(x + y)^3 = x^3 + 3x^2y + 3xy^2 + y^3$. First relate this to balls and boxes: The number of terms in the expansion is the same as the number of ways 3 balls can be placed in 2 boxes.

Distribution of 3 balls in 2 boxes	Variable part of corresponding term
x: 3 balls, y: 0 balls	x^3
x: 2 balls, y: 1 ball	x^2y
x: 1 ball, y: 2 balls	xy^2
x: 0 balls, y: 3 balls	y^3

Then apply the theorem in this lesson. Here $n = 2$ and $r = 3$, so the number of terms is $\binom{r + (n - 1)}{r} = \binom{3 + (2 - 1)}{3} = \binom{4}{3} = 4$.

QUESTIONS

Covering the Reading

1. What is the answer to Problem 1 at the beginning of this lesson? **105**
2. What is the answer to Problem 2 at the beginning of this lesson? **105**
3. How many 7-element collections with repetitions allowed can be constructed by using the letters x, y, and z? **36**

In 4 and 5, write a 12-symbol collection consisting of 8 ❍s and 4 blanks to represent the distribution of 8 identical balls in 5 different boxes.

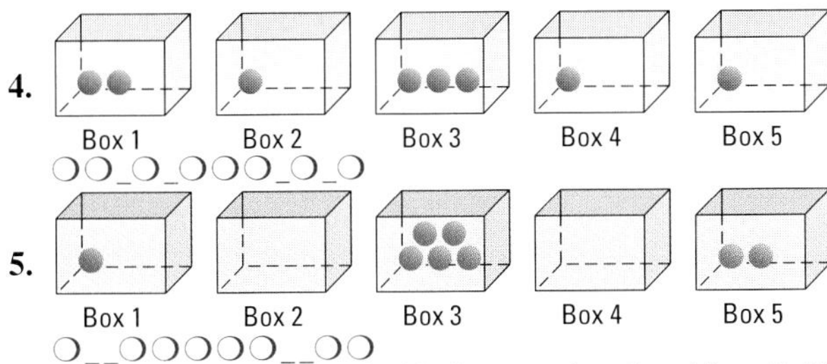

4. **❍❍_❍_❍❍❍_❍_❍**
5. **❍__❍❍❍❍❍__❍❍**

In 6–8, suppose that 8 identical balls are to be placed into 5 different boxes. How many balls are in each box?

6. ❍_❍_❍_❍❍_❍❍❍ **1, 1, 1, 2, 3**
7. _❍❍❍_❍❍_❍❍❍_ **0, 3, 2, 3, 0**
8. ❍__❍❍❍_❍❍❍_❍ **1, 0, 3, 3, 1**
9. In how many ways can 8 balls be placed in 5 boxes? **495**
10. How many different terms are in the expansion of the trinomial power $(a + b + c)^9$? **55**
11. How many different terms are in the expansion of $(x_1 + x_2 + x_3 + x_4 + x_5)^{11}$? **1365**
12. How many integers from 1 to 9999 have the property that the sum of their digits is 6? **84**

Applying the Mathematics

13. The Tastee Donut Shoppe charges $3.00 for its Mix N' Match Selection that allows you to select a dozen doughnuts from among the following varieties: plain, maple frosted, chocolate, glazed, and French. How many different Mix 'N' Match Selections are possible? **1820**
14. Fill in the blanks. The number of terms in the expansion of $(w + x + y + z)^5$ equals the number of strings of _?_ nonnegative integers with the sum _?_. **4, 5**

Notes on Questions

Questions 4–8 These questions test understanding of the balls-in-boxes model and should be carefully covered.

Questions 9–13 These questions sample the variety of situations that can be treated as combinations with repetition.

Question 12 Error Alert Students may need help interpreting this situation in the language of this lesson. It is useful to think of six balls to be placed into 4 boxes, representing the four digits of a number between 1 and 9999. If box 1 gets 3 balls, box 2 gets no ball, box 3 gets 1 ball, and box 4 gets 2 balls, then the number is 3012.

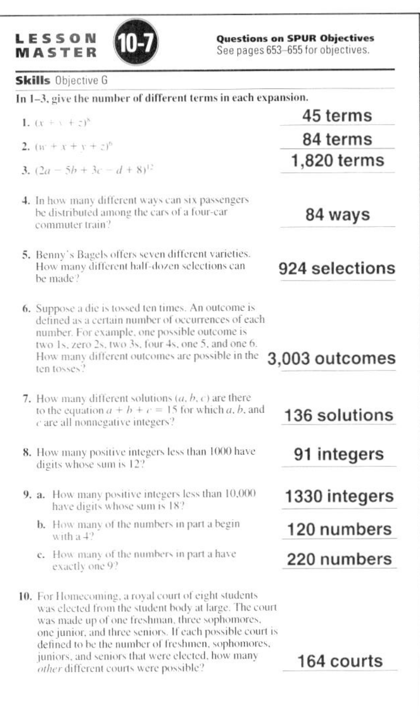

LESSON MASTER 10-7 — **Questions on SPUR Objectives** See pages 653–655 for objectives.

Skills Objective G

In 1–3, give the number of different terms in each expansion.

1. $(x + y + z)^8$ — **45 terms**
2. $(w + x + y + z)^6$ — **84 terms**
3. $(2a - 5b + 3c - d + 8)^{12}$ — **1,820 terms**
4. In how many different ways can six passengers be distributed among the cars of a four-car commuter train? **84 ways**
5. Benny's Bagels offers seven different varieties. How many different half-dozen selections can be made? **924 selections**
6. Suppose a die is tossed ten times. An outcome is defined as a certain number of occurrences of each number. For example, one possible outcome is two 1s, zero 2s, two 3s, four 4s, one 5, and one 6. How many different outcomes are possible in the ten tosses? **3,003 outcomes**
7. How many different solutions (a, b, c) are there to the equation $a + b + c = 15$ for which a, b, and c are all nonnegative integers? **136 solutions**
8. How many positive integers less than 1000 have digits whose sum is 12? **91 integers**
9. a. How many positive integers less than 10,000 have digits whose sum is 18? **1330 integers**
   b. How many of the numbers in part a begin with a 4? **120 numbers**
   c. How many of the numbers in part a have exactly one 9? **220 numbers**
10. For Homecoming, a royal court of eight students was elected from the student body at large. The court was made up of one freshman, three sophomores, one junior, and three seniors. If each possible court is defined to be the number of freshmen, sophomores, juniors, and seniors that were elected, how many *other* different courts were possible? **164 courts**

Notes on Questions

Question 18 Treat this situation as a binomial experiment. Since the number of circuit boards is finite, the actual distribution, as noted in the previous lesson, is hypergeometric.

Follow-up for Lesson 10-7

Practice

For more questions on SPUR Objectives, use **Lesson Master 10-7** (shown on page 643).

Assessment

Written Communication Give students another problem like **Question 10 or 11.** Have students do the following three things.

1. Give the related balls-and-boxes problem.
2. Explain one possible distribution and tell the variable part of the corresponding term.
3. Find the total number of terms in the expansion.

[Students apply their understanding of combinations with repetition to count the number of terms in the expansion of a multinomial.]

Extension

Project Update Project 1, *Integer Partitions,* and Project 2, *Card Game Odds,* on page 649, relate to the content of this lesson.

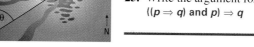

15. In a game at a school fair, a $1 ticket at the fishing pool allows the participant to choose three prizes from four bags, each of which contains a different type of prize. Any combination of selections is acceptable. That is, all selections can be made from the same bag, two can be made from one bag and one from a different bag, or all three can be made from different bags. How many different selections are possible? **20**

16. Suppose four identical dice are rolled. Define an outcome to be a particular collection of four numbers that come up on the four dice. For example, 2, 1, 5, 2 is the same outcome as 1, 2, 2, 5, but not the same as 2, 1, 6, 1. How many different outcomes are possible? **126**

17. How many different solutions (w, x, y, z) of the equation $w + x + y + z = 20$ are there for which w, x, y, and z are all nonnegative integers? **1771**

Review

18. Suppose that 0.5% of the circuit boards produced on a certain assembly line are defective. If a sample of 100 circuit boards are selected at random to be tested, what is the probability that at least one of them will be defective? *(Lesson 10-6)* **≈ .394**

19. Find the coefficient of x^3y^5 in the expansion of $(2x + y)^8$. *(Lesson 10-5)* **448**

20. Find the number of committees which can be formed from a group of 25 people if each committee must contain at least 5 members, but no more than 8 members. *(Lesson 10-4)* **1,792,505**

21. Consider the word *boxes.*

a. How many permutations of the letters of *boxes* are there? **120**

b. How many permutations of the letters in *boxes* end in a vowel? *(Lesson 10-3)* **48**

22. Let f be the function defined by $f(x) = x^3 + 4$. Find the average rate of change of f from $x = 2$ to $x = 3$. *(Lesson 9-1)* **19**

23. Evaluate $\sum_{k=1}^{\infty} 4\left(\frac{3}{5}\right)^{k-1}$. *(Lesson 7-6)* **10**

24. A ship is on a bearing such that its position after 1 hour is 30 miles east of its starting position. Express the bearing, θ, as a function of the ship's northerly distance from its original location. *(Lesson 6-7)* $\theta = \tan^{-1}\frac{30}{d}$

25. Write the argument form for *modus ponens.* *(Lesson 1-6)* $((p \Rightarrow q) \text{ and } p) \Rightarrow q$

Exploration

26. a. As in Question 5, count the number of different distributions of 5 identical balls into 3 different boxes for which each box contains at least one ball. **6**

b. Use the model to count the number of different distributions of 15 identical balls into 7 different boxes for which each box contains at least one ball. **3003**

c. Find a formula for the number of distributions of r identical balls into n different boxes for which each box contains at least one ball. **See left**

26c) A general formula is $\binom{r-1}{r-n}$.

644

Setting Up Lesson 10-8

For each of the problems in which the number of terms of a multinomial expansion is asked, emphasize that we have not in this lesson determined the coefficients of the terms. That is the subject of Lesson 10-8.

LESSON

10-8

Multinomial Coefficients

To expand a power of a trinomial or other polynomial, such as $(x + y + z)^{13}$, you need to know the terms of the expansion and the coefficients of each term. The last lesson showed that there are 105 terms in the expansion of $(x + y + z)^{13}$. The variable part of each term contains $x^a y^b z^c$, where a, b, and c are nonnegative integers and $a + b + c = 13$. But this is not enough to expand $(x + y + z)^{13}$ because the coefficients of the terms were not mentioned. These coefficients are called *multinomial coefficients*. In this lesson, you will see how to determine these coefficients.

As with binomial coefficients, there is a combinatorial interpretation to multinomial coefficients. Write out $(x + y + z)^{13}$ as a product of 13 factors.

$$\underbrace{(x + y + z)(x + y + z)(x + y + z) \cdot \ldots \cdot (x + y + z)}_{13 \text{ factors}}$$

The expansion is found by choosing an x, y, or z from each factor, multiplying them, and adding the products. The sum of the exponents of x, y, and z is 13 in each term because there are 13 factors. Now consider a particular term, for instance, the one with $x^6y^2z^5$. This term arises when x is chosen 6 times, y 2 times, and z 5 times. The coefficient of $x^6y^2z^5$ is the number of different ways in which this set of choices can be made.

To calculate this number, note that the 6 xs can be selected from the 13 factors in $\binom{13}{6}$ ways. There are now 7 factors remaining, so the 2 ys can be selected in $\binom{7}{2}$ ways. This leaves 5 factors from which to choose the 5 zs, and this can be done in only $\binom{5}{5} = 1$ way. Since the selections are made one after the other, by the Multiplication Counting Principle the total number of selections is the product of these three combinations, $\binom{13}{6} \cdot \binom{7}{2} \cdot \binom{5}{5}$.

In doing the actual calculation of this product, many of the factorials appear in both the numerator and denominator. So what seems to be a difficult calculation is not at all complicated.

$$\binom{13}{6}\binom{7}{2}\binom{5}{5} = \frac{13!}{6!7!} \cdot \frac{7!}{2!5!} \cdot \frac{5!}{5!0!} = \frac{13!}{6!2!5!}$$

Thus the coefficient of $x^6y^2z^5$ in the expansion of $(x + y + z)^{13}$ is $\frac{13!}{6!2!5!}$. You can see how the power of the polynomial and the exponents of the term are related to the factorials in the coefficient. The pattern is that simple.

> **Theorem**
> Let k and n be positive integers. In the expansion of $(x_1 + x_2 + \ldots + x_k)^n$, the coefficient of $x_1^{a_1}x_2^{a_2} \ldots x_k^{a_k}$ is $\frac{n!}{a_1!a_2! \ldots a_k!}$.

Lesson 10-8

Objectives

There are no SPUR objectives for any reading lesson.

Resources

From the ***Teacher's Resource File***
- Answer Master 10-8
- Teaching Aid 105: Warm-up

Additional Resources
- Visual for Teaching Aid 105

Teaching Lesson 10-8

Warm-up

1. According to the work in Lesson 10-7, how many terms are in the expansion of $(x + y + z)^4$?
   $C(6, 4) = 15$
2. $(x + y + z)^2 = x^2 + y^2 + z^2 + 2xy + 2xz + 2yz$. Square this six-term polynomial to obtain the full expansion of $(x + y + z)^4$.
   $\mathbf{x^4 + y^4 + z^4 + 4x^3y + 4x^3z + 4y^3x + 4y^3z + 4z^3x + 4z^3y + 6x^2y^2 + 6x^2z^2 + 6y^2z^2 + 12x^2yz + 12xy^2z + 12xyz^2}$

Notes on Reading

The word *multinomial* refers to any polynomial with more than one term; thus binomials and trinomials are multinomials. The *Multinomial Theorem* is that $(x_1 + x_2 + \ldots + x_k)^n = \sum\left(\frac{n!}{a_1!a_2! \ldots a_k!}\right)x_1^{a_1}x_2^{a_2} \ldots x_k^{a_k}$, where the summation ranges over all nonnegative integers a_i such that $a_1 + a_2 + \ldots + a_k = n$. We did not state the theorem in this lesson

Lesson 10-8 Overview

Broad Goals This lesson completes the task begun in Lesson 10-8, namely that of raising the multinomial $x_1 + x_2 + \ldots + x_k$ to the nth power. In Lesson 10-7, the number of terms was found. In this lesson, the coefficient of each term is derived.

Perspective The Binomial Theorem indicates that $(x + y)^n$ has $n + 1$ terms, each with variables of the form x^ky^{n-k}, and that the coefficient of the term x^ky^{n-k} is $\binom{n}{k}$. A natural generalization is to the expansion of the multinomial $(x_1 + x_2 + \ldots + x_k)^n$. Each term in the expansion has variables of the form $x_1^{a_1}x_2^{a_2} \ldots x_k^{a_k}$, where $a_1 + a_2 + \ldots + a_k = n$. We found the number of terms in Lesson 10-7 to be $\binom{k+n-1}{k}$. The coefficient of this term, $\frac{n!}{a_1!a_2! \ldots a_k!}$, is the number of permutations from a set with n elements of k different kinds, a_1 of one kind, a_2 of a second kind, ..., a_k of the kth kind. Much of this lesson is devoted to seeing the equivalence of the problem of the power of the multinomial and this number of permutations.

using this sort of summation because it would take some time to explain, but you should do so if you think it appropriate for your class.

❶ The power of the multinomial theorem is shown with the expansion of $(x + y + z)^4$. Even with a small number of terms (3) and a small exponent (4), the expansion is not easy, but by combining the theorem at the bottom of page 645 with the theorem from the last lesson, the power can be expanded.

Point out that the lesson discusses the number of permutations using *all* the letters of the word PROPORTION. The number of permutations using some of these letters is a more difficult question.

Error Alert When expanding a multinomial completely, have students first determine the number of terms using the theorem in the last lesson. This may prevent their inadvertently skipping some terms.

The general proof of this theorem requires mathematical induction. Here is a proof of the special case $k = 4$ without induction. The coefficient of $x_1^{a_1}x_2^{a_2}x_3^{a_3}x_4^{a_4}$ in the expansion of $(x_1 + x_2 + x_3 + x_4)^n$ is equal to the number of choices in the following counting problem. A set has n elements. You wish to choose a_1 of them. Then from the remaining $n - a_1$ you choose a_2. Then from the $n - a_1 - a_2$ that remain after this second choice, you choose a_3. Lastly, from the $n - a_1 - a_2 - a_3$ that remain after the third choice, you choose a_4. The number of ways to make these four selections is

$$\binom{n}{a_1}\cdot\binom{n-a_1}{a_2}\cdot\binom{n-a_1-a_2}{a_3}\cdot\binom{n-a_1-a_2-a_3}{a_4}$$

$$= \frac{n!}{a_1!(n-a_1)!}\cdot\frac{(n-a_1)!}{a_2!(n-a_1-a_2)!}\cdot\frac{(n-a_1-a_2)!}{a_3!(n-a_1-a_2-a_3)!}\cdot\frac{(n-a_1-a_2-a_3)!}{a_4!(n-a_1-a_2-a_3-a_4)!}$$

$$= \frac{n!}{a_1!a_2!a_3!a_4!}$$

since $(n - a_1 - a_2 - a_3 - a_4)! = 0! = 1$.

❶ Notice now how what you have learned in this and the previous lessons makes it possible to expand any polynomial to any power. For instance, by the Theorem on page 642, $(x + y + z)^4$ has 15 terms. The coefficients and variable parts of those terms can be determined by the Theorem on page 645. Here is the complete expansion.

$$\begin{aligned}(x+y+z)^4 &= \tfrac{4!}{4!}x^4 + \tfrac{4!}{3!1!}x^3y + \tfrac{4!}{3!1!}x^3z + \tfrac{4!}{2!2!}x^2y^2 + \tfrac{4!}{2!1!1!}x^2yz + \\ &\quad \tfrac{4!}{2!2!}x^2z^2 + \tfrac{4!}{1!3!}xy^3 + \tfrac{4!}{1!2!1!}xy^2z + \tfrac{4!}{1!1!2!}xyz^2 + \tfrac{4!}{1!3!}xz^3 + \\ &\quad \tfrac{4!}{4!}y^4 + \tfrac{4!}{3!1!}y^3z + \tfrac{4!}{2!2!}y^2z^2 + \tfrac{4!}{1!3!}yz^3 + \tfrac{4!}{4!}z^4 \\ &= x^4 + 4x^3y + 4x^3z + 6x^2y^2 + 12x^2yz + 6x^2z^2 + 4xy^3 + \\ &\quad 12xy^2z + 12xyz^2 + 4xz^3 + y^4 + 4y^3z + 6y^2z^2 + 4yz^3 + z^4\end{aligned}$$

A problem equivalent to the multinomial coefficient problem is the problem of determining the number of permutations of a string when some of the n objects are alike. (Until now all the permutations you have seen have been from a set of different objects.) For instance, how many distinguishable permutations are there of the letters of *PROPORTION*?

You can think of this problem as being like that of determining the coefficient of $INO^3P^2R^2T$ in the expansion of $(I + N + O + P + R + T)^{10}$. That is, we want to know the number of different arrangements of 1 I, 1 N, 3 Os, 2 Ps, 2 Rs, and a T. There are $\binom{10}{1}$ possible locations for the I. Then once the I has been located, there are $\binom{9}{1}$ locations for the N. Then there are $\binom{8}{3}$ locations for the three Os, $\binom{5}{2}$ locations for the two Ps, $\binom{3}{2}$ locations for the two Rs, and finally the last location in $\binom{1}{1}$ way for the T. The product is

$$\binom{10}{1}\binom{9}{1}\binom{8}{3}\binom{5}{2}\binom{3}{2}\binom{1}{1} = \frac{10!}{1!1!3!2!2!1!} = 151{,}200.$$

Optional Activities

Refer to **Question 7.** Ask students how many six digit license plate numbers have two occurrences of one digit, two occurrences of another, and two occurrences of a third. [64800] Then ask if they would expect the probability of this event to be greater or smaller than the event in the text. [The probability is greater, 0.0648.] Ask them how many six digit license plate numbers have six different digits and find the probability of this event. They may find it smaller than they expected! [151200; the probability is 0.1512.]

Some people prefer another way to analyze this problem. Let x be the number of distinguishable permutations of the letters of *PROPORTION*. If the three *O*s in *PROPORTION* are labeled as O_1, O_2, and O_3, then there are 3! as many distinguishable permutations. Similarly, if the *P*s are labeled P_1 and P_2, the number of permutations would be multiplied by 2!, and if the *R*s are labeled R_1 and R_2, the number of permutations is again multiplied by 2!. The result is the same as dealing with the number of permutations of the word $P_1R_1O_1P_2O_2R_2TIO_3N$, with 10 distinct letters. There are 10! permutations of $P_1R_1O_1P_2O_2R_2TIO_3N$, so $x \cdot 3! \cdot 2! \cdot 2! = 10!$. This implies that $x = \frac{10!}{3!2!2!}$, the same value as found by the multinomial coefficient analysis. The letters that appear only once in *PROPORTION* do not affect the number of permutations; according to the analysis, each of them could be considered as multiplying the denominator by 1!, which does not change the value of the denominator.

QUESTIONS

Covering the Reading

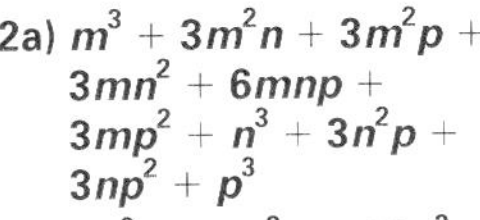

2a) $m^3 + 3m^2n + 3m^2p + 3mn^2 + 6mnp + 3mp^2 + n^3 + 3n^2p + 3np^2 + p^3$

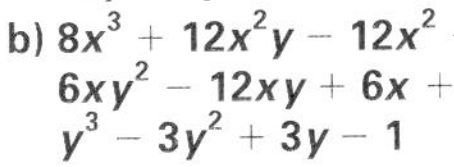

b) $8x^3 + 12x^2y - 12x^2 + 6xy^2 - 12xy + 6x + y^3 - 3y^2 + 3y - 1$

1. Consider the expansion of $(x + y + z)^5$.
   a. How many terms are in this expansion? **21**
   b. What is the coefficient of x^2y^3 in this expansion? **10**

2. a. Expand $(m + n + p)^3$ completely. **See left.**
   b. Apply your answer to part **a** to expand $(2x + y - 1)^3$. **See left.**

3. a. How many distinct permutations are there of the letters of the word *NONILLION*? **7560**
   b. What is a nonillion? **10^{30}**

4. A biology class has 12 microscopes. Four of these are identical and of one type, two are identical and of a second type, and six are identical and of a third type. In how many distinct ways can these microscopes be placed on 12 lab desks? **13,860**

5. Prove the theorem of this lesson for the special case $k = 3$. You may assume that the problem is equivalent to a counting problem. **See margin.**

6. Discuss the theorem of this lesson for the special case $k = 2$. **See left.**

6) For $k = 2$, in the expansion of $(x + y)^n$, the coefficient of $x^{n-r}y^r$ is $\frac{n!}{(n-r)!\,r!} = \binom{n}{r}$, which is a restatement of the Binomial Theorem.

7. While driving, Laronda noticed that the license plate of the car ahead of her had the number 226266, with three occurrences of one digit and three occurrences of another.
   a. How many six-digit numbers have this property? (Hint: First you need to determine how many pairs of digits are possible.) **900**
   b. What is the probability that a randomly selected 6-digit number has this property? **0.0009**

Notes on Questions

Question 2b The answer can be checked by multiplying $(2x + y - 1)(2x + y - 1)(2x + y - 1)$. Or let $x = 3$ and $y = 2$. The values of the given expression and the answer are both 343.

Question 7a Here we assume that a 6-digit "number," being on a license plate, can begin with zeros. In some states, there are licenses such as 0648 which are different from 648.

Additional Answers

5. The coefficient of $x_1^{a_1}x_2^{a_2}x_3^{a_3}$ in the expansion of $(x_1 + x_2 + x_3)^n$ is equal to the number of choices in the following counting problem. A set has n elements. You wish to choose a_1 of them. Then, from the remaining $n - a_1$, you choose a_2. Then, from the $n - a_1 - a_2$ that remains, you choose a_3 The number of ways to make the 3 selections is

$$\binom{n}{a_1} \cdot \binom{n-a_1}{a_2} \cdot \binom{n-a_1-a_2}{a_3} = \frac{n!}{a_1!(n-a_1)!} \cdot \frac{(n-a_1)!}{a_2!(n-a_1-a_2)!} \cdot \frac{(n-a_1-a_2)!}{a_3!(n-a_1-a_2-a_3)!} = \frac{n!}{a_1!a_2!a_3!},$$ **since**

$$(n - a_1 - a_2 - a_3)! = 0! = 1.$$

Adapting to Individual Needs

Extra Help

Some students may have difficulty listing all the different variable parts in the terms of an expansion. Spend some time discussing the systematic method used in the expansion of $(x + y + z)^4$. The terms are written in order with the powers of x decreasing. Then for terms with the same power of x, the powers of y decrease. The powers of z are determined by the powers of x and y since the three exponents must always add up to 4.

Challenge

Have students expand $(x + 1 + 2i)^5$ using the Binomial Theorem with $y = 1 + 2i$, and using the Multinomial Theorem. Have them check that they get the same results. Then ask which they find easier. [There are 21 terms; answers will vary about which one is easier.]

Notes on Questions

Question 9 Since jelly beans are normally taken from a bowl to be eaten, it is assumed that there are at least 8 jelly beans of each color.

Question 12 The answer given in scientific notation on some calculators is the exact answer.

Follow-up for Lesson 10-8

Extension

Project Update Project 2, *Card Game Odds,* on page 649, relates to the content of this lesson.

Additional Answers

14. $s(1)$: $a_1 = c$, so a_1 is divisible by c.
$s(2)$: $a_2 = c$, so a_2 is divisible by c.
Assume $s(k)$: a_k is divisible by c, for all $k \le n$.
Then $a_{k+1} = a_k - 4a_{k-1}$
$= cq - 4cp$ for some integers p and q
$= c(q - 4p)$,
where $q - 4p$ is an integer.
So a_{k+1} is divisible by c.
So $s(k) \Rightarrow s(k+1)$, and, therefore by the Strong Form of Mathematical Induction, every term is divisible by c.

8a) Think of the exponent 6 as 6 identical balls. Think of the variables x, y, z, and w as boxes. Each distribution of all 6 balls in the four boxes can be thought of as a term in the expansion of $(x + y + z + w)^6$.

8b) Suppose that S is the set $\{x, y, z, w\}$. The number of 6-element collections selected from these 4 elements of S gives the number of terms in the expansion of $(x + y + z + w)^6$.

15a) It is one less than the degree of $p(x)$.
b) $p(x) = (3x + 2)d(x) + x + 2$, so some samples are:

$d(x)$	$p(x)$
x	$3x^2 + 3x + 2$
x^2	$3x^3 + 2x^2 + x + 2$
$x + 5$	$3x^2 + 18x + 12$

Review

8. Consider the problem of finding the number of terms in the expansion of $(x + y + z + w)^6$. **a, b) See left.**
a. Explain how it is equivalent to counting ways of distributing identical balls in boxes.
b. Explain how it is equivalent to counting collections of symbols.
c. How many terms are there in the expansion of $(x + y + z + w)^6$? *(Lesson 10-7)* **84**

9. A bowl contains red, orange, yellow, purple, and green jelly beans. In how many different ways can 8 jelly beans be taken from the bowl? *(Lesson 10-7)* **495**

10. Suppose that 2% of all clovers in a field are four-leaved. What is the probability that out of 40 clovers picked at random, at least two will be four-leaved? *(Lesson 10-6)* **≈ 0.19**

11. A photo is to be taken of 5 tall people and 8 average people standing in a line. If the tall people are to stand together in the middle with 4 average people on each side, in how many different ways can the people be arranged? *(Lessons 10-2, 10-3)* **4,838,400**

12. A phone number consists of a three-digit area code, a three-digit exchange number, and then four more digits. The first digit of the area code cannot be 0 or 1, the first digit of the exchange number cannot be 0 or 1, and the exchange number cannot end in 11 or be 555. If those are the only restrictions on telephone numbers, how many are possible? *(Lesson 10-2)* **6,328,000,000**

13. Let $[r, \theta]$ and (x, y) represent the same point in the fourth quadrant. If $r = 6$ and $x = 4$, find θ and y. *(Lesson 8-2)* **$y \approx -4.47$; $\theta \approx 5.44$**

14. Let c be an integer. Prove that every term of the sequence defined by

$$\begin{cases} a_1 = c \\ a_2 = c \\ a_{k+1} = a_k - 4a_{k-1} & \text{for integers } k \ge 2 \end{cases}$$

is divisible by c. *(Lesson 7-7)* **See margin.**

15. When a polynomial $p(x)$ is divided by a polynomial $d(x)$, the quotient is $3x + 2$ and the remainder is $x + 2$.
a. What do you know about the degree of $d(x)$?
b. Find possible formulas for $p(x)$ and $d(x)$. *(Lesson 4-3)*
a, b) See left.

Exploration

16. In the word *nonillion*, the subject of Question 3, every letter that appears occurs more than once. Find at least three other English words with this property and calculate the number of distinct permutations of their letters.

Samples: deed: $\frac{4!}{2!\,2!} = 6$ tomtom: $\frac{6!}{2!\,2!\,2!} = 90$
noon: $\frac{4!}{2!\,2!} = 6$ deeded: $\frac{6!}{3!\,3!} = 20$

Possible Responses, page 649

1. Sample: There are 11 partitions of the number 6:

6	2 + 2 + 2
1 + 5	1 + 1 + 1 + 3
2 + 4	1 + 1 + 2 + 2
3 + 3	1 + 1 + 1 + 1 + 2
1 + 1 + 4	1 + 1 + 1 + 1 + 1 + 1
1 + 2 + 3	

There are 15 partitions of the number 7:

7	1 + 1 + 1 + 4
1 + 6	1 + 1 + 2 + 3
2 + 5	1 + 2 + 2 + 2
3 + 4	1 + 1 + 1 + 1 + 3
1 + 1 + 5	1 + 1 + 1 + 2 + 2
1 + 2 + 4	1 + 1 + 1 + 1 + 1 + 2
1 + 3 + 3	1 + 1 + 1 + 1 + 1 + 1 + 1
2 + 2 + 3	

The following program is an example of a method which generates partitions of n in increasing length, in dictionary order for each fixed length.

```
10  REM PARTITIONING INTEGERS
    PROGRAM
20  DIM P(100)
30  INPUT "ENTER A POSITIVE
    INTEGER TO PARTITION:";N
40  PRINT
```

A project presents an opportunity for you to extend your knowledge of a topic related to the material of this chapter. You should allow more time for a project than you do for a typical homework question.

1 Integer Partitions

The number 5 has the following positive integer *partitions*:

1 + 1 + 1 + 1 + 1
1 + 1 + 1 + 2
1 + 1 + 3
1 + 2 + 2
1 + 4
2 + 3
5

In general, a **partition** of a positive integer n is a finite sequence of positive integers whose sum is n. Investigate the number of partitions of any positive integer n.

2 Card Game Odds

Combinations can be used to analyze card games such as poker and bridge. These games are played with a deck of 52 cards. There are four *suits*: hearts ♥, diamonds ♦, clubs ♣, and spades ♠. Each suit has one card of each of the following *ranks*: 2, 3, 4, 5, 6, 7, 8, 9, 10, *J, Q, K, A*. A *poker hand* is any set of 5 cards. A *bridge hand* has 13 cards. The order in which the cards in a poker or bridge hand are dealt is unimportant. Many almanacs contain information on the number of possible poker and bridge hands of particular types and/or the odds against obtaining such hands. Pick one of these games. Use your knowledge of counting techniques to determine how these numbers were calculated.

3 Extending Pascal's Triangle

You know that Pascal's triangle represents the coefficients of $(x + y)^n$. The variable portions can also be included in the triangle to obtain the figure at the right.

$$\mathbf{1}$$
$$\mathbf{1x + 1y}$$
$$\mathbf{1x^2 + 2xy + 1y^2}$$

To illustrate the terms of $(x + y + z)^n$, a tetrahedron can be used. The top layer is a single 1. The second layer, which corresponds to $(x + y + z)^1$, is shown below at the left. The third layer is shown below at the right.

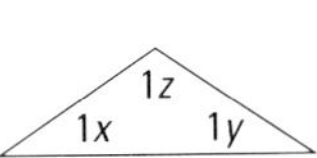

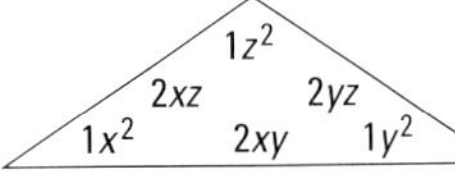

The variable portions of the fourth layer, representing $(x + y + z)^3$, are shown below.

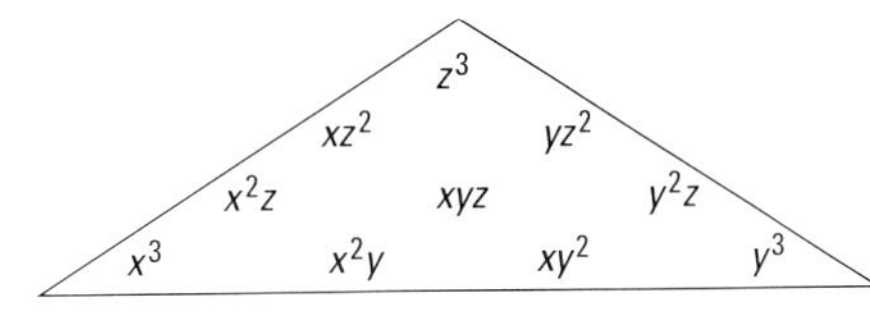

a. Fill in the coefficients of the terms of the fourth layer.
b. Find the fifth and sixth layers.
c. Describe some of the patterns that occur.
d. Make a 3-dimensional model of the first few layers.
e. Find Pascal's triangle in the tetrahedron. It appears in several places. Explain why.

Chapter 10 Projects

The projects relate chiefly to the content of the lessons of this chapter as follows:

Project	Lesson(s)
1	10-1, 10-7
2	10-4, 10-7, 10-8
3	10-5, 10-6
4	10-2, 10-3
5	10-6
6	10-1, 10-2

1 Integer Partitions This project is closely related to the content of Lesson 10-7. Students might think of this as balls in boxes. An alternate solution is to count the partitions for 6 and 7 and look for a pattern. Note: the number 5 itself is an integer partition of 5.

2 Card Game Odds The odds for some card games can be found in almanacs. We have seen odds for pinochle, for instance. But pinochle is not as rich in combinations as bridge or poker.

3 Extending Pascal's Triangle Because of the detail of the directions given, this is a rather straightforward project, but it requires some time.

4 License Plate Numbers Since you do not wish to deluge a state office with requests for the ways in which license plates "numbers" are determined, you might have all students doing this project work as a team to make one request. Or, if you wish to make things easier, you could determine the information about your state in advance.

```
50  NUMP = 0
100 L = 1
110 P(1) = N
120 P(0) = -1
130 IF (L > N) THEN 280
140 FOR J = 1 TO L
150 PRINT P(J);" ";
160 NEXT J
170 PRINT
180 NUMP = NUMP + 1
190 I = L - 1
200 IF ((P(L) - P(I)) > = 2) THEN
    GOTO 230
210 I = I - 1
220 GOTO 200
230 IF (I <> 0) THEN FOR J = L TO I
    STEP -1:P(J) = P(I) + 1:NEXT J
240 IF (I = 0) THEN FOR J = 1 TO
    L:P(J) = 1:NEXT J: L = L + 1
250 SUM = 0:FOR J = 1 TO L - 1:
    SUM = SUM + P(J):NEXT J
260 P(L) = N - SUM
270 GOTO 130
280 PRINT:PRINT "THERE ARE
    ";NUMP;"PARTITIONS."
290 END
```

Students may also attempt a method which generates/counts partitions of an integer in dictionary order regardless of length.

(Responses continue on page 650)

5 Simulated Sampling You might expand this project by having students contact the quality control department of a local manufacturing or distributing company. Students might be able to talk with a quality control engineer to learn how samples are tested for that industry.

6 Scheduling Problems The number of possibilities for some students in some schools may be quite large. The schedules of other students may have been uniquely determined by the courses they are taking. You may wish to consider separately schedules with activities, such as yearbook or band, and schedules without taking activities into account.

Additional Responses, page 649

2. **Sample (for poker): The following odds may be found in an almanac.**

Hand	Odds Against
Nothing	1 to 1
One pair	1.37 to 1
Two pairs	20 to 1
Three of a kind	46 to 1
Straight	254 to 1
Flush	508 to 1
Full house	693 to 1
Four of a kind	4,164 to 1
Straight flush	72,192 to 1
Royal flush	649,739 to 1

The odds against being dealt a particular hand is simply $\frac{\text{total no. of hands}}{\text{no. possible of particular hand}} - 1$ to 1. Combinatorics may be used to compute the number possible of each poker hand as discussed below.

(continued)

4 License Plate Numbers

Recall from Lesson 10-2 that there are 6,760,000 different 6-symbol license plate identifications if the first two symbols can be any of the 26 letters of the alphabet and the last 4 symbols can be any of the digits 0 through 9. In 1997, the state of California had over 26 million vehicles registered for plates. Clearly, the state of California must allow more types of license plates than those described in Example 3. Find out what types of license plates are used in your state and count the number of different license plates possible. In most states, certain license plate combinations are reserved for official vehicles and some kinds of "vanity" plates are not allowed. Find out about such restrictions in your state and estimate the number of license plate combinations available to private citizens. Estimate how many of these combinations are actually in use in your state this year.

PI 2000

5 Simulated Sampling

Refer to Example 3 of Lesson 10-6. The BASIC program below simulates taking 10 samples, each consisting of a twelve-bulb carton. The probability of a bulb being defective is .01. The program represents each carton with a twelve-letter string in which the letter "G" represents a good bulb and the letter "D" represents a defective bulb.

```
10 RANDOMIZE
20 FOR SAMPLE = 1 TO 10
30   FOR I = 1 TO 12
40     IF RND(1) < .99 THEN PRINT "G";
       ELSE PRINT "D";
50   NEXT I
60   PRINT
70 NEXT SAMPLE
80 END
```

a. Enter and run the program or run an equivalen program on a calculator. Approximately how many defective bulbs should you expect to find in the ten samples? How many appeared in the simulation?

b. Find the probability that a 12-bulb carton will contain exactly 2 defective bulbs. Run the program 10 times. (Use a different random number seed for each run.) How many cartons containing exactly 2 defective bulbs appeared? How many should you expect?

c. Modify the program to simulate an assembly line in which the probability that any one light bulb is defective is 5%. Repeat part **b** with the new program.

d. Run the program from part **c** and compute the quotient $\frac{\text{total number of defective bulbs}}{\text{total number of bulbs}}$. How does this compare with the probability that any one bulb is defective? Run the program several more times and keep track of the above quotient. Is it getting closer to the probability that any one bulb is defective? Explain your answer.

e. Repeat the "experiment" in part **d** with a partner. Have one of you determine the probability p that any one bulb is defective and modify the program to simulate it. Have the other person conduct the experiment in part **d** (without looking at a list of the program) and try to determine p experimentally.

6 Scheduling Problems

When you scheduled your classes for this year you chose perhaps five classes to take during a seven-period school day. Some of your classes may have been required and others electives. Among all of the classes offered by your school, some, such as freshman English, you could not sign up for this year. Find out about the classes which were actually available to you and count the number of different schedules which you could have chosen.

650

Royal flush: There are four possible suits, so 4 royal flushes are possible. **Straight flush:** The first card may be an A, 2, 3, 4, ..., 9, and there are 4 suits, so there are $4 \cdot 9 = 36$ possible other straight flushes. **Four of a kind:** There are 13 different card ranks possible. For the fifth card there are $52 - 4 = 48$ that could be dealt, so $13 \cdot 48 = 624$ possible hands which contain four of a kind.

Full house: There are 13 ranks possible for the triple and $\binom{4}{3}$ ways the suits could appear on these three cards. This leaves 12 ranks from which the pair may be dealt. There are $\binom{4}{2}$ ways the suits could appear on the pair. So there are $13 \cdot \binom{4}{3} \cdot 12 \cdot \binom{4}{2} = 13 \cdot 4 \cdot 12 \cdot 6 = 3744$ possible full houses.

Flush: There are $\binom{13}{5}$ ways that 5 cards from one suit can be dealt, and there are 4 suits. Subtracting the number of royal flushes and other straight flushes yields $4 \cdot \binom{13}{5} - 4 - 36 = 4 \cdot 1287 - 40 =$ 5108 possible flushes. **Straight:** The lowest ranked card in a straight may be A, 2, 3, ..., 10. There is only one way the ranks of the four remaining cards may appear. But, the

SUMMARY

This chapter begins by discussing four types of counting problems. Some counting problems can be considered as counting strings of symbols in which the order of the symbols distinguishes among the different items to be counted. Other problems can be considered as counting collections of symbols in which order is not important. In determining the essential features of a problem, you must determine whether order is or is not important and whether repetition of symbols is or is not allowed.

A possibility tree provides a visual representation of the various outcomes in a situation that involves a sequence of steps, each of which has several possible choices or results. By counting the number of "leaves" in the tree, the total number of possible outcomes can be obtained.

The Multiplication Counting Principle is one tool that can be used to count the number of different ways that something can occur. If k successive steps can be done in $n_1, n_2, \ldots,$ and n_k ways, respectively, then the total number of ways all k steps can be done is given by the product $n_1 n_2 \ldots n_k$.

Formulas useful for solving counting problems follow from the Multiplication Counting Principle. If a collection of r symbols is to be chosen from among n symbols, then the number of different collections is as given in the following chart.

	repetition allowed	repetition not allowed
ordered symbols (permutations)	n^r	$P(n, r) = \frac{n!}{(n-r)!}$
unordered symbols (combinations)	$\binom{r + (n-1)}{r}$	$C(n, r) = \binom{n}{r} = \frac{n!}{r!(n-r)!}$

The number of permutations of n objects is $n!$. Permutations and combinations are related by the fact that $P(n, r) = r!\, C(n, r)$. Counting the number of terms in the expansion of $(x_1 + x_2 + \ldots + x_n)^r$ and the number of ways r balls can be placed in n boxes are both equivalent to counting the number of r-element collections taken from n objects, with repetition allowed.

The Binomial Theorem provides an efficient means to expand $(x + y)^n$. The coefficient of $x^{n-k}y^k$ is given by $\binom{n}{k}$. The Binomial Theorem can help to compute the number of ways an event consisting of a sequence of trials can occur when each trial has two possible outcomes. It can also be used to compute the probability that an outcome occurs a certain number of times if the probability of each outcome is known.

VOCABULARY

Below are the most important terms and phrases for this chapter. You should be able to give a general description and a specific example of each and a precise definition for those marked with an asterisk (*).

Lesson 10-1
combinatorics
string
set

Lesson 10-2
possibility tree
branch points, nodes
leaves
Multiplication Counting Principle
complement

Lesson 10-3
* permutation
Permutation Theorem
* permutation of n elements taken r at a time, $P(n, r)$, ${}_nP_r$
$P(n, r)$ Calculation Theorem

Lesson 10-4
* combination of n elements taken r at a time, $C(n, r)$, ${}_nC_r$, $\binom{n}{r}$
$C(n, r)$ Calculation Theorem
Basic Properties of Combinations Theorem

Lesson 10-5
Pascal's triangle
binomial coefficients
Binomial Theorem

Lesson 10-6
Sum of Binomial Coefficients Theorem
trial
binomial probability

Lesson 10-7
collection

Summary

The Summary gives an overview of the entire chapter and provides an opportunity for students to consider the material as a whole. Thus, the Summary can be used to help students relate and unify the concepts presented in the chapter.

Vocabulary

Terms, symbols, and properties are listed by lesson to provide a checklist of concepts a student must know. Emphasize to students that they should read the vocabulary list carefully before starting the Progress Self-Test. If students do not understand the meaning of a term, they should refer back to the indicated lesson.

cards need not be of the same suit, so there are 4^5 ways the suits may be uniquely dealt. Subtracting the number of royal and straight flushes yields
$10 \cdot 4^5 - 4 - 36 = 10{,}240 - 40 = 10{,}200$ possible straights.
<u>Three of a kind:</u> There are 13 ranks which may be dealt for the triple and $\binom{4}{3}$ ways the suits may be dealt for these three cards. The remaining two cards dealt must not be a pair and must not match the rank of the first three cards; this yields $\binom{12}{2}$ possible ways the ranks may appear on the last two cards. Since any suit is possible for these last two cards, there are 4^2 ways the suits may appear on them. So there are $13 \cdot \binom{4}{3} \cdot \binom{12}{2} \cdot 4^2 = 54{,}912$ possible three-of-a-kind hands.

<u>Two pairs:</u> There are $\binom{13}{2}$ different ways the ranks may be dealt for two pairs. And there are $\binom{4}{2}$ different ways that the suits may appear for each pair of cards. The fifth card in the hand must have unique rank and may have any suit which means there are $11 \cdot 4$ ways it may be dealt. So there are $\binom{13}{2} \cdot \binom{4}{2} \cdot \binom{4}{2} \cdot 11 \cdot 4 =$
$78 \cdot 6 \cdot 6 \cdot 11 \cdot 4 = 123{,}552$ possible hands that contain two pairs.
<u>One pair:</u> There are 13 ranks possible for the pair and $\binom{4}{2}$ ways that the suits may appear on these two cards. The three remaining cards must each have a different rank to avoid having a full house, four of a kind, three of a kind, or two pairs. There are $\binom{12}{3}$ ways that this may occur. The last three cards may be of any suit, hence there are 4^3 ways that the suits may appear. So there are $13 \cdot \binom{4}{2} \cdot \binom{12}{3} \cdot 4^3 = 13 \cdot 6 \cdot 220 \cdot 64 = 1{,}098{,}240$ possible one pair hands.

(Responses continue on page 652.)

 CHAPTER TEN

Progress Self-Test

For the development of mathematical competence, feedback and correction, along with the opportunity to practice, are necessary. The Progress Self-Test provides the opportunity for feedback and correction; the Chapter Review provides additional opportunities and practice. We cannot overemphasize the importance of these end-of-chapter materials. It is at this point that the material "gels" for many students, allowing them to solidify skills and understanding. In general, student performance should be markedly improved after these pages.

Assign the Progress Self-Test as a one-night assignment. Worked-out *solutions* for all questions are in the Selected Answers section of the student book. Encourage students to take the Progress Self-Test honestly, grade themselves, and then be prepared to discuss the test in class.

Advise students to pay special attention to those Chapter Review questions (pages 653–655) that correspond to questions missed on the Progress Self-Test.

Additional Answers

3. 7 possible rolls

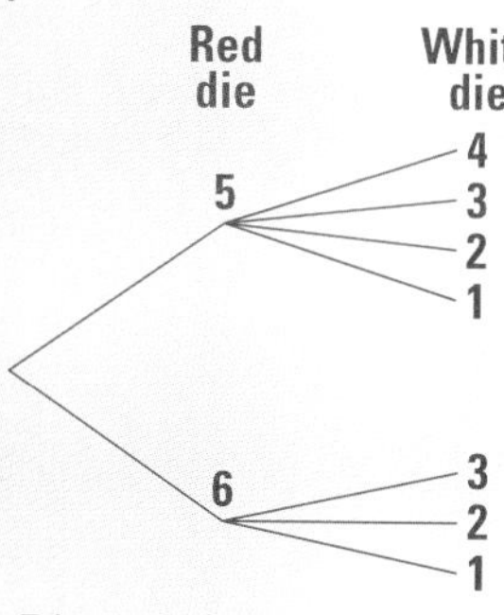

15. $P(n+1, r+1) = \dfrac{(n+1)!}{(n+1-(r+1))!} = \dfrac{(n+1)!}{(n-r)!}$;
$(n+1) \cdot P(n, r) = (n+1)\dfrac{n!}{(n-r)!} = \dfrac{(n+1)!}{(n-r)!}$
So, $P(n+1, r+1) = (n+1) \cdot P(n, r)$.

PROGRESS SELF-TEST

3, 15) See margin.

Take this test as you would take a test in class. Then check the test yourself using the solutions at the end of this volume.

In 1 and 2, a problem is given. **a.** Describe the essential features of each problem. **b.** Solve the problem. **a) See below.**

1. You wish to know how many different outcomes are possible when five identical dice are rolled. **b) 252**

2. A pizza parlor has the following toppings available: anchovy, pepperoni, sausage, black olive, double cheese, green pepper, mushroom, and onion. Thick or thin crust is offered. The problem is to determine the number of different 4-topping pizzas available. **b) 140**

3. A red die and a white die are rolled. Use a possibility tree to determine the number of rolls possible in which the red die is a five or six and the total showing on the two dice is less than ten.

4. Consider the computer program below.

```
10 FOR I = 1 TO 2
20   FOR J = 3 TO 8
30     FOR K = 10 TO 20
40     PRINT I+J+K
50     NEXT K
60   NEXT J
70 NEXT I
80 END
```

When the program is run, how many times is line 40 executed? **132**

5. In how many ways can you answer a ten-question multiple-choice test if each question has four possible answers? **1,048,576**

In 6 and 7, evaluate the expression.

6. $P(18, 4)$ **73,440** **7.** $\binom{8}{4}$ **70**

8. A committee of twelve people is to choose a chairperson, assistant chairperson, and secretary from among the members of the committee. In how many ways can the selection be made? **1320**

9. The alphabet has 21 consonants and 5 vowels. Suppose five-letter strings are to be created in which the first letter is a vowel. **2,284,880**
a. How many such strings are there if the same letter can occur more than once?
b. How many are there if a letter can only occur once? **1,518,000**

10. A caterer must choose three vegetable dishes from nine vegetable dishes which are available. In how many ways can this be done? **84**

11. Find the fourth term in the expansion of $(2x - y)^9$. $-5376x^6y^3$

12. A coin is flipped seven times. How many of the possible sequences of heads and tails have exactly 4 tails? **35**

13. How many subsets of a set with 11 elements are there that contain 3 or fewer members of that set? **232**

14. A soda machine offers a choice of cola, diet cola, lemon-lime soda, and grape soda. If 7 cans are to be purchased, in how many different ways can this be done? **120**

15. Prove that for positive integers n and r with $r \le n$, $P(n+1, r+1) = (n+1)P(n, r)$.

16. Suppose that the probability is 3% that a Snacko does not have enough cream filling. If a box of 10 Snackos is purchased, what is the probability that two Snackos are inadequately filled? $\approx$ **0.0317**

1a) unordered symbols; repetition allowed

2a) unordered symbols; repetition not allowed

Additional Responses, pages 649
Project 2, continued

Nothing: The total number of hands that can be dealt is $\binom{52}{5} = \left(\dfrac{52!}{47!\,5!}\right) = \left(\dfrac{52 \cdot 51 \cdot 50 \cdot 49 \cdot 48}{5!}\right) =$ 2,598,960. A nothing hand is simply none of the hands described above and may be calculated by subtracting these from the total number of hands.

So there are 2,598,960 − 4 − 36 − 624 − 3744 − 5108 − 10,200 − 54,912 − 123,552 − 1,098,240 = 1,302,540 possible nothing hands.

(Responses continue on page 654.)

 CHAPTER TEN

CHAPTER REVIEW

Questions on SPUR Objectives

SPUR stands for **S**kills, **P**roperties, **U**ses, and **R**epresentations. The Chapter Review questions are grouped according to the SPUR Objectives for this chapter.

SKILLS DEAL WITH THE PROCEDURES USED TO GET ANSWERS.

1–5, 11, 12) See margin.

Objective A: *Describe the essential features of counting problems.* *(Lesson 10-1)*

In 1–5, describe the essential features of the problem. You do not have to solve the problem.

1. An ice cream shop carries 32 different flavors. How many different double cones (2 dips) can be made?
2. At the school cafeteria, a standard lunch offers a choice of salad or fruit cup, two of three vegetable dishes, one of four entrees, and one of two desserts. How many different lunches can a student choose?
3. How many different 4-letter code words can be constructed from the letters in the words *mind power*?
4. A company plans to hire 8 new employees with 4 men and 4 women. If 15 men and 7 women apply for the positions, in how many ways can the company hire its new employees?
5. How many four-digit integers have digits which alternate between even and odd when read from left to right?

Objective B: *Evaluate expressions indicating permutations or combinations.* *(Lessons 10-3, 10-4)*

In 6–10, evaluate the expression.

6. $P(17, 3)$ **4080**
7. $C(14, 9)$ **2002**
8. $C(18, 6)$ **18,564**
9. ${}_9P_6$ **60,480**
10. $\binom{9}{7}$ **36**

Objective C: *Apply the Binomial Theorem to expand binomials or find specific terms.* *(Lesson 10-5)*

In 11 and 12, expand, using the Binomial Theorem.

11. $(x + y)^8$
12. $(2a - 3b)^4$
13. Without computing the entire expansion of $(4a - 2b)^6$, find the coefficient of a^3b^3. **-10240**
14. Find the fifth term of $(x + 5y)^9$. $\mathbf{78750x^5y^4}$

PROPERTIES DEAL WITH THE PRINCIPLES BEHIND THE MATHEMATICS.

15–18) See margin.

Objective D: *Use properties of permutations and combinations to prove identities.* *(Lessons 10-3, 10-4)*

15. Show that $C(n, r) = C(n, n - r)$ for all positive integers n and r with $r \le n$.
16. Show that $P(n, n) = n!$.
17. Provide an explanation in terms of combinations to justify the relationship $P(n, r) = r!C(n, r)$.

Objective E: *Apply the Binomial Theorem to deduce properties of sets.* *(Lesson 10-6)*

18. How can the Binomial Theorem be used to find the number of different subsets that can be formed from a 10-element set?
19. What binomial coefficient, expressed as a combination, gives the number of 4-element subsets that can be formed from a 20-element set? $\binom{20}{4}$

Chapter 10 Review

Resources

From the ***Teacher's Resource File***

- Answer Master for Chapter 10 Review
- Assessment Sourcebook: Chapter 10 Test, Forms A–D Chapter 10 Test, Cumulative Form

Additional Resources

- TestWorks CD-ROM

The main objectives for the chapter are organized in the Chapter Review under the four types of understanding this book promotes—Skills, Properties, Uses, and Representations.

Whereas end-of-chapter material may be considered optional in some texts, in UCSMP *Precalculus and Discrete Mathematics* we have selected these objectives and questions with the expectation that they will be covered. Students should be able to answer these questions with about 85% accuracy after studying the chapter.

You may assign these questions over a single night to help students prepare for a test the next day, or you may assign the questions over a two-day period. If you work the questions over two days, then we recommend assigning the *evens* for homework the first night so that students get feedback in class the next day, then assigning the *odds* the night before the test, because answers are provided to the odd-numbered questions.

It is effective to ask students which questions they still do not understand and use the day or days as a total class discussion of the material which the class finds most difficult.

Additional Answers, page 653

1. **unordered symbols; repetition allowed**
2. **unordered symbols; repetition not allowed**
3. **ordered symbols; repetition not allowed**
4. **unordered symbols; repetition not allowed**
5. **ordered symbols; repetition allowed**

11. $x^8 + 8x^7y + 28x^6y^2 + 56x^5y^3 + 70x^4y^4 + 56x^3y^5 + 28x^2y^6 + 8xy^7 + y^8$
12. $16a^4 - 96a^3b + 216a^2b^2 - 216ab^3 + 81b^4$
15. $C(n, r) = \frac{n!}{r!(n-r)!} = \frac{n!}{(n-(n-r))!(n-r)!} = C(n, n - r)$
16. $P(n, n) = \frac{n!}{(n-n)!} = \frac{n!}{0!} = n!$
17. **For each of the $C(n, r)$ combinations of n objects taken r at a time, there are $r!$ arrangements. So $C(n, r) \cdot r! = P(n, r)$, or $P(n, r) = r!C(n, r)$.**
18. **Add the coefficients;** $\sum_{k=0}^{10} \binom{10}{k} = 2^{10}$.

Assessment

Evaluation The Assessment Sourcebook provides five forms of the Chapter 10 Test. Forms A and B present parallel versions in a short-answer format. Forms C and D offer performance assessment. The fifth test is Chapter 10 Test, Cumulative Form. About 50% of this test covers Chapter 10, 25% of it covers Chapter 9, and 25% of it covers earlier chapters.

For information on grading, see *General Teaching Suggestions: Grading* in the *Professional Sourcebook,* which begins on page T20 in the Teacher's Edition.

Feedback After students have taken the test for Chapter 10 and you have scored the results, return the tests to students for discussion. Class discussion of the questions that caused trouble for the most students can be very effective in identifying and clarifying misunderstandings. You might want to have them write down the items they missed and work, either in groups or at home, to correct them. It is important for students to receive feedback on every chapter test, and we recommend that students see and correct their mistakes before proceeding too far into the next chapter.

Additional Answers, page 654

23. $\approx 1.2165 \times 10^{17}$
24. $\approx 5.0215 \times 10^{14}$
25. $\approx 1.40 \times 10^{10}$
26. 87,500
32. ${}_{50}C_{23} \approx 1.0804 \times 10^{14}$

CHAPTER TEN

USES DEAL WITH APPLICATIONS OF MATHEMATICS IN REAL SITUATIONS.

23–26, 32) See margin.

Objective F: *Use the Multiplication Counting Principle and permutations to solve counting problems.* *(Lessons 10-2, 10-3)*

20. a. How many 6-letter strings can be created from the 26 letters of the English alphabet?

b. How many 6-letter strings are possible if the first letter must be *d* and the last letter must be *t*? **331,776** **a) 308,915,776**

21. At a ceremony, seven people are to be seated on the podium. How many different seatings are possible? **5040**

22. A combination lock on a briefcase has three dials with the digits from 0 through 9 on each dial. How many different possible combinations are there for this lock? **1000**

In 23–25, 15 old books and 4 old bookmarks are to be displayed in a row at an art exhibit.

23. How many different displays are possible?

24. How many displays are possible if the 4 bookmarks must be displayed together?

25. How many displays are possible if only 7 of the books and 2 of the bookmarks are displayed?

26. How many integers from 10,000 through 99,999 have at least one digit which is odd?

27. Consider the computer program below.

```
10 FOR I = 3 TO 5
15   FOR J = 6 TO 10
20     FOR K = 4 TO 11
25       B = I * J * K
30       PRINT B
35     NEXT K
40   NEXT J
50 NEXT I
60 END
```

How many numbers does line 30 print? **120**

28. Consider the computer program below.

```
10 FOR I = 1 TO 4
20   FOR J = 2 TO 7
30     PRINT I, J
40   NEXT J
50   FOR K = 1 TO 3
60     PRINT I, K
70   NEXT K
80 NEXT I
90 END
```

How many lines of data are printed? **36**

Objective G: *Use combinations and the Binomial Theorem to solve counting problems.* *(Lessons 10-4, 10-6, 10-7)*

29. An ice cream shop has 20 flavors.

a. How many triple cones (3 dips) are possible if no flavor can be repeated? (Do not count different arrangements of the same flavors as different.) **1140**

b. How many triple cones are possible if flavors can be repeated? **8000**

30. Solve the problem in Question 4. **47,775**

31. For a literature class, a teacher must choose four novels from a list of ten. In how many ways can this choice be made? **210**

32. A dance company has 50 dancers. In how many ways can the company choose 23 of these dancers for a production?

Members of the Irish dance troupe Riverdance in Los Angeles, 1996

Additional Responses, pages 649–650

3. See Additional Answers at the back of this Teacher's Edition.
4. Answers will vary from state to state.
5. a. $10 \cdot 12 = 120$ bulbs, so there should be $120(.01) = 1.2$, or approximately 1 defective bulb. Sample: None appeared in the first simulation.
   b. $\binom{12}{2}(.99)^{10}(.01)^2 \approx 0.00597$ is the probability of exactly 2 defective bulbs. $10 \cdot 10 \cdot (0.00597) = 0.597$. About 1 carton should be expected to have exactly 2 defective bulbs after 10 runs of the program. Sample: Running the program 10 times, there was one carton that had 2 defective bulbs.
   c. Change line 40 to:
   40 IF RND(1) < .95 THEN PRINT "G"; ELSE PRINT "D";
   The probability of a carton with exactly two defective bulbs becomes $\binom{12}{2}(.95)^{10}(.01)^2 \approx$ 0.0983. So $10 \cdot 10 \cdot 0.0983 = 9.83 \approx 10$ such cartons should appear after running the program 10 times. Sample: In 10 trial runs, 5 cartons appeared that had 2 defective bulbs.
   d. Sample: In the first run, there were 5 defective bulbs out of 120.

CHAPTER TEN

33. In how many ways is it possible to obtain at least two heads in a sequence of five coin tosses? 26

34. Student council members are to be selected from the general student body. Suppose a high school has 2000 students: 620 freshmen, 580 sophomores, 450 juniors, and 350 seniors. Leave your answers to the following questions in $C(n, r)$ form. a, b) See below.

a. How many 50-member councils can be formed from the whole student body?

b. How many 50-member councils can be formed if there must be 12 freshmen, 12 sophomores, 13 juniors, and 13 seniors in the council?

35. A Mix-n-Match selection of 10 cookies is to be made from three varieties: oatmeal, peanut butter, and sugar. How many different selections are possible? 66

34a) $C(2000, 50)$
b) $C(620, 12) \cdot C(580, 12) \cdot C(450, 13) \cdot C(350, 13)$

Objective H: *Find binomial probabilities in realistic situations.* *(Lesson 10-6)*

36. A jar contains purple jelly beans and green jelly beans. There are three times as many purple ones as green ones. If an individual chooses 5 beans from the jar, what is the probability that 3 of the beans will be green? ≈ 0.0879

37. Suppose the probability is 0.2% that a pencil sharpener produced at a factory is defective.

a. If the quality control department randomly selects 100 sharpeners for testing, find the probability that two of those sharpeners are defective. ≈ 0.0163

b. Find the probability that at least one sharpener is defective. ≈ 0.1814

c. If the quality control department selects 500 sharpeners, find the probability that at least one of those sharpeners is defective. ≈ 0.6325

REPRESENTATIONS DEAL WITH PICTURES, GRAPHS, OR OBJECTS THAT ILLUSTRATE CONCEPTS.

38–40) See margin for diagrams.

Objective I: *Use a possibility tree to determine the number of outcomes in a given situation.* *(Lesson 10-2)*

38. Make a possibility tree to determine the number of two-letter strings that can be created from the letters *d, e, f,* and *g* if *d* and *e* can be repeated but *f* and *g* cannot. 14 strings

39. Three-digit numbers are to be made from the digits 1, 2, 3, and 4. Use a possibility tree to count the number of three-digit numbers that can be made if digits must alternate even-odd-even or odd-even-odd and digits cannot repeat. 8 numbers

40. In a tournament, two teams play each other until one team wins two in a row or a total of four games. Use a possibility tree to count the number of different possible outcomes of this tournament. 14 outcomes

Additional Answers, page 655

38.

d: d, e, f, g
e: d, e, f, g
f: d, e, g
g: d, e, f

39.

1 — 2 — 3
1 — 4 — 3
2 — 1 — 4
2 — 3 — 4
3 — 2 — 1
3 — 4 — 1
4 — 1 — 2
4 — 3 — 2

40.

A — A
A — B — A — A
A — B — A — B — A — A
A — B — A — B — A — B
A — B — A — B — B
A — B — B
B — A — A
B — A — B — A — A
B — A — B — A — B
B — A — B — B
B — A — B — A — B — A
B — B

Project 5d, continued

So the quotient is $\frac{5}{120} \approx 0.0417$. This is close to the probability of any one bulb being defective (0.05). The results after several runs are summarized below.

Number of Runs	Quotient
2	.0375
3	.0389
4	.0354
5	.0417
6	.0444
7	.0452

The quotient gets closer to the probability that any one bulb is defective after more and more runs. This is true because

(probability any one bulb is defective) • (total number of bulbs) ≈ (total number of defective bulbs). In the long run,

(probability any one bulb is defective) = (total number of defective bulbs) / (total number of bulbs).

5. e. Sample: After 24 runs of the program, the quotient calculated was ≈ 0.0167. Assuming my partner put up a whole number probability for defective bulbs, I guessed p to be .02 and was correct.

6. Answers will vary from school to school.

Chapter 11 Pacing Chart		
Day	**Full Course**	**Minimal Course**
1	11-1	11-1
2	11-2	11-2
3	11-3	11-3
4	11-4	11-4
5	Quiz*; 11-5	Quiz*; begin 11-5.
6	11-6	Finish 11-5.
7	11-7	11-6
8	Self-Test	11-7
9	Review	Self-Test
10	Test*	Review
11		Review
12		Test*

*in the Teacher's Resource File

Adapting to Individual Needs

The student text is written for the vast majority of students. The chart at the right suggests two pacing plans to accommodate the needs of your students. Students in the Full Course should complete the entire text by the end of the year. Students in the Minimal Course will spend more time when there are quizzes and more time on the Chapter Review. Therefore, these students may not complete all of the chapters in the text.

Options are also presented to meet the needs of a variety of teaching and learning styles. For each lesson, the Teacher's Edition provides a section entitled *Adapting to Individual Needs.* This section regularly includes **Optional Activities, Challenge** problems, **English Language Development** suggestions, and suggestions for providing **Extra Help.** The Teacher's Edition also frequently includes an **Error Alert,** an **Extension,** and an **Assessment** alternative. The options available in Chapter 11 are summarized in the chart below.

In the Teacher's Edition...

Lesson	Optional Activities	Extra Help	Challenge	English Language Development	Error Alert	Extension	Cooperative Learning	Ongoing Assessment
11-1	●	●	●		●	●	●	Written
11-2	●	●	●		●	●	●	Written
11-3	●	●	●		●	●		Oral
11-4	●	●	●		●	●	●	Quiz
11-5	●	●	●		●	●	●	Written
11-6	●	●	●		●	●		Oral
11-7	●	●	●			●		

In the Additional Resources...

	In the Teacher's Resource File							
Lesson	**Lesson Masters**	**Teaching Aids***	**Answer Masters**	**Technology Sourcebook**	**Assessment Sourcebook**	**Visual Aids****	**Technology**	**Explorations Software**
11-1	11-1	110, 112, 113, 114, 115	11-1			110, 112, 113, 114, 115, AM		
11-2	11-2	110, 116, 117, 118, 119	11-2			110, 116, 117, 118, 119, AM		
11-3	11-3	110	11-3			110, AM		
In-class Activity		120	11 4			120, AM		
11-4	11-4	111, 121, 122, 123	11-4		Quiz	111, 121, 122, 123, AM		
11-5	11-5	111, 124, 125, 126, 127	11-5			111, 124, 125, 126, 127, AM		11-5
11-6	11-6	111, 128, 129	11-6	Calc 16		111, 128, 129, AM		11-6
11-7		111, 130, 131	11-7			111, 130, 131, AM		11-7
End of chapter					Tests			

*Teaching Aids, except Warm-ups, are pictured on pages 656C and 656D.

**Visual Aids provide transparencies for all Teaching Aids and all Answer Masters.

Also available is the Study Skills Handbook which includes study-skill tips related to reading, note-taking, and comprehension.

Integrating Strands and Applications

	11-1	11-2	11-3	11-4	11-5	11-6	11-7
Mathematical Connections							
Number Sense	●						
Algebra			●				●
Geometry	●						●
Logic and Reasoning	●	●	●	●	●	●	●
Probability	●						
Patterns and Functions		●	●	●	●	●	●
Discrete Mathematics	●	●	●	●	●	●	●
Interdisciplinary and Other Connections							
Literature							●
Science	●			●		●	
Social Studies				●	●	●	●
Multicultural	●	●		●	●	●	
Career						●	
Consumer	●	●	●				
Sports						●	

Teaching and Assessing the Chapter Objectives

Chapter 11 Objectives (Organized into the SPUR catetgories—Skills, Properties, Uses, and Representations)	**Lessons**	**Progress Self-Test Questions**	**Chapter Review Questions**	**In the Teacher's Resource File: Chapter Test, Forms A and B**	**Chapter Test, Forms C**	**Chapter Test, Forms D**
Skills						
A: Draw graphs given sufficient information.	11-2, 11-3	12	1–5			
Properties						
B: Identify parts of graphs and type of graphs.	11-2, 11-3, 11-4, 11-5	1, 2, 3, 4, 5, 6, 7, 9	6–11		1	X
C: Determine whether there exists a graph containing vertices with given degrees.	11-3	14	12–16		2	
D: Determine whether a graph has an Euler circuit.	11-4	8	17–20		3	X
Uses						
E: Use graphs to solve scheduling and probability problems.	11-1	15	21–23			
F: Use the Total Degree of a Graph Theorem and its corollaries to solve handshake problems.	11-3	16	24–26			
G: Solve application problems involving circuits.	11-1, 11-4	11	27–28		3	X
H: Use stochastic matrices to make long-term predictions.	11-6	17	29–30		5	
Representations						
I: Convert between the picture of a graph or directed graph, and its adjacency matrix.	11-2	13	31–35		1	
J: Use the powers of the adjacency matrix of a graph to find the number of walks of a given length, from a given starting vertex to a given ending vertex.	11-5	10	36–39		4	

Assessment Sourcebook
Quiz for Lessons 11-1 through 11-4
Chapter 11 Test, Forms A–D
Chapter 11 Test, Cumulative Form

TestWorks CD-ROM

Teaching Aids

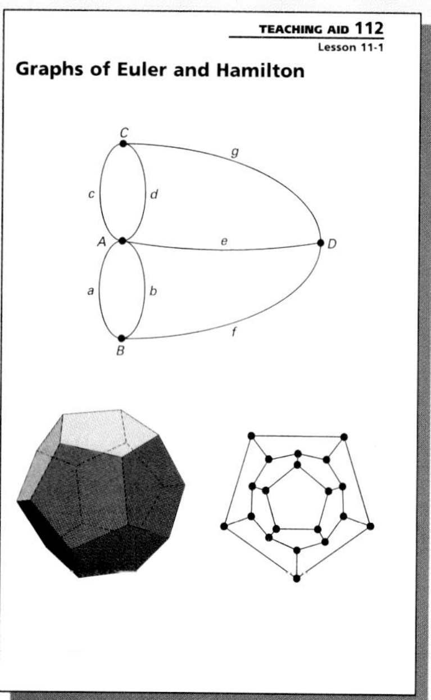
TEACHING AID 112
Lesson 11-1

Graphs of Euler and Hamilton

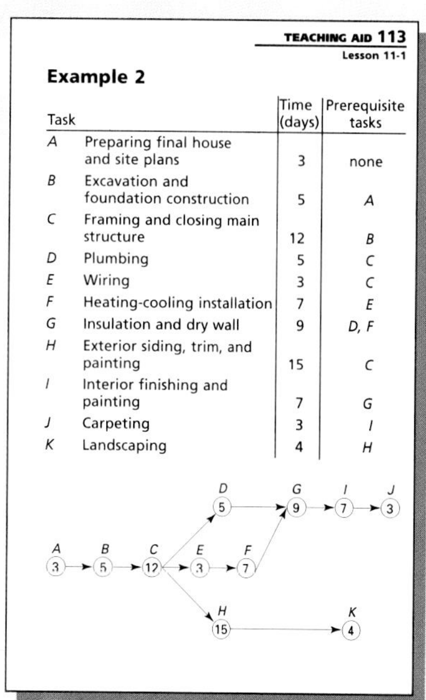
TEACHING AID 113
Lesson 11-1

Example 2

	Task	Time (days)	Prerequisite tasks
A	Preparing final house and site plans	3	none
B	Excavation and foundation construction	5	A
C	Framing and closing main structure	12	B
D	Plumbing	5	C
E	Wiring	3	C
F	Heating-cooling installation	7	E
G	Insulation and dry wall	9	D, F
H	Exterior siding, trim, and painting	15	C
I	Interior finishing and painting	7	G
J	Carpeting	3	I
K	Landscaping	4	H

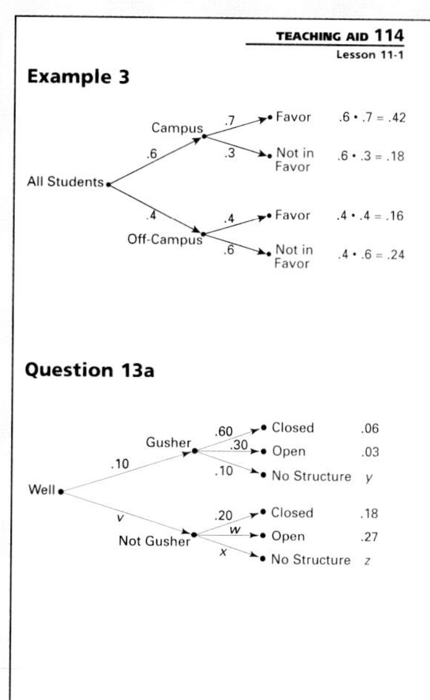
TEACHING AID 114
Lesson 11-1

Example 3

Question 13a

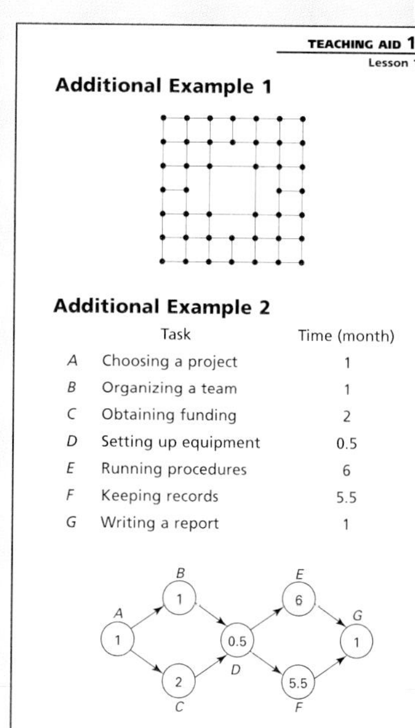
TEACHING AID 1
Lesson 1

Additional Example 1

Additional Example 2

	Task	Time (month)
A	Choosing a project	1
B	Organizing a team	1
C	Obtaining funding	2
D	Setting up equipment	0.5
E	Running procedures	6
F	Keeping records	5.5
G	Writing a report	1

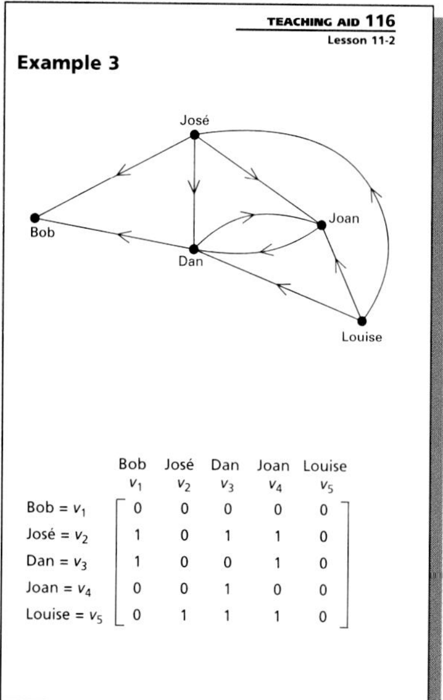
TEACHING AID 116
Lesson 11-2

Example 3

	Bob v_1	José v_2	Dan v_3	Joan v_4	Louise v_5
Bob = v_1	0	0	0	0	0
José = v_2	1	0	1	1	0
Dan = v_3	1	0	0	1	0
Joan = v_4	0	0	1	0	0
Louise = v_5	0	1	1	1	0

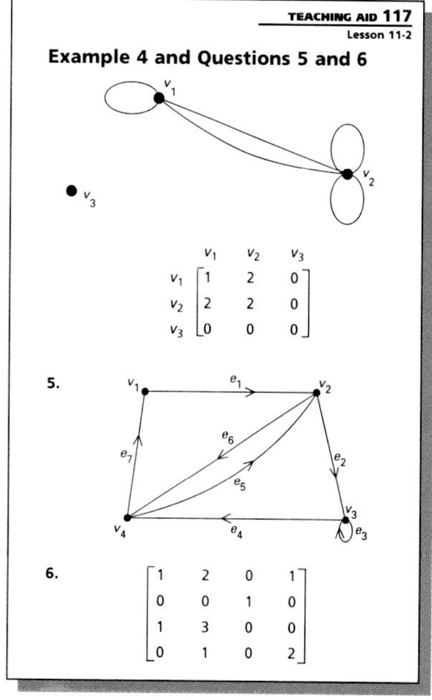
TEACHING AID 117
Lesson 11-2

Example 4 and Questions 5 and 6

	v_1	v_2	v_3
v_1	1	2	0
v_2	2	2	0
v_3	0	0	0

5.

6. $\begin{bmatrix} 1 & 2 & 0 & 1 \\ 0 & 0 & 1 & 0 \\ 1 & 3 & 0 & 0 \\ 0 & 1 & 0 & 2 \end{bmatrix}$

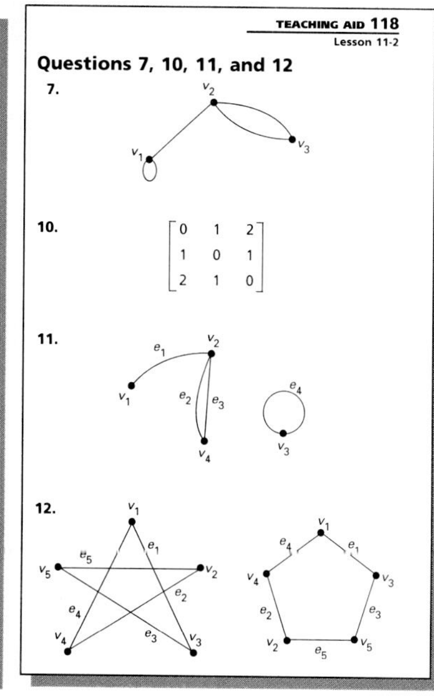
TEACHING AID 118
Lesson 11-2

Questions 7, 10, 11, and 12

7.

10. $\begin{bmatrix} 0 & 1 & 2 \\ 1 & 0 & 1 \\ 2 & 1 & 0 \end{bmatrix}$

11.

12.

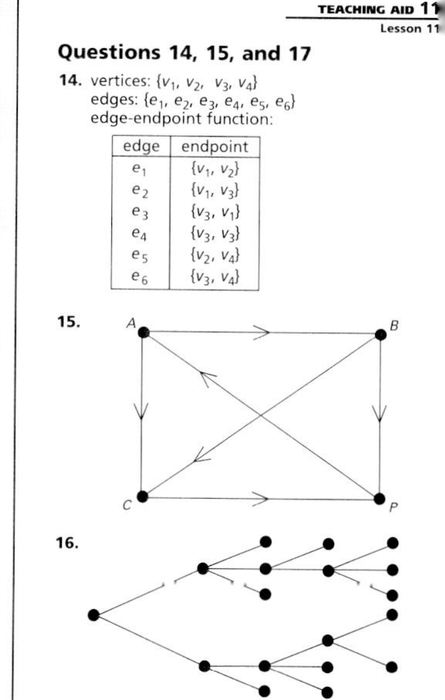
TEACHING AID 11
Lesson 11

Questions 14, 15, and 17

14. vertices: $\{v_1, v_2, v_3, v_4\}$
edges: $\{e_1, e_2, e_3, e_4, e_5, e_6\}$
edge-endpoint function:

edge	endpoint
e_1	$\{v_1, v_2\}$
e_2	$\{v_1, v_3\}$
e_3	$\{v_3, v_1\}$
e_4	$\{v_3, v_3\}$
e_5	$\{v_2, v_4\}$
e_6	$\{v_3, v_4\}$

15.

16.

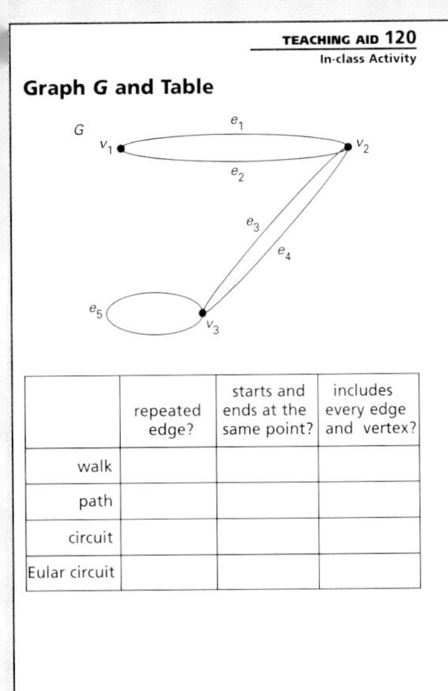

	repeated edge?	starts and ends at the same point?	includes every edge and vertex?
walk			
path			
circuit			
Eular circuit			

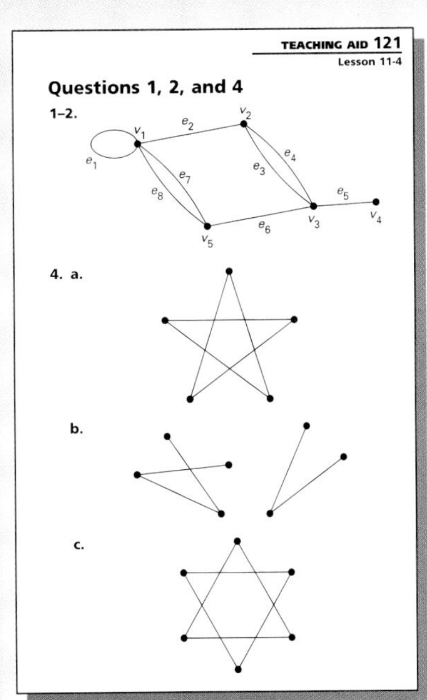

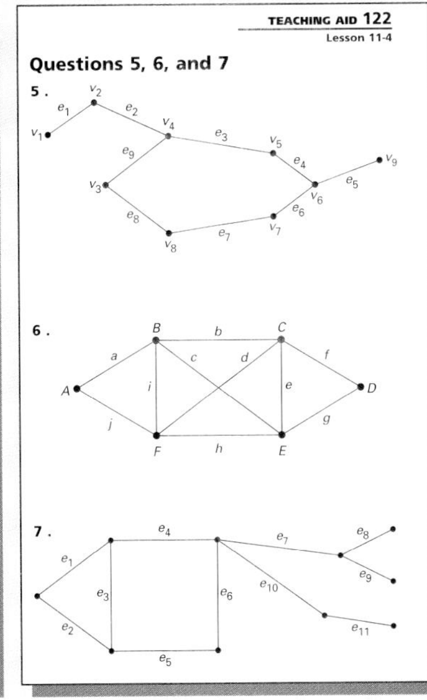

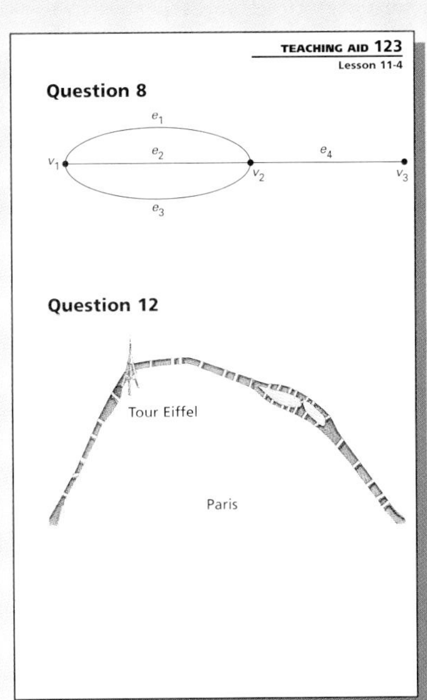

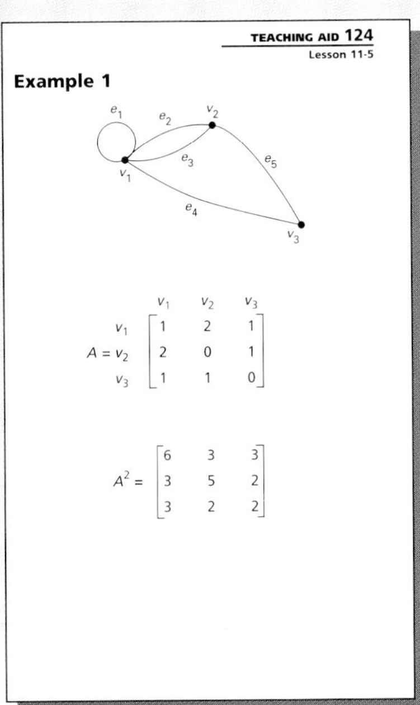

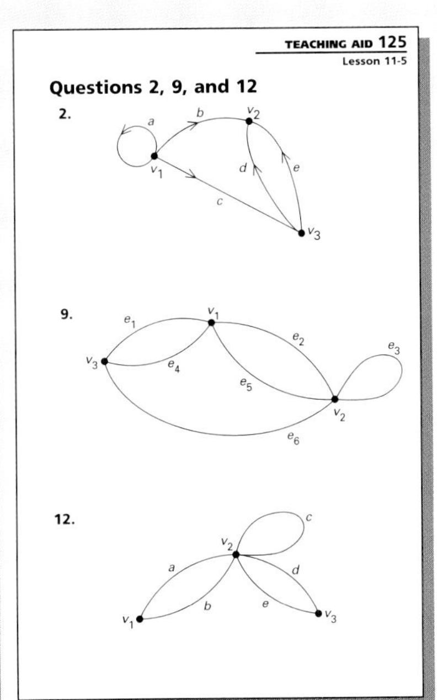

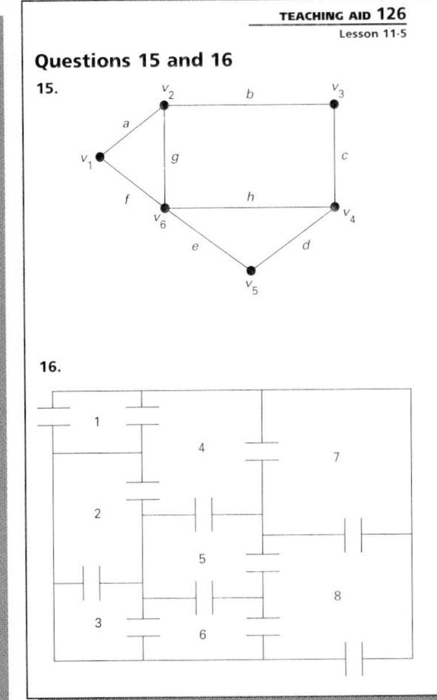

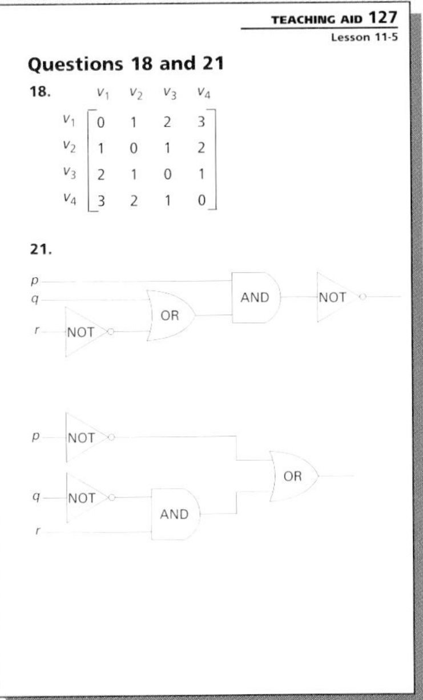

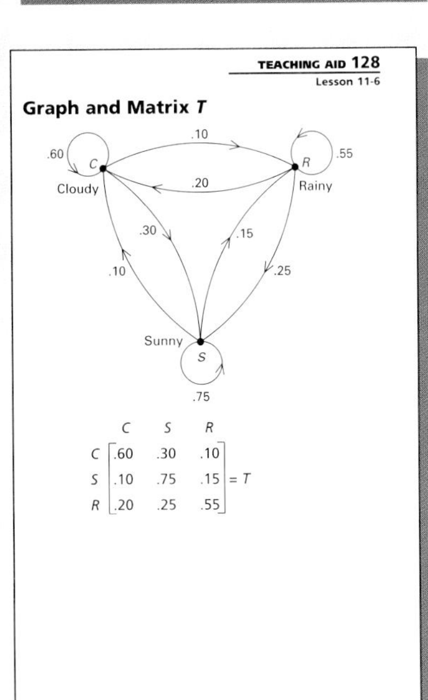

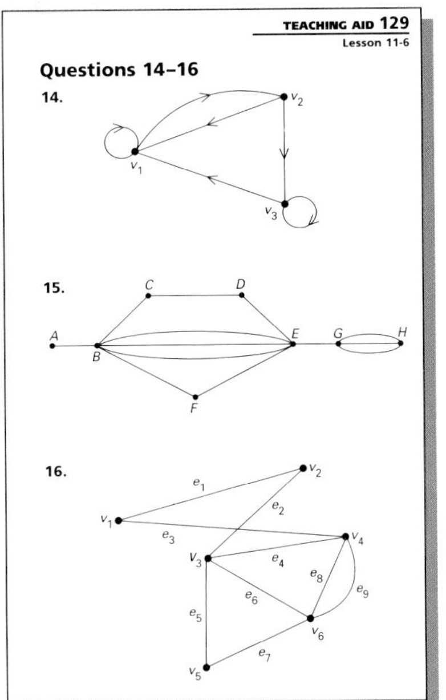

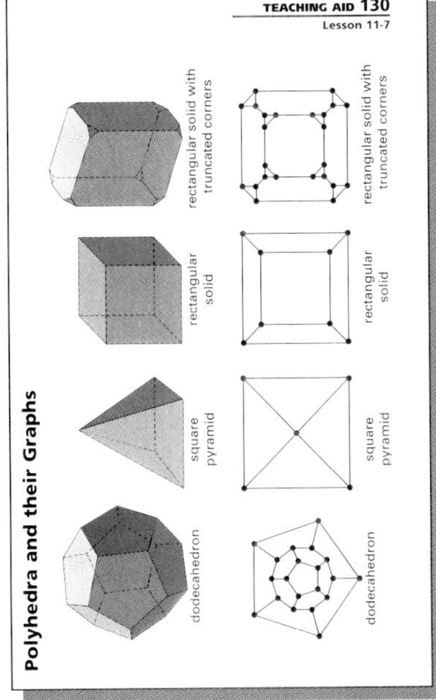

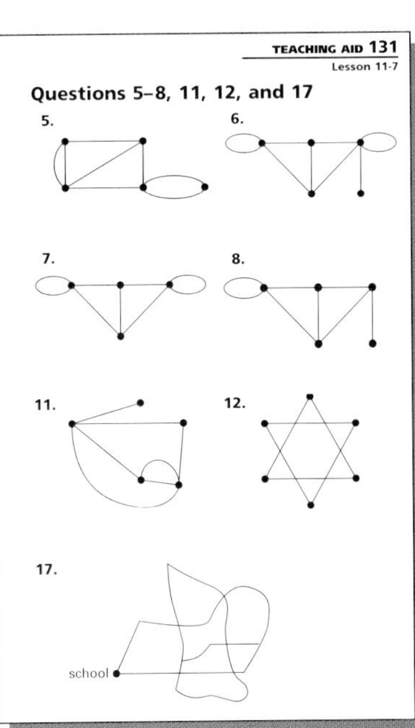

Chapter Opener

Pacing

All lessons in this chapter are designed to be covered in one day. At the end of the chapter, you should plan to spend 1 day to review the Progress Self-Test, 1–2 days for the Chapter Review, and 1 day for a test. You may wish to spend a day on projects, and possibly a day is needed for quizzes and the In-class Activity. This chapter should therefore take 10–12 days. Spending more than 14 days on this chapter is not recommended; there is important content in later chapters.

Using Pages 656–657

If your students have studied UCSMP *Geometry,* they will be familiar with the Königsberg bridge problem. Ask if any students have seen this problem before. If not,have them copy the diagram of the bridges on page 658 onto a sheet of paper and try to find a path for the walk. Although students may rapidly become convinced that no path is possible, few students unfamiliar with the problem can formulate an argument to prove that no path is possible.

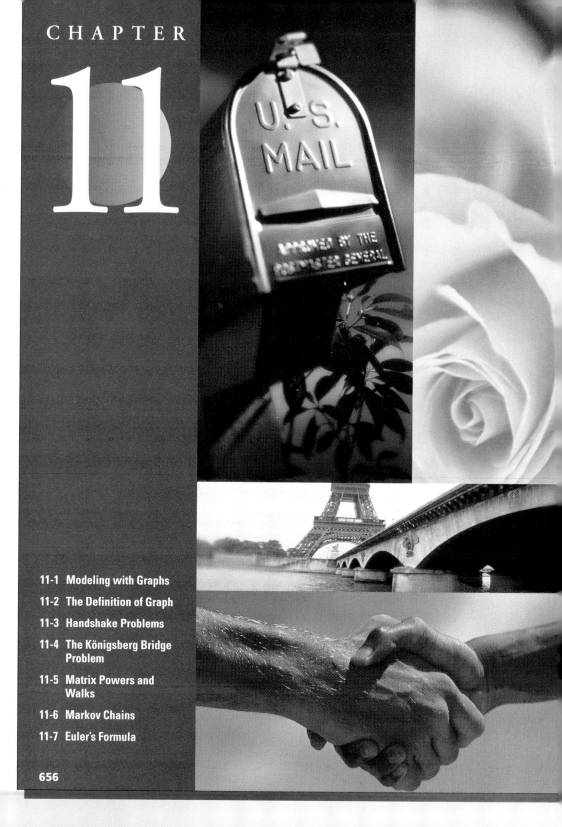

CHAPTER 11

Chapter 11 Overview

This chapter is an introduction to the study of *graphs* (also called *networks*) and *circuits*—mathematical objects that consist of points and segments or arcs connecting them. This area of mathematics is known as *graph theory*. The chapter discusses graphs and circuits from three viewpoints: as objects of study in themselves, as tools for interpreting applications and solving problems, and as links among mathematical ideas. Most discrete mathematics courses at the college level include the topics of graphs, circuits, probability, and matrices. Students who go through this chapter will have the prerequisites for that study.

Of all the topics of discrete mathematics, this may be the least familiar to most teachers. A generation ago, few colleges taught courses in graph theory. However, in recent years the study of graphs has become a fixture of discrete mathematics. One reason is that a diverse collection of problems (both theoretical and practical) can be modeled by graphs, and their solutions often involve working through the graphs. Another reason is that when computers are employed to solve problems of almost any size, the programs require branching and loops, and their logical structures are often most clearly described by graphs. A third reason is that the mathematics is very pretty and still being discovered.

GRAPHS AND CIRCUITS

The city of Kaliningrad in Russia is situated where two branches of the Pregol'a River come together. In 1736, this city was called Königsberg and was a part of East Prussia ruled from what is Germany today. At that time, parts of Königsberg were on the banks of the river, another part was on a large island in the middle, and a final part was between the two branches of the river. Seven bridges connected these four parts of the city. An unsolved problem of the time was:

Is it possible for a person to walk around the city traversing each bridge exactly once, starting and ending at the same point?

This problem is now known as the **Königsberg bridge problem**. It became famous because it was the subject of a research paper in that year by the great mathematician Leonhard Euler. A drawing like the one on page 658 was included in that paper. Take a minute or two to see if you can find such a walk.

To solve the Königsberg bridge problem, Euler constructed a simple and helpful geometric model of the situation called a *graph*, and his paper is usually acknowledged to be the origin of the subject called **graph theory**. (As you will see, these graphs are not the same as the graphs of functions or relations.) In the two-and-a-half centuries since his solution, graphs have been used to solve a wide variety of problems. In this chapter, you will be introduced to a selection of those problems.

Photo Connections

The photo collage makes real-world connections to the content of the chapter: graphs and circuits.

Mailbox: Several practical examples of Hamilton's problem, which is discussed in Lesson 11-1, can be modeled by a graph. One of these problems asks if a postal-truck driver can plan a route that begins and ends at the same place and allows the collection of the mail from all of the boxes without passing any box twice.

Roses: The **Example** in Lesson 11-6 on Markov Chains uses a transition matrix to find the proportion, after several generations, of pale and brilliant roses.

Paris Bridges: In Lesson 11-4, which discusses the Königsberg Bridge problem, **Exercise 12** poses a similar problem involving the bridges over the Seine River in Paris.

Handshake: If there are n people at a party, and each person shakes another person's hand, how many shakes will occur? Lesson 11-3 discusses handshake problems.

Oil Field: **Exercise 13** in Lesson 11-1 deals with an oil company's use of test drilling to determine what areas of its land will be worth developing.

Chapter 11 Projects

At this time, you might want to have students look over the projects on pages 707–708.

The chapter opener and Lesson 11-1 discuss the use of graphs to solve problems. The examples include scheduling problems, puzzles, and conditional probability, and they are a vehicle to introduce some of the terminology associated with graphs.

Lesson 11-2 provides a formal definition of graph and relates certain graphs to matrices. Lessons 11-3 and 11-4 build on those definitions, and some simple theorems with powerful applications are proved.

Lessons 11-5 and 11-6 continue the relationship between matrices and graphs. Powers of matrices give information about graphs which would be hard to acquire from direct examination of the graph.

Markov chains use ideas of large powers of probability matrices to show that the limiting effects of certain paths in a graph are predictable and stable.

Lesson 11-7 shows how theorems from the previous lessons can be employed to prove the famous relationship between the numbers of vertices V, faces F, and edges E of any polyhedron: $V - E + F = 2$.

Lesson 11-1

Objectives

E Use graphs to solve scheduling and probability problems.

G Solve application problems involving circuits.

Resources

From the ***Teacher's Resource File***

- Lesson Master 11-1
- Answer Master 11-1
- Teaching Aids
  - 110 Warm-up
  - 112 Graphs of Euler and Hamilton
  - 113 Example 2
  - 114 Example 3 and Question 13a
  - 115 Additional Examples 1 and 2

Additional Resources

- Visuals for Teaching Aids 110, 112–115

Teaching Lesson 11-1

Warm-up

Consider the cube below.

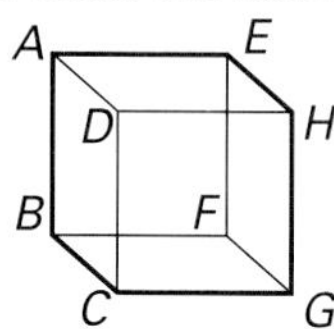

1. Is it possible to draw a path along the edges of the cube that contains each vertex exactly once and ends where it started? If so, draw such a path. **Possible; sample path: *ABCGFEHDA***
2. Is it possible to draw a path along its edges that contains each edge once and ends where it started? If so, draw such a path. **Not possible**

LESSON

11-1 *Modeling with Graphs*

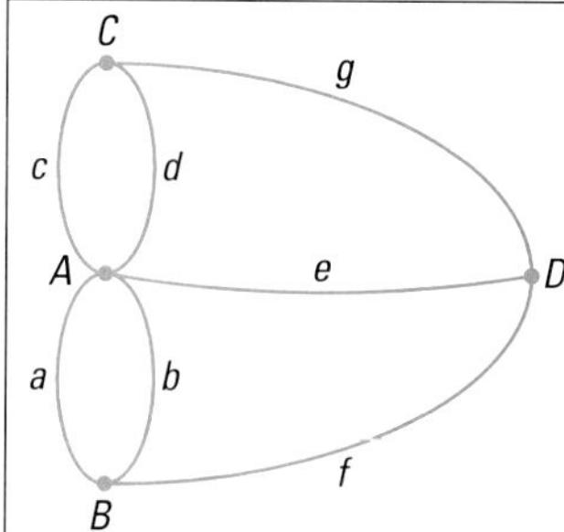

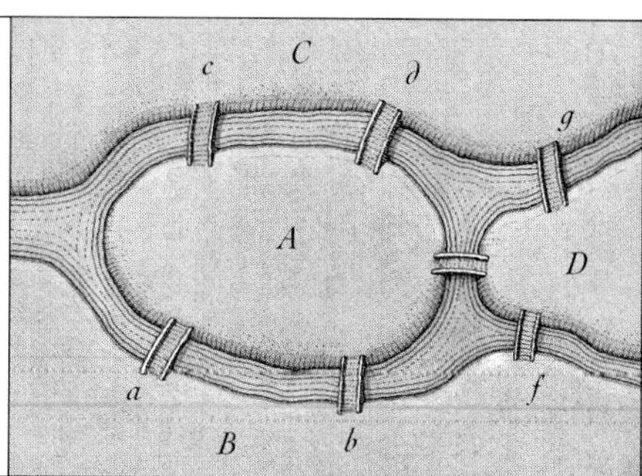

Traversing the Edges of a Graph

To solve the Königsberg bridge problem of the preceding page, Euler observed that, for this problem, each land mass could be represented by a point since it is possible to walk from any part of a land mass to any other part without crossing a bridge. The bridges could be thought of as arcs joining these points. Thus the situation of Königsberg could be represented by the following geometric model consisting of four points and seven arcs.

❶ This type of geometric model is called a graph. The four points are the **vertices** and the seven arcs are the **edges** of the graph. In terms of this graph, the Königsberg bridge problem can be stated:

> Is it possible to trace this graph with a pencil, traveling each edge exactly once, starting and ending at the same vertex, without picking up the pencil?

Euler's solution to the Königsberg bridge problem is given in Lesson 11-4.

Traversing the Vertices of a Graph

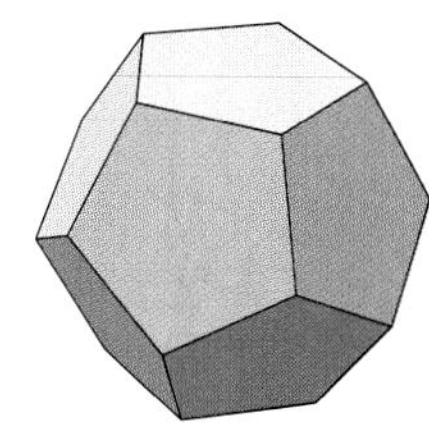

Another famous puzzle for which a graph is a very helpful model was invented in 1859 by the Irish mathematician Sir William Rowan Hamilton (1805–1865). The puzzle consisted of a wooden block in the shape of a regular dodecahedron, as shown at the right.

This polyhedron has 12 regular pentagons as its faces, 30 edges, and 20 vertices. Hamilton marked each vertex of the block with the name of a city, and the object of the puzzle was to find a travel route along the edges of the block that would visit each of the cities once and only once. A small pin protruded from each vertex so that the player could mark a route by wrapping string around each pin in order as its city was visited.

By thinking of the polyhedron as transparent, as shown at the top of page 659 at the left, you can count to determine that Hamilton's problem involves a graph with 20 vertices and 30 edges in which 3 edges meet at each vertex. The graph at the right shows the same relationships of vertices and edges in a 2-dimensional diagram; the two graphs are **equivalent**.

Lesson 11-1 Overview

Broad Goals This is an informal lesson that introduces students to some of the kinds of problems they will encounter in the chapter and gives them practice in drawing graphs.

Perspective The first situations in this lesson involve two different problems of traversing a graph: (1) The Königsberg bridge problem is a problem of traversing all the *edges* of a graph exactly once. It is like the practical problem of a snowplow having to traverse streets and wanting to do so efficiently. *Warm-up* Question 2 is of this type. (2) A problem of William Rowan Hamilton involves traversing all the *vertices* of a dodecahedron exactly once. It is like the practical problem of a mailman who has mailboxes at intersections of streets and wishes to be at each intersection exactly once for efficiency. (*Warm-up* Question 1 is of this type.)

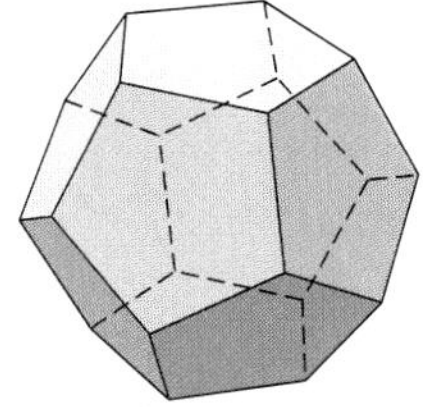

Hamilton's puzzle can be stated in terms of either graph as the following problem:

> Is it possible to trace this graph with a pencil, traveling through each *vertex* exactly once, without picking up the pencil?

In fact, Hamilton also sold the 2-dimensional version of his puzzle since it was easier to work with. Notice the similarity between the problems of Euler and Hamilton; in both the goal is to traverse all objects of one kind in the graph exactly once; in Euler's problem the objects are the edges; in Hamilton's the objects are the vertices.

Several practical situations are examples of Hamilton's problem.

❷ **Example 1**

One mailbox is located at each intersection of a city and a postal truck is required to collect the mail from all the boxes in the 42-block region in the map at the right.

Can the driver plan a pick-up route that begins and ends at the same place and allows collection of the mail from all of the boxes without passing one that has already been collected?

Solution

The problem can be modeled by a graph, with the mailboxes being the vertices and the streets being the edges. Experimentation gives several suitable routes such as the one pictured here.

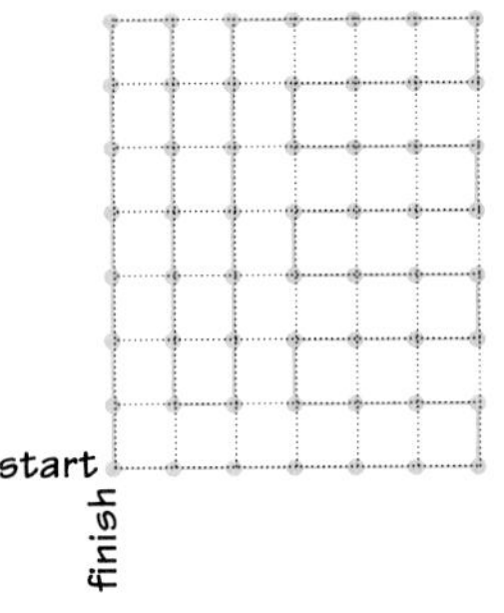

Notes on Reading

The chapter opener on page 657 begins this lesson and should not be ignored in the reading.

❶ **Reading Mathematics** In almost every lesson of this chapter, important terminology new to the students will be introduced. While the number of terms per lesson is not large, the total is, so students should be forewarned to learn the vocabulary in each lesson as they read it. In this lesson, the terms *vertex* and *edge* are introduced before their formal definition in Lesson 11-2. Other key terms are *equivalent graphs* and *digraphs*.

❷ **Error Alert** The idea most likely to confuse students here is the distinction between the problems of Euler and Hamilton. Note that both are problems of traversing, but in Euler's we think of bridges as edges and in Hamilton's we think of mailboxes as vertices. **Teaching Aid 112** shows Euler's and Hamilton's graphs.

Although the snowplow and mailman problems might seem to be equivalent, they are not. Euler's solution to the Königsberg bridge problem is given in Lesson 11-4; there is no known general solution to problems of Hamilton's type. A third type of use of graphs for efficiency is with the scheduling of tasks to finish them in the shortest amount of time. Graphs used in scheduling have edges that can only be traversed in a particular direction; they are *digraphs*. An algorithm for a solution to the scheduling problem is known and given in this lesson.

A digraph in which vertices are labeled with probabilities is called a probability tree and is used in the final example of this lesson. This kind of graph clarifies the computation of conditional probabilities.

Consumer Connection The scheduling problem of **Example 2** is a fundamental problem in almost any business in which time is critical. At a muffler shop or other car repair installation that promises quick service, the speed is based on an efficiency of schedule. When an airplane stops, it needs to be serviced, its luggage and passengers unloaded and loaded, and its cabin cleaned all in the shortest total amount of time. **Teaching Aid 113,** which shows the table and graph on page 660, can be used in discussing **Example 2.**

Example 3, on page 662, connects the mathematics of probability with graphs. In constructing the graph, students are applying the formula for conditional probability, $P(A \cap B) = P(A) \cdot P(B \text{ given } A)$, when they complete the probabilities of the "leaves" of the tree. For example, $P(\text{Campus and Favor}) = P(\text{Campus}) \cdot P(\text{Favor given Campus}) = .6 \cdot .7 = .42$. The graph shown in the solution is on **Teaching Aid 114.** Also, **Question 13a** relates specifically to this example.

The work in this lesson with conditional probability sets the stage for work with Markov chains in Lesson 11-6.

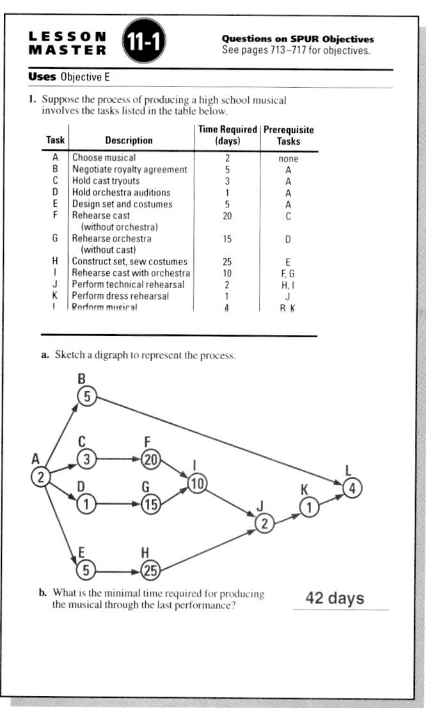

LESSON MASTER 11-1 **Questions on SPUR Objectives** See pages 713–717 for objectives.

Uses Objective E

1. Suppose the process of producing a high school musical involves the tasks listed in the table below.

Task	Description	Time Required (days)	Prerequisite Tasks
A	Choose musical	2	none
B	Negotiate royalty agreement	5	A
C	Hold cast tryouts	3	A
D	Hold orchestra auditions	1	A
E	Design set and costumes	5	A
F	Rehearse cast (without orchestra)	20	C
G	Rehearse orchestra (without cast)	15	D
H	Construct set, sew costumes	25	E
I	Rehearse cast with orchestra	10	F, G
J	Perform technical rehearsal	2	H, I
K	Perform dress rehearsal	1	J
L	Perform musical	4	B, K

a. Sketch a digraph to represent the process.

b. What is the minimal time required for producing the musical through the last performance? 42 days

A Non-Geometric Example

The two examples you have seen so far result from situations that themselves are geometric. The next example is quite different; it shows the use of graphs in scheduling a complex task. First, some background information is necessary.

Building a house is usually a team effort that involves specialists such as architects, excavators, concrete workers, framing carpenters, drywallers, electricians, plumbers, roofers, heating and air conditioning workers, finish carpenters, painters, and landscapers. Different specialists are often able to work at the same time provided that the work that must precede a particular specialist is completed before that specialist begins. By working simultaneously whenever possible, the house can be completed more quickly, and it is natural to wonder if there is some optimal way to schedule the various tasks for completion.

This can be done with a graph, but first the information to be graphed must be assembled. Here is a list of some of the tasks involved in building a house, along with the time they require and the tasks which must be completed prior to their beginning. (The list is simplified but the ideas are not.)

Task		Time (days)	Prerequisite tasks
A	Preparing final house and site plans	3	none
B	Excavation and foundation construction	5	*A*
C	Framing and closing main structure	12	*B*
D	Plumbing	5	*C*
E	Wiring	3	*C*
F	Heating-cooling installation	7	*E*
G	Insulation and dry wall	9	*D, F*
H	Exterior siding, trim, and painting	15	*C*
I	Interior finishing and painting	7	*G*
J	Carpeting	3	*I*
K	Landscaping	4	*H*

It would take 73 days to finish the house if only one task were done on any day. However, the following graph can help the builder decide which tasks can be done simultaneously in order to complete the job more quickly. The tasks are represented by vertices, drawn here as circles. The number of days needed for each job is indicated inside its circle. The arrows represent edges; when an arrow is drawn such as from vertex *A* to vertex *B*, it means that task *A* must be completed before task *B* can begin.

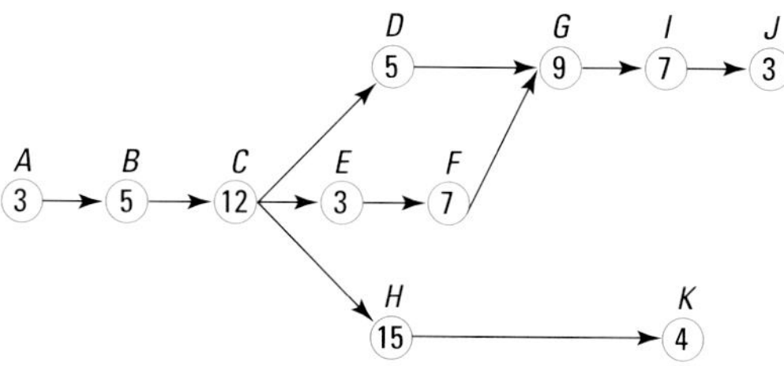

Optional Activities

Activity 1 For the graphs in **Questions 4–5,** ask students how many different paths can be drawn where the starting point and ending point are the same and all vertices are traversed exactly once.[See diagrams at the right. In **Question 4,** there are two paths; in **Question 5,** there are six paths.]

4. Two paths

5. Six paths a. b.

And 3 others formed by 90° rotations of (a) and one other formed by a 90° rotation of (b).

Example 2

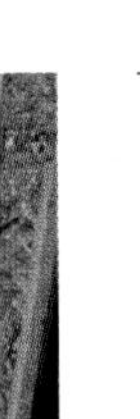

Use the graph on page 660 to determine the least number of days to complete the house.

Solution

From left to right along the graph, calculate for each task the least number of days in which it can be completed since the beginning of construction. Write this number beneath the circle representing the task. For instance, task *D* requires the completion of tasks *A*, *B*, and *C*, which takes 20 days. Since *D* requires 5 more days, write 25 beneath *D*. Through Task *F* similarly requires 30 days. Since both *D* and *F* must be done before *G*, *G* cannot be started before 30 days and will not be completed before 39 days.

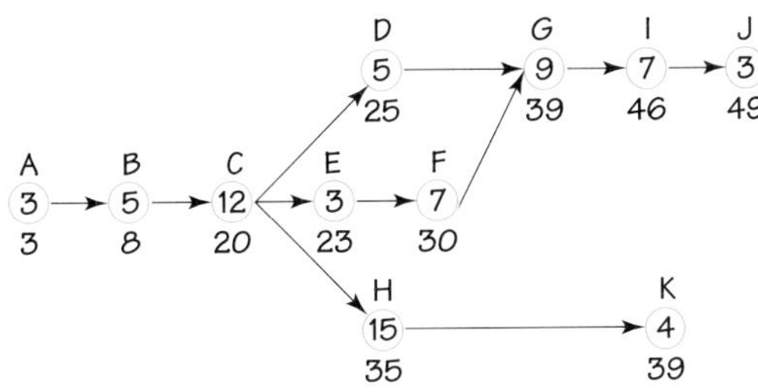

All the tasks will be completed when both *J* and *K* are done. Since *J* requires at least 49 days and *K* requires at least 39 days for its completion, **the house can be completed in 49 days.**

Notice that the algorithm used in Example 2 is recursive. Here is the general algorithm to calculate the number of days for a particular task:

> If there are no prerequisite tasks, use the number of days required by this task alone.
>
> Otherwise:
> (1) Calculate the number of days for each prerequisite task by using this algorithm.
> (2) Choose the largest of the numbers found in step (1), and add to it the number of days required by this task alone.

This algorithm is used to determine efficient job schedules for much more complex projects, and there exists computer software which will automatically create the graph and find the solution after the user inputs information like that given in Example 2.

The graph of Example 2 is different from the others in this lesson in that you can travel along each edge in only one direction. Such graphs are called **directed graphs** or **digraphs**. The graph in the solution differs in a second way; each vertex is labeled with a number.

Additional Examples

The graph in Additional Example 1 and the table and graph in Additional Example 2 are on **Teaching Aid 115.**

1. A mailbox is located at each intersection in the downtown section of a city and a postal truck is required to collect the mail from all 45 boxes shown in the diagram below. Is there a route that begins and ends at the same point without passing a box from which the mail has already been collected?

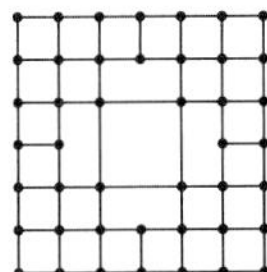

We have been unable to find such a route. This problem underscores the difficulty of such questions.

(Additional Examples continue on page 662.)

Optional Activities

Activity 2 Writing You might ask students to write and then answer three more questions about the situation described in **Question 13.** [Sample questions and answers given.]

1. Which is more likely to be found in "random" testing: a closed structure, open structure, or no structure? [No structure]
2. Suppose seismic testing indicates no structure. What is the probability that drilling there would produce a gusher? [$\approx$ 2%]
3. What type of structure gives the highest probability of finding a gusher? [Open]

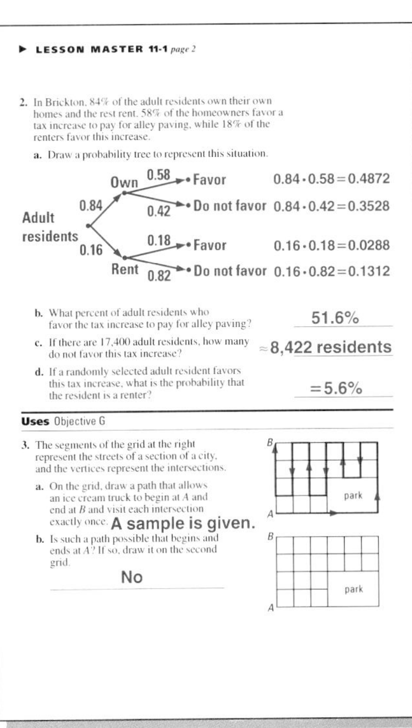

▶ **LESSON MASTER 11-1** *page 2*

2. In Brickton, 84% of the adult residents own their own homes and the rest rent. 58% of the homeowners favor a tax increase to pay for alley paving, while 18% of the renters favor this increase.
   a. Draw a probability tree to represent this situation.

   b. What percent of adult residents who favor the tax increase to pay for alley paving? **51.6%**
   c. If there are 17,400 adult residents, how many do not favor this tax increase? **≈ 8,422 residents**
   d. If a randomly selected adult resident favors this tax increase, what is the probability that the resident is a renter? **= 5.6%**

Uses Objective G

3. The segments of the grid at the right represent the streets of a section of a city, and the vertices represent the intersections.
   a. On the grid, draw a path that allows an ice cream truck to begin at *A* and end at *B* and visit each intersection exactly once. **A sample is given.**
   b. Is such a path possible that begins and ends at *A*? If so, draw it on the second grid. **No**

2. A scientific experiment involves the following tasks.

	Task	Time (months)
A	Choosing a project	1
B	Organizing a team	1
C	Obtaining funding	2
D	Setting up equipment	0.5
E	Running procedures	6
F	Keeping records	5.5
G	Writing a report	1

The graph below shows the tasks, the time it takes to complete each task, and the relationships among the tasks. Use the graph to determine the least number of months to complete the experiment.

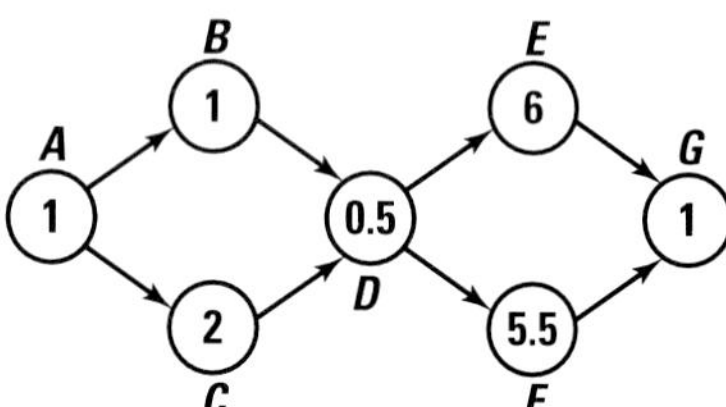

The diagram below shows the total number of months to complete each part of the experiment. For instance, tasks *A*, *B*, and *D* take $1 + 1 + 0.5 = 2.5$ months. Tasks *A*, *C*, and *D* take $1 + 2 + 0.5 = 3.5$ months. So task *D* cannot be completed before 3.5 months. Thus, 3.5 is written below the circle for *D*.

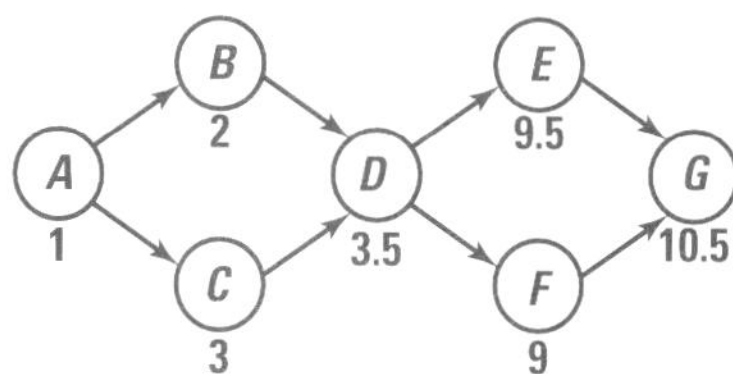

The total number of months needed to complete the experiment is 10.5.

A Probability Tree

A particular type of digraph, called a *probability tree*, is useful for solving certain problems involving probabilities. In a **probability tree**, a vertex represents an event, and the edge leading from vertex *A* to vertex *B* is labeled with the probability that event *B* occurs if *A* occurs. The last vertex of each branch is called a *leaf* of the tree.

Example 3

60% of the students in a college live on campus. 70% of those who live on campus favor improved student health services even if it means an increase in tuition. 40% of those who live off campus favor this increase. Draw a graph to answer the following.

a. What is the proportion of students who favor this increase to pay for improved student health services?

b. If a randomly selected student favors the tuition increase, what is the probability that the student lives on campus?

Solution

a. Draw a graph showing the division of students by residence: Campus or Off-Campus. Since 60% of the students live on campus, 40% must live off campus. Then break down each group by their opinions on the increase. The proportion of students who are both on campus and favor the increase is $.6 \cdot .7 = .42$. The proportion of students who are on campus and don't favor the increase is $.6 \cdot .3 = .18$. Similarly, you can compute the proportion of students in the two branches leading from the Off-Campus vertex.

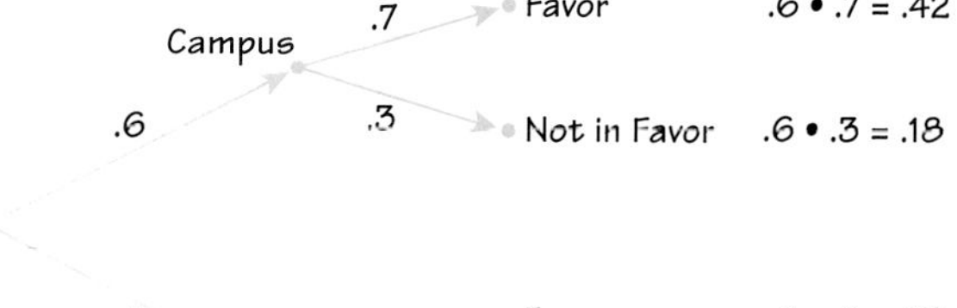

Notice that the proportions at the end of the graph add to 1.00; all students are represented by the leaves of the tree. The proportion of students who favor the tuition increase is .42 + .16 or 58% of the student body.

b. 58% of the student body are in favor of the increase, while 42% are in favor *and* live on campus. Therefore, given that a student favors the increase, there is a $\frac{.42}{.58} \approx 72\%$ probability that the student lives on campus.

Adapting to Individual Needs

Extra Help

Students might find it tedious to redraw complicated graphs, such as the one in Additional Example 1, as they experiment to find the required route. You might want to have them draw just one copy of the graph and then draw each tested route on a sheet of tracing paper or a transparency placed over the graph.

Challenge

Refer to the digraph of building a house on page 661. Ask students to think of other complex tasks where digraph modeling to determine the length of the project would be appropriate. Interested students might research their idea and produce a digraph. [Samples: building an airplane or car; cleaning a large office building or hotel; harvesting crops on a farm; filming a movie]

a)

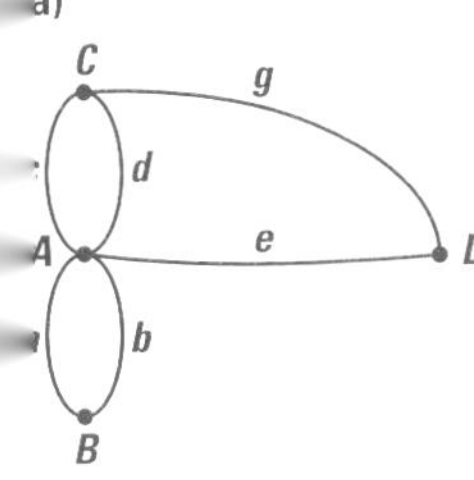

) Yes; Sample:

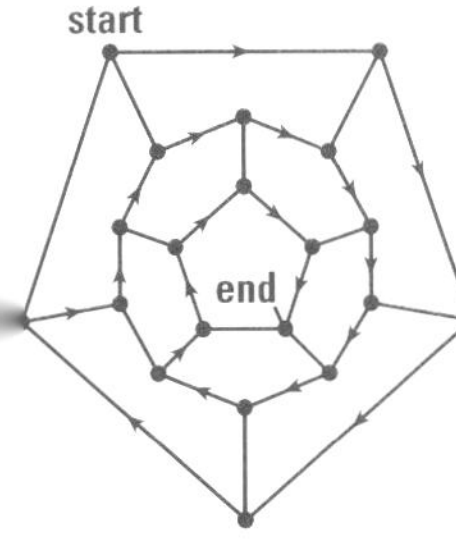

) Sample:

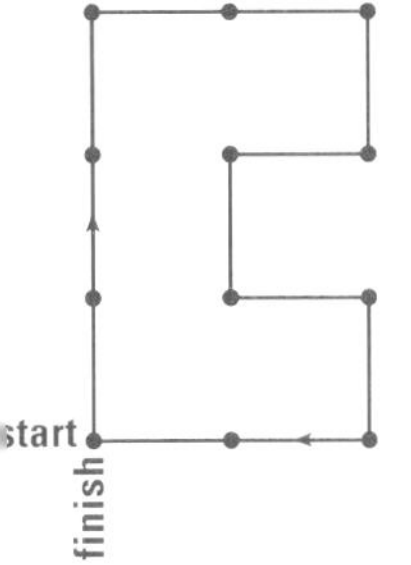

5) Sample:

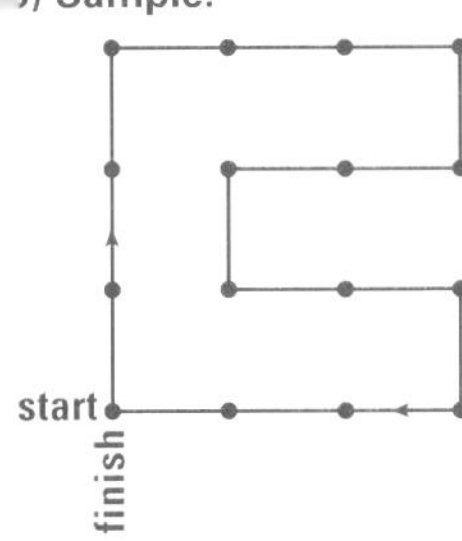

QUESTIONS

Covering the Reading

1. The seventh bridge of Königsberg to be built connected the land masses B and D in the drawing on page 658.
   a. Draw a graph of the Königsberg bridge problem when the city had only 6 bridges. **See left.**
   b. Show that there is a path around the city crossing each of the six bridges exactly once by listing the land masses and bridges, in order. Does your path begin and end at the same point? **Sample: *A, a, B, b, A, e, D, g, C, c, A, d, C*; no**
2. Copy the graph for Hamilton's dodecahedron. Determine whether there is a solution to Hamilton's problem. **See left.**
3. In Euler's problem, each __?__ is traversed exactly once, and in Hamilton's problem, each __?__ is traversed exactly once. **edge, vertex**

In 4 and 5, copy the graph. Think of the vertices of the graph as mailboxes and the edges as streets, and draw a path that will allow a driver to collect the mail from each box without passing one whose mail has already been collected, starting and finishing at the same point. **See left.**

4. 

5. 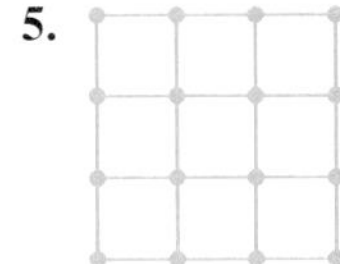

6. In the situation of Example 2, a new task L, the moving in of appliances, taking one day, and requiring the completion of task I, is added to the schedule.
   a. Draw a new graph including task L. **See margin.**
   b. How does this affect the time to finish the house? **does not affect it**

In 7–9, refer to Example 3.

7. If there are 2000 students at the college, how many live off campus *and* favor improved student health services? **320 students**
8. What is the proportion of students who don't favor a tuition increase for improved student health services? **.42**
9. If a student selected at random doesn't favor a tuition increase for improved student health services, what is the probability that he or she lives on campus? **≈ .43**
10. A store estimates that 80% of its customers are female. The probability that a female wears contact lenses is 6%. The probability that a male wears contact lenses is 5%.
    a. Draw a probability tree and label its edges with the appropriate probabilities to represent this situation. **See margin.**
    b. What proportion of customers of this store are male and don't wear contact lenses? **19%**
    c. What proportion wear contacts? **5.8%**

3. Suppose 75% of a class of students own automatic graphers. Suppose 80% of those who own graphers think they should be allowed on tests and 90% of those who do not own graphers think they should not be allowed on tests.
   a. Draw a graph of this situation.

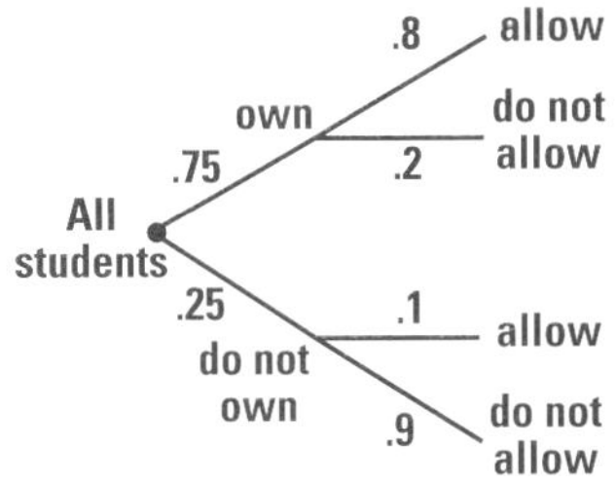

   b. What is the probability that a student from the class favors the use of these graphers on tests? **.625**
   c. If a randomly selected student opposes the use of these graphers, what is the probability that student does not own an automatic grapher? **.6**

Notes on Questions

Question 3 The differences between the problems of Hamilton and Euler can be easily seen by considering a graph that looks like a picture of a cube, as in the *Warm-up*. Traversing all the vertices exactly once is easy but traversing all the edges without repetition is impossible.

Additional Answers

6. a.

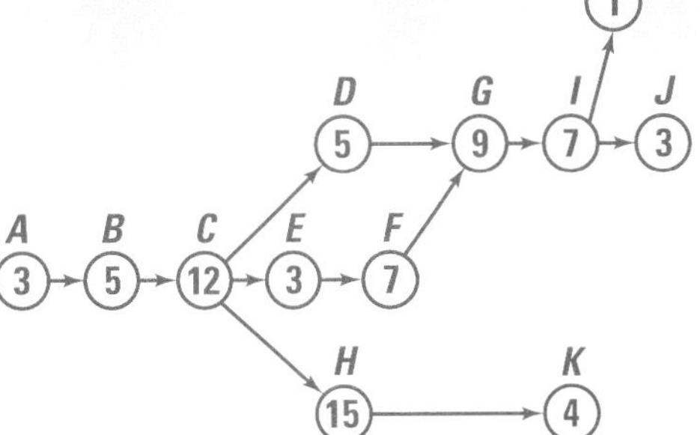

10. a.

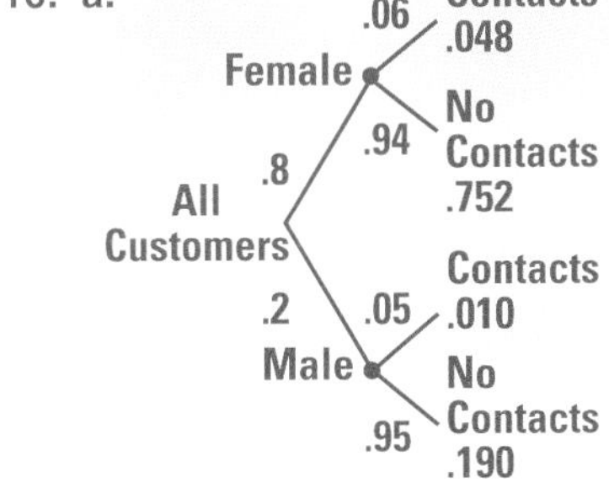

Notes on Questions

Question 13 Although there is a lot of reading here, the question is not difficult to do once a graph has been drawn. The probability tree is on **Teaching Aid 114.**

Question 14 Königsberg is the German equivalent of Kingstown or Kingston.

Question 15 Note that graphs are a natural way of organizing information about relations between sets. Students' graphs will differ depending on the definitions of trapezoid and isosceles trapezoid. For UCSMP *Geometry* students and some others, trapezoids include parallelograms, and isosceles trapezoids include rectangles.

Question 21b Hamilton's problem, of which this is an example, is more difficult than Euler's, and there is no known general criterion for determining traversability. Even for this simple example, a proof is beyond the scope of this course.

Applying the Mathematics

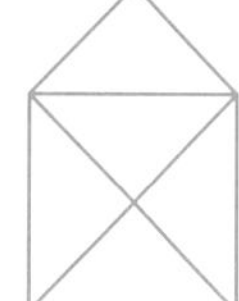

11. A common children's puzzle is to traverse the edges of the drawing at the left exactly once. Is this puzzle more like Euler's problem or Hamilton's problem? **Euler's**

12. The possibility tree of Example 1 in Lesson 10-2 is a graph.
 a. How many vertices does that graph have? **39**
 b. How many edges does that graph have? **38**

Oil Rig. *This roughneck, drenched in mud which acts as a lubricant, is attaching a new section of pipe.*

13. An oil company has used expensive test drilling to determine what areas of its land will be worth developing as oil fields. Only 10% of the test wells are gushers which indicate oil deposits worth developing. Test wells are extremely expensive to drill, so the company has been studying the use of less expensive seismic tests on a plot to predict whether drilling is worthwhile. Seismic tests indicate whether the underlying strata have a closed structure, open structure, or no structure. Over a period of time, the company performs seismic tests in conjunction with drilling. The table below shows the proportions of gushers and of nongushers that are associated with each structure. For example, 60% of the gushers came from closed structures.

	Closed	Open	No Structure
Gusher	.60	.30	.10
Not a gusher	.20	.30	.50

 a. Find the probabilities v, w, x, y, and z in the following probability tree.
 $v = .90$; $w = .30$; $x = .50$; $y = .01$; $z = .45$

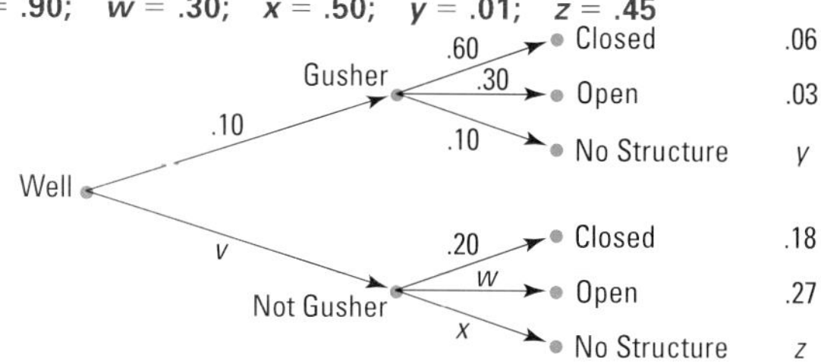

 b. What is the probability that the underlying strata of a randomly selected well has a closed structure? **.24**
 c. Suppose the company conducts a seismic test on one of its properties and finds a closed structure. According to the data above, what is the probability that drilling there would produce a gusher? **.25**
 d. Suppose a seismic test indicates an open structure. What is the probability that drilling there would produce a gusher? **.10**

14. In Queenstown there is a river with two islands and bridges connecting the islands to the shore, as depicted at the right. Is there a path traversing each bridge exactly once? **Yes**

664

15. Draw a digraph whose vertices represent the following nine types of figures: isosceles trapezoids, kites, parallelograms, polygons, quadrilaterals, rectangles, rhombuses, squares, and trapezoids. Draw an arrow connecting vertex X to vertex Y if and only if all Xs are Ys, but do not connect X to Z if X is connected to Y and Y is connected to Z. **See margin.**

Review

16. a. Sketch the graph of a function whose first derivative is negative on the interval [-5, -2) and positive on the interval (-2, 3]. **See left.**

b. Identify the location of a relative minimum or maximum. Which is it? *(Lesson 9-5)* **There is a relative minimum at $x = -2$.**

17. Consider the matrix at the right.

$$\begin{bmatrix} 5 & 1 & 0 \\ 3 & 2 & 0 \\ 8 & 0.5 & -3 \\ 4 & 6 & 10 \end{bmatrix}$$

a. What are its dimensions? **4×3**

b. If a_{ij} is the element in the ith row and jth column, what is a_{23}? **0**

c. Calculate $\sum_{i=1}^{3} a_{ii}$. *(Lesson 7-2)* **4**

18. Express in terms of tan x. *(Lesson 6-5)*

a. $\tan\left(x + \frac{\pi}{2}\right)$ **$-\frac{1}{\tan x}$** **b.** $\tan(x + \pi)$ **$\tan x$** **c.** $\tan\left(x + \frac{3\pi}{2}\right)$ **$-\frac{1}{\tan x}$**

19. Suppose p is a polynomial function whose graph is shown at the left. What is the smallest possible value for the degree of p? *(Lesson 4-4)* **7**

20. Solve $\sqrt{3y + 1} = 4$. Indicate which steps are reversible and which are not. *(Lesson 3-3)* **See left.**

Exploration

21. Example 1 and Questions 4 and 5 ask for the traversing of all the vertices of a rectangular array exactly once, going horizontally or vertically, and beginning and ending at the same point. In size, these arrays are 8 by 7, 4 by 3, and 4 by 4. **a) Samples: 3×3, 5×5**

a. Find a rectangular array that cannot be traversed in this way.

b. Find a criterion that seems to distinguish the dimensions of those arrays that can be traversed from those which cannot be traversed. **One dimension must be even for an array to be traversed.**

16a)

20) $\sqrt{3y + 1} = 4$
1. $3y + 1 = 16$ non reversible
2. $3y = 15$ reversible
3. $y = 5$ reversible

Practice

For more questions on SPUR Objectives, use **Lesson Master 11-1** (shown on pages 660–661).

Assessment

Written Communication Have students **work in small groups.** Ask each group to give the tasks and times for an activity of their choice. Possibilities include a craft project, putting on a concert, or producing a newspaper. Then have the groups represent their information in a digraph like the one above **Example 2.** [Students design schedules and represent them with a digraph.]

Extension

Project Update Project 5, *Dynamic Programming,* on page 708, relates to the content of this lesson.

Additional Answers

15. Sample:

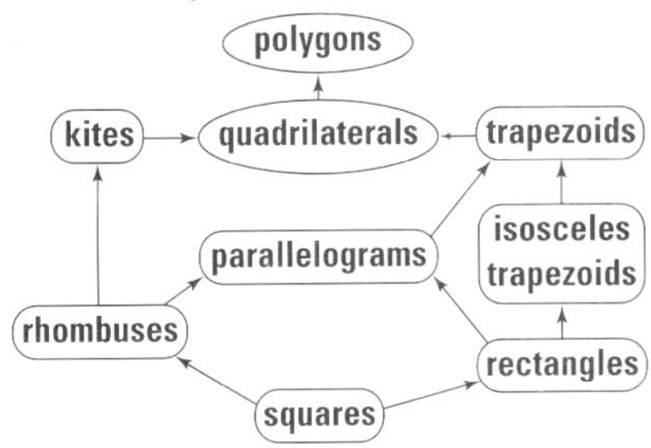

Setting Up Lesson 11-2

Be certain that students know the difference between the edges of a graph and the vertices of a graph.

Lesson 11-2

Objectives

A Draw graphs given sufficient information.
B Identify parts of graphs and types of graphs.
I Convert between the picture of a graph or directed graph, and its adjacency matrix.

Resources

From the ***Teacher's Resource File***

- Lesson Master 11-2
- Answer Master 11-2
- Teaching Aids
  - 110 Warm-up
  - 116 Example 3
  - 117 Example 4 and Questions 5 and 6
  - 118 Questions 7, 10, 11, and 12
  - 119 Questions 14, 15, and 17

Additional Resources

- Visuals for Teaching Aids 110, 116–119

Teaching Lesson 11-2

Warm-up

Draw a graph with 5 vertices and the following number of edges.

1. 3 edges

2. 5 edges

3. 11 edges

LESSON

11-2 The Definition of Graph

What Exactly Is a Graph?

In the last lesson you saw examples of problems that could be solved using graphs, but no definition of *graph* was given. In order to deduce general properties of graphs, a definition is needed. Consider the graph below.

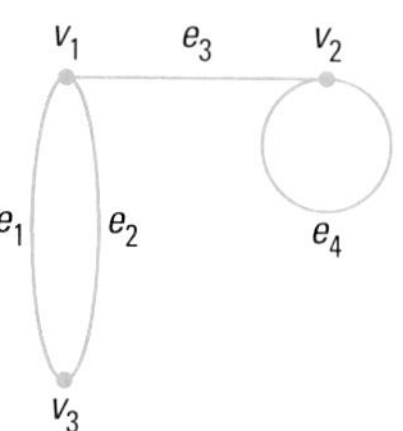

(1) Its vertices are v_1, v_2, and v_3.
(2) Its edges are e_1, e_2, e_3, and e_4.
(3) The endpoints of each edge are given by the following table.

edge	endpoints
e_1	$\{v_1, v_3\}$
e_2	$\{v_1, v_3\}$
e_3	$\{v_1, v_2\}$
e_4	$\{v_2\}$

This table describes an *edge-endpoint function.*

To specify a graph it is necessary to provide the kind of information given in (1)–(3) above, with words or a picture. Here is a formal definition of *graph.*

❶ **Definition**
A **graph** G consists of
1. a finite set of vertices,
2. a finite set of edges,
3. a function (the **edge-endpoint function**) that maps each edge to a set of either one or two vertices (the **endpoints** of the edge).

Some Vocabulary of Graphs

In a graph there must be a vertex at each end of every edge. An edge *connects* or *joins* its endpoints, but has no points other than its endpoints. So its shape—curve or segment—is not important. Two vertices connected by an edge are **adjacent vertices**. Two edges with a common endpoint are called **adjacent edges**. For instance, e_3 and e_2 above are adjacent edges.

Note that vertices v_1 and v_3 are connected by more than one edge. When this occurs the edges are said to be **parallel**. (This is a different meaning for "parallel" than that associated with lines.) Also edge e_4 joins vertex v_2 to itself. Such an edge is called a **loop**.

Lesson 11-2 Overview

Broad Goals The emphasis in this lesson is on the formal vocabulary of graphs. Students are expected to be able to convert between a geometric description (drawing), an algebraic description (definition), and an arithmetic description (matrix) of a graph.

Perspective The following etymology of the word "graph," from *The Words of Mathematics,* by Steven Schwartzman, published by the Mathematical Association of America, indicates how the graphs students have seen in algebra and the graphs here are part of the same tradition.

> **graph** (noun, verb): from the Greek verb *graphein* "to write," from the Indo-European root *gerbh-* "to scratch." Writing was originally scratched on wood, stone tablets, or the ground itself. Early geometers scratched pictures on the ground, too,

Example 1

Draw a picture of the graph G defined as follows.

1. set of vertices: $\{v_1, v_2, v_3, v_4, v_5\}$
2. set of edges: $\{e_1, e_2, e_3, e_4, e_5\}$
3. edge-endpoint function:

edge	endpoints
e_1	$\{v_1, v_2\}$
e_2	$\{v_1, v_4\}$
e_3	$\{v_1, v_4\}$
e_4	$\{v_5\}$
e_5	$\{v_4, v_5\}$

Solution

It is often convenient to start the graph by placing the vertices as though they were consecutive vertices of a convex polygon. Since there are 5 vertices, begin with a pentagon.

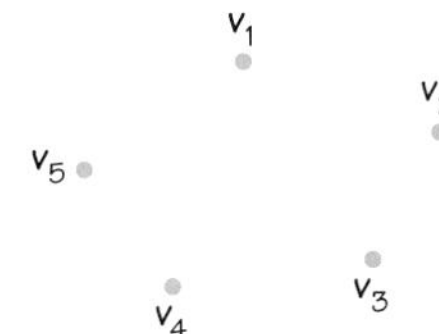

Then fill in edges as specified by the edge-endpoint function table.

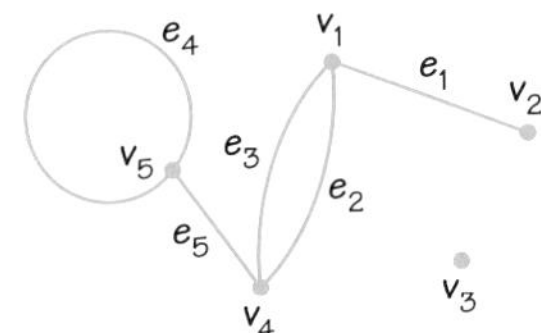

❷ In Example 1, vertex v_3 is not the endpoint of any edge. It is called **isolated**. The definition of graph allows isolated vertices. Although all edges must have endpoints, a vertex need not be the endpoint of an edge.

Simple Graphs

A picture of the graph from the housebuilding problem in Lesson 11-1 is repeated here with the vertices shown by dots.

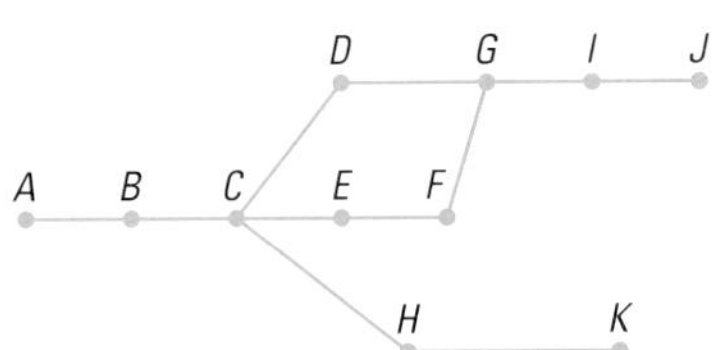

In this graph, there are no loops or parallel edges. Such a graph is called *simple*.

Notes on Reading

❶ **Reading Mathematics** The vocabulary of this lesson may be made easier by noting that there are three ways to describe a graph:

1. the geometric way, by a picture;
2. the algebraic way, by naming vertices, naming edges, and giving the edge-endpoint function; and
3. the arithmetic way, by writing a matrix that shows how many edges there are from any vertex v_i to any vertex v_j.

Example 1 gives an algebraic description of a graph (a definition), and students are asked to give a geometric description (drawing a picture). Students may wonder why the algebraic description is needed. There are two basic reasons: with the algebra, a problem involving graphs can be stated in computer language and so can be treated in a computer program; and with the algebra, theorems can be deduced about graphs.

❷ The terms *isolated, parallel,* and *simple* are easier for students to interpret in a setting involving a picture of a graph than by identifying the components of the formal definition. In terms of the edge-endpoint function, an isolated vertex is a vertex which does not appear on the table defining the function; parallel edges are those edges which map onto the same pair of vertices. The edge-endpoint function listing of a simple graph has no single vertices in the endpoints column and each pair of vertices occurs only once.

and that is how we acquired the word *graph* in the sense of a diagram or picture of a relation among variables. A related native English word is *crab,* since crabs scratch the ground as they walk along."

In this lesson, the type of graph found in network theory is formally defined by indicating its edges and then the vertices for each of the edges. There are natural meanings for adjacent edges, adjacent vertices, isolated vertices, and loops.

Parallel edges are two edges with the same endpoints, and a simple graph is one with no parallel edges and no loops.

Unlabeled graphs can be described by an adjacency matrix in which a_{ij} is the number of edges connecting vertex v_i to vertex v_j.

This matrix description is applied in Lessons 11-5 and 11-6. We assume students have studied matrices in a previous course.

You might wish to use **Teaching Aids 116 and 117** when discussing **Examples 3–4.**

Example 3 asks for the translation of geometric form (picture) into arithmetic form (matrix). Stress that before writing a matrix for a graph, the vertices should be ordered. If the graph is directed, then the rows stand for the origins of arrows and the columns for their destinations. **Example 4** translates from matrix to picture.

The adjacency matrix for a graph is symmetric unless the graph is a directed graph. The type of check in **Example 3** can be modified to check **Example 4.** Use the fact that the number of edges of an undirected graph equals the sum of the elements on or above the diagonal of the matrix. So the graph in **Example 4** must have 5 edges.

At this point, students do not need to know any operations on matrices, but by Lesson 11-5 multiplication of matrices must be well in hand. See the note with **Question 20.**

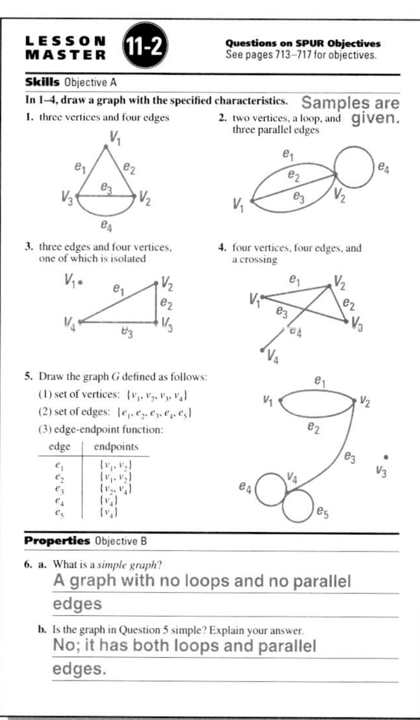

LESSON MASTER 11-2 Questions on SPUR Objectives
See pages 713–717 for objectives.

Skills Objective A

In 1–4, draw a graph with the specified characteristics. Samples are given.

1. three vertices and four edges
2. two vertices, a loop, and three parallel edges
3. three edges and four vertices, one of which is isolated
4. four vertices, four edges, and a crossing

5. Draw the graph G defined as follows:
(1) set of vertices: $\{v_1, v_2, v_3, v_4\}$
(2) set of edges: $\{e_1, e_2, e_3, e_4, e_5\}$
(3) edge-endpoint function:

edge	endpoints
e_1	$\{v_1, v_2\}$
e_2	$\{v_1, v_2\}$
e_3	$\{v_2, v_4\}$
e_4	$\{v_4\}$
e_5	$\{v_4\}$

Properties Objective B

6. a. What is a *simple graph*?
A graph with no loops and no parallel edges

b. Is the graph in Question 5 simple? Explain your answer.
No; it has both loops and parallel edges.

Definition
A graph is **simple** if and only if it does not have loops and it does not have parallel edges.

In a simple graph with vertices v and w, if edge $\{v, w\}$ exists, it is unique, since there is at most one edge joining any two of the graph's vertices.

Example 2

Draw all simple graphs with vertices $\{u, v, w\}$ if one of the edges is $\{u, v\}$.

Solution

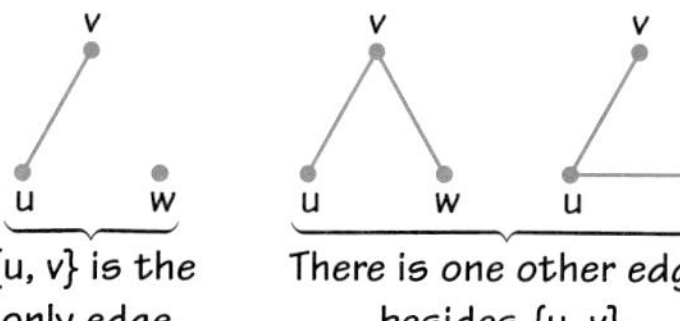

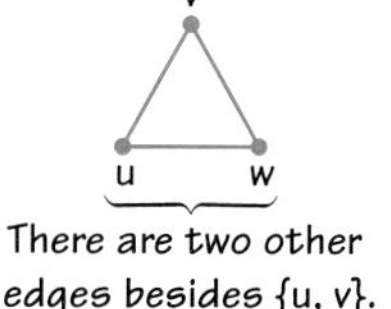

{u, v} is the only edge.

There is one other edge besides {u, v}.

There are two other edges besides {u, v}.

Consider the simple graph with vertices a, b, c, d and edges $\{a, c\}$, $\{b, d\}$, and $\{b, c\}$. Two pictures of this graph are shown below. In the left picture, the pictures of edges $\{a, c\}$ and $\{b, d\}$ intersect but the edges do not (because they have no points other than their endpoints). Such intersections in pictures are called **crossings**. The figure at the right illustrates the same graph but it avoids crossings.

Digraphs

Recall from Lesson 11-1 that it is sometimes useful to add direction to each edge of a graph. The resulting digraph is pictured like other graphs except that its edges are drawn with arrows. The formal definition of *digraph* is the same as the definition of graph except that the edge-endpoint function sends each edge to an *ordered pair* of vertices.

For instance, some group-behavior studies investigate the influence one person has on another in a social setting. The directed graph pictured at the right shows such a set of influence relationships.

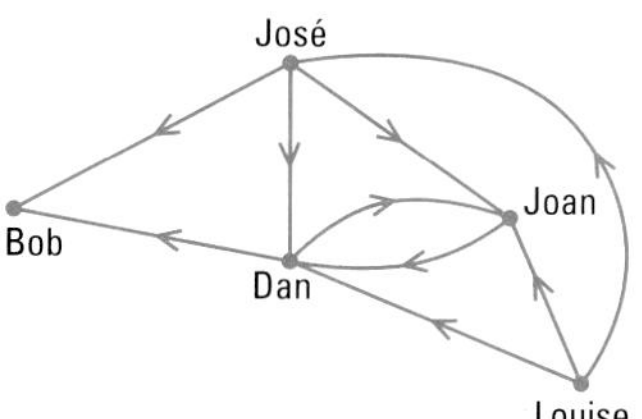

The arrows indicate that, for example, José influences Bob, Dan, and Joan, and Louise influences José, Dan, and Joan. The edge connecting Louise and Joan is said to go *from* the vertex for Louise *to* the vertex for Joan.

Optional Activities

After discussing the lesson, you might have students write adjacency matrices for the graphs in **Example 1** and **Questions 1–2.** Then ask them how they can tell from an adjacency matrix if an undirected graph has a loop, parallel edges, or an isolated vertex. [See matrices at the right. An undirected graph has a loop if there are nonzero numbers along the main diagonal (from upper left to lower right) of the matrix; a graph has parallel edges if the matrix contains numbers greater than one above or below the main diagonal; an isolated vertex is indicated by a row and column of zeros.]

Example 1:
$$\begin{bmatrix} 0 & 1 & 0 & 2 & 0 \\ 1 & 0 & 0 & 0 & 0 \\ 0 & 0 & 0 & 0 & 0 \\ 2 & 0 & 0 & 0 & 1 \\ 0 & 0 & 0 & 1 & 1 \end{bmatrix}$$

Question 1:
$$\begin{bmatrix} 0 & 1 & 0 & 0 \\ 1 & 0 & 3 & 0 \\ 0 & 3 & 0 & 0 \\ 0 & 0 & 0 & 0 \end{bmatrix}$$

Question 2:
$$\begin{bmatrix} 0 & 0 & 2 & 0 & 0 \\ 0 & 2 & 0 & 0 & 0 \\ 2 & 0 & 0 & 0 & 2 \\ 0 & 0 & 0 & 0 & 0 \\ 0 & 0 & 2 & 0 & 0 \end{bmatrix}$$

Using a Matrix to Describe a Graph

It is natural to want to describe a graph numerically. It may be somewhat surprising that this can be done using a matrix.

> **Definition**
> The **adjacency matrix** M for a graph with vertices $v_1, v_2, \ldots, v_n$ is the $n \times n$ matrix in which, $\forall$ i and j, the element in the ith row and jth column is the number of edges from vertex v_i to vertex v_j.

Example 3

Write the adjacency matrix for the directed graph of influence relationships pictured on page 668.

Solution

Because there are 5 vertices, the adjacency matrix has 5 rows and 5 columns. Label the rows and columns with the vertex names. To fill in the entry in the ith row and jth column, just count the number of edges from v_i to v_j. For instance, there are no edges from v_1 to v_1, so the entry in row 1, column 1 is 0. There is one edge from v_2 to v_3, so the entry in row 2, column 3 is 1. The entire adjacency matrix is given below.

$$\begin{array}{r} \\ \\ \text{Bob} = v_1 \\ \text{José} = v_2 \\ \text{Dan} = v_3 \\ \text{Joan} = v_4 \\ \text{Louise} = v_5 \end{array} \begin{array}{c} \begin{array}{ccccc} \text{Bob} & \text{José} & \text{Dan} & \text{Joan} & \text{Louise} \\ v_1 & v_2 & v_3 & v_4 & v_5 \end{array} \\ \begin{bmatrix} 0 & 0 & 0 & 0 & 0 \\ 1 & 0 & 1 & 1 & 0 \\ 1 & 0 & 0 & 1 & 0 \\ 0 & 0 & 1 & 0 & 0 \\ 0 & 1 & 1 & 1 & 0 \end{bmatrix} \end{array}$$

Check

In the matrix for a directed graph, each edge appears once, so the sum of all elements of the matrix equals the number of edges of the graph. Here the sum in the matrix is 9, which checks with the drawing on page 668.

Example 4

Draw a picture of a graph (*not* directed) that has the adjacency matrix shown at the left.

$$\begin{array}{c} \\ v_1 \\ v_2 \\ v_3 \end{array} \begin{array}{c} \begin{array}{ccc} v_1 & v_2 & v_3 \end{array} \\ \begin{bmatrix} 1 & 2 & 0 \\ 2 & 2 & 0 \\ 0 & 0 & 0 \end{bmatrix} \end{array}$$

Solution

Draw vertices v_1, v_2, and v_3 and connect them by edges as indicated in the matrix. For example, the 2 in the first row and second column indicates that two edges should go from v_1 to v_2. Since the graph is not directed, these two edges also go from v_2 to v_1, agreeing with the 2 in the second row and first column of the matrix. Note that when the graph is completed there is one loop at v_1 and two at v_2, that there are parallel edges joining v_1 and v_2, and that v_3 is an isolated vertex.

Additional Examples

1. Draw a picture of the graph G with vertices v_1, v_2, v_3, v_4, and v_5; edges e_1, e_2, e_3, e_4, and e_5, and the following edge-endpoint function:
   e_1 has endpoints $\{v_1, v_2\}$
   e_2 has endpoints $\{v_3\}$
   e_3 has endpoints $\{v_1, v_3\}$
   e_4 has endpoints $\{v_1, v_4\}$
   e_5 has endpoints $\{v_3, v_4\}$.

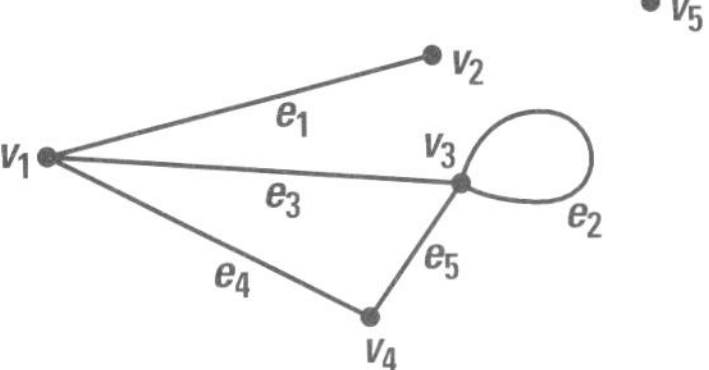

2. Draw a simple graph with 5 vertices and 7 edges.
   Sample:

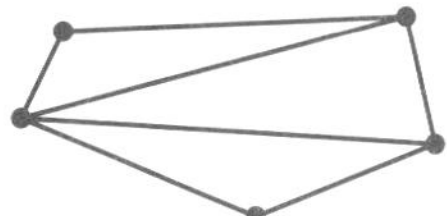

3. A, B, and C are three cities. Every day there are 2 nonstop flights from A to B, 3 from B to C, and 1 from A to C. There are 2 nonstop flights from B to A, 2 from C to B, and 1 from C to A. Write the adjacency matrix for this information.
   $\begin{bmatrix} 0 & 2 & 1 \\ 2 & 0 & 2 \\ 1 & 3 & 0 \end{bmatrix}$

(*Additional Examples continue on page 670.*)

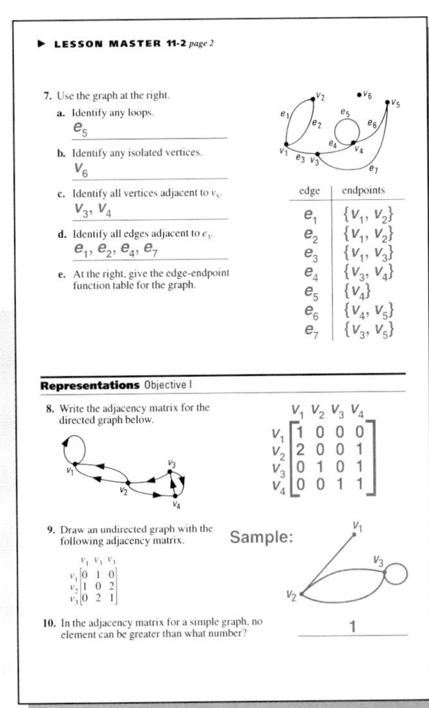

▶ **LESSON MASTER 11-2** *page 2*

7. Use the graph at the right.
   a. Identify any loops. e_5
   b. Identify any isolated vertices. v_6
   c. Identify all vertices adjacent to v_5. v_3, v_4
   d. Identify all edges adjacent to e_3. e_1, e_2, e_4, e_7
   e. At the right, give the edge-endpoint function table for the graph.

edge	endpoints
e_1	$\{v_1, v_2\}$
e_2	$\{v_1, v_2\}$
e_3	$\{v_1, v_3\}$
e_4	$\{v_3, v_4\}$
e_5	$\{v_4\}$
e_6	$\{v_4, v_5\}$
e_7	$\{v_3, v_5\}$

Representations Objective I

8. Write the adjacency matrix for the directed graph below.

$$\begin{array}{c} \\ v_1 \\ v_2 \\ v_3 \\ v_4 \end{array} \begin{array}{c} \begin{array}{cccc} v_1 & v_2 & v_3 & v_4 \end{array} \\ \begin{bmatrix} 1 & 0 & 0 & 0 \\ 2 & 0 & 0 & 1 \\ 0 & 1 & 0 & 1 \\ 0 & 0 & 1 & 1 \end{bmatrix} \end{array}$$

9. Draw an undirected graph with the following adjacency matrix.

$$\begin{array}{c} \\ v_1 \\ v_2 \\ v_3 \end{array} \begin{array}{c} \begin{array}{ccc} v_1 & v_2 & v_3 \end{array} \\ \begin{bmatrix} 0 & 1 & 0 \\ 1 & 0 & 2 \\ 0 & 2 & 1 \end{bmatrix} \end{array}$$

Sample:

10. In the adjacency matrix for a simple graph, no element can be greater than what number? 1

Adapting to Individual Needs

Extra Help

Be sure students understand that while some graphs with crossings can be redrawn without crossings, that it is not always the case. For example, suppose a graph has five vertices such that each pair of vertices is joined by exactly one edge. (Such a graph is called a *complete graph* and is discussed in the next lesson.) Students might try to draw such a graph without crossings, and may soon be convinced that it cannot be done.

4. Draw a picture of a graph that has the following adjacency matrix.

$$\begin{bmatrix} 1 & 2 & 1 & 0 \\ 0 & 0 & 1 & 3 \\ 0 & 0 & 2 & 0 \\ 1 & 1 & 0 & 0 \end{bmatrix}$$

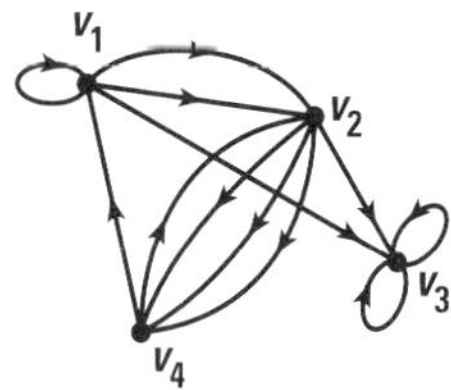

Notes on Questions

Question 2 Error Alert Students might forget to include v_4 since it is not in the table. Remind them that isolated vertices never appear in the table for an edge-endpoint function.

Questions 5–6 To save time in discussing these questions, **Teaching Aid 117** is provided with the given graph and matrix.

Questions 7, 10, 11, and 12 **Teaching Aid 118** is provided with the graphs and matrix for these questions.

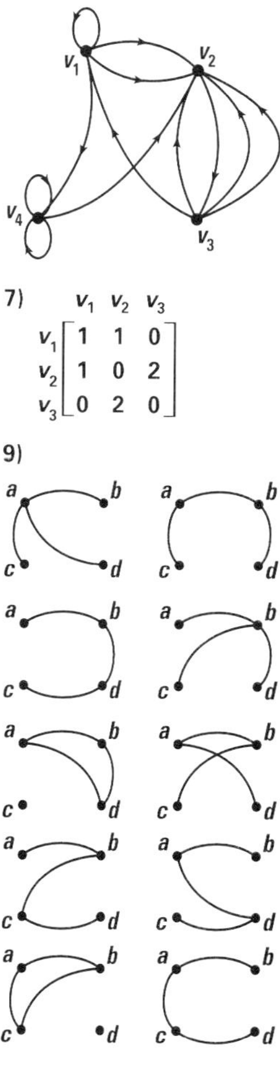

7)

	v_1	v_2	v_3
v_1	1	1	0
v_2	1	0	2
v_3	0	2	0

QUESTIONS

Covering the Reading

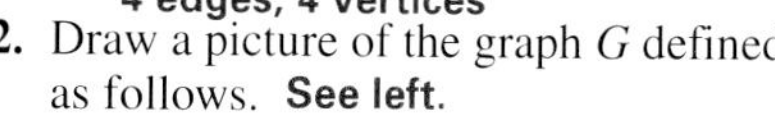

1. Refer to the figure at the right.
   a. Does the figure represent a graph? **Yes**
   b. If it does, tell how many edges and how many vertices it has. If it does not, explain why not. **4 edges, 4 vertices**

2. Draw a picture of the graph G defined as follows. **See left.**
   (1) set of vertices: $\{v_1, v_2, v_3, v_4, v_5\}$
   (2) set of edges: $\{e_1, e_2, e_3, e_4, e_5, e_6\}$
   (3) edge-endpoint function: (at right)

edge	endpoints
e_1	$\{v_1, v_3\}$
e_2	$\{v_1, v_3\}$
e_3	$\{v_2\}$
e_4	$\{v_2\}$
e_5	$\{v_3, v_5\}$
e_6	$\{v_3, v_5\}$

3. Use the graph G of Question 2.
   a. Are edges e_1 and e_5 adjacent? **Yes**
   b. Are vertices v_1 and v_2 adjacent? **No**
   c. Identify all isolated vertices. **v_4**
   d. Identify all parallel edges. **e_3 and e_4, e_1 and e_2, e_5 and e_6**
   e. Identify all loops. **e_3, e_4**

4. *True or false.* The directed graph following Example 2 shows that Bob influences Dan. **False**

5. Write the adjacency matrix for the directed graph pictured at the right.

	v_1	v_2	v_3	v_4
v_1	0	1	0	0
v_2	0	0	1	1
v_3	0	0	1	1
v_4	1	1	0	0

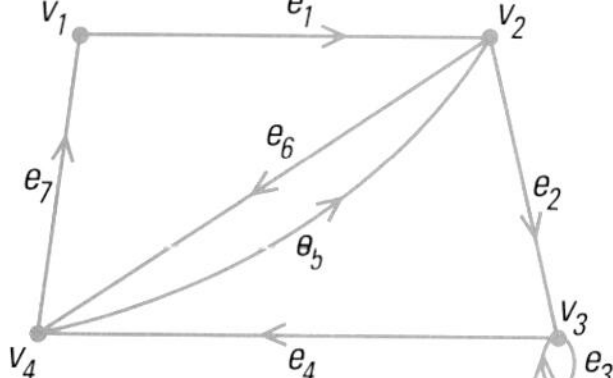

6. Draw a directed graph with the adjacency matrix shown below. **See left.**

$$\begin{bmatrix} 1 & 2 & 0 & 1 \\ 0 & 0 & 1 & 0 \\ 1 & 3 & 0 & 0 \\ 0 & 1 & 0 & 2 \end{bmatrix}$$

7. Write the adjacency matrix for the graph pictured at the right. **See left.**

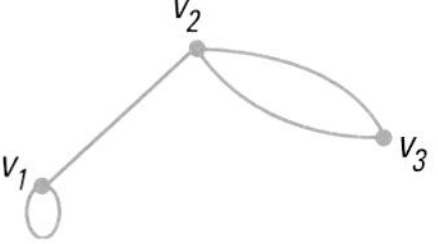

8. Give the numbers of vertices and edges of the graph in Example 2 of Lesson 11-1. **11 vertices, 11 edges**

9. Draw all simple graphs with vertices $\{a, b, c, d\}$, one edge $\{a, b\}$, and two other edges. **See left.**

Applying the Mathematics

10. **a.** Does the adjacency matrix below represent a simple graph? **No**

b. Explain your answer.

There are two edges between v_1 and v_3. Those edges are parallel, so the graph is not simple.

$$\begin{bmatrix} 0 & 1 & 2 \\ 1 & 0 & 1 \\ 2 & 1 & 0 \end{bmatrix}$$

11. Construct an edge-endpoint function table for the graph pictured at the right.

edge	endpoint
e_1	$\{v_1, v_2\}$
e_2	$\{v_2, v_4\}$
e_3	$\{v_2, v_4\}$
e_4	$\{v_3\}$

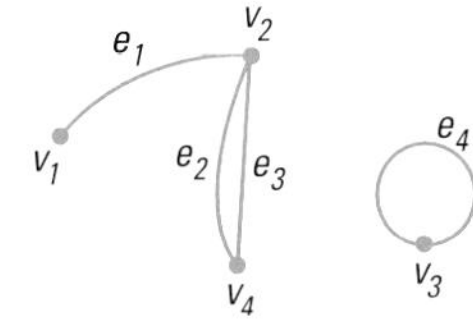

12. Do the following two pictures represent the same graph? Explain your answer. **See left.**

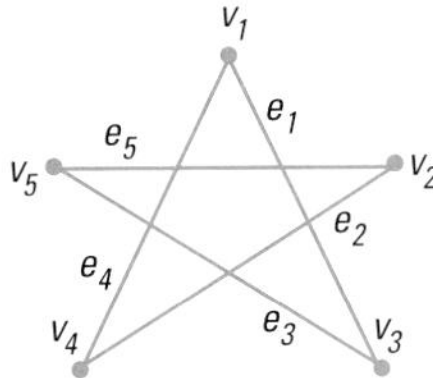

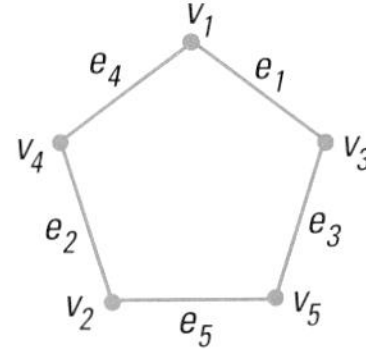

13. **a.** Write the negation of the following statement:

$\forall$ *graphs G, if G does not have any loops, then G is simple.*

b. Is the statement you obtained in part **a** *true* or *false*? Justify your answer.

See left.

14. The edge-endpoint function for a directed graph sends each edge to an ordered pair of vertices. For instance, suppose edge e is sent to the *ordered pair* $\{u, v\}$. When a picture of this graph is drawn, there will be an arrow pointing from u to v to show that the edge e goes from u to v. Draw a picture of the directed graph defined as follows. **See left.**

vertices: $\{v_1, v_2, v_3, v_4\}$

edges: $\{e_1, e_2, e_3, e_4, e_5, e_6\}$

edge-endpoint function:

edge	endpoints
e_1	$\{v_1, v_2\}$
e_2	$\{v_1, v_3\}$
e_3	$\{v_3, v_1\}$
e_4	$\{v_3, v_3\}$
e_5	$\{v_2, v_4\}$
e_6	$\{v_3, v_4\}$

15. A food P is being test-marketed against 3 leading brands A, B, and C. At the right, vertices A, B, C, and P represent the products, and an arrow is drawn from vertex x to vertex y if the taster prefers x to y. Explain why there is an inconsistency in the taster's preferences. **See left.**

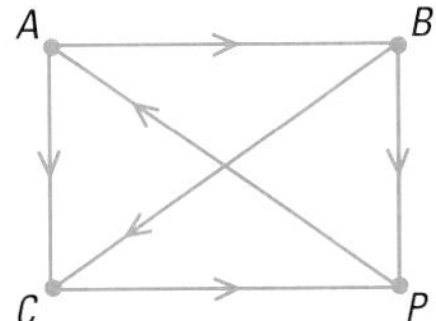

12) Yes, they have the same list of vertices and edges and the same edge-endpoint function.

13a) $\exists$ a graph *G* such that *G* does not have any loops and *G* is not simple.

b) True; *G* could have parallel edges and no loops.

14)

15) The taster prefers *A* to *C*, and prefers *C* to *P*. But in a direct comparison of *A* to *P*, the taster prefers *P*.

Question 12 The criterion for determining whether two pictures represent the same graph is: Do the graphs have the same algebraic definition? Here, because no other information is known, one assumes that the vertices are interchangeable. But that might not be the case in other situations, say if each vertex represents a person as in **Example 3.**

Questions 14, 15, and 17 The table for **Question 14** and the graphs for **Questions 15 and 17** are on **Teaching Aid 119.**

Adapting to Individual Needs

Challenge

Have students answer these questions.

1. Draw a graph and give an adjacency matrix for each situation.
   - **a.** A directed graph with 4 vertices, no loops, no crossings, 1 isolated point, and 2 parallel edges. [Many graphs are possible.]
   - **b.** A nondirected graph with 4 vertices, 6 edges, 3 loops, no isolated points, and no parallel edges. [Many graphs are possible.]
   - **c.** A simple graph with 4 vertices and 9 edges. [Not possible.]
2. Describe a list of tasks necessary for a group of 3 math students to make a presentation on graphs. Describe which tasks can or cannot be done simultaneously, and how many hours should realistically be spent on each task. Draw a simple graph and determine the minimum number of hours needed to complete the task.

Notes on Questions

Question 17 The formal definition of "tree" is given in Project 1, *Spanning Trees,* on page 707, and requires terminology to be given in Lesson 11-4, so this conjecture cannot be proved with what students have had thus far.

Question 20 Finding the powers of a matrix is needed in Lessons 11-5 and 11-6. Even students who have multiplied matrices may never have squared them. Anticipate the notation to be used there: if the given matrix here is named A, the answer to **part a** is A^2.

Follow-up for Lesson 11-2

Practice

For more questions on SPUR Objectives, use **Lesson Master 11-2** (shown on pages 668–669).

Assessment

Written Communication Have students **work in pairs.** Ask each student to make up an adjacency matrix. Then have students draw a graph for their partner's matrix. Begin again, but this time have each student draw a graph, and then have students write the adjacency matrix for their partner's graph. [Students convert between graphs and the related adjacency matrices.]

Extension

Ask students to draw another graph equivalent to those shown in **Question 12.** You might challenge the class to see how many different-looking but equivalent graphs they can create. [Samples:

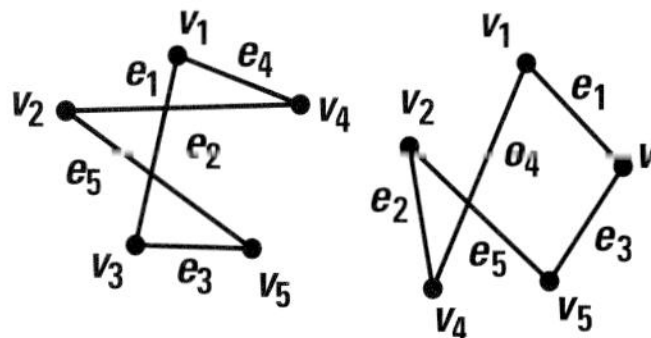

The two graphs above, the pentagon, and the star, are the four different types that can be drawn. All others will be reflection or rotation images of these.]

Project Update Project 3, *Constellations,* on page 708, relates to the content of this lesson.

16a)

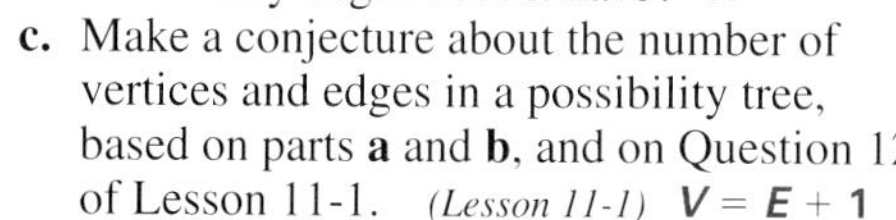

18) Sample: $p(x) = x^3 - x^2 - 7x + 15$

19) quotient: $6x^3 - 42x^2 + 287x - 2006$; remainder: 14,043

20a) $\begin{bmatrix} \cos 2\theta & -\sin 2\theta \\ \sin 2\theta & \cos 2\theta \end{bmatrix}$

b) $\begin{bmatrix} \cos\theta & -\sin\theta \\ \sin\theta & \cos\theta \end{bmatrix}^n = \begin{bmatrix} \cos(n\theta) & -\sin(n\theta) \\ \sin(n\theta) & \cos(n\theta) \end{bmatrix}$

Review

16. The green cookie jar in the kitchen contains five chocolate chip cookies and seven peanut butter cookies. The red cookie jar contains three chocolate chip cookies and five vanilla wafers. In the middle of the night little Freddy sneaks into the kitchen. He doesn't turn on the light for fear of waking his parents. He puts his hand in one of the jars at random and pulls out a cookie. *(Lesson 11-1)*
    a. Draw a probability tree and label its edges with probabilities to represent this situation. **See left.**
    b. What is the probability that he gets a chocolate chip cookie? **≈ .396**
    c. When he bites into the cookie, he finds it is chocolate chip. What is the probability that it came from the red jar? **≈ .474**

17. a. How many vertices does the possibility tree shown at the right have? **18**
    b. How many edges does it have? **17**
    c. Make a conjecture about the number of vertices and edges in a possibility tree, based on parts **a** and **b**, and on Question 12 of Lesson 11-1. *(Lesson 11-1)* $V = E + 1$

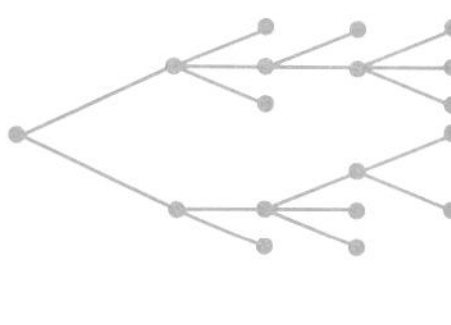

18. Let $p(x)$ be a polynomial with real coefficients such that $p(2 - i) = 0$ and $p(-3) = 0$. Find a possible formula for $p(x)$. *(Lesson 8-9)* **See left.**

19. Find the quotient and remainder when $p(x) = 6x^4 - 7x^2 + 3x + 1$ is divided by $d(x) = x + 7$. *(Lesson 4-3)* **See left.**

20. a. Multiply the matrix $\begin{bmatrix} \cos\theta & -\sin\theta \\ \sin\theta & \cos\theta \end{bmatrix}$ by itself and simplify the result.
    b. Generalize the result in part **a**. *(Previous course)*
See left.

Exploration

21. a. Consider simple graphs that have four vertices $\{a, b, c, d\}$, and at least the edges $\{a, b\}$ and $\{b, c\}$. How many such graphs have exactly the indicated number of edges?
    i. 2 **1** **ii.** 3 **4** **iii.** 4 **6** **iv.** 5 **4** **v.** 6 **1**
    b. Consider simple graphs which have vertices $\{a, b, c, d\}$ and at least the edges $\{a, b\}$, $\{b, c\}$, and $\{c, d\}$. How many such graphs have exactly the indicated number of edges?
    i. 3 **1** **ii.** 4 **3** **iii.** 5 **3** **iv.** 6 **1**
    c. What do the sequences of answers to parts **a** and **b** suggest?
    d. How is Example 2 and its answer similar to this problem?
    1, 2, 1 is row 2 of Pascal's Triangle.

c) Pascal's triangle; binomial coefficients

LESSON

11-3

Handshake Problems

Bill Clinton shaking hands with the crowd at the Lyndon Baines Johnson Library in Austin, TX, while he was running for president.

The Classic Handshake Problem

Suppose n people are at a party. If each person shakes hands with every other person, how many handshakes are required?

This *handshake problem* can be represented by a graph in the following way. Represent the n people by vertices and join two vertices by an edge if the corresponding people shake hands. Since each person shakes hands once with each other person, every pair of vertices is joined by exactly one edge. A graph with this property is called a **complete graph**. Here is a picture of the complete graph with 7 vertices.

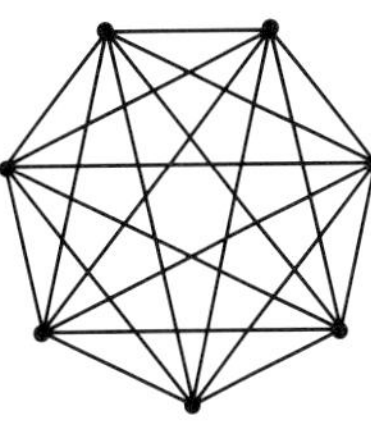

You can see that a complete graph can be pictured as the union of a polygon with its diagonals. Thus the number of edges in the complete graph with n vertices equals the total number of sides and diagonals in an n-gon, which in turn is the answer to the handshake problem.

There are a number of ways to solve the handshake problem. One way is to use combinations. Note that there are as many handshakes (edges) as there are ways to choose 2 people (vertices) to shake hands out of a group of n. This number is $\binom{n}{2}$, which equals $\frac{n(n-1)}{2}$. For the above graph, when $n = 7$, there are 21 handshakes, corresponding to the total of 7 sides and 14 diagonals for a heptagon.

Many other problems are equivalent to handshake problems. For instance, replacing handshakes by games and people by teams converts any handshake problem into a problem involving games and teams. The solution to the above problem implies that $\frac{n(n-1)}{2}$ games are required for each of n teams to play each of the other teams exactly once.

Lesson 11-3

Objectives

A Draw graphs given sufficient information.
B Identify parts of graphs and types of graphs.
C Determine whether there exists a graph containing vertices with given degrees.
F Use the Total Degree of a Graph Theorem and its corollaries to solve handshake problems.

Resources

From the ***Teacher's Resource File***
- Lesson Master 11-3
- Answer Master 11-3
- Teaching Aid 110: Warm-up

Additional Resources
- Visual for Teaching Aid 110

Teaching Lesson 11-3

Warm-up

Eight people are at a party. Identify them as *A, B, C, D, E, F, G,* and *H.*

1. If each person says "Hello" to everyone else individually, how many "Hellos" will be spoken? 56
2. List them. ***AB*** **(*A* says hello to *B*), *AC, AD, AE, AF, AG, AH, BC, BD, BE, BF, BG, BH, CD, CE, CF, CG, CH, DE, DF, DG, DH, EF, EG, EH, FG, FH, GH,* and each of these possibilities with the letters reversed. (The result is twice what one gets from handshakes since each person has to say hello to the other.)**

Lesson 11-3 Overview

Broad Goals This lesson develops some theorems about the degree of a graph so that they can be applied in the next lesson. Along the way, several "handshake problems" are solved.

Perspective An edge of a graph can be considered as a handshake between its vertices. The number of handshakes possible from a vertex is the number of edges, called the degree of the vertex.

Handshake problems are paradigms for many graph problems, in that other problems have the same structure. For instance, the problem on page 674 is isomorphic to the following: Is it possible to connect 47 points by segments so that each point is connected to 9 others? Could a chess tournament with 47 entrants be devised so that each entrant would play exactly 9 games?

Notes on Reading

It is not unusual that the classic handshake problem is solved using combinations. Graph theory often applies combinatorics.

To illustrate The Total Degree of a Graph Theorem and its use in **Example 1,** you might want to simplify the problem to one which involves fewer people, say 5 people each shaking hands with exactly three other people. Then you can have five students try to demonstrate how they could do the handshaking at the front of the room. Some students might not believe the theorem and will try to show how it could be done.

Have students go through the proof in **Example 2b** step by step.

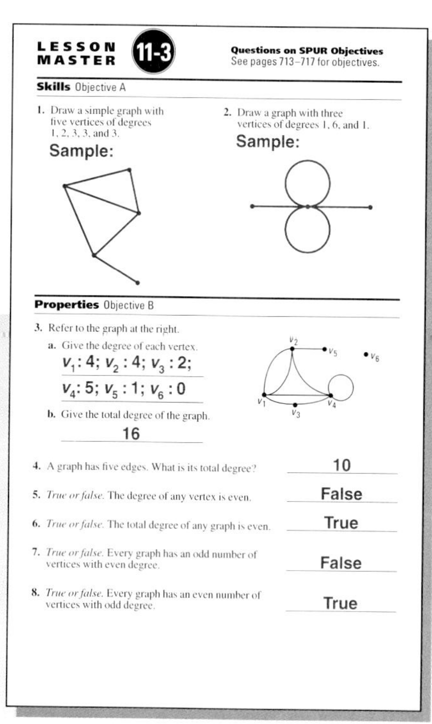

LESSON MASTER 11-3 — **Questions on SPUR Objectives** See pages 713–717 for objectives.

Skills Objective A

1. Draw a simple graph with five vertices of degrees 1, 2, 3, 3, and 3.
   Sample:

2. Draw a graph with three vertices of degrees 1, 6, and 1.
   Sample:

Properties Objective B

3. Refer to the graph at the right.
   a. Give the degree of each vertex. $v_1: 4$; $v_2: 4$; $v_3: 2$; $v_4: 5$; $v_5: 1$; $v_6: 0$
   b. Give the total degree of the graph. 16

4. A graph has five edges. What is its total degree? 10

5. *True or false.* The degree of any vertex is even. False

6. *True or false.* The total degree of any graph is even. True

7. *True or false.* Every graph has an odd number of vertices with even degree. False

8. *True or false.* Every graph has an even number of vertices with odd degree. True

The Degree of a Graph

Here is a different handshake problem, one which seems more difficult.

> Forty-seven people attend a social gathering. During the course of the event, various people shake hands. Is it possible for each person to shake hands with exactly nine other people?

The concept of *degree*, together with properties of even and odd integers, can help to solve this problem.

> **Definition**
> If v is a vertex of a graph G, the **degree of v**, denoted **deg(v)**, equals the number of edges that have v as an endpoint, with each edge that is a loop counted twice.

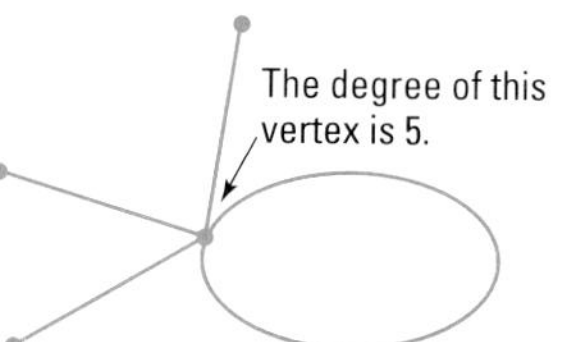

Consider the graph G pictured at the right. Its vertices have the following degrees:

$$\deg(v_1) = 3$$
$$\deg(v_2) = 4$$
$$\deg(v_3) = 3.$$

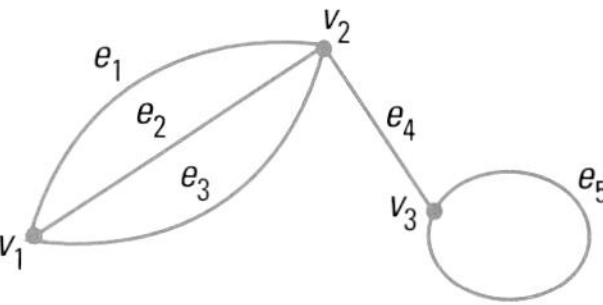

The Total Degree of a Graph

The **total degree of a graph** is the sum of the degrees of all the vertices of the graph. Thus the total degree of graph G above is 10, which is twice the number of edges. Is this always the case? The answer is yes. The reason is that each edge of a graph contributes 2 to the total degree whether or not the edge is a loop. For instance, in the graph pictured above,

Edge	contributes 1 to the degree of	and 1 to the degree of
e_1	v_1	v_2
e_2	v_1	v_2
e_3	v_1	v_2
e_4	v_2	v_3
e_5, a loop, contributes 2 to the degree of v_3.		

This argument proves the following theorem.

> **Theorem (Total Degree of a Graph)**
> The total degree of any graph equals twice the number of edges in the graph.

The theorem has corollaries, which you are asked to prove in the Questions.

Optional Activities

After discussing the lesson, and without referring to the Total Degree of a Graph Theorem, you might ask students to find an expression for the total degree of any complete graph with n vertices, $n \geq 2$. To lead up to this question, you could ask it first of the graph students drew for **Question 5.** [$(n-1)n$] Then ask students to show how this expression demonstrates the Total Degree of a Graph Theorem.

[The number of edges in a complete graph with n vertices is $\frac{n(n-1)}{2}$. The Total Degree of a Graph Theorem states the total degree of a graph will be twice the number of edges, or $n(n-1)$.]

Corollaries

1. Total Degree Is Even: The total degree of any graph is an even positive integer.
2. Number of Odd Vertices Is Even: Every graph has an even number of vertices of odd degree.

The second corollary helps to answer the question about handshakes at a social gathering.

Example 1

In a group of 47 people, can each person shake hands with exactly nine other people? Explain why or why not.

Solution

The answer is **no**. To see why, assume that each of the 47 people could shake hands with exactly 9 others. Represent each person as the vertex of a graph, and draw an edge joining each pair of people who shake hands. The graph would then have 47 vertices, each of which would have degree 9. So it would have an odd number of vertices of odd degree. But this contradicts the second corollary, so the assumption must be false. Thus it is impossible for each of 47 people to shake hands with exactly 9 others.

Drawing Graphs with Vertices of Specified Degrees

Example 2

In parts **a** and **b**, draw the specified graph, or show that no such graph exists.

a. a graph with three vertices of degrees 2, 2, and 0

b. a simple graph with three vertices of degrees 2, 2, and 0

Solution

a. This combination of degrees is not forbidden by the Total Degree of a Graph Theorem because the total degree of the graph would be 4, which is even. The number of edges in the graph would be half the total degree, or 2. If you experiment by drawing three vertices connected in various ways by two edges, you quickly find that each of the graphs below satisfies the given properties.

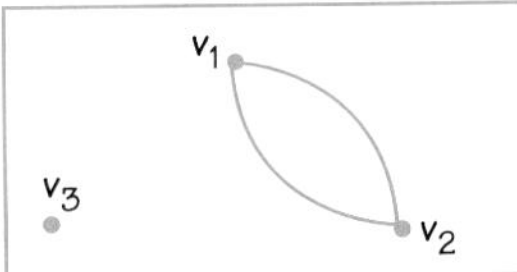

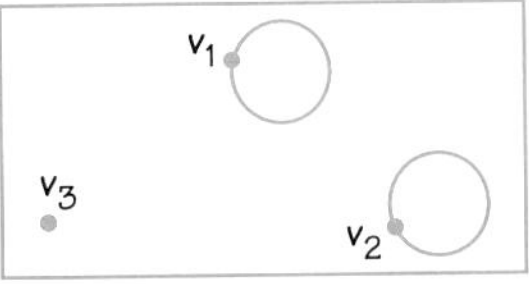

b. Neither graph in part **a** is simple. If you continue to experiment by shifting the positions of the edges in the graphs above, you continually come up with graphs that either are not simple or have vertices with different degrees ▶

Additional Examples

1. In a group of 10 people, can each person shake hands with exactly 3 others? **Yes. Call the people *A, B, C, D, E, F, G, H, I,* and *J*. Draw a polygon *ABCDEFGHIJ* and its diagonals $\overline{AF}$, $\overline{BG}$, $\overline{CH}$, $\overline{DI}$, and $\overline{EJ}$. Now, considered as a graph, each vertex is connected to three others.**
2. For each description, draw a graph or show that no such graph exists.
   a. A graph with three vertices, v_1 of degree 1, v_2 of degree 2, and v_3 of degree 3

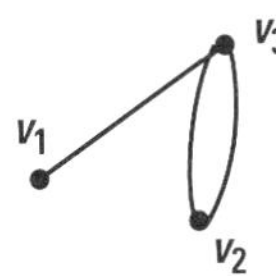

   b. A simple graph with three vertices, v_1 of degree 1, v_2 of degree 2, and v_3 of degree 3 **This cannot be done because v_3 has 3 edges from it, but there are only 2 other vertices, so it would be connected to one of the other vertices by 2 edges.**

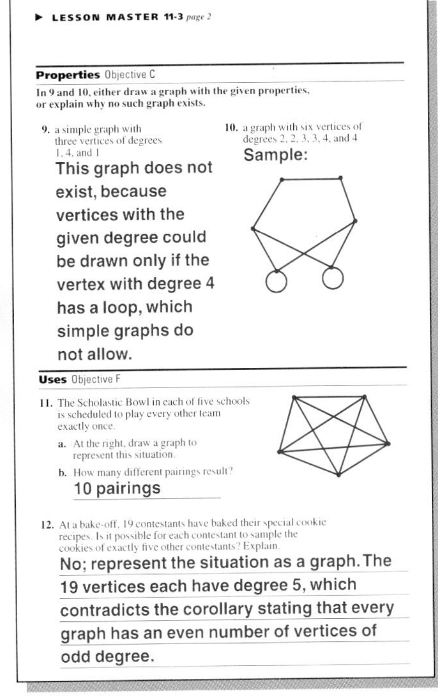

▶ **LESSON MASTER 11-3** *page 2*

Properties Objective C

In 9 and 10, either draw a graph with the given properties, or explain why no such graph exists.

9. a simple graph with three vertices of degrees 1, 4, and 1
This graph does not exist, because vertices with the given degree could be drawn only if the vertex with degree 4 has a loop, which simple graphs do not allow.

10. a graph with six vertices of degrees 2, 2, 3, 3, 4, and 4
Sample:

Uses Objective F

11. The Scholastic Bowl in each of five schools is scheduled to play every other team exactly once.

a. At the right, draw a graph to represent this situation.

b. How many different pairings result?
10 pairings

12. At a bake-off, 19 contestants have baked their special cookie recipes. Is it possible for each contestant to sample the cookies of exactly five other contestants? Explain.
No; represent the situation as a graph. The 19 vertices each have degree 5, which contradicts the corollary stating that every graph has an even number of vertices of odd degree.

Notes on Questions

Question 2 Error Alert This question is tricky and may confuse some students because the only counterexamples are loops.

(Notes on Questions continue on page 678.)

Practice

For more questions on SPUR Objectives, use **Lesson Master 11-3** (shown on pages 674–675).

Assessment

Oral Communication Have each student draw a graph. Then have students use their graph to explain the definitions, theorem, and corollaries in the lesson. [Students show understanding of degree of a vertex, total degree of a graph, and their properties.]

Extension

Consider variants of the handshake problem.

1. In a committee of 10 people, can subcommittees of 3 people be organized so that each person is on exactly 1 subcommittee? [No]
2. Can subgroups of 3 people be organized so that each person is on exactly 2 subcommittees? [No]
3. What numbers of subcommittees must a person be on so that each person could be on the same number of subcommittees? [3, 6, or 9]

than are required. At a certain point, you would probably conjecture that no such graph exists. Proof by contradiction is a natural approach to use to prove this conjecture.

To prove:
There is no simple graph with three vertices of degrees 2, 2, and 0.

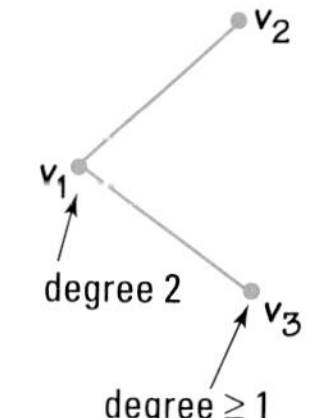

Proof (by contradiction): Assume that there is a simple graph with three vertices of degrees 2, 2, and 0. (A contradiction must be deduced.) Let G be such a graph and let its vertices of degree 2 be v_1 and v_2 and its vertex of degree 0 be v_3. Since v_1 has degree 2 and G has no loops or parallel edges (because it is simple), there must be edges joining v_1 to v_2 and v_1 to v_3. Consequently, the degree of v_3 will be at least 1. On the other hand, the degree of v_3 is required to be 0. This is a contradiction, so the assumption that there is such a simple graph is false and the conjecture that no such graph exists is true.

The result of Example 2b can be put into the language of handshakes. In a group of 3 people in which no pair shakes hands twice, it is impossible for 2 people to shake hands with 2 others and the third person not to shake any hands at all.

QUESTIONS

Covering the Reading

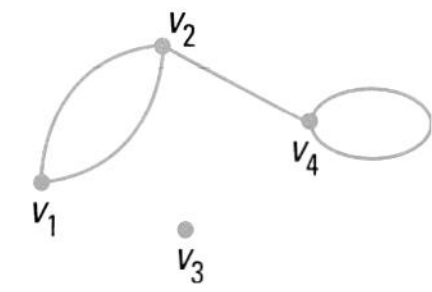

1. Consider the graph G pictured at the right.
   a. Find the degree of each vertex.
   b. What is the total degree of G? 8
   a) deg $(v_1) = 2$; deg $(v_2) = 3$; deg $(v_3) = 0$; deg $(v_4) = 3$

2. Explain why the following statement is *false*: The degree of a vertex equals the number of edges that have the vertex as an endpoint. See left.

2) The statement does not include the case when edges are loops which are counted twice.

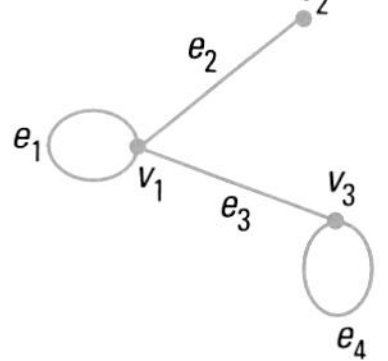

3. Consider the graph pictured at the right. Fill in the table below for this graph.
   a) 2 b) v_1 c) 1
   d) v_2 e) 1 f) v_1
   g) contributes 1 to the degree of v_3 and 1 to the degree of v_1.
   h) contributes 2 to the degree of v_3.

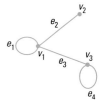

Edge e_1 contributes __a.__ to the degree of __b.__.
Edge e_2 contributes __c.__ to the degree of __d.__, and __e.__ to the degree of __f.__.
Edge e_3 ____________ g. ____________
Edge e_4 ____________ h. ____________

Adapting to Individual Needs

Extra Help
You might want to give students an informal way to find the degree of a vertex. Tell them to count how many ways there are to "leave" the vertex v. Refer to the diagrams at the right.

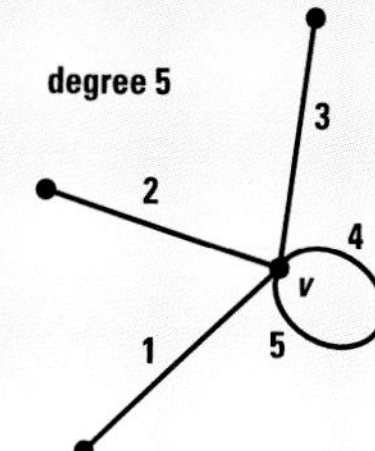

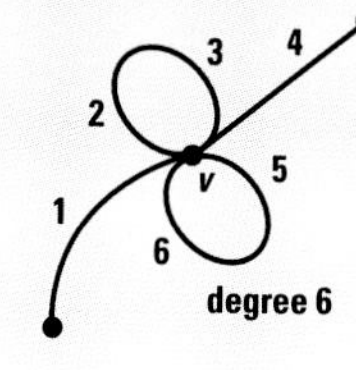

4. How many handshakes are needed for 23 people at a party if each person is to shake hands with every other person? 253

5. Draw a complete graph with 5 vertices. See margin.

6. At a family reunion, 8 cousins wish to reminisce with each other two at a time.
   a. How many conversations are needed? 28
   b. Verify your answer to part **a** with a graph. See margin.
   c. Explain how this problem is equivalent to a handshake problem. See margin.

7. What is the total degree of the graph given at the beginning of this lesson? 42

8. What is the total degree of the second graph of this lesson? 8

9. Prove that, in a group of 9 people, it is impossible for every person to shake hands with exactly 3 others. See margin.

10. Correct this false statement. *The number of edges in any graph equals twice the total degree of the graph.* **The total degree of any graph equals twice the number of edges in the graph.**

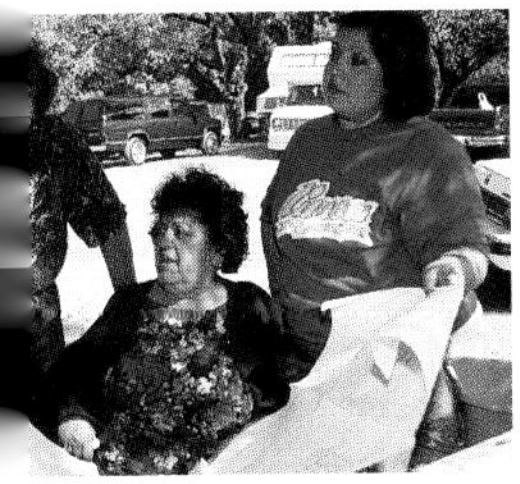

What's Buzz'n, cousin? *At their annual reunion, members of the Limon family look over the family tree.*

Applying the Mathematics

11. Prove or disprove. *A graph must have an odd number of vertices of even degree.* See left.

In 12–15, either draw a graph with the specified properties or explain why no such graph exists. See left.

12. a graph with 10 vertices of degrees 1, 1, 1, 2, 3, 3, 3, 4, 5, 6

13. a graph with 4 vertices of degrees 1, 1, 3, and 3

14. a simple graph with 4 vertices of degrees 1, 1, 2, and 2

15. a simple graph with 4 vertices of degrees 1, 1, 3, and 3

16. Let G be a simple graph with n vertices.
   a. What is the maximum degree of any vertex of G? $n - 1$
   b. What is the maximum total degree of G? $n(n - 1)$
   c. What is the maximum number of edges of G? $\frac{n(n-1)}{2}$

17. Use the answer to the handshake problem at the beginning of the lesson to deduce an expression for the number of diagonals of an n-gon. $\frac{n(n-3)}{2}$

18. At a party, the first guest to arrive shakes hands with the host. The second guest shakes hands with the host and the first guest, and so on.
   a. If there are n guests, how many handshakes are there in all?
   b. Relate part **a** to the first handshake problem of this lesson.
   See margin.

19. Explain why the Total Degree Is Even corollary follows immediately from the Total Degree of a Graph Theorem. See margin.

20. Explain how the Number of Odd Vertices Is Even corollary follows from the Total Degree of a Graph Theorem. See margin.

11) Counterexample:

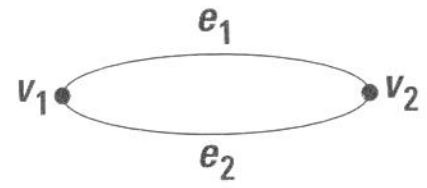

12) Impossible; it can't have an odd number of odd vertices

13) Sample:

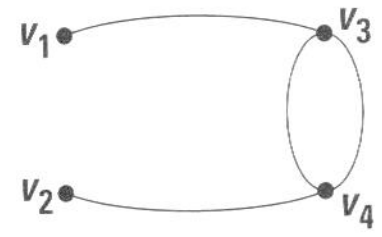

14) Sample:

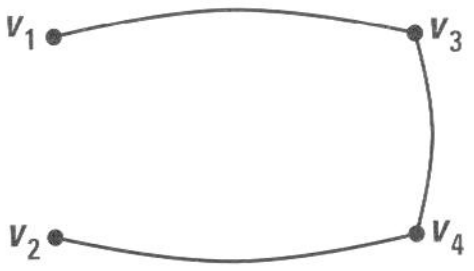

15) Impossible: one of the degree 3 vertices goes to each of the other vertices. But the other degree 3 vertex cannot connect to itself (the graph is simple), to the first degree 3 vertex (no parallel edges), or to the other two vertices (they already have one edge).

Additional Answers

5.

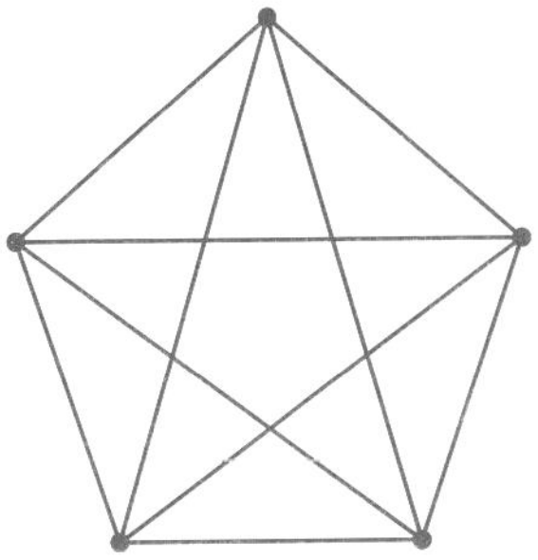

6. b.

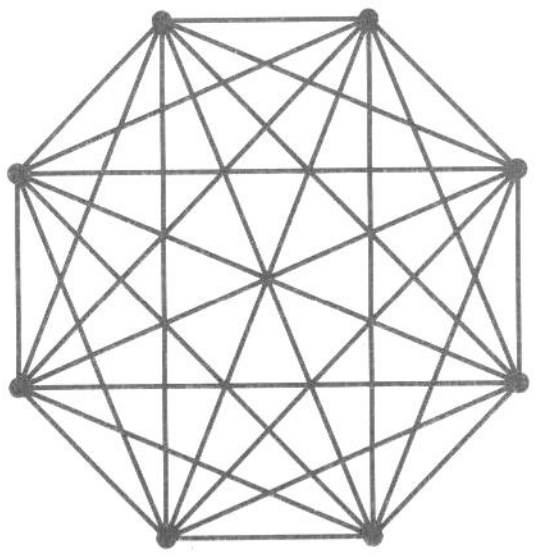

c. It is equivalent to 8 people shaking hands with each other.

9. Assume that each of the nine people could shake hands with exactly three others. Represent each person as the vertex of a graph, and draw an edge joining each pair of people who shake hands. To say that a person shakes hands with three other people is equivalent to saying that the degree of the vertex representing that person is 3. The graph would then have an odd number of vertices of odd degree. This contradicts Corollary 2 of the Total Degree of a Graph Theorem. Thus, the given situation is impossible.

18. a. $\frac{(n+1)n}{2}$
   b. It is the same problem but with one more person.

19. "Twice the number of edges" must be an even number.

20. The set of even vertices contributes an even number to the total degree of the graph. Since that total degree is even, the set of odd vertices must also contribute an even number to the total degree. An odd number of odd vertices would contribute an odd number, so the number of odd vertices must be even.

Adapting to Inividual Needs

Challenge

Have students answer the following questions.

1. a. For your math class, how many handshakes are necessary for each person to shake everyone else's hand? [$\frac{n(n-1)}{2}$ where n is the number of students]
   b. Is it possible for every person to shake hands with exactly 3 other people? [Only if n is even and $n \geq 4$]
   c. Is it possible for every person to shake hands with exactly 4 other people? [Yes, if $n \geq 4$]
2. Construct other problems that are variations of the handshake problem.

Notes on Questions

Question 25 This question continues the review of matrix multiplication. If needed, here are two additional questions.

a. $\begin{bmatrix} 1 & 5 \\ 2 & -1 \end{bmatrix} \cdot \begin{bmatrix} 4 \\ 8 \end{bmatrix}$ $\left[\begin{bmatrix} 44 \\ 0 \end{bmatrix}\right]$

b. $\begin{bmatrix} 1 & 2 & -1 \\ 0 & 1 & 1 \\ -1 & 0 & 1 \end{bmatrix} \cdot \begin{bmatrix} 3 & 1 & 8 \\ 2 & 0 & 1 \\ 1 & 3 & 2 \end{bmatrix}$

$\left[\begin{bmatrix} 6 & -2 & 8 \\ 3 & 3 & 3 \\ -2 & 2 & -6 \end{bmatrix}\right]$

Question 26 A corollary to this statement is that there is a simple graph with m edges and n vertices for every pair of positive integers m and n such that $m \leq \frac{n(n-1)}{2}$. (If an edge is deleted from a simple graph, the graph is still simple.)

Additional Answers

21. See below.

22. 10 hours

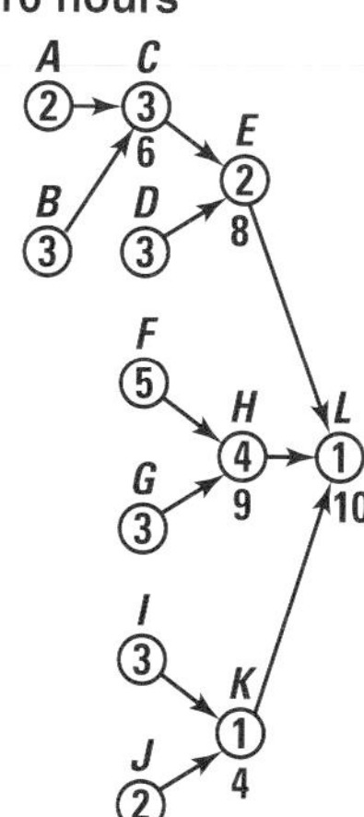

Review

21. The numbers by the arcs show the number of daily non-stop flights between those cities when this question was written. Write the adjacency matrix for the graph of non-stop flights between the indicated cities. List the cities alphabetically for the rows and columns. *(Lesson 11-2)* **See margin.**

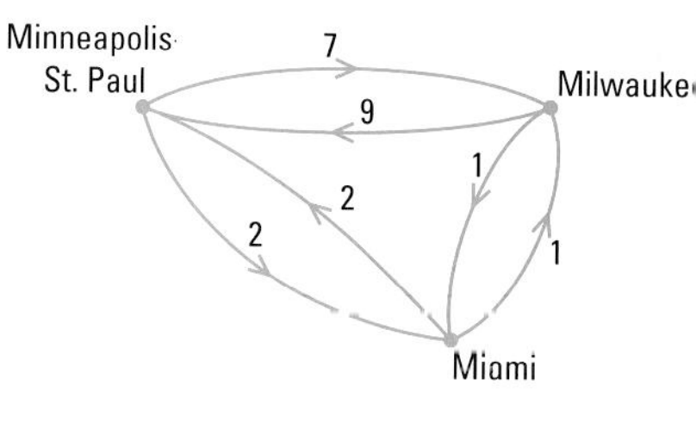

22. Suppose that the assembling of a computer consists of the following tasks

Task		Time required (hours)	Prerequisite tasks
A	Assemble memory & CPU chips	2	
B	Assemble I/O port components	3	
C	Assemble computer circuit board	3	A, B
D	Assemble disk drive	3	
E	Assemble computer	2	C, D
F	Assemble picture tube	5	
G	Assemble monitor circuit board	3	
H	Assemble monitor	4	F, G
I	Assemble key mechanism	3	
J	Assemble keyboard circuit board	2	
K	Assemble keyboard	1	I, J
L	Package computer and peripherals	1	E, H, K

Draw a digraph to determine the minimum time required for the entire assembling process. *(Lesson 11-1)* **See margin.**

23. Solve over the complex numbers: $20x^4 + 11x^2 - 3 = 0$. *(Lesson 3-6)* **See left.**

23) $x = \frac{\sqrt{5}}{5}, \frac{-\sqrt{5}}{5}, \frac{i\sqrt{3}}{2}, \frac{-i\sqrt{3}}{2}$

24. The graph of a function g is shown at the left. Approximate the values of x satisfying each condition. *(Lessons 2-1, 2-3)*

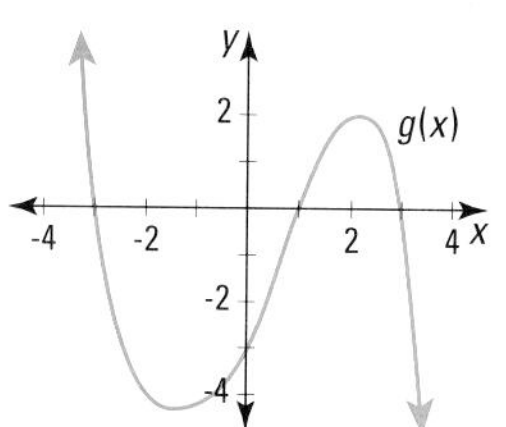

a. $g(x) > 0$ **$x < -3$, $1 < x < 3$**

b. $g(x) < 0$ **$-3 < x < 1$, $x > 3$**

c. g is increasing **$-1.5 < x < 2$**

25. If $A = \begin{bmatrix} 1 & 2 \\ 3 & 5 \end{bmatrix}$, calculate $A \cdot A$ (which is A^2). *(Previous course)* $\begin{bmatrix} 7 & 12 \\ 18 & 31 \end{bmatrix}$

Exploration

26. Consider the statement: *If G is a simple graph with m edges and n vertices, then* $m \leq \frac{n(n-1)}{2}$. **See margin.**

a. Write its contrapositive.

b. Prove or disprove either the statement or its contrapositive.

21.

	Miami	Milwaukee	Minn./St. Paul
Miami	0	1	2
Milwaukee	1	0	9
Minn./St. Paul	2	7	0

26. a. ***If*** $m > \frac{n(n-1)}{2}$***, then G is not a simple graph with m edges and n vertices.***

b. **Proof of statement: Given a simple graph *G* with *n* vertices and *m* edges, let k = maximum number of edges possible (that is, $m \leq k$). We know from the lesson that $k = \frac{n(n-1)}{2}$, so $m \leq \frac{n(n-1)}{2}$.**

Setting Up Lesson 11-4

Do the In-class Activity on page 679.

Introducing Lesson 11-4

Euler Circuits

IN-CLASS ACTIVITY

Here are definitions of four terms.

Suppose that G is a graph and v and w are vertices of G.

A **walk from v to w** is an alternating sequence of adjacent vertices and edges of G beginning with v and ending with w.

A **path from v to w** is a walk in G from v to w in which no edge is repeated.

A **circuit** is a path in G that starts and ends at the same vertex.

An **Euler circuit** is a circuit that contains every edge and vertex of G.

1 Consider the graph G shown here.

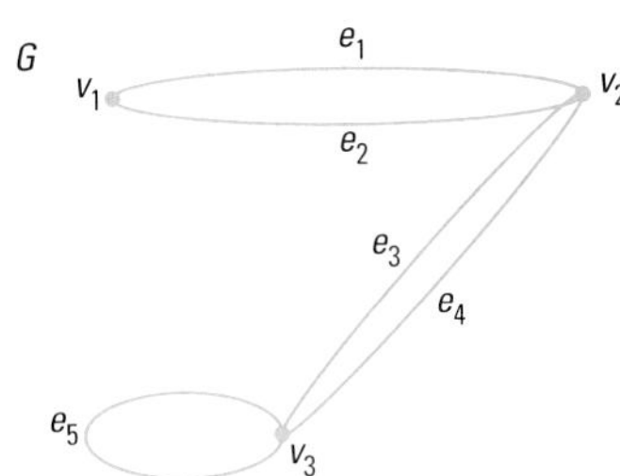

The following is a walk from v_3 to v_1: $v_3\ e_5\ v_3\ e_3\ v_2\ e_4\ v_3\ e_3\ v_2\ e_1\ v_1$. Is it a path? Why or why not? **No, edge 3 is repeated.**

2 When there is no confusion, we list only the edges of a walk. For the walk of Task 1, we can write $e_5\ e_3\ e_4\ e_3\ e_1$. Name three paths from v_3 to v_1. **Sample: $e_4\ e_1$; $e_3\ e_2$; $e_4\ e_2$**

3 **a.** Name two circuits from v_1 to v_1. **Sample: $e_1\ e_2\ e_1\ e_4\ e_3\ e_2$**
b. Name an Euler circuit in G, starting at v_1. **Sample: $e_1\ e_4\ e_5\ e_3\ e_2$**

4 Copy the table below. Fill in each cell of the table with one of the words "always," "sometimes," or "never."

	repeated edge?	starts and ends at the same point?	includes every edge and vertex?
walk	sometimes	sometimes	sometimes
path	never	sometimes	sometimes
circuit	never	always	sometimes
Euler circuit	never	always	always

In-class Activity

Resources

From the ***Teacher's Resource File***
- Teaching Aid 120: Graph *G* and the Table
- Answer Master 11-4

Additional Resources
- Visual for Teaching Aid 120

Without this activity, Lesson 11-4 would introduce too much technical vocabulary at one time. This activity is designed to ensure that students know some of the vocabulary of Lesson 11-4 before they embark on its reading.

Cooperative Learning The activity can be done by students **working in pairs,** with students stopping after each question to check with each other to see if their answers agree. Or it can be done as a whole-class activity, again stopping after each question to see that the terminology is clear.

Notice that the terms go from general to specific. *Walk* is the most general term. A *path* is a type of walk. A *circuit* is a type of path. An *Euler circuit* is a type of circuit.

You might ask: Could *Euler circuit* have been defined as a circuit that contains every edge of *G*? (This definition would not mention vertices.) [Yes, it could, but then it would not be as obvious that an Euler circuit is also a circuit.]

In Lesson 11-4, the Königsberg bridge problem is recast as a problem about Euler circuits.

Lesson 11-4

Objectives

B Identify parts of graphs and types of graphs.
D Determine whether a graph has an Euler circuit.
G Solve application problems involving circuits.

Resources

From the ***Teacher's Resource File***

- Lesson Master 11-4
- Answer Master 11-4
- Assessment Sourcebook: Quiz for Lessons 11-1 through 11-4
- Teaching Aids
  111 Warm-up
  121 Questions 1, 2, and 4
  122 Questions 5, 6, and 7
  123 Questions 8 and 12

Additional Resources

- Visuals for Teaching Aids 111, 121–123

Teaching Lesson 11-4

Warm-up

In each case a polygon is identified. Consider the polygon and all its diagonals as a network, but do not consider intersections of diagonals as vertices in the network. Does the network have an Euler circuit?

1. Convex quadrilateral **No**
2. Regular pentagon **Yes**
3. Hexagon **No**
4. Heptagon **Yes**

LESSON

11-4 *The Königsberg Bridge Problem*

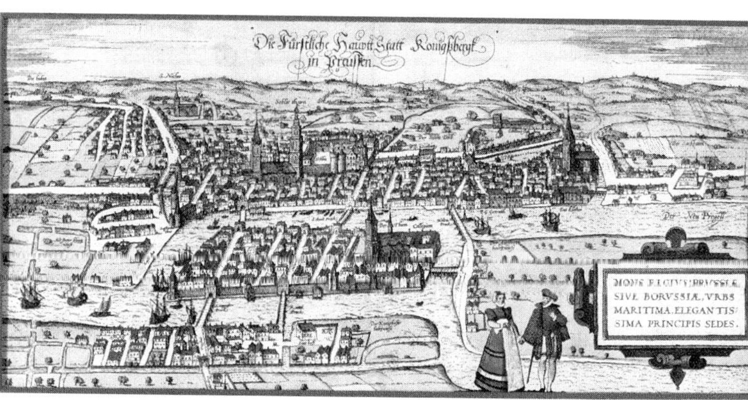

❶ *This historic etching, picturing Königsberg (now Kaliningrad), predates Euler. Note that only six bridges existed; the seventh was built later.*

Return to the Problem

At the beginning of this chapter, the Königsberg bridge problem was posed:

> In the city of Königsberg, is it possible for a person to walk around the city traversing each bridge exactly once, starting and ending at the same point?

It was pointed out in Lesson 11-1 that this problem is equivalent to the question of whether it is possible to trace the graph below without picking up your pencil, traversing each edge exactly once and starting and ending at the same vertex. Using the terminology in the In-class Activity, the Königsberg bridge problem asks if there is an Euler circuit for this graph.

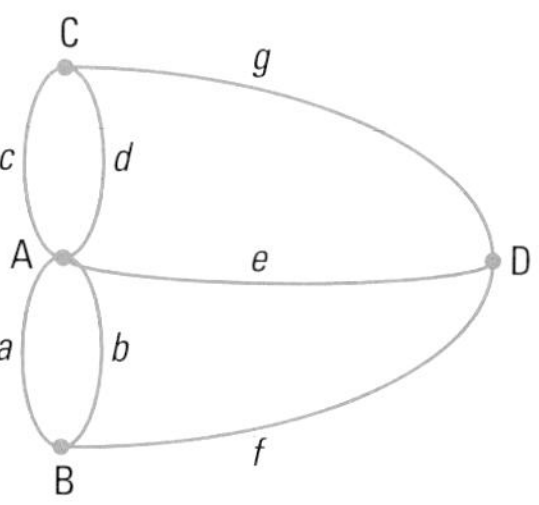

Euler's Solution

Euler proved the following theorem. It gives a necessary condition for a graph to have an Euler circuit, and it solves the Königsberg bridge problem.

> **Euler Circuit Theorem**
> If a graph has an Euler circuit, then every vertex of the graph has even degree.

Lesson 11-4 Overview

Broad Goals This lesson proves necessary and sufficient conditions for an Euler circuit, and uses those to solve the Königsberg bridge problem.

Perspective The Königsberg bridge problem requires an Euler circuit, a circuit in which no edge is repeated. The key to the solution of the Könisberg bridge problem is the theorem that every vertex of a graph with an Euler circuit has even degree. A sufficient condition for an Euler circuit is also given. This enables students to determine exactly which graphs have Euler circuits and solves the traversing problem for edges.

❷ **Proof**

Suppose *G* is any graph that has an Euler circuit. To show that every vertex of *G* has even degree, we take any particular but arbitrarily chosen vertex *v* and show that the degree of *v* must be even.

Either *v* is or is not the vertex where the Euler circuit starts and stops. If *v* is not, then each time the circuit enters *v* on one edge, it must leave *v* by a different edge. Thus the edges having *v* as an endpoint must occur in entry/exit pairs. This idea is illustrated by the diagram below.

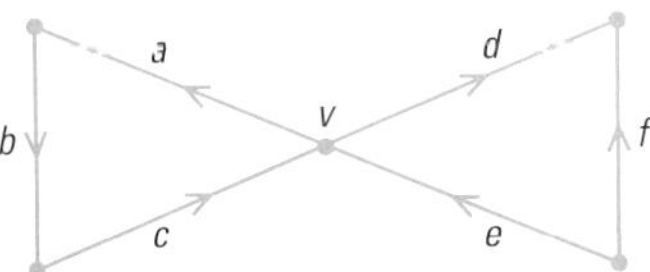

In an Euler circuit, each time *v* is entered by one edge it is exited by another edge.

If *v* is the initial vertex of the Euler circuit, then the first edge of the circuit (that leads out of *v*) can be paired with the last edge of the circuit (that leads into *v*). Also, as above, any other edges having *v* as an endpoint occur in entry/exit pairs.

It follows that, regardless of whether or not the circuit starts and ends at *v*, all the edges having *v* as an endpoint can be divided into pairs. Therefore, the number of such edges is even, which is what was to be shown.

Now examine the graph of the Königsberg bridges. All four vertices have odd degree. Since just one vertex of odd degree is enough to preclude there being an Euler circuit, the answer to the question of the Königsberg bridge problem is "No." The Königsberg bridge graph has no Euler circuit.

Connected Graphs

Does the converse of the Euler Circuit Theorem hold true? Is it true that if every vertex of a graph has even degree, then the graph has an Euler circuit? The answer is no. The following counterexample shows a graph with four vertices v_1, v_2, v_3, and v_4 in which every vertex has even degree yet there is no Euler circuit.

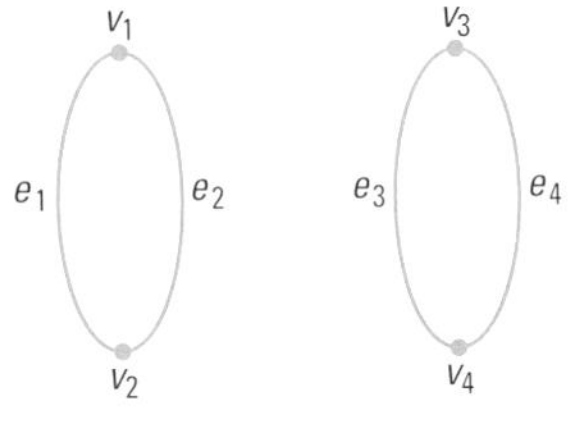

However, the converse to the Euler Circuit Theorem is true under certain conditions. To discuss these conditions requires the concept of connectedness. Roughly speaking, a graph is *connected* if it is possible to travel from any vertex to any other vertex along adjacent edges.

❸ **Definitions**

Suppose *G* is a graph. Two vertices *v* and *w* in *G* are **connected** if and only if there is a walk in *G* from *v* to *w*. *G* is a **connected graph** if and only if ∀ vertices *v* and *w* in *G*, ∃ a walk from *v* to *w*.

After discussing the Warm-up, help students make the following generalizations. When n is odd, the network of an *n*-gon and its diagonals has an Euler circuit (it satisfies the sufficient condition for an Euler circuit mentioned in the lesson). When *n* is even, the network does not have an Euler circuit (each vertex has an odd number of edges from it).

Notes on Reading

❶ **Geography Connection** After World War II, Königsberg became part of the Soviet Union and, in 1946, the name was changed to Kaliningrad. Kaliningrad is located near the Baltic Sea in a part of Russia between Poland and Lithuania.

Begin by reviewing the terminology necessary to discuss traversing a graph, terminology found in the In-class Activity on page 679. A *walk* is just a list of the vertices and edges traversed in order. A *path* is a walk that does not repeat edges, and a *circuit* is a path that starts and ends at the same vertex. The terms *walk, path, circuit,* and *Euler circuit* build, one to the next. The table in Part 4 of the Activity shows the successive restrictions on the terms from *walk* to *Euler circuit*. Use **Questions 1–2** as examples. Also see the suggestions in Extra Help in *Adapting to Individual Needs* on page 684.

❷ Students who have seen the Königsberg bridge problem before may remember the rule for determining whether a graph is traversable. Here a proof is given, and it requires that mathematical precision be given to ideas which emerge from the Königsberg bridge problem.

❸ Connectedness is a concept needed in order to give a sufficient condition for the existence of an Euler circuit. Guide your students through the definition of connectedness. We have made the definition more compact with symbolic logic notation. You might ask students in class to write this definition without those symbols.

Optional Activities

Activity 1 You might use this activity after discussing **Question 7.** Ask students to draw a simple graph with 4 vertices such that the following conditions are met. [Drawings for 1–4 are shown at the right.]

1. No edge can be removed without disconnecting the graph
2. At most 1 edge can be removed
3. At most 2 edges can be removed
4. At most 3 edges can be removed
5. At most 4 edges can be removed [Impossible]

1. 

2. 

3. 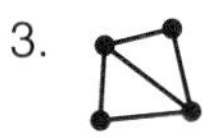

4.  

The Circuits and Connectedness Theorem is employed in the proof of Euler's Formula $V - E + F = 2$ in Lesson 11-7. There it is critical in reducing a figure with $n + 1$ edges to one that has n edges so that an induction hypothesis can be utilized. So it seems as if this theorem is so obvious it could not have any place in a nonobvious proof, but it does.

Additional Examples

1. Tell whether or not the graph is connected.

a. No

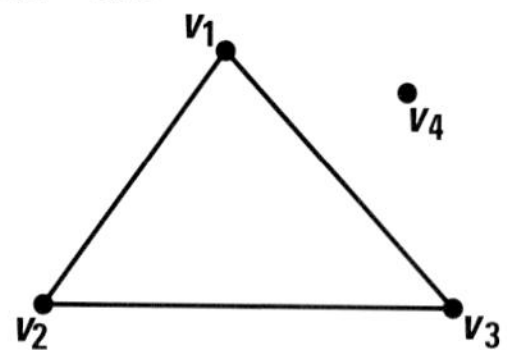

b. Yes

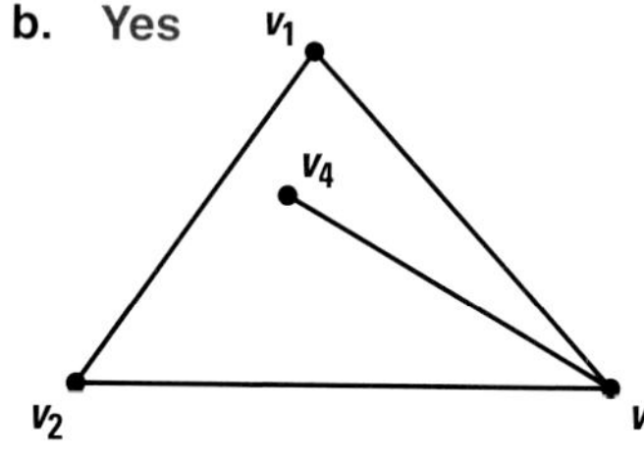

c. No

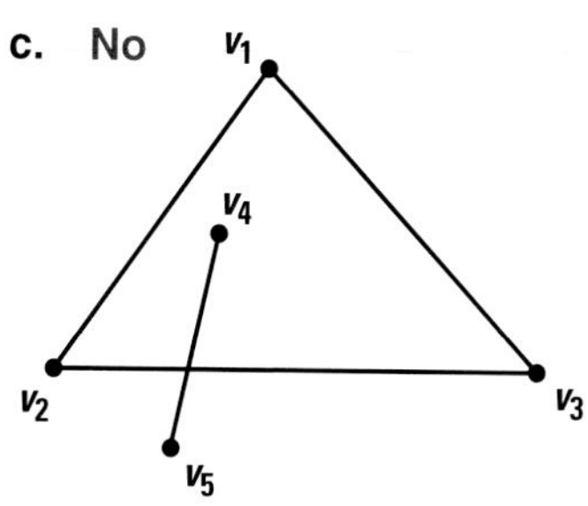

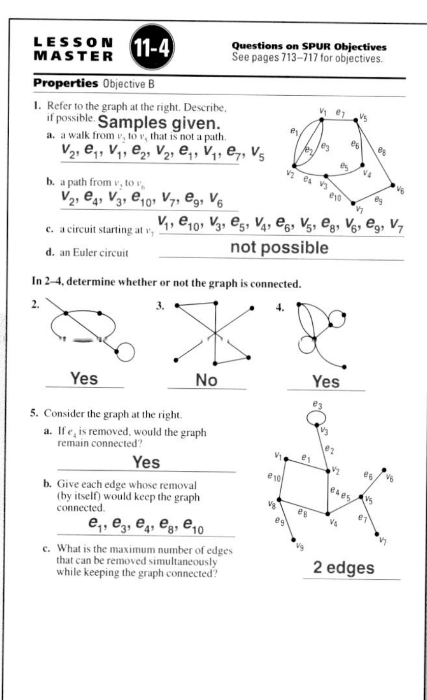

LESSON MASTER 11-4 **Questions on SPUR Objectives** See pages 713–717 for objectives.

Properties Objective B

1. Refer to the graph at the right. Describe, if possible. **Samples given.**
   a. a walk from v_2 to v_5 that is not a path. $v_2, e_1, v_1, e_2, v_2, e_1, v_1, e_7, v_5$
   b. a path from v_2 to v_6 $v_2, e_4, v_3, e_{10}, v_7, e_9, v_6$
   c. a circuit starting at v_7 $v_1, e_{10}, v_3, e_5, v_4, e_6, v_5, e_8, v_6, e_9, v_7$
   d. an Euler circuit not possible

In 2–4, determine whether or not the graph is connected.

2. Yes
3. No
4. Yes

5. Consider the graph at the right.
   a. If e_4 is removed, would the graph remain connected? Yes
   b. Give each edge whose removal (by itself) would keep the graph connected. $e_1, e_3, e_4, e_8, e_{10}$
   c. What is the maximum number of edges that can be removed simultaneously while keeping the graph connected? 2 edges

Example 1

Tell whether or not the graph is connected.

a. b. c.

Solution

a. The graph is not connected. It is impossible to find a walk from v_1 to v_3, for instance.
b. The graph is connected; each vertex is connected to each other vertex by a walk.
c. There is no walk from w_1 to w_2. So the graph is not connected. This can also be shown by redrawing the graph without crossings.

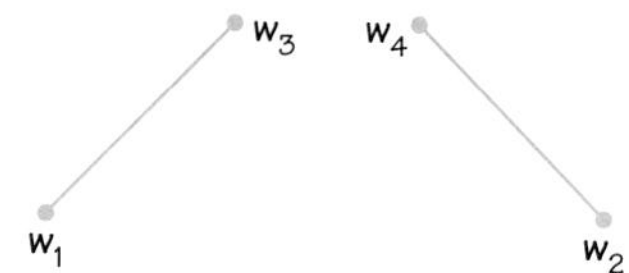

When Does a Graph Have an Euler Circuit?

With the idea of connectedness, a sufficient condition for an Euler circuit can be given.

Theorem (Sufficient Condition for an Euler Circuit)
If a graph G is connected and every vertex of G has even degree, then G has an Euler circuit.

The proof is omitted because it is quite long.

Example 2

Does the following graph have an Euler circuit? If so, find such a circuit.

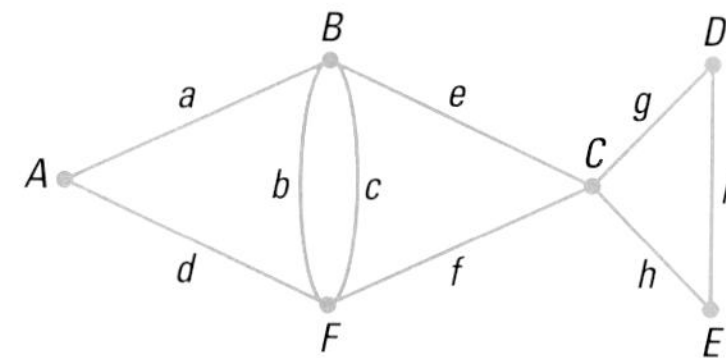

Solution

This graph is connected and every vertex has even degree: deg(A) = deg(D) = deg(E) = 2, deg(B) = deg(C) = deg(F) = 4. Hence this graph has an Euler circuit. One such circuit starting at A is a b c e g i h f d.

Optional Activities

Activity 2 You might use this activity after discussing **Question 8.** Ask students to investigate the number of possible walks from v_1 to v_3 that pass through

1. 2 edges [3]
2. 3 edges [Not possible]
3. 4 edges [6]
4. 6 edges [120]
5. 8 edges. [5040]

Encourage students to generalize their findings, that is, to state the number of possible walks from v_1 to v_3 that pass through n edges. [If n is an even integer greater than 2, the number of possible walks through n edges is $(n - 1)!$.]

Now consider a connected graph which contains a circuit.

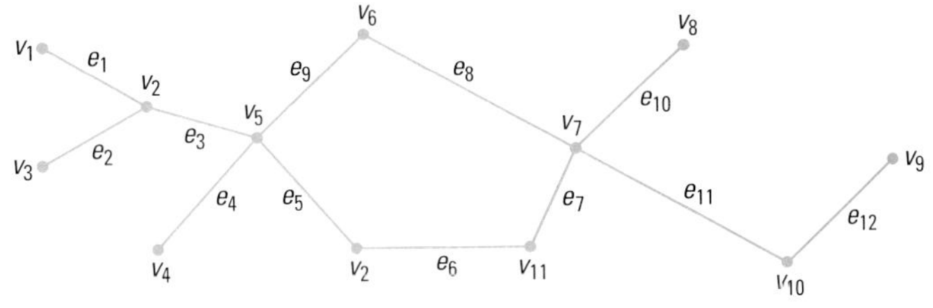

This graph has the following circuit starting at v_6: $e_9e_5e_6e_7e_8$. Suppose one edge is removed from the circuit. For instance, suppose edge e_6 is removed. Is the resulting graph connected?

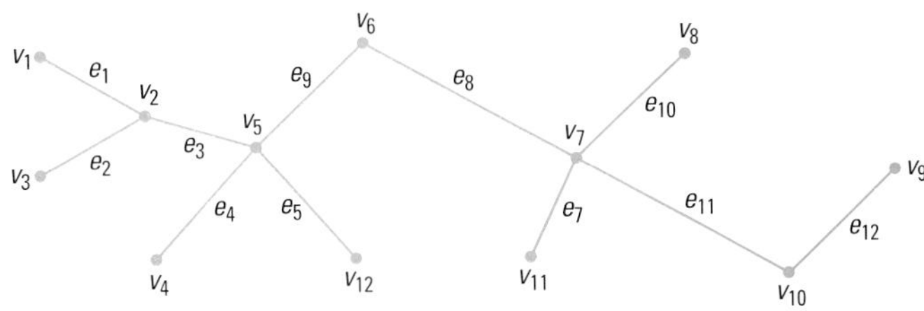

The answer, of course, is yes. Although the direct connection from v_{12} to v_{11} has been removed, the indirect connection obtained by traveling the other way around the circuit $e_5\ e_9\ e_8\ e_7$ remains. By the same reasoning, any other pair of vertices connected using the original edge e_6 can also be connected by using this indirect route.

This discussion can be formalized to prove the following theorem, which seems obvious but has a nonobvious application in Lesson 11-7.

> **Theorem (Circuits and Connectedness)**
> If a connected graph contains a circuit and an edge is removed from the circuit, then the resulting graph is also connected.

QUESTIONS

Covering the Reading

In 1 and 2, refer to the graph pictured below. A walk is given. **a.** Is it a path? **b.** Is it a circuit? **c.** Is it an Euler circuit? **See left.**

1. $v_5\ e_7\ v_1\ e_8\ v_5\ e_7\ v_1$

2. $e_4\ e_6\ e_7\ e_2$

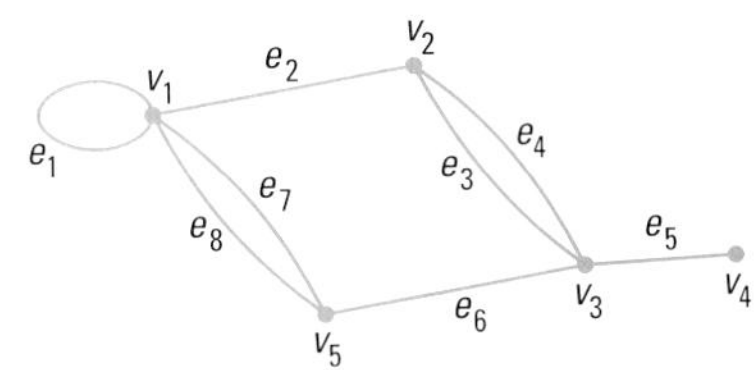

1a) No
b) No
c) No

2a) Yes
b) Yes
c) No

2. Does the following graph have an Euler circuit? If so, find such a circuit. If not, why not?

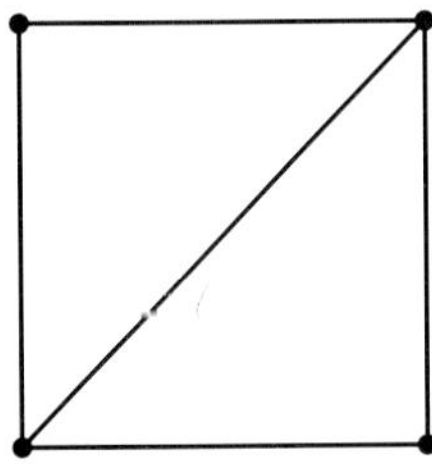

No, it has two vertices of odd degree.

Notes on Questions

Questions 1, 2, and 4 The graphs for these questions are on **Teaching Aid 121.**

Activity 3 Cooperative Learning
After completing the lessons, some students might enjoy **working in groups** to find and solve problems similar to the Königsberg bridge problem. Have each group pose one or more of their problems for the class to solve.

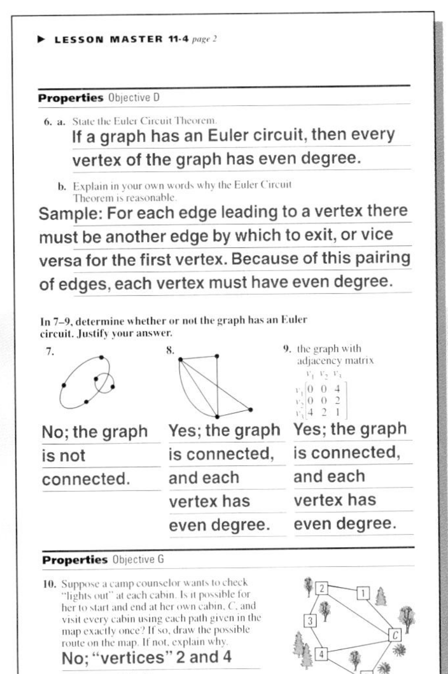

▶ **LESSON MASTER 11-4** *page 2*

Properties Objective D

6. a. State the Euler Circuit Theorem.
If a graph has an Euler circuit, then every vertex of the graph has even degree.

b. Explain in your own words why the Euler Circuit Theorem is reasonable.
Sample: For each edge leading to a vertex there must be another edge by which to exit, or vice versa for the first vertex. Because of this pairing of edges, each vertex must have even degree.

In 7–9, determine whether or not the graph has an Euler circuit. Justify your answer.

7. No; the graph is not connected.

8. Yes; the graph is connected, and each vertex has even degree.

9. the graph with adjacency matrix

$$\begin{array}{c} \\ v_1 \\ v_2 \\ v_3 \end{array}\begin{array}{c} \begin{array}{ccc} v_1 & v_2 & v_3 \end{array} \\ \begin{bmatrix} 0 & 0 & 4 \\ 0 & 0 & 2 \\ 4 & 2 & 1 \end{bmatrix} \end{array}$$

Yes; the graph is connected, and each vertex has even degree.

Properties Objective G

10. Suppose a camp counselor wants to check "lights out" at each cabin. Is it possible for her to start and end at her own cabin, C, and visit every cabin using each path given in the map exactly once? If so, draw the possible route on the map. If not, explain why.
No; "vertices" 2 and 4 have odd degree.

Notes on Questions

Question 4 Error Alert Watch for students who incorrectly assume that crossings give an indication of whether or not a graph is connected. Emphasize that crossings do not give any indication of whether a graph is connected or not. All these graphs have crossings, but two of them are not connected. And, of course, there can be a connected graph without crossings (students should think of a polygon).

Questions 5, 6, 7 These graphs are on **Teaching Aid 122.**

Questions 8 and 12 The graph and map for these questions are on **Teaching Aid 123.**

3a) If at least one vertex of a graph has an odd degree, then the graph does not have an Euler circuit.
b) The presence of an odd vertex is sufficient to show that a graph cannot have an Euler circuit.

7a) e_1, e_2, e_3, e_4, e_5, e_6

3. a. Write the contrapositive of the Euler Circuit Theorem.
b. How is the contrapositive used to test whether a given graph has an Euler circuit?
See left.

4. Tell whether the graph pictured is connected.

a. Yes

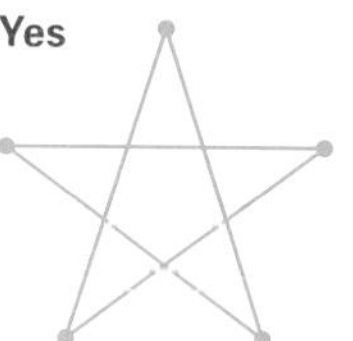

b. No

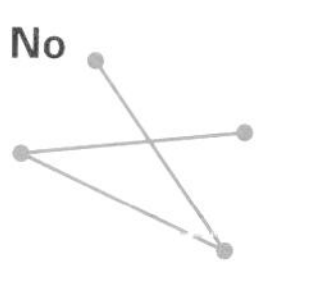

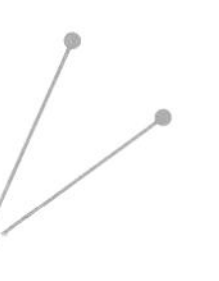

c. No

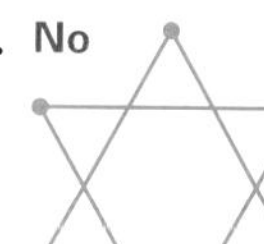

5. In the graph pictured below, the walk $e_1\ e_2\ e_3\ e_4\ e_5$ connects v_1 and v_9.

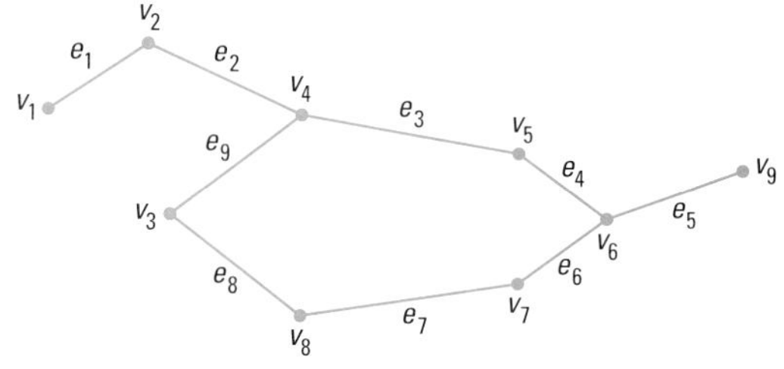

Now consider the graph obtained by removing edge e_3. Find a walk in this graph that connects v_1 and v_9. $\mathbf{e_1\ e_2\ e_9\ e_8\ e_7\ e_6\ e_5}$

6. Does the graph at the right have an Euler circuit? If so, describe the circuit. **Yes, sample from vertex *A*: *a b f g h i c e d j***

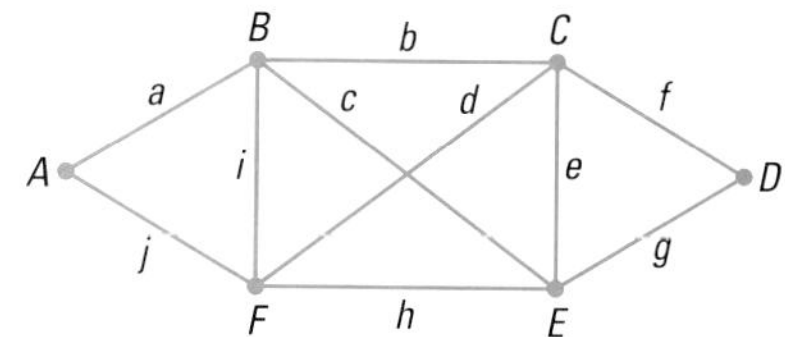

Applying the Mathematics

7. a. In the graph pictured below, list each edge that could be removed individually without disconnecting the graph. **See left.**
b. What is the maximum number of edges that can be removed at the same time without disconnecting the graph? **2**

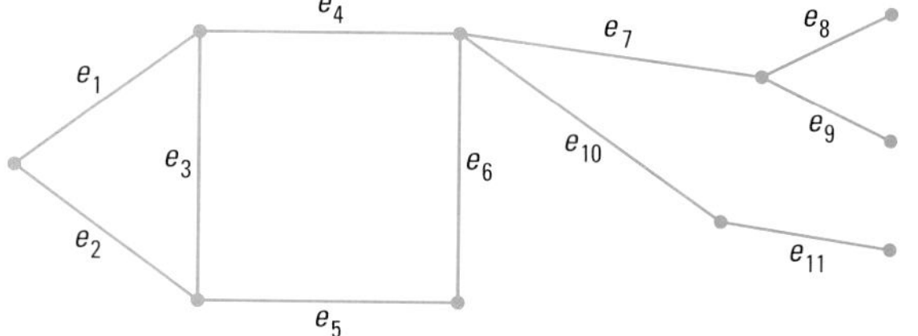

Adapting to Individual Needs

Extra Help

To help students understand the terms *walk*, *path*, *circuit*, and *Euler circuit*, you may use the following chart. Discuss how each term builds on previous ones.

	Sequence of vertices and edges traversed in order	No edge is repeated	Starts and ends with same vertex	Contains every edge and vertex
Walk	√			
Path	√	√		
Circuit	√	√	√	
Euler circuit	√	√	√	√

Challenge

Writing Have students write a report on the city of Königsberg (modern day Kaliningrad). Suggest that they discuss the history of the city; how wars have affected it; famous citizens; and how the city got its current name. Explain that the city now has two other bridges, one connecting *B* and *C* and the other connecting *B* and *D*. Ask: "Does this new graph have an Euler circuit?" [No]

3a) e_1e_4; e_2e_4; e_3e_4; $e_1e_2e_3e_4$; $e_1e_3e_2e_4$; $e_2e_1e_3e_4$; $e_2e_3e_1e_4$; $e_3e_1e_2e_4$; $e_3e_2e_1e_4$
b) Samples: $e_1e_1e_1e_4$; $e_1e_2e_2e_4$; $e_1e_3e_3e_4$; $e_1e_2e_1e_4$; $e_1e_3e_1e_4$
c) 3
d) No, you can use pairs of e_1, e_2, and e_3 as many times as you wish.

8. Consider the graph pictured below. **See left.**

a. Find all paths from v_1 to v_3.

b. Find five walks from v_1 to v_3 that are not paths.

c. How many walks from v_1 to v_3 have no repeated vertex?

d. Can you list all possible walks from v_1 to v_3? Explain.

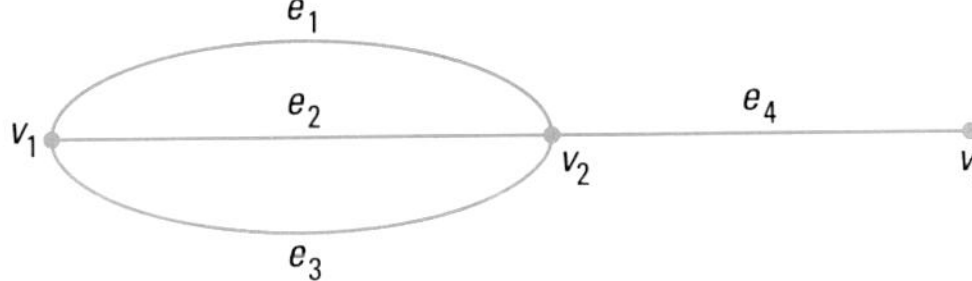

9. If a graph has an Euler circuit, must the graph be connected? Explain your answer. **Yes, if the graph is not connected, there is no way a circuit could contain every vertex**

10. Suppose G is a graph with five vertices of degrees 2, 2, 2, 4, and 4. Answer *yes, no,* or *not necessarily* to the question: Does G have an Euler circuit? Justify your answer. **See margin.**

11. Could a citizen of Königsberg have taken a walk around the city crossing each bridge exactly twice before returning to the starting point? Explain your answer. **See margin.**

12. Paris, France, is built along the banks of the Seine river and includes two islands in the river. The map below shows the bridges of Paris. Is it possible to take a walk around Paris starting and ending at the same point and crossing each bridge exactly once? **No**

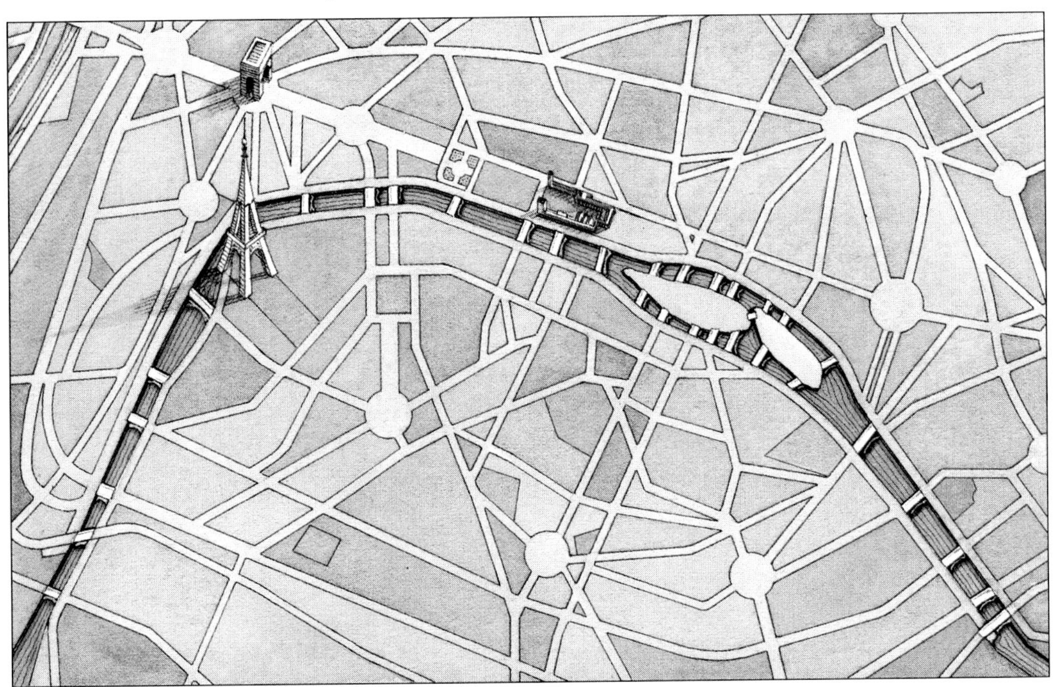

13. If a graph contains a walk from one vertex v to a different vertex w, must it contain a path from v to w? Explain your answer. **See margin.**

Additional Answers

10. Not necessarily; there is a connected graph (which must have an Euler circuit) and a nonconnected graph (which cannot).

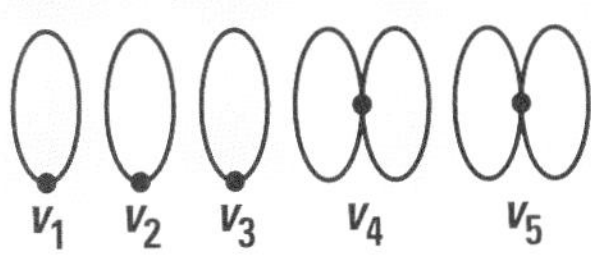

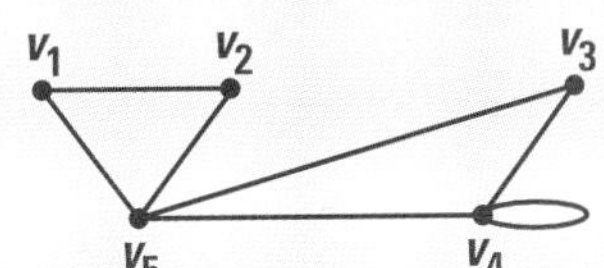

11. Yes; think of replacing each bridge by two bridges. Such a walk exists by the sufficient condition for an Euler Circuit Theorem, since every vertex will have an even degree.

13. Yes, if the walk repeats an edge, then there is a circuit. Remove edges from the graph until there is no circuit. Then connect v to w.

Notes on Questions

Question 16 Health Connection The percentages give a false impression of the accuracy of the test. That is, there are many more false positives than one would like, so expect discussion on the answers. This is why it is critical that tests be far more accurate even than 98% of the time.

Follow-up for Lesson 11-4

Practice

For more questions on SPUR Objectives, use **Lesson Master 11-4** (shown on pages 682–683).

Assessment

Quiz A quiz covering Lessons 11-1 through 11-4 is provided in the *Assessment Sourcebook.*

Extension

Ask students to determine the maximum number of edges that can be removed in a complete graph with three vertices or more without disconnecting the graph. [The maximum number of edges that can be removed is one more than all the diagonal edges of the polygon; i.e., for $n \geq 3$, the maximum number of edges that can be removed is $\frac{(n-2)(n-1)}{2}$, which produces the triangular numbers.]

Project Update Project 1, *Spanning Trees,* Project 2, *Ringel's Conjecture,* Project 3, *Constellations,* and Project 4, *The Traveling Salesman Problem,* on pages 707–708, relate to the content of this lesson.

14) Sample:

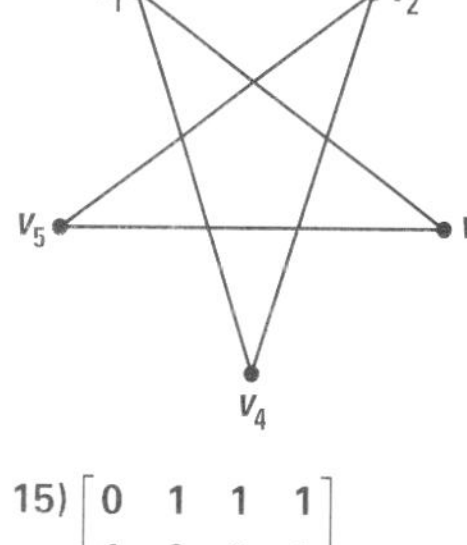

15)

$$\begin{bmatrix} 0 & 1 & 1 & 1 \\ 1 & 0 & 1 & 1 \\ 1 & 1 & 0 & 1 \\ 1 & 1 & 1 & 0 \end{bmatrix}$$

16a)

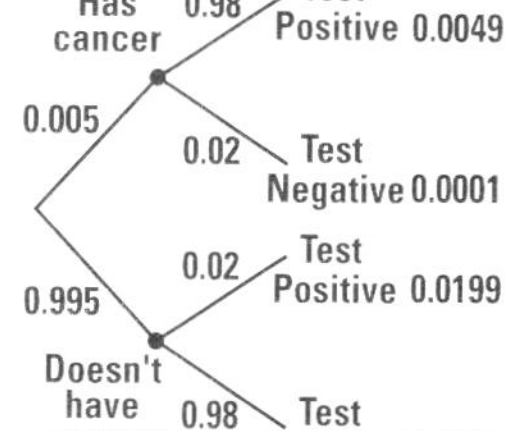

Review

14. Show, with a graph, that it is possible for 5 people on a committee each to shake the hands of two others. *(Lesson 11-3)* **See left.**

15. Write the adjacency matrix for the vertices of a tetrahedron. *(Lesson 11-2)* **See left.**

16. Assume that there is a test for cancer which is 98 percent accurate; that is, if someone has cancer, the test will be positive (signifying a cancer) 98 percent of the time, and if one doesn't have it, the test will be negative (signifying no cancer) 98 percent of the time. Also assume that 0.5% of the population has cancer.

a. Draw a probability tree and label its edges with probabilities to represent this situation. **See left.**

b. Imagine that you are tested for cancer. What is the probability that the test will be positive? **2.48%**

c. What is the probability that if the test is positive, then you have cancer? **≈ 19.76%**

d. What is the probability that if the test is positive, then you don't have cancer? *(Lesson 11-1)* **≈ 80.24%**

17. Who founded the subject of graph theory and in what century did he live? *(Lesson 11-1)* **Leonhard Euler, eighteenth**

18. How many whole numbers less than 10,000 have the property that the sum of their digits is 7? *(Lesson 10-7)* **120**

19. Suppose $\frac{\pi}{2} < x < \pi$ and $\csc x = 5$. Find $\tan x$. *(Lesson 5-7)* **≈ −.204**

20. Describe a transformation that transforms the graph of $y = e^x$ onto the graph of $y = 3e^{x-5} + 4$. *(Lesson 3-8)* **$(x, y) \rightarrow (x + 5, 3y + 4)$**

Exploration

21. Let K_n denote the complete graph with n vertices. For what values of n does K_n have an Euler circuit? Justify your answer.
n must be an odd number. For the complete graph of an n-gon, the degree of each vertex is $n - 1$. That degree is even if n is odd.

Setting Up Lesson 11-5

If you have not done so, discuss the questions from earlier lessons that review matrix ideas: **Question 17** of Lesson 11-1, **Question 20** of Lesson 11-2, and **Question 25** of Lesson 11-3. Students need to know how to multiply a matrix by itself.

LESSON

11-5

Matrix Powers and Walks

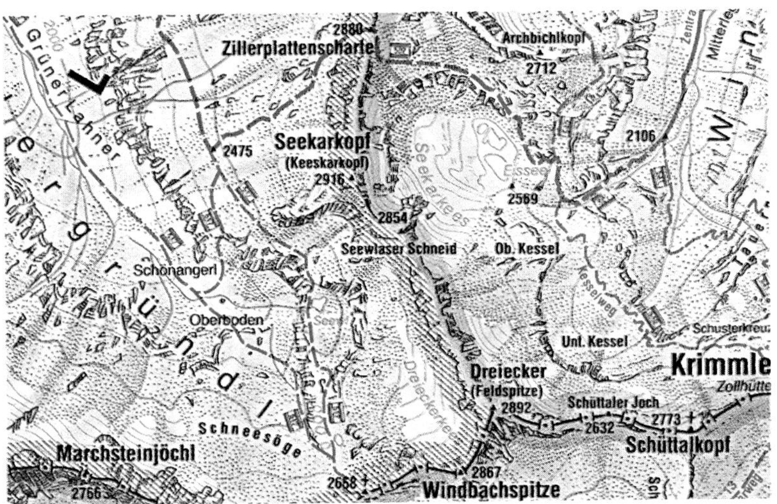

How many paths? *This map of part of the Austrian Alps shows trails (in red) for hikers. Matrices can be used to represent the choices of paths.*

In a matrix A, the element in the ith row and jth column is often denoted by a_{ij}. This notation is quite useful with adjacency matrices. For example, consider the directed graph pictured below along with its adjacency matrix.

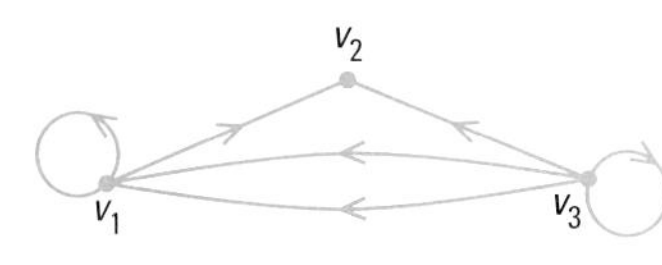

$$\begin{array}{c} \\ v_1 \\ v_2 \\ v_3 \end{array}\begin{array}{c} \begin{array}{ccc} v_1 & v_2 & v_3 \end{array} \\ \begin{bmatrix} 1 & 1 & 0 \\ 0 & 0 & 0 \\ 2 & 1 & 1 \end{bmatrix} \end{array} = A = \begin{bmatrix} a_{11} & a_{12} & a_{13} \\ a_{21} & a_{22} & a_{23} \\ a_{31} & a_{32} & a_{33} \end{bmatrix}$$

The Length of a Walk

The **length** of a walk is defined to be the number of edges in the walk. Then the entry $a_{31} = 2$ can be interpreted as indicating that there are two walks of length 1 from v_3 to v_1. The first number of the subscript in a_{31} indicates the starting vertex; the second number, the ending vertex. The entry $a_{33} = 1$ indicates that there is one walk of length 1 from v_3 to itself. The entries a_{ii} make up the **main diagonal** of the matrix, the diagonal from upper left to lower right.

Now consider the undirected graph and its adjacency matrix B pictured below.

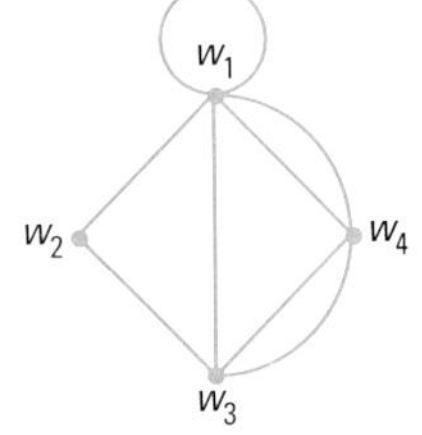

$$B = \begin{bmatrix} 1 & 1 & 1 & 2 \\ 1 & 0 & 1 & 0 \\ 1 & 1 & 0 & 2 \\ 2 & 0 & 2 & 0 \end{bmatrix}$$

main diagonal

Lesson 11-5

Objectives

B Identify parts of graphs and types of graphs.

J Use the powers of the adjacency matrix of a graph to find the number of walks of a given length, from a given starting vertex to a given ending vertex.

Resources

From the ***Teacher's Resource File***

- Lesson Master 11-5
- Answer Master 11-5
- Teaching Aids
  - 111 Warm-up
  - 124 Example 1
  - 125 Questions 2, 9, and 12
  - 126 Questions 15 and 16
  - 127 Questions 18 and 21

Additional Resources

- Visuals for Teaching Aids 111, 124–127
- Exploration 11-5

Teaching Lesson 11-5

Warm-up

1. If $A = \begin{bmatrix} 1 & 2 \\ 3 & 4 \end{bmatrix}$, find A^4 by hand.

$\begin{bmatrix} 199 & 290 \\ 435 & 634 \end{bmatrix}$

2. If you have technology that multiplies matrices, check your work using that technology.

Lesson 11-5 Overview

Broad Goals This lesson uses the matrix description of a graph to determine the number of walks from one vertex to another.

Perspective The length of a walk is the number of edges in it. The method for finding how many walks there are of a given length is surprising and elegant: If A is the adjacency matrix for a graph, then the elements a_{ij} of A^n indicate the number of walks of length n from a_i to a_j.

The computation of powers will not be difficult for students who have seen matrix multiplication before. If your students have not seen it, expect to spend an extra day on this lesson while your students become comfortable with the multiplication procedure.

Notes on Reading

The mathematics of this lesson may amaze some of your students. While it is a surprise that matrix operations have an interpretation with graphs, the matrix seems merely to be a recording device. Furthermore, matrix multiplication tends to be viewed as an artificial operation even by those familiar with it. Now, putting the two together, the powers of an adjacency matrix turn out to have a simple interpretation. Wow! This is an opportunity to point out the unity of mathematics.

The discussion on page 688 is designed to show that the connection between A^2 and walks of length 2 is not coincidence; it can be predicted from the multiplications which are done to get each element of the square of A. Briefly, to get from a vertex v_1 to a vertex v_3 with a walk of length 2, you must get from v_1 to an intermediate vertex v_i and then to v_3. The rows show how to get from v_1 to v_i for all i; the columns show how to get from v_i to v_3; multiplying them gives the number of possible walks. **Teaching Aid 124,** which shows the diagram for **Example 1** and matrix A on page 688 and matrix A^2 on page 689, can be used in this discussion.

The three missing walks from the answer to **Example 2** are the subject of **Question 8.**

Notice that this matrix has an interesting characteristic. The entries are symmetric to the main diagonal. For instance, $b_{12} = b_{21}$ and $b_{32} = b_{23}$. This is true since an edge from w_i to w_j also goes from w_j to w_i. Every matrix representation of an undirected graph has this characteristic. Such a matrix is called **symmetric**.

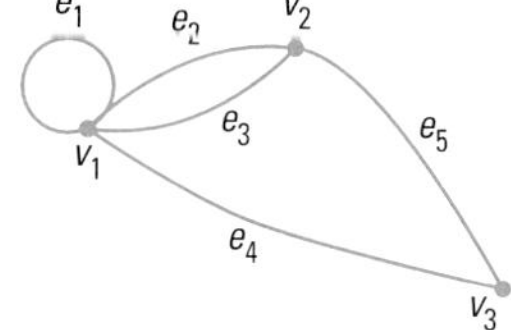

Example 1

How many walks of length 2 are there from v_1 to v_3 in the graph at the left?

Solution

A walk of length 2 from v_1 to v_3 will go through an "intermediate" vertex. There are two such walks with v_2 as the intermediate vertex (e_2e_5 and e_3e_5). There is one such walk with v_1 as the intermediate vertex (e_1e_4), but none with v_3 as the intermediate vertex. Thus, there are three walks of length 2 from v_1 to v_3.

Walks of Length 2

The length of a walk has a wonderful connection with matrices. Consider the adjacency matrix A of the graph in Example 1.

$$A = \begin{matrix} & v_1 & v_2 & v_3 \\ v_1 & 1 & 2 & 1 \\ v_2 & 2 & 0 & 1 \\ v_3 & 1 & 1 & 0 \end{matrix}$$

Each entry a_{ij} gives the number of walks of length 1 from vertex v_i to vertex v_j. Thus $a_{21} = 2$ indicates that there are 2 walks of length 1 from vertex v_2 to vertex v_1. Now multiply A by itself.

$$A \cdot A = A^2 = \begin{bmatrix} 1 & 2 & 1 \\ 2 & 0 & 1 \\ 1 & 1 & 0 \end{bmatrix}\begin{bmatrix} 1 & 2 & 1 \\ 2 & 0 & 1 \\ 1 & 1 & 0 \end{bmatrix}$$

The element a_{13} in A^2 is the product of row 1 and column 3, by the rule for matrix multiplication.

$$a_{13} = [1 \quad 2 \quad 1]\begin{bmatrix} 1 \\ 1 \\ 0 \end{bmatrix} = 1 \cdot 1 + 2 \cdot 1 + 1 \cdot 0 = 3$$

Notice that this computation of a_{13} also computes the number of walks of length 2 from v_1 to v_3:

$$\begin{bmatrix}\text{number of walks of length 1} \\ \text{from } v_1 \text{ to } v_1\end{bmatrix} \times \begin{bmatrix}\text{number of walks of length 1} \\ \text{from } v_1 \text{ to } v_3\end{bmatrix}$$
$$+ \begin{bmatrix}\text{number of walks of length 1} \\ \text{from } v_1 \text{ to } v_2\end{bmatrix} \times \begin{bmatrix}\text{number of walks of length 1} \\ \text{from } v_2 \text{ to } v_3\end{bmatrix}$$
$$+ \begin{bmatrix}\text{number of walks of length 1} \\ \text{from } v_1 \text{ to } v_3\end{bmatrix} \times \begin{bmatrix}\text{number of walks of length 1} \\ \text{from } v_3 \text{ to } v_3\end{bmatrix}$$

Optional Activities

Activity 1 Technology Connection
Materials: *Explorations* software

Students may use *Exploration 11-5: Adjacency Matrices and Walks,* to explore the relationship between a graph, its adjacency matrix, and the number of walks of a given length between vertices. Students can create an adjacency matrix for an undirected graph and then find the number of walks between any two vertices by examining the power matrix.

Activity 2 You might use this activity in conjunction with **Question 10.** Have students draw a graph for the matrix and verify some of the paths of lengths 2 and 3 computed by the matrix powers. [See sample answer at the right.]

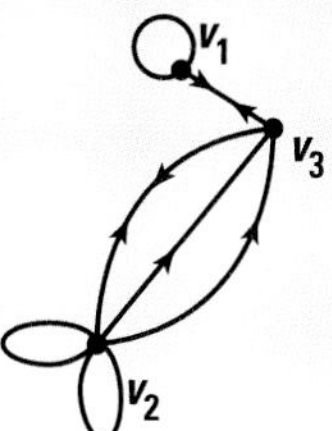

The entire matrix A^2 is computed in the same way.

$$A^2 = \begin{bmatrix} 6 & 3 & 3 \\ 3 & 5 & 2 \\ 3 & 2 & 2 \end{bmatrix}$$

The entry in row 1 and column 3 of A^2 is 3, the number of walks of length 2 between v_1 and v_3 that was found in Example 1. Using similar reasoning, since $a_{22} = 5$, there are 5 walks of length 2 from v_2 to v_2. You should try to find these 5 walks.

Activity

e_2e_3; e_3e_2; e_3e_3; e_2e_2; e_5e_5

Describe the 5 walks of length 2 from v_2 to v_2. **See left.**

Walks of Length n

The discussion on page 688 is a special case of the following wonderful theorem, whose proof is too long to be included. (It can be proved using mathematical induction.) As usual,

$$A^n = \underbrace{A \cdot A \cdot \ldots \cdot A.}_{n \text{ factors}}$$

Theorem
Let G be a graph with vertices $v_1, v_2, \ldots, v_m$, and let n be a positive integer. Let A be the adjacency matrix for G. Then the element a_{ij} in A^n is the number of walks of length n from v_i to v_j.

Example 2

Determine the number of walks of length 3 between v_1 and v_2 in the graph of Example 1.

Solution

The answer is given by the element a_{12} of A^3.

$$A^3 = \begin{bmatrix} 1 & 2 & 1 \\ 2 & 0 & 1 \\ 1 & 1 & 0 \end{bmatrix}^3 = \begin{bmatrix} 15 & 15 & 9 \\ 15 & 8 & 8 \\ 9 & 8 & 5 \end{bmatrix} \text{ and so } a_{12} = 15.$$

Thus, there are 15 walks of length 3 between v_1 and v_2.

Check

The walks can be listed. Here are 12 of them. Which three are missing?

$e_1e_1e_2$ $e_1e_1e_3$ $e_2e_3e_2$ $e_3e_2e_3$ $e_2e_2e_2$ $e_3e_3e_3$ $e_1e_4e_5$
$e_2e_5e_5$ $e_3e_5e_5$ $e_4e_4e_3$ $e_4e_4e_2$ $e_2e_2e_3$

Additional Examples

1. Find the number of walks of length 2 from v_2 to v_1 in this graph.

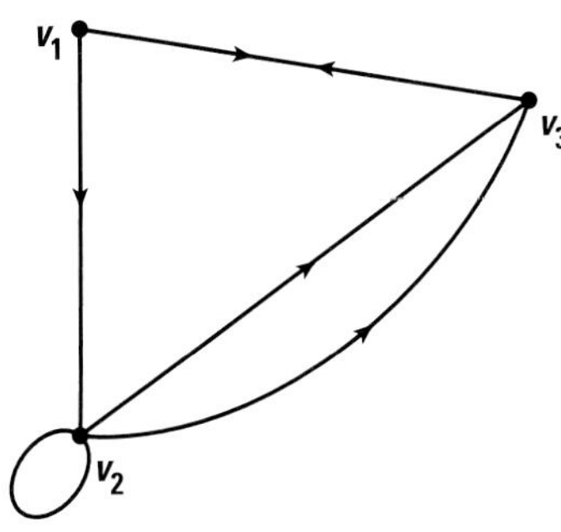

2; This can be verified by taking the second power of this adjacency matrix:
$$\begin{bmatrix} 0 & 1 & 1 \\ 0 & 1 & 2 \\ 1 & 0 & 0 \end{bmatrix}.$$

2. In the graph of Additional Example 1, find the number of walks of length 3 from v_1 to v_3.
3; This can be done by matrix multiplication. (Only one element of the matrix for the cube needs to be calculated.) It can be verified by examining the graph and seeing that there are three ways to get from v_1 to v_3 in a walk of length 3.

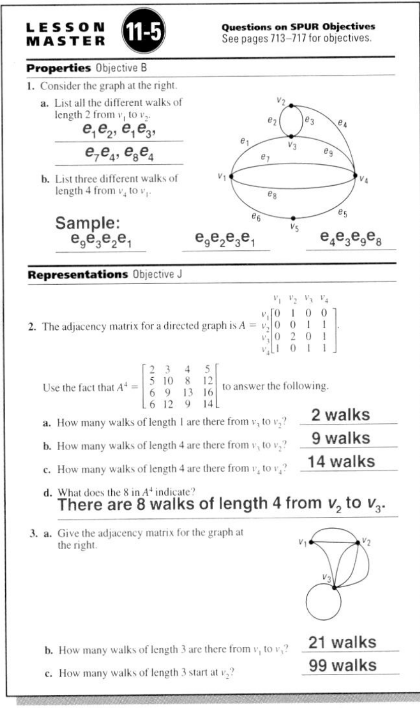

LESSON MASTER 11-5 **Questions on SPUR Objectives** See pages 713–717 for objectives.

Properties Objective B

1. Consider the graph at the right.
   a. List all the different walks of length 2 from v_1 to v_2. **e_1e_2, e_1e_3, e_7e_4, e_8e_4**
   b. List three different walks of length 4 from v_4 to v_1. **Sample: $e_9e_3e_2e_1$ $e_9e_2e_3e_1$ $e_4e_3e_9e_8$**

Representations Objective J

2. The adjacency matrix for a directed graph is $A = \begin{matrix} & v_1 & v_2 & v_3 & v_4 \\ v_1 & 0 & 1 & 0 & 0 \\ v_2 & 0 & 0 & 1 & 1 \\ v_3 & 0 & 2 & 0 & 1 \\ v_4 & 1 & 0 & 1 & 1 \end{matrix}$.

   Use the fact that $A^4 = \begin{bmatrix} 2 & 3 & 4 & 5 \\ 5 & 10 & 8 & 12 \\ 6 & 9 & 13 & 16 \\ 6 & 12 & 9 & 14 \end{bmatrix}$ to answer the following.
   a. How many walks of length 1 are there from v_3 to v_2? **2 walks**
   b. How many walks of length 4 are there from v_3 to v_2? **9 walks**
   c. How many walks of length 4 are there from v_4 to v_4? **14 walks**
   d. What does the 8 in A^4 indicate? **There are 8 walks of length 4 from v_2 to v_3.**
3. a. Give the adjacency matrix for the graph at the right.
   b. How many walks of length 3 are there from v_1 to v_3? **21 walks**
   c. How many walks of length 3 start at v_2? **99 walks**

Activity 3 After completing the lesson, you might have students investigate how many walks of length 2 begin and end at the same vertex for a complete graph with 3 or more vertices. Incidentally, there are many patterns apparent in powers of adjacency matrices for complete graphs—you may want students to explore further and list some. [In a complete graph of n vertices, from each vertex there are $n - 1$ walks of length 2 which lead back to itself, and $n - 2$ walks of length 2 which end at a different vertex. From each vertex, there is exactly one more walk of even length that leads back to itself than ends at a different vertex, and exactly one less walk of odd length that leads back to itself than ends at a different vertex.]

Notes on Questions

Questions 2, 9, and 12 Teaching Aid 125 contains these graphs.

Question 9 Do this question both with and without matrices. How many students did it each way? Did any do it both ways to check? Give plaudits if they did.

Question 10 You might check a few elements of A^2 and A^3 by examining a graph for A.

Question 11 This kind of question brings home the relationship between graphs and their adjacency matrices.

Questions 15 This graph is on **Teaching Aid 126.**

Question 16 Error Alert Many students will need guidance here. Tell them to think of this like the Königsberg bridge problem, with the doors like bridges and the rooms (and outside) like pieces of land. This floor plan is on **Teaching Aid 126.**

(Notes on Questions continue on page 692.)

It can be proved that the powers of a symmetric matrix are symmetric. Since the matrix A of Example 1 is symmetric, its cube A^3 in Example 2 should also be symmetric. This provides another way of checking the multiplication in Example 2.

QUESTIONS

Covering the Reading

1. *True or false.* If in a graph there are 2 walks from v_2 to itself, then the entry in the second row, second column of the adjacency matrix for the graph will be 4. **False**

2. In the adjacency matrix of the graph at the right, the entry a_{32} = __?__ and a_{23} = __?__. **2; 0**

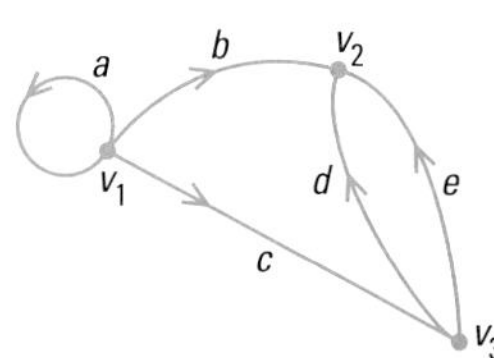

In 3 and 4, consider the matrix B shown at the right.

$$B = \begin{matrix} & v_1 & v_2 & v_3 \\ v_1 \\ v_2 \\ v_3 \end{matrix}\begin{bmatrix} 1 & 1 & 0 \\ 0 & 0 & 0 \\ 2 & 1 & 1 \end{bmatrix}$$

3. Give the element.

a. b_{21} = __?__ **0**

b. b_{13} = __?__ **0**

c. b_{33} = __?__ **1**

4. *True or false.* The matrix represents an undirected graph. **False**

5. *True or false.* There is only one walk from v_1 to v_2 in the graph at the right. **False**

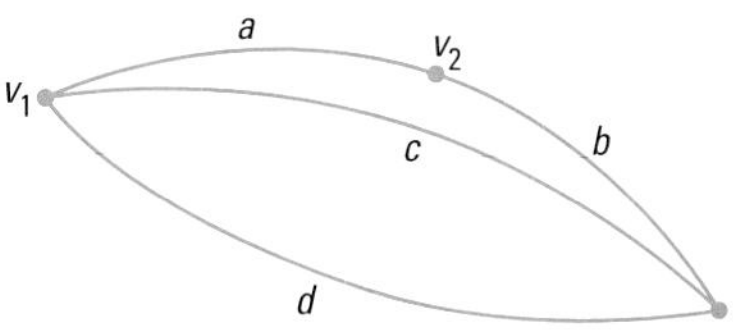

6. Describe the 5 walks of length 2 from v_2 to v_2 in the graph of Example 1. **See left.**

7. Describe all of the walks of length 3 from v_3 to v_3 in Example 2. **See left.**

8. In Example 2, find the 3 missing walks of length 3 from v_1 to v_2. **See left.**

6) e_2e_3; e_3e_2; e_3e_3; e_2e_2; e_5e_5

7) $e_4e_1e_4$; $e_4e_2e_5$; $e_4e_3e_5$; $e_5e_2e_4$; $e_5e_3e_4$

8) $e_2e_3e_3$; $e_3e_2e_2$; $e_3e_3e_2$

9. Find the number of walks of length 2 from v_3 to v_2 in the graph at the right. **5 walks; e_1e_2; e_1e_5; e_4e_2; e_4e_5; e_6e_3**

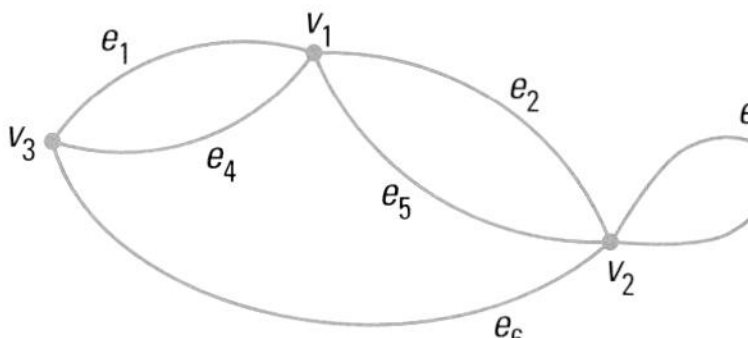

10. If $A = \begin{bmatrix} 1 & 0 & 1 \\ 0 & 2 & 3 \\ 1 & 1 & 0 \end{bmatrix}$, calculate A^2 and A^3. **See margin.**

Adapting to Individual Needs

Extra Help

Some students might be confused by the double subscript notation a_{ij}. Point out that the numbers indicate the row and the column of the element in the matrix. (See **Question 3.**) Stress that a_{ij} in an adjacency matrix gives the number of walks of length 1 from v_i to v_j. (See **Question 2.**) Then explain that a_{ij} in the nth power of the adjacency matrix gives the number of walks of length n from v_i to v_j.

Additional Answers

10. $A^2 = \begin{bmatrix} 2 & 1 & 1 \\ 3 & 7 & 6 \\ 1 & 2 & 4 \end{bmatrix}$;

$A^3 = \begin{bmatrix} 3 & 3 & 5 \\ 9 & 20 & 24 \\ 5 & 8 & 7 \end{bmatrix}$

Applying the Mathematics

11) If the main diagonal is all zeros, there are no loops, and if all other entries are zero or one, there are no parallel edges, so the graph is simple.

14a) If the adjacency matrix for a graph is symmetric, then its graph is not directed.
b) Sample:

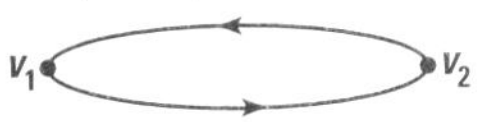

15)

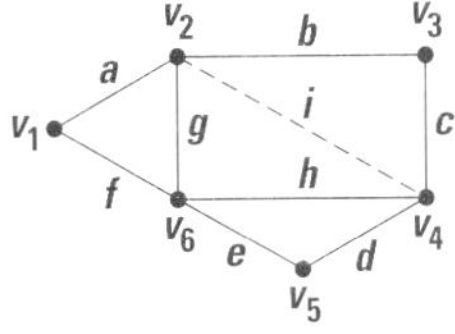

11. If all the entries on the main diagonal of the adjacency matrix for a graph are zero and the other entries are zero or one, then the graph is a simple graph. Explain why. **See left.**

12. Determine the total number of walks of length 3 for the graph given at the right. **105**

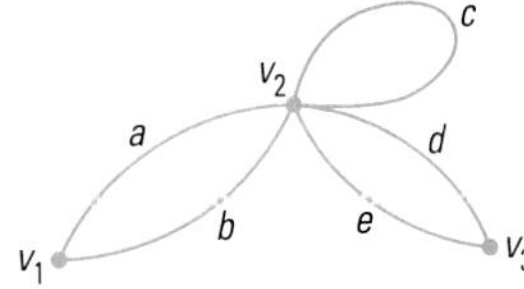

13. Refer to the graph on page 680. Determine the number of walks over exactly 3 bridges of Königsberg that begin and end at C. **4**

14. Consider the following true statement: **See left.**

If a graph is not directed, then its adjacency matrix is symmetric.

a. Write the converse.
b. Give a counterexample to show that the converse is false.

Review

15. Does the graph at the right have an Euler circuit? If so, find it. If not, draw an edge that will make an Euler circuit possible. *(Lesson 11-4)*
No, add edge i, see left.

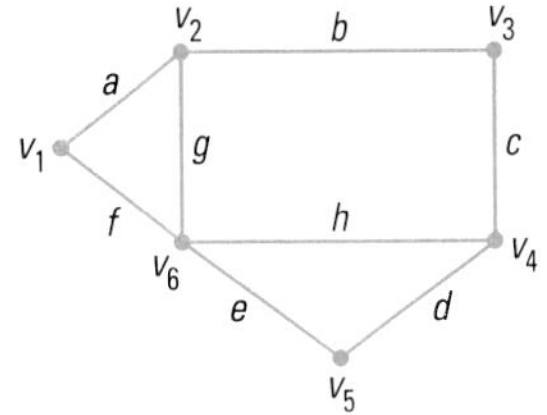

16. A house is open for public viewing. An outline of the floor plan is shown below. Is it possible to enter into room 1, pass through every interior doorway of the house exactly once, and exit from room 8? If so, how can this be done? If not, where could you put a new door to make such a tour possible? (Hint: Construct a graph to model this situation.) *(Lesson 11-4)*

sitting room in the 1875 home of Senator Wilbur Sanders in Helena, Montana

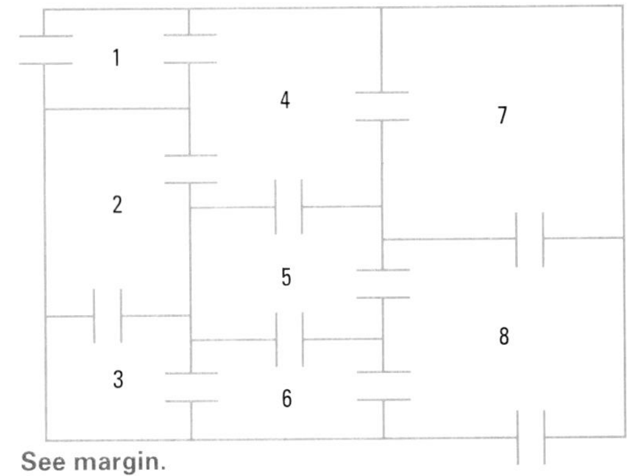

See margin.

Follow-up for Lesson 11-5

Practice

For more questions on SPUR Objectives, use **Lesson Master 11-5** (shown on page 689).

Assessment

Written Communication Ask students to **work in pairs.** Have each student draw a graph and write a problem like **Example 2.** Students should solve their partner's problem and verify their answer by listing the walks. [Students count the walks of a given length from one given vertex to another by finding powers of adjacency matrices and making a list.]

Extension

Extend the idea of **Question 11** by asking students these questions.

1. Can you tell if a graph has an isolated vertex from its adjacency matrix? [Yes, it will have a row and a column with all entries equal to 0.]
2. What can be said about a directed graph if one row of its adjacency matrix consists of all 0s? [No paths lead out from one of its vertices.]
3. What can be said if one column consists of all 0s? [No paths lead to one of its vertices.]

Adapting to Individual Needs

Challenge

Have students exemplify each of the following graph theorems by drawing a graph with the stated conditions and showing that the result is true.

1. One of Euler's theorems says that a graph with exactly 2 odd vertices has a complete path starting at one odd vertex and ending at the other.
2. Another Euler theorem says that a graph with more than 2 odd vertices can be traversed completely, but it requires more than 1 circuit.
3. A corollary to the second theorem above says that a graph with $2n$ odd vertices can be traversed completely in n separate circuits. [Many graphs are possible.]

Additional Answers

16.

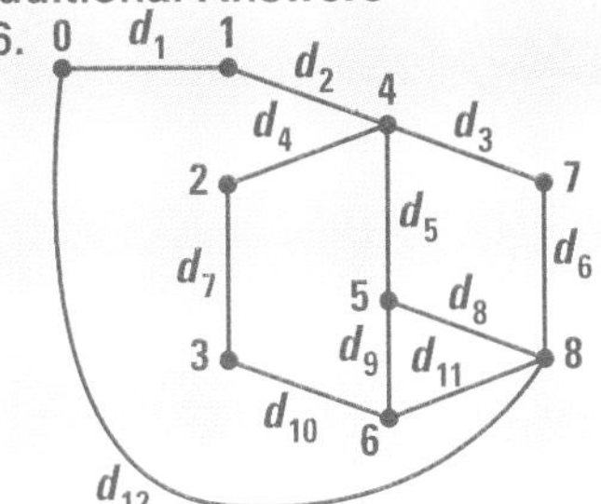

Add d_{13} between room 5 and room 6.

Notes on Questions

Questions 18 and 21 Teaching Aid 127 has the matrix and the networks for these questions.

Question 22 The solving of a 2×2 system is needed for Lesson 11-5. It does not have to be solved using matrices, but you might wish to do so just to review another application of matrices.

Additional Answers

21. Top network
$\equiv \sim (p \text{ and } (q \text{ or } \sim r))$
$\equiv \sim p \text{ or } \sim (q \text{ or } \sim r)$
$\equiv \sim p \text{ or } (\sim q \text{ and } r)$
$\equiv$ Bottom network
Therefore, the two networks are equivalent.

23. a. $A = \begin{bmatrix} 0 & 1 & 0 \\ 0 & 0 & 1 \\ 1 & 0 & 0 \end{bmatrix}$,

$A^2 = \begin{bmatrix} 0 & 0 & 1 \\ 1 & 0 & 0 \\ 0 & 1 & 0 \end{bmatrix}$,

$A^3 = \begin{bmatrix} 1 & 0 & 0 \\ 0 & 1 & 0 \\ 0 & 0 & 1 \end{bmatrix}$,

$A^4 = \begin{bmatrix} 0 & 1 & 0 \\ 0 & 0 & 1 \\ 1 & 0 & 0 \end{bmatrix}$,

$A^4 = A^1$, $A^5 = A^2$, $A^6 = A^3$. The pattern is $A^n = A^{n \pmod 3}$.

b. The paths between vertices are circular.

c. 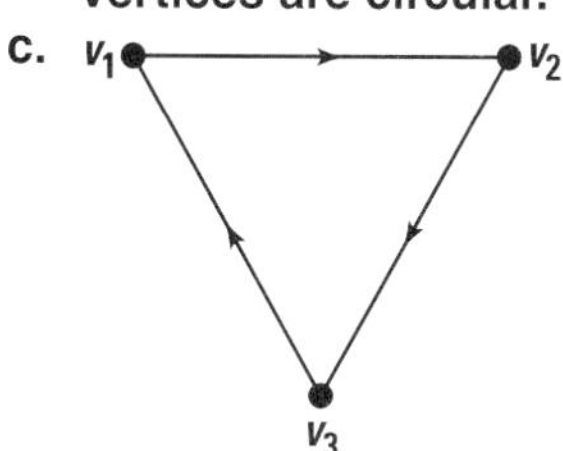

18)

v_1 v_2 v_4 v_3

19)

imaginary
$1 + 2i$
$-2 + i$
real
$2 - i$
$-1 - 2i$

22b) There are an infinite number of solutions. For all real x, $y = \frac{4}{9}x + \frac{2}{3}$.

17. If there are 27 people at a party, is it possible for each one to shake hands with exactly 4 other people? *(Lesson 11-3)* **Yes**

18. Draw a graph which has the adjacency matrix at the right. *(Lesson 11-2)* **See left.**

$$\begin{array}{c} \\ v_1 \\ v_2 \\ v_3 \\ v_4 \end{array}\begin{array}{c} \begin{matrix} v_1 & v_2 & v_3 & v_4 \end{matrix} \\ \begin{bmatrix} 0 & 1 & 2 & 3 \\ 1 & 0 & 1 & 2 \\ 2 & 1 & 0 & 1 \\ 3 & 2 & 1 & 0 \end{bmatrix} \end{array}$$

19. Suppose that $2 - i$ is the fourth root of some complex number z. Find and graph the other fourth roots. *(Lessons 8-6, 8-7)* **See left.**

20. Simplify the expression $\left(\frac{1 + z^{-2}}{1 - z^{-2}}\right) \cdot (1 + z)$, and state the restrictions on z. *(Lesson 5-1)* $\frac{z^2 + 1}{z - 1}$ **for** $z \neq 0, 1, -1$

21. Show that the two computer logic networks given below are equivalent. *(Lessons 1-3, 1-4)* **See margin.**

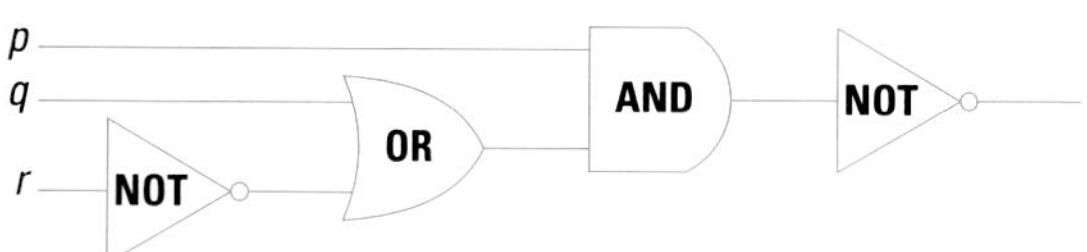

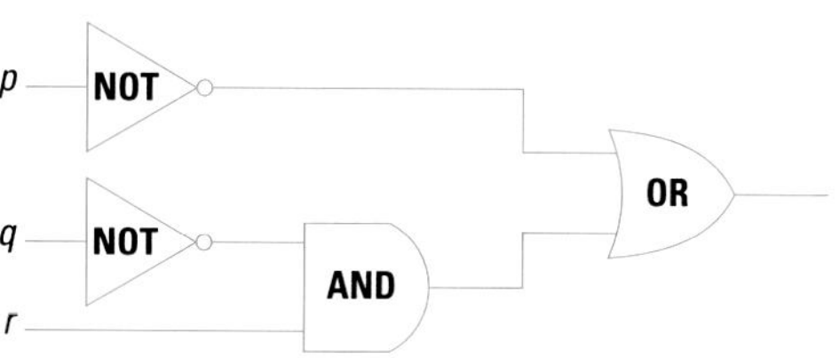

22. Solve the following systems. *(Previous course)*

a. $\begin{cases} 3x + 4y = 10 \\ 2x - y = 1 \end{cases}$ $x = \frac{14}{11}, y = \frac{17}{11}$

b. $\begin{cases} 8x = 18y - 12 \\ 24 = -16x + 36y \end{cases}$ **See left.**

Exploration

23. Let $A = \begin{bmatrix} 0 & 1 & 0 \\ 0 & 0 & 1 \\ 1 & 0 & 0 \end{bmatrix}$. **See margin.**

a. Calculate A^n for $n = 1, 2, 3, 4, \ldots$. Find a pattern in A^n.
b. What does this pattern tell you about the directed graph whose adjacency matrix is A?
c. Draw the graph to confirm your answer to part **b**.

Setting Up Lesson 11-6

The system $\{.6a + .3b = a, a + b = 1\}$ is found in the **Example** in Lesson 11-6. You might wish to ask students to solve this system in class before the lesson if you feel that they need work on this skill.

LESSON

11-6

Markov Chains

Our Milky Way Galaxy. *Some astronomers have used Markov chains to study galaxies and their distribution in the universe.* *See page 696.*

In this lesson, graphs and powers of matrices are combined with probability, limits, and systems of equations in a display of the interconnectedness of mathematics. The ideas of this lesson have wide applicability.

A Markov Chain Weather Situation

Suppose that weather forecasters in a particular town have come up with data, represented in the following directed graph, concerning the probabilities of occurrence of sunny days (S), rainy days (R), and cloudy days (C).

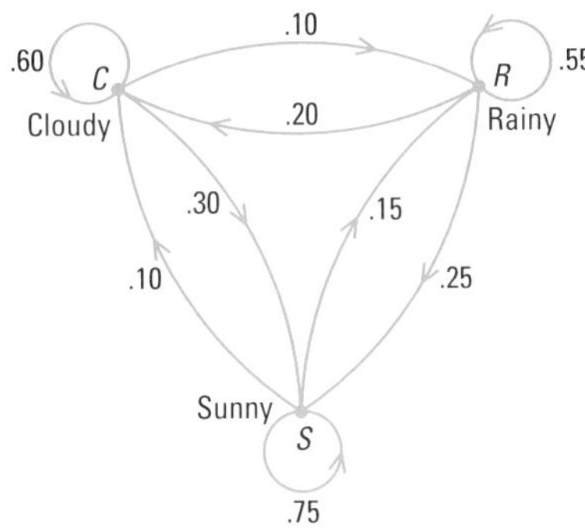

Interpret this directed graph as follows. The loop about point C, labeled .60, means that 60% of the time a cloudy day is followed by another cloudy day. The .10 by edge (C, R) means that 10% of cloudy days are followed by a rainy day. The .30 by edge (C, S) means that 30% of cloudy days are followed by a sunny day.

Lesson 11-6

Objectives

H Use stochastic matrices to make long-term predictions.

Resources

From the ***Teacher's Resource File***
- Lesson Master 11-6
- Answer Master 11-6
- Teaching Aids
  - 111 Warm-up
  - 128 Graph and Matrix T
  - 129 Questions 14–16
- Technology Sourcebook
  - Calculator Master 16

Additional Resources
- Visuals for Teaching Aids 111, 128–129
- Exploration 11-6

Teaching Lesson 11-6

Warm-up

Let A be a 2×2 matrix in which the elements of the two rows are identical and the elements of each row sum to 1. Prove that $A^2 = A$.

Let $A = \begin{bmatrix} x & 1-x \\ x & 1-x \end{bmatrix}$.

Then $A^2 = \begin{bmatrix} x & 1-x \\ x & 1-x \end{bmatrix} \bullet \begin{bmatrix} x & 1-x \\ x & 1-x \end{bmatrix}$

$= \begin{bmatrix} x^2 + (1-x)x & x(1-x) + (1-x)^2 \\ x^2 + (1-x)x & x(1-x) + (1-x)^2 \end{bmatrix}$

Carrying out the multiplications and adding the elements in the rows of A^2 shows that $A^2 = A$.

Lesson 11-6 Overview

Broad Goals This lesson considers the application of networks and their matrices to situations in which states at time $n + 1$ depend on states at time n with fixed probabilities.

Perspective The adjacency matrices of Lesson 11-2 become probability matrices here. Instead of the a_{ij} element of the matrix representing the number of paths from vertex i to vertex j, the element a_{ij} is the probability of moving from vertex i to vertex j. A Markov chain is a situation that can be described by these transition probabilities.

In a matrix for a Markov chain, the elements of any row are nonnegative and add to 1, that is, the matrix is a stochastic matrix. If A is a stochastic matrix, so is A^n. Furthermore, the elements of A^n represent the probability of moving from vertex i to vertex j in exactly n transitions. So, for example, if the probabilities of particular weather changes from one day to the next are considered constant, the probability of a particular kind of weather any number of days from now can be calculated.

We have not considered all the possibilities of stochastic matrices in this lesson. For example, if a row has a 1 on the diagonal, then the 1 creates what is called an *absorbing state*. For example, a situation represented by

(Overview continues on page 694.)

The Warm-up is one generalization of Question 8. It shows that when the transition probabilities are the same regardless of the current state, then these transition probabilities represent also the long range probabilities, for by mathematical induction, if $A^2 = A$, then for all n, $A^n = A$.)

Notes on Reading

The language can be confusing here. A Markov chain is neither a chain nor a sequence. It is a *situation* in which enough information is given so that a sequence of states can be determined with their probabilities.

Markov chain matrices are sometimes called *Markov matrices*. That multiplying them gives probabilities of going from state n to state $n + 2$ is a combination of the idea of the last lesson and the notion, first encountered in Lesson 11-1, that conditional probabilities can be represented by graphs.

Teaching Aid 128 shows the graph on page 693 and matrix T.

❶ **Science Connection** Students should expect that the powers of the Markov weather matrix gradually approach a limit in which all rows are the same. This merely represents the idea that weather n days from now is less and less dependent on today's weather as n increases and more and more dependent on the probabilities of a particular type of weather condition.

Now suppose today is cloudy. What will the weather be two days from now?

To answer this question, represent the graph by a matrix T, where the rows and columns of T are labeled C, S, and R. The entries of T are probabilities that one type of weather on one day is followed by a particular type of weather the next day. For instance, $t_{23} = .15$ because t_{23} is in row S and column R and 15% of sunny days are followed by a rainy day.

$$\begin{array}{c} \\ C \\ S \\ R \end{array}\begin{array}{c} \begin{array}{ccc} C & S & R \end{array} \\ \begin{bmatrix} .60 & .30 & .10 \\ .10 & .75 & .15 \\ .20 & .25 & .55 \end{bmatrix} \end{array} = T$$

Notice that each element is nonnegative (since each is a probability), and that the entries in each row add to 1 (since the next day is always either cloudy, sunny, or rainy). A matrix with these properties is called a **stochastic matrix**. We call this matrix T to indicate that it contains the **transition probabilities** from one time period to the next.

In Lesson 11-5, you saw that the square of the adjacency matrix for a graph represents the number of walks of length two from one vertex to another. Here the square of T has a similar interpretation: its elements are the probabilities connecting weather two days apart.

$$T^2 = T \cdot T = \begin{bmatrix} .60 & .30 & .10 \\ .10 & .75 & .15 \\ .20 & .25 & .55 \end{bmatrix} \cdot \begin{bmatrix} .60 & .30 & .10 \\ .10 & .75 & .15 \\ .20 & .25 & .55 \end{bmatrix} = \begin{bmatrix} .410 & .430 & .160 \\ .165 & .630 & .205 \\ .255 & .385 & .360 \end{bmatrix}$$

Notice that the entries in each row still add up to 1, so T^2 is also a stochastic matrix. Reading across the first row of T^2 shows that if today is cloudy, there is a 41% chance that it will be cloudy two days from now, a 43% chance that it will be sunny, and a 16% chance of rain.

T^2 can be multiplied by itself to yield T^4, which indicates the probabilities of various types of weather occuring 4 days later. Similarly $T^4 \cdot T^4 = T^8$ and $T^8 \cdot T^2 = T^{10}$. In general, each entry of T^k indicates the probability that one type of weather will be followed by a particular type k days later.

$$T^4 \approx \begin{bmatrix} .27985 & .50880 & .21135 \\ .22388 & .54678 & .22935 \\ .25988 & .49080 & .24932 \end{bmatrix}$$

$$T^8 \approx \begin{bmatrix} .24715 & .52432 & .22853 \\ .24466 & .52544 & .22990 \\ .24740 & .52295 & .22965 \end{bmatrix}$$

$$T^{10} \approx \begin{bmatrix} .24612 & .52458 & .22930 \\ .24563 & .52474 & .22962 \\ .24628 & .52426 & .22946 \end{bmatrix} \approx \begin{bmatrix} .25 & .52 & .23 \\ .25 & .52 & .23 \\ .25 & .52 & .23 \end{bmatrix}$$

❶ The three rows of T^{10} are almost identical. This means that no matter what the weather is today, there is approximately a 25% chance of a cloudy day 10 days from now, a 52% chance of a sunny day, and a 23% chance of rain.

Lesson 11-6 Overview, continued

$\begin{bmatrix} .6 & .4 \\ 0 & 1 \end{bmatrix}$ will cause all objects to end in the second state (vertex). This is the absorbing state. If there are two rows with 1's, you can have oscillating states. For example, the matrix $\begin{bmatrix} 0 & 1 \\ 1 & 0 \end{bmatrix}$ will never lead to a stable situation. The Convergence of Powers Theorem explicitly excludes matrices with entries of zero.

Optional Activities

Activity 1 Technology Connection
Materials: *Explorations* software

You may use *Exploration 11-6: Markov Chains,* to introduce the relationship between a directed graph, its corresponding matrix with transition probabilities, and increasing powers of the matrix. You can create a transition matrix and then display a directed graph and different powers of that matrix.

Activity 2 In conjunction with the **Example** on page 696, you might ask how the probability matrix for the flowers would have to change if the desired outcome was to be 50% pale flowers and 50% brilliant flowers. [The probabilities for pale flowers producing pale offspring and brilliant flowers producing pale offspring would have to sum to 1. So, if brilliant flowers produced pale offspring 40% of the time, then eventually the offspring would be equally split between pale and brilliant.]

Weather is dependent on many factors. The key assumption in the model used here is that the probability of a certain type of weather tomorrow is only dependent on the weather today. When a situation can exist in only a finite number of states (above there are 3 states: C, S, and R), and the probabilities of having one state precede another depend only on the earlier state, then the situation is said to be an example of a **Markov chain**.

Markov chains are named after the Russian mathematician who first studied them, Andrei Andreevich Markov (1856-1922). Markov worked in a variety of areas of mathematics, with his greatest contributions being in the area of probability theory. He developed the concept of Markov chain from the theory of probability and applied it to a study of the distributions of vowels and consonants in Russian literature. His work is frequently considered to be the first research in mathematical linguistics, the mathematical study of language structure.

Squares of Stochastic Matrices Are Stochastic

Recall that for the stochastic matrix T on the previous page, T^2 is also stochastic. In general, the kth power of any stochastic matrix is stochastic. This can be seen for the 2nd power of a 2×2 stochastic matrix as follows.

Because the entries in each row add to 1, the matrix has the form $\begin{bmatrix} x & 1-x \\ y & 1-y \end{bmatrix}$, where $0 \le x \le 1$ and $0 \le y \le 1$. Its square is

$$\begin{bmatrix} x & 1-x \\ y & 1-y \end{bmatrix} \cdot \begin{bmatrix} x & 1-x \\ y & 1-y \end{bmatrix} = \begin{bmatrix} x^2+y-xy & 1-x^2-y+xy \\ xy+y-y^2 & 1+y^2-y-xy \end{bmatrix},$$

which is also stochastic.

Furthermore, if a stochastic matrix T has no zero entries, the rows of T^k will be nearly identical for large k. This indicates that over the long term the proportions of the occurrences of the different states stabilizes. You also saw this for the matrix T on the previous page. The rows of T^{10} are nearly identical.

> **Theorem (Convergence of Powers)**
> Let T be an $n \times n$ stochastic matrix with no zero entries. Then $\lim_{k \to \infty} T^k$ is a stochastic matrix with n identical rows.

A Markov Chain Situation in Biology

Stable populations occur in populations of plants and animals, as the example on page 696 illustrates.

Additional Examples

In a particular desert climate, 80% of rainy days are followed by sunny days, and 95% of sunny days are followed by sunny days. Over the long run, what portion of days are sunny? **16/17**

Activity 3 After discussing **Question 10,** you might ask students to draw a labeled digraph to represent the matrix of data based on Galton's research in this question. They should see how similar it looks to the digraph that opens this lesson. [See the digraph at the right.]

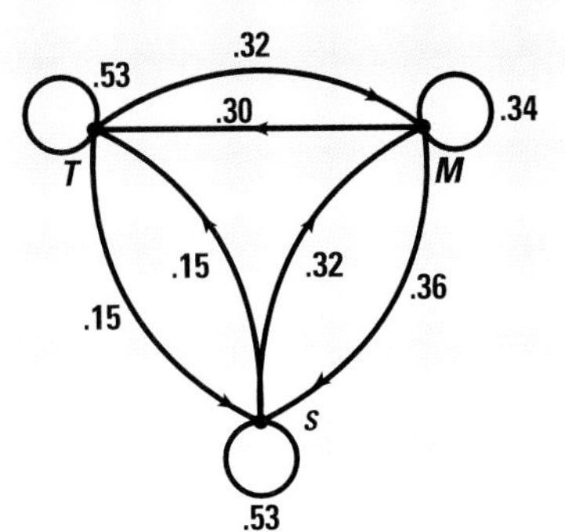

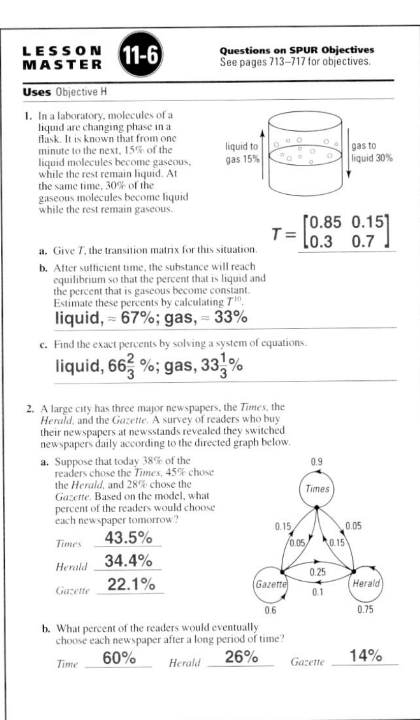

LESSON MASTER 11-6

Questions on SPUR Objectives
See pages 713–717 for objectives.

Uses Objective H

1. In a laboratory, molecules of a liquid are changing phase in a flask. It is known that from one minute to the next, 15% of the liquid molecules become gaseous, while the rest remain liquid. At the same time, 30% of the gaseous molecules become liquid while the rest remain gaseous.

 a. Give T, the transition matrix for this situation. $T = \begin{bmatrix} 0.85 & 0.15 \\ 0.3 & 0.7 \end{bmatrix}$

 b. After sufficient time, the substance will reach equilibrium so that the percent that is liquid and the percent that is gaseous become constant. Estimate these percents by calculating T^{10}.
 liquid, ≈ 67%; gas, ≈ 33%

 c. Find the exact percents by solving a system of equations.
 liquid, $66\frac{2}{3}$ %; gas, $33\frac{1}{3}$%

2. A large city has three major newspapers, the *Times*, the *Herald*, and the *Gazette*. A survey of readers who buy their newspapers at newsstands revealed they switched newspapers daily according to the directed graph below.

 a. Suppose that today 38% of the readers chose the *Times*, 45% chose the *Herald*, and 28% chose the *Gazette*. Based on the model, what percent of the readers would choose each newspaper tomorrow?
 Times **43.5%**
 Herald **34.4%**
 Gazette **22.1%**

 b. What percent of the readers would eventually choose each newspaper after a long period of time?
 Time **60%** *Herald* **26%** *Gazette* **14%**

Example

Consider a variety of rose that can have either a pale hue or a brilliant hue. It is known that seeds from a pale blossom yield plants of which 60% have pale flowers and 40% have brilliant flowers. Seeds from a brilliant flower yield plants of which 30% are pale and 70% are brilliant. After several generations of plants, what will be the proportion of pale and brilliant flowering plants?

Solution

The transition matrix for this situation is

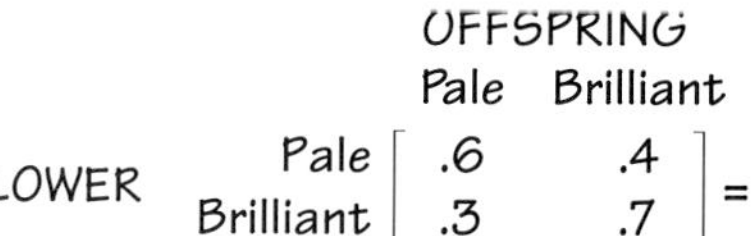

$$\text{FLOWER} \begin{array}{r} \\ \text{Pale} \\ \text{Brilliant} \end{array} \overset{\text{OFFSPRING}}{\begin{array}{cc} \text{Pale} & \text{Brilliant} \\ \end{array}} \begin{bmatrix} .6 & .4 \\ .3 & .7 \end{bmatrix} = T.$$

Let a and b be the proportion of plants with pale and brilliant flowers, respectively, when the population stabilizes. Then $a + b = 1$, since no other flowers are possible. Yet the proportion of the flowers of the next generation that are pale will be $.6a + .3b$ because .6 of those produced by the pale flowers are pale, and .3 of those produced by the brilliant ones are pale. But since the population has stabilized, the fraction of the next generation that is pale must still be a. This results in the equation

$$.6a + .3b = a.$$

Thus the following system must be satisfied.

$$\begin{cases} .6a + .3b = a \\ a + b = 1 \end{cases}$$

This system has the solution $(a, b) = \left(\frac{3}{7}, \frac{4}{7}\right) \approx (.43, .57)$. So when the population stabilizes, about 43% of the plants will have pale flowers and 57% will have brilliant flowers.

Check 1

The fraction of flowers in the next generation that are brilliant is $.4a + .7b$. When the population has stabilized, the fraction that is brilliant is b. So we must have $.4a + .7b = b$. This is true when $a = \frac{3}{7}$ and $b = \frac{4}{7}$.

Check 2

The result matches the result obtained by calculating powers of T. For instance,

$$T^{10} \approx \begin{bmatrix} .42857 & .57143 \\ .42857 & .57143 \end{bmatrix} \approx \begin{bmatrix} \frac{3}{7} & \frac{4}{7} \\ \frac{3}{7} & \frac{4}{7} \end{bmatrix}.$$

After Markov published his theory, his techniques were adopted by scientists in a wide range of fields. Albert Einstein used these ideas to study the Brownian motion of molecules. Physicists have employed them in the theory of radioactive transformation, nuclear fission detectors, and the theory of tracks in nuclear emulsions. Astronomers have used Markov theory to study fluctuations in the brightness of the Milky Way and the spatial distribution of

Optional Activities

Activity 4 Technology Connection You might wish to assign *Technology Sourcebook, Calculator Master 16.* In this activity, students use the programming features of a graphics calculator to explore Markov chains and matrices. Students enter a program that will compute the population of a region for several years based on the transition matrix and the current population. Another program allows them to examine the powers of a matrix in order to understand the population trends.

Activity 5 Writing You might have students describe a situation for matrix T in **Question 12.** Suggest that they refer to the last paragraph of the lesson for topic ideas. Read different descriptions aloud to comment on the variety of situations in which Markov chains apply. [Sample: Suppose two candidates, A and B, are running for a state office. Pollsters predict that 50% of the voters who voted for A in the primary will vote for A in the final election while 40% of the voters who voted for B in the primary will vote for A in the final election.]

galaxies. Biologists have used Markov chains to describe population growth, evolution, molecular genetics, pharmacology, tumor growth, and epidemics. Sociologists have modeled voting behavior, geographical mobility, growth and decline of towns, sizes of businesses, changes in personal attitudes, and deliberations of trial juries with Markov chains.

QUESTIONS

Covering the Reading

In 1–4, consider the weather situation on page 693.

1. **a.** If it is sunny today, what is the probability that tomorrow is rainy?
b. If it is sunny today, what is the probability that tomorrow is sunny?
a) 15% b) 75%

2. **a.** If it is rainy today, what is the probability that two days from now is rainy? **36%**
b. If it is sunny today, what is the probability that four days from now is rainy? **≈ 22.9%**

3. Is T^{10} a stochastic matrix? **Yes**

4. **a.** In the matrix T^{10}, what does the number .24612 represent?
b. What is the significance of the fact that the rows of T^{10} are nearly identical?
See left.

In 5–8, consider the flower situation of this lesson's Example.

5. **a.** If a rose is brilliant, what is the probability that its offspring are brilliant? **0.7**
b. If a rose is pale, what is the probability that its offspring are pale? **0.6**

6. Solve the system to verify the solution. $b = \frac{4}{7}$; $a = \frac{3}{7}$

7. Verify Check 1. $.4\left(\frac{3}{7}\right) + .7\left(\frac{4}{7}\right) = \frac{4}{10}\left(\frac{3}{7}\right) + \frac{7}{10}\left(\frac{4}{7}\right) = \frac{12}{70} + \frac{28}{70} = \frac{40}{70} = \frac{4}{7} = b$

8. Using $T^{10} = \begin{bmatrix} \frac{3}{7} & \frac{4}{7} \\ \frac{3}{7} & \frac{4}{7} \end{bmatrix}$, calculate T^{20} and explain your result. **See left.**

Applying the Mathematics

9. At each four-month interval, two TV stations in a small town go through "ratings week." They try to offer special programs which will draw viewers from the other station. During each period, MBC (Markov Broadcasting Company) wins over 20% of SBS (Stochastic Broadcasting System) viewers, but loses 10% of its viewers to SBS.
a. Draw a graph (like that shown at the beginning of this lesson) to represent the movement of viewers between stations.
b. Write down the transition matrix.
c. Using the method of the rose example, find the long-term distribution of viewers watching each station.
See left.

4a) the probability that it will be cloudy 10 days after a cloudy day
b) No matter what the weather is today, the probabilities for the weather in 10 days are about the same.

8) $T^{20} = \begin{bmatrix} \frac{3}{7} & \frac{4}{7} \\ \frac{3}{7} & \frac{4}{7} \end{bmatrix}$

In 20 generations, $\frac{3}{7}$ of the seeds will produce pale flowers, and $\frac{4}{7}$ brilliant flowers, no matter what seeds you start with.

9a)
MBC .2 SBS
.9 .8
.1

b)

	MBC	SBS
MBS	.9	.1
SBS	.2	.8

c) MBC: 67%; SBS: 33%

Adapting to Individual Needs

Extra Help
Some students may need more details in the discussion that verifies that squares of stochastic matrices are stochastic. Do the appropriate row-by-column multiplications to find the square. Then have students add the elements in each row of the square to show that their sum is 1.

Challenge
Have students answer the following questions.

1. Suppose $D = [\ .3\ .7]$ is a 1×2 matrix describing the initial distribution of colors in the roses Example; i.e. 30% of the original group of roses were pale and 70% were brilliant.
a. Calculate $D \cdot T$, $D \cdot T^2$, and $D \cdot T^3$. What do you think these represent? [The distribution of colors in the second, third, and fourth generations.]
b. The Equilibrium Matrix, $E = \lim\limits_{k \to \infty} D \cdot T^k$, is the long range distribution of colors. Find E for this situation. Is this the same result as obtained in the Example? [Yes]

2. Find E using the initial distributions $D = [.5\ .5]$ and $D = [.7\ .3]$. What happens? [E is the same.]

Notes on Questions

Question 10 The work of Galton led to some significant early work in modern statistics. His work is mentioned in conjunction with applications of ellipses in UCSMP *Functions, Statistics, and Trigonometry.*

Question 11 Error Alert Students may not realize that this result is not shown in the reading. In the reading, it is shown that if A is stochastic then A^2 is stochastic. You might want to alert your students to the fact that they need to define a second matrix B for this question.

Questions 14–16 Teaching Aid 129 has these graphs.

Question 15 If paths containing circuits are included, the problem is harder but a very nice example of a problem in permutations. There are $P(5, 5) + P(5, 3) + P(5, 1)$ paths from A to E and $P(3, 3) + P(3, 1)$ paths from E to H. Applying the Multiplication Counting Principle, the total number of paths possible is 1665.

Additional Answers

11. Let $A = \begin{bmatrix} a_1 & a_2 \\ a_3 & a_4 \end{bmatrix}$, and $B = \begin{bmatrix} b_1 & b_2 \\ b_3 & b_4 \end{bmatrix}$. If A and B are stochastic, then each row sums to 1 and each entry is nonnegative.

$$AB = \begin{bmatrix} a_1b_1 + a_2b_3 & a_1b_2 + a_2b_4 \\ a_3b_1 + a_4b_3 & a_3b_2 + a_4b_4 \end{bmatrix}.$$

Row 1 sums to

$a_1b_1 + a_2b_3 + a_1b_2 + a_2b_4$
$= a_1b_1 + a_1b_2 + a_2b_3 + a_2b_4$
$= a_1(b_1 + b_2) + a_2(b_3 + b_4)$
$= a_1 + a_2 = 1$, since $b_1 + b_2 = b_3 + b_4 = a_1 + a_2 = 1$.

Row 2 sums to

$a_3b_1 + a_4b_3 + a_3b_2 + a_4b_4$
$= a_3b_1 + a_3b_2 + a_4b_3 + a_4b_4$
$= a_3(b_1 + b_2) + a_4(b_3 + b_4)$
$= a_3 + a_4 = 1$, since $b_1 + b_2 = b_3 + b_4 = a_3 + a_4 = 1$.

Each entry of AB is nonnegative since it is the sum of two terms, each of which is the product of two nonnegative numbers. Hence, the product of two 2×2 stochastic matrices is stochastic.

10. The British scientist Sir Francis Galton studied inheritance by looking at distributions of the heights of parents and children. In 1886 he published data from a large sample of parents and their adult children showing the relation between their heights. The following matrix is based on his data. Since he had to use volunteers in his study, he could not be sure that his sample accurately reflected the English population.

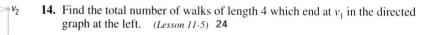

		CHILD		
		Tall	Med	Short
PARENT	Tall	.53	.32	.15
	Med	.30	.34	.36
	Short	.15	.32	.53

$= T$

According to this matrix,

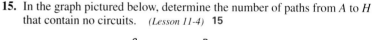

$$T^2 \approx \begin{bmatrix} .399 & .326 & .274 \\ .315 & .327 & .358 \\ .255 & .326 & .419 \end{bmatrix} \text{ and } T^{10} \approx \begin{bmatrix} .321 & .327 & .353 \\ .321 & .327 & .353 \\ .321 & .327 & .353 \end{bmatrix}.$$

a. What proportion of the children of tall parents were short? **15%**

b. Use T^2 to tell what proportion of grandchildren of tall people were short. **27.4%**

c. Use T^{10} to predict the approximate proportion of tall, medium, and short people in the population in the long run. **See left.**

11. Prove for 2×2 matrices: *If A is stochastic and B is stochastic, the product AB must be stochastic.* **See margin.**

12. Consider the matrix T at the right. $\begin{bmatrix} .5 & .5 \\ .4 & .6 \end{bmatrix}$

a. Is T stochastic? **Yes**

b. Calculate T^2, T^4, T^8, and T^{16}. **See margin.**

c. Find two numbers a and b such that $vT = v$ where $v = [a \quad b]$ and $a + b = 1$. **See left.**

d. What do a and b represent? **See left.**

13. Generalize the result of Question 8 and prove your generalization. **See margin.**

10c) 32.1% tall, 32.7% medium, 35.3% short

12c) $a = \frac{4}{9}$, $b = \frac{5}{9}$

d) Over the long term, the proportion of occurrences stabilize to a and b.

Review

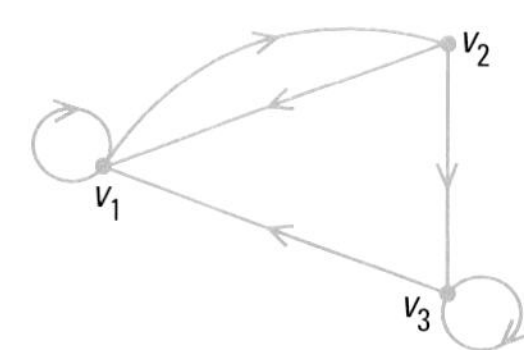

14. Find the total number of walks of length 4 which end at v_1 in the directed graph at the left. *(Lesson 11-5)* **24**

15. In the graph pictured below, determine the number of paths from A to H that contain no circuits. *(Lesson 11-4)* **15**

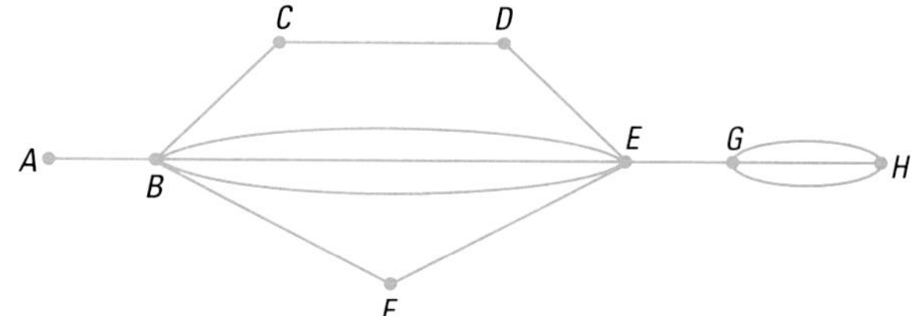

12. b.

$$T^2 = \begin{bmatrix} .45 & .55 \\ .44 & .56 \end{bmatrix}$$

$$T^4 = \begin{bmatrix} .4445 & .5555 \\ .4444 & .5556 \end{bmatrix}$$

$$T^8 \approx \begin{bmatrix} .4444 & .5556 \\ .4444 & .5556 \end{bmatrix}$$

$$T^{16} \approx \begin{bmatrix} .4444 & .5556 \\ .4444 & .5556 \end{bmatrix}$$

Setting Up Lesson 11-7

Draw a rectangular solid (box). Have students count the number of edges, vertices, and faces of this solid. (12, 8, 6, respectively) This terminology is necessary to understand the next lesson.

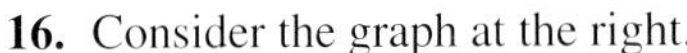

16. Consider the graph at the right.

a. Does the graph have an Euler circuit? Justify your answer.

b. What is the maximum number of edges that could be removed while keeping the graph connected? *(Lesson 11-4)* **4**

a) Yes, because all vertices are even, and it is connected.

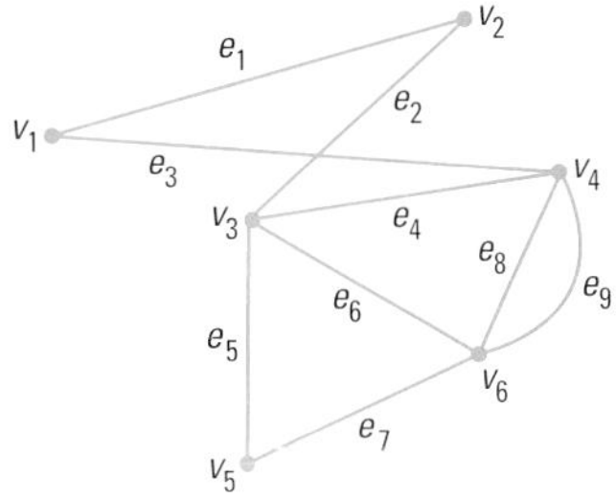

17. In a league of nine teams, is it possible for each team to play exactly seven other teams? Explain why or why not. *(Lesson 11-3)*
See left.

18. Suppose the height (in feet) of an object t seconds after it is thrown is given by $h(t) = -16t^2 + 50t + 10$. *(Lessons 9-3, 9-4, 9-5)* **See left.**

a. Find the object's velocity 1 second after it is thrown.

b. When is the object's velocity the opposite of the velocity found in part **a**?

c. When does the object reach its maximum height?

d. How are the times in parts **a**, **b**, and **c** related?

e. When is the object's acceleration positive?

19. Solve the inequality $2\sin^2 x + \cos^2 x < \frac{1}{4}$ when $0 \le x \le 2\pi$. *(Lesson 6-8)*
no solution

20. Use limit notation to describe the end behavior of the function f given by

$f(n) = \dfrac{2n^2 + 3n + 1}{6n^2}$. *(Lesson 5-5)* **See left.**

21. Prove: *Exactly one of every four consecutive integers is divisible by 4.* (Hint: Use the Quotient-Remainder Theorem.) *(Lesson 4-2)*
See margin.

Exploration

22. Find an example in a book or article that describes how a Markov chain is used in biology, linguistics, or politics.
A good source is *Markov Chains: Theory and Applications* by Dean Isaacson and Richard Madsen.

17) No, a graph cannot have an odd number of odd vertices.

18a) $v(1) = 18$ ft/sec

b) $t = \frac{68}{32} = 2.125$ sec

c) $t = \frac{50}{32} = 1.5625$ sec

d) The time in part c is midway between the times in parts a and b.

e) Never, it is always -32 ft/sec^2

20) $\lim_{n \to -\infty} f(n) = \frac{1}{3}$; $\lim_{n \to \infty} f(n) = \frac{1}{3}$

Follow-up for Lesson 11-6

Practice

For more questions on SPUR Objectives, use **Lesson Master 11-6** (shown on page 695).

Assessment

Oral Communication Have students show their work for **Question 10** and explain how they determined their answers. Then point to some specific entries in the matrices and ask what these numbers represent. [Students show understanding of how to use stochastic matrices to calculate long-term predictions.]

Extension

Technology In general, the questions in this lesson do not require a computer program or technological support to compute high powers of matrices. We have provided the relevant power of a matrix and asked for interpretation of the elements. A possible additional project is to write a computer program or develop a template on a spreadsheet which will compute powers of 3×3 matrices.

Additional Answers

13. T stabilizes to $\begin{bmatrix} \frac{3}{7} & \frac{4}{7} \\ \frac{3}{7} & \frac{4}{7} \end{bmatrix}$. Proof: If $[a\ b]\begin{bmatrix} .6 & .4 \\ .3 & .7 \end{bmatrix} = [a\ b]$, then

$.6a + .3b = a \Rightarrow -.4a + .3b = 0$ and $.4a + .7b = b \Rightarrow -.4a + .3b = 0$

Since $a + b = 1$,

$\begin{aligned} -.4a + .3b &= 0 \\ a + b &= 1 \end{aligned} \Rightarrow \begin{aligned} -.4a + .3b &= .0 \\ .4a + .4b &= .4 \end{aligned}$

$.7b = .4$ So $b = \frac{4}{7}$ and $a = \frac{3}{7}$

21. Let n, $n + 1$, $n + 2$, and $n + 3$ represent the four consecutive integers. By the Quotient-Remainder Theorem, $n = 4q + r$ where q is an integer and $r = 0, 1, 2,$ or 3.
If $r = 0$, then n is divisible by 4.
If $r = 1$, $n + 3 = (4q + 1) + 3 = 4(q + 1)$ is divisible by 4.
If $r = 2$, $n + 2 = (4q + 2) + 2 = 4(q + 1)$ is divisible by 4.
If $r = 3$, $n + 1 = (4q + 3) + 1 = 4(q + 1)$ is divisible by 4.
So, exactly one of every four consecutive integers is divisible by 4.

Lesson 11-7

Objectives
There are no SPUR objectives for any reading lesson.

Resources
From the ***Teacher's Resource File***
- Answer Master 11-7
- Teaching Aids
  - 111 Warm-up
  - 130 Polyhedra and their Graphs
  - 131 Questions 5–8, 11, 12, and 17

Additional Resources
- Visuals for Teaching Aids 111, 130–131
- Exploration 11-7

Teaching Lesson 11-7

Warm-up
A regular octahedron can be formed by drawing two square pyramids with the same base whose faces are equilateral triangles. Draw such an octahedron and find the number of its vertices, edges, and faces.

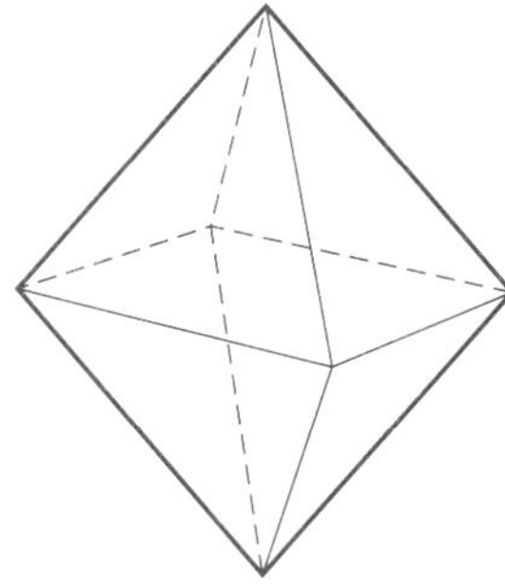

$V = 6$, $E = 12$, $F = 8$; notice that $V - E + F = 2$

LESSON

11-7 Euler's Formula

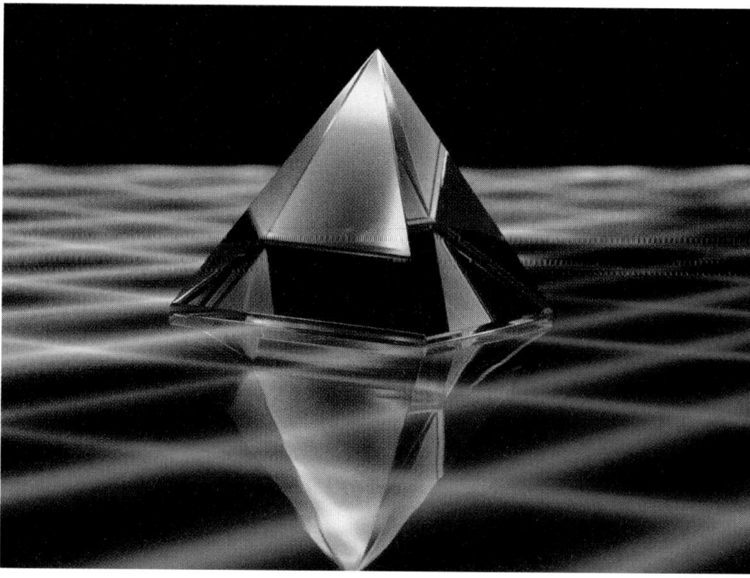

A surprisingly simple relationship exists between the number of vertices, edges, and faces of a polyhedron. Although the ancient Greeks studied polyhedra extensively, no one seems to have known of this relationship until Descartes discovered it in the seventeenth century. Furthermore, it was not until the next century that it was proved by Euler, whose name it now bears. In this lesson, Euler's formula is interpreted in terms of the ideas of graph theory that you have seen in this chapter. These ideas are combined along with mathematical induction to deduce the formula.

The Vertices, Edges, and Faces of a Polyhedron
Consider the regular dodecahedron drawn below. Let V, E, and F be the numbers of its vertices, edges, and faces, respectively. In Lesson 11-1, it was noted that $V = 20$, $E = 30$, and $F = 12$. In the table on page 701 are the corresponding values for several other polyhedra.

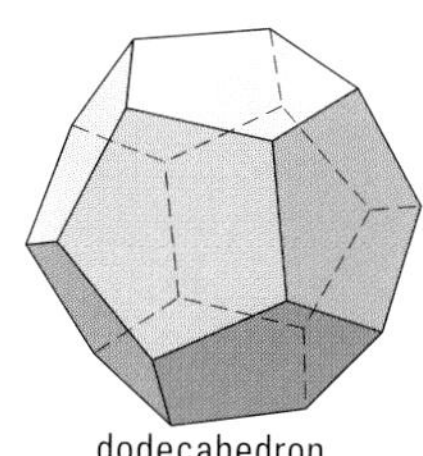
dodecahedron

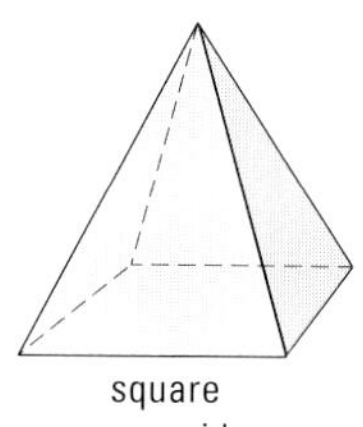
square pyramid

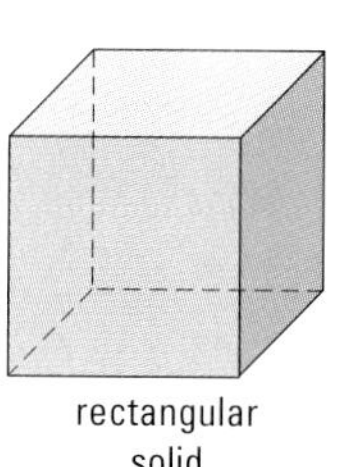
rectangular solid

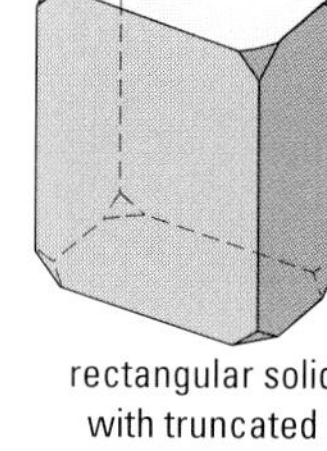
rectangular solid with truncated corners

Lesson 11-7 Overview

Broad Goals In this lesson, Euler's formula $V - E + F = 2$ for the vertices, edges, and faces of any polyhedron is explored for figures other than polyhedra, and it is proved for polyhedra using many theorems from earlier lessons.

Perspective Euler is famous for many things, and his name is associated with a number of formulas and theorems. The formula referred to by the title is the formula relating the vertices, edges, and faces of any polyhedron.

It is surprising that the Greeks did not know of the relationship $V - E + F = 2$, for polyhedra were very important to them. Perhaps they did and it has been lost.

The value of $V - E + F$ is called the *Euler characteristic* of a surface. The key to the proof of Euler's formula is the reduction of a graph with $k + 1$ edges to one that has k edges without changing the value of Euler's characteristic. That reduction is accomplished with the aid of the first two theorems of this lesson (page 702 and the middle of page 703). These theorems thus have the role of *lemmas,* theorems that are stated and proved for the purpose of shortening the proof of a theorem that follows.

polyhedron	V	E	F
dodecahedron	20	30	12
square pyramid	5	8	5
rectangular solid	8	12	6
rectangular solid with truncated corners	24	36	14

The relationship discovered by Descartes is that, for any polyhedron, $V - E + F = 2$. Euler reformulated this conjecture in terms of graphs.

Graphs of Polyhedra

Recall that in Lesson 11-1, the dodecahedron was distorted into the graph shown below at the left. This distortion can be thought of in the following way: one face is removed to create a hole, allowing the remaining figure to be stretched and flattened. The same process was used to obtain the other figures shown below.

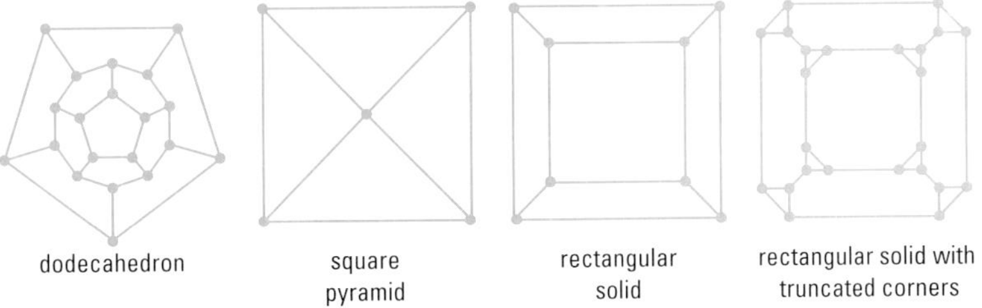

dodecahedron   square pyramid   rectangular solid   rectangular solid with truncated corners

Another way of visualizing this distortion is to imagine that the polyhedron is placed on a table top with a light source placed only slightly above it. If the faces of the polyhedron are transparent, but the edges are not, the light will project shadows of the edges and vertices onto the table top. These shadows will form the 2-dimensional graph.

V, E, and *F* for a Graph

In the distorting process, each face of the polyhedron becomes a region separated from the others by edges of the graph. The face that is removed for the flattening process (or that is on top for the shadowing process) corresponds to the region exterior to the graph and must be included in the count. These regions are called the **faces** of the graph. Since the distorting process does not change the number of vertices, edges, or faces, the relationship $V - E + F = 2$ holds for polyhedra if and only if it holds for the resulting graphs.

Note that these graphs are simple and connected, that they have no crossings or vertices of degree less than 3, and that every edge is part of a circuit. A graph without crossings can always be obtained when the original polyhedron is **convex**; that is, when any two points in the polyhedron can be connected by a line segment lying completely inside it. This can be seen by noting that if a light source is placed close enough to the top of a transparent, convex polyhedron, the shadows of the edges will never cross.

Notes on Reading

The formula we call Euler's Formula is sometimes called the Euler-Descartes formula.

❶ Go through this table with students. You will find these polyhedra and their graphs on **Teaching Aid 130.**

You may also wish to consider the *Warm-up* and other polyhedra. In addition to **Questions 2–4,** ask students to give the values of *V, E,* and *F* for figures such as a tetrahedron ($V = 4$, $E = 6$, $F = 4$); a hexagonal prism ($V = 12$, $E = 18$, $F = 8$), and an icosahedron ($V = 12$, $E = 30$, $F = 20$).

In Imre Lakatos's book *Proofs and Refutations: The Logic of Mathematical Discovery* (Cambridge University Press, 1976), Euler's formula and its extensions are discussed in some detail, presented as a dialogue between a teacher and his students. One of these extensions is that if a polyhedral hole is drilled through a polyhedron, then the numbers of vertices, edges, and faces of the resulting surface satisfy $V - E + F = 0$. (See the *Extension* for this lesson on page 705.)

Optional Activities

Activity 1 After discussing the lesson, you might have students draw all the different connected graphs that have exactly 2 edges. Have them show that in all cases, the graphs satisfy Euler's formula. [The three possibilities are shown at the right.]

$V = 2, E = 2, F = 2$
$2 - 2 + 2 = 2$

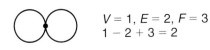

$V = 2, E = 2, F = 2$
$2 - 2 + 2 = 2$

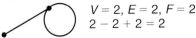

$V = 1, E = 2, F = 3$
$1 - 2 + 3 = 2$

Reading Mathematics The proofs of the theorems on pages 702–704 are difficult reading for most people. They need to be read slowly, carefully, and probably more than once. You may wish to go through these proofs line by line with the class to show how one reads mathematics. If so, begin at the start of the section Modifying Graphs without Changing $V - E + F$, having students read every word out loud. Wait after every sentence or two. Then ask students to raise their hands if, after this time, they do not understand what was just read.

As you do this, often you will find that the problem lies in the vocabulary. Words such as *circuit* and *degree* are new for students and they may need explanation when they appear in a new context.

Although this process can take a great deal of time, it can illuminate how a theorem (in this case, Euler's Formula) that would seem so general as to be rather impossible to prove is deduced from other theorems using careful logical arguments.

The question arises as to whether all graphs satisfy $V - E + F = 2$. Two of the figures below show that under certain circumstances the value of $V - E + F$ can be different from 2.

The graph is not connected.

$V = 5$ $E = 4$ $F = 2$
$V - E + F = 3$

Not all edges are part of a circuit.

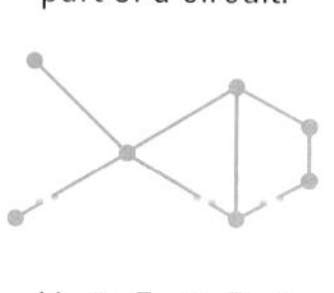

$V = 7$ $E = 8$ $F = 3$
$V - E + F = 2$

The graph has crossings.

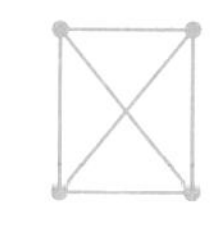

$V = 4$ $E = 6$ $F = 5$
$V - E + F = 3$

In the Questions, you will determine the values of $V - E + F$ for some other graphs that are not simple.

Modifying Graphs without Changing $V - E + F$

It turns out that Euler's formula, $V - E + F = 2$, holds for any graph that is connected and has no crossings. We deduce this formula in two stages. First we prove that a graph can be altered without changing the value of $V - E + F$. For example, one edge of the graph shown below is removed to obtain the other, but the value of $V - E + F$ remains the same because both E and F are decreased by 1.

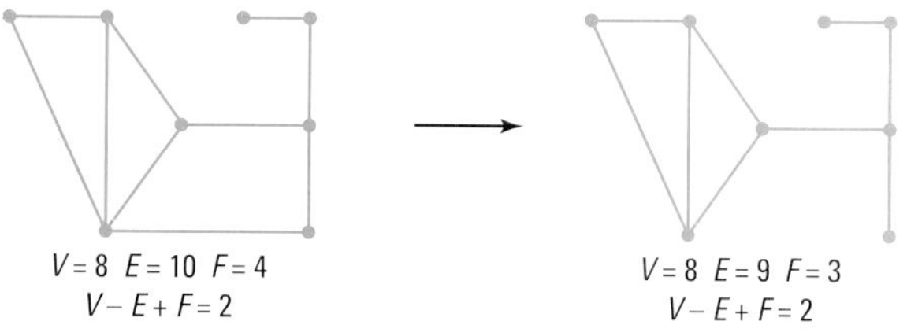

$V = 8$ $E = 10$ $F = 4$
$V - E + F = 2$

$V = 8$ $E = 9$ $F = 3$
$V - E + F = 2$

Theorem
Let G be a connected graph with no crossings, and let V, E, and F be the number of vertices, edges, and faces of G. The following alterations to G do not change the value of $V - E + F$.

(1) removing a vertex of degree 1 along with its adjacent edge, and
(2) removing an edge that is part of a circuit.

Proof
(1) Let v be a vertex of degree 1, and let e be the edge emanating from it. (A vertex of degree 1 can only have 1 such edge.) Then, removing v and e decreases both V and E by 1 and does not affect F. But decreasing both V and E by 1 does not change the value of $V - E$, so the value of $V - E + F$ remains the same.

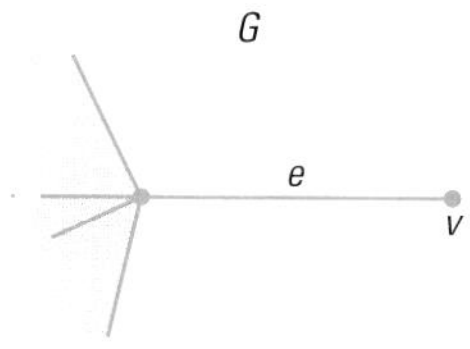

Optional Activities

Activity 2 Technology Connection
Materials: *Explorations* software

Students may use *Exploration 11-7: Euler's Formula,* to explore connected graphs with no crossings. Students can alter the graph by turning the edges either on or off, then count the number of faces, edges, and vertices to see if their graph satisfies Euler's formula. Students can verify their results by clicking on a button to show the calculations for the formula.

Activity 3 This activity relates to **Question 13.** After discussing that question, you might have students list other combinations of degrees of vertices and then draw a graph based on their list. They may find some lists do not produce a possible connected graph with no crossings. Have them modify their lists until they create such a graph and then have them test Euler's formula for their graph.

[Sample: The vertices of the graph below have degrees 1, 1, 2, 3, 4, and 5.

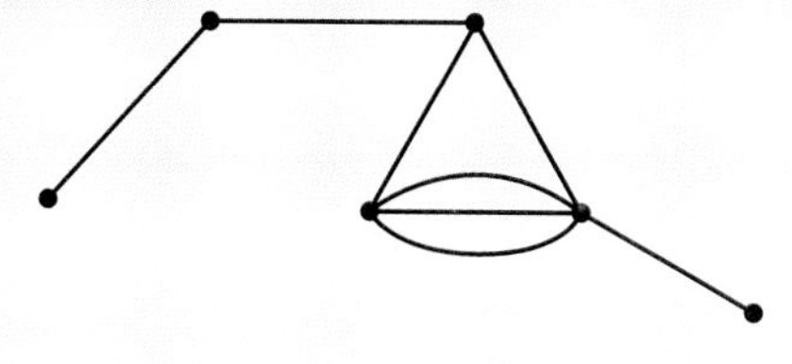

$V = 6$; $E = 8$; $F = 4$; $V - E + F = 2$.]

(2) Let e be an edge that is part of a circuit, and let f_1 and f_2 be the faces separated by e (as shown at the right). Removing e combines the two faces f_1 and f_2 into one. (Note that f_1 and f_2 could not have already been the same face, because otherwise e wouldn't have been part of a circuit.) Thus, removing e decreases both E and F by 1 and leaves V unchanged. But decreasing both E and F by 1 does not change $-E + F$, so $V - E + F$ remains the same.

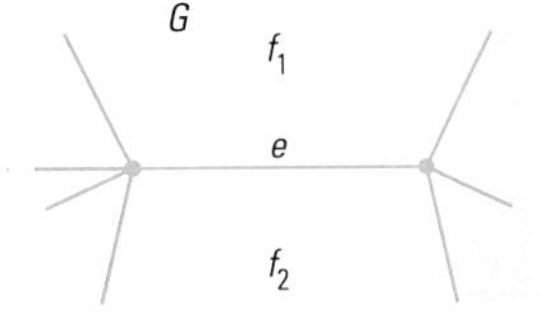

Part (2) of the preceding theorem gives information about graphs that have circuits. The next theorem applies to graphs that have no circuits. It says that part (1) of the preceding theorem can be applied to such graphs.

Theorem
Let G be a graph with at least one edge. If G has no circuits, then G has a vertex of degree 1.

Proof
Choose any vertex of G and traverse a path from that vertex in the following way. Whenever you arrive at a vertex of degree greater than 1, leave the vertex via one of its other edges. (Note that this other edge will not have been used before because otherwise you would have traversed a circuit). Since there are only a finite number of vertices and none will ever be repeated (because there are no circuits), the path will eventually have to end. The ending vertex will have degree 1, because otherwise the path could continue.

For example, consider the graph below. Starting at any vertex, if you follow any path eventually you will come to a vertex with degree 1.

A Proof of Euler's Formula

With these two theorems, Euler's formula can now be proved.

Theorem (Euler's Formula)
Let G be a connected graph with no crossings, and let V, E, and F be the number of vertices, edges, and faces of G. Then

$$V - E + F = 2.$$

Adapting to Individual Needs

Extra Help
Some students may need help counting faces in the graph with crossings. It might help to label the vertices and list the faces.

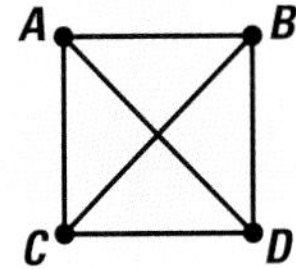

Faces:
(1) ABC (2) BCD
(3) CDA (4) DAB
(5) region exterior to graph

Remind students that edges $\overline{AC}$ and $\overline{BD}$ do not intersect.

Challenge
Writing History Connection
The name Leonhard Euler has been mentioned many times in this book. He was one of the most prolific writers in the history of mathematics and his name appears in almost every branch of mathematics. Students may have written a short report on him earlier (Challenge Questions for Lesson 2-1). Have them write a more detailed account of his life and describe some of the advances in mathematics associated with his name. One reference they might enjoy for this and other research is William Dunham's *Journey Through Genius.*

Additional Answers

2. a.

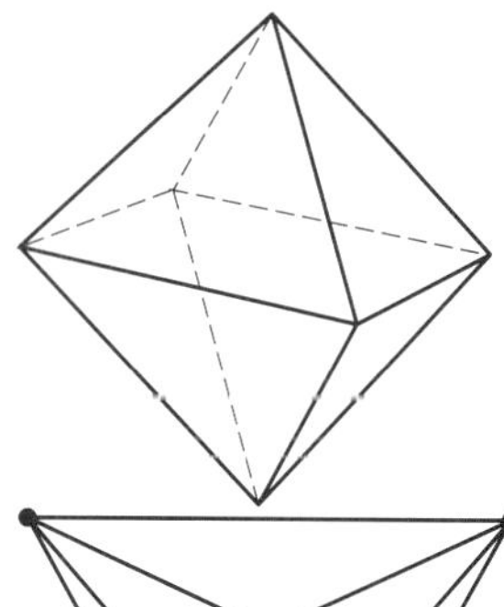

b.

c. $V - E + F = 6 - 12 + 8 = 2$

3. a.

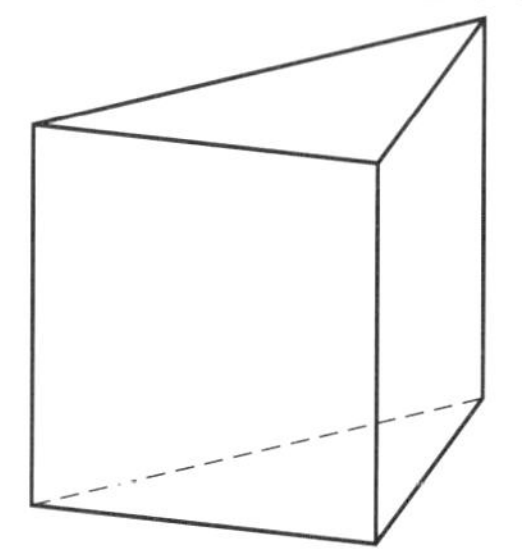

b.

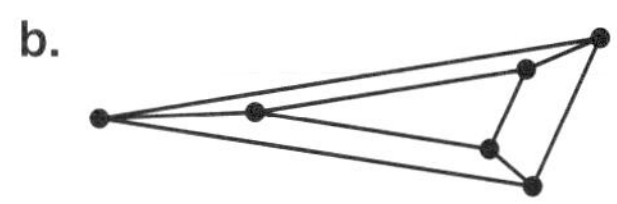

c. $V - E + F = 6 - 9 + 5 = 2$

4. a.

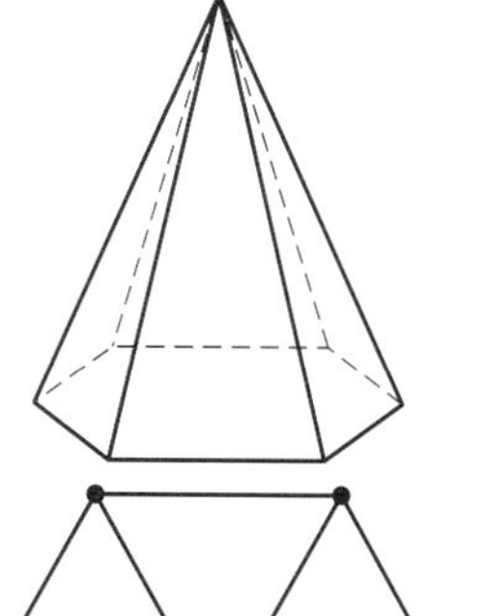

b.

c. $V - E + F = 7 - 12 + 7 = 2$

Proof

The proof uses induction. Let $S(n)$ be the statement that Euler's formula holds for any graph with n edges.

First, prove $S(0)$: Let G be a connected graph with 0 edges. The only such graph consists of a single vertex. It has one face—the entire region surrounding it. For this graph, $V = 1$, $E = 0$, and $F = 1$. Thus, $V - E + F = 1 - 0 + 1 = 2$.

Now assume $S(k)$ is true for an arbitrarily chosen nonnegative integer k, and prove that $S(k + 1)$ is true. That is, assume that $V - E + F = 2$ for a connected graph with no crossings and with k edges. It must be proved that the formula holds for such a graph with $k + 1$ edges. Let G be such a graph. Either G has a circuit, or it doesn't.

If G has a circuit, remove one edge from the circuit. By part (2) of the theorem on page 702, this does not affect the value of $V - E + F$. The new graph is still connected, by the Circuits and Connectedness Theorem in Lesson 11-4, and it has only k edges. Therefore, by the inductive assumption, it satisfies $V - E + F = 2$. Since the value of $V - E + F$ is the same for both graphs, the formula also holds for G.

If G does not have a circuit, then by the theorem on page 703, it has a vertex of degree 1. Remove this vertex as well as its adjacent edge. By part (1) of the theorem on page 702, this does not affect the value of $V - E + F$. The new graph is connected and has only k edges, so by the inductive assumption, it satisfies $V - E + F = 2$. Since $V - E + F$ is the same for both graphs, the formula also holds for G.

Thus, assuming that Euler's formula holds for a graph with k edges leads to the conclusion that it holds for a graph with $k + 1$ edges, whether it has a circuit or not. That is, assuming that $S(k)$ is true leads to the conclusion that $S(k + 1)$ is true. Since $S(0)$ is true and $S(k) \Rightarrow S(k + 1)$, $S(n)$ is true for all nonnegative integers n by the Principle of Mathematical Induction. In other words, Euler's formula holds for all connected graphs with no crossings.

So Euler's formula is true for polyhedra: In a polyhedron with V vertices, E edges, and F faces, $V - E + F = 2$, or as it is sometimes written, $V + F = E + 2$.

QUESTIONS

Covering the Reading

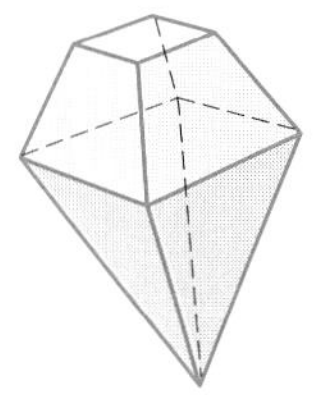

1. Show that the polyhedron drawn at the left satisfies Euler's formula. $V - E + F = 9 - 16 + 9 = 2$

In 2–4, a type of polyhedron is described. **a.** Draw a polyhedron of the given type. **b.** Draw the graph obtained from it by the distorting process described in the lesson. **c.** Show that this graph satisfies Euler's formula. **See margin.**

2. regular octahedron
3. triangular prism
4. hexagonal pyramid

8. a. An edge was removed.
   b. Both E and F were reduced by 1, so $-E + F$ was not changed. Since V did not change, $V - E + F$ did not change.
9. True, by the contrapositive of the second theorem of this lesson: Let G be a graph with at least one edge. If G has no vertex of degree 1, then G has a circuit.

10.

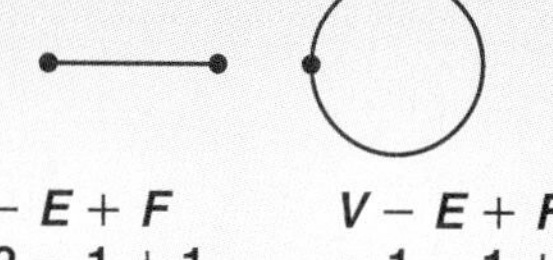

$V - E + F = 2 - 1 + 1 = 2$

$V - E + F = 1 - 1 + 2 = 2$

11. a. Sample:

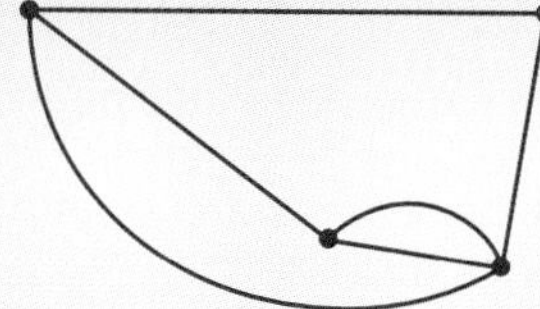

b. Since the graph in part a has no crossings and 6 edges, $V - E + F = 2$ holds true. Remove a vertex of degree 1 and its adjacent edge does not

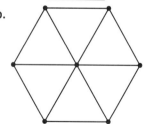

In 5 and 6, the graphs are not simple. Show that they still satisfy Euler's formula.

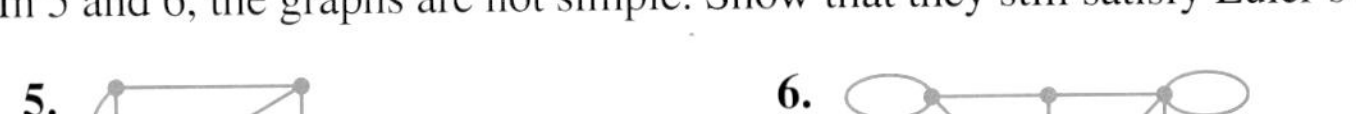

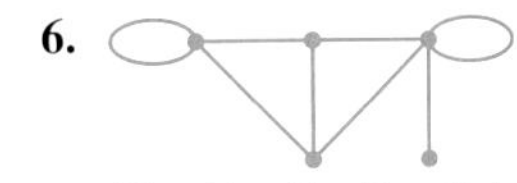

5. $V - E + F = 5 - 8 + 5 = 2$

6. $V - E + F = 5 - 8 + 5 = 2$

In 7 and 8, the graph was obtained by altering the graph in Question 6. **a.** Tell what change was made. **b.** Explain why this change did not alter the value of $V - E + F$.

7. See left.

8. See margin.

7a) The vertex of degree 1 and its adjacent edge were removed.
b) Both V and E were reduced by 1, so $V - E$ stayed the same. Since F did not change, $V - E + F$ did not change.

9. *True or false.* If G is a graph such that every vertex has degree greater than 1, then G has a circuit. If *true*, explain why. If *false*, give a counterexample. See margin.

10. Draw two different connected graphs, each of which has only one edge. Show that both satisfy Euler's formula. See margin.

11. Consider the graph with 7 edges shown at the left. See margin.
- **a.** Draw a graph obtained from this one by performing one of the changes described in the theorem on page 702.
- **b.** Suppose you know that $V - E + F = 2$ for all connected graphs with no crossings and with 6 edges. Based on your work in part **a**, what can you conclude about the graph shown at the left? Justify your answer.

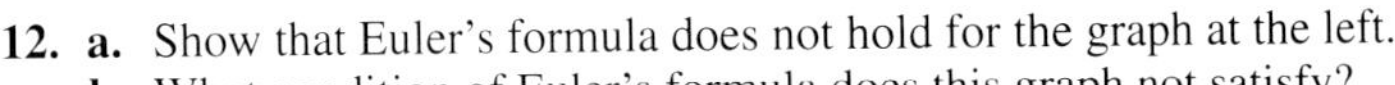

12. **a.** Show that Euler's formula does not hold for the graph at the left.
b. What condition of Euler's formula does this graph not satisfy?
See margin.

13. Suppose a connected graph with no crossings has vertices of the following degrees: 1, 2, 2, 3, 5, 5.
- **a.** How many edges does the graph have? 9
- **b.** How many faces does it have? 5

14. Suppose that 3 houses are each to be connected to 3 utilities: electricity, gas, and telephone, and that the connecting lines are not to cross.
- **a.** This situation may be represented as a graph in which vertices represent houses and utilities, and edges represent the connecting lines. How many vertices and edges must it have? See left.
- **b.** Try drawing a graph in the plane for this situation if there must be no crossings. impossible
- **c.** Use Euler's formula to determine the number of faces the graph must have. 5
- **d.** Explain why a face must have at least 4 edges. (Hint: It cannot have 3 edges, because that would mean that either two houses or two utilities would be connected to each other.) See margin.
- **e.** Use part **d** along with the fact that an edge borders exactly 2 faces to explain why $4F \leq 2E$, or $2F \leq E$. See margin.
- **f.** Use parts **c** and **e** to explain why it is impossible to connect 3 houses to 3 utilities without any lines crossing. See margin.

14a) 6 vertices, 9 edges

Notes on Questions

Questions 5–8, 11, 12, and 17 The graphs for these questions are on **Teaching Aid 131.**

Question 10 There are only two graphs of this type. You might ask students to draw all connected graphs with two edges. (There are three types, with 0 loops, 1 loop, and 2 loops.) Show that they too satisfy Euler's formula.

Question 14b This is a rather well-known puzzle.

Follow-up for Lesson 11-7

Extension

Euler's characteristic does not change as a result of continuous distortions, so it is an example of a topological property. It is 2 for any surface topologically equivalent to a sphere and 0 for any surface topologically equivalent to a torus (doughnut). Students may find it interesting to read books that discuss this idea (e.g., Courant and Robbins, *What Is Mathematics?*) and find out which figures have an Euler characteristic equal to 1.

change the value of $V - E$. This was done in part a, and F did not change, so $V - E + F = 2$ holds for the original graph.

12. a. $V - E + F = 6 - 6 + 8 = 8$
b. It is not connected and contains crossings.

14. d. In this graph, a face cannot have 1 edge, since this would mean a line connects a house or utility to itself. A face cannot have 2 edges, since this would mean a house and a utility have two lines connecting them. Finally, a face cannot have 3 edges, since the restrictions prevent two houses or two utilities from being connected to each other. So a face must have at least 4 edges.
e. Since each edge borders exactly two faces, if we sum for every face the number of edges bordering it, we get $2E$. Since there are at *least* 4 edges bordering each face, there must be at *most* $\frac{2E}{4}$ faces. So $F \leq \frac{2E}{4}$. Multiplying, $4F \leq 2E$, or $2F \leq E$.
f. By part a, $E = 9$. If there are no crossings, by part c, $F = 5$. This contradicts part e, since $2(5) \leq 9$ does not hold true. Therefore, it is impossible to connect three houses and three utilities without lines crossing.

Additional Answers

15\. d. $.95a + .02b = a$

$-5a + 2b = 0$

$5a + 5b = 5$

$7b = 5$

$b = \frac{5}{7} \approx .714$; $a = \frac{2}{7} \approx .286$

17\. a. No, there are two vertices with odd degrees.

b. Sample:

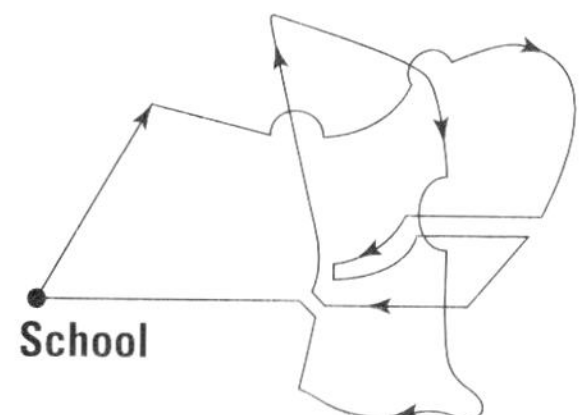

18\. No; for example, let v_1, v_2, v_3 have degree 3, and v_4 have degree 1. Then $\{v_1, v_2\}$, $\{v_1, v_3\}$, and $\{v_1, v_4\}$ are the three edges from v_1. $\{v_2, v_1\}$ and $\{v_2, v_3\}$ are 2 edges from v_2. Now there must be another edge from v_2. But that edge cannot connect v_2 to v_4, since v_4 must remain with degree 1. It cannot connect to v_1 or v_3, since a simple graph cannot contain parallel edges. And it cannot connect to itself, since a simple graph does not have any loops. So, there is no such graph.

15a)

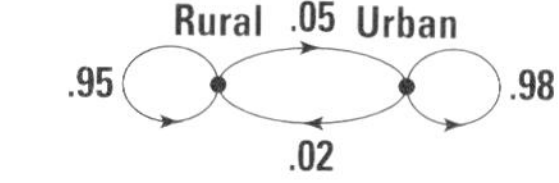

b)
$$\begin{array}{c|cc} & R & U \\ \hline R & .95 & .05 \\ U & .02 & .98 \end{array}$$

c) Urban ≈ 71%;
Rural ≈ 29%

Review

15. Suppose that in a particular country, each year 5% of the rural population moves to urban areas, and 2% of the urban population moves to rural areas *(Lesson 11-6)*

a. Sketch a digraph with edges labeled by numbers to represent the movement of the population. **See left.**

b. Write the transition matrix T. **See left.**

c. Find a large power of T and use it to predict the proportion of the population in rural and urban areas in the long run. **See left.**

d. Solve a system of equations to check your prediction. **See margin.**

16. A digraph has the adjacency matrix given at the right. Find the number of paths of length 3 from v_3 to v_3. *(Lesson 11-5)* **5**

$$\begin{bmatrix} 1 & 2 & 0 \\ 1 & 0 & 1 \\ 2 & 0 & 1 \end{bmatrix}$$

17. **a.** Can a school bus start and end at the school and pick up students along every section of road shown in the map at the right without repeating any road? Justify your answer.

b. If so, draw the route the bus would follow. If not, draw a route which would duplicate as few of the roads as possible. *(Lesson 11-4)*

See margin.

18. Determine whether there is a simple graph with four vertices: one of degree 1, and three of degree 3. Justify your answer. *(Lesson 11-3)* **See margin.**

19. If 6 dice are rolled, find the probability that exactly two 2s will come up. *(Lesson 10-6)* **≈ 20%**

20. Prove that ∀ positive integers n,

$$\sum_{i=1}^{n} i(i + 3) = \frac{n(n + 1)(n + 5)}{3}.$$ *(Lesson 7-3)* **See margin.**

Exploration

21. Consider a regular polyhedron where each face is an n-sided regular polygon and m edges meet at each vertex. **See margin.**

a. Explain why $nF = 2E$.

b. Explain why $mV = 2E$.

c. Solve the equations in parts **a** and **b** for F and V, respectively, and substitute into Euler's formula to obtain

$$\frac{1}{n} + \frac{1}{m} = \frac{1}{2} + \frac{1}{E}.$$

d. Find all positive integer values for n and m for which the equation in part **c** gives reasonable values for E.

e. Use the results of part **d** to give a proof different from that in Lesson 5-9 that there are only five regular polyhedra: the tetrahedron, cube, octahedron, dodecahedron, and icosahedron.

20\. To prove $S(n)$: $\sum_{i=1}^{n} i(i+3) = \frac{n(n+1)(n+5)}{3}$. $S(1)$: $\sum_{i=1}^{1} i(i+3) = 1(4) = 4$, and $\frac{1(2)(6)}{3} = 4$, so $S(1)$ is true.

Assume $S(k)$: $\sum_{i=1}^{k} i(i+3) = \frac{k(k+1)(k+5)}{3}$. Then $\sum_{i=1}^{k+1} i(i+3) =$

$\sum_{i=1}^{k} i(i+3) + (k+1)((k+1)+3) = \frac{k(k+1)(k+5)}{3} + (k+1)(k+4) =$

$\frac{k(k+1)(k+5)}{3} + \frac{3(k+1)(k+4)}{3} = \frac{(k+1)[k(k+5) + 3(k+4)]}{3} =$

$\frac{(k+1)(k^2+5k+3k+12)}{3} = \frac{(k+1)(k+2)(k+6)}{3} = \frac{((k+1)(k+1)+1)(k+1+5)}{3}.$

So, $S(k) \Rightarrow S(k+1)$, and by mathematical induction $S(n)$ is true for all positive integers n.

21\. a. The faces are n-gons, so each face has n edges. For all F faces, each edge appears in 2 faces, so the total number of edges is $E = \frac{nF}{2}$, or $nF = 2E$.

b. At each vertex, m edges meet. So for all V vertices, the total degree would be mV. But each edge meets at two vertices, so

A project presents an opportunity for you to extend your knowledge of a topic related to the material of this chapter. You should allow more time for a project than you do for a typical homework question.

1 Spanning Trees

A **tree** is a connected graph that has no circuits. Given a connected graph G, a **spanning tree** is a tree consisting of a subset of the edges of G but all of the vertices of G. Thus, by definition, it is a part of G which is simple and keeps all the vertices of G connected. For example, a graph G is shown below followed by a spanning tree for G.

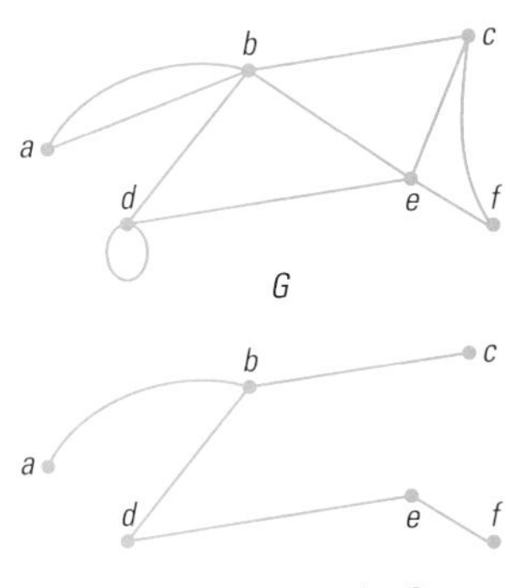

A spanning tree for G

a. Find another spanning tree for G.

b. Describe a systematic algorithm that could be used to find a spanning tree given a connected graph, and demonstrate it on a graph of your choice.

c. Suppose each edge of the graph G is labeled with a number, as is done below. Find a spanning tree for G such that the sum of the labels on its edges is the smallest possible. Such a tree is called a **minimal spanning tree**.

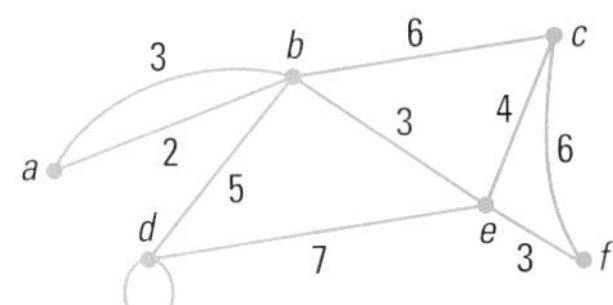

d. Find a systematic algorithm for finding a minimal spanning tree given a connected graph, and demonstrate it on a graph of your choice. (You might look up Kruskal's algorithm or Pimm's algorithm in a book.)

e. What would be some real life applications for such an algorithm?

2 Ringel's Conjecture

The following unsolved problem was posed by G. Ringel and offered by Richard K. Guy in the December 1989 issue of the *American Mathematical Monthly*. Consider the connected graph drawn below. Note that it has no circuits, and that all of its vertices have degree 1 or 3. Its 29 edges have been numbered from 1 to 29 in such a way that the sum of the numbers on the three edges leading into any vertex of degree 3 is always 45.

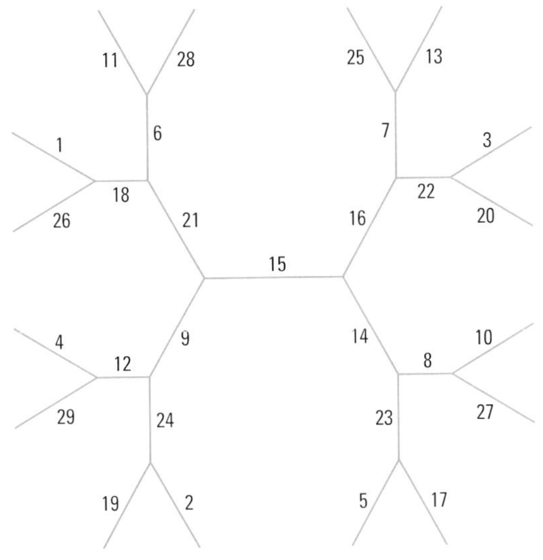

Ringel's conjecture is as follows:

Suppose you are given any connected graph which has no circuits and all of whose vertices have degree 1 or 3. Let n be the number of edges in the graph. Then you can

Chapter 11 Projects

The projects relate chiefly to the content of the lessons of this chapter as follows:

Project	Lesson(s)
1	11-4
2	11-4
3	11-2, 11-4
4	11-4
5	11-1

1 Spanning Trees Entire books are devoted to algorithms; many of these books discuss minimal spanning trees.

2 Ringel's Conjecture If any student (or teacher) is able to prove or disprove the conjecture stated in this project, you should write the editors of the *American Mathematical Monthly*. (If you write UCSMP, we will tell you whom to contact.) We expect that finding either a proof or a counterexample is quite difficult. However, finding instances is a worthy project.

(Responses begin on page 708.)

the number of edges is $E = \frac{mV}{2}$, so $mV = 2E$.

21. c. $V - E + F = 2$. From parts a and b, $F = \frac{2E}{n}$ and $V = \frac{2E}{m}$. So by substitution, $\frac{2E}{m} - E + \frac{2E}{n} = 2$. Divide both sides by 2E to obtain $\frac{1}{m} - \frac{1}{2} + \frac{1}{n} = \frac{1}{E}$. Thus, $\frac{1}{n} + \frac{1}{m} = \frac{1}{2} + \frac{1}{E}$.

d. A regular n-gon must have at least 3 sides, hence $n \geq 3$. In a polyhedron, at least 3 edges must meet at a vertex, hence $m \geq 3$. m and n cannot both be greater than 3, because $\frac{1}{m} + \frac{1}{n} \leq \frac{1}{4} + \frac{1}{4} = \frac{1}{2} < \frac{1}{2} + \frac{1}{E}$. Thus, either $m = 3$ or $n = 3$. Neither m nor n can be greater than 5, because $\frac{1}{m} + \frac{1}{n} \leq \frac{1}{6} + \frac{1}{3} = \frac{1}{2} < \frac{1}{2} + \frac{1}{E}$.

Computing values for E when m and n range from 3 to 5, five solutions are found.

n	m	E	polyhedron
3	3	6	tetrahedron
3	4	12	octahedron
3	5	30	icosahedron
4	3	12	cube
5	3	30	dodecahedron

e. These solutions relate to the five polyhedra given in the column at the right above.

3 Constellations This is a relatively easy project, though it takes time. Students should be advised that different books may connect the brighter stars in a constellation in different ways, so that the graph of a constellation in one source may not have the same properties as the graph of the same constellation in a different source.

4 The Traveling Salesman Problem There has been a huge amount of work on this problem, so much that there exists a home page on the Internet devoted to it. Search first for mathematics and then for "traveling salesman."

5 Dynamic Programming The algorithm used in the solution of the scheduling problem of Lesson 11-1 is an example of dynamic programming. Students who enjoyed that problem might be interested in this project.

(continued)

number the edges of the graph from 1 to n in such a way that the sum of the numbers on the edges leading into any vertex of degree 3 is a constant.

This conjecture has been neither proved nor disproved. Explore this problem by trying to verify the conjecture for smaller graphs. Is there a systematic way of numbering the edges? If so, can it be used to prove the conjecture? Or, can you find a counterexample?

3 Constellations

Astronomers recognize 88 constellations of stars. Constellations historically were imagined patterns among the brighter stars in the nighttime sky. Each constellation can be described by a graph. Pick 50 of the 88 constellations and display their graphs. Determine whether each graph is simple or not, connected or not, traversable or not, or whether it contains circuits. Which of the graphs do you find most interesting, and why?

4 The Traveling Salesman Problem

a. Suppose a salesperson wishes to travel to each city on the map at the top of the next column exactly once, starting and ending in New York, and using only the roads shown. The numbers on the roads indicate distances (in miles) between cities. Find the shortest route that the salesperson could use.

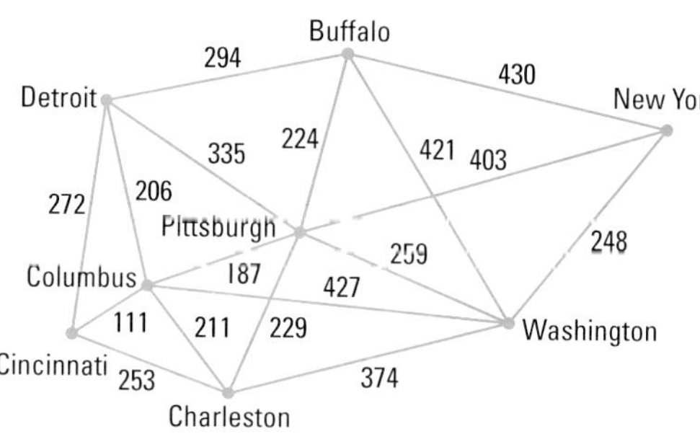

b. Explain why it would be impossible for the salesperson to visit each city below exactly once, using only the roads shown, and end at the starting point.

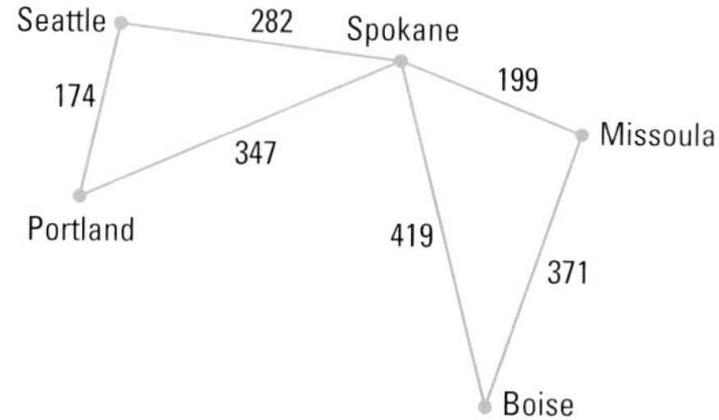

c. The general problem of parts **a** and **b** is known as the *traveling salesman problem*. Refer to a book or the Internet to find out how much is known about this problem. Write a report on your findings, along with your solutions to parts **a** and **b**.

5 Dynamic Programming

Find out what *dynamic programming* is. Give some examples of problems that can be solved using dynamic programming and demonstrate their solutions. Describe the recursive algorithm that is used in solving these types of problems. For assistance, refer to books on artificial intelligence or discrete mathematics.

Possible Responses, page 707

1. a. sample:

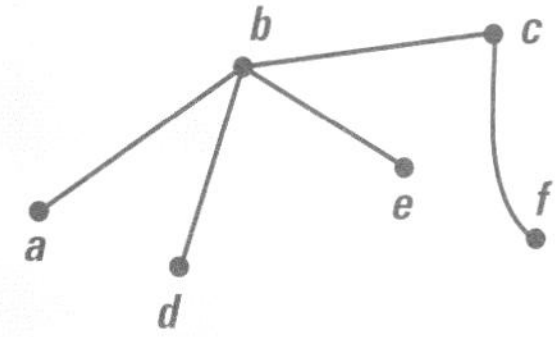

b. Sample: Examine the graph G for circuits. If it has none, than it is already a spanning tree. Otherwise remove one edge from a circuit in the graph to obtain a subgraph G_1 that is still connected. Repeat this process until a connected subgraph without circuits is obtained. The result is a spanning subtree.

Sample graph:

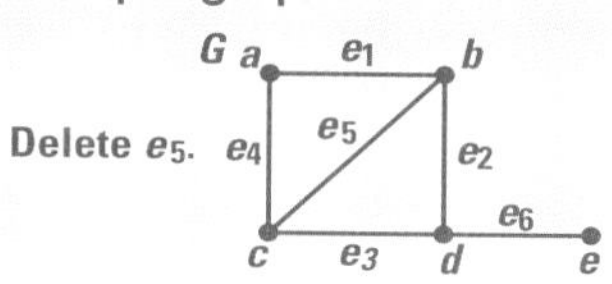

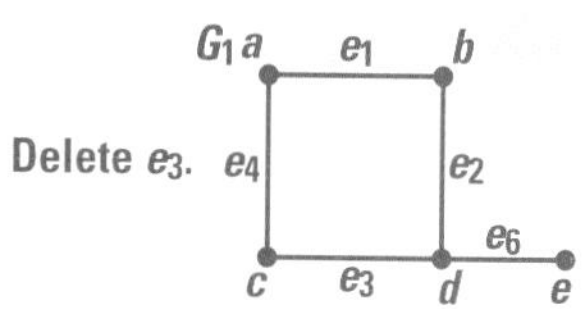

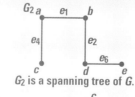

G_2 is a spanning tree of G.

c.

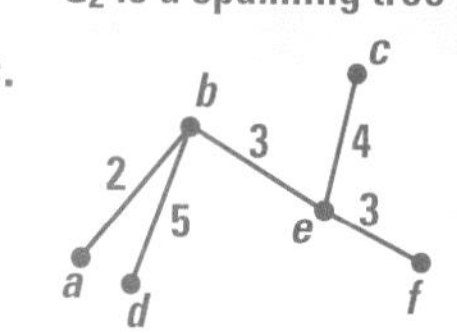

d. Sample: Kruskal's algorithm

Step 1: Start the tree by selecting an edge with smallest weight from all the edges in the graph. If more than one edge has this weight, pick any one of them.

Step 2: Add an edge with smallest weight that has not yet been included in the tree and that can be added without forming a circuit.

Step 3: Stop, if a spanning tree has been formed; otherwise, repeat Step 2.

SUMMARY

Problems in medicine, science, and business, as well as various puzzles, can be represented and solved using graphs. Directed graphs are useful for solving scheduling problems, and probability trees are helpful in situations involving the probability that one event occurs if another event occurs.

Because the total degree of any graph is twice the number of edges, the total degree of any graph is even. Thus every graph has an even number of vertices of odd degree. These facts can be used to determine that certain types of graphs do not exist, providing solutions to a special class of problems referred to as handshake problems.

Euler proved that if a graph has an Euler circuit, then every vertex of the graph has even degree, and that if every vertex of a connected graph has even degree, then the graph has an Euler circuit. These results can be used to determine whether a given graph has an Euler circuit, and thus can be used to solve practical problems as well as puzzles such as the Königsberg bridge problem.

If an edge is removed from a circuit in a connected graph, then the graph remains connected. This theorem helps to prove Euler's formula: In any connected graph with no crossings, V vertices, E edges, and F faces, $V - E + F = 2$. This relation can be applied to any polyhedron, where V, E, and F are the number of vertices, edges, and faces of the polyhedron.

Every graph can be represented by an adjacency matrix which contains the numbers of edges from each vertex to each other vertex. The adjacency matrix for an undirected graph is always symmetric. The number of walks of length n from a given vertex to another given vertex can be obtained from the nth power of the adjacency matrix.

A Markov chain is a system involving a succession of changes from one state (or condition) to another, where the probability of moving to one state depends only on the previous state. It can be modeled by a stochastic matrix which contains those probabilities. It can be proved that for large values of n, the nth power of a stochastic matrix approaches a matrix in which every row is the same. This implies that in a Markov chain, after a long period of time, the probability of being in each state approaches a constant.

Summary

The Summary gives an overview of the entire chapter and provides an opportunity for students to consider the material as a whole. Thus, the Summary can be used to help students relate and unify the concepts presented in the chapter.

Sample graph:

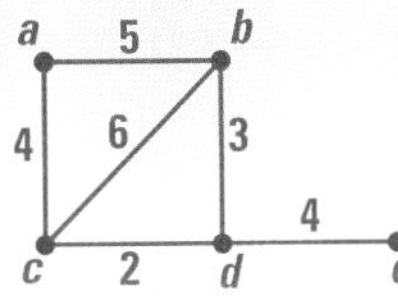

Step 1: Choose $\{c, d\}$.
Step 2: Choose $\{b, d\}$.
Step 3: Continue.
Step 2: Choose $\{d, e\}$.
Step 3: Continue.
Step 2: Choose $\{a, c\}$.
Step 3: Stop.

Minimal spanning tree:

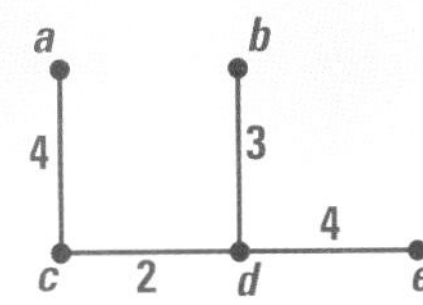

e. Sample: One real-life application could involve considering the vertices of a graph to be cities. Each number assigned to an edge between two vertices could

Continued

1. e. represent the cost of setting up and maintaining a communication or transport link between the corresponding pair of cities. Determining a minimal spanning tree would correspond to setting up a communication or transport network with the minimum cost.

2. Sample:
Ringel's conjecture can be verified on some smaller graphs, for example:

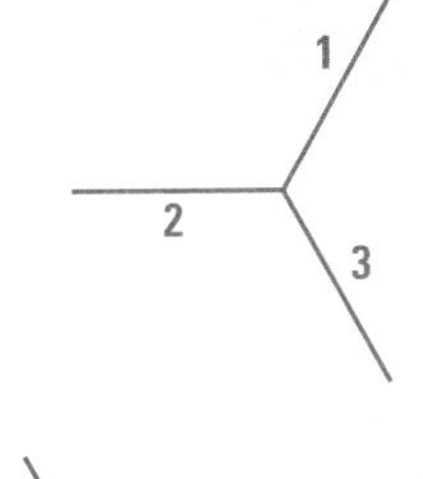

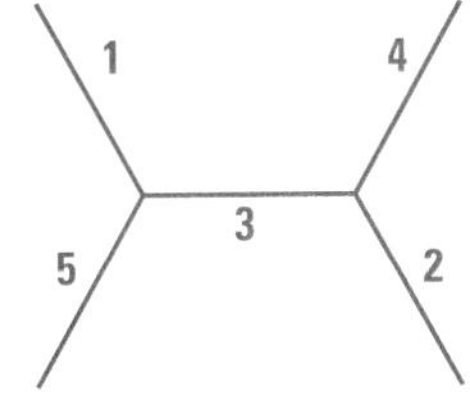

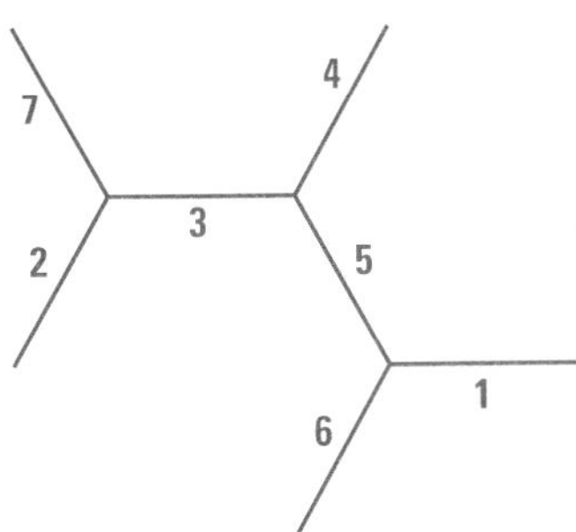

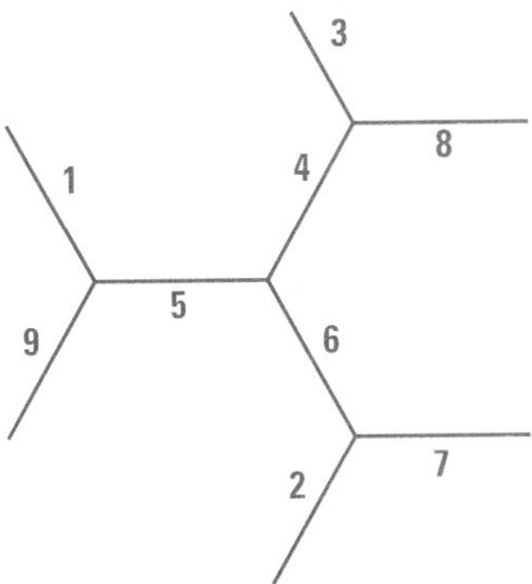

(Responses continue on page 710.)

Vocabulary

Terms, symbols, and properties are listed by lesson to provide a checklist of concepts a student must know. Emphasize to students that they should read the vocabulary list carefully before starting the Progress Self-Test. If students do not understand the meaning of a term, they should refer back to the indicated lesson.

Additional Responses, pages 707–708

Note that in each example, the sum of the numbers of the edges leading into any vertex of degree 3 is $\frac{3}{2}(n + 1)$, where n is the number of edges in the graph. This observation may be useful in constructing additional examples. However, a proof of the conjecture cannot be based simply on examples.

3. Answers may include the following 88 constellations.

Andromeda
Antlia
Apus
Aquarius
Aquila
Ara
Aries
Auriga
Bootes
Caelum
Camelopardalis
Cancer
Canes Venatici
Canis Major
Canis Minor
Capricornus
Carina
Cassiopeia
Centaurus
Cepheus
Cetus
Chamaeleon
Circinus
Columba
Coma Berenices
Corona Australis
Corona Borealis
Corvus
Crater
Crux
Cygnus
Delphinus
Dorado
Draco
Equuleus
Eridanus
Fornax
Gemini
Grus
Hercules
Horologium
Hydra
Hydrus
Indus
Lacerta
Leo
Leo Minor
Lepus
Libra
Lupus
Lynx
Lyra
Mensa
Microscopium
Monoceros
Musca
Norma
Octans
Ophiuchus
Orion
Pavo
Pegasus
Perseus
Phoenix
Pictor
Pisces
Piscis Austrinus
Puppis
Pyxis
Reticulum
Sagitta
Sagittarius
Scorpius
Sculptor
Scutum
Serpens
Sextans
Taurus
Telescopium
Triangulum
Triangulum Australe
Tucana
Ursa Major
Ursa Minor
Vela
Virgo
Valans
Vulpecula

VOCABULARY

Below are the most important terms and phrases for this chapter. You should be able to give a general description and a specific example of each and a precise definition for those marked with an asterisk (*)

Lesson 11-1
Königsberg bridge problem
graph theory
vertex
edge
equivalent graphs
directed graph, digraph
probability tree

Lesson 11-2
* graph
edge-endpoint function
endpoint
adjacent vertices
adjacent edges
parallel edges
loop
isolated vertex
* simple graph
crossing
adjacency matrix

Lesson 11-3
handshake problem
complete graph
* degree of a vertex, deg(v)
* total degree of a graph
Total Degree of a Graph Theorem

Lesson 11-4
* walk
* path
* circuit
* Euler circuit
Euler Circuit Theorem
connected vertices
* connected graph
Sufficient Condition for an Euler Circuit Theorem
Circuits and Connectedness Theorem

Lesson 11-5
length of a walk
main diagonal
symmetric matrix

Lesson 11-6
* stochastic matrix
transition probabilities
Markov chain
Convergence of Powers Theorem

PROGRESS SELF-TEST

ake this test as you would take a test in class. hen check the test yourself using the solutions the back of the book.

n 1–3, use the following graph.

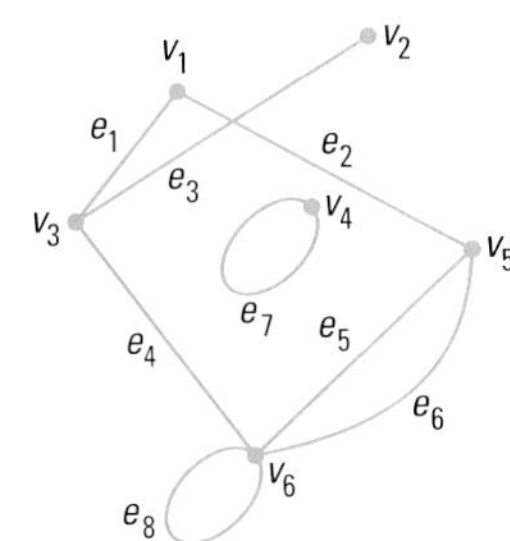

1. List all vertices adjacent to v_2. **v_3**
2. List all sets of parallel edges. **e_5 and e_6**
3. How can the graph be altered to make it simple? **Remove e_7 and e_8 and either e_5 or e_6**

In 4–8, use the following graph.

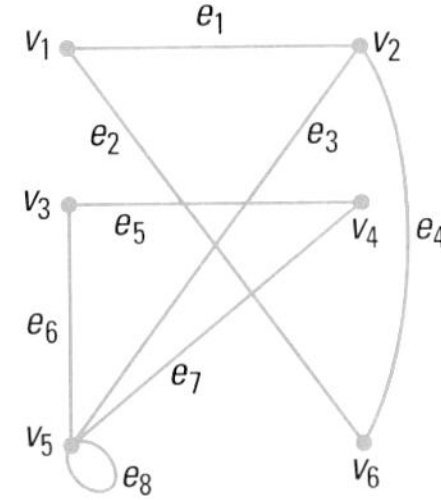

4. What is the degree of v_5? **5**
5. What is the total degree of the graph? **16**
6. Starting at v_3, consider the walk $e_6\ e_8\ e_7\ e_5$.
   a. Is this walk a path? **Yes**
   b. Is this walk a circuit? **Yes**
   c. Is this walk an Euler circuit? **No**
7. List each edge which, if only it were removed, would leave the graph connected. **all except e_3**
8. Does the graph have an Euler circuit? Justify your answer.
   No, there are vertices of odd degree.

In 9–11, consider the graph of airline routes below.

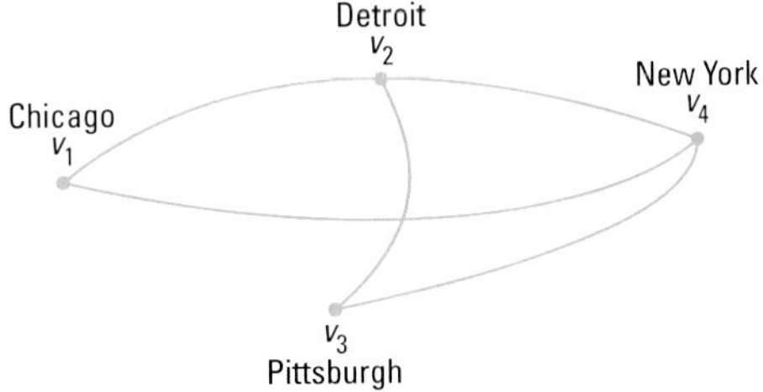

9. It is sometimes cheaper to fly through another city to get to your final destination. How many one-stop routes (i.e., walks of length 2) are there from Chicago to Pittsburgh? **2**

the Golden Triangle, Pittsburgh, PA

10. a. Write the adjacency matrix for the graph.
    b. Use the adjacency matrix to find the number of one-stop routes from Detroit to each of the other cities. **a, b) See margin.**
11. Is it possible for the airline to send a single plane so it covers every route exactly once and then returns to where it begins? Justify your answer. **No, this would be an Euler circuit, which is impossible since there are vertices with odd degree.**

Progress Self-Test

For the development of mathematical competence, feedback and correction, along with the opportunity to practice, are necessary. The Progress Self-Test provides the opportunity for feedback and correction; the Chapter Review provides additional opportunities and practice. We cannot overemphasize the importance of these end-of-chapter materials. It is at this point that the material "gels" for many students, allowing them to solidify skills and understanding. In general, student performance should be markedly improved after these pages.

Assign the Progress Self-Test as a one-night assignment. Worked-out *solutions* for all questions are in the Selected Answers section of the student book. Encourage students to take the Progress Self-Test honestly, grade themselves, and then be prepared to discuss the test in class.

Advise students to pay special attention to those Chapter Review questions (pages 713–717) that correspond to questions missed on the Progress Self-Test.

Additional Answers, page 712

10. a.

$$\begin{array}{c|cccc} & v_1 & v_2 & v_3 & v_4 \\ \hline v_1 & 0 & 1 & 0 & 1 \\ v_2 & 1 & 0 & 1 & 1 \\ v_3 & 0 & 1 & 0 & 1 \\ v_4 & 1 & 1 & 1 & 0 \end{array}$$

b. The numbers of 1-stop routes to Chicago, Pittsburgh, and New York are 1, 1, and 2, respectively.

Sample graphs are shown at the right:

The graph of Pisces is simple, not connected, and not traversable. It does not contain any circuits.

The graph of Sagittarius is simple, not connected, and not traversable. It contains one circuit.

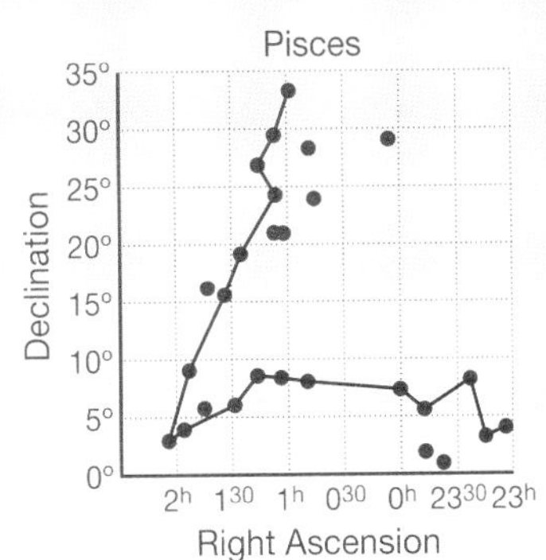

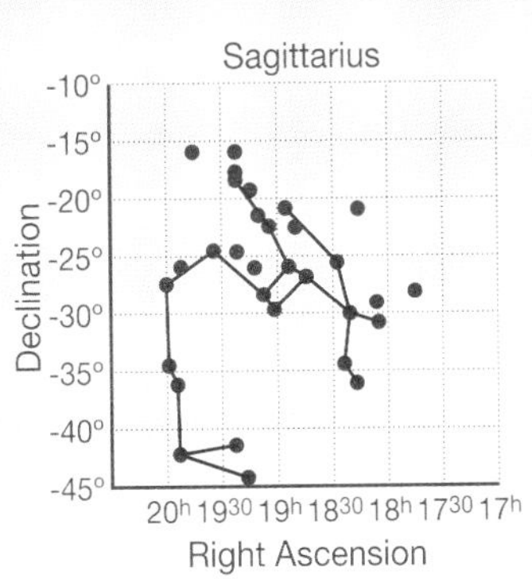

(Responses contiune on page 715.)

Additional Answers

12. e_2 v_1 v_2 e_3 e_5 e_1 e_4 v_4 v_3

13.

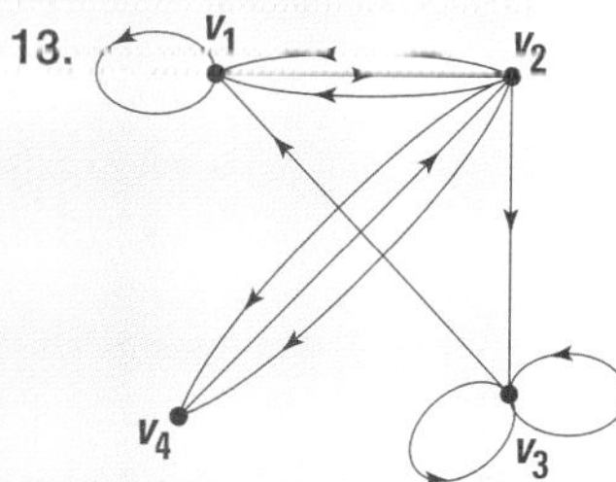

15. a.

Infected: .001; Positive .98 → .00098; Negative .02 → .00002

Not Infected: .999; Positive .002 → .001998; Negative .998 → .997002

Total Population

b. has HIV and tests positive: .00098; has HIV but tests negative: .00002; doesn't have HIV but tests positive: .001998; doesn't have HIV and tests negative: .997002

c. ≈ 67%

17. a.

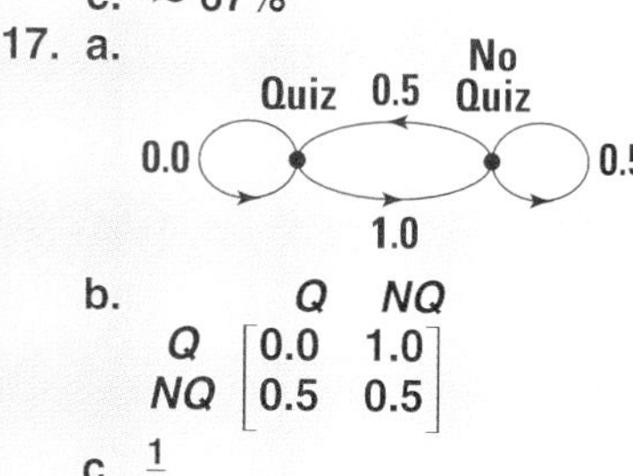

b.

$$\begin{array}{c c} & Q \quad NQ \\ \begin{array}{c} Q \\ NQ \end{array} & \begin{bmatrix} 0.0 & 1.0 \\ 0.5 & 0.5 \end{bmatrix} \end{array}$$

c. $\frac{1}{3}$

In 12 and 13, draw a graph satisfying the given conditions. **See margin.**

12. set of vertices: $\{v_1, v_2, v_3, v_4\}$
set of edges: $\{e_1, e_2, e_3, e_4, e_5\}$
edge-endpoint function:

edge	endpoints
e_1	$\{v_2, v_3\}$
e_2	$\{v_1\}$
e_3	$\{v_2, v_4\}$
e_4	$\{v_2, v_3\}$
e_5	$\{v_1, v_4\}$

13. adjacency matrix:

$$\begin{bmatrix} 1 & 1 & 0 & 0 \\ 2 & 0 & 1 & 2 \\ 1 & 0 & 2 & 0 \\ 0 & 1 & 0 & 0 \end{bmatrix}$$

14. Does there exist a graph with 4 vertices of degrees 0, 1, 2, and 2? If so, draw one. If not, explain why not. **See below.**

15. A drug manufacturer has developed a test for AIDS (Acquired Immune Deficiency Syndrome). A study shows that the test shows up positive for 98% of those who have HIV and for .2% of those who do not have HIV. Assume that .1% of the population has HIV.

a. Draw a graph and label its edges with probabilities to represent the situation.

b. Find the fraction of the population in each category: has HIV and tests positive; has HIV but tests negative; doesn't have HIV but tests positive; doesn't have HIV and tests negative.

c. What is the probability that a person who tests positive does not have HIV?

16. Explain why it is impossible to set up a tournament in which each of nine teams plays exactly five of the other teams.
A graph cannot have an odd number of odd vertices.

14) No, the total degree of a graph must be even.

15) See margin.

CHAPTER ELEVEN

17. A mathematics teacher has the following policy regarding pop quizzes: If he gives one on one day, he will not give one the next day. However, if he does not give a pop quiz on a particular day, there is a 50-50 chance he will give one the next day. **See margin.**

a. Draw a graph for this situation, and label the edges with the correct probabilities.

b. Write down the corresponding stochastic matrix.

c. Find the long-term probability that the teacher will give a pop quiz on any particular day.

Additional Answers, page 713

1. a. Sample: b. Yes, Sample:

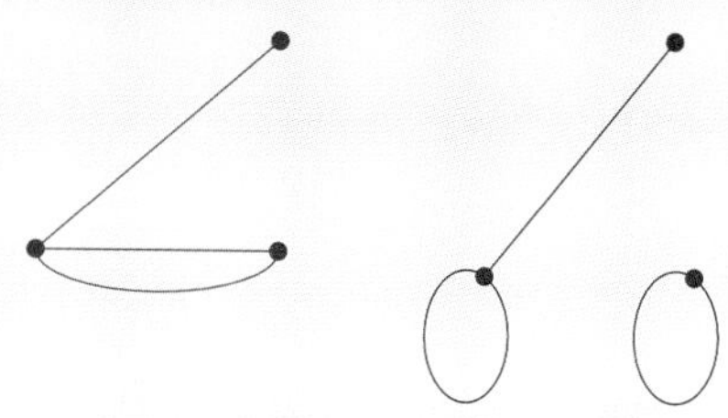

2. Sample:

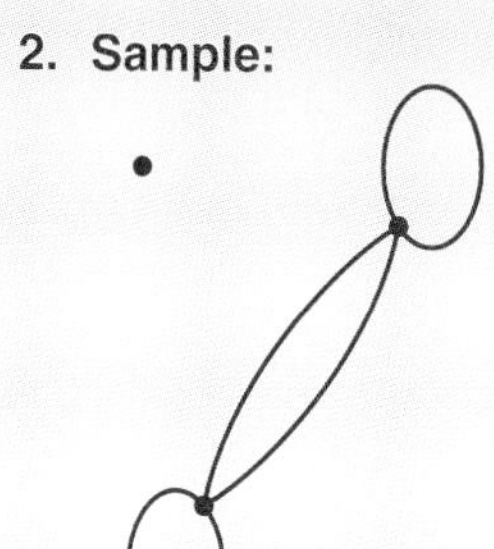

3.

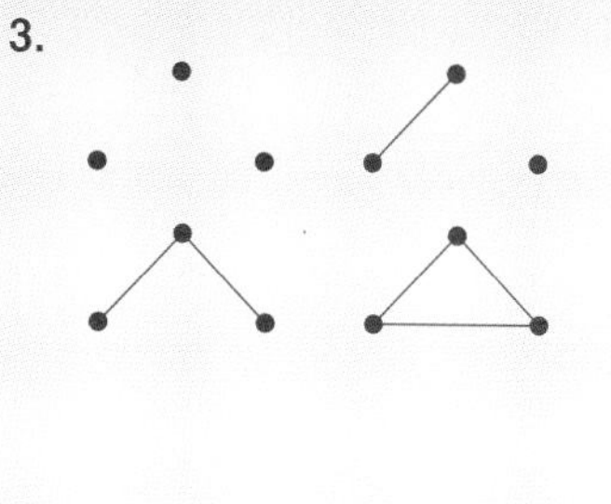

4. Sample:

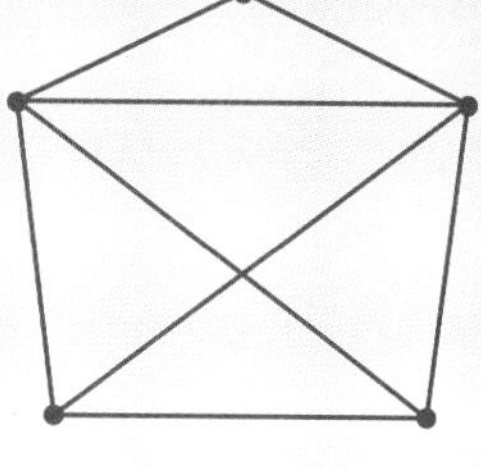

CHAPTER REVIEW

Questions on SPUR Objectives

SPUR stands for **S**kills, **P**roperties, **U**ses, and **R**epresentations. The Chapter Review questions are grouped according to the SPUR Objectives for this chapter

SKILLS DEAL WITH THE PROCEDURES USED TO GET ANSWERS.

1–5, 8c, 8d) See margin.

Objective A: *Draw graphs given sufficient information.* *(Lessons 11-2, 11-3)*

1. a. Draw a graph with three vertices and three edges.

b. Is it possible to draw a graph with three vertices and three edges such that two edges are not adjacent to each other? If so, do it. If not, explain why not.

2. Draw a graph with two loops, an isolated vertex, and two parallel edges.

3. Draw all the simple graphs with three vertices.

4. Draw a simple graph with five vertices of the following degrees: 2, 3, 3, 4, and 4.

5. Draw the graph defined below.

set of vertices: $\{v_1, v_2, v_3, v_4, v_5\}$
set of edges: $\{e_1, e_2, e_3, e_4, e_5\}$
edge-endpoint function:

edge	endpoints
e_1	$\{v_1, v_3\}$
e_2	$\{v_1, v_4\}$
e_3	$\{v_2, v_4\}$
e_4	$\{v_1\}$
e_5	$\{v_1, v_3\}$

PROPERTIES DEAL WITH THE PRINCIPLES BEHIND THE MATHEMATICS.

Objective B: *Identify parts of graphs and types of graphs.* *(Lessons 11-2, 11-3, 11-4, 11-5)*

6. Use the graph below.

a. *True or false.* There is exactly one walk from v_1 to v_2. **False**

b. *True or false.* There is exactly one path from v_1 to v_2. **False**

7. Is the graph below connected? **Yes**

8. Use the graph below.

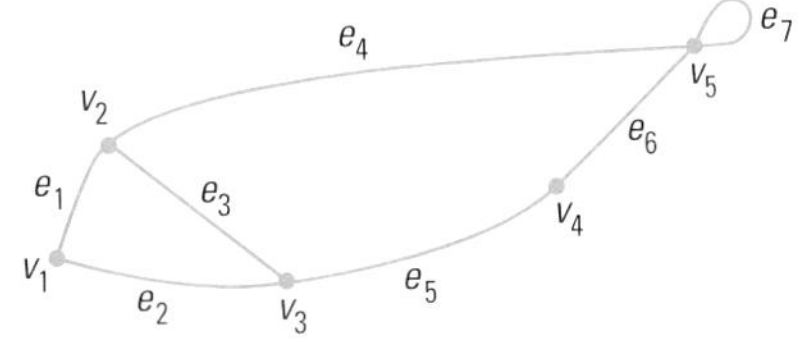

a. Starting at v_2, consider the walk $e_4\ e_7\ e_6\ e_5\ e_3$.

i. Is it a path? **Yes**

ii. Is it a circuit? **Yes**

iii. Is it an Euler circuit? **No**

b. Starting at v_2, consider the walk $e_4\ e_6\ e_5\ e_3\ e_1\ e_2\ e_3$.

i. Is it a path? **No**

ii. Is it a circuit? **No**

iii. Is it an Euler circuit? **No**

c. Identify all paths from v_1 to v_3 and give their lengths.

d. Identify three circuits that go through v_1.

Chapter 11 Review

Resources

From the ***Teacher's Resource File***

- Answer Master for Chapter 11 Review
- Assessment Sourcebook: Chapter 11 Test, Forms A–D Chapter 11 Test, Cumulative Form

Additional Resources

- TestWorks CD-ROM

The main objectives for the chapter are organized in the Chapter Review under the four types of understanding this book promotes—Skills, Properties, Uses, and Representations.

Whereas end-of-chapter material may be considered optional in some texts, in UCSMP *Precalculus and Discrete Mathematics* we have selected these objectives and questions with the expectation that they will be covered. Students should be able to answer these questions with about 85% accuracy after studying the chapter.

You may assign these questions over a single night to help students prepare for a test the next day, or you may assign the questions over a two-day period. If you work the questions over two days, then we recommend assigning the *evens* for homework the first night so that students get feedback in class the next day, then assigning the *odds* the night before the test, because answers are provided to the odd-numbered questions.

It is effective to ask students which questions they still do not understand and use the day or days as a total class discussion of the material which the class finds most difficult.

5.

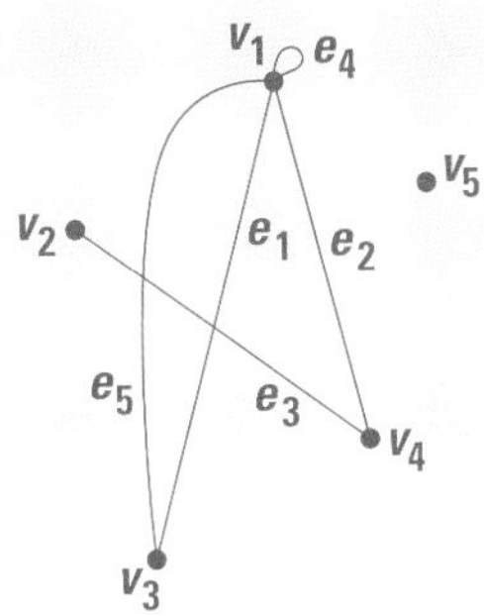

8. c.

length	path(s)
1	e_2
2	e_1e_3
3	none
4	$e_1e_4e_6e_5$
5	$e_1e_4e_7e_6e_5$
	$e_2e_3e_4e_6e_5$
	$e_2e_5e_6e_4e_3$
6	$e_2e_3e_4e_7e_6e_5$
	$e_2e_5e_6e_7e_4e_3$

d. Samples: $e_1e_2e_5e_6e_4$; $e_3e_2e_1$; $e_4e_7e_6e_5e_2e_1$

Assessment

Evaluation The Assessment Sourcebook provides five forms of the Chapter 11 Test. Forms A and B present parallel versions in a short-answer format. Forms C and D offer performance assessment. The fifth test is Chapter 11 Test, Cumulative Form. About 50% of this test covers Chapter 11, 25% of it covers Chapter 10, and 25% of it covers earlier chapters.

For information on grading, see *General Teaching Suggestions: Grading* in the *Professional Sourcebook*, which begins on page T20 in the Teacher's Edition.

Feedback After students have taken the test for Chapter 11 and you have scored the results, return the tests to students for discussion. Class discussion of the questions that caused trouble for the most students can be very effective in identifying and clarifying misunderstandings. You might want to have them write down the items they missed and work, either in groups or at home, to correct them. It is important for students to receive feedback on every chapter test, and we recommend that students see and correct their mistakes before proceeding too far into the next chapter

Additional Answers

11.

edge	endpoints
e_1	$\{v_1, v_5\}$
e_2	$\{v_1, v_2\}$
e_3	$\{v_1, v_3\}$
e_4	$\{v_2, v_3\}$
e_5	$\{v_2, v_4\}$
e_6	$\{v_4\}$
e_7	$\{v_4, v_5\}$
e_8	$\{v_1, v_5\}$

9. Use the graph drawn below.

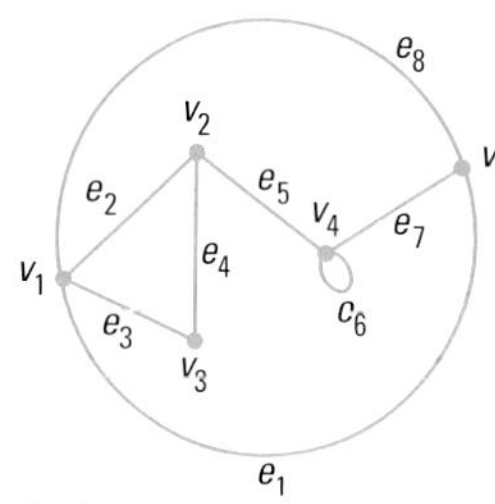

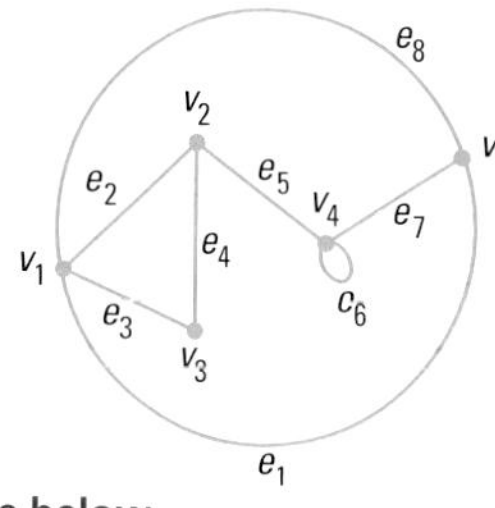

b, g) See below.

a. Identify all vertices adjacent to v_1. **v_2, v_3, v_5**

b. Identify all edges adjacent to e_5.

c. Identify any isolated vertices. **none**

d. Identify any parallel edges. **e_1 and e_8**

e. Identify any loops. **e_6**

f. *True or false.* If edge e_6 is removed, the graph is simple. **False**

g. Give the degree of each vertex.

h. Give the total degree of the graph. **16**

10. Consider the graph below.

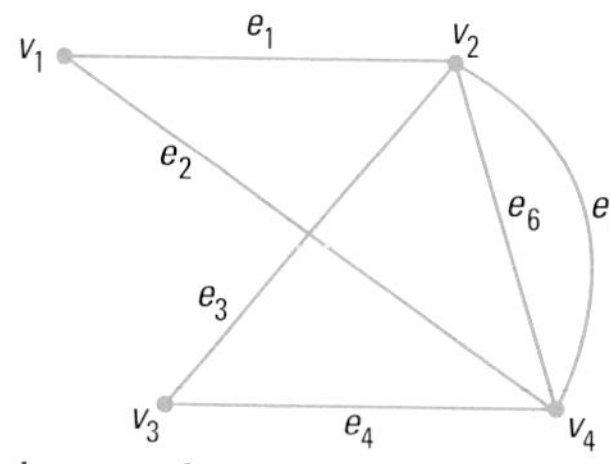

Samples are given.

a. Identify an Euler circuit. **$e_1e_5e_6e_3e_4e_2$**

b. Identify two circuits that are not Euler circuits. **$e_1e_6e_2$; $e_1e_5e_2$**

c. Identify a walk that is not a path. **e_1e_1; $e_1e_5e_4e_4$**

d. What is the minimum number of edges to remove so that the graph is no longer connected? **2**

e. What is the maximum number of edges that can be removed at the same time while keeping the graph connected? List one such set of edges. **3; Sample: e_1, e_3, e_6**

11. Give the edge-endpoint function table for the graph in Question 9. **See margin.**

9b) **e_2, e_4, e_6, e_7**
g) **$\deg(v_1) = 4$; $\deg(v_2) = 3$; $\deg(v_3) = 2$; $\deg(v_4) = 4$; $\deg(v_5) = 3$**

Objective C: *Determine whether there exists a graph containing vertices with given degrees.* *(Lesson 11-3)* **12–16) See margin.**

In 12–15, either draw a graph with the given properties or show that no such graph exists.

12. graph with 5 vertices of degrees 1, 2, 2, 3, and 5

13. graph with 5 vertices of degrees 1, 2, 2, 3, and 0

14. simple graph with 5 vertices of degrees 1, 2, 2, 3, and 0

15. graph with 9 vertices of degrees 0, 1, 1, 1, 2, 2, 2, 3, and 3

16. Suppose that the sum of the entries in a matrix is odd. Can this matrix be the adjacency matrix of a graph? Explain your answer.

Objective D: *Determine whether a graph has an Euler circuit.* *(Lesson 11-4)*

In 17–20, determine, if possible, whether the graph has an Euler circuit. Justify your answer.

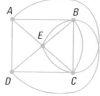

17. **See margin.**

18. **No, the graph is not connected.**

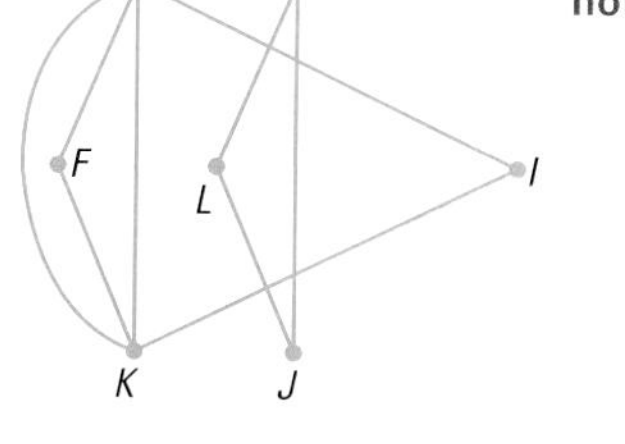

19. the graph whose adjacency matrix is $\begin{bmatrix}1 & 1 & 1\\ 1 & 0 & 2\\ 1 & 2 & 0\end{bmatrix}$ **See below.**

20. a graph with vertices of degrees 2, 2, 4, and 6 **It cannot be determined since the graph may not be connected.**

19) No, because v_2 and v_3 have odd degree.

12. **Impossible; a graph cannot have an odd number of odd vertices.**
13. **Sample:**

14. **Sample:**

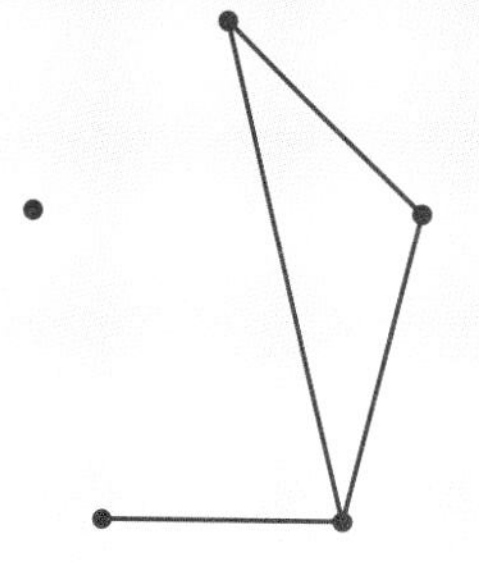

15. **Impossible; a graph cannot have an odd number of odd vertices.**
16. **No, the sum of the entries must be the total degree of the graph, which must be even.**
17. **The graph has an Euler circuit by the sufficient condition for an Euler Circuit Theorem, since it is connected and every vertex is of even degree.**

USES DEAL WITH APPLICATIONS OF MATHEMATICS IN REAL SITUATIONS.

(21a, 22a, 23a, 24–26) **See margin.**

Objective E: *Use graphs to solve scheduling and probability problems.* (*Lesson 11-1*)

21. Oiler Motorboats manufactures two models of motorboat: a compact model called the Pac, and a luxury model called the Lux. In 1997, 69% of the boats sold were Oiler Pacs, and 31% were Oiler Luxes. Since then, 5% of the owners of an Oiler Pac have had to replace the rudder; of the others, 3% have had to replace the fuel gauge. The rest have needed no repairs. 7% of the owners of an Oiler Lux have had to replace the rudder; of the others, 4% the fuel gauge. The rest have needed no repairs.

a. Draw a probability tree to represent this situation, labeling edges with the proper probabilities.

b. If a 1997 Oiler was brought in for rudder replacement, what is the probability that it was a Pac? **61.4%**

22. Suppose that at any given day in a particular city, the probability that a given car is being broken into is .01%. Also suppose that a Car-Safe alarm system installed on a car sounds 96% of the time that the car is broken into, but also sounds 2% of the time that the car is not being broken into.

a. Draw a probability tree to represent the situation.

b. Find the probability that the car is really being broken into when the alarm sounds. **≈ 0.48%**

23. Suppose the process of assembling a car at a particular plant can be broken down into the following tasks.

Task		Time required (hours)	Prerequisite tasks
A	Assemble body	6	
B	Paint exterior	3	A
C	Assemble engine	11	
D	Install engine	5	B, C
E	Assemble water pump	4	
F	Assemble carburetor	5	
G	Install fuel, exhaust, electrical, cooling systems	12	D, E, F
H	Assemble interior parts	5	
I	Install interior	5	G, H

a. Sketch a directed graph to represent the situation.

b. What is the minimal time required to assemble a car? **33 hours**

Objective F: *Use the Total Degree of a Graph Theorem and its corollaries to solve handshake problems.* (*Lesson 11-3*)

24. In a class of 25 students, is it possible for each student to shake hands with exactly fifteen other students? Justify your answer.

25. From 1970 to 1975, the National Football League had two conferences each with 13 teams. If the league office had decided that every team should play 11 games in its own conference, each against a different team, would this have been possible? Justify your answer.

26. Six authors are writing a textbook, each one writing a different part. In order to maintain some unity in the book, they decide that each author should show the part he or she has written to three other authors. They want to do this in the following way: Each author will make three copies of what he or she has written, then trade each copy with a different author. Is this possible? Justify your answer.

Additional Answers, page 715

21. a.

Pac .69: .05 Rudder .035; .95 → .03 Gauge .02; .97 None .64

Lux .31: .07 Rudder .022; .93 → .04 Gauge .01; .96 None .28

22. a.

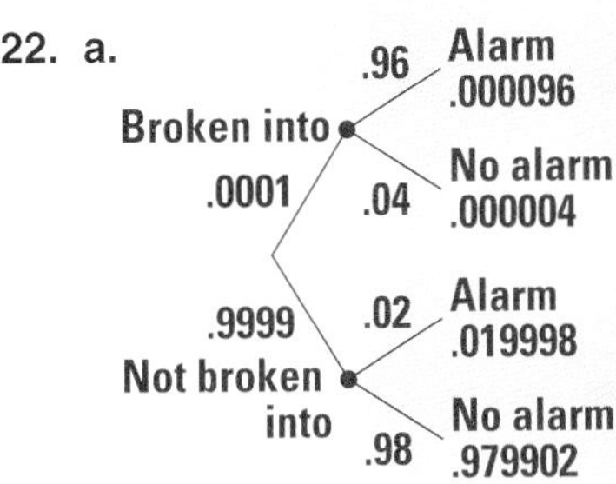

23. a.

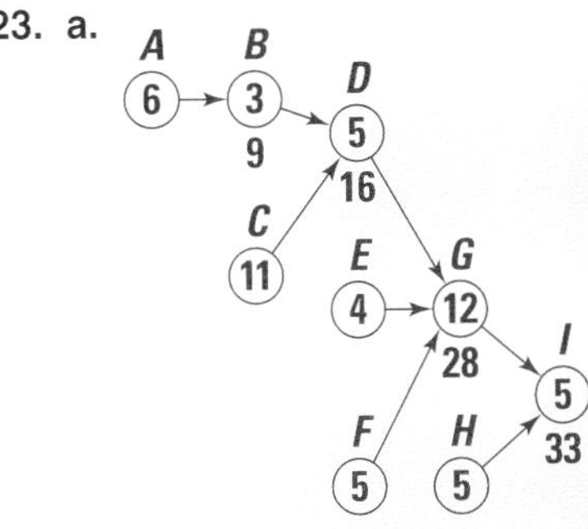

24. No; this situation may be represented as a graph with 25 vertices, each with 5 edges. This is not possible since a graph cannot have an odd number of odd vertices.

25. No, a graph cannot have an odd number of odd vertices

26. Yes; below is a Sample graph:

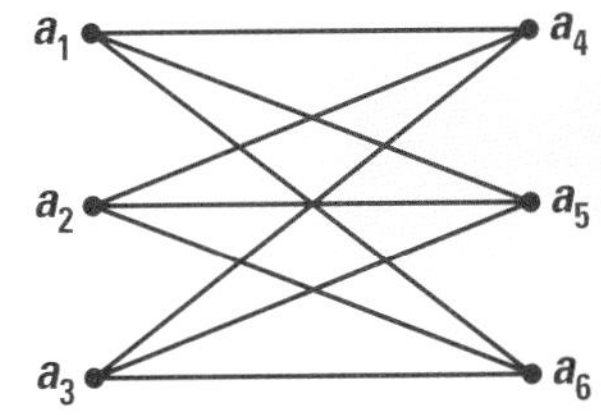

Additional Responses, page 708

4. a. A good route may be found by moving from city to city by choosing the next city to be the nearest city among all possible neighboring cities. Through some trial and error, the following route *appears* to be the shortest: New York–Washington–Pittsburgh–Charleston–Cincinnati–Columbus–Detroit–Buffalo–New York, which covers a total distance of 2030 miles.

b. A salesperson starting in Seattle or Portland must travel through Spokane to get to Boise and Missoula and then must return through Spokane. In the same way, a salesperson starting in Missoula or Boise must travel through Spokane to get to Portland and Seattle and then must return through Spokane. Similarly, a salesperson starting in Spokane will "visit" Spokane three times over such a trip so the described trip is impossible.

(Responses continue on page 716.)

CHAPTER ELEVEN

Additional Answers, page 716

27. a. Vertices F and G have odd degree, so there is not an Euler circuit.
    b. the edge between F and G

28. a. Yes, Sample:

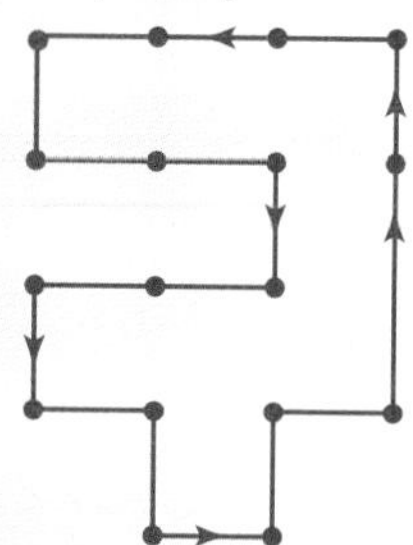

    b. No, some of the vertices have odd degree, so no Euler circuit is possible.

29. a.

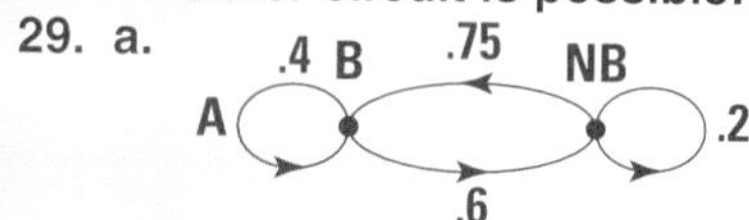

    b.
$$\begin{array}{c} \\ B \\ NB \end{array}\begin{array}{c} \begin{array}{cc} B & NB \end{array} \\ \begin{bmatrix} .4 & .6 \\ .75 & .25 \end{bmatrix} \end{array}$$

    c. $T^8 \approx \begin{bmatrix} .5557 & .4443 \\ .5554 & .4446 \end{bmatrix}$

    They bowl on about 56% of the Tuesdays.

    d. $\approx$ 56%

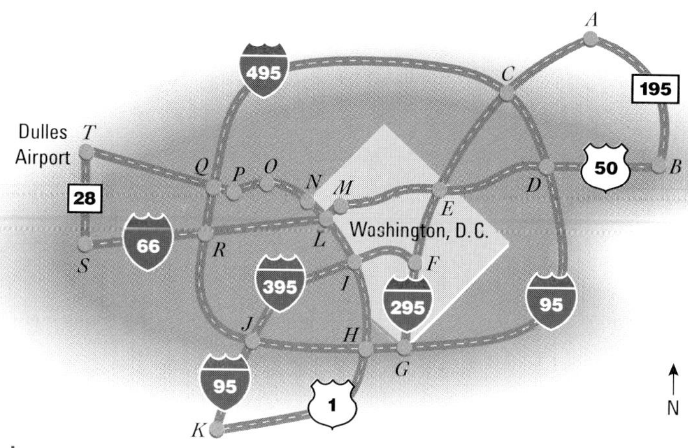

27–29) See margin.

Objective G: *Solve application problems involving circuits.* *(Lessons 11-1, 11-4)*

27. A map of the Washington, D.C., area is shown above.

a. Explain why it is impossible to travel each road shown above exactly once and return to where you started.

b. What one section of road (that is, one edge of the graph) can be removed to make it possible?

28. Consider the map of a section of a city shown below.

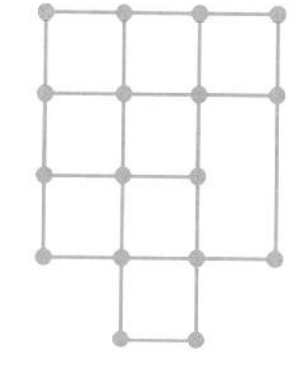

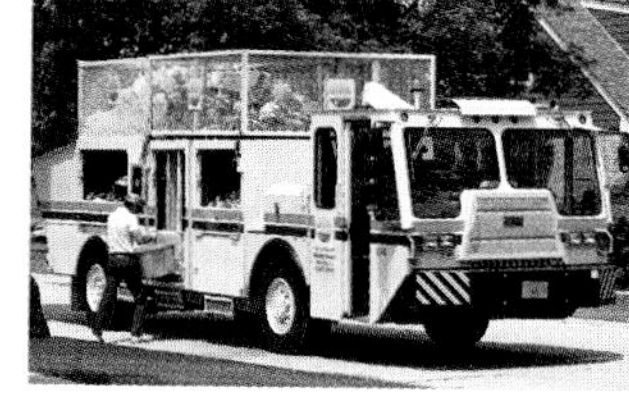

a. Each corner (indicated by a dot) is a recycling pick-up point. Is there a route that a truck could follow which would begin and end at the same place and go past each of the other pick-up points exactly once? If so, find it. If not, explain why not.

b. Is there a route that a street cleaner could follow which would begin and end at the same place and travel every section of road exactly once? If so, find it. If not, explain why not.

Objective H: *Use stochastic matrices to make long-term predictions.* *(Lesson 11-6)*

29. Some friends like to go bowling on Tuesdays. If they go on a particular Tuesday, there is a 40% chance they will go bowling the next Tuesday. Otherwise, there is a 75% chance that they will bowl the following Tuesday.

a. Draw a directed graph representing the situation.

b. Find T, the transition matrix.

c. Estimate how often the friends bowl on average over a long period of time by calculating T^8.

d. Find how often the friends bowl on average over a long period of time by solving a system of equations.

30. In a certain state, it was found that 60% of the daughters of women registered to vote as Democrats also register as Democrats, 15% register as Republicans, and the rest register as Independents. 70% of the daughters of Republicans are Republicans, 20% are Democrats, and the rest are Independents. 50% of the daughters of Independents are Independents, 30% are Democrats, and the rest are Republicans. Assume this pattern continues over many generations. What percentage of women will be registered in each group? **38% Democrat, 36% Republican, 26% Independent**

Additional Responses, page 708

4. c. Answers will vary. Reports may include the following main points:
    i. discussion of Hamiltonian circuits
    ii. formulation and physical interpretation of the Traveling Salesman Problem
    iii. mathematical difficulty in its solution
    iv. methods used to solve it (e.g., nearest-neighbor method)

5. Dynamic programming is a method for finding the shortest path between two nodes of a graph. It is based on the *dynamic-programming principle* which states that, when searching for the shortest path from a node S to a node G, all but the shortest path from S to any intermediate node I can be ignored. Here is an algorithm for this method. It builds a queue which holds partial paths. Notice that at each stage of the search, redundant paths are discarded, leaving only the shortest one.
    a. Put the path of length zero from the starting node to nowhere in the queue.
    b. If the queue is empty or the goal has been reached then go to step d, otherwise, do the following:
        i. Remove the first path from the queue.
        ii. Form new paths by extending the path you just removed by one step.

REPRESENTATIONS DEAL WITH PICTURES, GRAPHS, OR OBJECTS THAT ILLUSTRATE CONCEPTS.

31–34, 37a, 38a, 39) See margin.

Objective I: *Convert between the picture of a graph or directed graph, and its adjacency matrix.* *(Lesson 11-2)*

31. Write the adjacency matrix for the directed graph shown below.

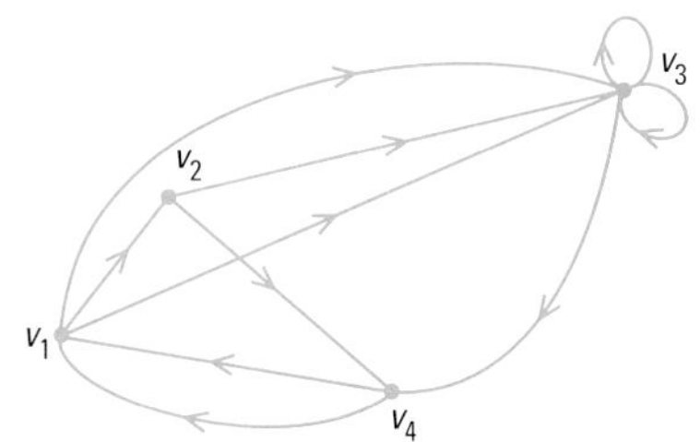

32. How can you tell from its adjacency matrix whether or not a graph is simple?

33. Consider the matrix shown below.

$$\begin{bmatrix} 0 & 1 & 2 & 1 \\ 0 & 0 & 1 & 0 \\ 1 & 0 & 1 & 0 \\ 1 & 2 & 1 & 0 \end{bmatrix}$$

a. Draw a directed graph whose adjacency matrix is the matrix given above.

b. Could the matrix above be the adjacency matrix of a graph that is not directed? If so, draw the graph. If not, explain.

34. Draw a graph (not directed) whose adjacency matrix is given below.

$$\begin{bmatrix} 0 & 2 & 1 \\ 2 & 2 & 0 \\ 1 & 0 & 0 \end{bmatrix}$$

35. In the adjacency matrix of the directed graph below, $a_{13} = $ __?__ and $a_{22} = $ __?__. **0; 0**

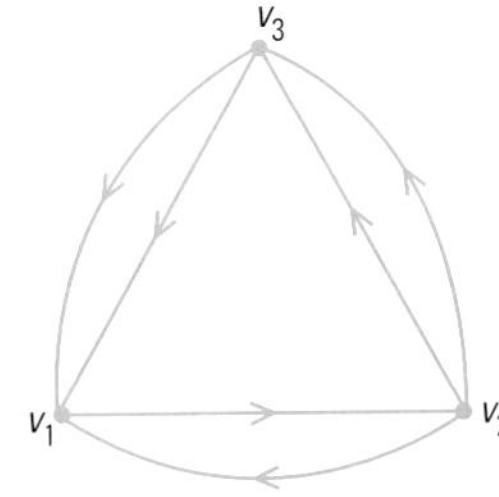

Objective J: *Use the powers of the adjacency matrix of a graph to find the number of walks of a given length, from a given starting vertex to a given ending vertex.* *(Lesson 11-5)*

36. The adjacency matrix for a graph is $\begin{bmatrix} 2 & 1 & 2 \\ 1 & 0 & 1 \\ 2 & 1 & 0 \end{bmatrix}$. How many walks of length 2 go from v_2 to v_3? **2**

37. a. Give the adjacency matrix for the graph below.

b. How many walks of length 3 are there which start at v_1? **39**

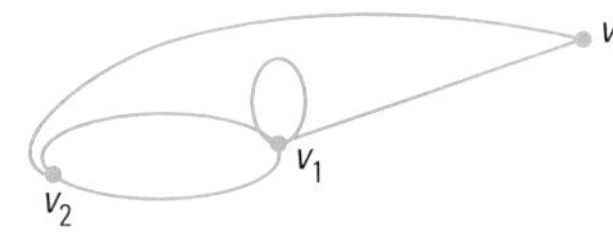

38. a. Give the adjacency matrix for the directed graph below.

b. How many walks of length 3 are there which start at v_1? **9**

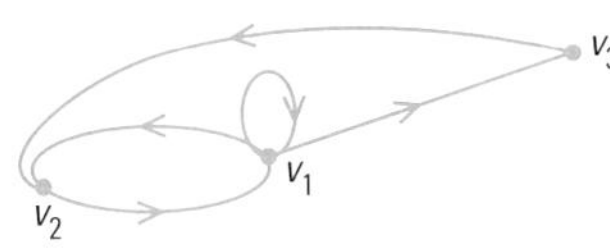

39. Consider the matrix $A = \begin{bmatrix} 0 & 1 & 1 & 1 \\ 0 & 0 & 1 & 1 \\ 0 & 0 & 0 & 1 \\ 0 & 0 & 0 & 0 \end{bmatrix}$.

a. A has the property that $A^4 = \begin{bmatrix} 0 & 0 & 0 & 0 \\ 0 & 0 & 0 & 0 \\ 0 & 0 & 0 & 0 \\ 0 & 0 & 0 & 0 \end{bmatrix}$.

In fact, $A^n = \begin{bmatrix} 0 & 0 & 0 & 0 \\ 0 & 0 & 0 & 0 \\ 0 & 0 & 0 & 0 \\ 0 & 0 & 0 & 0 \end{bmatrix}$ for all $n \geq 4$.

What does this imply about walks in the directed graph with adjacency matrix A?

b. Confirm your answer to part **a** by drawing the directed graph with adjacency matrix A.

Additional Answers, page 717

31.

	v_1	v_2	v_3	v_4
v_1	0	1	2	0
v_2	0	0	1	1
v_3	0	0	2	1
v_4	2	0	0	0

32. If the main diagonal has zeros, and all other entries are either zeros or ones, then the graph is simple.

33. a.

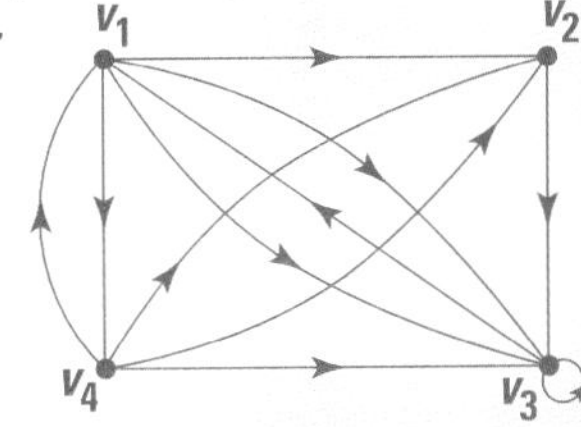

b. No, the matrix is not symmetric.

34.

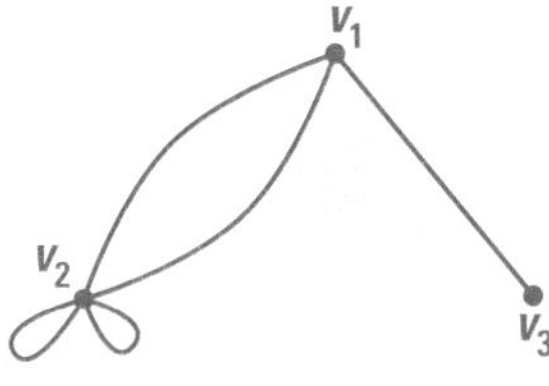

37. a.

	v_1	v_2	v_3
v_1	1	2	1
v_2	2	0	1
v_3	1	1	0

38. a.

	v_1	v_2	v_3
v_1	1	1	1
v_2	1	0	0
v_3	0	1	0

39. a. There are no walks of length 4 or more.

b.

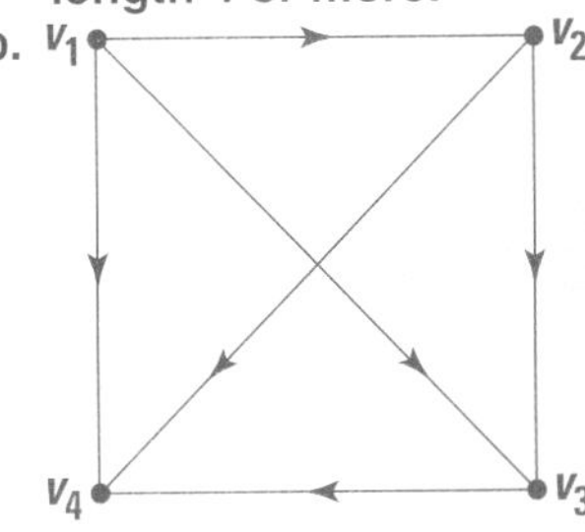

Project 5. b. continued

iii. Add these new paths to the queue.

iv. Sort the queue, putting the shortest paths in front.

v. If two or more paths reach a common node, delete all except the shortest one.

c. Return to step b.

d. If the goal has been reached, then the procedure was successful; otherwise it failed.

Chapter 12 Pacing Chart

Day	Full Course	Minimal Course
1	12-1	12-1
2	12-2	12-2
3	12-3	12-3
4	Quiz*; 12-4	Quiz*; begin 12-4.
5	12-5	Finish 12-4.
6	12-6	12-5
7	Quiz*; 12-7	12-6
8	12-8	Quiz*; begin 12-7.
9	Self-Test	Finish 12-7.
10	Review	12-8
11	Test*	Self-Test
12		Review
13		Review
14		Test*

*in the Teacher's Resource File

Adapting to Individual Needs

The student text is written for the vast majority of students. The chart at the right suggests two pacing plans to accommodate the needs of your students. Students in the Full Course should complete the entire text by the end of the year. Students in the Minimal Course will spend more time when there are quizzes and more time on the Chapter Review. Therefore, these students may not complete all of the chapters in the text.

Options are also presented to meet the needs of a variety of teaching and learning styles. For each lesson, the Teacher's Edition provides a section entitled *Adapting to Individual Needs.* This section regularly includes **Optional Activities, Challenge** problems, **English Language Development** suggestions, and suggestions for providing **Extra Help.** The Teacher's Edition also frequently includes an **Error Alert,** an **Extension,** and an **Assessment** alternative. The options available in Chapter 12 are summarized in the chart below.

In the Teacher's Edition...

Lesson	Optional Activities	Extra Help	Challenge	English Language Development	Error Alert	Extension	Cooperative Learning	Ongoing Assessment
12-1	●	●	●		●	●	●	Written
12-2	●	●	●		●	●		Written
12-3	●	●	●		●	●		Quiz
12-4	●	●	●			●	●	Written
12-5	●	●	●		●	●		Oral
12-6	●	●	●		●	●		Quiz
12-7	●	●	●		●	●	●	Written
12-8	●		●		●	●		

In the Additional Resources...

	In the Teacher's Resource File							
Lesson	Lesson Masters	Teaching Aids*	Answer Masters	Technology Sourcebook	Assessment Sourcebook	Visual Aids**	Technology	Explorations Software
12-1	12-1	132, 135	12-1			132, 135, AM		
12-2	12-2	132, 136, 137, 138	12-2			132, 136, 137, 138, AM		12-2
12-3	12-3	132, 139	12-3	Calc 17	Quiz	132, 139, AM		12-3
In-class Activity			12-4					
12-4	12-4	133, 140	12-4			133, 140, AM		12-4
12-5	12-5	133, 141, 142	12-5			133, 141, 142, AM		
12-6	12-6	133, 143, 144	12-6		Quiz	133, 143, 144, AM		
12-7	12-7	134, 145	12-7			134, 145, AM		
12-8		134, 146	12-8			134, 146, AM		
End of chapter					Tests			

*Teaching Aids are pictured on pages 718C and 718D.

**Visual Aids provide transparencies for all Teaching Aids and all Answer Masters.

Also available is the Study Skills Handbook which includes study-skill tips related to reading, note-taking, and comprehension.

Integrating Strands and Applications

	12-1	12-2	12-3	12-4	12-5	12-6	12-7	12-8
Mathematical Connections								
Algebra	●	●	●				●	●
Geometry		●	●	●	●	●	●	●
Measurement	●	●	●	●	●	●		
Patterns and Functions			●		●	●	●	●
Interdisciplinary and Other Connections								
Science	●	●	●	●	●	●		
Social Studies		●	●	●			●	
Technology		●	●	●		●		
Career	●	●				●		
Consumer	●							●
Sports		●						

Teaching and Assessing the Chapter Objectives

Chapter 12 Objectives (Organized into the SPUR categories—Skills, Properties, Uses, and Representations)	**Lessons**	**Progress Self-Test Questions**	**Chapter Review Questions**	**In the Teacher's Resource File:** Chapter Test, Forms A and B	Chapter Test, Forms C	Chapter Test, Forms D
Skills						
A: Find the magnitude and direction of two-dimensional vectors.	12-1	1	1–4		1	X
B: Find sums, opposites, scalar products, and dot products of two-dimensional vectors.	12-2, 12-3, 12-4	2, 3, 4	5–16		1	X
C: Find sums, lengths, scalar products, dot products, and cross products of vectors in 3-space.	12-6	6, 7, 8	17–24		4, 5	
D: Find the measure of the angle between two vectors.	12-4, 12-6	5	25–27		1	X
Properties						
E: Prove or disprove generalizations about vector operations.	12-2, 12-3, 12-4, 12-6	11	28–32			
F: Identify parallel and orthogonal vectors.	12-3, 12-4, 12-6	12	33–38		3, 4	
Uses						
G: Use vectors in a plane to decompose motion or force into *x*- and *y*-components.	12-1	13	39–40		2	
H: Use addition of vectors in a plane to solve problems involving forces or velocities.	12-2	13	41–44		2	X
Representations						
I: Represent two-dimensional vectors in their component or polar representation, or as directed segments.	12-1, 12-3	10	45–48			X
J: Represent addition, subtraction, and scalar multiplication of two-dimensional vectors graphically.	12-2, 12-3	14, 15	49–50			X
K: Geometrically interpret three-dimensional vectors and their operations.	12-6	9	51–53		5	
L: Represent lines in a plane using vector or parametric equations.	12-3, 12-4	16	54–59		3	
M: Represent lines, planes, and spheres in 3-space using parametric, vector, or coordinate equations.	12-5, 12-7	17, 18	60–67		5	

Assessment Sourcebook
Quiz for Lessons 12-1 through 12-3
Quiz for Lessons 12-4 through 12-6
Chapter 12 Test, Forms A–D
Chapter 12 Test, Cumulative Form

TestWorks CD-ROM

TEACHING AID 132

Warm-up
Lesson 12-1

1. A point has rectangular coordinates (-4, -7). What are its polar coordinates?
2. A point has polar coordinates $\left[2, \frac{\pi}{5}\right]$. What are its rectangular coordinates?

Warm-up
Lesson 12-2

A plane is going due west at a ground speed of $G\ \frac{km}{hr}$. There is a wind of $W\ \frac{km}{hr}$. How fast $\left(\text{in } \frac{km}{hr}\right)$ is the plane traveling in the west direction if the wind is coming from the following directions?

1. east
2. north
3. west
4. south

Warm-up
Lesson 12-3

1. Using a calculator, graph the parametric equations $\begin{cases} x = 2 + 3t \\ y = 5 - t \end{cases}$
2. Give an x-y equation for the graph.

TEACHING AID 133

Warm-up
Lesson 12-4

Let * be an operation on ordered pairs of real numbers, defined as follows: $(a, b) * (c, d) = ac + bd$.

1. Is * commutative?
2. Is the set of ordered pairs of real numbers closed under *?
3. Is * associative?

Warm-up
Lesson 12-5

A trunk is one meter long, 45 centimeters wide, and 28 centimeters high in its internal dimensions. To the nearest centimeter, what is the length of the longest inflexible thin rod that can fit inside this trunk?

Warm-up
Lesson 12-6

Find the area of the parallelogram with consecutive vertices (2, 10), (0, 0), and (4, 1).

TEACHING AID 134

Warm-up
Lesson 12-7

Refer to the diagram.

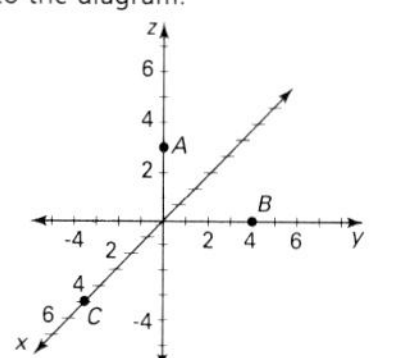

1. What are the coordinates of points A, B, and C?
2. How many lines contain points A and B? Points A and C? Points B and C?
3. How many planes contain points A, B, and C?

Warm-up
Lesson 12-8

Moe, Curly, and Shemp Howard were brothers and played the roles of the stooges in the "Three Stooges" movies. Curly was born 6 years after Moe and 8 years after Shemp. The sum of their years of birth was 5695. To find the years of their births, write a system of three linear equations and solve it.

TEACHING AID
Lesson

Definitions and Basic Theorems About Vectors

Definition
A **vector** is a quantity that can be characterized by its direction and its magnitude.

Definition
The **polar representation** of a two-dimensional vector $\vec{v}$ with non-negative **magnitude** r and **direction** θ measured from the polar axis is $[r, \theta]$.

Definition
The **component representation** of a plane vector $\vec{u}$ is the ordered pair (u_1, u_2), the rectangular coordinates of the point at the top of the standard position arrow for u. The numbers u_1 and u_2 are the ***x*-component** and ***y*-component** of u, respectively, or the **horizontal** and **vertical components** of u.

Theorem
If $\vec{u} = (u_1, u_2)$, then $|\vec{u}| = \sqrt{u_1^2 + u_2^2}$.

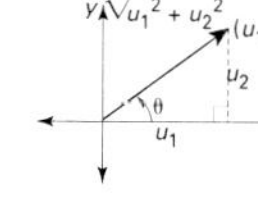

Theorem
For all plane vectors $\vec{u}$ with direction θ,
$[|\vec{u}|, \theta] = (|\vec{u}|\cos\theta, |\vec{u}|\sin\theta)$.

TEACHING AID 136
Lesson 12-2

Example and Definition of Vector Addition

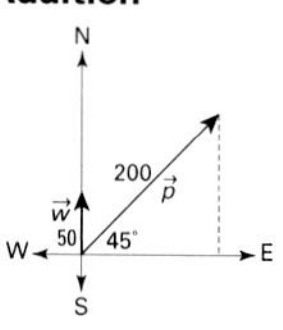

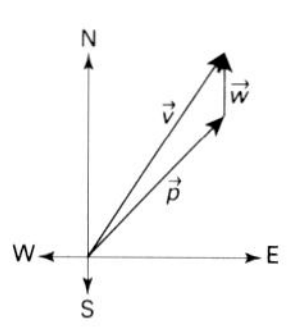

Definition
If $\vec{u} = (u_1, u_2)$ and $\vec{v} = (v_1, v_2)$, then the **sum of $\vec{u}$ and $\vec{v}$** written $\vec{u} + \vec{v}$, is the vector $(u_1 + v_1, u_2 + v_2)$.

TEACHING AID 137
Lesson 12-2

Example 1

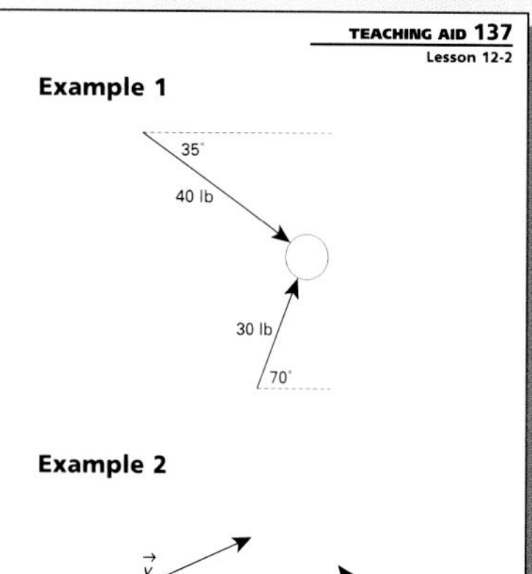

Example 2

$\vec{v}$ $\vec{w}$

TEACHING AID 138
Lesson 12-2

Questions 4, 6, and 15

4.

30 lb $\vec{f}$ y 125° -10° x $\vec{g}$ 90 lb

6.

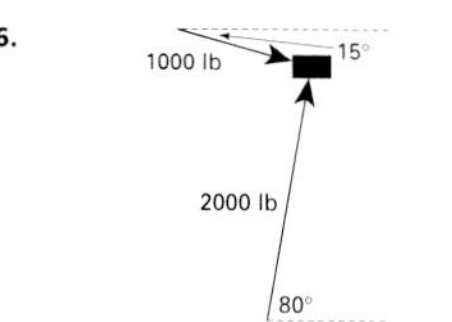

15.

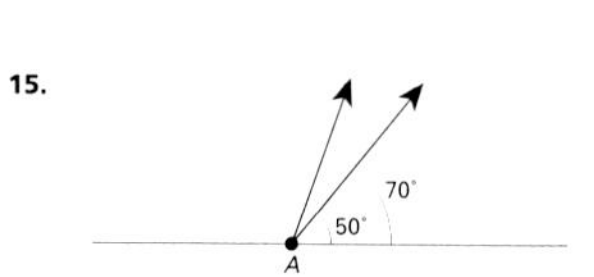

TEACHING AID 1
Lesson

Vector and Parametric Equations for Lines

Theorem
A point $Q = (x, y)$ is on the line through $P = (x_0, y_0)$ parallel to the vector $\vec{v} = (v_1, v_2)$ if and only if there is a real number t with $\overrightarrow{PQ} = t\vec{v}$, or $(x - x_0, y - y_0) = t(v_1, v_2)$.

Theorem
The line through (x_0, y_0) that is parallel to the vector $\vec{v} = (v_1, v_2)$ has parametric equations

$$\begin{cases} x = x_0 + tv_1 \\ y = y_0 + tv_2, \end{cases}$$

where t may be any real number.

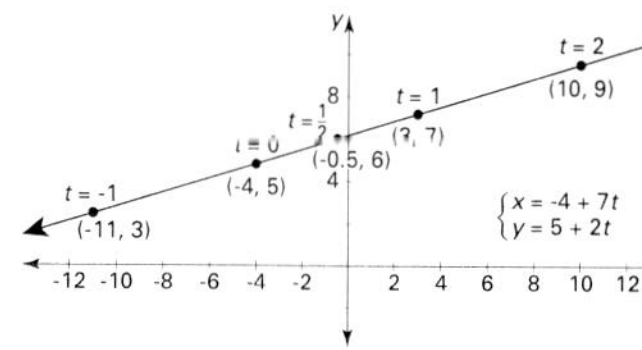

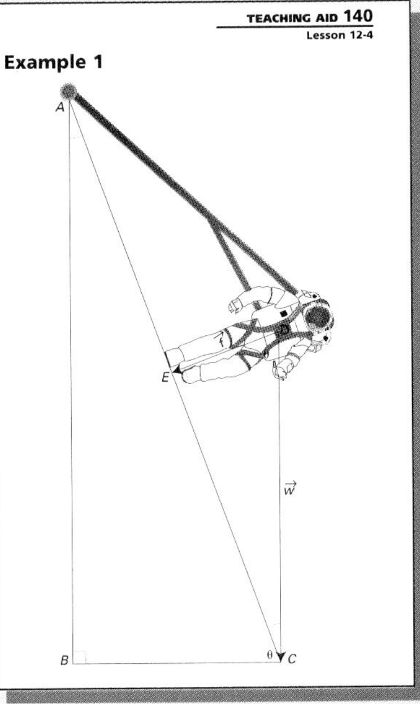

TEACHING AID 140
Lesson 12-4
Example 1
A
E
$\vec{f}$
$\vec{w}$
B
θ
C

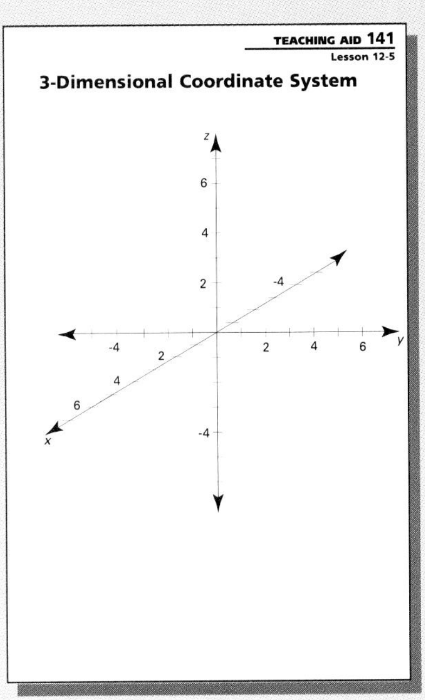

TEACHING AID 141
Lesson 12-5
3-Dimensional Coordinate System
z
6
4
2
-4
-4
2
4
6
y
2
4
6
x
-4

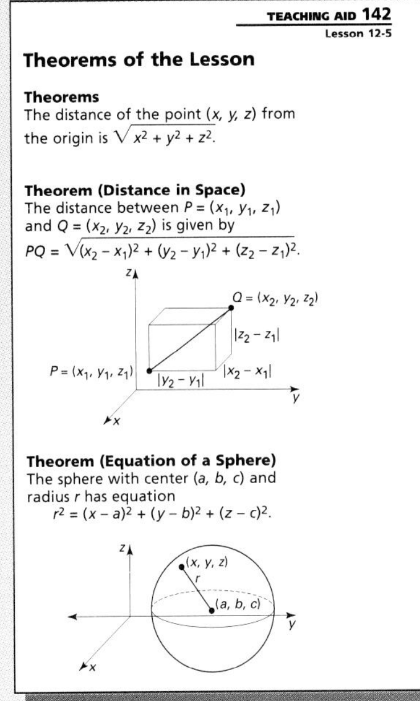

TEACHING AID 142
Lesson 12-5
Theorems of the Lesson
Theorems
The distance of the point (x, y, z) from the origin is $\sqrt{x^2 + y^2 + z^2}$.
Theorem (Distance in Space)
The distance between $P = (x_1, y_1, z_1)$ and $Q = (x_2, y_2, z_2)$ is given by
$PQ = \sqrt{(x_2 - x_1)^2 + (y_2 - y_1)^2 + (z_2 - z_1)^2}$.
z
$Q = (x_2, y_2, z_2)$
$|z_2 - z_1|$
$P = (x_1, y_1, z_1)$
$|y_2 - y_1|$
$|x_2 - x_1|$
y
x
Theorem (Equation of a Sphere)
The sphere with center (a, b, c) and radius r has equation
$r^2 = (x - a)^2 + (y - b)^2 + (z - c)^2$.
z
(x, y, z)
r
(a, b, c)
y
x

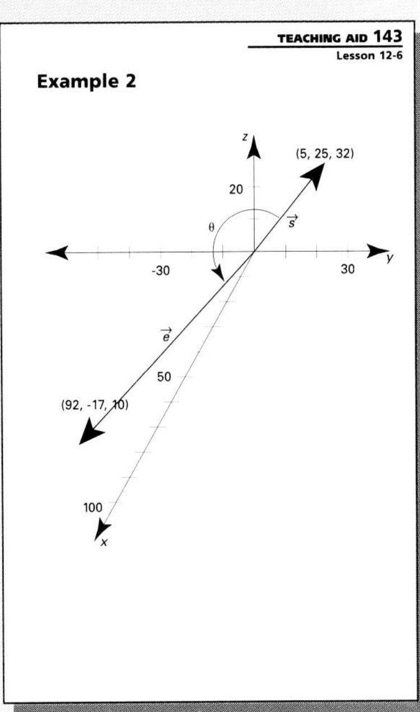

TEACHING AID 143
Lesson 12-6
Example 2
z
(5, 25, 32)
20
θ
$\vec{s}$
-30
30
y
$\vec{e}$
50
(92, -17, 10)
100
x

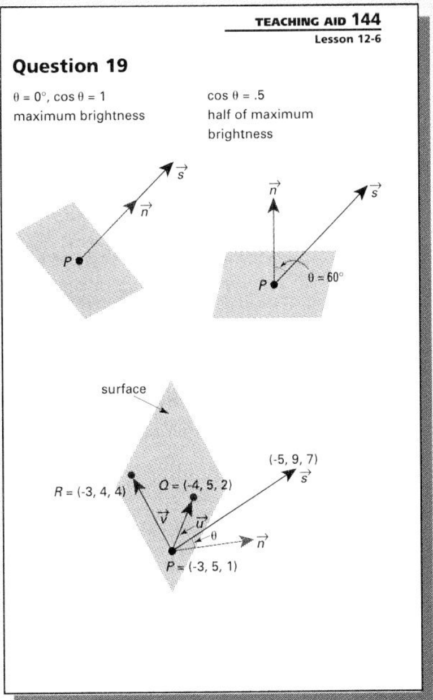

TEACHING AID 144
Lesson 12-6
Question 19
θ = 0°, cos θ = 1
maximum brightness
cos θ = .5
half of maximum brightness
$\vec{s}$
$\vec{n}$
P
$\vec{n}$
$\vec{s}$
P
θ = 60°
surface
(-5, 9, 7)
$\vec{s}$
R = (-3, 4, 4)
Q = (-4, 5, 2)
$\vec{v}$
$\vec{u}$
θ
$\vec{n}$
P = (-3, 5, 1)

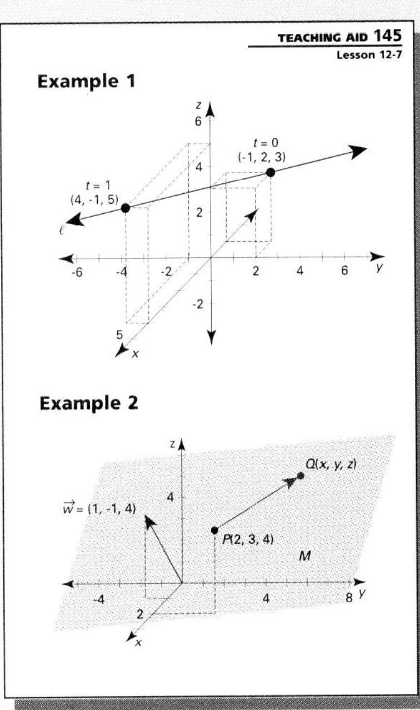

TEACHING AID 145
Lesson 12-7
Example 1
z
6
t = 0
(-1, 2, 3)
t = 1
(4, -1, 5)
4
2
ℓ
-6
-4
-2
2
4
6
y
-2
5
x
Example 2
z
Q(x, y, z)
$\vec{w}$ = (1, -1, 4)
4
P(2, 3, 4)
M
-4
4
8
y
2
x

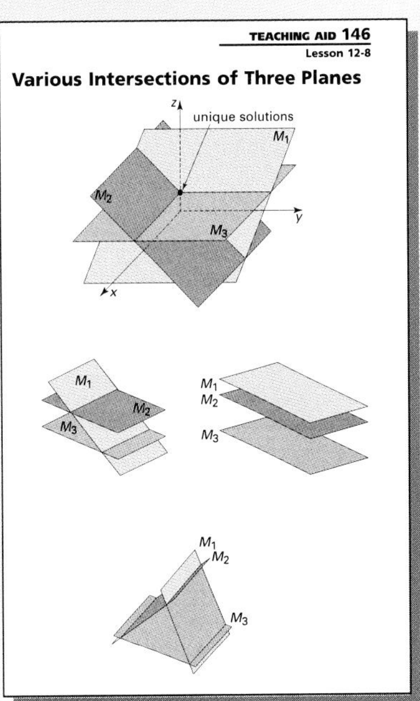

TEACHING AID 146
Lesson 12-8
Various Intersections of Three Planes
z
unique solutions
M_1
M_2
y
M_3
x
M_1
M_2
M_3
M_1
M_2
M_3
M_1
M_2
M_3

Chapter Opener

Pacing

All lessons in this chapter are designed to be covered in one day. At the end of the chapter, you should plan to spend 1 day to review the Progress Self-Test, 1–2 days for the Chapter Review, and 1 day for a test. You may wish to spend a day on projects, and possibly a day is needed for quizzes and the In-class Activity. This chapter should therefore take 11–14 days. Spending more than 15 days on this chapter is not recommended.

Using Pages 718–719

Another name for ordered pair is *2-tuple*; another name for ordered triple is *3-tuple.* All of the ideas here can be extended to *n-tuples*, that is, strings with *n* objects. You might ask students if they can see how. [Sample: There are 4-dimensional coordinate systems (though they are difficult to picture); points can be located with time as the 4th dimension; a sports meet might have 4 teams; there can be an extended ratio for sides in a quadrilateral; there can be a 1×4 matrix; and an identification number might have four parts.]

Some of your students may be taking or have taken physics. If so, by this time of the year they should have encountered vectors. Find out how many have; they very likely will be able to help you in explaining some of the ideas in this chapter to others in the class.

CHAPTER 12

Chapter 12 Overview

Three fundamental uses of vectors are found in this chapter. First, vectors describe forces and motion in the physical world. Second, vectors provide a means for lines and planes to be described algebraically in a way that is consistent regardless of the dimension of space. Third, vectors are a useful tool for solving systems. The first two are studied here in some detail; the last, which is the subject of linear algebra courses, is only briefly introduced in the last lesson of the chapter. Vectors as elements of vector spaces, a fourth important role for these objects, are not mentioned.

The chapter begins by considering vectors in two dimensions. Lesson 12-1 introduces these vectors as quantities that have both magnitude and direction and gives their polar and component (rectangular coordinate) representations. Lesson 12-2 introduces vector addition and subtraction by means of physical problems involving combinations of forces and motions. In Lesson 12-3, vectors lead to new ways to describe lines in a plane: vector equations and parametric equations. The dot product of two vectors is introduced in Lesson 12-4. It gives us an easy way to calculate the angle between two vectors and to deal with perpendicularity.

Vectors

An ordered pair (x, y) may stand for many different things. Here are some examples.

(4, -5)	location on the coordinate plane
(36°N, 112°W)	point in the Grand Canyon on the surface of Earth
(a, b)	the complex number $a + bi$
95–86	score in a basketball game
2:3	the ratio of 2 to 3
[17.6 8.8]	1 × 2 matrix
123–456789	identification number

Since two numbers are involved, ordered pairs are generally thought of as representing two-dimensional ideas. All but the complex number example can be extended to three dimensions using *ordered triples* (x, y, z).

(10, 0, -19.2)	location on a three-dimensional coordinate system
(48°50′N, 2°20′E, 100 m)	a point in Paris, France, 100 meters above the ground
(32, 28, 12)	scores in a wrestling meet with three teams
$1:1:\sqrt{2}$	extended ratio of sides in an isosceles right triangle
[6.7 -2.9 8.0]	1 × 3 matrix
312-555-5555	telephone number

You can extend these ideas to involve still more numbers.

In this chapter, you will encounter *vectors*, which involve yet another use of ordered pairs and triples, and you will learn certain operations on them. Historically, the primary application of vectors has been to represent physical forces, and the operation called addition of vectors corresponds to the combining of forces. In recent years, many applications for vectors have been found in business; information is often conveniently stored in ordered pairs, triples, and longer sequences of numbers. Vectors also have applications to geometry. They provide a very nice way to describe lines and planes in both two and three dimensions. In fact, they provide a way to think about lines and planes in higher dimensions, but that is beyond the scope of this course.

Photo Connections

This photo collage makes real-world connections to the content of the chapter: vectors.

Airplane: The speed and direction of an airplane can be represented by a vector.

Boat: Vectors are used to solve problems involving a boat traveling through moving water. One such problem appears on page 730.

Volleyball: When a volleyball is hit by two people at the same time, the resulting force on the ball can be shown by a vector. **Example 1** on page 728 illustrates such a situation.

Tree in Wind: Weather forecasters often mention both the speed and direction of wind. This is another example of vectors that occur in everyday situations.

Satellite Dishes: Satellites are often launched into space so they will remain at a fixed position. Reception dishes on the ground can then be aimed directly at the satellite. Three numbers determine the position of the satellite: latitude, longitude, and height above the earth. Three-dimensional coordinates are discussed in Lesson 12-5.

Chapter 12 Projects

At this time, you might want to have students look over the projects on pages 773–774.

One powerful aspect of vectors is that they can be extended from two to three (and higher) dimensions; the extension to three dimensions occupies the rest of the chapter. Lesson 12-5 prepares the way by discussing coordinates of points and the distance between points in 3-space. In Lesson 12-6 the basic properties of vectors are extended to three dimensions, and the new operation of cross-product is introduced to find a vector that is perpendicular to two others. This enables the use of vectors in Lesson 12-7 to deduce equations for lines and planes in space. Lesson 12-8 looks back at a familiar topic, systems of linear equations, and uses the understanding gained in this chapter to connect the algebra of linear systems with three variables and the geometry of planes in space.

Lesson 12-1

Objectives

A Find the magnitude and direction of two-dimensional vectors.

G Use vectors in a plane to decompose motion or force into x- and y-components.

I Represent two-dimensional vectors in their component or polar representation, or as directed segments.

Resources

From the ***Teacher's Resource File***

- Lesson Master 12-1
- Answer Master 12-1
- Teaching Aids
  - 132 Warm-up
  - 135 Definitions and Basic Theorems About Vectors

Additional Resources

- Visuals for Teaching Aids 132, 135

Teaching Lesson 12-1

Warm-up

1. A point has rectangular coordinates (-4, -7). What are its polar coordinates?
   $\left[\sqrt{65}, \tan^{-1}\frac{7}{4} + \pi\right] \approx [8.06, 4.19]$
2. A point has polar coordinates $\left[2, \frac{\pi}{5}\right]$. What are its rectangular coordinates?
   $\left(2\cos\frac{\pi}{5}, 2\sin\frac{\pi}{5}\right) \approx (1.618, 1.176)$

These exercises give practice in the skills needed to convert back and forth between polar and component form of vectors.

LESSON

12-1 Vectors in a Plane

Full Speed Ahead. *The direction in which a sailboat moves is mainly a result of the force of the wind and the force of the water against the rudder.*

What Is a Vector?

Many quantities can be described by specifying a *direction* and a *magnitude*. For instance, when a weather forecaster says, "The winds are from the southwest at 15 miles per hour," the forecaster is describing the velocity of the winds by giving their direction ("from the southwest") and their magnitude ("15 miles per hour"). You could represent this quantity by drawing an arrow 15 units long pointing in a northeasterly direction relative to given compass headings. This arrow does not represent a ray; its length is finite.

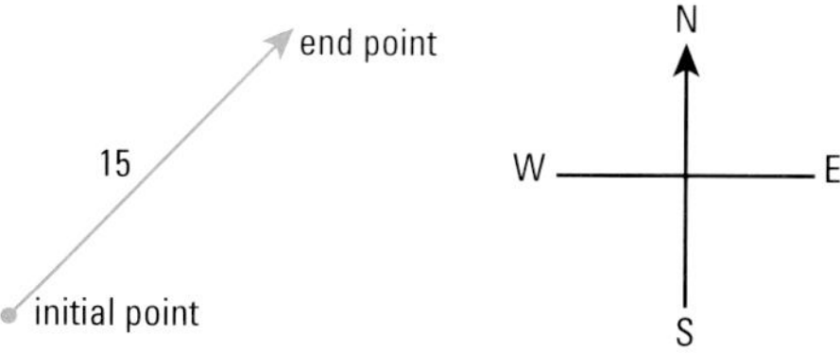

❶ Notice that the arrow can begin at any point. The starting position of the arrow (its *initial point*) does not matter; any other arrow with the same magnitude (its *length*) and direction represents the same wind velocity. Velocity is an example of a vector quantity.

> **Definition**
> A **vector** is a quantity that can be characterized by its direction and its magnitude.

Vectors are named by single letters, with arrows above them, as in $\vec{u}$ and $\vec{v}$, or with boldface, as in $\boldsymbol{u}$ and $\boldsymbol{v}$.

Lesson 12-1 Overview

Broad Goals This lesson covers the meaning of vector (a quantity with magnitude and direction) and the description of vectors by arrows, by coordinates (polar or rectangular), and with letters.

Perspective A vector is normally pictured by an arrow whose direction indicates the direction of the vector and whose length indicates the magnitude of the vector. Symbolically, a vector may be described in many ways: (1) by a boldface letter $\boldsymbol{v}$ or by a letter with an arrow above it, such as $\vec{v}$; (2) by indicating its initial point P and endpoint Q, perhaps with the symbol $\overrightarrow{PQ}$; or (3) by indicating its endpoint if the initial point is taken as the origin (the standard position of the vector). Each of these types of descriptions can be used for vectors in the plane or in space, but description (3) will have two coordinates if the vector is a plane vector, and three coordinates if the vector is in 3-space.

The arrow picture for vectors begins this lesson. Quickly we look for a symbolic description. The natural first description is with polar coordinates, since they involve magnitude and direction just as a vector does. The translation into rectangular coordinates gives a vector in terms of its horizontal (x-) and vertical (y-) components.

Polar Representation of Plane Vectors

If all the vectors under consideration lie in a single plane, then the vectors are called **plane vectors** or **two-dimensional vectors**. Descriptions of plane vectors can take several forms. The arrow describing wind velocity given on page 720 can also be represented by the ordered pair [15, 45°]. The ordered pair [magnitude, direction] is called the *polar representation* of a vector.

Definition
The **polar representation** of a two-dimensional vector $\vec{v}$ with non-negative **magnitude** r and **direction** θ measured from the polar axis is $[r, \theta]$.

The arrow for $\vec{v}$ that joins the pole to the point $[r, \theta]$ is in **standard position**. Any arrow in the plane which is parallel to, in the same direction as, and the same length as the arrow in standard position is also a geometric representation of $\vec{v}$.

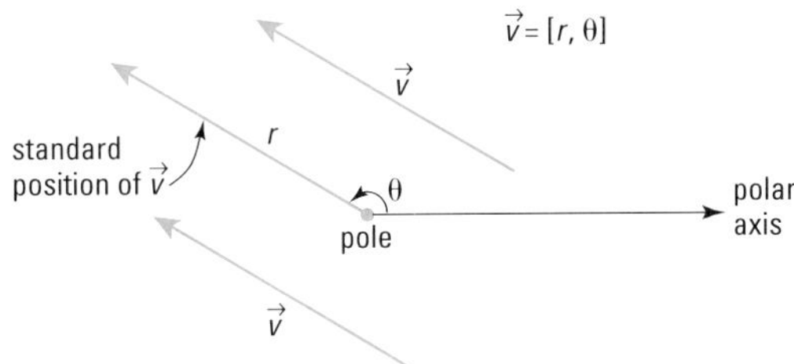

The Component Representation of a Plane Vector

Trigonometry can be used to change the polar representation of a vector into a rectangular coordinate representation.

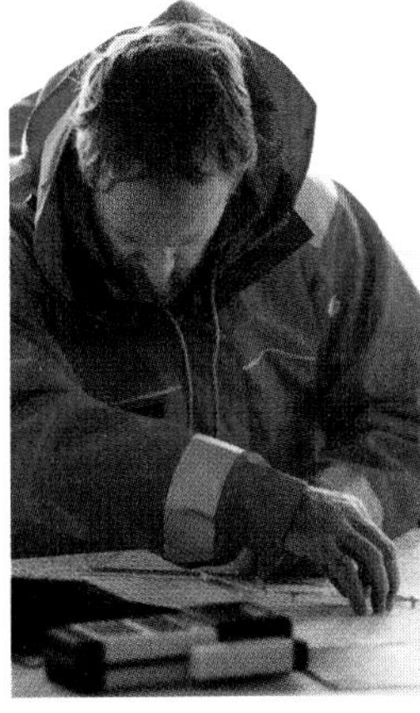
Sailors use nautical charts to determine their position and course.

Example 1

A ship's velocity is represented by [12, 82°], where the first component is measured in miles per hour and the second is the number of degrees north of east that the ship travels.

a. Draw the arrow in standard position representing the velocity.
b. Describe the ship's movement each hour in terms of a number of miles east and a number of miles north.

Solution

a.

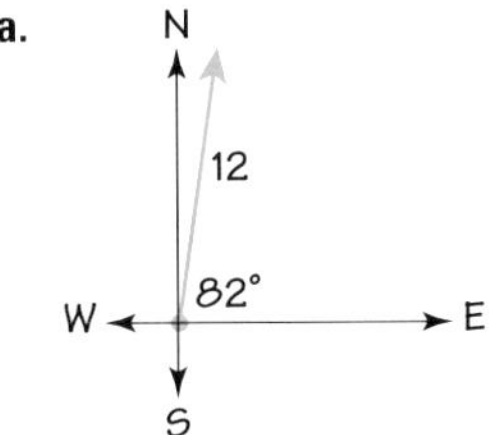

Notes on Reading

Perhaps the hardest notion to get across when teaching vectors is that there is this *one* object that has *both* magnitude and direction. Students want to constantly think that two objects are needed, and the fact that two coordinates are used for describing plane vectors does not help. To overcome this difficulty, use arrows for pictures and single letters to represent vectors when you can; do not always use the coordinate representations.

❶ We begin by using vectors to describe velocity. It is important to point out to students who have not had physics that, although in common English usage, "velocity" and "speed" are synonyms, to physical scientists and in any discussion of vectors, they do not mean the same thing. Speed is merely the magnitude of velocity; velocity includes direction as well. So, when you say you are traveling at 50 mph, you are giving a speed, but when you say you are traveling north at 50 mph, you are giving a velocity.

Much of the work in this lesson centers on the two coordinate representations for vectors: *polar form* and *component form*. As we did for polar coordinates, we use square brackets in polar representations and parentheses for component form. This helps students to differentiate the two forms and stop to think about which one they are using. However, students may see some books where vectors in component form are represented with brackets. Remind students that a sentence like $[6, 45°] = (3\sqrt{2}, 2\sqrt{2})$ does not mean that the corresponding listings are equal, but that the vectors are. Note that with vectors (as with complex numbers), in $[r, \theta]$, r is nonnegative, whereas with polar coordinates r can be negative.

Finding the length of a vector is easy in polar coordinates and done with the Pythagorean Theorem in rectangular coordinates.

Although no binary operations on vectors are done in this lesson, their use to describe forces runs throughout.

Optional Activities

Have students give the polar and component representations of the vectors in **Questions 1–3.** Have them write a sentence to describe each representation.

[**1.** [180, 170°]; (-177.27, 31.26); the plane is flying 180 mph at a 170° angle counterclockwise from east; the plane has velocity components of 177.27 mph west and 31.26 mph north.
2. [150, 90°]; (0, 150); the force of 150 newtons is exerted at a 90° angle to the ground; 0 newtons of force are exerted horizontally and 150 newtons of force are exerted vertically.
3. [6.71, 296.57°]; (3, -6); the graph is translated 6.71 units from its original position at an angle of 296.57°; the graph is translated 3 units to the right and 6 units down on the coordinate plane.]

b. Draw a right triangle whose hypotenuse is the arrow and whose legs are parallel to the axes, as shown at the right.

Use the definitions of sine and cosine.

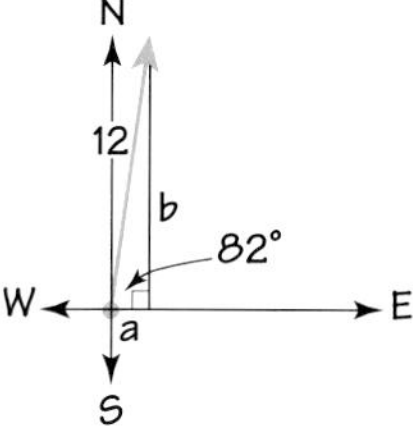

$\frac{a}{12} = \cos 82°$ $\qquad$ $\frac{b}{12} = \sin 82°$

$a = 12 \cos 82° \approx 1.67$ $\qquad$ $b = 12 \sin 82° \approx 11.88$

Each hour the ship's new position is approximately 1.67 miles east and 11.88 miles north of its old position.

In Example 1, the ordered pair $(12 \cos 82°, 12 \sin 82°) \approx (1.67, 11.88)$ describes the ship's motion. It also gives the rectangular coordinates of the endpoint of the arrow in standard position. This ordered pair is the *component representation* of the vector of Example 1.

> **Definitions**
> The **component representation** of a plane vector $\vec{u}$ is the ordered pair (u_1, u_2), the rectangular coordinates of the point at the tip of the standard position arrow for $\vec{u}$. The numbers u_1 and u_2 are the ***x*-component** and ***y*-component** of $\vec{u}$, respectively, or the **horizontal** and **vertical components** of $\vec{u}$.

Example 2

The arrow from (-1, 2) to (3, 5) represents a plane vector $\vec{v}$.

a. Find the length and direction of $\vec{v}$.

b. Draw the standard position arrow for $\vec{v}$.

Solution

a. Using the diagram at the right and the Pythagorean Theorem, the length of $\vec{v}$ is $\sqrt{3^2 + 4^2} = 5$. The direction of $\vec{v}$ is given by the angle θ between the positive x-axis and the vector. From the diagram, $\tan \theta = \frac{3}{4}$, and so $\theta = \tan^{-1}(0.75) \approx 36.9°$.

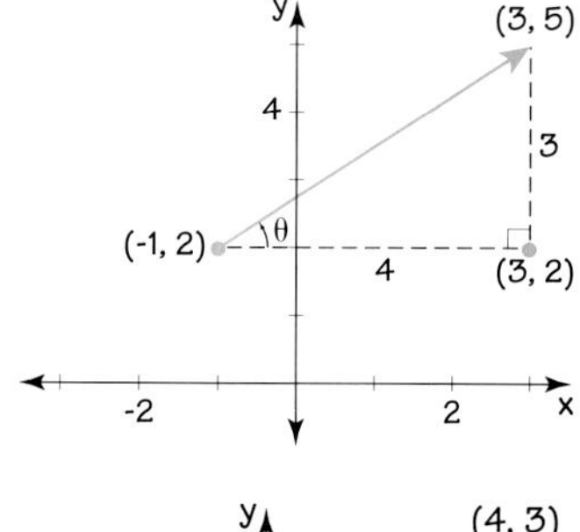

b. The translation from (-1, 2) to (3, 5) is a translation of 4 units horizontally and 3 units vertically. Thus, the standard position for $\vec{v}$ is drawn from the origin to the point (4, 3).

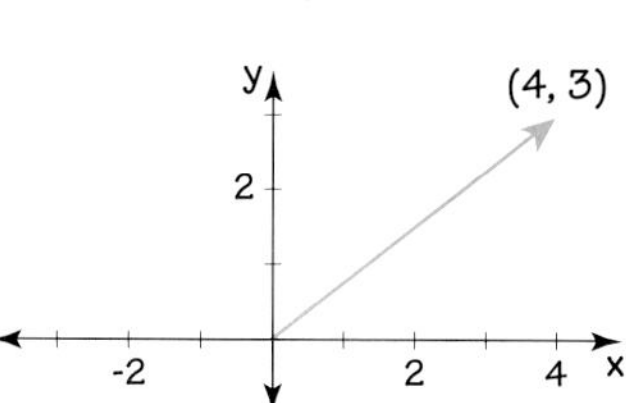

Because of their work with polar coordinates, students should find it easy to change between these two representations of vectors.

❷ The diagram explaining the formula for $|\vec{u}|$ is important. (**Teaching Aid 135** contains this diagram and the definitions and theorems of the lesson.) When students see it they should think of several ways that the legs of the right triangle are used: in applying the Pythagorean Theorem to find the length of $\vec{u}$, in determining the tangent of the direction angle of $\vec{u}$ and thus finding the size of the angle, and in determining the slope of the line containing the vector, an idea applied in Lesson 12-3. Students should realize that a similar drawing can be made for vectors that are not in standard position.

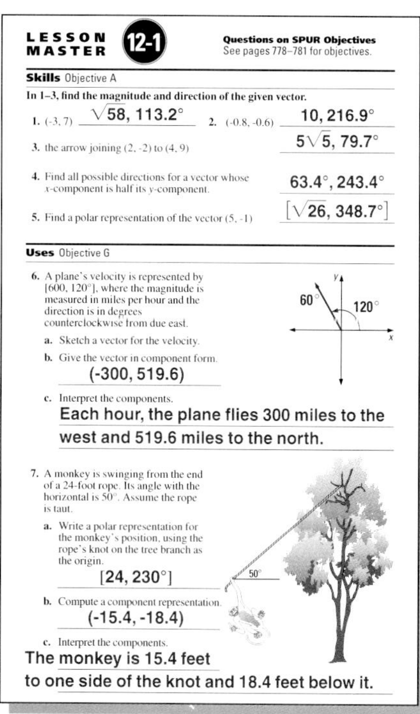

LESSON MASTER 12-1

Questions on SPUR Objectives
See pages 778–781 for objectives.

Skills Objective A

In 1–3, find the magnitude and direction of the given vector.

1. (-3, 7) $\sqrt{58}$, 113.2°
2. (-0.8, -0.6) 10, 216.9°
3. the arrow joining (2, -2) to (4, 9) $5\sqrt{5}$, 79.7°
4. Find all possible directions for a vector whose x-component is half its y-component. 63.4°, 243.4°
5. Find a polar representation of the vector (5, -1) $[\sqrt{26}, 348.7°]$

Uses Objective G

6. A plane's velocity is represented by [600, 120°], where the magnitude is measured in miles per hour and the direction is in degrees counterclockwise from due east.
   a. Sketch a vector for the velocity.
   b. Give the vector in component form. (-300, 519.6)
   c. Interpret the components. Each hour, the plane flies 300 miles to the west and 519.6 miles to the north.

7. A monkey is swinging from the end of a 24-foot rope. Its angle with the horizontal is 50°. Assume the rope is taut.
   a. Write a polar representation for the monkey's position, using the rope's knot on the tree branch as the origin. [24, 230°]
   b. Compute a component representation. (-15.4, -18.4)
   c. Interpret the components. The monkey is 15.4 feet to one side of the knot and 18.4 feet below it.

Adapting to Individual Needs

Extra Help

As you discuss the two theorems in the lesson, point out their connection to polar-rectangular conversions. For the vector $\vec{u}$, in standard position, $|\vec{u}| = r$, $u_1 = x$, and $u_2 = y$. So the familiar formula $r = \sqrt{x^2 + y^2}$ becomes $|\vec{u}| = \sqrt{u_1^2 + u_2^2}$, and $[r, \theta] = (r \cos \theta, r \sin \theta)$ becomes $[|\vec{u}|, \theta] = (|\vec{u}| \cos \theta, |\vec{u}| \sin \theta)$.

The vector quantity in Example 2 can be described by the arrow, by the ordered pair (4, 3), or by the polar representation $[5, \tan^{-1} 0.75]$, which is about [5, 36.9°].

Notice that in Example 2, $(4, 3) = (3 - (-1), 5 - 2)$. In general, if $\vec{u} = (u_1, u_2)$ is the vector from (a, b) to (c, d), then $(u_1, u_2) = (c - a, d - b)$. That is, the horizontal component of $\vec{u}$ is $c - a$, and the vertical component of $\vec{u}$ is $d - b$.

Example 3

A vector $\vec{u}$ represents a force of 5 pounds that is being exerted at an angle of $\frac{5\pi}{6}$ with the positive x-axis. Find the x- and y-components of $\vec{u}$.

Solution

The arrow in standard position for $\vec{u}$ is shown in the diagram below. The coordinates (u_1, u_2) of the tip of this arrow are found as follows:

$$u_1 = 5 \cos \frac{5\pi}{6} = 5 \cdot \left(-\frac{\sqrt{3}}{2}\right) = -\frac{5\sqrt{3}}{2},$$

and

$$u_2 = 5 \sin \frac{5\pi}{6} = 5 \cdot \left(\frac{1}{2}\right) = \frac{5}{2}.$$

Consequently, $\left(-\frac{5\sqrt{3}}{2}, \frac{5}{2}\right)$ is the component representation of $\vec{u}$. The x-component of $\vec{u}$ is $-\frac{5\sqrt{3}}{2}$ and the y-component of $\vec{u}$ is $\frac{5}{2}$.

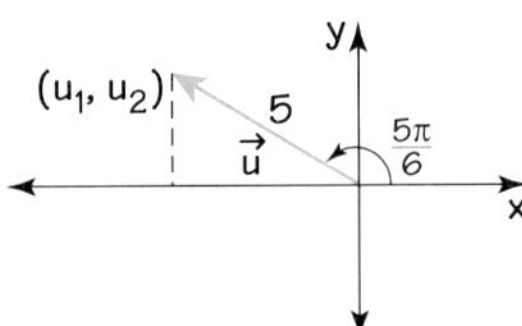

This means that $-\frac{5}{2}\sqrt{3}$ or about 4.33 lb of force is being exerted to the left and 2.5 lb of force is being exerted up by the 5 lb of force exerted at the $\frac{5\pi}{6}$ angle.

❷ The Norm of a Vector

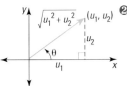

If $\vec{u}$ is a vector, then the symbol $|\vec{u}|$ denotes the length of $\vec{u}$. ($|\vec{u}|$ is sometimes called the **norm** of $\vec{u}$.) The length of a plane vector $\vec{u}$ is the first coordinate of its polar representation. The length can be easily determined from the vector's component representation, using the Pythagorean Theorem.

Theorem

If $\vec{u} = (u_1, u_2)$, then

$$|\vec{u}| = \sqrt{u_1^2 + u_2^2}.$$

Additional Examples

1. An airplane is flying at a constant altitude, at 600 km/hr in a direction 27° W of N. Express the airplane's velocity in each of the following ways.
   a. with an arrow

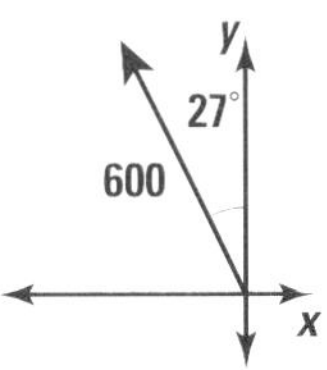

   b. as a vector in polar coordinates **[600, 117°]**
   c. as a vector in rectangular coordinates **(600 cos 117°, 600 sin 117°) ≈ (-272, 535)**
2. The arrow from (13, 6) to (-27, 42) represents a plane vector $\vec{v}$.
   a. Find the length of $\vec{v}$. **$\sqrt{2896} \approx 53.8$**
   b. What is the endpoint of the standard position arrow for $\vec{v}$? **(-40, 36)**
   c. Find the direction of $\vec{v}$. **≈ 138°**

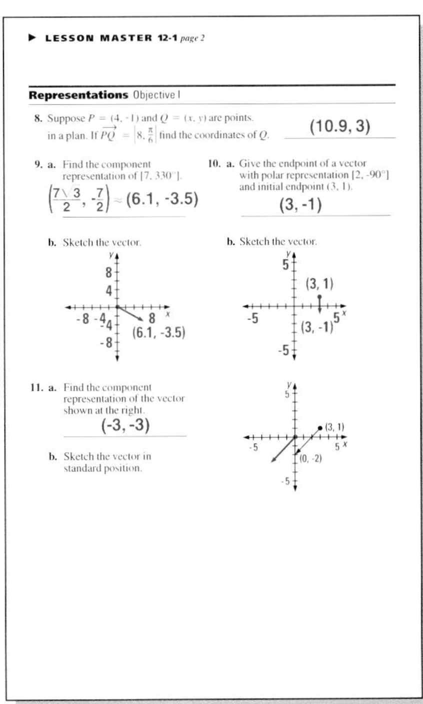

▶ LESSON MASTER 12-1 *page 2*

Representations Objective I

8. Suppose $P = (4, -1)$ and $Q = (x, y)$ are points in a plan. If $\overrightarrow{PQ} = \left[8, \frac{\pi}{6}\right]$ find the coordinates of Q. **(10.9, 3)**

9. a. Find the component representation of [7, 330°]. $\left(\frac{7\sqrt{3}}{2}, -\frac{7}{2}\right) \approx (6.1, -3.5)$
   b. Sketch the vector.

10. a. Give the endpoint of a vector with polar representation [2, -90°] and initial endpoint (3, 1). **(3, -1)**
   b. Sketch the vector.

11. a. Find the component representation of the vector shown at the right. **(-3, -3)**
   b. Sketch the vector in standard position.

Adapting to Individual Needs

Challenge

Have students answer the following.

1. The terminal point of each vector below is rotated 47° counterclockwise. Give the component representation (to the nearest thousandth) of the resulting vector.
   a. $\vec{v} = (3, 9)$ [(-4.536, 8.332)]
   b. $\vec{u} = (-2, 5)$ [(-5.021, 1.947)]
   c. $\vec{w} = (-3, -7)$ [(3.073, -6.968)]
2. Show that $\vec{u} = (\sin\theta, \cos\theta)$ is a unit vector, for any θ. $\left[|\vec{u}| = \sqrt{\sin^2\theta + \cos^2\theta} = 1\right]$
3. Let $\vec{u} = (a, b)$ be any nonzero vector. Give the component representation of the unit vector in the direction of $\vec{u}$. $\left[\left(\frac{a}{|\vec{u}|}, \frac{b}{|\vec{u}|}\right)\right]$

Notes on Questions

Question 3 Mathematically, vectors are very much like translations; addition of vectors is isomorphic to composition of translations.

Question 4 Stress that students should be able to take any vector given as an arrow, in polar form, or in component form, and put it in the other two forms.

Question 12 All unit vectors have the form (cos θ, sin θ).

Questions 13–14 Pictures help to explain why there are two answers.

Question 15 This question previews the idea of a scalar multiple of a vector, covered in Lesson 12-3.

Question 21 Error Alert Be sure students find all three possibilities.

Graphing the sum of two vectors, to be discussed in the next lesson, involves finding the fourth vertex of a parallelogram. In particular, the sum of the vectors (2, 7) and (-3, 6) is (-1, 13). You could use this question to introduce the next lesson.

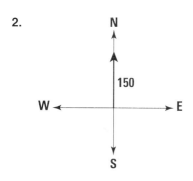

The following relationship between the polar and component representations of a vector generalizes Examples 1 and 3.

> **Theorem**
> For all plane vectors $\vec{u}$ with direction θ,
> $$[|\vec{u}|, \theta] = (|\vec{u}| \cos \theta, |\vec{u}| \sin \theta).$$

The point (0, 0) in the plane corresponds to the **zero vector** $\vec{0}$. The zero vector has length zero, and it can have any direction.

pilot's map

QUESTIONS

Covering the Reading

In 1–3, draw an arrow to represent each vector. **See margin.**

1. the velocity of a plane flying at a speed of 180 miles per hour in the direction 10° north of west

2. a force upward of 150 newtons

3. the translation of the graph of a relation 3 units horizontally and -6 units vertically

4. A car is driving east-southeast (22.5° south of east) at a speed of 55 miles per hour. Give the indicated representation of this velocity.
   a. polar **[55, -22.5°]** **b.** component
   b) (55 cos (-22.5°), 55 sin (-22.5°)) ≈ (50.8, -21.0)

5. Give the component representation of a vector with length 1 and direction 218° from the polar axis. **(cos 218°, sin 218°) ≈ (-0.788, -0.616)**

6. **a.** Give the component representation of the vector shown at the left.
   b. Sketch the vector in standard position. **See margin.**
   a) (5, -6)

7. **a.** Find the length and direction of the plane vector represented by the arrow joining the point (3, 4) to (7, -1). **See below left.**
   b. Sketch the standard position vector. **See margin.**

7a) length = $\sqrt{41}$, direction ≈ 308.7°

8. Find $|\vec{v}|$ when $\vec{v}$ = (-6, 11). **$\sqrt{157}$ ≈ 12.5 units**

9. Sketch the vector described by (8 cos 10°, 8 sin 10°). **See margin.**

10. Give the polar representation of the vector (-16, 19).
    $\left[\sqrt{617}, \tan^{-1}\left(-\frac{19}{16}\right)\right] \approx$ [24.8, 130°]

Applying the Mathematics

11. Prove that the arrow joining (-1, 2) to (4, -1) represents the same vector as the arrow joining (3, -2) to (8, -5). **See margin.**

12. A **unit vector** is a vector whose length is 1. Give the components of the unit vector with the same direction as the vector of Example 1.
    (cos 82°, sin 82°) ≈ (0.139, 0.990)

Additional Answers

1.

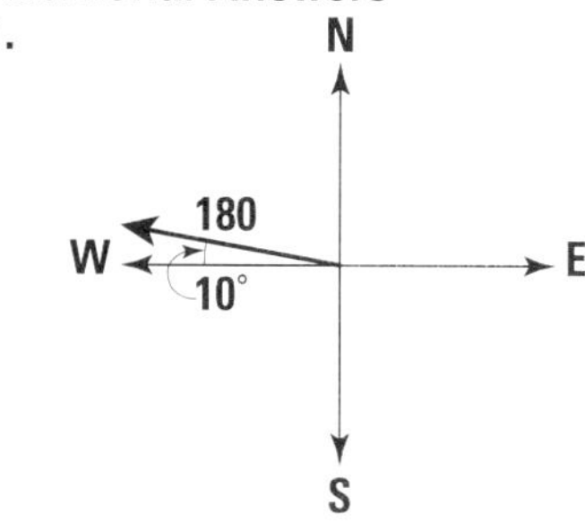

2.

3.

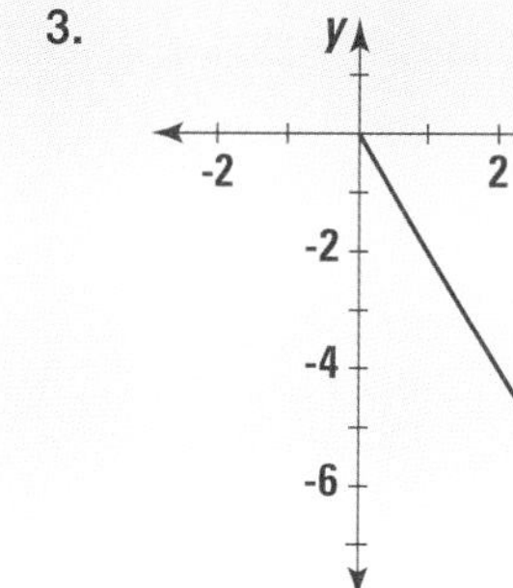

6. b.

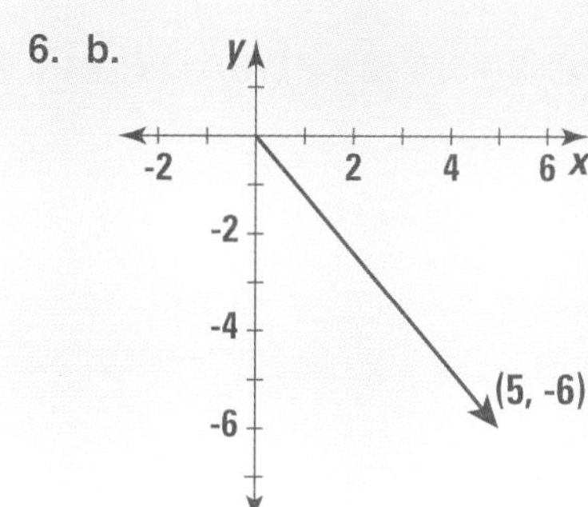

13. Find the directions of all nonzero plane vectors whose x-components are 3 times their y-components. **$\tan^{-1}\left(\frac{1}{3}\right) \approx 18.4°$ or $198.4°$**

14. $\vec{v}$ is the vector from (3, 8) to (7, k) and $|\vec{v}| = 2\sqrt{13}$. Find the value of k. **$k = 2$ or $k = 14$**

15. Let $\vec{v} = [15, 45°]$. Suppose $\vec{w}$ has the same direction as $\vec{v}$, and $|\vec{w}| = \frac{1}{3}|\vec{v}|$. Give the polar and component representations of $\vec{w}$. **$\vec{w} = [5, 45°] = \left(\frac{5\sqrt{2}}{2}, \frac{5\sqrt{2}}{2}\right)$**

Review

16. a. Sketch the graph of a function f with *all* of the following properties:
(i) $\lim_{x\to\infty} f(x) = 2$ (ii) f is an odd function
(iii) $f'(x) > 0$ for $0 < x < 2$ (iv) $f'(x) < 0$ for $2 < x < 4$

b. Identify all points where f must have a relative minimum or maximum. *(Lessons 2-4, 9-5)* **relative maximum at $x = 2$; relative minimum at $x = -2$**
a) See left.

17. At the beginning of month 1, the buyer of a car owes \$8,000 on the car. At the beginning of each month thereafter, 0.8% interest is added to the amount owed, and the owner then pays off \$200 of the loan. Let A_k represent the amount owed during month k. **See left.**
a. Write a recursive definition for the sequence $A_1, A_2, A_3, \ldots$.
b. Find the amount owed at the beginning of month 5. *(Lesson 7-1)*

18. a. *Multiple choice.* Which expression equals $\sin \frac{7\pi}{12}$? **ii**
(i) $\sin\frac{\pi}{3}\sin\frac{\pi}{4} - \cos\frac{\pi}{3}\cos\frac{\pi}{4}$
(ii) $\sin\frac{\pi}{3}\cos\frac{\pi}{4} + \cos\frac{\pi}{3}\sin\frac{\pi}{4}$
(iii) $\sin\frac{\pi}{3}\cos\frac{\pi}{4} - \cos\frac{\pi}{3}\sin\frac{\pi}{4}$
(iv) $\cos\frac{\pi}{3}\cos\frac{\pi}{4} - \sin\frac{\pi}{3}\sin\frac{\pi}{4}$

b. Which two of the other three choices are equal to each other? *(Lessons 6-4, 6-5)* **i and iii**

In 19 and 20, what curve is described by each pair of parametric equations? *(Lessons 2-5, 2-6)* **See left.**

19. $\begin{cases} x = t \\ y = t^2 + 1 \end{cases}$ **20.** $\begin{cases} x = \cos t \\ y = 2\sin t \end{cases}$

21. Three vertices of a parallelogram (not necessarily in order) are (0, 0), (2, 7), and (-3, 6). Find all possible locations for the fourth vertex. *(Previous course)* **(-1, 13), (-5, -1), (5, 1)**

Exploration

22. Is there a vector whose polar and coordinate representations consist of the same numbers? In other words, is there a vector $\vec{v} = (x, y) = [r, \theta]$ such that $x = r$ and $y = \theta$? If so, find its components. If not, prove that such a representation cannot exist.
Yes; any vector of the form (r, 0) with r positive has polar form [r, 0].

16a) [graph]

17a) $A_1 = 8000$;
$A_2 = 7864$;
$A_k = 1.008A_{k-1} - 200$ for $k > 1$

b) $\approx$ \$7449.44

19) This is a graph of half of a parabola whose y-intercept is (0, 1).

20) This is a graph of an ellipse with vertices (1, 0), (0, 2), (-1, 0), and (0, -2).

Practice

For more questions on SPUR Objectives, use **Lesson Master 12-1** (shown on pages 722–723).

Assessment

Written Communication Have students **work in pairs.** Ask each student to sketch a vector in the coordinate plane. Then have students sketch their partner's vector in standard position, give its component representation, its length, and its polar representation. [Students give component and polar representations for two-dimensional vectors.]

Extension

Refer students to **Question 12.** Have them find the unit vector with the same direction as the vector of **Example 2b.** $\left[\left(\frac{4}{5}, \frac{3}{5}\right)\right]$ Then have them generalize how to find the component form of a unit vector in the same direction as
1. A vector given in polar form [Given $[r, \theta]$, the unit vector is $(\cos\theta, \sin\theta)$.]
2. A vector given in component form [Given (a, b), the unit vector is $\left(\frac{a}{\sqrt{a^2+b^2}}, \frac{b}{\sqrt{a^2+b^2}}\right)$.]
Students should be able to show that these forms are equivalent. [Since $\sqrt{a^2+b^2} = r$, the second expression is $\left(\frac{x}{r}, \frac{y}{r}\right) = (\cos\theta, \sin\theta)$.]

7. b.

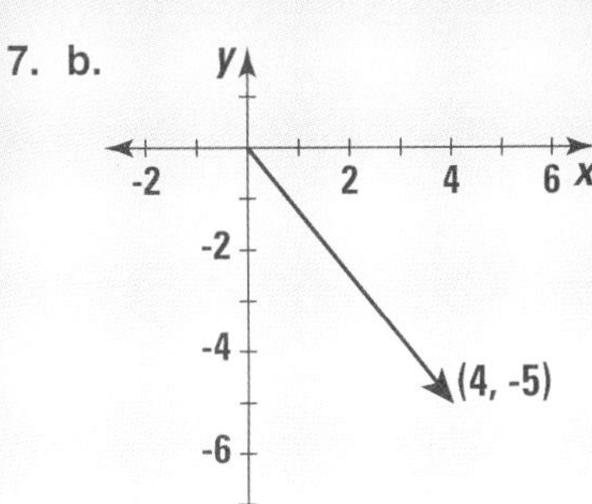

9.

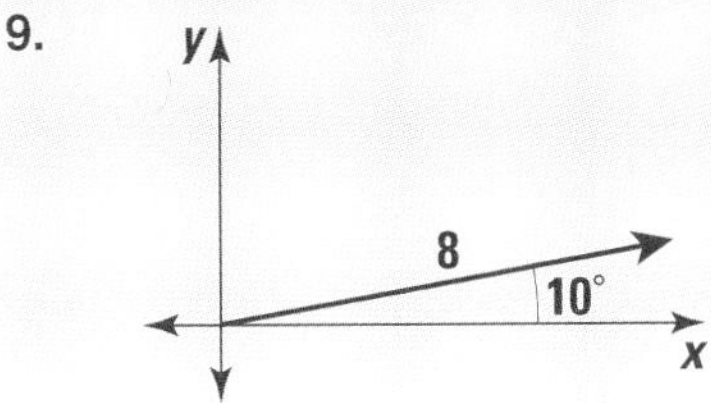

11. The standard position arrow for the vector from (-1, 2) to (4, -1) has endpoint (4 – (-1), -1 – 2) = (5, -3); the standard position arrow for the vector from (3, -2) to (8, -5) has endpoint (8 – 3, -5 – (-2)) = (5, -3). So the vectors are the same.

Lesson 12-2

Objectives

B Find sums and opposites of two-dimensional vectors.
E Prove or disprove generalizations about vector operations.
H Use addition of vectors in a plane to solve problems involving forces or velocities.
J Represent addition and subtraction of two-dimensional vectors graphically.

Resources

From the ***Teacher's Resource File***
- Lesson Master 12-2
- Answer Master 12-2
- Teaching Aids
  - 132 Warm-up
  - 136 Example and Definition of Vector Addition
  - 137 Example 1 and Example 2
  - 138 Questions 4, 6, and 15

Additional Resources
- Visuals for Teaching Aids 132, 136, 137, and 138
- Exploration 12-2

Teaching Lesson 12-2

Warm-up

A plane is going due west at a ground speed of $G\frac{\text{km}}{\text{hr}}$. There is a wind of $W\frac{\text{km}}{\text{hr}}$. How fast (in $\frac{\text{km}}{\text{hr}}$) is the plane traveling in the west direction if the wind is coming from the following directions?

1. east $G + W$
2. north G
3. west $G - W$
4. south G

LESSON

12-2 Adding and Subtracting Vectors

An Example of Addition of Vectors

❶ Consider an airplane whose instrument panel indicates that its airspeed (that is, the speed of the airplane relative to the surrounding air) is 200 miles per hour and that its compass heading (that is, the direction in which the airplane is pointing) is due northeast. However, suppose there is a steady 50-mph wind blowing from the south. Because of the wind, the plane's airspeed and compass heading do not give the true direction and speed of the plane as measured by a control tower. The true velocity $\vec{v}$ of the plane is found by combining the instrument-panel velocity (airspeed and compass heading) $\vec{p} = [200, 45°]$ with the wind velocity $\vec{w} = [50, 90°]$.

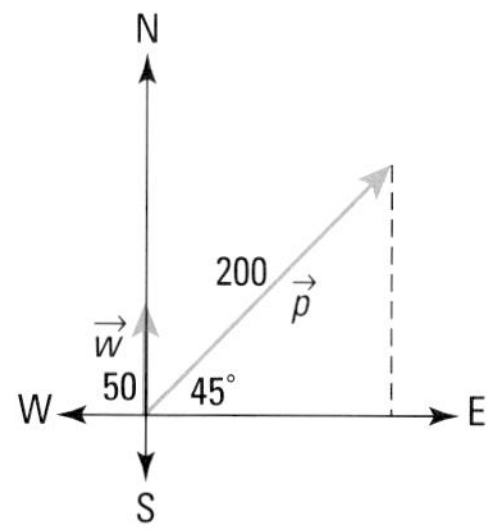

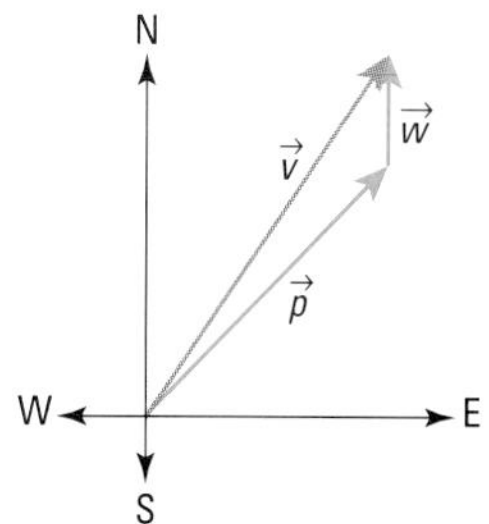

To find the true velocity, separate the wind and instrument-panel velocities into their horizontal (east-west) and vertical (north-south) components. The sums of corresponding components are the components of the true velocity.

$$\vec{p} = [200, 45°] = (200 \cos 45°, 200 \sin 45°)$$
$$= \left(100\sqrt{2}, 100\sqrt{2}\right)$$
$$\vec{w} = [50, 90°] = (0, 50)$$

Lesson 12-2 Overview

Broad Goals This lesson discusses how to add vectors given their representations by rectangular coordinates (add the corresponding components), arrows (use the parallelogram law), or when their polar representations are given (translate into rectangular coordinates).

Perspective Historically, the importance of vectors in applications has been primarily due to their ability to represent forces and the fact that addition gives the resultant force. The applications in this lesson are to the calculation of the true velocity of an airplane (by adding the wind velocity to its instrument velocity) and the calculation of the direction a volleyball will travel (by adding the forces exerted by two players on it). More recently, vectors have been used in social science and statistical applications. (See Project 3 on page 773.)

In their rectangular coordinate representation, addition of vectors is the most normal operation possible. Subtraction of vectors is defined as adding the opposite; the questions in this lesson explore some of the properties of addition and subtraction.

Therefore, the true velocity of the plane is

$$\vec{v} = \left(100\sqrt{2},\ 50 + 100\sqrt{2}\right).$$

The true speed of the plane is the length of $\vec{v}$:

$$|\vec{v}| = \sqrt{(100\sqrt{2})^2 + (50 + 100\sqrt{2})^2}$$
$$\approx 238 \text{ miles per hour.}$$

The direction θ satisfies

$$\tan\theta = \frac{50 + 100\sqrt{2}}{100\sqrt{2}}$$
$$\approx 1.35.$$
$$\therefore \quad \theta \approx 53.5°.$$

Therefore, the plane is traveling at about 238 miles per hour in the direction 53.5° north of east.

A General Definition for Vector Addition

This example exhibits the rule for adding vectors: add their x-components to get the x-component of the sum and add their y-components to get the y-component of the sum.

Definition
If $\vec{u} = (u_1, u_2)$ and $\vec{v} = (v_1, v_2)$, then the **sum of $\vec{u}$ and $\vec{v}$**, written $\vec{u} + \vec{v}$, is the vector $(u_1 + v_1, u_2 + v_2)$.

There are two equivalent ways to picture the sum of two vectors. In the diagram at the left below, the second arrow begins at the end of the first arrow. In the middle diagram, both vectors are placed in standard position. Either way the two vectors represent sides of a parallelogram. The sum vector is a diagonal of the parallelogram!

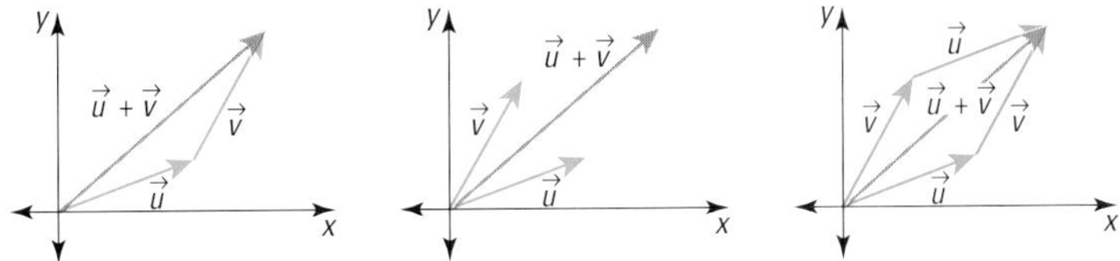

Adding Forces

The procedure that was used to compute the true velocity of the plane from its instrument velocity and the wind velocity is often used with other types of vector quantities. *Forces* are among the most important of these. A **force** is an influence that changes the motion of an object. Anytime an object speeds up, slows down, stops, starts to move, or changes direction, one or more forces must be at work. For example, you might give an object a push to start it sliding. Then the friction of the object with the floor will cause it to stop. Both your initial push and the influence of friction are forces.

Notes on Reading

❶ In the airplane velocity example opening the lesson, the airplane's true velocity is the resultant of two forces $\vec{p}$ and $\vec{w}$ that act simultaneously, as shown in the first diagram. However, the sum can be envisioned by imagining $\vec{p}$ occurring first, then $\vec{w}$, as the second diagram illustrates. A third drawing for the situation could show $\vec{w}$ happening first, then $\vec{p}$. By combining all three of these drawings, students can see a parallelogram diagram like that found on page 727.

Teaching Aid 136 shows the diagrams at the beginning of the lesson, as well as the definition for vector addition.

Alternate Approach One reason for studying vectors is that they give us easier methods for solving familiar problems. In the airplane velocity example, the Law of Cosines could be used to find the plane's speed and direction. Showing students this alternate approach illustrates the convenience of vector methods and helps to set up Lesson 12-4 on the angle between vectors.

You may wish to set a theme for your discussions of plane vectors, namely that everything that is done be interpreted by students with arrows, in polar form, and in component form. Then, for each idea, you can ask for the interpretation. So, for instance, start with the basic idea of how to describe a vector. Which interpretation is given first? [polar form, on page 726] Which next? [component form, used for the definition of addition on page 727] Addition with arrows is shown after the component definition.

Optional Activities

Activity 1 Technology Connection
Materials: *Explorations* software

Students may use *Exploration 12-2: Vector Addition of Forces,* as an alternative to **Example 1** in Lesson 12-2. Students can designate two vector forces in polar form. Each vector will be shown on a coordinate grid and algebraically in polar coordinates and rectangular coordinates. The sum of the two vectors is also shown algebraically and graphically.

Activity 2 Refer students to **Question 15.** Ask them to find the velocity of the current and the speed of the boat if the current acts so that the boat travels "straight" across the river, at a 90° angle to the banks. [The current must have a velocity of 5.13 knots due west; the boat will travel at 14 knots (due north).]

Adapting to Individual Needs

Extra Help
Be sure students understand why the quadrilateral in the third diagram illustrating $\vec{u} + \vec{v}$ is a parallelogram. [The two drawings of $\vec{v}$ are parallel as are both drawings of $\vec{u}$. So, since the quadrilateral has opposite sides parallel, it is a parallelogram.]

The theorem following the definition of the opposite of a vector shows both polar and component representations of the opposite; the arrow interpretation is used next.

Subtraction with arrows is given on page 729. Subtraction with vectors given in component representation can be discussed with **Question 14.** Subtraction with vectors given in polar representation is the essence of **Question 15.**

In **Example 1,** point out that in the original drawing the arrows terminate at the ball, representing the forces exerted on it. We then redraw the diagram with the arrows emanating from the ball. In a way they now show the result of each force on the ball's motion. **Teaching Aid 137** has the drawings for **Example 1 and Example 2.**

A force is a vector quantity whose length represents the size of the force and whose direction is the direction in which the force is applied. The size of a force is measured in *pounds* in the customary system and in *newtons* in the metric system. For example, the statement that a person weighs 180 pounds means that the size of the force due to the influence of gravity on that person is 180 pounds.

If two forces, $\vec{f}$ and $\vec{g}$, influence the motion of an object at the same time, then the sum of these two forces $\vec{h} = \vec{f} + \vec{g}$ is a single force that produces the same resulting change in the motion of the object as the two forces $\vec{f}$ and $\vec{g}$ combined. For this reason, the force $\vec{h}$ is called the **resultant force** for the forces $\vec{f}$ and $\vec{g}$.

Example 1

Two volleyball players hit the ball at the same time. The forces they exert are represented by the arrows drawn at the right. Describe the vector representing the total force exerted on the ball.

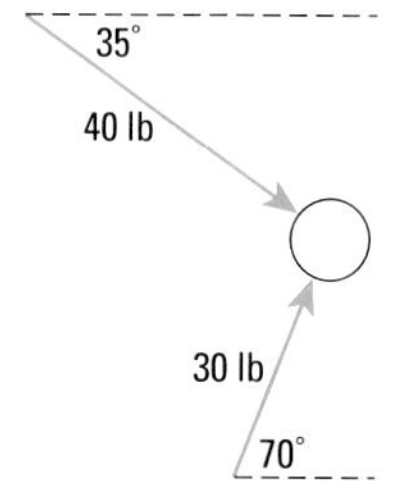

Solution

First show each force as a vector in standard position. (Notice that one vector has direction -35°.) Each component of the total force on the ball will be the sum of the corresponding components of the two force vectors. So express each vector in component form.

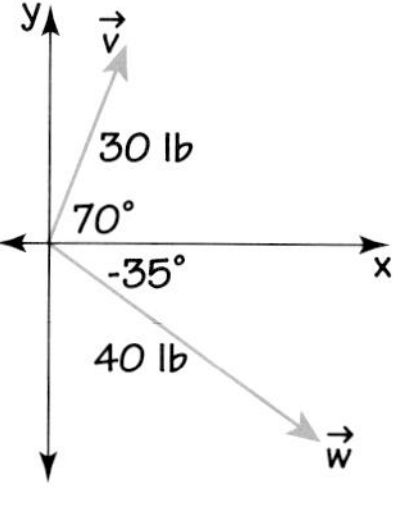

$\vec{v} = (30 \cos 70°, 30 \sin 70°)$
$\approx (10, 28)$
$\vec{w} = (40 \cos (\text{-}35°), 40 \sin (\text{-}35°))$
$\approx (33, \text{-}23)$

The total force in the x-direction is approximately 10 + 33 = 43 lb. The force in the y-direction is approximately 28 + -23 = 5 lb. Thus, the resulting force has components of about (43, 5). The ball will travel in the direction shown at the right.

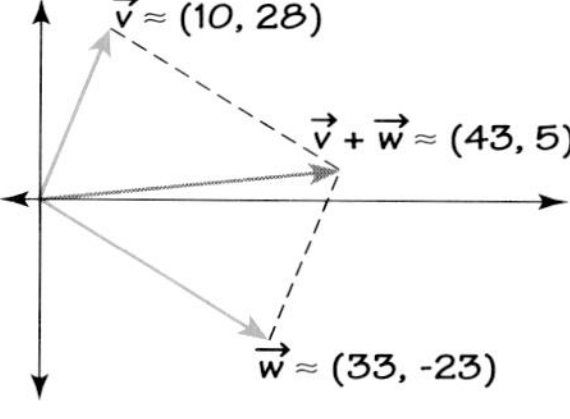

Check

The origin and the tips of the arrows of $\vec{v}$, $\vec{w}$, and $\vec{v} + \vec{w}$ in standard position should be vertices of a parallelogram, which they are.

LESSON MASTER 12-2 **Questions on SPUR Objectives**
See pages 778–781 for objectives.

Skills Objective B

In 1–4, let $\vec{u}$ = (-2, -5), $\vec{v}$ = (4, 1), and $\vec{w}$ = (-6, 0). Find the sum or difference.

1. $\vec{u} + \vec{w}$ (-8, -5)
2. $\vec{u} - \vec{v}$ (-6, -6)
3. $-\vec{u}$ (2, 5)
4. $\vec{w} - \vec{v} + \vec{u}$ (-12, -6)

In 5 and 6, let $\vec{s}$ = [4, 75°] and $\vec{t}$ = [1, 20°]. Compute and express the answer in its polar representation.

5. $\vec{s} + \vec{t}$ [4.6, 64.8°]
6. $\vec{s} - \vec{t}$ [3.5, 88.45°]

Properties Objective E

7. Prove that if $\vec{v} + \vec{u} = \vec{v} + \vec{w}$, then $\vec{u} = \vec{w}$. Samples are given.
Let $\vec{v} = (v_1, v_2)$, $\vec{u} = (u_1, u_2)$, and $\vec{w} = (w_1, w_2)$. Then $\vec{v} + \vec{u} = (v_1 + u_1, v_2 + u_2)$, and $\vec{v} + \vec{w} = (v_1 + w_1, v_2 + w_2)$. But, $\vec{v} + \vec{u} = \vec{v} + \vec{w}$, so $(v_1 + u_1, v_2 + u_2) = (v_1 w_1, v_2 w_2)$. Thus, $u_1 = w_1$ and $u_2 = w_2$. Therefore, $\vec{u} = (u_1, u_2) = (w_1, w_2) = \vec{w}$.

8. Show that $\vec{v}$ = (cos 50°, 5 sin 50°) is the opposite of $\vec{w}$ = (5 cos 230°, 5 sin 230°).
$\vec{v}$ = (5 cos 50°, 5 sin 50°) ≈ (3.2, 3.8).
$\vec{w}$ = (5 cos 230°, 5 sin 230°) ≈ (3.2, 3.8).
Thus $\vec{v}$ and $\vec{w}$ are opposites.

Adapting to Individual Needs

Challenge

1. Have students compare $|\vec{u}| + |\vec{v}|$ and $|\vec{u} + \vec{v}|$ for each of the following.
   a. $\vec{u}$ = (5, 3); $\vec{v}$ = (2, 9)
   b. $\vec{u}$ = (-4, -3); $\vec{v}$ = (5, 2)
   c. $\vec{u}$ = (6, -2); $\vec{v}$ = (3, -1)
   d. $\vec{u}$ = (0, 3); $\vec{v}$ = (2, 0)
   [In all cases, $|\vec{u}| + |\vec{v}| \geq |\vec{u} + \vec{v}|$.]

2. Use vectors to prove that the diagonals of a parallelogram bisect each other.
   [Let $\vec{u}$ = (a, b) and $\vec{v}$ = (c, d).
   The vector $\vec{u} + \vec{v}$ is one diagonal and is in standard position. The vector $\vec{u} - \vec{v}$ is the other diagonal, with endpoints at (a, b) and (c, d). Both vectors have midpoints $\left(\frac{a+c}{2}, \frac{b+d}{2}\right)$.]

Subtraction of Vectors

If it makes sense to add two vectors, is it possible to subtract them? The answer is yes. As is commonly done in mathematical systems, subtraction is defined as adding the opposite, so the *opposite of a vector* must be defined. The definition is what you might expect.

> **Definition**
> The vector $-\vec{v}$, the **opposite of** $\vec{v}$, is the vector with the same magnitude as $\vec{v}$ and direction opposite to $\vec{v}$.

Part **a** of the following theorem follows immediately from the definition of $-\vec{v}$. In the Questions you are asked to prove part **b**.

> **Theorem**
> **a.** If $\vec{v}$ is a vector with polar representation $[r, \theta°]$, then $-\vec{v} = [r, 180° + \theta°]$.
> **b.** If $\vec{v}$ has component representation (v_1, v_2), then $-\vec{v} = (-v_1, -v_2)$.

Opposite vectors are quite important in the study of forces. One of Newton's laws is (in his words): "To every action there is always opposed an equal reaction, or the mutual reactions of two bodies upon each other are always equal and directed to contrary directions." This means that the forces in interactions between two bodies can be represented by opposite vectors.

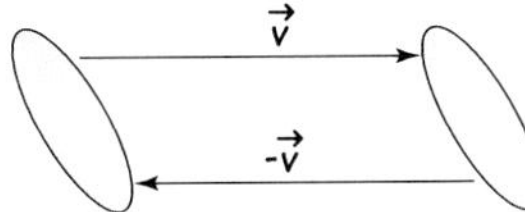

Using the definition of opposite vectors, it is possible to define vector subtraction.

> **Definition**
> The **difference** $\vec{u} - \vec{v}$ is the vector
> $$\vec{u} + (-\vec{v}).$$

Example 2

The vectors $\vec{v}$ and $\vec{w}$ are shown at the right. Sketch the following.

a. $\vec{v} - \vec{w}$ 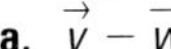 **b.** $\vec{w} - \vec{v}$ 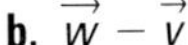

Solution

First sketch the opposites of the two vectors.

Example 2 can be extended by asking students to draw an arrow diagram to show that $(\vec{v} - \vec{w}) + \vec{w} = \vec{v}$. Another extension is to ask students to write a computer program to give the sum of two vectors that are entered in polar form. A student familiar with graphics could also have the program draw the arrows on the screen.

You may want to instruct your students that, unless directed otherwise, vector answers should be written in the same form (polar or component) as the given information.

Additional Examples

1. Suppose that two volleyball players hit a ball at the same time, and the force of the first was 40 lb in the direction -35° as in **Example 1,** but the force of the second was 40 lb in the direction 35°. Show that the ball would go in the 0° direction as expected and find the magnitude of the force on it.
   If $\vec{v} = [40, 35°]$ and $\vec{w} = [40, -35°]$, then $\vec{v} + \vec{w} = (40 \cos 35° + 40 \cos (-35°), 40 \sin 35° + 40 \sin (-35°)) = (80 \cos 35°, 0)$, a vector in the direction 0° with magnitude $\approx$ 66 lb.

(Additional Examples continue on page 730.)

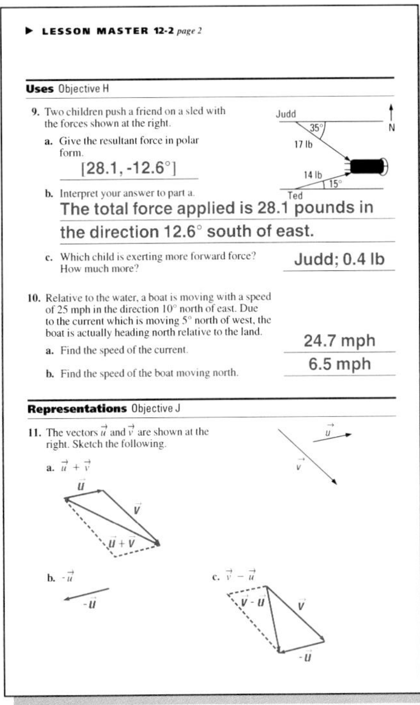

▶ **LESSON MASTER 12-2** *page 2*

Uses Objective H

9. Two children push a friend on a sled with the forces shown at the right.
   a. Give the resultant force in polar form. **[28.1, -12.6°]**
   b. Interpret your answer to part a. **The total force applied is 28.1 pounds in the direction 12.6° south of east.**
   c. Which child is exerting more forward force? How much more? **Judd; 0.4 lb**

10. Relative to the water, a boat is moving with a speed of 25 mph in the direction 10° north of east. Due to the current which is moving 5° north of west, the boat is actually heading north relative to the land.
    a. Find the speed of the current. **24.7 mph**
    b. Find the speed of the boat moving north. **6.5 mph**

Representations Objective J

11. The vectors $\vec{u}$ and $\vec{v}$ are shown at the right. Sketch the following.
    a. $\vec{u} + \vec{v}$
    b. $-\vec{u}$
    c. $\vec{v} - \vec{u}$

2. Let $\vec{u} = (2, 7)$ and $\vec{v} = (3, 5)$.
   a. Draw $\vec{u}$, $\vec{v}$, and $\vec{u} - \vec{v}$.

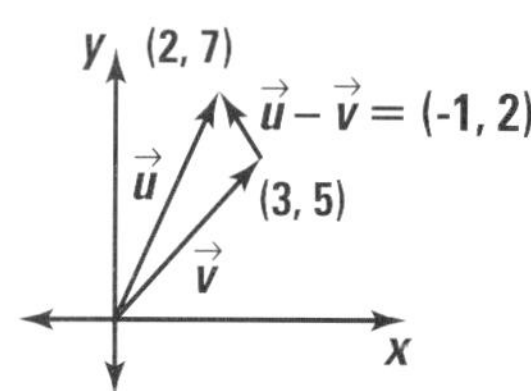

   b. Give the components of $\vec{u} - \vec{v}$. **(-1, 2)**

Notes on Questions

Questions 3–4 Note that in the questions the arrows are not drawn to scale. Encourage students to draw accurate diagrams to check the reasonableness of their answers.

Questions 4, 6, and 15 Teaching Aid 138 provides these drawings.

Question 6 Students should begin by drawing the two vectors beginning at the barge.

Question 12 Error Alert Students may have a hard time getting started. It may help if you give a hint to let $\vec{v} = (v_1, v_2) = [r, \theta]$, so that $v_1 = r\cos\theta$ and $v_2 = r\sin\theta$. Then use the definition of *opposite*.

Question 14a Generalize to give a rule for subtracting vectors given their components: If $\vec{s} = (a, b)$ and $\vec{t} = (c, d)$, then $\vec{s} - \vec{t} = (a - c, b - d)$.

(Notes on Questions continue on page 732.)

a. $\vec{v} - \vec{w} = \vec{v} + -\vec{w}$, so sketch $-\vec{w}$ as done above, and add, using a parallelogram. The result is shown at the right.

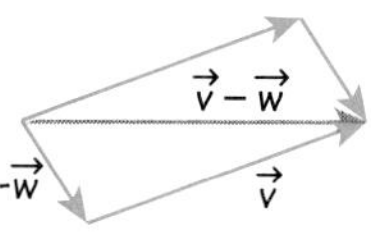

b. $\vec{w} - \vec{v} = \vec{w} + -\vec{v}$, so sketch $-\vec{v}$ and add it to $\vec{w}$ as shown at the right.

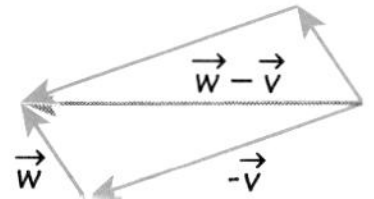

Notice that $\vec{v} - \vec{w}$ is the opposite of $\vec{w} - \vec{v}$. Addition and subtraction of vectors have many of the same properties as addition and subtraction of real numbers.

QUESTIONS

Covering the Reading

In 1 and 2, find $\vec{u} + \vec{w}$.

1. $\vec{u} = (18, -3)$ and $\vec{w} = (-6, -11)$ **(12, -14)**

2. $\vec{u} = [9, 55°]$ and $\vec{w} = [3, 140°]$ **≈ [9.73, 72.9°]**

3. Consider the resultant vector in Example 1. **See left.**
   a. Give its magnitude and direction.
   b. What is the physical meaning of the answer to part **a**?

3a) magnitude: ≈ 43.3 lb; direction: ≈ 6.6° *N of E*
b) The resultant force is 43.3 lb in the direction 6.6° *N of E*.

4. Find the resultant force $\vec{h}$ for the forces $\vec{f}$ and $\vec{g}$ shown below.

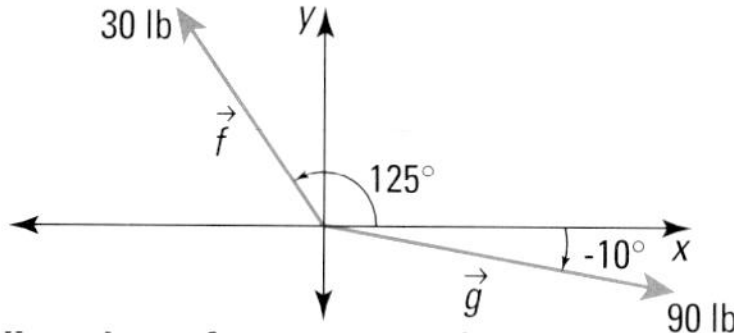

71.96 lb in the direction of ≈ 7.18° *N of E*.

5. A motorboat is crossing a river at an angle of 60° to the shore at a speed of 20 mph in the water. The river is flowing at 6 mph. Describe the resulting velocity (speed and direction) of the boat.

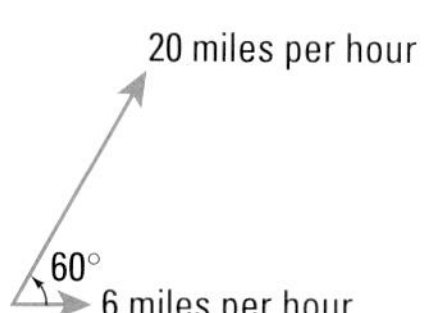

Speed: $\sqrt{556} \approx 23.6$ mph; direction: $\theta = \tan^{-1}\left(\frac{10\sqrt{3}}{16}\right) \approx 47°$ *N of E*

Additional Answers

9. a.

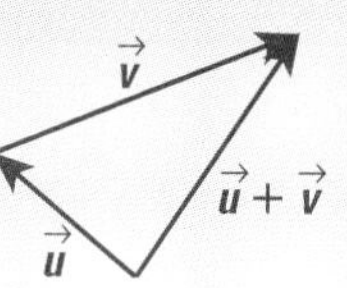

9. b.

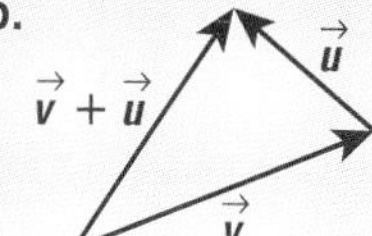

9. c.

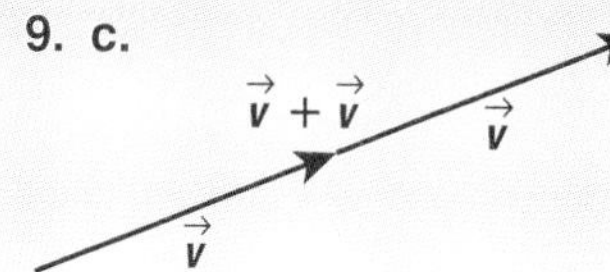

10. a.

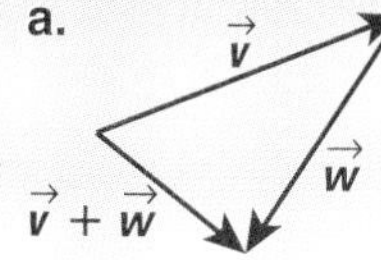

10. b.

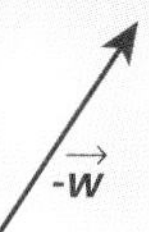

6. Two tugboats push a barge with the forces shown at the right. Describe the resultant force. **≈ 2157 lb in the direction of ≈ 52.5° *N* of *E***

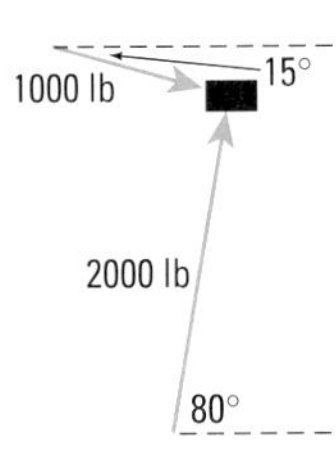

7. A ship sails for 10 hours at a speed of 14 knots (nautical miles per hour) at a heading of 72° north of east. It then turns to a heading of 57° north of east and travels for 2 hours at 11 knots. Find its position north and east of its starting point. (Assume Earth is flat.) **See left.**

8. If $\vec{w} = [6, 20°]$, express $-\vec{w}$ in the indicated form. **See left.**
   a. polar
   b. component

In 9 and 10, trace the arrows shown below. Then sketch the indicated vectors. **See margin.**

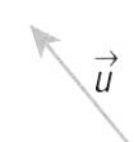

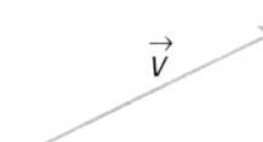

$\vec{w}$

9. a. $\vec{u} + \vec{v}$ b. $\vec{v} + \vec{u}$ c. $\vec{v} + \vec{v}$

10. a. $\vec{v} + \vec{w}$ b. $-\vec{w}$ c. $\vec{v} - \vec{w}$

Applying the Mathematics

11. Show that this statement is false: *If* $\vec{u} = [r, \alpha]$ *and* $\vec{v} = [s, \beta]$, *then* $\vec{u} + \vec{v} = [r + s, \alpha + \beta]$. **See left.**

12. Use the polar representation of $-\vec{v}$ and trigonometric identities to prove that if $\vec{v} = (v_1, v_2)$, then $-\vec{v} = (-v_1, -v_2)$. **See margin.**

13. a. Prove: *For any vector* $\vec{v}$, $\vec{v} - \vec{v}$ *is the zero vector.* **See left.**
    b. Give a geometric interpretation for the result of part **a**. **See left.**

14. Let $\vec{s} = (-6, 5)$ and $\vec{t} = (-3, 1)$. Solve for the components of $\vec{v}$ under the given condition.
    a. $\vec{s} + \vec{v} = \vec{t}$ **(3, -4)** b. $\vec{v} - \vec{s} = \vec{t}$ **(-9, 6)**

15. A boat leaves point *A* on the south bank of a river and heads at a 70° angle with an engine speed of 15 knots.

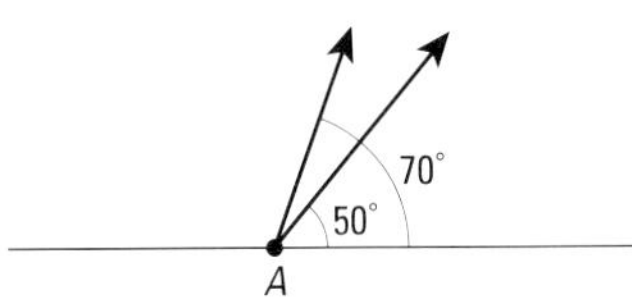

However, the eastward force of the current carries the boat along so it actually travels at a 50° angle with the shore.
   a. How fast is the current? **The current is about 6.7 knots.**
   b. How fast does the boat actually travel? **The boat travels about 18.4 knots.**

7) ≈ 55.2 nautical miles east and ≈ 151.6 nautical miles north of its starting point

8a) [-6, 20°] or [6, 200°]
b) (6 cos 200°, 6 sin 200°) ≈ (-5.64, -2.05)

11) Sample counter-example: If $\vec{u} = [1, 45°]$ and $\vec{v} = [1, 45°]$, then $\vec{u} + \vec{v} = [2, 45°] \neq [2, 90°]$.

13a) If $\vec{v} = (v_1, v_2)$ then $\vec{v} - \vec{v} = \vec{v} + -\vec{v}$ then $(v_1, v_2) + (-v_1, -v_2) = (v_1 + -v_1, v_2 + -v_2) = (0, 0)$, which is the zero vector.
b) Sample: The arrow for $\vec{v} - \vec{v}$ is a point.

Follow-up for Lesson 12-2

Practice

For more questions on SPUR Objectives, use **Lesson Master 12-2** (shown on pages 728–729).

Assessment

Written Communication Give students problems like **Question 14.** Have students solve the problems and verify their answers with accurate drawings in the coordinate plane. [Students add and subtract two-dimensional vectors and represent these operations graphically.]

Extension

In **Question 5,** the river current is speeding up the boat. You might ask students under what conditions the river slows the boat down rather than speeds it up. Relate this to the parallelogram diagram. Under what conditions is the length of the diagonal of a parallelogram less than the length of its sides? Can it be equal to one side or both? What is the maximum length?

Project Update Project 2, *Vectors Applied to Computer Simulations,* and Project 4, *Vectors Applied to Physics,* on pages 773–774, relate to the content of this lesson.

10. c.

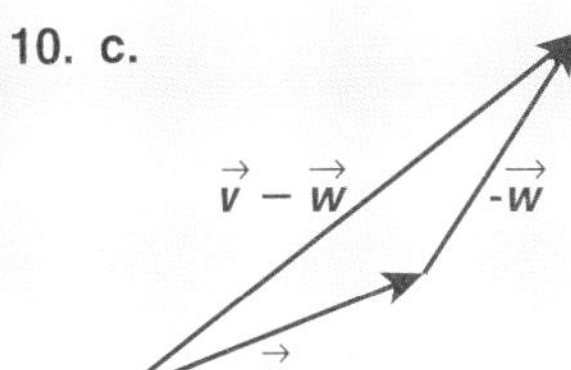

12. Let $\vec{v} = (v_1, v_2)$ be a vector with polar representation $[r, \theta]$.
Hence, $\vec{v} = (r\cos\theta, r\sin\theta)$, and $v_1 = r(\cos\theta)$, $v_2 = r(\sin\theta)$.
$-\vec{v} = [r, \theta + 180°] = (r[\cos(\theta + 180°)], r[\sin(\theta + 180°)])$
$= (r[\cos\theta\cos 180° - \sin\theta\sin 180°], r[\sin\theta\cos 180° + \cos\theta\sin 180°])$
$= (r[(\cos\theta)(-1) - (\sin\theta)(0)], r[(\sin\theta)(-1) + (\cos\theta)(0)])$
$= (-r(\cos\theta), -r(\sin\theta))$
$= (-v_1, -v_2)$

Notes on Questions

Question 16 This is important to discuss, because in the next lesson on scalar multiplication, this property will indicate that the magnitude of a scalar product is the product of the absolute value of the scalar and the magnitude of the original vector. Note the different, but related, use of the absolute value symbol for real numbers and for vectors.

16) The length of (kv_1, kv_2) is $\sqrt{(kv_1)^2 + (kv_2)^2}$
$= \sqrt{k^2v_1^2 + k^2v_2^2}$
$= \sqrt{k^2(v_1^2 + v_2^2)}$
$= |k|\sqrt{(v_1^2 + v_2^2)}$
$= |k|\,|\vec{v}|$.

Review

16. If $\vec{v} = (v_1, v_2)$ and k is a real number, show that the length of the vector (kv_1, kv_2) is $|k|\,|\vec{v}|$. *(Lesson 12-1)* See left.

17. Four women and four men are to be seated around a circular table so that no two women and no two men are beside each other. In how many ways can this be done? *(Lessons 10-2, 10-3)* 144

18. Suppose the voltage across an AC circuit is 120V and the impedance is $6 - 5i$ ohms.

a. Find the current. $\approx 11.8 + 9.84i$ amps

b. Interpret the answer to part **a** in terms of the graph of the current shown by an oscilloscope. (Hint: See Question 15 of Lesson 8-3.) *(Lessons 8-1, 8-3)* a sine curve with amplitude $\approx$ 15.4 and phase shift $\approx -39.8°$

19. Simplify $\frac{4}{x^2 + 2x - 8} - \frac{3}{x^2 + 5x + 4}$. *(Lesson 5-2)* $\frac{x + 10}{(x + 4)(x - 2)(x + 1)}$

20. Approximate the smallest positive solution to $\tan x = (x - 1)^2$ to within 0.1. *(Lesson 3-4)* 0.4

Exploration

21. Describe some of the forces involved in the motions of the following objects.

a. an apple falling from a tree gravity

b. a plane doing acrobatics gravity, engine thrust, lift due to wing designs

c. a pitcher throwing a baseball See below.

d. a sled coasting down a hill gravity, friction, initial push

c) gravity, torque, initial velocity of ball

Setting Up Lesson 12-3

Discuss **Question 16.** You may wish to define the operation of scalar multiplication before students read the lesson.

LESSON

12-3

Parallel Vectors and Equations of Lines

Tug-o-War. *The fish and the angler are exerting force on the line in opposite directions.*

Vectors are very valuable! In Lesson 12-2 they were applied to physical forces. In this lesson, vectors are applied to geometry.

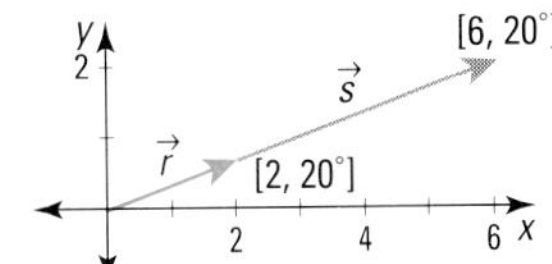

Parallel Vectors

Two vectors with the same or opposite directions are called **parallel**. That is, the polar representations of parallel vectors differ by a multiple of π.

Consider two such vectors, $\vec{r} = [2, 20°]$ and $\vec{s} = [6, 20°]$. If they are drawn in standard position it is clear that they lie on the same ray with initial point at the origin. Clearly the length of $\vec{s}$ is three times that of $\vec{r}$. The component representations of the two vectors can be found by converting their polar representations to rectangular:

$$\vec{r} = (2 \cos 20°, 2 \sin 20°) \text{ and } \vec{s} = (6 \cos 20°, 6 \sin 20°).$$

Thus the x- and y-components of $\vec{s}$ are three times those of $\vec{r}$. $\vec{s}$ is called a *scalar multiple* of $\vec{r}$ because the components of $\vec{r}$ are *scaled*, or multiplied, by the same number to get the components of $\vec{s}$. That scale factor is called a **scalar** to emphasize that it is not a vector.

> **Definition**
> A vector $\vec{w} = (w_1, w_2)$ is a **scalar multiple** of vector $\vec{u} = (u_1, u_2)$, written $\vec{w} = k\vec{u}$ if and only if $\exists$ a real number k such that $(w_1, w_2) = (ku_1, ku_2)$.

Notice that $w = k(u_1, u_2)$, so it is natural to define a **scalar multiplication** $k(u_1, u_2) = (ku_1, ku_2)$. For $\vec{r}$ and $\vec{s}$ above, the scale factor $k = 3$, and

Lesson **12-3**

Objectives

- **B** Find scalar products involving two-dimensional vectors.
- **E** Prove or disprove generalizations about vector operations.
- **F** Identify parallel vectors.
- **I** Represent two-dimensional vectors in their component or polar representation, or as directed segments.
- **J** Represent scalar multiplication of two-dimensional vectors graphically.
- **L** Represent lines in a plane using vector or parametric equations.

Resources

From the ***Teacher's Resource File***
- Lesson Master 12-3
- Answer Master 12-3
- Assessment Sourcebook: Quiz for Lessons 12-1 through 12-3
- Teaching Aids
  132 Warm-up
  139 Vector and Parametric Equations for Lines
- Technology Sourcebook Calculator Master 17

Additional Resources
- Visuals for Teaching Aids 132, 139
- Exploration 12-3

Teaching Lesson **12-3**

Warm-up

1. Using a calculator, graph the parametric equations
$$\begin{cases} x = 2 + 3t \\ y = 5 - t \end{cases}$$
line through (2, 5) and (5, 4)

Lesson 12-3 Overview

Broad Goals This lesson defines scalar multiplication and develops it to yield parametric equations for a line in the plane.

Perspective Multiplying a vector $\vec{v}$ by the real number k (the scalar) yields a vector $k\vec{v}$ whose length is k times the length of $\vec{v}$ and whose direction is the same as that of $\vec{v}$ if $k > 0$ and opposite that of $\vec{v}$ if $k < 0$.

That a vector $\vec{v} = (v_1, v_2)$ and its scalar multiple $k\vec{v} = (kv_1, kv_2)$ have the same direction if $k > 0$ can be seen by examining the similar right triangles associated with each vector, as shown at the right.

(Overview continues on page 734.)

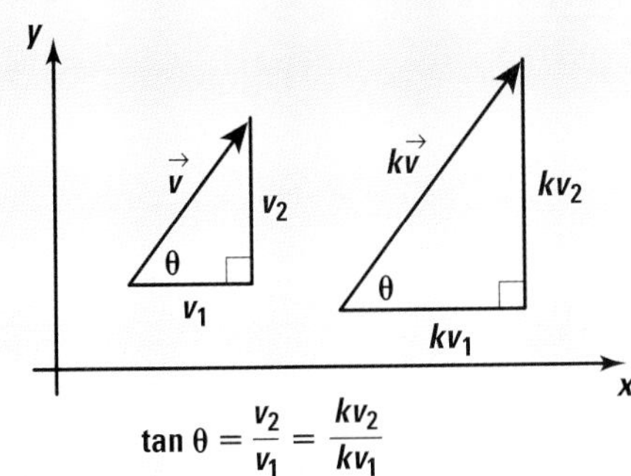

2. Give an x-y equation for the graph. $y = -\frac{1}{3}x + \frac{17}{3}$

Notes on Reading

Be sure that students understand the difference between a scalar and a vector. *Scalar* is merely another name for real number when vectors are being discussed.

In earlier UCSMP courses, there is experience with scale factor multiplication and scale changes with negative magnitude. Students who have taken these courses should be accustomed to the idea that a negative scale factor reverses direction, and most other students do not find this difficult.

Your students may notice that the vector and parametric forms of the equation of a line look very similar to point-slope form. Both are related to the definition of slope. If the line is not vertical, the quotient $\frac{v_2}{v_1}$ of the components (v_1, v_2) of the vector is its slope, as follows:
From the definition of slope, $\frac{y - y_1}{x - x_1} = m$. Thus $\frac{y - y_1}{x - x_1} = \frac{v_2}{v_1} = \frac{tv_2}{tv_1}$, from which there exists a t such that $y - y_1 = tv_2$ and $x - x_1 = tv_1$. Similarly, point-slope form can be derived from the parametric form by solving each equation for t and substituting.

LESSON MASTER 12-3 **Questions on SPUR Objectives**
See pages 778–781 for objectives.

Skills Objective B

In 1–4, let $\vec{u} = (-4, 12)$, and $\vec{v} = (-6, 1)$, and compute.

1. $\frac{2}{3}\vec{u}$ $\left(-\frac{8}{3}, 8\right)$
2. $5\vec{v}$ (-30, 5)
3. $\frac{2}{3}\vec{u} + 5\vec{v}$ $\left(-\frac{98}{3}, 13\right)$
4. $3\vec{u} - 4\vec{v}$ (12, 32)

Properties Objective E

5. Show that $\vec{v} = (-2, 5)$ and $\vec{w} = (12, -30)$ are parallel.
$\vec{w} = (12, -30) = -6(-2, 5) = -6\vec{v}$

6. Show that the line passing through (-2, -2) and (0, 8) is parallel to the vector $\vec{v} = (-1, -5)$.
$(0 - (-2), 8 - (-2)) = (2, 10) = -2(-1, -5) = -2\vec{v}$

Properties Objective F

In 7–9, is the given vector parallel to $\vec{u} = (12, 2)$?

7. $\vec{v} = \left(-4, -\frac{2}{3}\right)$ Yes
8. $\vec{w} = (-24, 4)$ No
9. $\vec{n} = (12, 2)$ Yes
10. Are $\vec{u} = [2, 40°]$ and $\vec{v} = [3, 220°]$ parallel? Yes

Representations Objective I

11. Sketch $\vec{v} = (-2, -5)$ and $-2\vec{v}$ on the grid at the right.

$\vec{s} = (6 \cos 20°, 6 \sin 20°)$. $3\vec{r} = 3(2 \cos 20°, 2 \sin 20°)$. Also, $\vec{r} = \frac{1}{3}\vec{s}$, so that $\vec{r}$ is a scalar multiple of $\vec{s}$ with $k = \frac{1}{3}$. That is, $(2 \cos 20°, 2 \sin 20°) = \frac{1}{3}(6 \cos 20°, 6 \sin 20°)$.

Notice that the definition of scalar multiple allows a scalar to be negative.

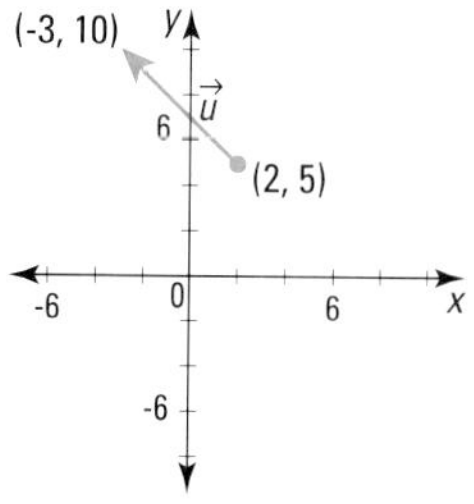

Example 1

The vector $\vec{u}$ is pictured at the left. Sketch the vector $\vec{w} = -2\vec{u}$ in standard position.

Solution

Subtract the coordinates of the endpoint and initial point of the arrow for $\vec{u}$ to give the component representation of $\vec{u}$.

$$\vec{u} = (-3 - 2, 10 - 5) = (-5, 5).$$

Therefore

$$\vec{w} = -2\vec{u} = -2(-5, 5) = (10, -10).$$

$\vec{w}$ is sketched at the right.

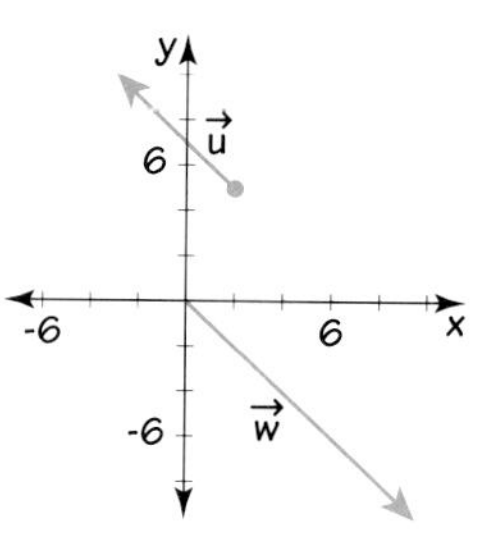

Notice that in Example 1, $\vec{u}$ and $\vec{w}$ have opposite direction and that $\vec{w}$ is twice as long as $\vec{u}$. In fact, Question 16 of Lesson 12-2 shows that multiplying a vector by a scalar multiplies its length by the absolute value of the scalar. If $\vec{v}$ is a vector and k is a real number, then $|k\vec{v}| = |k|\,|\vec{v}|$.

Notice also that in the graph of Example 1, $\vec{u}$ and $\vec{w}$ lie on parallel lines. They are parallel vectors. In general, it is possible to prove the following.

> **Theorem**
> Nonzero vectors $\vec{u}$ and $\vec{v}$ are parallel if and only if one of the vectors is a nonzero scalar multiple of the other.

Example 2

Show that the vectors (2, 5) and (18, 45) are parallel.

Solution

$$(18, 45) = (9 \cdot 2, 9 \cdot 5) = 9(2, 5)$$

Since (18, 45) is a scalar multiple of (2, 5), the vectors are parallel.

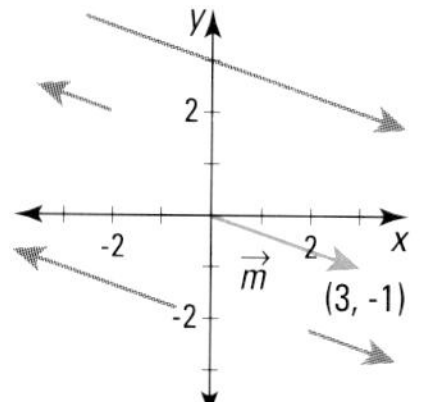

The diagram at the left shows several vectors that are parallel to $\vec{m} = (3, -1)$. Each one lies on a line with slope $-\frac{1}{3}$. If $a \neq 0$, a vector (a, b) will always lie on a line with slope $\frac{b}{a}$. If $a = 0$, the vector $(0, b)$ lies on a vertical line.

Lesson 12-3 Overview, continued

Since scalar multiples of vectors all go in the same or opposite directions, they lie on parallel lines. So any point on a given line can be thought of as the sum of (1) a vector from the origin to a point on the line and (2) a scalar multiple of a vector parallel to the line. The scalars by which the vector is multiplied are the values of the parameter.

The algebraic description of lines using vectors is a parametric description, that is, both x- and y-coordinates are expressed in terms of a third variable t, the parameter. This description uses the second basic operation with vectors, scalar multiplication. The same ideas as used in this lesson are employed in Lesson 12-7 to develop parametric equations for a line in space.

Vector Equations for Lines

Since vectors are related to slopes, vectors can be used to describe lines. In Euclidean geometry, Playfair's Parallel Postulate states: There is exactly one line parallel to a given line through a given point. This uniqueness of this line suggests how to find a vector equation for a line.

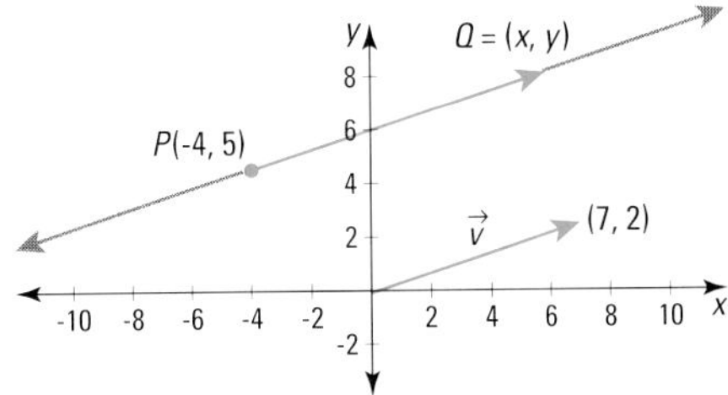

Consider the line through the point $P = (-4, 5)$ parallel to the vector $\vec{v} = (7, 2)$. For any point $Q = (x, y)$ on the line, the vector $\overrightarrow{PQ}$ connecting $P = (-4, 5)$ to $Q = (x, y)$, satisfies the equation

$$\overrightarrow{PQ} = t\vec{v}$$

for some number t. Now $\overrightarrow{PQ}$ has x-component $x - (-4)$ and y-component $y - 5$. Substituting, we obtain

$$(x + 4, y - 5) = t(7, 2).$$

This is a **vector equation for the line.**

The preceding argument can be generalized to any given point and vector.

> **Theorem**
> A point $Q = (x, y)$ is on the line through $P = (x_0, y_0)$ parallel to the vector $\vec{v} = (v_1, v_2)$ if and only if there is a real number t with $\overrightarrow{PQ} = t\vec{v}$, or $(x - x_0, y - y_0) = t(v_1, v_2)$.

Parametric Equations for Lines

The vector equation $(x - x_0, y - y_0) = t(v_1, v_2)$ can be written as two equations, one relating the x-components of the two vectors and one relating the y-components.

$$\begin{cases} x - x_0 = tv_1 \\ y - y_0 = tv_2 \end{cases}$$

When these are solved for x and y, the result is another form of an equation for a line, the **parametric form of an equation for a line**.

> **Theorem**
> The line through (x_0, y_0) that is parallel to the vector $\vec{v} = (v_1, v_2)$ has parametric equations
> $$\begin{cases} x = x_0 + tv_1 \\ y = y_0 + tv_2, \end{cases}$$
> where t may be any real number.

Error Alert Be sure students don't assume that the parametric form for the equation of a line is unique. For example, the line through (-4, 5) and parallel to the vector $\vec{v} = (7, 2)$, discussed in the lesson, also goes through (3, 7). So another set of parametric equations for this line would be

$$\begin{cases} x = 3 + 7t. \\ y = 7 + 2t. \end{cases}$$

Have students verify that this set also yields the points on the line. (See the Notes on **Questions 5a, 6b, 8, and 9.**) The parametric form can be made more concrete by looking at an example. Suppose a puppy weighs 8 pounds and is 15 inches long, and each month it grows $\frac{1}{2}$ inch and gains 3 pounds. Then, after t months, its weight is $8 + 3t$ pounds and its length is $15 + \frac{1}{2}t$ inches. The pairs $\left(8 + 3t, 15 + \frac{1}{2}t\right)$ all lie on the same line. The parametric form examines the changes in the two quantities weight and length individually.

The two theorems on page 735 and the diagram on page 736 are on **Teaching Aid 139.**

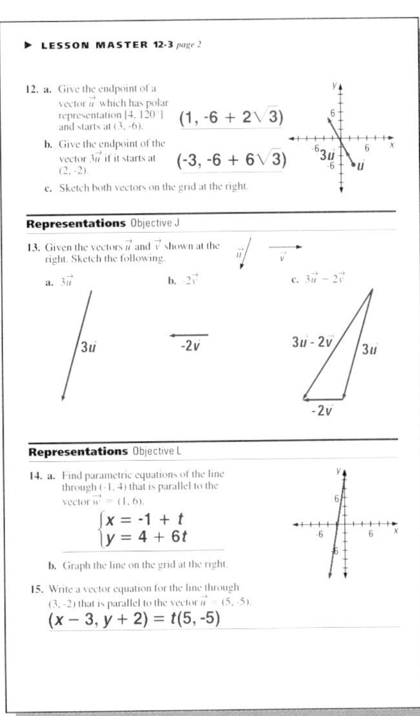
▶ **LESSON MASTER 12-3** *page 2*

12. a. Give the endpoint of a vector $\vec{u}$ which has polar representation [4, 120°] and starts at (3, -6). $(1, -6 + 2\sqrt{3})$

b. Give the endpoint of the vector $3\vec{u}$ if it starts at (2, -2). $(-3, -6 + 6\sqrt{3})$

c. Sketch both vectors on the grid at the right.

Representations Objective J

13. Given the vectors $\vec{u}$ and $\vec{v}$ shown at the right. Sketch the following.

a. $3\vec{u}$ b. $-2\vec{v}$ c. $3\vec{u} - 2\vec{v}$

Representations Objective L

14. a. Find parametric equations of the line through (-1, 4) that is parallel to the vector $\vec{w} = (1, 6)$.

$$\begin{cases} x = -1 + t \\ y = 4 + 6t \end{cases}$$

b. Graph the line on the grid at the right.

15. Write a vector equation for the line through (3, -2) that is parallel to the vector $\vec{u} = (5, -5)$.
$(x - 3, y + 2) = t(5, -5)$

Optional Activities

Activity 1 Technology Connection
Materials: *Explorations* software

Students may use *Exploration 12-3: Parametric Equations for Lines,* to explore vector equations. Students can choose a vector and a point to see the parametric equations of the line through the point and parallel to the vector. They can observe the relationship between the parameter t and the line by choosing other values for the parameter.

Activity 2 In **Question 5,** have students find the x- and y-intercepts of the line. Have them briefly explain their process. [x-intercept is $-\frac{31}{5}$; y-intercept is $\frac{31}{2}$. To find the x-intercept of a line written in parametric equations, set $y = 0$ and solve for t. Substitute this value of t into the equation for x. To find the y-intercept, set $x = 0$ and continue the process.]

Additional Examples

1. If $\vec{v} = (3, -4)$, calculate $|5\vec{v}|$. **25**
2. Show that the vectors (-1, 6) and (6, -1) are not parallel.
   If there is a k such that $k(6, -1) = (-1, 6)$, then $6k = -1$ and $-1k = 6$, from which $k = \frac{-1}{6}$ and $k = -6$ simultaneously, which is impossible.
3. Find parametric equations for the line through (2, 8) parallel to the vector $\vec{v} = (-5, 4)$.
   Sample: $x = 2 - 5t$, $y = 8 + 4t$

Additional Answers

5. a. $x = -3 + 2t$; $y = 8 + 5t$

   b.

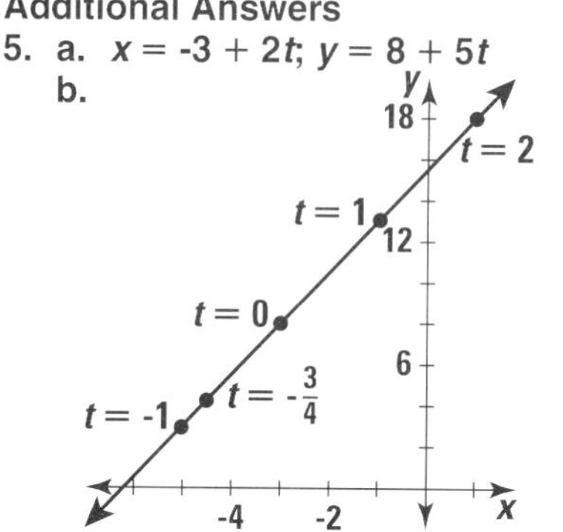

t	0	1	2	-1	$-\frac{3}{4}$
x	-3	-1	1	-5	-4.5
y	8	13	18	3	4.25

6. a.

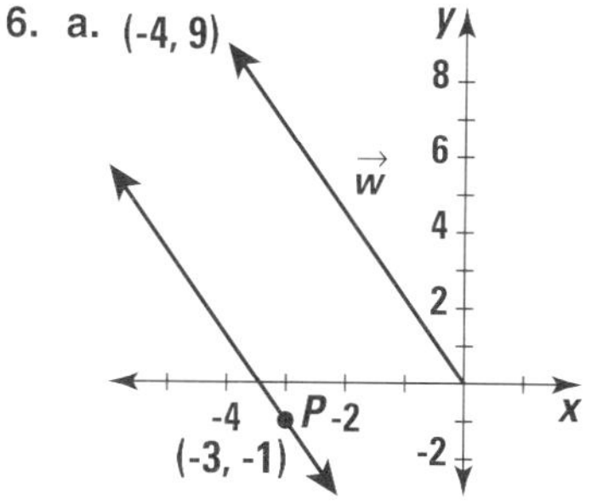

   b. **Sample: $x = -3 - 4t$; $y = -1 + 9t$**

For example, the line through (-4, 5) parallel to $\vec{v} = (7, 2)$ pictured on page 735 has parametric equations

$$\begin{cases} x = -4 + 7t \\ y = \ \ 5 + 2t. \end{cases}$$

In many physical situations, t represents time. Think of a point moving at a constant speed along the line. The location of the point at time t is given by $(x, y) = (-4 + 7t, 5 + 2t)$. Each value of t corresponds to a different point on the line. For example, if $t = 1$, then $x = 3$, and $y = 7$, yielding the point (3, 7) on the line.

Straight stretches of track allow trains to travel at constant speeds along a line.

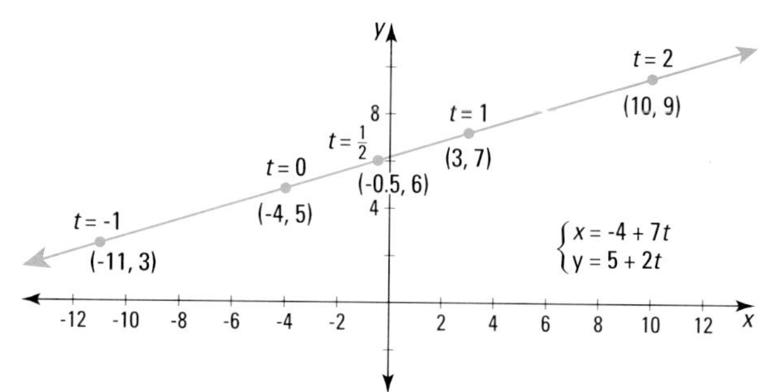

You are familiar with other forms of equations for lines in the plane: $y = mx + b$ (slope-intercept form), $Ax + By = C$ (standard form), and $y - y_0 = m(x - x_0)$ (point-slope form). An advantage of the vector and parametric equations for a line is that they generalize to describe lines in three dimensions. Some examples are given in Lesson 12-7.

QUESTIONS

Covering the Reading

1. Suppose $\vec{s} = [5, 52°]$. In the indicated form, describe the vector with the same direction as $\vec{s}$ and $\frac{1}{4}$ its magnitude.
   a. polar $\left[\frac{5}{4}, 52°\right]$
   b. component **See left.**

   1b) $\left(\frac{5}{4}\cos 52°, \frac{5}{4}\sin 52°\right)$
2. Let $\vec{u}$ be the vector from (-3, 1) to (1, -5). Give the component form for the vector $\vec{v} = -3\vec{u}$. **(-12, 18)**
3. Give an example of a vector parallel to (-6, 14). **See left.**

   3) **Samples: (-12, 28), (6, -14); in general, $k(-6, 14)$ where k is any real number.**
4. Is the vector (8, -3) parallel to the vector (-48, 18)? Why or why not? **(-48, 18) = -6(8, -3), so the vectors are parallel.**
5. A vector equation of a line is $(x + 3, y - 8) = t(2, 5)$. **See margin.**
   a. Give parametric equations for this line.
   b. Graph the line and identify the points on it determined by $t = 0, 1, 2, -1$, and $-\frac{3}{4}$.
6. a. Sketch the line through $P = (-3, -1)$ that is parallel to $\vec{w} = (-4, 9)$.
   b. Write parametric equations for this line.
   See margin.

Optional Activities

Activity 3 Technology Connection
You might wish to assign *Technology Sourcebook, Calculator Master 17.* In this activity, students use a graphics calculator to explore how parametric equations for lines are plotted on a graph and to understand the correspondence between the parametric equations and the slope-intercept equation of a line.

Adapting to Individual Needs

Extra Help
Be sure students understand that the notation $k(u_1, u_2)$ indicates the same ordered pair as (ku_1, ku_2). Students might be reminded of the Distributive Property as they multiply each coordinate of the ordered pair by k.

Challenge
Have students use vectors to prove that the line segment joining the midpoints of two sides of a triangle is parallel to, and one-half the length of, the third side. [If $\vec{u}$ and $\vec{v}$ are the vectors corresponding to two sides, then $\vec{u} - \vec{v}$ corresponds to the third side. The vector connecting the midpoints of $\vec{u}$ and $\vec{v}$ is $\frac{1}{2}\vec{u} - \frac{1}{2}\vec{v} = \frac{1}{2}(\vec{u} - \vec{v})$.]

7) Sample:
$x = -1 - 5t$;
$y = 5 - 5t$

8) Sample:
$(x + 8, y - 5) = t(7, 2)$

9) Sample:
$x = 2 + 3t$;
$y = 8 + t$

10) $-1\vec{v} = -1(v_1, v_2) = (-v_1, -v_2) = -\vec{v}$

11d) $a(b\vec{v}) = a(bv_1, bv_2) = (abv_1, abv_2) = ab(v_1, v_2) = (ab)\vec{v}$

Applying the Mathematics

7. Find parametric equations for the line through (-1, 5) and (4, 10). **See left.**

8. Write a vector equation for the line that contains (-8, 5) and is parallel to the line with vector equation $(x - 4, y + 3) = t(7, 2)$. **See left.**

9. A ship is currently 2 miles east and 8 miles north of port. It is moving in the direction parallel to the vector (3, 1). Find parametric equations for the path of this ship. **See left.**

10. Show that for any vector $\vec{v} = (v_1, v_2)$, $-1\vec{v} = -\vec{v}$. (This shows that $\vec{v}$ and $-1\vec{v}$ have opposite directions.)

11. Let $\vec{v} = (3, -4)$.

a. Find $-5\vec{v}$. **(-15, 20)**

b. Multiply your answer to part **a** by the scalar 2. **(-30, 40)**

c. Find $-10\vec{v}$. **(-30, 40)**

d. Note that part **b** gave you $2(-5\vec{v})$, while part **c** gave you $(2 \cdot -5)\vec{v}$. Generalize parts **a–c** by proving that for any vector $\vec{v} = (v_1, v_2)$ and real numbers a and b, $a(b\vec{v}) = (ab)\vec{v}$. **See left.**

12. Let $\begin{cases} x = x_0 + tv_1 \\ y = y_0 + tv_2 \end{cases}$ be parametric equations for a line. **See margin.**

a. Prove: the point determined when $t = \frac{1}{2}$ is the midpoint of the points determined when $t = 0$ and $t = 1$.

b. Generalize the result of part **a**. (You do not have to prove your generalization.)

Review

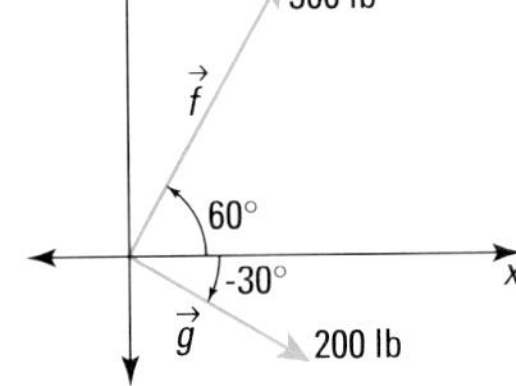

13. Find the resultant force $\vec{h}$ for the forces $\vec{f}$ and $\vec{g}$ shown at the left. *(Lesson 12-2)* **about 360.6 lb in the direction about 26.3°**

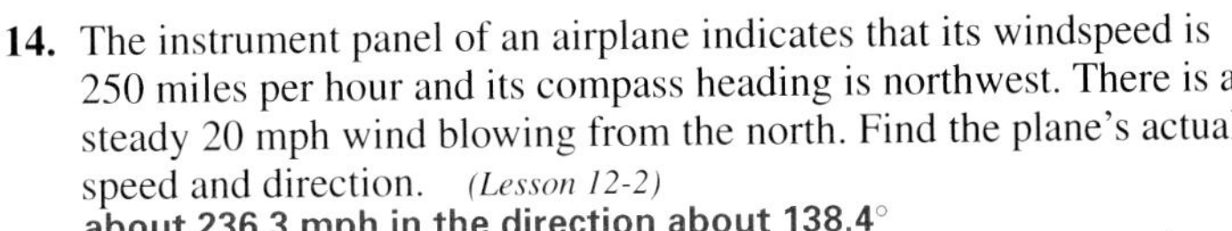

14. The instrument panel of an airplane indicates that its windspeed is 250 miles per hour and its compass heading is northwest. There is a steady 20 mph wind blowing from the north. Find the plane's actual speed and direction. *(Lesson 12-2)*
about 236.3 mph in the direction about 138.4°

15. A vector $\vec{w} = (w_1, w_2)$ in standard position is perpendicular to $\vec{u} = (7, 1)$ and twice as long. Find two sets of values for (w_1, w_2). *(Lesson 12-1)*
(-2, 14), (2, -14)

16. In the matrix of 4 cities shown at the right, a "1" indicates that a flight goes from the city on the left to the city above. A "0" indicates that no such flight exists. Find the number of different 2-stop (that is, 3-leg) routes from Los Angeles to Paris through these cities. *(Lesson 11-5)* **4**

	LA	NY	Paris	London
Los Angeles	0	1	1	1
New York	1	0	1	0
Paris	0	1	0	1
London	1	1	0	0

Notes on Questions

Questions 5a, 6b, 8, and 9 Because there are many parametric equations for a line, students could have different answers here. The given answer is typically the one that would be found by directly applying the techniques of the lesson. But note that any point on the line could be (x_0, y_0) in the parametric equations for it, and t could be replaced by any nonzero multiple kt.

Question 7 Students will have different answers depending on which point they use as a starting point. The values of t will be opposites.

Question 12 Another type of generalization is that the point determined when $t = \frac{a}{b}$, $0 < \frac{a}{b} < 1$, is the point that is $\frac{a}{b}$ of the way from the points determined when $t = 0$ and $t = 1$. This generalization is found in **Question 21.**

Additional Answers

12. a.

t	0	$\frac{1}{2}$	1
x	x_0	$x_0 + \frac{v_1}{2}$	$x_0 + v_1$
y	y_0	$y_0 + \frac{v_2}{2}$	$y_0 + v_2$

$$\frac{(x_0 + y_0) + (x_0 + v_1 + y_0 + v_2)}{2}$$
$$= \frac{(2x_0 + v_1, 2y_0 + v_2)}{2}$$
$$= \left(x_0 + \frac{v_1}{2}, y_0 + \frac{v_2}{2}\right)$$

b. **Sample: The midpoint of the points determined by $t = a$ and $t = b$ is the point determined by $t = \frac{a + b}{2}$.**

Notes on Questions

Question 20 This question is preparation for the discussion of perpendicular vectors in the next lesson.

Follow-up for Lesson 12-3

Practice

For more questions on SPUR Objectives, use **Lesson Master 12-3** (shown on pages 734–735).

Assessment

Quiz A quiz covering Lessons 12-1 through 12-3 is provided in the *Assessment Sourcebook.*

Extension

Project Update Project 4, *Vectors Applied to Physics,* on page 774, relates to the content of this lesson.

Additional Answers

17. a. -0.267 words per sec; the subjects forget 8 words per 30 second period when the wait-time changes from 0 sec to 30 sec.
    b. -.13 words per sec; the subjects forget 4 words per 30-second period when the wait time changes from 30 sec to 60 sec.

Wait-time (sec)	Mean number of words remembered
0	25
30	17
60	13
300	10

17. A psychologist conducts a study in which subjects (the people being studied) are given a list of 40 words to memorize. Some of the subjects are then asked to recall as many words as they can. Others are told to wait 30 seconds, 1 minute, or 5 minutes, and then asked to recall the words. The table at the left shows that, on the average, the longer that the subjects are told to wait, the fewer words they remember. **See margin.**

a. Find and interpret the average rate of change in words remembered with respect to wait-time from 0 sec to 30 sec.

b. Repeat part **a** for wait-times from 30 sec to 60 sec. *(Lesson 9-1)*

18. Here is a "proof" that all positive integers are even. Where does the argument go wrong?

Let $S(n)$: *n is even.*
Use the Strong Form of the Principle of Mathematical Induction and start with the inductive assumption that all of the statements $S(1), S(2), \dots, S(k)$ are true. Show that this assumption implies that $S(k+1)$ is true:

$$S(k+1)\text{: } k+1 \text{ is even.}$$

The number $k+1$ can be expressed as

$$k+1 = k-1+2.$$

Since $k-1$ is less than k, $k-1$ is even by the inductive assumption. That is, $k-1$ can be expressed as $2m$ for some integer m. Substituting into the equation for $k+1$ yields

$$k+1 = 2m+2,$$

or

$$k+1 = 2(m+1)$$

by the Distributive Property. Thus, $k+1$ is twice an integer, $m+1$. Thus $k+1$ is even, so $S(k+1)$ is true. By the Principle of Mathematical Induction, $S(n)$ is true for all positive integers n. All positive integers are even! *(Lesson 7-7)* **See left.**

19. *Multiple choice.* If a is even, and b is odd, then $ab + a + b$ is which of the following? **b**
(a) always even
(b) always odd
(c) sometimes even, sometimes odd *(Lesson 4-1)*

20. Given $A = (3, -4)$, $B = (5, 1)$, $C = (-1, 6)$, and $D = (8, -2)$. Of the lines $\overleftrightarrow{AB}$, $\overleftrightarrow{AC}$, and $\overleftrightarrow{AD}$, which two are perpendicular to each other? *(Previous course)* $\overleftrightarrow{AC}$ **and** $\overleftrightarrow{AD}$

18) The initial conditions do not hold because $S(1)$, $S(3)$, . . . are not true.

21) Since $x = x_0 + v_1t$ and $y = y_0 + v_2t$, when $t = 0$, $P = (x_0, y_0)$ is determined. When $t = 1$, $Q = (x_0 + v_1, y_0 + v_2)$ is determined. Create a number line with P at 0 and Q at 1. Then each value of t will determine the corresponding point on the number line.

Exploration

21. In the parametric equations for a line, there is a 1-1 correspondence between values of t and points on the line. Using Questions 5 and 12 as a guide, how can you tell geometrically, given x_0, y_0, v_1, and v_2, what points will be determined by various values of t? That is, what point is given when $t = 0$, when $t = 1$, and so on? **See left.**

Setting Up Lesson 12-4

Discuss **Question 20** to ensure that students remember how to determine whether lines in the plane are perpendicular by using their slopes. Do the In-class Activity on page 739.

Introducing
Lesson 12-4

Finding the Angle Between Two Vectors

IN-CLASS ACTIVITY

By positioning vectors at certain angles to each other, the forces they represent can be maneuvered. You can determine the angle between two vectors by using the Law of Cosines and other theorems you know. Consider the vectors $\vec{r} = (3, 2)$ and $\vec{s} = (-2, 9)$ as drawn here. Let θ be the measure of the angle between them.

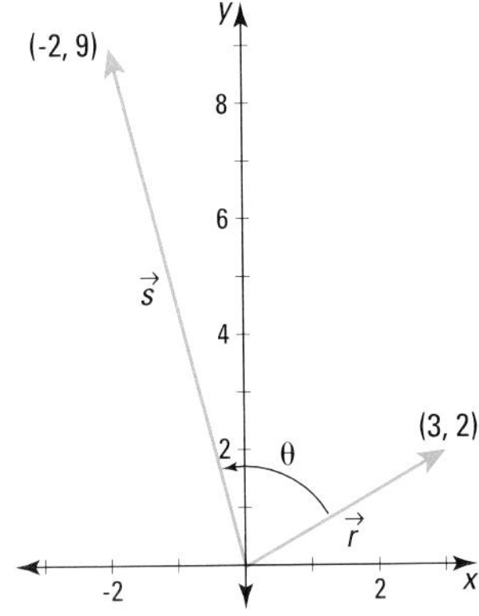

1 **a.** Find the lengths of the vectors r and s. **$|\vec{r}| = \sqrt{13}$; $|\vec{s}| = \sqrt{85}$**
b. Find the distance between (-2, 9) and (3, 2). **$\sqrt{74}$**

2 **a.** Using the Law of Cosines, find cos θ. **≈ .361**
b. From part **a**, find θ to the nearest tenth of a degree. **θ = 68.8°**

3 Use the ideas of parts 1 and 2 to find the angle between the vectors $\vec{t} = (3.5, 6)$ and $\vec{u} = (-12, 7)$. **cos θ = 0; θ = 90°**

4 Examine the components of the vectors $\vec{t}$ and $\vec{u}$. How could you have predicted the result of part 3 with just one calculation?
Sample: The product of the slopes of perpendicular lines is -1 and the ratio of second to first components is the slope of the line containing the vector. Since $\frac{6}{3.5} \cdot \frac{7}{-12} = -1$, the lines containing the vectors are perpendicular.

In-class Activity

Resources

From the ***Teacher's Resource File***
- Answer Master 12-4

This activity is related to **Example 3** of Lesson 12-4. In that Example, the angle between two vectors is derived by using the dot product of vectors, which is introduced just before **Example 2.** The activity shows how this angle can be found without using the dot product. By doing so, it runs through the process of deriving the formula that precedes **Example 3.** Consequently, doing the Activity will make it easier to read and understand the next lesson.

Lesson 12-4

Objectives

B Find dot products of two-dimensional vectors.
D Find the measure of the angle between two vectors.
E Prove or disprove generalizations about vector operations.
F Identify orthogonal vectors.
L Represent lines in a plane using vector or parametric equations.

Resources

From the ***Teacher's Resource File***
- Lesson Master 12-4
- Answer Master 12-4
- Teaching Aids
  133 Warm-up
  140 Example 1

Additional Resources
- Visuals for Teaching Aids 133, 140
- Exploration 12-4

Teaching Lesson 12-4

Warm-up

Let * be an operation on ordered pairs of real numbers, defined as follows: $(a, b) * (c, d) = ac + bd$.

1. Is * commutative? **Yes**
2. Is the set of ordered pairs of real numbers closed under *? **No**
3. Is * associative? *** could not be associative because there is no closure after the first operation.**

LESSON

12-4 *The Dot Product and the Angle Between Two Vectors*

Computing an Angle for a Ratio of Forces

Because of the difference between the force of gravity on Earth and on the moon, a person's weight on the moon is about one-sixth of what it is on Earth. In the 1960s, when the United States decided to send astronauts to the moon, NASA engineers built an apparatus that simulated the effect of gravity on the moon, and on which astronauts practiced walking and jumping. The apparatus consisted of an inclined plane with a trolley that ran back and forth along the top of the plane. A cable from the trolley to a harness held the astronaut so that his body was perpendicular to the plane and he was able to move back and forth along the plane. The idea was to fix the angle θ between the horizontal and the incline so that the force of the astronaut's feet against the plane was equal to one-sixth of his weight. Thus the force on his feet would feel like the force he would experience on the moon.

Example 1

Compute the angle of inclination θ for the lunar gravity simulator.

Solution

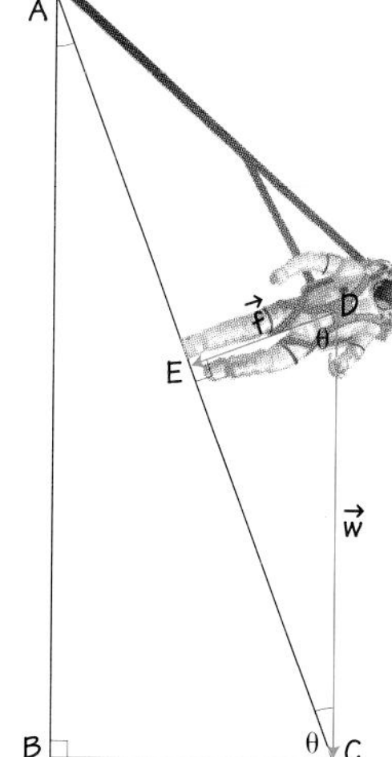

The weight of the astronaut is indicated by the length of a vector $\vec{w}$ pointing straight downward toward the center of Earth. The force $\vec{f}$ exerted by the astronaut's feet against the inclined plane ($\overline{CA}$ in the picture) is
❶ a vector perpendicular to the plane.

The angle $\theta \cong \angle BCA$ (the angle of inclination of the plane) must be chosen so that

$$|\vec{f}| = \frac{1}{6}\text{(astronaut's weight)} = \frac{1}{6}|\vec{w}|.$$

Since $\overline{BA} \,//\, \overline{CD}$, $\angle BAC \cong \angle DCE$. This makes $\triangle ABC \sim \triangle CED$ and thus θ is equal to the angle between $\vec{f}$ and $\vec{w}$. It follows that

$$\cos\theta = \frac{DE}{CD} = \frac{|\vec{f}|}{|\vec{w}|}.$$

Since $|\vec{f}| = \frac{1}{6}|\vec{w}|$, $\cos\theta = \frac{1}{6}$. So the angle of inclination θ of the lunar simulator plane is given by $\theta = \cos^{-1}\left(\frac{1}{6}\right) \approx 80.4°$.

Lesson 12-4 Overview

Broad Goals This lesson introduces the dot product of two vectors and gives some of its algebraic and geometric properties.

Perspective A third binary operation on vectors is the dot product, also called the *inner product*. The result of this operation is a real number that has certain very nice properties. (1) When the dot product of two nonzero vectors is divided by the product of the lengths of the vectors, the quotient is the cosine of the angle between the vectors. (2) When the dot product of two nonzero vectors is zero, the vectors are orthogonal (perpendicular). (3) The dot product of a vector with itself is the square of the length of the vector. As with the properties in the previous lesson, all these properties extend to three dimensions, so the mathematics is quite powerful.

Optional Activities

Activity 1 Technology Connection
Materials: *Explorations* software

Students may use *Exploration 12-4: The Angle Between Two Vectors,* as an alternative to Example 3 in this lesson. Students can enter two vector forces in rectangular form. Each vector will be shown on a coordinate grid. The algebraic computation for finding the angle between the vectors is also shown.

What Is the Dot Product of Two Vectors?

In Example 1, the angle between $\vec{f}$ and $\vec{w}$ could be determined from $|\vec{f}|$ and $|\vec{w}|$ because a right triangle is formed. This, of course, is not always the case. However, the angle between two nonzero vectors can always be determined from the components of the vectors. The process begins by first defining another operation on vectors.

> **Definition**
> The **dot product** of $\vec{u} = (u_1, u_2)$ and $\vec{v} = (v_1, v_2)$, denoted by $\vec{u} \cdot \vec{v}$, is the real number $u_1v_1 + u_2v_2$.

Notice that the dot product of two vectors is a number, not a vector.

Example 2

If $\vec{u} = (2, 3)$ and $\vec{v} = (7, -1)$, calculate $\vec{u} \cdot \vec{v}$.

Solution

Here $u_1 = 2$, $u_2 = 3$, $v_1 = 7$, and $v_2 = -1$.
$\vec{u} \cdot \vec{v} = u_1v_1 + u_2v_2 = 2 \cdot 7 + 3 \cdot -1 = 11$

The dot product of a vector with itself is related to its length.

> **Theorem**
> The dot product of a vector with itself equals the square of its length: For all vectors $\vec{w}$, $\vec{w} \cdot \vec{w} = |\vec{w}|^2$.

> **Proof**
> Let $\vec{w} = (w_1, w_2)$. Then $\vec{w} \cdot \vec{w} = w_1w_1 + w_2w_2 = w_1^{\ 2} + w_2^{\ 2} = |\vec{w}|^2$.

Computing the Angle Between Two Vectors

With the dot product, the angle between two nonzero vectors $\vec{u}$ and $\vec{v}$ can easily be described. Consider the triangle ABC formed by the standard position arrows for $\vec{u}$ and $\vec{v}$, as shown at the right. The arrow extending from B to C represents the vector $\vec{u} - \vec{v}$ and is the third side of this triangle. If θ is the angle between $\vec{u}$ and $\vec{v}$, then according to the Law of Cosines,

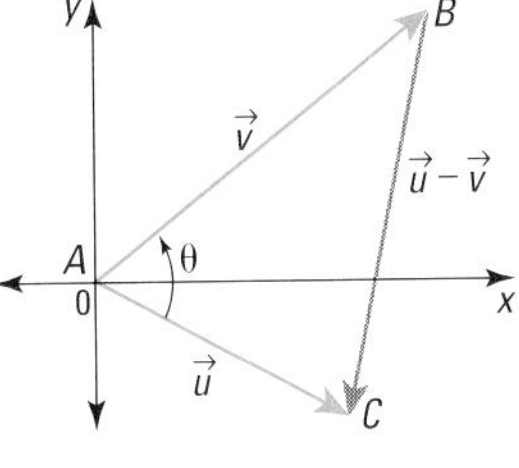

$$BC^2 = AC^2 + AB^2 - 2 \cdot AC \cdot AB \cdot \cos\theta.$$

In the language of vectors, the Law of Cosines is

$$|\vec{u} - \vec{v}|^2 = |\vec{u}|^2 + |\vec{v}|^2 - 2\,|\vec{u}|\,|\vec{v}|\cos\theta.$$

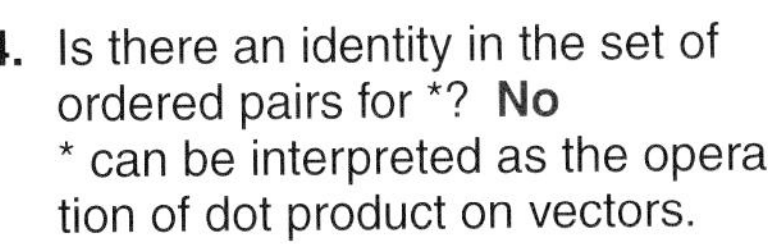

4. Is there an identity in the set of ordered pairs for *? **No**
* can be interpreted as the operation of dot product on vectors.

Notes on Reading

Example 1 is designed to show that the angle between two vectors can be a rather significant idea; in the lunar gravity simulator, finding this angle is part of the process of equalizing gravitational forces. **Teaching Aid 140** with the picture is provided.

Summarize the remainder of the lesson by asking students for the three major properties of the dot product given here. Although they are found in the three theorems of the lesson, there is a lot to be read and students may not focus on them.

Alternate Approach Students may appreciate a picture of the theorem on this page.
$\vec{w} \cdot \vec{w} = |\vec{w}|^2 = w_1^{\ 2} + w_2^{\ 2}$

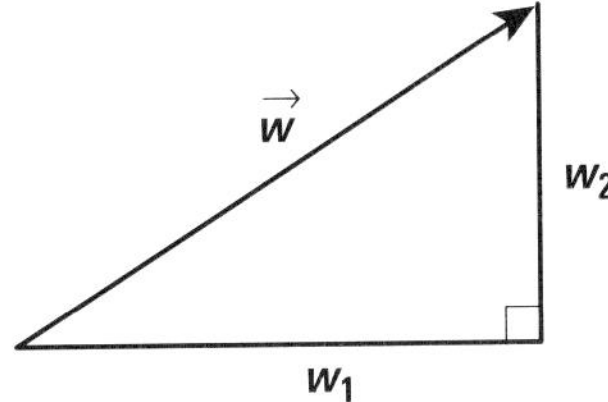

❶ When dealing with vectors, the word *orthogonal* is more commonly used than the word *perpendicular*. It is related to orthodontia ("straight tooth") and orthodox ("having right opinion"). One nonobvious application of orthogonal vectors is found in Lesson 12-7; in deriving an equation for a plane, a vector orthogonal to the plane is used.

Activity 2 In **Question 7,** ask students to find y if the angle between $\vec{u}$ and $\vec{v}$ is 180°. $\left[y = \frac{10}{3}\right.$; students may solve $\frac{-6 - 5y}{\sqrt{34}\sqrt{4 + y^2}}$ or (more simply) consider that the slopes of the two vectors must be the same: $\left.\frac{5}{3} = \frac{y}{2}.\right]$ As a challenge, ask them to find y if the angle between $\vec{u}$ and $\vec{v}$ is 60°. $[y = -3.6]$

Adapting to Individual Needs

Extra Help

To help students remember the important ideas about dot products, you might want to summarize them on the chalkboard.

Definition and Properties of Dot Products:
For all vectors $\vec{u} = (u_1, u_2)$ and $\vec{v} = (v_1, v_2)$ with θ the angle between them,

(1) $\vec{u} \cdot \vec{v} = u_1v_1 + u_2v_2$
(2) $\vec{u} \cdot \vec{u} = |\vec{u}|^2$
(3) $\frac{\vec{u} \cdot \vec{v}}{|\vec{u}|\,|\vec{v}|} = \cos\theta$
(4) $\vec{u} \cdot \vec{v} = 0 \Leftrightarrow \vec{u} \perp \vec{v}$.

❷ The formula for cos θ in the Angle Between Vectors Theorem is used so often it is worth discussing calculator keystrokes. Students should be careful to enter $a \div (b \cdot c)$ rather than $a \div b \cdot c$.

Example 4 asks for a geometric meaning of a negative dot product. The **Activity** which follows it, repeated in **Question 6,** asks for a geometric meaning of a positive dot product. Here is a more inclusive geometric interpretation. $\vec{u} \cdot \vec{v}$ equals the product of two lengths: the length of $\vec{u}$ and the length of the projection of $\vec{v}$ onto $\vec{u}$. If $\vec{u}$ and $\vec{v}$ are perpendicular, then the length of the projection of $\vec{v}$ onto $\vec{u}$ is zero, so the dot product is zero.

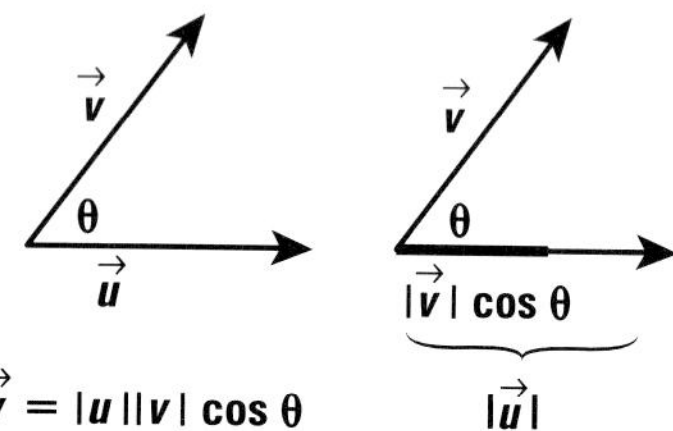

Also, see Extra Help in *Adapting to Individual Needs* on page 741.

Now rewrite the squares of the lengths of the vectors $|\vec{u} - \vec{v}|^2$, $|\vec{u}|^2$, and $|\vec{v}|^2$ as the sum of the squares of their components.

$$(u_1 - v_1)^2 + (u_2 - v_2)^2 = u_1^2 + u_2^2 + v_1^2 + v_2^2 - 2|\vec{u}||\vec{v}| \cos\theta$$
$$u_1^2 - 2u_1v_1 + v_1^2 + u_2^2 - 2u_2v_2 + v_2^2 = u_1^2 + u_2^2 + v_1^2 + v_2^2 - 2|\vec{u}||\vec{v}| \cos\theta$$
$$-2u_1v_1 - 2u_2v_2 = -2|\vec{u}||\vec{v}| \cos\theta$$
$$u_1v_1 + u_2v_2 = |\vec{u}||\vec{v}| \cos\theta$$
$$\vec{u} \cdot \vec{v} = |\vec{u}||\vec{v}| \cos\theta$$

Dividing both sides by $|\vec{u}||\vec{v}|$ yields the following result.

Angle Between Vectors Theorem

Suppose that θ is the measure of the angle between two nonzero vectors $\vec{u}$ and $\vec{v}$ and $0 \le \theta \le \pi$. Then

$$\cos\theta = \frac{\vec{u} \cdot \vec{v}}{|\vec{u}||\vec{v}|}.$$

The preceding proof was based on the assumption that the vectors $\vec{u}$ and $\vec{v}$ determine a triangle; that is, that $\vec{u}$ and $\vec{v}$ are not parallel. In Question 11, you are asked to show that the Angle Between Vectors Theorem holds even if this condition is not met.

With the Angle Between Vectors Theorem, you can verify the result of the In-class Activity on page 739.

Example 3

Find the angle θ between the vectors $\vec{r} = (3, 2)$ and $\vec{s} = (-2, 9)$.

Solution

By the Angle Between Vectors Theorem,

$$\cos\theta = \frac{\vec{r} \cdot \vec{s}}{|\vec{r}||\vec{s}|}.$$

Here

$$|\vec{r}| = \sqrt{3^2 + 2^2} = \sqrt{13},$$
$$|\vec{s}| = \sqrt{(-2)^2 + (9)^2} = \sqrt{85},$$

and

$$\vec{r} \cdot \vec{s} = (3)(-2) + (2)(9) = 12.$$

It follows that

$$\cos\theta = \frac{12}{\sqrt{13}\sqrt{85}} \approx 0.361.$$

Therefore

$$\theta \approx \cos^{-1}(.361)$$
$$\approx 68.8°$$
$$\approx 1.201 \text{ radians.}$$

LESSON MASTER 12-4 Questions on SPUR Objectives
See pages 778–781 for objectives.

Skills Objective B

In 1–4, let $\vec{u} = (3, 8)$, $\vec{v} = (4, -2)$ and $\vec{w} = (-7, 6)$, and compute.

1. $\vec{v} \cdot \vec{w}$ -40
2. $\vec{u} \cdot \vec{u}$ 73
3. $\vec{u} \cdot (\vec{v} \cdot \vec{w})$ (-120, -320)
4. $(\vec{v} - \vec{w}) \cdot (\vec{u} + \vec{v})$ 29

Skills Objective D

In 5–8, find the measure of the angle between the two vectors.

5. (-3, -3) and (1, 2) 161.6°
6. (4, 6) and (2, 7) 17.7°
7. (-5, 0) and (0, -12) 90°
8. [4, 94°] and [19, 211°] 117°

Properties Objective E

9. Show that $\vec{v} = (-4, 7)$ and $\vec{w} = (-12, -9)$ are not orthogonal.
$\vec{v} \cdot \vec{w} = -4 \cdot -12 + 7 \cdot -9 = 48 - 63 = -15 \ne 0$

10. If $\vec{u}$ and $\vec{v}$ are perpendicular vectors, prove that for all nonzero real numbers j and k, $j\vec{u}$ and $k\vec{v}$ are perpendicular. Sample is given.
Let $\vec{u} = (u_1, u_2)$ and $\vec{v} = (v_1, v_2)$. Since $\vec{u}$ and $\vec{v}$ are perpendicular, $u_1v_1 + u_2v_2 = 0$. Also, $j\vec{u} = (ju_1, ju_2)$ and $k\vec{v} = (kv_1, kv_2)$. So $j\vec{u} \cdot k\vec{v} = ju_1 \cdot kv_1 + ju_2 \cdot kv_2 = jk(u_1, v_1) + jk(u_2, v_2) = jk(u_1, v_1 + u_2, v_2) = jk \cdot 0 = 0$. Therefore, $j\vec{u}$ and $k\vec{v}$ are perpendicular.

Adapting to Individual Needs

Challenge

Have students answer the following.

1. Let $\vec{u} = (\cos\alpha, \sin\alpha)$ and $\vec{v} = (\cos\beta, \sin\beta)$, where $\alpha > \beta$. Use $\vec{u} \cdot \vec{v}$ to give a different proof of a previous identity: $\cos(\alpha - \beta) = \cos\alpha\cos\beta + \sin\alpha\sin\beta$. [$\alpha - \beta$ is the measure of the angle between $\vec{u}$ and $\vec{v}$, so $\cos(\alpha - \beta) = \frac{\vec{u} \cdot \vec{v}}{|\vec{u}||\vec{v}|} = \cos\alpha\cos\beta + \sin\alpha\sin\beta$.]
2. Use vectors to prove that the diagonals of a rhombus are perpendicular. [Let $\vec{u}$ and $\vec{v}$ be vectors corresponding to adjacent sides. Because $\vec{u}$ and $\vec{v}$ are sides of a rhombus, $|\vec{u}| = |\vec{v}|$. Also, $\vec{u} + \vec{v}$ and $\vec{u} - \vec{v}$ are vectors corresponding to the diagonals. So $(\vec{u} + \vec{v}) \cdot (\vec{u} - \vec{v}) = u_1^2 - v_1^2 + u_2^2 - v_2^2 = \vec{u} \cdot \vec{u} - \vec{v} \cdot \vec{v} = |\vec{u}|^2 - |\vec{v}|^2 = 0$, since $\vec{u}$ and $\vec{v}$ have the same length.]

How Is the Dot Product Related to Right, Obtuse, and Acute Angles?

In the Angle Between Vectors Theorem, the denominator of the formula for $\cos \theta$ is always positive. Thus the sign of $\cos \theta$ is the same as the sign of the dot product $\vec{u} \cdot \vec{v}$.

Example 4

If $\vec{u}$ and $\vec{v}$ are nonzero vectors, explain the geometric meaning of the inequality $\vec{u} \cdot \vec{v} < 0$.

Solution

The question asks what it means for the dot product of two vectors to be negative. Since $|\vec{u}||\vec{v}|$ is always positive, $\vec{u} \cdot \vec{v}$ has the same sign as $\cos \theta$, where θ is the angle between the two vectors with $0 \le \theta \le \pi$. For these values of θ, $\cos \theta < 0$ only when $\frac{\pi}{2} < \theta \le \pi$. Therefore the dot product of two vectors is negative only if the angle between them is obtuse or if they have opposite directions.

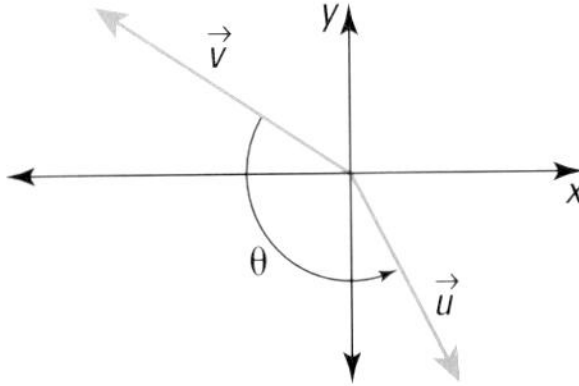

Activity

If $\vec{u}$ and $\vec{v}$ are nonzero vectors, explain the geometric meaning of the inequality $\vec{u} \cdot \vec{v} > 0$. **See Question 6 on page 745.**

The dot product also provides a simple criterion for testing whether two vectors are perpendicular. Let θ be the angle between the two nonzero vectors $\vec{u}$ and $\vec{v}$. Then, $\vec{u}$ and $\vec{v}$ are perpendicular

$$\Leftrightarrow \quad \theta = \frac{\pi}{2}$$

$$\Leftrightarrow \quad \cos \theta = 0 \quad \text{(since } 0 \le \theta \le \pi\text{)}$$

$$\Leftrightarrow \quad \frac{\vec{u} \cdot \vec{v}}{|\vec{u}|\,|\vec{v}|} = 0 \quad \text{Angle Between Vectors Theorem}$$

$$\Leftrightarrow \quad \vec{u} \cdot \vec{v} = 0.$$

This proves the following theorem.

> **Theorem**
> Two nonzero vectors $\vec{u}$ and $\vec{v}$ are perpendicular if and only if their dot product is zero.

Perpendicular vectors are also called **orthogonal**.

Additional Examples

1. The force of gravity on the planet Venus is about 88% of the force of gravity on Earth. To simulate such gravity, what should be the angle of the inclined plane? **$\cos^{-1} .88 \approx 28°$**
2. Calculate $\vec{u} \cdot \vec{v}$ when $\vec{u} = (10, 3)$ and $\vec{v} = (-4, -1)$. **-43**
3. Give the measure of the angle between the two vectors of Additional Example 2. **$\cos^{-1} \frac{-43}{\sqrt{109}\sqrt{17}} \approx 177°$**
4. How are two vectors related if their dot product equals half the product of their lengths? **The angle between them is 60°.**
5. a. Find all vectors in a plane that are orthogonal to [3, 72°] and have length 2. **[2, 162°] and [2, -18°]**
   b. Find all vectors in a plane that are orthogonal to (6, -2) and have length $10\sqrt{2}$. **$(2\sqrt{5}, 6\sqrt{5})$ and $(-2\sqrt{5}, -6\sqrt{5})$**

▶ **LESSON MASTER 12-4** *page 2*

Properties Objective F

In 11–13, determine whether $\vec{u}$ and $\vec{v}$ are perpendicular, parallel, or neither.

11. $\vec{u} = (7, 7), \vec{v} = (-3, 8)$ — neither
12. $\vec{u} = (4, -10), \vec{v} = (-5, -2)$ — perpendicular
13. $\vec{u} = (3, -5), \vec{v} = (12, -20)$ — parallel
14. Find x so that the vectors $\vec{u} = (10, -12)$ and $\vec{v} = (x, 5)$ are orthogonal. — $x = 6$
15. Find all plane vectors with length $10\sqrt{2}$ that are orthogonal to $\vec{w} = (1, -7)$. — (14, 2) or (-14, -2)

Representations Objective L

In 16 and 17, let $\vec{v} = (-2, 9)$. Write a vector equation for the line through $P = (1, 4)$ that is

16. parallel to $\vec{v}$. — $(x - 1, y - 4) = t(-2, 9)$
17. perpendicular to $\vec{v}$. — $(x - 1, y - 4) = t(9, 2)$

Notes on Questions

Questions 1–3 Students should be able to tell if the answer is a scalar or a vector by looking at the expression. Point out that an expression like $(\vec{u} \cdot \vec{v}) \cdot \vec{w}$ is meaningless, since the dot product is performed on two vectors and $\vec{u} \cdot \vec{v}$ is a scalar.

Question 4 Check the answer by drawing a picture.

Question 9 Alternate Approach Use the idea that (v_1, v_2) and $(v_2, -v_1)$ are perpendicular. This gives (4, 3) as a direction vector of the line and leads easily to a vector equation. You can point out that the dot product can be used to give a coordinate equation of the line. Let $(x - 6, y - 2)$ be a vector lying on the line. Then $(x - 6, y - 2) \cdot (-3, 4) = 0$, from which $-3(x - 6) + 4(y - 2) = 0$, or $-3x + 4y = -10$. You can preview Lesson 12-7 by pointing out that, in general, the vector (a, b) is perpendicular to the line with equation $ax + by = c$.

Question 13 Students may be surprised that the angle between two lines is unaffected by their y-intercepts. Ask why. [Translations do not affect slopes of lines; parallel lines have the same slope.]

Question 16 In this situation, one subtracts the wind velocity from the desired velocity to get the necessary plane velocity.

(Notes on Questions continue on page 746.)

Example 5

Find all vectors in a plane that are orthogonal to $\vec{w} = (1, 4)$ and have length 2.

Solution

Let $\vec{u} = (u_1, u_2)$ be any such vector. Since $\vec{u}$ and $\vec{w}$ are orthogonal,

$$0 = \vec{u} \cdot \vec{w} = u_1 + 4u_2.$$

Since

$$|\vec{u}| = 2,$$
$$u_1^2 + u_2^2 = 4.$$

This is now a system of equations in u_1 and u_2. From the first equation, $u_1 = -4u_2$. Substituting into the second equation yields

$$(-4u_2)^2 + u_2^2 = 4.$$

Therefore, $17u_2^2 = 4$ and so $u_2^2 = \frac{4}{17}$. Consequently, $u_2 = \frac{\pm 2}{\sqrt{17}}$ and $u_1 = -4u_2 = \frac{\mp 8}{\sqrt{17}}$. Thus, the two vectors of length 2 that are orthogonal to $\vec{w} = (1, 4)$ are $\vec{r} = \left(\frac{-8}{\sqrt{17}}, \frac{2}{\sqrt{17}}\right)$ and $\vec{s} = \left(\frac{8}{\sqrt{17}}, \frac{-2}{\sqrt{17}}\right)$.

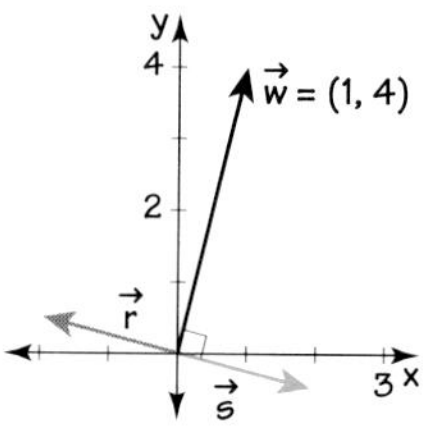

Check

You should check that $|\vec{r}| = |\vec{s}| = 2$ and that $\vec{r} \cdot \vec{w} = \vec{s} \cdot \vec{w} = 0$.

QUESTIONS

Covering the Reading

In 1–4, let $\vec{u} = (-10, 20)$, $\vec{v} = (3, -2)$, and $\vec{w} = (5, 6)$. Compute the following.

1. $\vec{u} \cdot \vec{w}$ 70

2. $(\vec{u} \cdot \vec{v})\vec{w}$ (-350, -420)

3. $(\vec{u} + \vec{v}) \cdot \vec{w}$ 73

4. the measure of the angle between $\vec{u}$ and $\vec{v}$ 150° 5) $\cos^{-1}\frac{3}{8} \approx 68°$

5. The force of gravity on Mars is about $\frac{3}{8}$ the force of gravity on Earth. To simulate Mars' force of gravity in a way similar to that described in Example 1, at what angle should the inclined plane be constructed?

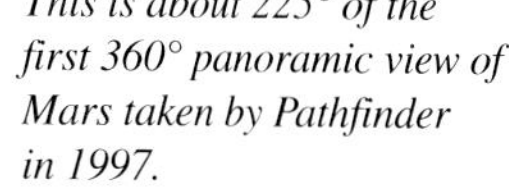
This is about 225° of the first 360° panoramic view of Mars taken by Pathfinder in 1997.

Additional Answers

6. The meaning of the dot product of two vectors being positive is the same as asking what it means for $\cos\theta$ to be positive, where θ is the angle between the two vectors and $0 \le \theta \le \pi$. For these values of θ, $\cos\theta > 0$ only when $0 \le \theta < \frac{\pi}{2}$. Therefore the dot product of two vectors is positive only if the angle between them is acute.

8. $|\vec{r}| = \sqrt{\left(\frac{-8}{\sqrt{17}}\right)^2 + \left(\frac{2}{\sqrt{17}}\right)^2} = \sqrt{\frac{64}{17} + \frac{4}{17}} = \sqrt{\frac{68}{17}} = \sqrt{4} = 2$

$|\vec{s}| = \sqrt{\left(\frac{8}{\sqrt{17}}\right)^2 + \left(\frac{-2}{\sqrt{17}}\right)^2} = \sqrt{\frac{64}{17} + \frac{4}{17}} = \sqrt{\frac{68}{17}} = \sqrt{4} = 2$

$\vec{r} \cdot \vec{w} = \left(\frac{-8}{\sqrt{17}}\right)(1) + \left(\frac{2}{\sqrt{17}}\right)(4) = \frac{-8}{\sqrt{17}} + \frac{8}{\sqrt{17}} = 0;$

$\vec{s} \cdot \vec{w} = \left(\frac{8}{\sqrt{17}}\right)(1) + \left(\frac{-2}{\sqrt{17}}\right)(4) = \frac{8}{\sqrt{17}} + \frac{-8}{\sqrt{17}} = 0$

6. Give the results that you found for the Activity in this lesson. **See margin.**

7. Find y so that the vectors $\vec{u} = (-3, -5)$ and $\vec{v} = (2, y)$ are orthogonal. **$y = -\frac{6}{5}$**

8. Finish the check to Example 5. **See margin.**

9. Find all plane vectors that are orthogonal to the vector $\vec{u} = (3, 4)$ that have length 10. **(-8, 6) or (8, -6)**

Applying the Mathematics

10. Write a vector equation for the line through (6, 2) that is perpendicular to the vector (-3, 4). **Sample: $(x - 6, y - 2) = k(4, 3)$**

11. Suppose two nonzero vectors $\vec{u}$ and $\vec{v}$ are parallel, and let $\vec{v} = (v_1, v_2)$. Then $\vec{u} = k\vec{v}$ where $k \neq 0$. Let θ be the angle between $\vec{u}$ and $\vec{v}$. **a–d) See left.**
    a. Write $\vec{u} \cdot \vec{v}$ in terms of v_1 and v_2.
    b. Write $|\vec{u}|\,|\vec{v}|$ in terms of v_1 and v_2.
    c. If $k > 0$, then $\vec{u}$ and $\vec{v}$ have the same direction, so $\theta =$ __?__. If $k < 0$, then $\vec{u}$ and $\vec{v}$ have opposite directions, so $\theta =$ __?__.
    d. Use part **c** to explain why $|k| \cos \theta = k$.
    e. Use parts **a**, **b**, and **d** to show that the Angle Between Vectors Theorem holds when $\vec{u}$ and $\vec{v}$ are parallel. **See margin.**

12. a. Find a vector of length 2 that is perpendicular to the line given by $x = -8 + 5t$, $y = 6 - 12t$. **See left.**
    b. Use that vector to find parametric equations for the line through (-8, 6) and perpendicular to the line given in part **a**.

13. Give the measure of the acute angle between the lines $y = 3x$ and $y = 2x + 4$. (Hint: Graph the lines first.) **8.13°**

14. Show that the dot product has the following algebraic properties for all vectors $\vec{u}$, $\vec{v}$, and $\vec{w}$, and for any real number k. **See margin.**
    a. $\vec{u} \cdot \vec{v} = \vec{v} \cdot \vec{u}$
    b. $\vec{u} \cdot (\vec{v} + \vec{w}) = \vec{u} \cdot \vec{v} + \vec{u} \cdot \vec{w}$
    c. $(k\vec{u}) \cdot \vec{v} = k(\vec{u} \cdot \vec{v})$

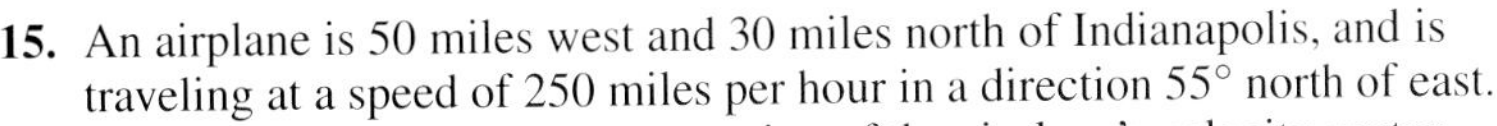

Review

15. An airplane is 50 miles west and 30 miles north of Indianapolis, and is traveling at a speed of 250 miles per hour in a direction 55° north of east.
    a. Find the component representation of the airplane's velocity vector.
    b. Find parametric equations for the path of the airplane.
    c. Find the point on this path for $t = 0.5$. What does this answer tell you about the airplane? *(Lessons 12-1, 12-3)*

See margin.

16. Suppose that a pilot wants to fly directly east at a ground speed of 225 mph, but that there is a wind from the northwest at a speed of 40 mph. What airspeed and compass heading should the pilot select? *(Lesson 12-2)*
airspeed ≈ 198.7 mph, compass heading ≈ 8.18° N of E

11a) $k(v_1)^2 + k(v_2)^2$
b) $|k|\,[(v_1)^2 + (v_2)^2]$
c) 0°, 180°
d) If $k > 0$, $|k| \cdot \cos 0° = k \cdot 1 = k$; if $k < 0$, $|k| \cdot \cos 180° = -k \cdot -1 = k$. Hence, $|k| \cos \theta = k$

12a) $\left(\frac{24}{13}, \frac{10}{13}\right)$ or $\left(\frac{-24}{13}, \frac{-10}{13}\right)$
b) $x = -8 + \frac{24}{13}t$; $y = 6 + \frac{10}{13}t$

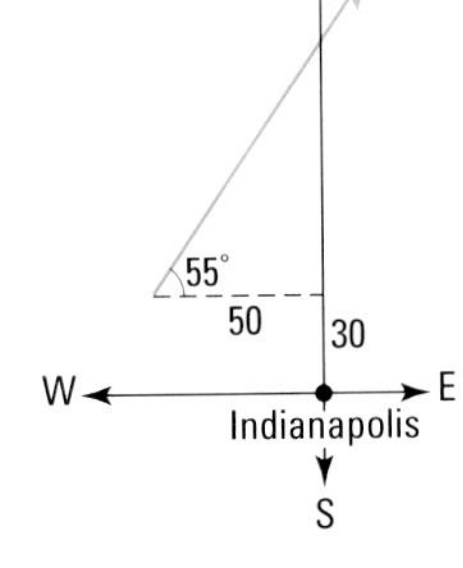

Follow-up for Lesson 12-4

Practice

For more questions on SPUR Objectives, use **Lesson Master 12-4** (shown on pages 742–743).

Assessment

Written Communication Ask students to **work in pairs.** Have each student write a problem like **Example 5.** Students should solve their partner's problem. Then partners should check each other's work using the method discussed in the Check for **Example 5.** [Students use dot products to find orthogonal vectors.]

Extension

Refer students to **Question 14.** Ask them if there is an identity property for the dot product. [No; $\vec{u} \cdot \vec{v}$ can never equal $\vec{u}$, since the dot product yields a scalar.] Then ask if there is an inverse property for the dot product. [No, since there is no identity element, there can be no inverse property.]

Project Update Project 3, *Vectors Applied to Statistics,* and Project 4, *Vectors Applied to Physics,* on pages 773–774, relate to the content of this lesson.

Additional Answers

14. a. $\vec{u} \cdot \vec{v} = u_1v_1 + u_2v_2 = v_1u_1 + v_2u_2 = \vec{v} \cdot \vec{u}$

b. $\vec{u} \cdot (\vec{v} + \vec{w}) = \vec{u} \cdot (v_1 + w_1, v_2 + w_2) = u_1(v_1 + w_1) + u_2(v_2 + w_2) = u_1v_1 + u_1w_1 + u_2v_2 + u_2w_2 = u_1v_1 + u_2v_2 + u_1w_1 + u_2w_2 = \vec{u} \cdot \vec{v} + \vec{u} \cdot \vec{w}$

c. $(k\vec{u}) \cdot \vec{v} = (ku_1, ku_2) \cdot \vec{v} = ku_1v_1 + ku_2v_2 = k(u_1v_1 + u_2v_2) = k(\vec{u} \cdot \vec{v})$

15. a. $(250 \cos 55°, 250 \sin 55°) \approx (143, 205)$

b. Sample: $x = -50 + 143t$; $y = 30 + 205t$

c. (21.5, 132.5); it is 21.5 miles east and 132.5 miles north of Indianapolis.

11. e.

$\cos \theta = \dfrac{\vec{u} \cdot \vec{v}}{\lvert\vec{u}\rvert\,\lvert\vec{v}\rvert}$	**Angle Between Vectors Theorem**
$\dfrac{k}{\lvert k\rvert} = \dfrac{\vec{u} \cdot \vec{v}}{\lvert\vec{u}\rvert\,\lvert\vec{v}\rvert}$	**From part d, $\cos \theta = \frac{k}{\lvert k\rvert}$**
$\dfrac{k}{\lvert k\rvert} = \dfrac{k(v_1)^2 + k(v_2)^2}{\lvert k\rvert\,[(v_1)^2 + (v_2)^2]}$	**From parts a and b**
$\dfrac{k}{\lvert k\rvert} = \dfrac{k[(v_1)^2 + (v_2)^2]}{\lvert k\rvert\,[(v_1)^2 + (v_2)^2]}$	**Distributive Law**
$\dfrac{k}{\lvert k\rvert} = \dfrac{k}{\lvert k\rvert}$	**Simplify**

Therefore, the Angle Between Vectors Theorem holds true for parallel vectors.

Notes on Questions

Question 21 The vectors $\vec{i}$ and $\vec{j}$ here are orthogonal unit vectors. The generalization shows that any vector $\vec{v}$ in the plane can be written as a linear combination of $\vec{i}$ and $\vec{j}$, and the coefficients are the dot products of $\vec{v}$ with $\vec{i}$ and $\vec{j}$. Geometrically, this says that $\vec{v}$ is the sum of its vector projections on the horizontal and the vertical axes.

17a) $\vec{u} + \vec{v}$ is 3; $\vec{u} - \vec{v}$ is 4

b) Sample: $\vec{u} = (3, 4)$ and $\vec{v} = (12, 5)$; $|\vec{u} + \vec{v}|^2 + |\vec{u} - \vec{v}|^2 = 306 + 82 = 388$; $2(|\vec{u}|^2 + |\vec{v}|^2) = 2(25 + 169) = 2(194) = 388$

19) The units digit of the fourth power of a number is the fourth power of the units digit, and 2^4, 4^4, 6^4, and 8^4 each have units digis 6.

17. The following equation is called the Parallelogram Identity.

$$|\vec{u} + \vec{v}|^2 + |\vec{u} - \vec{v}|^2 = 2(|\vec{u}|^2 + |\vec{v}|^2)$$

a. Of the arrows numbered 1, 2, 3, or 4 in the diagram below, identify those representing the vectors $\vec{u} + \vec{v}$ and $\vec{u} - \vec{v}$. **See left.**

b. Verify that the Parallelogram Identity is true for two vectors of your choosing. *(Lesson 12-2)* **See left.**

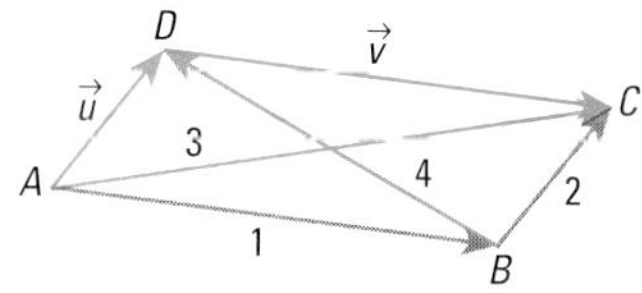

18. a. Find $\sum_{k=0}^{12} 4\left(\frac{6}{5}\right)^k$. **≈ 194**

b. Does $\sum_{k=0}^{\infty} 4\left(\frac{6}{5}\right)^k$ converge? If so, find its value. If not, tell why not. *(Lesson 7-6)* **No, $r = \frac{6}{5} > 1$**

19. Prove that if the units digit of an even number is nonzero, then the units digit of its fourth power is 6. *(Lesson 4-5)* **See left.**

20. Solve: $\log_3 (x + 2) = 2 - \log_3 x$. *(Lesson 3-2)* **≈ 2.162**

Exploration

21. Let $\vec{v} = (-3, 4)$, $\vec{i} = (1, 0)$, and $\vec{j} = (0, 1)$.

a. Find $\vec{v} \cdot \vec{i}$. **-3**

b. Find $\vec{v} \cdot \vec{j}$. **4**

c. Find $(\vec{v} \cdot \vec{i})\vec{i} + (\vec{v} \cdot \vec{j})\vec{j}$. **(-3, 4)**

d. Generalize the result of part **c** by letting $\vec{v} = (v_1, v_2)$. **$(\vec{v} \cdot \vec{i})\vec{i} + (\vec{v} \cdot \vec{j})\vec{j} = \vec{v}$**

Setting Up Lesson 12-5

Lesson 12-5 should be review for students. Ask how many students have seen three-dimensional coordinates (x, y, z) for points in space. How many have seen the distance formula? Do they remember it? What about an equation for a sphere? This will tell you where you need to devote your energies in discussing Lesson 12-5.

LESSON

12-5

Three-Dimensional Coordinates

What Is 3-Space?

A communications satellite is usually launched so that it stays in a fixed position above Earth. Reception dishes on the ground can then be aimed directly at the satellite. Three numbers determine the position of the satellite: latitude, longitude, and height above Earth. When three numbers are needed to determine the position of a point, the space in which the point lies is called **3-space** or **three-dimensional space**.

Rectangular Coordinates in 3-Space

For many applications in 3-space, rectangular coordinates are better than coordinates which reference a sphere, like those above for the satellite. A corner of a room provides a model for how three numbers can locate a point in the room. Suppose you want a light to be 3 feet from the side wall, 1 foot from the back wall, and 7 feet above the floor. If you were to consider the corner from which you measured as the origin of a coordinate system, you could write the position of the light as the ordered triple (3, 1, 7). Note that the intersections of the walls and floor are lines which are perpendicular to each other at the corner of the room.

Customarily, two-dimensional coordinate axes are drawn as if the plane is vertical with respect to the ground. A typical three-dimensional coordinate system is drawn as if the customary x- and y-axes are in a *horizontal* plane and located so that the positive x-axis points toward the viewer.

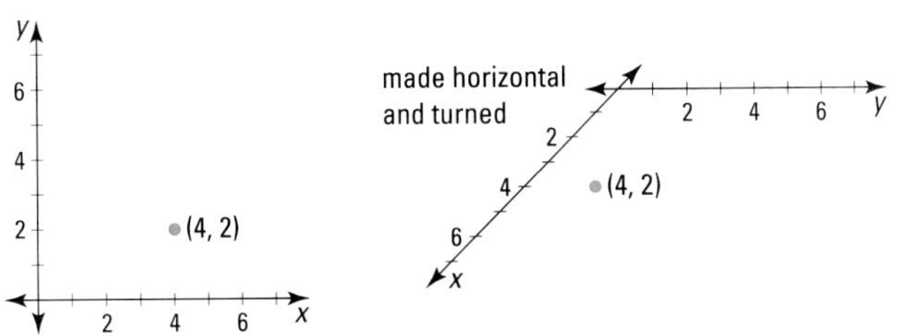

Lesson 12-5

Objectives

M Represent lines, planes, and spheres in 3-space using parametric, vector, or coordinate equations.

Resources

From the ***Teacher's Resource File***

- Lesson Master 12-5
- Answer Master 12-5
- Teaching Aids
  - 133 Warm-up
  - 141 3-dimensional Coordinate System
  - 142 Theorems of the Lesson

Additional Resources

- Visuals for Teaching Aids 133, 141, 142

Teaching Lesson 12-5

Warm-up

A trunk is one meter long, 45 centimeters wide, and 28 centimeters high in its internal dimensions. To the nearest centimeter, what is the length of the longest inflexible thin rod that can fit inside this trunk? **113 cm**

Notes on Reading

The next three lessons extend the ideas of vectors into three dimensions. This lesson prepares the way. Students who have studied from any of the three previous UCSMP courses may be familiar with its content. Probe your students to see how many are familiar with the content.

Lesson 12-5 Overview

Broad Goals This lesson should be review for all students. It covers graphing in 3-space, equations for the planes containing two axes and for planes parallel to the axes, the distance formula (proved from the Pythagorean Theorem), and the equation of a sphere.

Perspective This lesson affords an opportunity to point out once again how deductive proof enables a body of results to be derived from simpler principles. The theorems in the lesson are derived from the Pythagorean Theorem. That theorem is traditionally proved either from properties of area or properties of similar triangles. The Pythagorean Theorem enables us to obtain a formula for the longest diagonal of a box (see the *Warm-up*). That idea is the same as is used to find the distance of a point (x, y, z) from the origin in a 3-dimensional coordinate system.

The formula for the distance between two points can be interpreted as what happens when (0, 0, 0) and (x, y, z) are translated so that the image of (0, 0, 0) is (x_1, y_1, z_1). The image of (x, y, z) becomes $(x + x_1, y + y_1, z + z_1)$. Now we can prove the Distance in Space Theorem. Let $x + x_1 = x_2$, $y + y_1 = y_2$,

(Overview continues on page 748.)

Graphing 3-dimensional figures on a 2-dimensional sheet of paper is quite difficult for many people. Expect it to take quite a bit of time. A blank 3-dimensional graph is provided as **Teaching Aid 141.**

You should draw analogies between the following 2-D and 3-D ideas: Points: from (x, y) to (x, y, z), Distance: from $\sqrt{(x_2 - x_1)^2 + (y_2 - y_1)^2}$ to $\sqrt{(x_2 - x_1)^2 + (y_2 - y_1)^2 + (z_2 - z_1)^2}$; Simple equations: from the horizontal and vertical lines $x = a$, $y = b$ to the three planes $x = a$, $y = b$, $z = c$; from the circle $(x - a)^2 + (y - b)^2 = r^2$ to the sphere $(x - a)^2 + (y - b)^2 + (z - c)^2 = r^2$; Diagonals: from rectangle—$\sqrt{a^2 + b^2}$, to box—$\sqrt{a^2 + b^2 + c^2}$. The diagonal formula, the distance formula, and the equation of a sphere are shown on **Teaching Aid 142.**

If you have computer software that graphs three-dimensional functions, some of the graphs in this lesson can be illustrated. The sphere $x^2 + y^2 + z^2 = r^2$ can be graphed using the two functions $z = \sqrt{r^2 - x^2 - y^2}$ and $z = -\sqrt{r^2 - x^2 - y^2}$. You can ask your students to solve the equation in **Example 3** for z so that it can be graphed on the computer. $[z = \pm\sqrt{36 - (x - 1)^2 - y^2} - 5]$

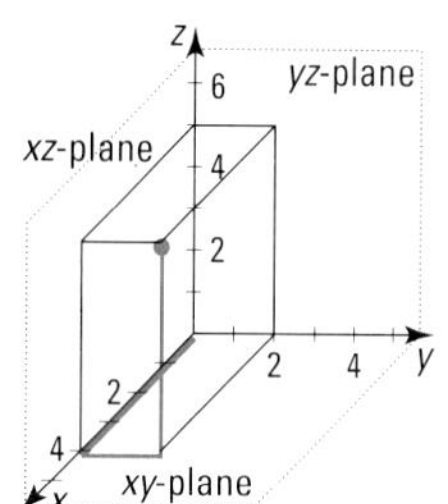

Then a z-axis is put into the picture as a vertical axis coming up from the origin. The location of a point is determined by three numbers, its x-, y-, and z-coordinates. The point (4, 2, 5), for instance, has x-coordinate 4, y-coordinate 2, and z-coordinate 5. To graph this point, think of graphing (4, 2) as you normally would. Then go up 5 units from (4, 2) to graph (4, 2, 5). Many people like to think of a box, as shown at the left.

The edges of the box are parallel to the axes. The origin (0, 0, 0) is one corner of the box and the point (4, 2, 5) is the opposite corner. In the drawing, the back of the box is in the ***yz*-plane**, the left side of the box is in the ***xz*-plane**, and the bottom of the box is in the ***xy*-plane**. Notice that the xy-plane is the set of points for which the z-coordinate is 0; it has the equation $z = 0$. All horizontal and vertical planes have simple equations, just like their counterparts in 2-space, horizontal and vertical lines. Similarly, the axes can be characterized by equations.

Example 1

Consider a 3-dimensional coordinate system.

a. Sketch the graph of all points (x, y, z) with $z = 5$.

b. Describe the y-axis with equations.

Solution

a. Points like (3, 2, 5), (2, -1, 5), (0, 0, 5), and $(x, y, 5)$ are all on the graph of $z = 5$. This is therefore a plane 5 units above the xy-plane. To sketch it, draw a parallelogram so that it appears to "float" above the xy-plane with all the named points in it.

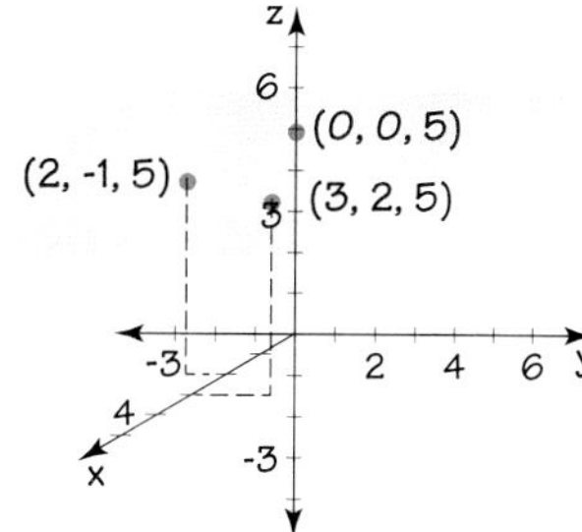

b. The y-axis contains points of the form $(0, a, 0)$, where a is any real number. So the y-axis is

$$\{(x, y, z): x = 0 \text{ and } z = 0\}.$$

Example 1**a** shows how a horizontal or vertical plane can be described by a single linear equation. Example 1**b** shows that an axis can be described by a system of two linear equations.

Distance in 3-Space

The longest diagonal of a box with dimensions a, b, and c, as shown at the right, has length $\sqrt{a^2 + b^2 + c^2}$. The formula for the distance of a point in 3-space from the origin is an immediate consequence of this fact.

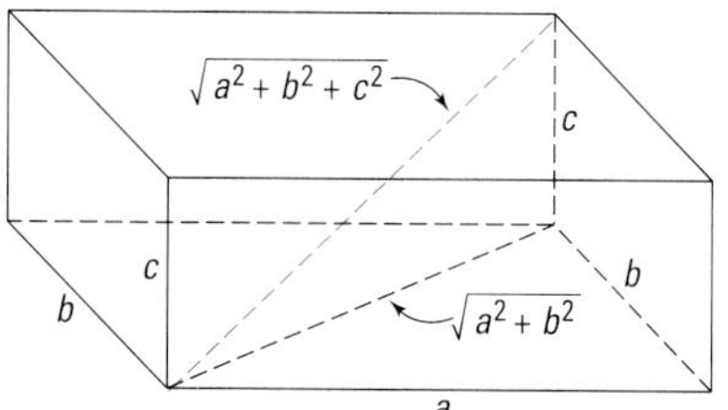

Lesson 12-5 Overview, continued

and $z + z_1 = z_2$. From this $x = x_2 - x_1$, $y = y_2 - y_1$, and $z = z_2 - z_1$. The original distance $\sqrt{x^2 + y^2 + z^2}$ is unchanged under the translation, and substitution for x, y, and z gives the formula.

Optional Activities

Refer students to **Question 6.** To gain more practice sketching planes, ask students to sketch the plane $x = 3$ on the same coordinate grid. Ask them what figure is described by the intersection of these two planes. [a line parallel to the z-axis and $3\sqrt{2}$ units away from it] Ask them what figure is described by the intersection of the planes $y = 3$, $x = 3$, and $z = 3$. [The point (3, 3, 3)]

Adapting to Individual Needs

Extra Help

Some students might have trouble visualizing the xy-plane as a horizontal plane. Have them draw an xy-coordinate system on graph paper. Then have them place it on their desk with the positive x-axis pointing toward themselves. A pencil can be held vertically at the origin to represent the positive z-axis.

Theorem
The distance of the point (x, y, z) from the origin is $\sqrt{x^2 + y^2 + z^2}$.

For instance, the light pictured on page 747 is

$$\sqrt{3^2 + 1^2 + 7^2} = \sqrt{59} \approx 7.7 \text{ feet}$$

from the corner of the walls and floor.

The formula for the distance between two points in space is a generalization of the preceding theorem.

Theorem (Distance in Space)
The distance between $P = (x_1, y_1, z_1)$ and $Q = (x_2, y_2, z_2)$ is given by
$PQ = \sqrt{(x_2 - x_1)^2 + (y_2 - y_1)^2 + (z_2 - z_1)^2}$.

Proof
The sides of the box at the right have lengths $|x_2 - x_1|$, $|y_2 - y_1|$, and $|z_2 - z_1|$. The proof is left for you to finish in Question 14.

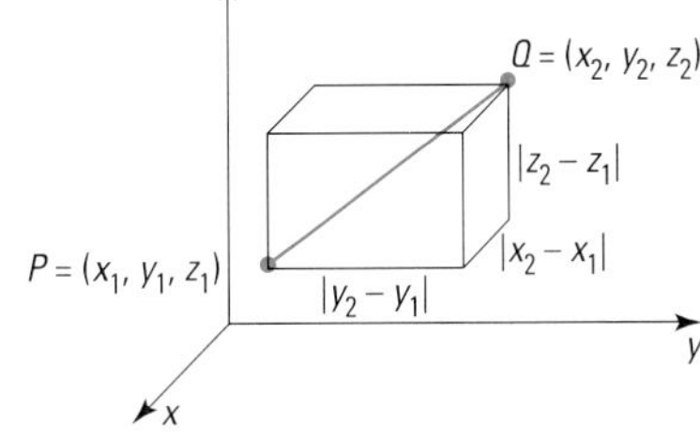

Example 2

Consider the points $A = (4, 3, 0)$ and $B = (1, -3, 5)$.
a. Sketch the points in a three-dimensional coordinate system.
b. Find AB.

Solution
a. Point A is in the xy-plane, so locate it in the xy-plane at (4, 3). Since the y-coordinate of B is negative, show the negative part of the y-axis in the sketch. Find (1, -3) in the xy-plane, then go up 5 units.

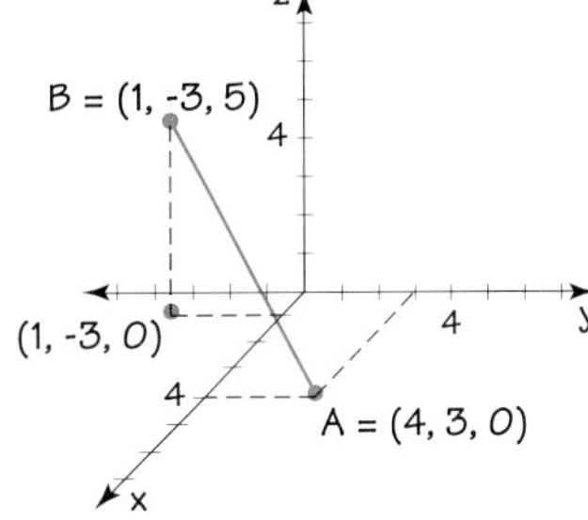

b. $AB = \sqrt{(4 - 1)^2 + (3 - -3)^2 + (0 - 5)^2}$
$= \sqrt{70}$.

Additional Examples

1. **a.** Describe the graph of all points (x, y, z) with $y = -1$. **a plane 1 unit to the left of the x-z plane (the plane determined by the x-axis and z-axis)**
   b. Give equations for the x-axis. **$y = 0$ and $z = 0$; you can think of the x-axis as the intersection of the planes with these equations.**
2. Sketch $A = (3, 4, 2)$ and $B = (-1, 5, 0)$ and find AB.

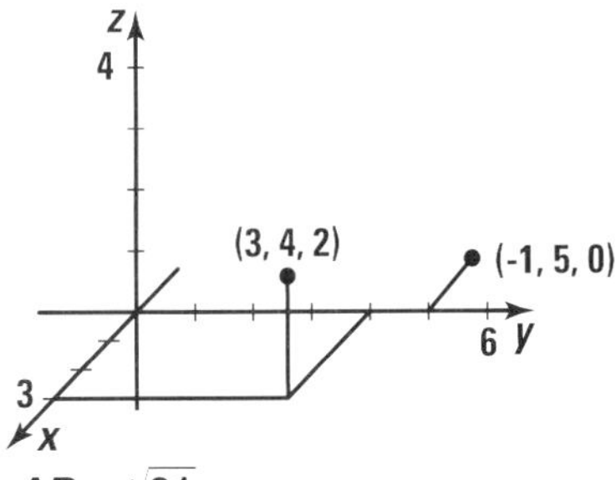

$AB = \sqrt{21}$

3. Find the center and radius of the sphere with equation $x^2 + y^2 + z^2 + 6x + 5y - 2z - 4 = 0$. **center (-3, -2.5, 1), radius 4.5**

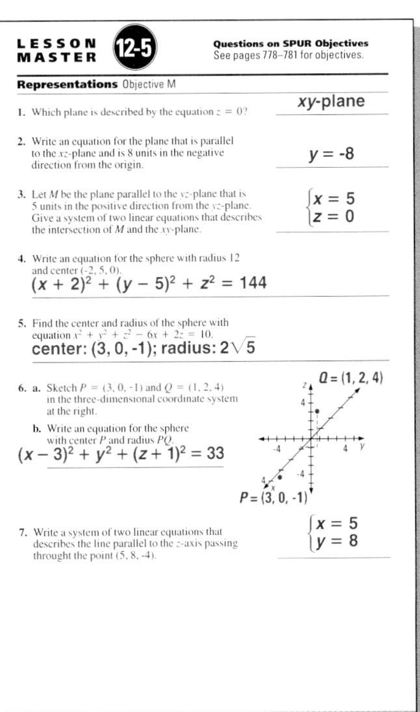

LESSON MASTER 12-5 — **Questions on SPUR Objectives** See pages 778–781 for objectives.

Representations Objective M

1. Which plane is described by the equation $z = 0$? ***xy*-plane**
2. Write an equation for the plane that is parallel to the xz-plane and is 8 units in the negative direction from the origin. **$y = -8$**
3. Let M be the plane parallel to the yz-plane that is 5 units in the positive direction from the yz-plane. Give a system of two linear equations that describes the intersection of M and the xy-plane. **$\begin{cases} x = 5 \\ z = 0 \end{cases}$**
4. Write an equation for the sphere with radius 12 and center (-2, 5, 0). **$(x + 2)^2 + (y - 5)^2 + z^2 = 144$**
5. Find the center and radius of the sphere with equation $x^2 + y^2 + z^2 - 6x + 2z = 10$. **center: (3, 0, -1); radius: $2\sqrt{5}$**
6. **a.** Sketch $P = (3, 0, -1)$ and $Q = (1, 2, 4)$ in the three-dimensional coordinate system at the right.
   b. Write an equation for the sphere with center P and radius PQ. **$(x - 3)^2 + y^2 + (z + 1)^2 = 33$**

7. Write a system of two linear equations that describes the line parallel to the z-axis passing throught the point (5, 8, -4). **$\begin{cases} x = 5 \\ y = 8 \end{cases}$**

Adapting to Individual Needs

Challenge
Have students answer the following.

1. Use a computer graphics program such as DERIVE to graph the following 3-dimensional graphs. Describe the results by describing cross sections parallel to the xy-plane, xz-plane, and yz-plane.
   a. $z = x^2 + y^2 + 1$ [circular cross sections parallel to the xy-plane; parabolic cross sections parallel to the xz- and yz-planes; shaped like a bullet.]
   b. $z = x^2 - y^2 + 1$ [hyperbolic cross sections parallel to the xy-plane; parabolic cross sections parallel to the xz- and yz-planes; looks like a saddle.]

Notes on Questions

Question 6 Error Alert Students may find it difficult to make the drawing. Suggest that they draw lines parallel to the *x*- and *z*-axes as the outlines of the plane. Making drawings like this helps them to interpret the diagrams they see and makes use of fundamental ideas like "parallel planes are everywhere equidistant."

Question 13 Here the rod is called thin so that we do not have to worry about its thickness. A thicker rod could not be as long. This question should be very easy if the *Warm-up* for this lesson has been done.

Question 15 A diagram can help explain the underlying geometry. All points satisfying (5, *y*, 2) lie in a line parallel to the *y*-axis. The question asks for the two points of intersection of this line and the sphere with radius $\sqrt{33}$ and center *A*.

Question 16 With the mathematics of this lesson, students can calculate how close airplanes come to each other in "near misses."

Question 22 The surface here is an example of a quadric surface. The equations and graphs of all these surfaces are often given in calculus textbooks. Your students may enjoy looking these up. They can be graphed with computer software that graphs 3-D functions.

Equations for Spheres

Since a sphere is formed by all points in 3-space at a fixed distance from a center point, the distance formula leads to an equation for a sphere.

Theorem (Equation of a Sphere)
The sphere with center (*a*, *b*, *c*) and radius *r* has equation
$$r^2 = (x - a)^2 + (y - b)^2 + (z - c)^2.$$

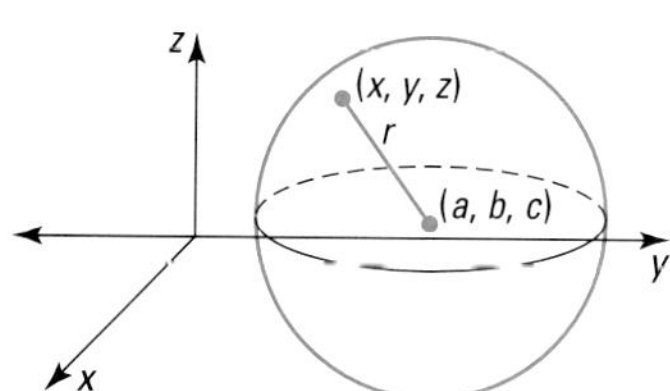

You can determine the center and radius of a sphere from its equation.

Example 3

Verify that the equation $x^2 + y^2 + z^2 - 2x + 10z = 10$ describes a sphere, and find its center and radius.

Solution

Regroup and complete the square for the expressions in *x* and *z*.

$$x^2 - 2x + y^2 + z^2 + 10z = 10$$
$$x^2 - 2x + 1 + y^2 + z^2 + 10z + 25 = 10 + 1 + 25$$
$$(x - 1)^2 + y^2 + (z + 5)^2 = 36$$

This is an equation of the sphere with center (1, 0, -5) and radius 6.

6)

QUESTIONS

Covering the Reading

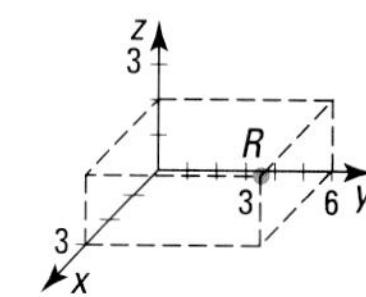

1. Point *R* shown at the left has integer coordinates. What are they? **(3, 6, 2)**

In 2–4, sketch the point in three-dimensional space. **See margin.**

2. (4, 2, 8)
3. (3, -2, 4)
4. (1, 5, -2)

5. *Multiple choice.* In 3-space, the equation $x = 0$ describes which of the following? **d**
   (a) the *x*-axis (b) the *z*-axis (c) the *xy*-plane (d) the *yz*-plane

6. Sketch the plane $y = 3$. **See above left.**

7. Describe the *z*-axis with linear equations. **$x = 0$ and $y = 0$**

8. How far is (-1, 5, -8) from the origin? **$3\sqrt{10}$**

Additional Answers

2.

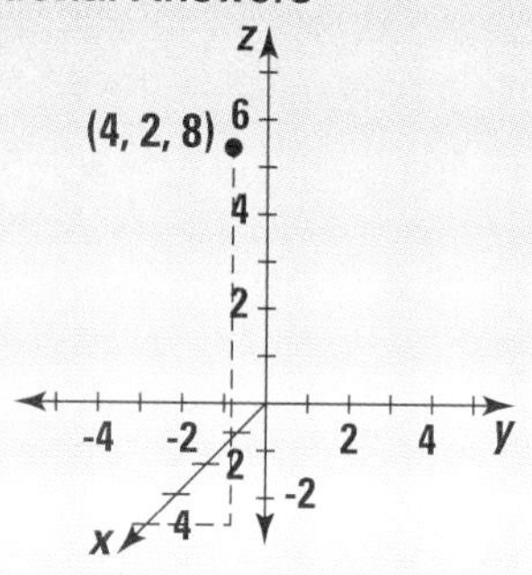

3.

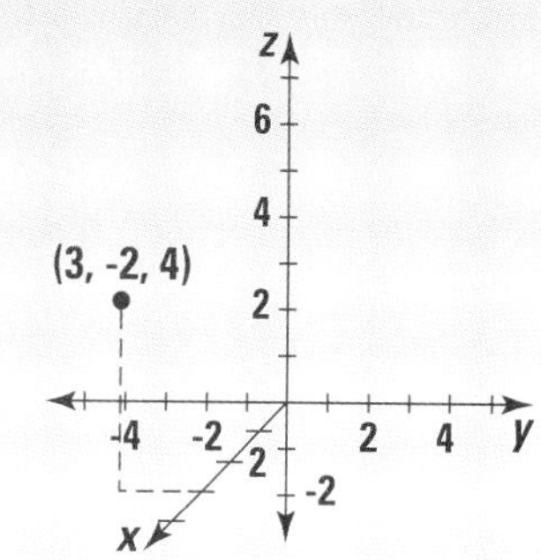

4.

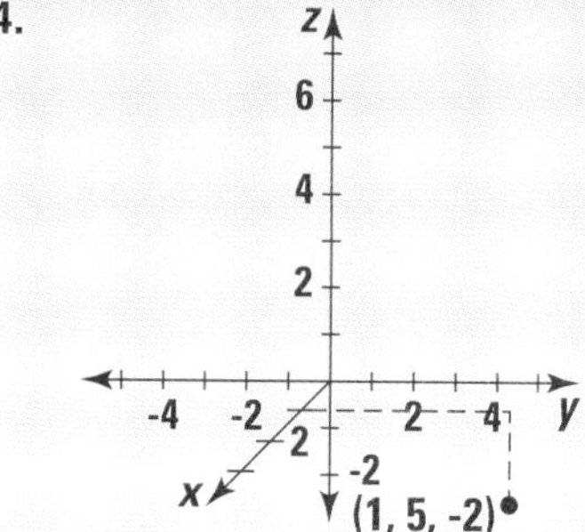

10) $(x + 1)^2 + (y - 2)^2 + (z - 8)^2 = 25$

9. What is the distance between (1, 0, -1) and (4, -4, 11)? **13**

10. Write an equation for the sphere with radius 5 and center (-1, 2, 8). **See left.**

11. Find the center and radius of the sphere with equation $x^2 + y^2 + z^2 - 2x + 6y + 8z = 10$. **center: (1, -3, -4); radius: 6**

Applying the Mathematics

12. Find the center and radius of the sphere with equation $x^2 + y^2 + z^2 = 15y$. **center: (0, 7.5, 0); radius: 7.5**

13. A wooden crate is 60 cm long, 40 cm wide, and 32 cm high in its internal dimensions. What is the length of the longest thin steel rod that can fit in the crate? **≈ 79 cm**

14. Finish the proof of the Distance in Space Theorem. **See margin.**

15. If $AB = \sqrt{33}$, $A = (1, 2, 3)$, and $B = (5, y, 2)$, find y. **$y = 6$ or $y = -2$**

16. At a particular point in time, one plane is 3 km south and 2 km west of another. One of the planes is flying at 8500 meters altitude, the other at 6500 meters. How far are the planes from each other? **≈ 4.1 km**

Review

17. *True or false.* If $\vec{u} = (-2, 3)$, $\vec{v} = (5, -1)$, and $\vec{w} = (-7, -2)$, then $(\vec{u} \cdot \vec{v})\vec{w} = (\vec{u} \cdot \vec{w})\vec{v}$. *(Lesson 12-4)* **False**

18a) Sample: $x = 2 - 4t$; $y = 1 + 2t$

b) $\left(\frac{3\sqrt{5}}{5}, \frac{6\sqrt{5}}{5}\right)$ or $\left(-\frac{3\sqrt{5}}{5}, \frac{-6\sqrt{5}}{5}\right)$

c) Sample: $x = 2 + t$; $y = 1 + 2t$

18. Suppose point P has coordinates (2, 1) and line ℓ has parametric equations **See left.**

$$\begin{cases} x = -7 - 4t \\ y = 3 + 2t. \end{cases}$$

a. Find parametric equations for the line through P and parallel to ℓ.

b. Find a vector with length 3 perpendicular to ℓ.

c. Find parametric equations for the line through P and perpendicular to ℓ. *(Lessons 12-3, 12-4)*

19a)

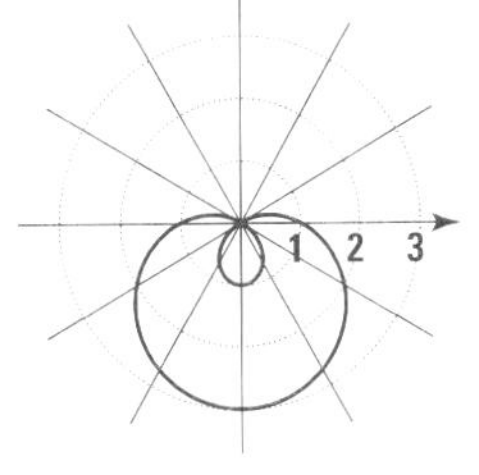

19. a. Sketch the polar graph of $r = 1 - 2 \sin \theta$. **See left.**

b. Identify the shape of the curve that results. *(Lesson 8-4)* **limaçon**

20. Prove that 3 is a factor of $n^3 + 2n$ for all integers $n \geq 1$. *(Lesson 7-4)* **See margin.**

21. Prove or disprove: For all real numbers x for which $\tan x$ is defined,

$$\tan^2 x - \sin^2 x = \tan^2 x \sin^2 x.$$ *(Lessons 6-1, 6-2)* **See margin.**

Exploration

22. Describe the shape of the three-dimensional figure whose equation is $\frac{x^2}{a^2} + \frac{y^2}{b^2} + \frac{z^2}{c^2} = 1$. **an ellipsoid that intersects the x-axis at $(\pm a, 0, 0)$, the y-axis at $(0, \pm b, 0)$, and the z-axis at $(0, 0, \pm c)$**

Follow-up for Lesson 12-5

Practice

For more questions on SPUR Objectives, use **Lesson Master 12-5** (shown on page 749).

Assessment

Oral Communication Have students show their sketches for **Questions 2, 3, and 4.** For one of these problems, ask students to explain how they located the point. [Students show understanding of how to make sketches of points in space.]

Extension

This is an appropriate time to examine dimensions higher than three. Students interested in this topic might want to examine either of two classics, *Flatland* by Edwin A. Abbott, or *One Two Three...Infinity* by George Gamow; or *Geometry, Relativity and the Fourth Dimension* by Rudolf V. B. Rucker; or the 1990 book *Beyond the Third Dimension: Geometry, Computer Graphics, and Higher Dimensions* by Thomas F. Banchoff. A book report could be a project.

Additional Answers

14.

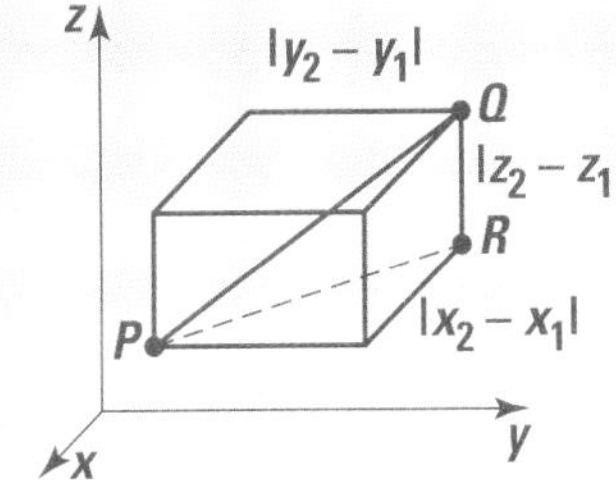

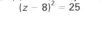

$PR = \sqrt{(y_2 - y_1)^2 + (x_2 - x_1)^2}$,

$PQ = \sqrt{PR^2 + QR^2}$

$= \sqrt{(y_2 - y_1)^2 + (x_2 - x_1)^2 + (z_2 - z_1)^2}$

20. For $n = 1$, 3 is a factor of $n^3 + 2n = 3$. Assume 3 is a factor of $n^3 + 2n$ for $n = k$. For $n = k + 1$, $n^3 + 2n$
$= (k + 1)^3 + 2(k + 1)$
$= k^3 + 3k^2 + 5k + 3$
$= (k^3 + 2k) + 3(k^2 + k + 1)$.
As both terms are divisible by 3, so is the sum, $n^3 + 2n$. Hence, by mathematical induction, 3 is a factor of $n^3 + 2n$, for all integers $n \geq 1$.

21. left side $= \tan^2 x - \sin^2 x$
$= \frac{\sin^2 x}{\cos^2 x} - \sin^2 x$
$= \frac{\sin^2 x - \sin^2 x \cos^2 x}{\cos^2 x}$
$= \frac{\sin^2 x(1 - \cos^2 x)}{\cos^2 x}$
$= \frac{\sin^2 x \sin^2 x}{\cos^2 x}$
$= \tan^2 x \sin^2 x$
= right side

Lesson 12-6

Objectives

C Find sums, lengths, scalar products, dot products, and cross products of vectors in 3-space.
D Find the measure of the angle between two vectors.
E Prove or disprove generalizations about vector operations.
F Identify parallel and orthogonal vectors.
K Geometrically interpret three-dimensional vectors and their operations.

Resources

From the ***Teacher's Resource File***
- Lesson Master 12-6
- Answer Master 12-6
- Assessment Sourcebook: Quiz for Lessons 12-4 through 12-6
- Teaching Aids
  133 Warm-up
  143 Example 2
  144 Question 19

Additional Resources
- Visuals for Teaching Aids 133, 143, 144

Teaching Lesson 12-6

Warm-up

Find the area of the parallelogram with consecutive vertices (2, 10), (0, 0), and (4, 1).
38 square units

LESSON

12-6 *Vectors in 3-Space*

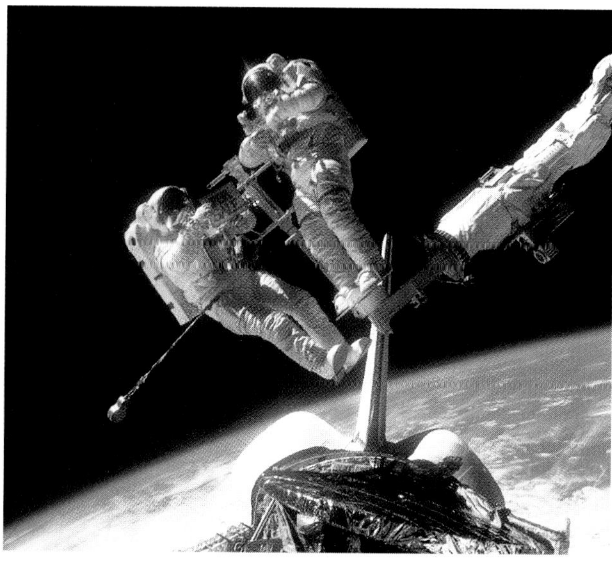

Astronauts Joseph P. Allen IV and Dale A. Gardner have just used a robot arm to recapture the malfunctioning satellite at the bottom of the picture.

Three-Dimensional Coordinate Systems in Space

One of the purposes of the space shuttle is to deliver communication satellites to their operating positions above Earth. The shuttle also retrieves damaged or inoperable satellites and returns them to Earth for repair. A robot arm is used to move satellites to and from the cargo bay of the shuttle. The crew uses a variety of devices for controlling the arm from the safety of the cockpit. Their manipulation of levers and buttons is translated by microcomputers into movement of the arm, using a three-dimensional coordinate system.

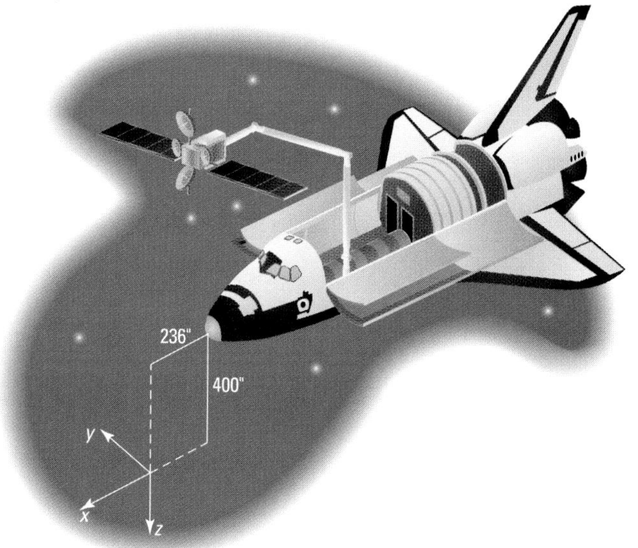

Lesson 12-6 Overview

Broad Goals In this lesson, addition, scalar multiplication, and the dot product, are extended to apply to three-dimensional vectors, and the same properties that were proved for these operations in 2-space are shown to hold in 3-space. Also introduced is an operation on 3-space vectors that is not an extension of a 2-space operation, the *cross product* (or *vector product*).

Perspective This and the next lesson provide a natural review of the first half of the chapter. Most of this lesson consists of examples of the same ideas that were covered in Lessons 12-2 to 12-4, but now in 3-space.

The cross product of two vectors is the vector that is orthogonal to each of them and whose length is the area of the parallelogram with those vectors as sides. The cross product can be used to obtain a vector equation of a plane (see **Question 8** of Lesson 12-7 or **Question 20** of Lesson 12-8).

❶ In the actual *orbiter body axis system* used by the shuttle, shown on page 752, the origin is not positioned at the nose of the shuttle. Instead, it is placed ahead of and below the nose. Also, the positive z-axis points downward and the positive y-axis points to the right (as viewed from the cockpit). Measured in inches, the nose is at the point (-236, 0, -400). The left-hand side of the cargo bay has a clip to secure a payload. That clip is about 691 inches behind the nose, 98 inches left of center, and 14 inches higher than the nose. In this coordinate system, the clip is at the point with coordinates (-236, 0, -400) + (-691, -98, -14) = (-927, -98, -414).

Basic Operations with 3-Dimensional Vectors

The addition of ordered triples, component by component, is the 3-dimensional analog to the addition of vectors in a plane. Vectors in three dimensions, like vectors in two dimensions, have direction and magnitude. When drawn in standard position (beginning at the origin), they can be represented by the coordinates of their endpoints. Operations on vectors in 3-space can then be generalized from those on vectors in a plane.

Definitions

Let $\vec{u} = (u_1, u_2, u_3)$ and $\vec{v} = (v_1, v_2\ v_3)$ be vectors in 3-space, and let k be a real number.

a. The **sum** of $\vec{u}$ and $\vec{v}$ is the vector $\vec{u} + \vec{v} = (u_1 + v_1, u_2 + v_2, u_3 + v_3)$.

b. The **scalar multiple** of $\vec{u}$ by the real number k is the vector $k\vec{u} = (ku_1, ku_2, ku_3)$.

c. The **dot product** of $\vec{u}$ and $\vec{v}$ is the number $\vec{u} \cdot \vec{v} = u_1v_1 + u_2v_2 + u_3v_3$.

It follows from the Distance in Space Theorem that the length of $\vec{u} = (u_1, u_2, u_3)$ is given by $|\vec{u}| = \sqrt{u_1^2 + u_2^2 + u_3^2} = \sqrt{\vec{u} \cdot \vec{u}}$. That is, just as in 2-space, the norm of a 3-space vector is the square root of the dot product of a vector with itself. The opposite of $\vec{u}$ is $-\vec{u} = (-u_1, -u_2, -u_3)$ and can be used for subtraction of 3-space vectors just as the opposite of a 2-dimensional vector is used in subtracting vectors in 2-space.

Example 1

Suppose that $\vec{u} = (5, -1, 1)$ and $\vec{v} = (2, 0, 4)$. Find the following.

a. $\vec{u} - \vec{v}$ **b.** $\vec{u} + \frac{1}{2}\vec{v}$ **c.** $\vec{u} \cdot \vec{v}$ **d.** $|\vec{v}|$

Solution

a. $\vec{u} - \vec{v} = \vec{u} + -\vec{v}$
$= (5, -1, 1) + (-2, 0, -4)$
$= (5 + -2, -1 + 0, 1 + -4)$
$= (3, -1, -3)$

Notes on Reading

❶ Students should wonder why the origin of the orbiter body axis system is not placed at the nose of the shuttle. (You might ask them for ideas.) The reason seems to be that, by placing the origin in front of the nose, objects more often do not intersect the origin; when objects would intersect the origin then any of the three coordinates could change sign, and keeping track of the coordinates would be confusing.

Example 1 requires only that students extend their knowledge of vectors in 2 dimensions to apply to 3-dimensional vectors.

Example 2 covers the same for the angle between two vectors, but in three dimensions students may have difficulty visualizing the angle. Remind them that two intersecting lines determine a plane, so the angle they are measuring is indeed an angle in a plane. The graph is provided on **Teaching Aid 143.** In **part b** of the example, the fact that the distance is the norm of the vector makes sense if they realize that the components of the vector are exactly the quantities that are used in the distance formula.

The cross product yields a vector orthogonal to two others. This idea is applied in the next lesson. **Example 3c** shows that the cross product is a valuable tool by illustrating how difficult it is to work without it.

Optional Activities

Refer students to **Question 15.** Ask them to investigate whether there is a commutative property with the cross product. Ask them to prove their discovery and interpret their findings geometrically. [$\vec{u} \times \vec{v} = -(\vec{v} \times \vec{u})$, since $\vec{u} \times \vec{v} = (u_2v_3 - u_3v_2, u_3v_1 - u_1v_3, u_1v_2 - u_2v_1)$ and $\vec{v} \times \vec{u} = (u_3v_2 - u_2v_3, u_1v_3 - u_3v_1, u_2v_1 - u_1v_2)$; that is, switching order in a cross product produces an orthogonal vector of the same magnitude but with opposite direction.]

Additional Examples

1. If $\vec{u} = (2, 3, 4)$ and $\vec{v} = (-5, -3, -1)$, find:
   a. $\vec{u} + 2\vec{v}$ **(-8, -3, 2)**
   b. $-\vec{v}$ **(5, 3, 1)**
   c. $\vec{u} \cdot \vec{v}$ **-23**
   d $|\vec{u} - \vec{v}|$ **$\sqrt{110}$**
2. Suppose the robot arm in **Example 2** moves an object from (3.50, 12.50, 20) to (7.50, 16, -5.50). (Use **Teaching Aid 143.**)
   a. At which point, start or end, is the arm more extended? **start**
   b. What is the distance between the starting and ending positions? **$\sqrt{678.5} \approx 26.05$ cm**
   c. Through what angle did the arm rotate? **$\approx 74.7°$**

b.
$$\frac{1}{2}v = \frac{1}{2}(2, 0, 4)$$
$$= \left(\frac{1}{2} \cdot 2, \frac{1}{2} \cdot 0, \frac{1}{2} \cdot 4\right)$$
$$= (1, 0, 2)$$
$$u + \frac{1}{2}v = (5, -1, 1) + (1, 0, 2)$$
$$= (6, -1, 3)$$

c. $u \cdot v = 5 \cdot 2 + -1 \cdot 0 + 1 \cdot 4 = 14$

d. $|\vec{v}| = \sqrt{2^2 + 0^2 + 4^2} = \sqrt{20} = 2\sqrt{5}$

Notice that the answers to parts **a** and **b** of Example 1 are vectors, while the answers to parts **c** and **d** are real numbers. This is the same as it would be if $\vec{u}$ and $\vec{v}$ were 2-dimensional vectors.

The Angle Between 3-Dimensional Vectors

Using the definition of dot product for 3-dimensional vectors, theorems about the angle between two vectors can be proved for 3-dimensional vectors in precisely the same way they were deduced in Lesson 12-4 for 2-dimensional vectors.

Theorem
Let $\vec{u}$ and $\vec{v}$ be any three-dimensional vectors and let θ be the measure of the angle between them. Then:
(1) $\cos\theta = \dfrac{\vec{u} \cdot \vec{v}}{|\vec{u}||\vec{v}|}$
(2) $\vec{u}$ and $\vec{v}$ are orthogonal $\Leftrightarrow \vec{u} \cdot \vec{v} = 0$.

Example 2

In an automobile factory, a robot arm is monitored with a coordinate system whose origin is at the base of the arm, and where distance is measured in centimeters. Suppose the arm moves an object from a starting position of (5.00, 25.00, 32.00) to an ending position of (92.00, -17.00, 10.00).
a. At which point, start or finish, is the arm more extended?
b. What is the distance between the starting and ending positions?
c. Through what angle did the arm rotate?

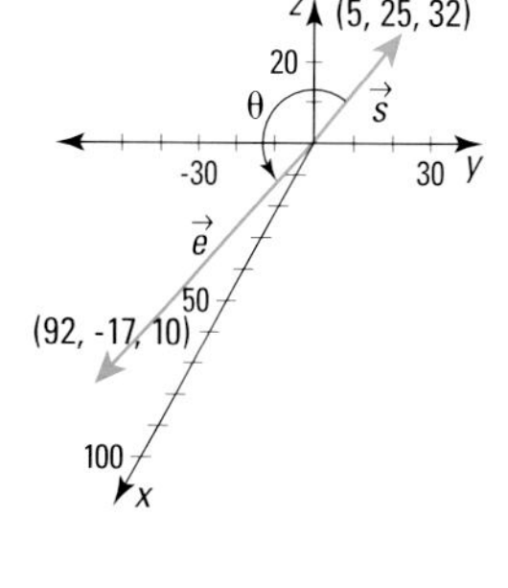

Solution

Let the starting position be given by $\vec{s} = (5, 25, 32)$ and the ending position by $\vec{e} = (92, -17, 10)$.

a.
$$|\vec{s}| = \sqrt{5^2 + 25^2 + 32^2} \approx 40.91 \text{ cm}$$
$$|\vec{e}| = \sqrt{92^2 + (-17)^2 + 10^2} \approx 94.09 \text{ cm}$$
The arm is extended more in its final position.

LESSON MASTER 12-6 Questions on SPUR Objectives
See pages 778–781 for objectives.

Skills Objective C

In 1–6, let $\vec{u} = (3, -2, 1)$, and $\vec{v} = (-4, 4, 5)$, and compute.

1. $\vec{u} + \vec{v}$ (-1, 2, 6)
2. $-8\vec{v}$ (32, -32, -40)
3. $|\vec{u}|$ $\sqrt{14}$
4. $\vec{u} \cdot \vec{v}$ -15
5. $5\vec{u} - 3\vec{v}$ (27, -22, -10)
6. $\vec{u} \times \vec{v}$ (-14, -19, 4)
7. Find a vector orthogonal to both $\vec{r} = (1, 1, 3)$ and $\vec{s} = (-2, 0, 6)$. Sample: (6, -12, 2)

Skills Objective D

In 8–10, find the measure of the angle between the two vectors.

8. $\vec{u} = (2, 3, 4)$, $\vec{v} = (-6, 0, 3)$ 90°
9. $\vec{u} = (0, -1, 7)$, $\vec{v} = (8, -2, -2)$ 101.5°
10. $\vec{u} = (3, 6, -5)$, $\vec{v} = (-6, -12, 10)$ 180°

Properties Objective E

11. Prove that if $\vec{u}$, $\vec{v}$, and $\vec{w}$ are vectors in 3-space, then $\vec{u} \cdot (\vec{v} + \vec{w}) = \vec{u} \cdot \vec{v} + \vec{u} \cdot \vec{w}$. Sample is given.

Let $\vec{u} = (u_1, u_2, u_3)$, $\vec{v} = (v_1, v_2, v_3)$ and $\vec{w} = (w_1, w_2, w_3)$. Then, $\vec{u} \cdot (\vec{v} + \vec{w})$
$= (u_1, u_2, u_3) \cdot (v_1 + w_1, v_2 + w_2, v_3 + w_3)$
$= (u_1(v_1 + w_1), u_2(v_2 + w_2), u_3(v_3 + w_3))$
$= (u_1v_1 + u_1w_1, u_2v_2 + u_2w_2, u_3v_3 + u_3w_3)$
$= (u_1v_1, u_2v_2, u_3v_3) + (u_1w_1, u_2w_2, u_3w_3)$
$= \vec{u} \cdot \vec{v} + \vec{u} \cdot \vec{w}$

Adapting to Individual Needs

Extra Help

Some students may have trouble visualizing angles and orthogonal vectors in three dimensions. Have students hold yard sticks to model the following:

1. angle formed by two vectors (A sheet of cardboard can be held against these two yardsticks to show that the angle is, in fact, a two-dimensional figure.)
2. vectors orthogonal to the first two
3. vectors orthogonal to a single vector (Lead students to discuss that even for vectors of a fixed length, in three dimensions there are an infinite number of vectors orthogonal to a given vector.)

b. The distance from start to end is the length of the difference vector.

$$|\vec{e} - \vec{s}| = \sqrt{(92 - 5)^2 + (-17 - 25)^2 + (10 - 32)^2}$$
$$= \sqrt{87^2 + 42^2 + 22^2}$$
$$\approx 99.08 \text{ cm}$$

The distance between start and end is almost one meter.

c. The angle is found using part (1) of the theorem on page 754.

$$\vec{s} \cdot \vec{e} = 5(92) + 25(-17) + 32(10)$$
$$= 355$$
$$\cos\theta = \frac{\vec{s} \cdot \vec{e}}{|\vec{s}|\,|\vec{e}|} \approx \frac{355}{(40.91)(94.09)} \approx .0922$$
$$\therefore \quad \theta \approx \cos^{-1}(.0922) \approx 84.7°$$

Orthogonal Vectors in 3-Space

The second part of the theorem on page 754 provides a test for orthogonality of vectors.

Example 3

Consider the vectors $\vec{u} = (3, -1, 2)$ and $\vec{v} = (4, -5, 6)$.

a. Are they orthogonal?
b. Find p so that $(3, p, -2)$ is orthogonal to $\vec{u}$.
c. Find a vector that is orthogonal to both $\vec{u}$ and $\vec{v}$.

Solution

a. $\vec{u} \cdot \vec{v} = 3 \cdot 4 + -1 \cdot -5 + 2 \cdot 6 = 29 \neq 0$, so they are not orthogonal.

b. $\vec{u} \cdot (3, p, -2) = 3 \cdot 3 + -1 \cdot p + 2 \cdot -2 = 5 - p$. This must be zero for the vectors to be orthogonal, so $p = 5$.

c. Let an orthogonal vector be $\vec{w} = (w_1, w_2, w_3)$. Then $\vec{u}$ and $\vec{w}$ are orthogonal

$$\Leftrightarrow \vec{u} \cdot \vec{w} = 0 \Leftrightarrow 3w_1 - w_2 + 2w_3 = 0.$$

$\vec{v}$ and $\vec{w}$ are orthogonal

$$\Leftrightarrow \vec{v} \cdot \vec{w} = 0 \Leftrightarrow 4w_1 - 5w_2 + 6w_3 = 0.$$

This system of two equations with three variables has an infinite number of solutions. But think of it as a system of two linear equations in the variable w_2 and w_3. Solve for w_2 and w_3 in terms of w_1.

$$\begin{cases} -w_2 = -3w_1 - 2w_3 \\ 6w_3 = -4w_1 + 5w_2 \end{cases} \Rightarrow \begin{cases} w_2 = 3w_1 + 2w_3 \\ w_3 = -\frac{2}{3}w_1 + \frac{5}{6}w_2 \end{cases}$$

3. Let $\vec{u} = (4, -2, 7)$ and $\vec{v} = (-3, 1, 2)$.
a. Are $\vec{u}$ and $\vec{v}$ orthogonal? Yes
b. Find z if $(6, 3, z)$ is orthogonal to $\vec{v}$. $z = 7.5$
c. Find all vectors orthogonal both to $\vec{u}$ and to $\vec{v}$. any vector of the form $(11k, 29k, 2k)$

4. Find $\vec{u} \times \vec{v}$ using the vectors from Additional Example 3 and check your answer using the dot product. $\vec{u} \times \vec{v} = (-11, -29, -2)$; both $(\vec{u} \times \vec{v}) \cdot \vec{u}$ and $(\vec{u} \times \vec{v}) \cdot \vec{v}$ equal 0.

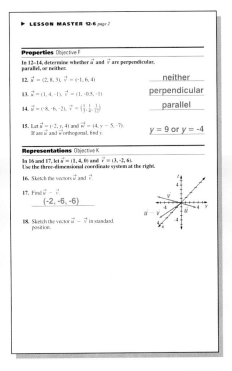

LESSON MASTER 12-6 *page 2*

Properties Objective F

In 12–14, determine whether $\vec{u}$ and $\vec{v}$ are perpendicular, parallel, or neither.

12. $\vec{u} = (2, 8, 3)$, $\vec{v} = (-1, 6, 4)$ neither

13. $\vec{u} = (1, 4, -1)$, $\vec{v} = (1, -0.5, -1)$ perpendicular

14. $\vec{u} = (-8, -6, -2)$, $\vec{v} = \left(\frac{1}{3}, \frac{1}{4}, \frac{1}{12}\right)$ parallel

15. Let $\vec{u} = (-2, y, 4)$ and $\vec{w} = (4, y - 5, -7)$. If are $\vec{u}$ and $\vec{w}$ orthogonal, find y. $y = 9$ or $y = -4$

Representations Objective K

In 16 and 17, let $\vec{u} = (1, 4, 0)$ and $\vec{v} = (3, -2, 6)$. Use the three-dimensional coordinate system at the right.

16. Sketch the vectors $\vec{u}$ and $\vec{v}$.

17. Find $\vec{u} - \vec{v}$. (-2, -6, -6)

18. Sketch the vector $\vec{u} - \vec{v}$ in standard position.

Science Connection A basic gyroscope consists of a spinning wheel or ball, called the rotor, which is supported by a frame. Once the rotor is set in motion, the gyroscope resists any attempt to change its direction of rotation. Because of this property, gyroscopes are used widely in navigation and flight instruments.

Notes on Questions

Question 10 Teaching Aid 143, which shows the diagram with **Example 2,** may be helpful.

Question 13 Error Alert Students may make mistakes in computing the cross product. Stress that they must be very careful to find each term of the cross product vector by following the definition on page 753.

Question 16 This asks for a generalization of **Example 4** and **Question 13.**

Substituting the expression for w_3 in the first equation and the expression for w_2 in the second equation, then solving yields:

$$w_2 = -\frac{5}{2}w_1$$
$$w_3 = -\frac{11}{4}w_1$$

So all vectors orthogonal to $\vec{u}$ and $\vec{v}$ have the form $\left(w_1, -\frac{5}{2}w_1, -\frac{11}{4}w_1\right)$. Letting $w_1 = 1$, one such vector is $\left(1, -\frac{5}{2}, -\frac{11}{4}\right)$. Letting $w_1 = -4$, another vector is $(-4, 10, 11)$. All the orthogonal vectors are parallel to each other.

The Cross Product of Two Vectors

gyroscope

The vectors found in part **c** of Example 3 are perpendicular to the plane determined by $\vec{u}$ and $\vec{v}$. Perpendiculars to planes are used in many applications. In physics, for example, a rotating object, such as a rotating disk or wheel (like that found in a gyroscope), produces a force called *torque* which is represented by a vector perpendicular to the plane of rotation. In computer graphics, vectors perpendicular to surfaces are used in the computation of shadings which represent light intensity and reflections. The vector operation called the *cross product* computes orthogonal vectors directly and so is useful in these and many other applications.

Definition
The **cross product** of two vectors
$\vec{u} = (u_1, u_2, u_3)$ and $\vec{v} = (v_1, v_2, v_3)$ is
$\vec{u} \times \vec{v} = (u_2v_3 - u_3v_2, u_3v_1 - u_1v_3, u_1v_2 - u_2v_1)$

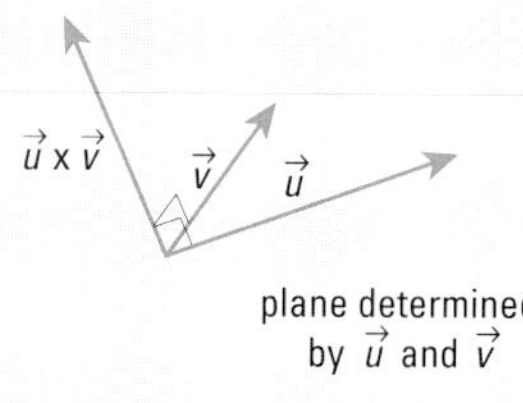

Example 4

a. Find $\vec{u} \times \vec{v}$ for the vectors $\vec{u} = (3, -1, 2)$ and $\vec{v} = (4, -5, 6)$.
b. Verify that $\vec{u} \times \vec{v}$ is perpendicular to both $\vec{u}$ and $\vec{v}$.

Solution

a. $(3, -1, 2) \times (4, -5, 6) = (-1 \cdot 6 - 2 \cdot -5, 2 \cdot 4 - 3 \cdot 6, 3 \cdot -5 - -1 \cdot 4)$
$= (4, -10, -11)$

Adapting to Individual Needs

Challenge
Have students answer the following.

1. Let $\vec{u} = (u_1, u_2, u_3)$. The angles, α, β, and γ, that $\vec{u}$ makes with the positive x-axis, positive y-axis, and positive z-axis, respectively, are called the *direction angles* for $\vec{u}$. They can be found by using the formulas:
$\cos\alpha = \frac{u_1}{|\vec{u}|}$; $\cos\beta = \frac{u_2}{|\vec{u}|}$; $\cos\gamma = \frac{u_3}{|\vec{u}|}$.
   a. Find α, β, and γ when $\vec{u} = (2, -5, 7)$. [$\alpha = 76.91°$; $\beta = 124.48°$; $\gamma = 37.57°$]
   b. Find α, β, and γ when $\vec{u} = (3, 0, -4)$. [$\alpha = 53.13°$; $\beta = 90°$; $\gamma = 143.13°$]
   c. Simplify: $\cos^2\alpha + \cos^2\beta + \cos^2\gamma$. [1]
2. Find the angle between the diagonal of a cube and one of its edges. [≈54.7°]
3. Find the angle between the diagonal of a cube and the diagonal of one of its sides. [≈35.26°]

b. Two vectors are orthogonal if and only if their dot product is 0. $(\vec{u} \times \vec{v}) \cdot \vec{u} = (4, -10, -11) \cdot (3, -1, 2) = 4 \cdot 3 + (-10)(-1) + -11 \cdot 2 = 12 + 10 - 22 = 0$, so $\vec{u} \times \vec{v}$ is orthogonal to $\vec{u}$. You are ask to verify that $\vec{u} \times \vec{v}$ is orthogonal to $\vec{v}$ in Question 12.

Notice that the cross-product vector in Example 4**b** is a scalar multiple of the vector $\left(1, -\frac{5}{2}, -\frac{11}{4}\right)$ found to be perpendicular to $\vec{u}$ and $\vec{v}$ in Example 3**c**. So it is perpendicular to them. This is true in general. (See Question 16.)

QUESTIONS

Covering the Reading

1. The right-hand clip in the space shuttle cargo bay is 691 inches behind the nose, 14 inches higher, and 98 inches right of center. Give the coordinates of this clip using the orbiter body axis system. **(-927, 98, -414)**

In 2–7, suppose $\vec{u} = (5, -1, -1)$ and $\vec{v} = (-2, 0, 7)$. Compute.

2. $\vec{u} + \vec{v}$ **(3, -1, 6)**

3. $\vec{v} - \vec{u}$ **(-7, 1, 8)**

4. $|\vec{u}|$ **$3\sqrt{3}$**

5. $\vec{u} \cdot \vec{v}$ **-17**

6. $2\vec{u} + 3\vec{v}$ **(4, -2, 19)**

7. $\vec{u} \times \vec{u}$ **(0, 0, 0)**

8. The length of a vector is the __?__ of its dot product with itself. **Square root**

9. Let $\vec{u} = (1, 3, 2)$ and $\vec{v} = (5, 0, -1)$. Find the measure of the angle between $\vec{u}$ and $\vec{v}$. **≈ 81°**

10. Suppose the robot arm in Example 2 had moved an object from (10.00, 50.00, 64.00) to (23.00, -4.25, 2.50).
  a. How far was the finishing point from the starting point?
  b. Through what angle did the arm rotate? **≈ 84.7°** **a) ≈ 83cm**

11. Tell why $\vec{r} = (1, 0, 1)$ is orthogonal to $\vec{s} = (\sqrt{2}, 10, -\sqrt{2})$. **$\vec{r} \cdot \vec{s} = 0$**

12. Verify the second part to Example 4**b** by direct computation. **See left.**

13. When $\vec{u} = (3, 4, 5)$ and $\vec{v} = (-2, 5, 9)$, verify that $\vec{u} \times \vec{v}$ is orthogonal to $\vec{u}$. **See left.**

14. **a.** Find z so that $\vec{u} = (3, -1, z)$ is orthogonal to $\vec{v} = (2, 5, -2)$. **$z = \frac{1}{2}$**
  b. Find a vector orthogonal to both $\vec{u}$ and $\vec{v}$.
  Sample: $\left(-\frac{1}{2}, 7, 17\right)$

12) $(\vec{u} \times \vec{v}) \cdot \vec{v} = (4, -10, -11) \cdot (4, -5, 6) = 4(4) + (-10)(-5) + (-11)(6) = 0$

13) $\vec{u} \times \vec{v} = (11, -37, 23)$; $\vec{u} \cdot (\vec{u} \times \vec{v}) = 3 \cdot 11 + 4 \cdot -37 + 5 \cdot 23 = 0$

Applying the Mathematics

15. **a.** Prove that $\vec{u} \cdot \vec{v} = \vec{v} \cdot \vec{u}$ for all three-dimensional vectors $\vec{u}$ and $\vec{v}$.
  b. What property does this illustrate?
See margin.

16. Prove that $\vec{u} \times \vec{v}$ is orthogonal to $\vec{u}$, and $\vec{u} \times \vec{v}$ is orthogonal to $\vec{v}$, for all three-dimensional vectors $\vec{u}$ and $\vec{v}$. **See margin.**

Additional Answers

15. a. $\vec{u} \cdot \vec{v} = u_1v_1 + u_2v_2 + u_3v_3 = v_1u_1 + v_2u_2 + v_3u_3 = \vec{v} \cdot \vec{u}$

b. Commutative Property of the Dot Product

16. $(\vec{u} \times \vec{v}) \cdot \vec{u} = (u_2v_3 - u_3v_2, u_3v_1 - u_1v_3, u_1v_2 - u_2v_1) \cdot \vec{u} = u_1u_2v_3 - u_1u_3v_2 + u_2u_3v_1 - u_1u_2v_3 + u_1u_3v_2 - u_2u_3v_1 = 0$; $(\vec{u} \times \vec{v}) \cdot \vec{v} = (u_2v_3 - u_3v_2, u_3v_1 - u_1v_3, u_1v_2 - u_2v_1) \cdot \vec{v} = v_1u_2v_3 - v_1u_3v_2 + v_2u_3v_1 - v_2u_1v_3 + v_3u_1v_2 - v_3u_2v_1 = 0$

Notes on Questions

Question 19 This question leads nicely into the next lesson by dealing with two vectors that determine a plane and a third vector perpendicular to it (and them). **Teaching Aid 144** is provided. Advise students not to be awed by the length of the question; each part leads to the next. Students may not realize how to use the result from **part d** to answer **part e.** Think of cos θ as the fraction of the maximum brightness at P. We need to find that fraction of 255, the maximum brightness in the computer's scale. So we find 255 cos θ.

Question 25 A general proof deserves extra credit.

Additional Answers

18. a. The angle between $a\vec{u}$ and $b\vec{v}$ is $\cos^{-1}\left(\frac{a\vec{u} \cdot b\vec{v}}{|a\vec{u}|\,|b\vec{v}|}\right)$

$= \cos^{-1}\left(\frac{ab(\vec{u} \cdot \vec{v})}{a|\vec{u}|\,b|\vec{v}|}\right)$

$= \cos^{-1}\left(\frac{\vec{u} \cdot \vec{v}}{|\vec{u}|\,|\vec{v}|}\right)$, which is the angle between $\vec{u}$ and $\vec{v}$.

b. Scalar multiplication does not change the measure of the angle between two vectors.

17) $(a\vec{u})(b\vec{v}) = (au_1, au_2, au_3) \cdot (bv_1, bv_2, bv_3) = abu_1v_1 + abu_2v_2 + abu_3v_3 = ab(u_1v_1 + u_2v_2 + u_3v_3) = ab(\vec{u} \cdot \vec{v})$

17. Prove that $(a\vec{u}) \cdot (b\vec{v}) = (ab)(\vec{u} \cdot \vec{v})$ for all three-dimensional vectors $\vec{u}$ and $\vec{v}$ and real numbers a and b. **See left.**

18. a. Prove that the angle between $a\vec{u}$ and $b\vec{v}$ is the same as the angle between $\vec{u}$ and $\vec{v}$, for any positive real numbers a and b.

b. Give a geometric interpretation for part **a**.

See margin.

19. Three-dimensional vectors are used in computer graphics. Suppose a *matte surface* (one which reflects and scatters light equally in all directions) is illuminated by a light source. Then the brightness of a point P on that surface depends on the angle at which the surface faces the light. In fact, if $\vec{s}$ is the vector from P to the light source, and $\vec{n}$ is a vector perpendicular to the surface at P, then the brightness of P is proportional to the cosine of the angle θ between $\vec{n}$ and $\vec{s}$. Thus, when the light hits the surface head on, so that θ = 0°, the point has maximum brightness because cos θ = 1.

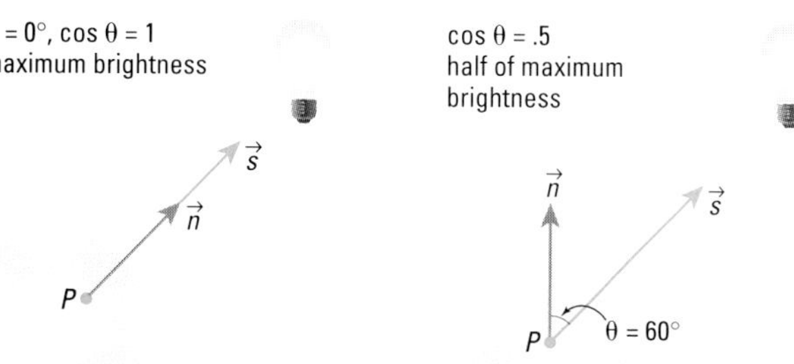

When the surface is tilted so that θ = 60°, the brightness is only half of the maximum because $\cos \theta = \frac{1}{2}$.

Suppose $P = (-3, 5, 1)$, and the surface is a plane which contains P as well as the points $Q = (-4, 5, 2)$ and $R = (-3, 4, 4)$.

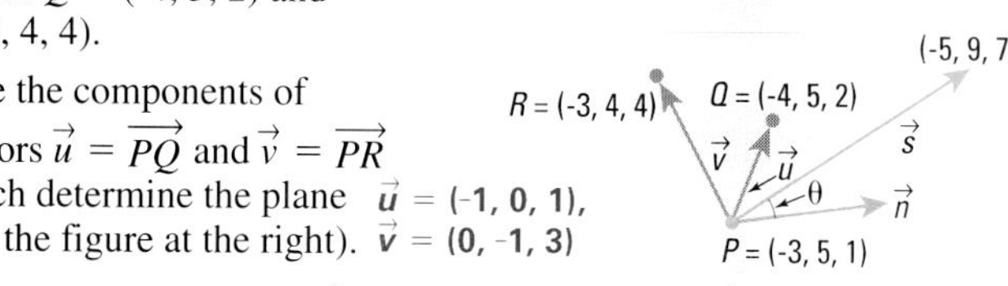

a. Give the components of vectors $\vec{u} = \overrightarrow{PQ}$ and $\vec{v} = \overrightarrow{PR}$ which determine the plane (see the figure at the right). **$\vec{u}$ = (-1, 0, 1), $\vec{v}$ = (0, -1, 3)**

b. Give the components of $\vec{n}$, a vector perpendicular to the surface. **Sample: (1, 3, 1)**

c. Give the components of $\vec{s}$, the vector from P to the light source at (-5, 9, 7). **(-2, 4, 6)**

d. Find cos θ, where θ is the angle between $\vec{n}$ and $\vec{s}$. **≈ 0.645**

e. Brightness is represented in many computers by an integer from 0 (pitch black) to 255 (maximum brightness). What integer represents the brightness of the surface at point P? **164**

0) center: $\left(2, -\frac{3}{2}, 0\right)$;
radius: $\frac{1}{2}\sqrt{17}$

2a) Sample: $(x - 1, y + 2) = t(-4, 7)$
b) Sample: $x = 1 - 4t$; $y = -2 + 7t$

Review

20. Find the center and radius of the sphere whose equation is $x^2 - 4x + y^2 + 3y + z^2 = -2$. *(Lesson 12-5)* **See left.**

21. Find all vectors in a plane that are orthogonal to $\vec{u} = (-4, 2)$ and that have length 5. *(Lesson 12-4)* **$(\sqrt{5}, 2\sqrt{5})$ and $(-\sqrt{5}, -2\sqrt{5})$**

22. Let ℓ be the line through the points (-3, 5) and (1, -2) in the plane.
a. Find a vector equation for ℓ. **See left.**
b. Find parametric equations for ℓ. *(Lesson 12-3)* **See left.**

23. Write the base 10 representation of 11111111_2. (This is the largest integer that can be stored by a computer in a single *byte*.) *(Lesson 4-6)* **255**

24. Suppose f is the function defined by $f(x) = \lfloor 2x \rfloor$ on the domain $0 \le x \le 1$.
a. Find the range of f. **{0, 1, 2}**
b. Is f a discrete function? *(Lessons 2-1, 2-2)* **No**

Exploration

25. Let $\vec{u} = (8, 10, 0)$ and $\vec{v} = (4, 5, 1)$. Show that the length of $\vec{u} \times \vec{v}$ is the area of the parallelogram having $\vec{u}$ and $\vec{v}$ as sides.
$\vec{u} \times \vec{v} = (10, -8, 0)$ whose length is $2\sqrt{41}$. The parallelogram with $\vec{u}$ and $\vec{v}$ as sides has base $|\vec{u}| = 2\sqrt{41}$ and height $= 1$, so its area is $2\sqrt{41}$.

Follow-up for Lesson 12-6

Practice

For more questions on SPUR Objectives, use **Lesson Master 12-6** (shown on pages 754–755).

Assessment

Quiz A quiz covering Lessons 12-4 through 12-6 is provided in the *Assessment Sourcebook.*

Extension

Ask students the following question. If two vectors are parallel then what can be said about their cross product? [It is the zero vector.]

Project Update Project 1, *Four-Dimensional Vectors,* and Project 3, *Vectors Applied to Statistics,* on pages 773–774, relate to the content of this lesson.

Setting Up Lesson 12-7

Go through **Question 19** in detail. You also may wish to discuss **Question 22** to review vector and parametric equations.

Lesson 12-7

Objectives

M Represent lines, planes, and spheres in 3-space using parametric, vector, or coordinate equations.

Resources

From the ***Teacher's Resource File***
- Lesson Master 12-7
- Answer Master 12-7
- Teaching Aids
  134 Warm-up
  145 Example 1 and Example 2

Additional Resources
- Visuals for Teaching Aids 134, 145

Teaching Lesson 12-7

Warm-up

Refer to the diagram.

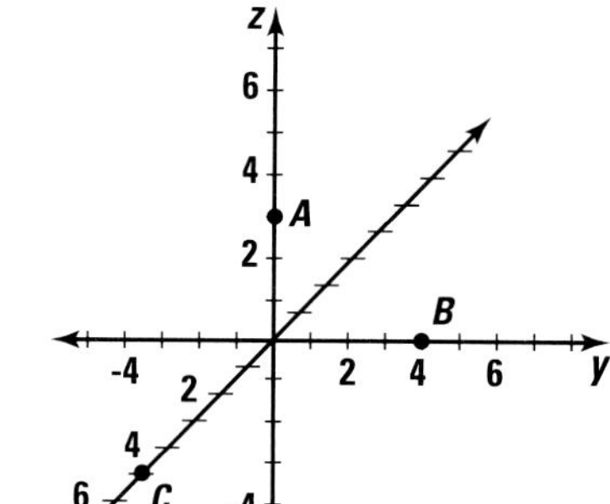

1. What are the coordinates of points A, B, and C? **(0, 0, 3), (0, 4, 0), (5, 0, 0)**
2. How many lines contain points A and B? Points A and C? Points B and C? **one, one, one**
3. How many planes contain points A, B, and C? **one**

LESSON

12-7 Lines and Planes in 3-Space

From the last lesson, you may realize that one advantage of using vectors is that they enable 3-dimensional figures to be dealt with just like their 2-dimensional counterparts. Addition, scalar multiplication, the dot product, and orthogonality are developed in the same way regardless of dimension. This is also true about vector equations for lines. (You may wish to compare what you read here with what is in Lesson 12-3.)

Equations for a Line in 3-Space

Suppose that $P = (x_0, y_0, z_0)$ is a fixed point in 3-space and that $\vec{v} = (v_1, v_2, v_3)$ is a fixed nonzero vector. Then there is one and only one straight line ℓ in space that passes through P and is parallel to $\vec{v}$.

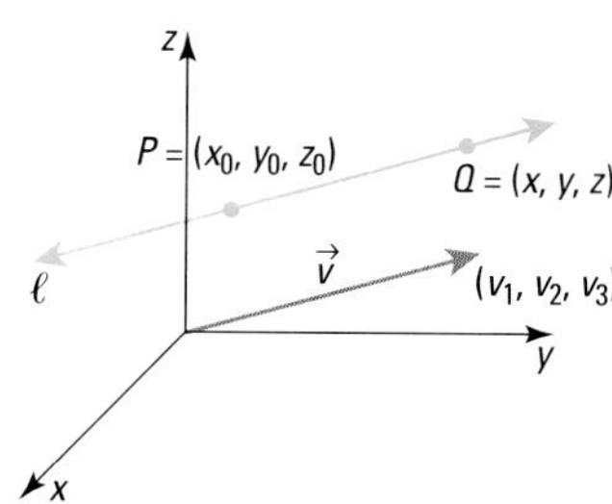

A point $Q = (x, y, z)$ lies on the line ℓ if and only if the vector $\overrightarrow{PQ}$ joining P to Q is parallel to the vector $\vec{v}$. However, recall that two nonzero vectors are parallel to one another if and only if one is a nonzero scalar multiple of the other. Therefore, the point $Q = (x, y, z)$ is on the line ℓ if and only if there is a real number t such that

$$\overrightarrow{PQ} = t\vec{v}.$$

This is a *vector equation* for ℓ.

The vector $\overrightarrow{PQ}$ has the component representation

$$\overrightarrow{PQ} = (x - x_0, y - y_0, z - z_0).$$

Substituting the components for $\overrightarrow{PQ}$ and $\vec{v}$, the vector equation for ℓ becomes

$$(x - x_0, y - y_0, z - z_0) = t(v_1, v_2, v_3).$$

Equating the components on the two sides of the equation yields parametric equations for the line ℓ in 3-space. These arguments prove the following theorem.

Lesson 12-7 Overview

Broad Goals The same process that was used to determine a parametric equation of a line in 2-space is extended here to lines in 3-space, and cross products are used to determine equations for planes.

Perspective The form of a vector equation of a line in 3-space is identical to the form of the equation in 2-space. But, in translating into parametric form, because there are 3 components to the vector, we need three equations. Whereas the parametric equations extend quite nicely, what would seem to be the 3-dimensional extension of the linear equation $ax + by = c$, the equation $ax + by + cz = d$, is not a line but a plane. This result is proved in this lesson by noting there is exactly one plane perpendicular to a line m and passing through a particular point P. All vectors in the plane through P are perpendicular to m. Thus the dot product of a vector parallel to m and a vector in the plane is 0. The upshot of all this is that the vector (a, b, c) is perpendicular to any plane with equation $ax + by + cz = d$. This is analogous to the fact that the vector (a, b) is perpendicular to any line with equation $ax + by = c$.

Although we discuss parametric equations in 3-space only for lines, students should realize that curves in 3-space can be described parametrically. This enables the

Theorem (Equations for a Line in 3-Space)
A point $Q = (x, y, z)$ is on the line ℓ through $P = (x_0, y_0, z_0)$ parallel to $\vec{v} = (v_1, v_2, v_3)$ if and only if there is a real number t such that

a. $\overrightarrow{PQ} = t\vec{v}$ **Vector equation for ℓ**

or b. $\begin{cases} x = x_0 + tv_1 \\ y = y_0 + tv_2 \\ z = z_0 + tv_3. \end{cases}$ **Parametric equations for ℓ**

Example 1

Let ℓ be the line passing through the two points (-1, 2, 3) and (4, -1, 5).

a. Describe ℓ with a vector equation.

b. Describe ℓ by parametric equations.

Solution

a. The vector $\vec{v}$ that joins (-1, 2, 3) to (4, -1, 5) has the component representation

$$\vec{v} = (4 - (-1), -1 - 2, 5 - 3) = (5, -3, 2).$$

If P is the point (-1, 2, 3) and Q = (x, y, z) is any point on ℓ, then $\overrightarrow{PQ} = (x + 1, y - 2, z - 3)$.
Since ℓ is parallel to $\vec{v}$, a vector equation of ℓ is
$(x + 1, y - 2, z - 3) = t(5, -3, 2)$.

b. Equating components in the vector equation yields $x + 1 = 5t$, $y - 2 = -3t$, and $z - 3 = 2t$. Thus, parametric equations for ℓ are

$$\begin{cases} x = -1 + 5t \\ y = 2 - 3t \\ z = 3 + 2t. \end{cases}$$

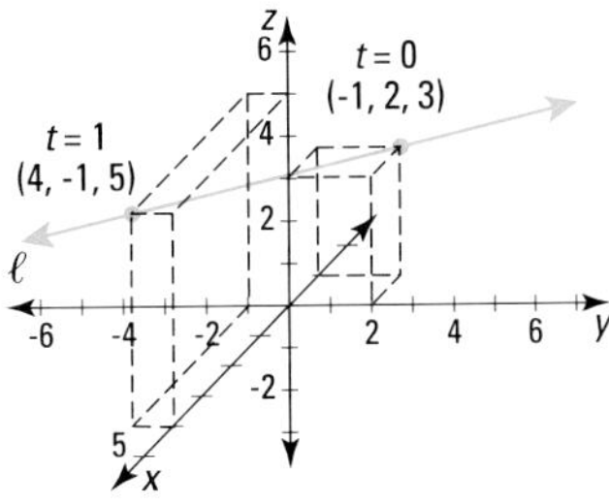

As in 2-space, each value of t in the parametric equations for a line determines a point on the line. In Example 1, $t = 0$ yields the point (-1, 2, 3), and $t = 1$ yields (4, -1, 5). Values of t between 0 and 1 yield points between (-1, 2, 3) and (4, -1, 5).

Notes on Reading

The diagrams in **Examples 1–2** are on **Teaching Aid 145.**

Example 1 is straightforward. Notice that these 3-space problems are essentially the same as the corresponding problems in 2-space.

Error Alert As in Lesson 12-3, be sure students don't assume that the parametric form of the equation of a line is unique. In **Example 1,** for instance, had (9, -4, 7), another point on line ℓ, been used for the second point, the set of parametric equations for this line would be

$$\begin{cases} x = -1 + 10t \\ y = 2 - 6t \\ z = 3 + 4t. \end{cases}$$

Whereas Lesson 12-6 contained topics where two-dimensional ideas were virtually identical to their counterparts in 3-space, the equations of lines and planes are not identical, but analogous. In 2-space $\{(x, y): ax + by = c\}$ is a line, but in 3-space $\{(x, y, z): ax + by + cz = d\}$ is a plane, not a line. In two dimensions the slope of a line helps to characterize it, but in 3-D a plane contains infinitely many vectors with infinitely many different directions. To describe the tilt of the plane we use a vector that is not even in the plane! This is shown in **Example 2.**

Go through the proof of the Equation for a Plane Theorem so that students see why the coefficients a, b, and c in the equation for a plane are also the components of a vector perpendicular to the plane.

Following **Example 3,** the plane M is graphed by finding its intersections with the axes. The lines through these points lie entirely in the xy-, xz-, and yz-planes and are sometimes called *traces* of the plane M.

paths of moving objects such as robots; astronomical objects such as planets, artificial and real satellites; drills and other equipment; and all sorts of other man-made and natural objects to be described.

Optional Activities

Refer students to **Question 9.** Ask them whether the result changes if they use $\overrightarrow{P_2Q} \cdot (\overrightarrow{P_2P_1} \times \overrightarrow{P_2P_3}) = 0$ to determine the plane. [No, although the perpendicular vector will be opposite in direction] Ask them to write a third expression that will yield the same plane.
[$\overrightarrow{P_3Q} \cdot (\overrightarrow{P_3P_1} \times \overrightarrow{P_3P_2}) = 0$]

Adapting to Individual Needs

Extra Help
Caution students not to confuse $\overrightarrow{PQ}$ as used to name a vector with $\overrightarrow{PQ}$, a ray in geometry. Review the difference between a vector and a ray and explain that students must be aware of the context in which the symbol $\overrightarrow{PQ}$ is being used.

Additional Examples

1. Consider the line containing the points (6, 0, -4) and (-5, 1, 2).
   a. Find a vector equation for this line. **Sample:** $(x - 6, y, z + 4) = t(-11, 1, 6)$
   b. Find a parametric equation for this line. **Sample:** $x = 6 - 11t$, $y = t$, $z = -4 + 6t$
2. Find an equation for the plane that contains $P = (4, 2, 4)$ and is perpendicular to the vector $\vec{v} = (1, 4, 3)$. $x + 4y + 3z = 24$
3. a. Find parametric equations for the line that contains (-5, 4, 2) and is perpendicular to the plane with equation $-2x + 3y + 9z = 7$. **Sample:** $x = -5 - 2t$, $y = 4 + 3t$, $z = 2 + 9t$
   b. Is (-5, 4, 2) in that plane? **No**

LESSON MASTER 12-7

Questions on SPUR Objectives
See pages 778–781 for objectives.

Representations Objective M

1. Let ℓ be a line passing through the two points (8, 3, -5) and (-7, -3, 1). Describe ℓ with
   a. a vector equation.
   Sample: $(x - 8, y - 3, z + 5) = t(15, 6, -6)$
   b. parametric equations.
   $\begin{cases} x = 8 + 15t \\ y = 3 + 6t \\ z = -5 - 6t \end{cases}$
2. Find a vector equation for the line through (-2, 5, -1) that is perpendicular to the plane given by $2x - 3y - 4z = 12$.
   $(x + 2, y - 5, z + 1) = t(2, -3, -4)$
3. Find a vector perpendicular to the plane defined by the equation $x - 5y + 10z = 20$. (1, -5, 10)
4. Consider the line in 3-space through the point (4, -2, -2) that is parallel to the vector (7, 5, -2).
   a. Find a vector equation for the line.
   $(x - 4, y + 2, z + 2) = t(7, 5, -2)$
   b. Find parametric equations for the line.
   $\begin{cases} x = 4 + 7t \\ y = -2 + 5t \\ z = -2 - 2t \end{cases}$
   c. Find a point other than (4, -2, -2) that lies on the line. Sample: (11, 3, -4)
5. Find an equation for the plane that is perpendicular to $\vec{u} = (2, 16, -10)$ and contains the point (3, -5, 0).
   $2(x - 3) + 16(y + 5) - 10z = 0$ or $x + 8y - 5z = -37$
6. Show that the planes defined by the equations $2x + y - 4z = 5$ and $-x + 2y + 3z = 8$ are not parallel.
   The vectors (2, 1, -4) and (-1, 2, 3), which are perpendicular to the planes, are not parallel.

An Equation for a Plane in 3-Space

Recall from your work in geometry that a plane M is perpendicular to a lin ℓ at a point P if and only if every line in M through P is perpendicular to ℓ (Imagine a pencil perpendicular to a table at its tip. Any line on the table through the tip is perpendicular to the pencil.)

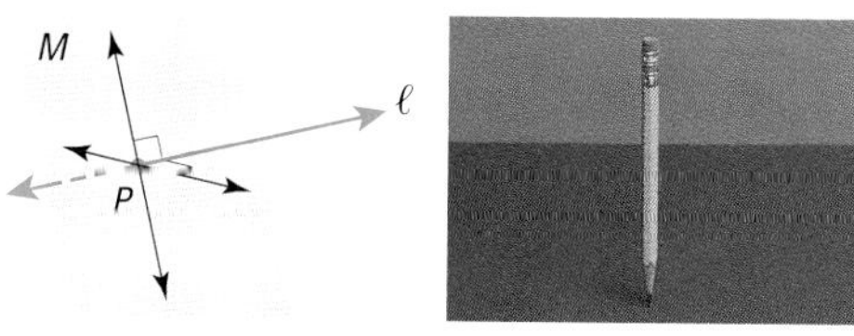

In Lesson 12-6, you learned that if $\vec{u}$ and $\vec{v}$ are nonzero 3-dimensional vectors, then $\vec{u} \cdot \vec{v} = 0$ if and only if $\vec{u}$ and $\vec{v}$ are orthogonal. This fact is very helpful for working with planes in space.

Example 2

Find vector and rectangular coordinate equations for the plane M that passes through the point $P = (2, 3, 4)$ and is perpendicular to the vector $\vec{w} = (1, -1, 4)$.

Solution

Suppose that $Q = (x, y, z)$ is a point on M, as shown below. Then

$$\overrightarrow{PQ} = (x - 2, y - 3, z - 4).$$

Now $\overrightarrow{PQ}$ lies in M if and only if $\vec{w}$ is perpendicular to $\overrightarrow{PQ}$. But $\vec{w} \perp \overrightarrow{PQ} \Leftrightarrow \vec{w} \cdot \overrightarrow{PQ} = 0$. Therefore, a vector equation of the plane M is $\vec{w} \cdot \overrightarrow{PQ} = 0$. Substitute for $\vec{w}$ and $\overrightarrow{PQ}$.

$(1, -1, 4) \cdot (x - 2, y - 3, z - 4) = 0.$

A rectangular coordinate equation for M can be obtained by using the definition of dot product.

$$(x - 2) - (y - 3) + 4(z - 4) = 0$$
$$x - y + 4z = 15$$

Thus, the plane M is the set of all points (x, y, z) in space that satisfy the equation

$$x - y + 4z = 15.$$

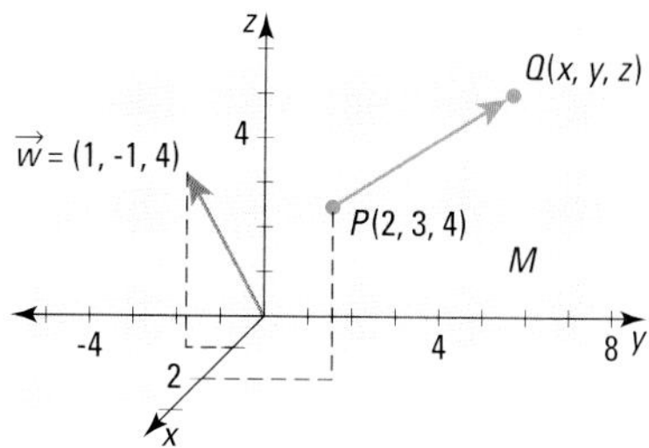

Adapting to Individual Needs

Challenge

Have students answer the following.

1. The shortest distance, D, from the point (x_0, y_0, z_0) to the plane $ax + by + cz + d = 0$ is given by:
   $$D = \frac{|ax_0 + by_0 + cz_0 + d|}{\sqrt{a^2 + b^2 + c^2}}.$$
   Find the distance between the point (5, 11, -2) and the plane $2x - 3y + z - 2 = 0$. $\left[\frac{27\sqrt{14}}{14}\right]$
2. Explain how vectors can be used to decide whether or not a group of three points is collinear. [Sample: P, Q, and R are collinear if and only if $\overrightarrow{PQ}$ and $\overrightarrow{PR}$ are parallel vectors.]
   a. Are (1, 5, 2), (8, 5, 3), (-2, 4,-9) collinear? [No]
   b. Are (3,-1, 0), (5, 2, -1), (7, 5, -2) collinear? [Yes]

Activity

Refer to Example 2. **See left.**

a. Check that the coordinates of P satisfy the equation found for M.

b. Find another point Q on M. Verify that $\overleftrightarrow{PQ} \perp \overrightarrow{w}$.

a) $2 - 3 + 4(4) = 15$ It checks.
b) Sample: $Q = (-2, -1, 4)$
$\overrightarrow{PQ} \perp \overrightarrow{w} \Leftrightarrow \overrightarrow{PQ} \cdot \overrightarrow{w} = 0$
$\overrightarrow{PQ} \cdot \overrightarrow{w} = (1 \cdot -4) + (-1 \cdot -4) + (0 \cdot 4) = 0$

Notice that the coefficients of x, y, and z in Example 2 are the components of $\overrightarrow{w}$. This wonderfully simple pattern is true in general.

Theorem (Equation for a Plane)
The set of points $\{(x, y, z)\colon ax + by + cz = d\}$, where at least one of the coefficients a, b, or c is nonzero, is a plane perpendicular to the vector $\overrightarrow{v} = (a, b, c)$.

Proof
Let M be the plane containing the fixed point $P = (x_0, y_0, z_0)$ and perpendicular to a fixed nonzero vector $\overrightarrow{v} = (a, b, c)$. Let $Q = (x, y, z)$ be any point. Then Q lies on M if and only if

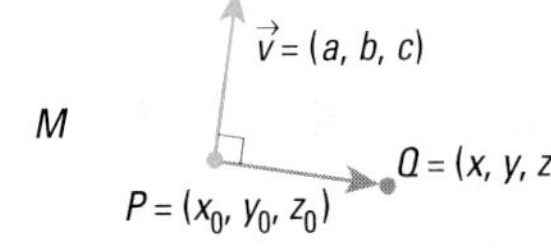

$$\overrightarrow{v} \cdot \overrightarrow{PQ} = 0.$$

This equation can be expressed in coordinates as

$$(a, b, c) \cdot (x - x_0, y - y_0, z - z_0) = 0.$$

Calculating the dot product,

$$a(x - x_0) + b(y - y_0) + c(z - z_0) = 0.$$

$$\therefore ax + by + cz = ax_0 + by_0 + cz_0.$$

The right side is a constant. Call this d. Thus (x, y, z) lies on the plane M if and only if

$$ax + by + cz = d.$$

Example 3

Find parametric equations of the line ℓ through $P = (1, 2, 4)$ that is perpendicular to the plane M defined by the equation

$$3x - y + 2z = 9.$$

Solution

According to the Equation for a Plane Theorem, the coefficients in the equation of M give the components of the vector $\overrightarrow{v} = (3, -1, 2)$ which is perpendicular to M. Any line ℓ through P perpendicular to M must be parallel to $\overrightarrow{v}$. Thus, if (x, y, z) is on ℓ, $(x - 1, y - 2, z - 4) = t(3, -1, 2)$ for any real number t, and so parametric equations of ℓ are

$$\begin{cases} x = 1 + 3t \\ y = 2 - t \\ z = 4 + 2t. \end{cases}$$

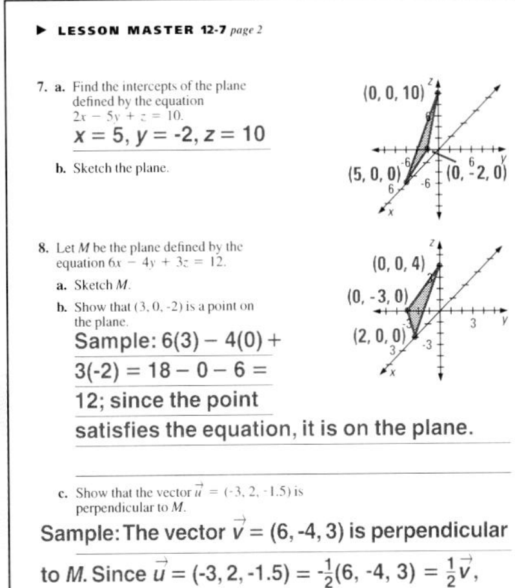
▶ **LESSON MASTER 12-7** *page 2*

7. a. Find the intercepts of the plane defined by the equation $2x - 5y + z = 10$.
$x = 5, y = -2, z = 10$

b. Sketch the plane.

8. Let M be the plane defined by the equation $6x - 4y + 3z = 12$.

a. Sketch M.

b. Show that $(3, 0, -2)$ is a point on the plane.
Sample: $6(3) - 4(0) + 3(-2) = 18 - 0 - 6 = 12$; since the point satisfies the equation, it is on the plane.

c. Show that the vector $\overrightarrow{u} = (-3, 2, -1.5)$ is perpendicular to M.
Sample: The vector $\overrightarrow{v} = (6, -4, 3)$ is perpendicular to M. Since $\overrightarrow{u} = (-3, 2, -1.5) = -\frac{1}{2}(6, -4, 3) = \frac{1}{2}\overrightarrow{v}$, $\overrightarrow{u}$ is parallel to $\overrightarrow{v}$ and thus perpendicular to M.

d. Find equation for the plane N that is parallel to M and passes through $(3, -1, 4)$.
$6(x - 3) - 4(y + 1) + 3(z - 4) = 0$

Notes on Questions

Questions 1–3 Notice that the vector whose components are the coefficients of t in the parametric equations of a line is parallel to the line, but the vector whose components are the coefficients in the equation of a plane is perpendicular to the plane (as in **Questions 5–7**).

Question 4 This plane has intercepts on the same rays of the coordinate axes as the plane graphed in the lesson. These and the planes with all coefficients positive are the easiest to graph. You may want to have your students graph a variety of planes.

Question 8 Students should realize that a method is being described, rather than a formula that they should learn. This method is applied in **Question 9.**

Question 9 Encourage students to check their answer by substituting the given points into the equation they write.

Question 11 One way to show that M_1 and M_2 are not parallel is to find a point in common. An easier way (usually) is to realize that vectors perpendicular to parallel planes must be scalar multiples of each other. Thus the coefficients a_i, b_i, and c_i must be proportional. We employ the latter method in **part a** but then ask for the former method in **part b.**

Question 12 All possible ordered triples are the points in the plane all of whose coordinates are nonnegative integers.

Additional Answers

5. $\vec{w} = (-4, 2, -6) = -2(2, -1, 3)$; $\vec{w}$ is parallel to (2, -1, 3), since it is a scalar multiple of it. (2, -1, 3) is perpendicular to the plane N, and hence $\vec{w}$ is perpendicular to N.

Graphing Planes in 3-Space

To graph the plane M of Example 3, recall that three noncollinear points determine a plane. Three points on M that are easy to find are its points of intersection with the axes. To find its point of intersection with the z-axis, note that a point (x, y, z) is on the z-axis if and only if $x = 0$ and $y = 0$. Suppose the point is also on M. Then $3 \cdot 0 - 0 + 2z = 9$, so $z = 4.5$. Consequently (0, 0, 4.5) is on M. In a similar manner, (0, -9, 0) is the point where M intersects the y-axis, and (3, 0, 0) is the point where M intersects the x-axis. The numbers 3, -9, and 4.5 are the x-, y-, and z-intercepts of the plane, respectively.

At the right is a sketch of M, along with the perpendicular vector $\vec{v}$. The three intercepts have been connected and the resulting region has been shaded to produce a look of flatness.

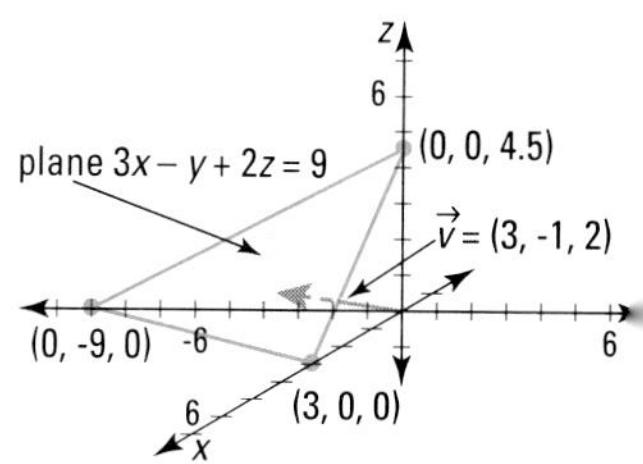

QUESTIONS

Covering the Reading

1a) $(x - 1, y - 5, z + 2) = t(-3, 0, 4)$
b) $x = 1 - 3t$; $y = 5$; $z = -2 + 4t$

1. Consider the line containing (1, 5, -2) parallel to the vector (-3, 0, 4).
   a. Find a vector equation for the line. See left.
   b. Find parametric equations for the line. See left.
   c. Find a point other than (1, 5, -2) that lies on the line. Sample: (-2, 5, 2)
2. Let ℓ be the line with parametric equations
$$\begin{cases} x = -2 + 3t \\ y = 3 - 2t \\ z = 2 - 3t. \end{cases}$$
   a. Is the point (10, -5, -8) on the line ℓ? Explain how you arrived at your answer. No, when $x = 10$, $t = 4$, but then $z \neq -8$.
   b. Find a vector $\vec{v}$ that is parallel to ℓ. (3, -2, -3)
   c. Find parametric equations for the line ℓ' that is parallel to ℓ and contains the point (1, 2, 3). Sample: $x = 1 + 3t$; $y = 2 - 2t$; $z = 3 - 3t$
3. Find an equation for the plane that is perpendicular to $\vec{u} = (2, 1, -2)$ and contains the point (0, 5, 3). $2x + y - 2z = -1$

In 4–7, let N be the plane defined by the equation $2x - y + 3z = 4$.

4. Sketch N. See left.

4)

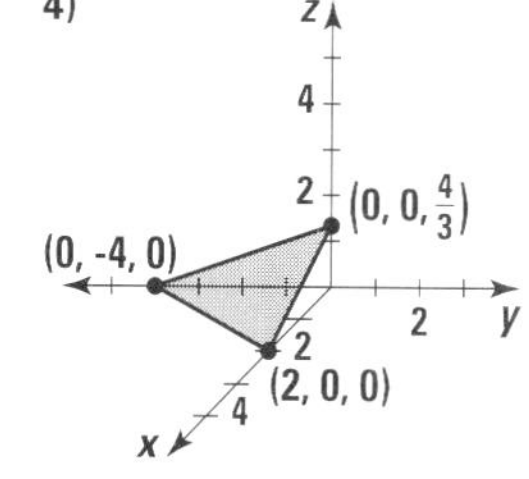

5. Show that the vector $\vec{w} = (-4, 2, -6)$ is perpendicular to N. See margin.

6. Find parametric equations for the line m that is perpendicular to N and that passes through the point (2, 3, -1).
Sample: $x = 2 + 2t$; $y = 3 - t$; $z = -1 + 3t$
7. Find an equation for the plane K that is parallel to N and that passes through the point (2, 3, -1). $2x - y + 3z = -2$

Applying the Mathematics

8. If P_1, P_2, and P_3 are three distinct noncollinear points in space, explain why a point $Q = (x, y, z)$ lies on the plane M through P_1, P_2, and P_3 if and only if $\overrightarrow{P_1Q} \cdot (\overrightarrow{P_1P_2} \times \overrightarrow{P_1P_3}) = 0$. (This is a vector equation of the plane through three points P_1, P_2, and P_3.) See margin.

9. Find an equation of the plane M through the points $P_1 = (1, 0, -1)$, $P_2 = (2, 3, -2)$, and $P_3 = (1, 2, 3)$ by the given method.
   a. using the result of Question 8 $7x - 2y + z = 6$
   b. solving the system of equations which results from substituting the coordinates of P_1, P_2, and P_3 into $ax + by + cz = d$ (Note that substitution yields three linear equations with four variables. Therefore, you can solve for a, b, and c in terms of d. If $d \neq 0$, then any value of d can be used to find specific values of a, b, and c.)
   $7x - 2y + z = 6$

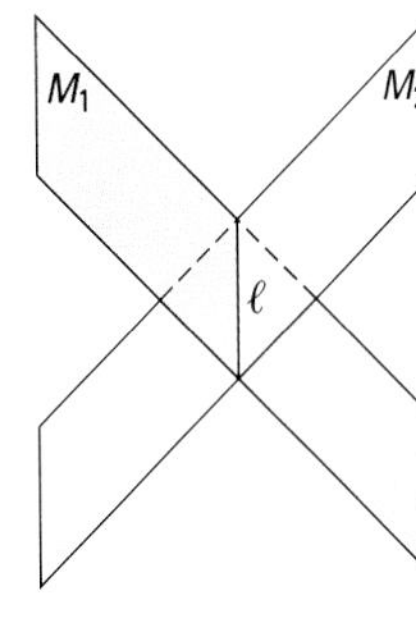

10. Suppose that the planes M_1 and M_2 are not parallel and that equations for M_1 and M_2 are

$$M_1\text{: } a_1x + b_1y + c_1z = d_1$$
$$M_2\text{: } a_2x + b_2y + c_2z = d_2.$$

Explain geometrically why the vector

$$\vec{w} = (a_1, b_1, c_1) \times (a_2, b_2, c_2)$$

is parallel to the line ℓ of intersection of M_1 and M_2. See margin.

11. Suppose that the planes M_1 and M_2 are defined by the equations

$$M_1\text{: } 3x - 2y + z = 4$$
$$M_2\text{: } x + 2y - z = 3.$$

   a. Show that M_1 and M_2 are not parallel planes.
   b. Find a point $P = (x_0, y_0, z_0)$ on the line ℓ of intersection of M_1 and M_2.
   c. Use the result of Question 10 to determine parametric equations for the line ℓ of intersection of M_1 and M_2.

See left.

11a) (3, -2, 1) and (1, 2, -1), the vectors perpendicular to the planes M_1 and M_2 are not parallel.
b) Sample: $\left(\frac{7}{4}, 1, \frac{3}{4}\right)$
c) Sample: $x = \frac{7}{4}$;
$y = 1 + 4t$;
$z = \frac{3}{4} + 8t$

12. A person has n nickels, d dimes, and q quarters whose total value is \$10.00. What is an equation for the plane containing all possible ordered triples (n, d, q)? $5n + 10d + 25q = 1000$

Review

13. The angle between $\vec{u} = (1, 2, 0)$ and $\vec{v} = (1, 2, p)$ has measure $\frac{\pi}{4}$. Find p. *(Lesson 12-6)* $p = \pm\sqrt{5}$

14. Let $\vec{u} = (u_1, u_2, u_3)$, $\vec{v} = (v_1, v_2, v_3)$, and $\vec{w} = (w_1, w_2, w_3)$. Prove that $\vec{u} \cdot (\vec{v} + \vec{w}) = \vec{u} \cdot \vec{v} + \vec{u} \cdot \vec{w}$. *(Lesson 12-6)* See margin.

Additional Answers

8. Since $\overrightarrow{P_1P_2}$ and $\overrightarrow{P_1P_3}$ lie in M, $\overrightarrow{P_1P_2} \times \overrightarrow{P_1P_3}$ gives the vector perpendicular to M. Thus, Q is on M (so that $\overrightarrow{P_1Q}$ is on M) if and only if $\overrightarrow{P_1Q}$ is perpendicular to $\overrightarrow{P_1P_2} \times \overrightarrow{P_1P_3}$.

10. M_1, is perpendicular to (a_1, b_1, c_1), and M_2 is perpendicular to (a_2, b_2, c_2), so ℓ is perpendicular to both (a_1, b_1, c_1) and (a_2, b_2, c_2). Since $\vec{w}$ is also perpendicular to both (a_1, b_1, c_1) and (a_2, b_2, c_2), $\vec{w}$ is parallel to ℓ.

14. $\vec{u} \cdot (\vec{v} + \vec{w}) = (u_1, u_2, u_3) \cdot$
$(v_1 + w_1, v_2 + w_2, v_3 + w_3) =$
$(u_1v_1 + u_1w_1) +$
$(u_2v_2 + u_2w_2) +$
$(u_3v_3 + u_3w_3) =$
$(u_1v_1 + u_2v_2 + u_3v_3) +$
$(u_1w_1 + u_2w_2 + u_3w_3) =$
$\vec{u} \cdot \vec{v} + \vec{u} \cdot \vec{w}$

Follow-up for Lesson 12-7

Practice

For more questions on SPUR Objectives, use **Lesson Master 12-7** (shown on pages 762–763).

Assessment

Written Communication Ask students to **work in pairs.** Have each student write a problem like **Example 2.** Students should solve their partner's problem. Then partners should work together to complete the Activity on page 763 for each of the problems. [Students find vector and rectangular coordinate equations for a plane.]

Extension

This lesson can be extended in many ways by bringing in ideas from geometry. Have students recall the ways to determine a plane: 3 noncollinear points, a line and a point not on it, two parallel lines, two intersecting lines. Given the information describing one of these situations, ask students to derive the equation of the plane determined. In three dimensions lines can either be intersecting, parallel or skew. Given the equation of a line and a point off the line, have students find the equations of lines parallel, intersecting, and skew to the given line passing through the given point.

Project Update Project 1, *Four-Dimensional Vectors,* on page 773, relates to the content of this lesson.

15. *Multiple choice.* In 3-space, $\{(x, y, z): x = 0 \text{ and } y = 0\}$ represents which set of points? **e**
(a) yz-plane
(b) xy-plane
(c) x-axis
(d) y-axis
(e) z-axis *(Lesson 12-5)*

16. Suppose that 4% of all students who are well one day are ill the next day, and that 50% of all students who are ill one day are well the next day.
a. Set up a stochastic matrix to model the situation. **See left.**
b. In the long run, what proportion of students will be ill on any given day? *(Lesson 11-6)* **≈ 7.4%**

17. a. Use summation notation to write the sum **See left.**

$$\left(\frac{1}{n}\right)^2 \cdot \frac{1}{n} + \left(\frac{2}{n}\right)^2 \cdot \frac{1}{n} + \left(\frac{3}{n}\right)^2 \cdot \frac{1}{n} + \ldots + \left(\frac{n}{n}\right)^2 \cdot \frac{1}{n}.$$

b. Simplify the sum in part **a**. *(Lesson 7-2)* **See left.**

18. Solve the equation $\frac{x+3}{3x} - \frac{x+6}{3x+2} = 0$. *(Lesson 5-8)* $x = \frac{6}{7}$

19. a. Sketch the region in the coordinate plane bounded by the x-axis, the line $y = \frac{1}{2}x$, and the line $x = 4$. **See left.**
b. What geometric figure is generated by rotating this region about the x-axis? **a cone**
c. Find the volume of the figure in part **b**. *(Previous course)* $\frac{16\pi}{3}$ **cubic uni**

16a)

$$\begin{array}{c|cc} & W & I \\ \hline W & .96 & .04 \\ I & .5 & .5 \end{array}$$

17a) $\sum_{j=1}^{n} \left(\frac{j}{n}\right)^2 \cdot \left(\frac{1}{n}\right)$

b) $\frac{(n+1)(2n+1)}{6n^2}$

19)

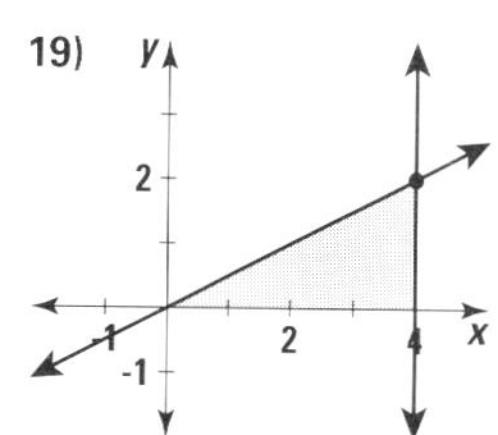

Exploration

20. a. Describe the plane in 3-space whose equation is $5z = 5$.
b. What happens to the plane with equation $ax + 5z = 5$ as a varies from 0 to 5? (Hint: What happens to vectors perpendicular to it?)
As a increases, vectors perpendicular to the plane rotate from the z-axis toward the x-axis, so the plane tilts more steeply.

a) a plane parallel to and 1 unit above the xy-plane

Setting Up Lesson 12-8

Discuss **Question 11.** Note that if there were a third plane and we knew its equation, the plane might or might not intersect the line of intersection of M_1 and M_2. If it did, then there is a solution to the system of 3 equations in 3 variables. If not, there is no solution to that system. Lesson 12-8 takes up all of the possibilities.

LESSON

12-8

The Geometry of Systems of Linear Equations in Three Variables

In Lesson 12-7, you saw that a linear equation

$$ax + by + cz = d,$$

in which at least one of the coefficients a, b, and c is nonzero, is the equation of a plane M in 3-space, and that the vector

$$\vec{v} = (a, b, c)$$

is perpendicular to M. Consequently, the solution set to a system of k linear equations in three unknowns

$$\begin{cases} a_1x + b_1y + c_1z = d_1 \\ a_2x + b_2y + c_2z = d_2 \\ \vdots \quad \vdots \quad \vdots \quad \vdots \\ a_kx + b_ky + c_kz = d_k \end{cases}$$

has a geometric interpretation; it is the set of points common to the k planes defined by the k equations in the system.

Finding the Intersection of Two Planes

When there are two planes, that is, when $k = 2$, then there are three possible situations for the location of the planes: they intersect in a line, or they are parallel and not coincident, or they coincide.

For instance, consider the following system of two equations in three unknowns.

$$\begin{cases} 2x + 5y - z = 6 & (1) \\ x - 8y + 4z = 7 & (2) \end{cases}$$

Its solution is the intersection of the two planes. Notice that plane (1) is perpendicular to the vector (2, 5, -1) and plane (2) is perpendicular to the vector (1, -8, 4). Since these vectors are not parallel, the planes are neither parallel nor do they coincide. So the planes intersect in a line. To describe this line, solve for two of the variables in terms of the third variable. Here we solve for x and z in terms of y.

$$\begin{aligned} 2x - z &= 6 - 5y & (1) \\ x + 4z &= 7 + 8y & (2) \end{aligned}$$

To solve this system for x, we multiply equation (1) by 4 and add the result to equation (2).

$$\begin{aligned} 8x - 4z &= 24 - 20y & 4 \cdot (1) \\ x + 4z &= 7 + 8y & (2) \\ 9x &= 31 - 12y & \end{aligned}$$

So, $$x = \frac{31 - 12y}{9}.$$

Lesson 12-8

Objectives

There are no SPUR Objectives for any reading Lesson.

Resources

From the ***Teacher's Resource File***
- Answer Master 12-8
- Teaching Aids
  - 134 Warm-up
  - 146 Various Intersections of Three Planes

Additional Resources
- Visuals for Teaching Aids 134, 146

Teaching Lesson 12-8

Warm-up

Moe, Curly, and Shemp Howard were brothers and played the roles of the stooges in the "Three Stooges" movies. Curly was born 6 years after Moe and 8 years after Shemp. The sum of their years of birth was 5695. To find the years of their births, write a system of three linear equations and solve it.
Sample:
***C* = 6 + *M*,**
***C* = 8 + *S*,**
***M* + *C* + *S* = 5695;**
***C* = 1903, *M* = 1897, *S* = 1895**

Lesson 12-8 Overview

Broad Goals Since an equation of the form $ax + by + cz = d$ is a plane, solving a system of linear equations in three variables means finding the intersection of planes. Although we expect that students have solved such systems when they have exactly one solution, this lesson considers all the other possibilities.

Perspective A system of two linear equations in three variables may represent (1) planes that intersect in a line, (2) parallel planes, or (3) coincident planes. In the first case, parametric equations for the line can be found. In the second case, there is no solution. In the third case, the equations are equivalent and represent the same plane.

A system of three linear equations in three unknowns may represent (1) planes that have exactly one point in common, such as students are accustomed to seeing; (2) three parallel planes; (3) two parallel planes and the third plane not parallel; (4) pairs of planes intersecting along parallel lines; (5) planes that have a line in common; or (6) planes that are all coincident. Students are asked to explore these situations.

Notes on Reading

We end the chapter by returning to more familiar ground. Solving systems of two equations in three unknowns to obtain a line nicely parallels the 2-dimensional situation of solving systems of two equations in two unknowns to obtain a point.

Regarding the solving of a 3×3 system of linear equations, do not strive for mastery here, for the analysis is most efficiently done in a linear algebra course using row reduction of matrices. Be content if students are aware of the possible types of solutions. A list is given in the Perspectives for this lesson. The configurations in the lesson are shown on **Teaching Aid 146.**

Now repeat the process to solve for z. This time we multiply equation (2) by -2 and add the result to equation (1).

$$\begin{aligned} -2x - 8z &= -14 - 16y \qquad -2 \cdot (\\ 2x - z &= 6 - 5y \qquad (\\ \hline -9z &= -8 - 21y \end{aligned}$$

So, $$z = \frac{8 + 21y}{9}.$$

Thus $$(x, y, z) = \left(\frac{31 - 12y}{9}, y, \frac{8 + 21y}{9}\right).$$

Because all three components depend on y, y is a parameter in this situation To write the parametric equations with the usual variable t, set $y = t$. Then parametric equations for the line are as given below.

$$\begin{cases} x = \dfrac{31 - 12t}{9} \\ y = t \\ z = \dfrac{8 + 21t}{9} \end{cases}$$

To find a point on the line, pick a value of t. For example, $t = 0$ gives the point $\left(\frac{31}{9}, 0, \frac{8}{9}\right)$, while $t = 2$ gives $\left(\frac{7}{9}, 2, \frac{50}{9}\right)$. These two points satisfy the equations for both planes. This checks that the above parametric equations are for the line of intersection of the planes.

If for two planes,

$$a_1x + b_1y + c_1z = d_1$$

and $$a_2x + b_2y + c_2z = d_2,$$

there is a constant k such that

$$k(a_1, b_1, c_1) = (a_2, b_2, c_2),$$

then the vectors perpendicular to these planes are parallel. Thus the planes are distinct and parallel, or they coincide. If $kd_1 = d_2$, then the equations are equivalent and so the planes coincide. If $kd_1 \neq d_2$, then there is no point in common.

Finding the Points Common to Three Planes

Now consider a system (*) of 3 linear equations in 3 unknowns.

$$(*) \quad \begin{cases} a_1x + b_1y + c_1z = d_1 \\ a_2x + b_2y + c_2z = d_2 \\ a_3x + b_3y + c_3z = d_3 \end{cases}$$

Optional Activities

Have students point out real world examples of the four configurations of planes in 3 space that are noted in the lesson. [Samples: two adjacent walls and a floor meet at a single point; ceilings in a three (or more) story apartment building are parallel; three walls of a typical room form two parallel planes with one intersecting the parallel pair; a triangular prism has pairs of planes intersecting along parallel lines.]

If the solution set to (*) consists of a single point, then no two of the three planes M_1, M_2, and M_3, defined by these equations respectively, are parallel. This can be determined by examining the vectors perpendicular to the planes, (a_1, b_1, c_1), (a_2, b_2, c_2), and (a_3, b_3, c_3).

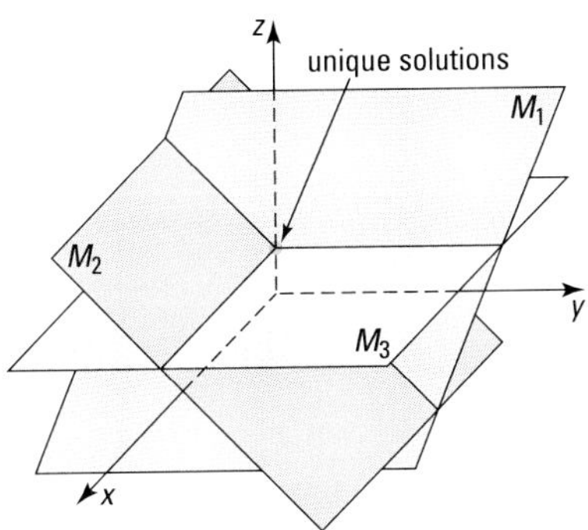

If the system (*) does not have a unique solution, then it either has infinitely many solutions or no solutions.

Possible Configurations of Planes with No Point in Common

The following three configurations of planes show the geometric situations possible when a system has no solutions.

Three parallel planes. All pairs of equations in the system have no solution.

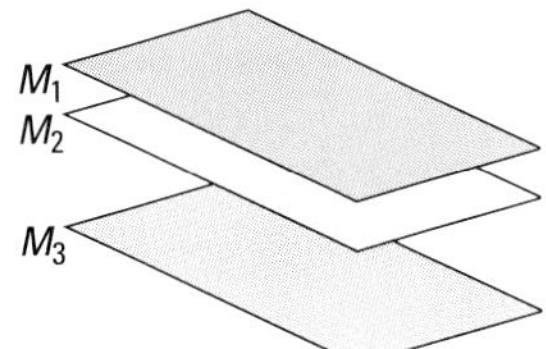

For example: $\begin{cases} x + y + 3z = 1 \\ x + y + 3z = 2 \\ 2x + 2y + 6z = 7 \end{cases}$

Two parallel planes with the third plane intersecting the parallel pair. One pair of equations in the system has no solution while each of the other two pairs has infinitely many solutions.

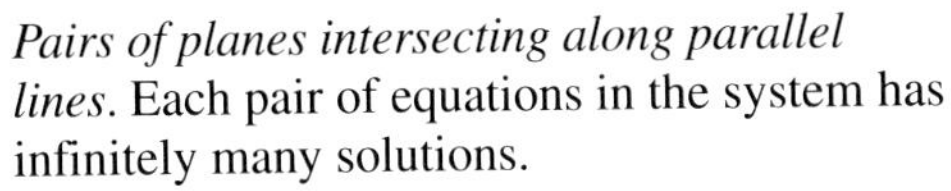

For example: $\begin{cases} x + y + 3z = 1 \\ x + y + 3z = 2 \\ 2x - y + z = 8 \end{cases}$

Pairs of planes intersecting along parallel lines. Each pair of equations in the system has infinitely many solutions.

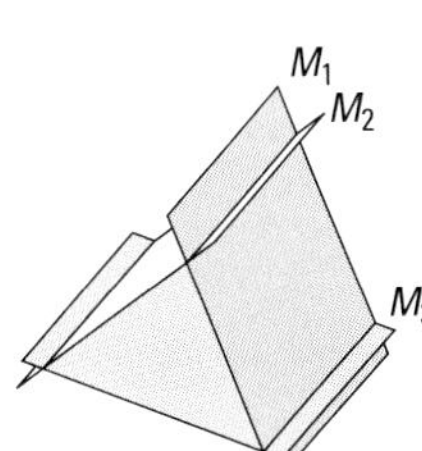

For example: $\begin{cases} x + 2y + z = 4 \\ 2x - y + z = 3 \\ 3x + y + 2z = -2 \end{cases}$

Adapting to Individual Needs

Challenge

Have students answer the following.

1. Find an equation for the plane through each set of points.
   a. (2, 1, -2), (3, 0, -4), (1, 2, 0)
   [$2x - 4y + 3z + 6 = 0$]
   b. (0, 0, 3), (0, -3, 0), (2, 0, 0)
   [$3x - 2y + 2z - 6 = 0$]
2. Find a, b, and c so that:
   $\frac{11x + 7}{x^3 - 2x^2 - 3x} = \frac{a}{x} + \frac{b}{x + 1} + \frac{c}{x - 3}$
   [$a = -1$; $b = -3$; $c = 4$]

Notes on Questions

Question 2 Error Alert If your students have trouble with the drawing, suggest that they make individual sketches of the two planes, then combine them into one drawing.

Questions 4–5 Suggest that students look before they leap. Determine whether the planes are parallel, coincident, or intersecting before trying to solve the system. Again make use of the fact that if planes are parallel or coincident, then their coefficients will be proportional.

Question 12 This parabola goes through the points on the graph of the sequence of triangular numbers. That is, with T_n standing for the nth triangular number, the point (n, T_n) is on this parabola.

Question 13 In geometrical terms, this traditional word problem asks for the point of intersection of three planes.

Follow-up for Lesson 12-8

Extension

Ask students the following questions. How are vectors used to describe hyperplanes? What are the possible intersections of 4-dimensional hyperplanes? Students could consult a book on linear algebra to find out. This could be a project.

Additional Answers

1. b. When $z = \frac{8}{9}$, the point $\left(\frac{31}{9}, 0, \frac{8}{9}\right)$ is generated; when $z = \frac{50}{9}$, the point $\left(\frac{7}{9}, 2, \frac{50}{9}\right)$ is derived. These points are the same as those on the intersection line shown on page 768 of the textbook. Since two points determine a line, this is the same line.

3. b. $3x - 2y + 4z = 2$ plane N
$3x - 2y + 4z = 1$ plane M
$0 = 1$ subtracting
Therefore, the system has no solution.

1a) $x = \frac{-12z + 83}{21}$, $y = \frac{9z - 8}{21}$

2a)

z
1
y − z = 0
1
y
1
x
x + y + z = 1

b) Sample:
$$\begin{cases} x = t \\ y = \frac{1}{2} - \frac{1}{2}t \\ z = \frac{1}{2} - \frac{1}{2}t \end{cases}$$

4) the line
$$\begin{cases} x = \frac{49 + 11t}{21} \\ y = t \\ z = \frac{7 + 8t}{21} \end{cases}$$

5) The plane $-x + 3y - 2z = -6$

7a) the first and second equations, because the vector (1, 1, 3) is perpendicular to both

b) (2, -1, 1) is perpendicular to the third plane, so that plane is not parallel to the first two, and must intersect both of them.

You are asked to explore the situation where the system (*) has infinitely many solutions in Question 6.

QUESTIONS

Covering the Reading

1. **a.** Solve the equations for planes (1) and (2) on page 767 for x and y in terms of z. **See left.**
   b. Show that the line of intersection is the same line as found on page 768. **See margin.**
2. **a.** Sketch the planes corresponding to the two equations in the system $\begin{cases} x + y + z = 1 \\ y - z = 0. \end{cases}$ **See left.**
   b. Give parametric equations for the line of intersection of the planes. **See left.**
3. Consider the plane M with equation $3x - 2y + 4z = 1$.
   a. Write an equation for a plane N that is parallel to (but not coincident with) M. **Sample: $3x - 2y + 4z = 2$**
   b. Solve the system consisting of the equations for M and N to show that there is no solution. **See margin.**

In 4–5, describe all solutions to the system. **See left.**

4. $\begin{cases} 5x - 3y + z = 12 \\ x + y - 4z = 1 \end{cases}$

5. $\begin{cases} -x + 3y - 2z = -6 \\ 2x - 6y + 4z = 12 \end{cases}$

6. When the system (*) in this lesson has infinitely many solutions, draw all possible configurations of the three planes M_1, M_2, and M_3. **See margin.**

7. Consider the following system of equations given in this lesson:
$$\begin{cases} x + y + 3z = 1 \\ x + y + 3z = 2 \\ 2x - y + z = 8. \end{cases}$$ **See left.**
   a. Which pair of equations corresponds to the parallel planes? How do you know?
   b. How can you tell that the other equation corresponds to a plane that intersects the parallel planes?

8. Consider the following system given in this lesson: **See margin.**
$$\begin{cases} x + 2y + z = 4 \\ 2x - y + z = 3 \\ 3x + y + 2z = -2. \end{cases}$$
   a. Show that the system has no solution.
   b. Choose one pair of the equations, and show that their graphs intersect in a line.

6.

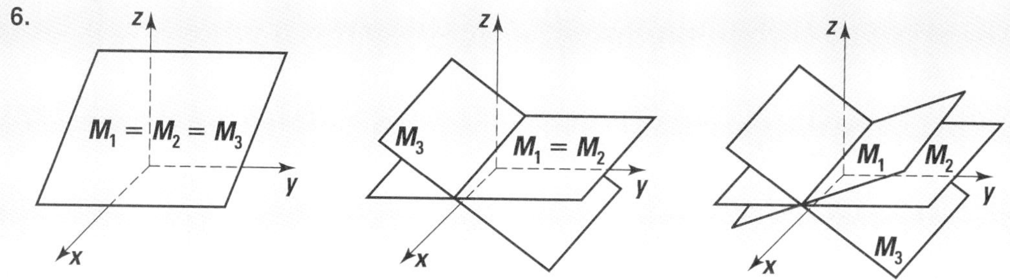

In 9–11, describe the graph of all solutions to the system.

9. $\begin{cases} a + b + c = 1 \\ 4a + 2b + c = 3 \\ 9a + 3b + c = 6 \end{cases}$ **the point** $\left(\frac{1}{2}, \frac{1}{2}, 0\right)$

10. $\begin{cases} 5u - 3v = w \\ 10u - 2w = 6v \\ u + v = 9 \end{cases}$ **the line** $\begin{cases} u = t \\ v = 9 - t \\ w = -27 + 8t \end{cases}$

11. $\begin{cases} x + y - z = 2 \\ x + 3y - z = 16 \\ -x + y + z = 12 \end{cases}$ **the line** $\begin{cases} x = t \\ y = 7 \\ z = 5 + t \end{cases}$

12. The points (1, 1), (2, 3), and (3, 6) are on the graph of $y = ax^2 + bx + c$. Find a, b, and c. **$a = b = \frac{1}{2}$, $c = 0$**

13. To get from the O'Neill farm to the city, you must travel d miles over a dirt road, g miles over a gravel road, and h miles over a highway. When Mr. O'Neill averages 20 mph on dirt, 15 mph on gravel, and 60 mph on the highway, it takes him 68 minutes to get to the city. Mrs. O'Neill averages 5 mph slower than Mr. O'Neill on dirt and gravel, but averages 60 mph on the highway, and it takes her 82 minutes. The total distance is 42 miles. How many of these miles are over each surface?
$d = 10$ mi, $g = 2$ mi, $h = 30$ mi

Review

14. Describe the graph of the set of points (x, y, z) such that $y + z = 10$. *(Lesson 12-7)* **a plane parallel to the x-axis containing (0, 0, 10) and (0, 10, 0)**

15) $\begin{cases} x = -7 + 3t \\ y = 2 - 4t \\ z = -t \end{cases}$

15. Find parametric equations for the line ℓ passing through (-7, 2, 0) and perpendicular to the plane with equation $3x - 4y - z = -1$. *(Lesson 12-7)*
See left.

16. a. Find an equation for the plane containing the point (-7, 2, 0) which is perpendicular to line ℓ given in Question 15. **$3x - 4y - z = -29$**

b. How is this plane related to the plane in Question 15? *(Lesson 12-7)*
The planes are parallel.

17. Explain why three nonzero 3-dimensional vectors $\vec{u_1}$, $\vec{u_2}$, and $\vec{u_3}$ with the same initial point are coplanar if and only if $\vec{u_1} \cdot (\vec{u_2} \times \vec{u_3}) = 0$. *(Lesson 12-7)* **See margin.**

18. Suppose g is a polynomial function such that

$g'(x) < 0$ when $-4 < x < -1$ or $x > 4$
and $g'(x) > 0$ when $x < -4$ or $-1 < x < 4$.

What is the smallest possible degree of g? *(Lessons 4-4, 9-5)* **4**

8. a. Subtracting the second equation from the first, we get $-x + 3y = 1$. Subtracting the third equation from twice the second equation, we get $x - 3y = 8$, or $x = 3y - 8$. Substituting for x, $-(3y - 8) + 3y = 1$, which simplifies to $8 = 1$. Hence, there is no solution to this system.

b. The first two equations intersect at the line $x = \frac{10 - 3t}{5}$, $y = \frac{5 - t}{5}$, $z = t$.

17. $\vec{u_2} \times \vec{u_3}$ is perpendicular to both $\vec{u_2}$ and $\vec{u_3}$. $\vec{u_1} \cdot (\vec{u_2} \times \vec{u_3}) = 0$ if and only if $\vec{u_1}$ is also perpendicular to $\vec{u_2} \times \vec{u_3}$. Thus $\vec{u_1}$, $\vec{u_2}$ and $\vec{u_3}$ being all perpendicular to the same vector at the same point, are coplanar.

19. Is the following argument valid? Explain. Yes, it is an example of modus tollens.

If school is not closed, then I go to school.
I don't go to school.
$\therefore$ *School is closed.* (Lessons 1-6, 1-7)

Exploration

20. a. Find an equation for the plane containing the lines ℓ_1 and ℓ_2 with the following parametric equations. $13x + 18y + 2z = 55$

$$\ell_1: \begin{cases} x = 1 + 4t \\ y = 2 - 3t \\ z = 3 + t \end{cases} \qquad \ell_2: \begin{cases} x = 1 - 2t \\ y = 2 + t \\ z = 3 + 4t \end{cases}$$

b. Generalize part **a** to find an equation for the plane containing the lines with the following parametric equations.

$$\ell_1: \begin{cases} x = x_0 + u_1 t \\ y = y_0 + u_2 t \\ z = z_0 + u_3 t \end{cases} \qquad \ell_2: \begin{cases} x = x_0 + v_1 t \\ y = y_0 + v_2 t \\ z = z_0 + v_3 t \end{cases}$$

$(\vec{u} \times \vec{v}) \cdot (x - x_0, y - y_0, z - z_0) = 0$ or
$(u_2v_3 - u_3v_2)x + (u_3v_1 - u_1v_3)y + (u_1v_2 - u_2v_1)z =$
$(u_2v_3 - u_3v_2)x_0 + (u_3v_1 - u_1v_3)y_0 + (u_1v_2 - u_2v_1)z_0$

Possible Responses, page 773

1. sum of vectors:
$\vec{u} + \vec{v} = (u_1, u_2, u_3, u_4) + (v_1, v_2, v_3, v_4)$
$= (u_1 + v_1, u_2 + v_2, u_3 + v_3, u_4 + v_4)$
distance between points:
$d = \sqrt{(x_2 - x_1)^2 + (y_2 - y_1)^2 + (z_2 - z_1)^2 + (w_2 - w_1)^2}$
length of vector: $|\vec{v}| = \sqrt{v_1^2 + v_2^2 + v_3^2 + v_4^2}$
dot product: $\vec{u} \cdot \vec{v} = u_1v_1 + u_2v_2 + u_3v_3 + u_4v_4$
scalar product: $k\vec{u} = (ku_1, ku_2, ku_3, ku_4)$
angle between vectors: $\cos\theta = \frac{\vec{u} \cdot \vec{v}}{|\vec{u}||\vec{v}|}$
perpendicular vectors: $\vec{u}$ is perpendicular to $\vec{v} \Leftrightarrow \vec{u} \cdot \vec{v} = 0$
parametric equations for a line:
$$\ell = \begin{cases} w = w_0 + w_1 t \\ x = x_0 + x_1 t \\ y = y_0 + y_1 t \\ z = z_0 + z_1 t \end{cases}$$

A project presents an opportunity for you to extend your knowledge of a topic related to the material of this chapter. You should allow more time for a project than you do for a typical homework question.

1 Four-Dimensional Vectors

This chapter discusses vectors in two and three dimensions. Develop formulas for the following in four dimensions:

sum of vectors,
distance between points,
length of vector,
dot product,
scalar product,
angle between vectors,
determination of perpendicular vectors, and
parametric equation of a line.

(Picturing these is difficult. But, surprisingly, four-dimensional vectors simplify computational procedures in computer graphics.)

2 Vectors Applied to Computer Simulations

Describe a computer simulation of your route from home to school by doing the following.

a. Draw a map of your route from home to school. (Change any curved paths to segments). Choose a measurement system (miles, kilometers, feet, or meters) which seems appropriate. Use your home as the origin of a coordinate system with North being the positive part of the y-axis and East being the positive part of the x-axis.

b. Write each segment of your trip as a vector in rectangular form. Verify that the sum of the vectors of paths gives the location of your school with respect to your home.

c. Repeat part **b**, but this time write each segment of your path as a vector in polar form. Use this form to write instructions in English giving direction and distance for each segment of your path to school.

3 Vectors Applied to Statistics

Given a vector, its corresponding *adjusted vector* is found by subtracting from each of its coordinates the average of those coordinates. For example, the vector (3, 2, 4) has the adjusted vector $(3 - 3, 2 - 3, 4 - 3) = (0, -1, 1)$. Given two vectors, their *correlation coefficient* is the cosine of the angle between their adjusted vectors. Do two of the following.

a. Look up the formula for correlation coefficient in a statistics book. Relate the formula given in the book to the cosine of the angle between adjusted vectors. Report the formula and an example from the statistics book that shows how data is used with it. (Note: Some books might not give the formula directly. Also, many books use capital letters (such as X_i) for data coordinates, bars over the letters to indicate means (such as $\overline{X}$), and small letters to represent data adjusted by the mean (such as $x_i = X_i - \overline{X}$).

b. Write a calculator or computer program which inputs two vectors and calculates their correlation coefficient.

c. Ask your counselor for SAT Quantitative and Verbal scores (or other pairs of scores) on seven to ten randomly selected people. (Of course, you should not ask for the names of the students.) Let the coordinates of one vector be the quantitative scores, and the coordinates of a second vector be the verbal scores.

Chapter 12 Projects

The projects relate chiefly to the content of the lessons of this chapter as follows:

Project	Lesson(s)
1	12-6, 12-7
2	12-2
3	12-4, 12-6
4	12-2, 12-3, 12-4

1 Four-Dimensional Vectors This project allows for a wide range of performance. You should demand a reasonably detailed and accurate map and analysis.

2 Vectors Applied to Computer Simulations This is a straightforward mathematical project.

3 Vectors Applied to Statistics Students who are taking AP Statistics or thinking of taking that course should seriously consider doing this project.

2. a. Sample:

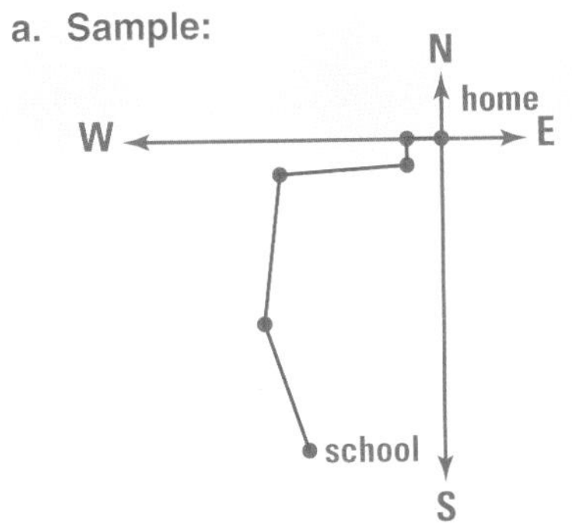

b. Sample: Vector representation of path to school: (-0.5, 0), (0, -0.4), (-2.1, -0.1), (-0.3, -3.2), (0.7, -2.8). The location of the school is then $(-0.5 - 2.1 - 0.3 + 0.7, -0.4 - 0.1 - 3.2 - 2.8) = (-2.2, -6.5)$ which checks.

c. Sample: In polar form, the path becomes [0.5, 180°], [0.4, 270°], [2.10, 183°], [3.21, 265°], [2.89, 104°]. The location of the school is then [6.86, 251°] which checks. These vectors can be translated into directions in English as follows: From home go 0.5 km west. Then go 0.4 km south. Next go 2.1 km 3° south of west. Next go 3.21 km 5° west of south. Finally, go 2.89 km 14° east of south to arrive at school.

(Responses continue on page 774.)

(continued)

Use the formula from part **a** or the computer program in part **b** to calculate their correlation coefficient. Compute the angle between the adjusted vectors. If the angle is under 30°, then the scores are considered to be "highly correlated" and are measuring nearly the same thing. If the angle is over 60°, then the scores are measuring relatively independent characteristics. Your result, of course, is highly dependent on the people chosen for your sample.

4 Vectors Applied to Physics

In the water sport of windsurfing, the windsurfer usually sets the boom at shoulder height and holds the boom perpendicular to his or her arms. There are three main forces, P, W, and R, which must balance in order for the windsurfer not to fall. Each force can be represented by a vector.

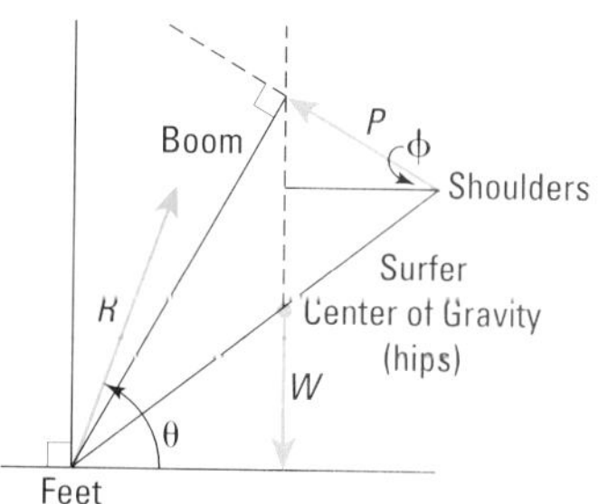

P is the pull in the arms (a force perpendicular to the boom), W is the weight of the windsurfer (a force downward), and R is the resultant reaction between the board and the windsurfer's feet. Let ϕ be the angle from the horizontal of the windsurfer's arms, and let θ be the angle between the force on the board and the horizontal. ϕ can be accurately measured from photographs or observations, but θ cannot because the windsurfer might bend his or her legs or put most pressure on the balls of his or her feet. (However, θ can be conjectured from other angles.) If the windsurfer does not fall off the board, then the following relationships must hold.

$$R \cos \theta - P \cos \phi = 0$$
$$R \sin \theta + P \sin \phi = W$$

a. Use vectors to explain why the equations must hold.

b. Solve the equations for P. You will get an expression involving the weight of the surfer and trigonometric functions of θ and ϕ.

c. Assume that a value of P that equals more than half the weight of the surfer is hard to sustain over any length of time. Compute P for the following situations and determine which would be hard.

- **i.** Weight of surfer = 140 lb, $\phi = 45°$, $\theta = 50°$.
- **ii.** Your weight in pounds, $\phi = 45°$, $\theta = 50°$.
- **iii.** Your weight in pounds, $\phi = 30°$, $\theta = 70°$.

d. Select values for ϕ and θ which you might believe to be reasonable in a very strong wind, and compute P for these values.

774

4 Vectors Applied to Physics Physics students may find this project to be straightforward. If any student doing this project has wind surfed, you might wish to ask for a companion essay discussing the practical implications of the various forces on the wind surfer (how grips are maintained, how weight is maneuvered, etc.).

Possible Responses, page 773

3. a. **Sample: Given two vectors X and Y, we may represent their adjusted vectors as $(X - \bar{X})$ and $(Y - \bar{Y})$. The formula for the angle between two vectors yields the following formula for the angle between the adjusted vectors:**

$$\cos \theta = \frac{(X - \bar{X}) \cdot (Y - \bar{Y})}{|(X - \bar{X})| \cdot |(Y - \bar{Y})|}.$$

The formula for the correlation coefficient from statistics is

$$r = \frac{\text{covariance of } X \text{ and } Y}{S_X \cdot S_Y}.$$

This relates to the cosine of the angle between two adjusted vectors in the following way. The coefficient r corresponds to the cosine of the angle between the two adjusted vectors. The covariance of X and Y is equal to

$$\frac{\text{the sum of } (X - \bar{X}) \cdot (Y - \bar{Y})}{N},$$

which corresponds to the dot product of the adjusted vector X with the adjusted vector Y. Finally, S_X and S_Y, the standard deviations for X and Y, are calculated as

$$S_X = \sqrt{\text{variance of } X} = \sqrt{\frac{\text{sum of } (X - \bar{X})^2}{N}} \text{ and}$$

$$S_Y = \sqrt{\text{variance of } Y} = \sqrt{\frac{\text{sum of } (Y - \bar{Y})^2}{N}},$$

which correspond to the length of the adjusted vector X and the length of the adjusted vector Y, respectively. Examples students use may vary.

b.

```
80  REM CORRELATION
    COEFFICIENT FOR
90  REM ADJUSTED VECTORS
100 DIM X(10), Y(10), AX(10),
    AY(10)
110 INPUT "Enter dimension of
    vector:" ;N
120 XSUM = 0: YSUM = 0
130 FOR I = 1 TO N
140   PRINT "X";I;"=";
150   INPUT X(I)
160   PRINT "Y";I;"=";
170   INPUT Y(I)
180   XSUM = XSUM + X(I):
      YSUM = YSUM + Y(I)
190 NEXT I
200 XBAR = XSUM/N
210 YBAR = YSUM/N
220 SUM = 0: XSUM = 0:
    YSUM = 0
230 FOR I = 1 TO N
240   AX(I) = X(I) – XBAR
250   AY(I) = Y(I) – YBAR
260   SUM = SUM + AX(I) * AY(I)
```

SUMMARY

A vector is a quantity with magnitude and direction. Vectors have applications in physics and engineering, for instance, in their use to represent velocity and force. Two- and three-dimensional vectors were discussed in this chapter, although the concept of vector can be extended to any number of dimensions.

In two dimensions, vectors can be represented by single letters with arrows above them $\vec{v}$, as ordered pairs of real numbers (a, b), polar coordinates $[r, \theta]$, or arrows. These representations are related by the equations $r = \sqrt{a^2 + b^2}$ and $(a, b) = (r \cos \theta, r \sin \theta)$, where $|\vec{v}|$ or r is the length (or norm or magnitude) of the vector v, and θ is its direction.

Sums, opposites, and scalar multiples of vectors can be found, respectively, by adding corresponding components, taking the opposites of components, and multiplying each component by the same real number. Two vectors are parallel if and only if one is a scalar multiple of the other. As a result, the vector equation of the line through a point P parallel to a vector $\vec{v}$ is $\overrightarrow{PQ} = k\vec{v}$, where Q is a variable point on the line. Equating components yields parametric equations for the line.

Vector operations have graphical representations. To add vectors on a coordinate plane, place them in standard position. If the vectors are not parallel, they then form adjacent sides of a parallelogram. The sum is the diagonal of the parallelogram with one endpoint at the origin. The opposite of a vector is the collinear vector of the same length drawn in the opposite direction. If $\vec{v}$ is a vector and $k > 0$, the scalar multiple $k\vec{v}$ has the same direction as $\vec{v}$ but is k times as long.

Vector operations also have physical interpretations. When vectors represent forces, their sum represents the resultant force. Their opposites represent forces of equal magnitude in the opposite direction. Scalar multiples represent forces k times as intense in the same direction if $k > 0$.

The dot product of two vectors $\vec{u}$ and $\vec{v}$, denoted by $\vec{u} \cdot \vec{v}$, is the sum of the products of corresponding coordinates. The Law of Cosines implies that the angle θ between $\vec{u}$ and $\vec{v}$ can be found from $|\vec{u}|\,|\vec{v}| \cos \theta = \vec{u} \cdot \vec{v}$. Two vectors are orthogonal if and only if their dot product is zero.

The formula for distance between two points in 3-space leads to an equation for a sphere: $(x - a)^2 + (y + b)^2 + (z - c)^2 = r^2$, where (a, b, c) is the center and r is the radius.

Addition, scalar multiplication, opposites, length, and the angle between two vectors can be generalized to three dimensions. The criteria for parallel and orthogonal vectors are unchanged from two dimensions, and vector and parametric equations for a line through a point parallel to a vector are essentially the same as in two dimensions. The geometric idea of finding a perpendicular to the plane formed from two vectors gives rise to the operation of cross product. The fact that the dot product of two orthogonal vectors is 0 leads to the fact that a plane perpendicular to the vector $\vec{v} = (a, b, c)$ has an equation of the form $ax + by + cz = d$.

The solution to a system of linear equations in three variables is the intersection of the planes corresponding to those equations. A unique solution exists if and only if the planes intersect at a single point. No solution exists if two of the planes are parallel or if each pair of planes intersects at a different parallel line. An infinite number of solutions exists if the intersection of all the planes is a straight line or if the planes are identical.

Summary

The Summary gives an overview of the entire chapter and provides an opportunity for students to consider the material as a whole. Thus, the Summary can be used to help students relate and unify the concepts presented in the chapter.

```
270     XSUM = XSUM +
        AX(I) * AX(I)
280     YSUM = YSUM +
        AY(I) * AY(I)
290  NEXT I
300  XLEN = SQR(XSUM)
310  YLEN = SQR(YSUM)
320  CTHETA =
     SUM/(XLEN*YLEN)
330  PRINT "Correlation
     coefficient:";CTHETA
340  END
```

c. Sample:

SAT Scores

Quantitative	Verbal
251	264
623	715
644	504
596	665
740	530
323	416
636	542
743	341
455	652
654	634

3. c. (Continued) The correlation coefficient is about .387159, so the angle between the adjusted vectors is about 67.2°. These scores are measuring relatively independent characteristics.

4. a. Draw the vectors *P*, *R*, and *W* with a common initial point. These vectors must balance (sum to zero) in order for the windsurfer to stay on the board.

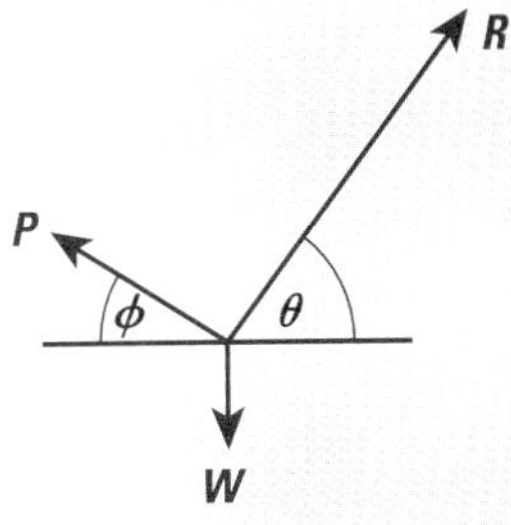

For the horizontal component to balance,
$P\cos(180° - \phi) + R\cos\theta + W\cos 270° = 0$
$\Leftrightarrow P(\cos 180° \cos(-\phi) - \sin 180° \sin(-\phi)) + R\cos\theta + W \cdot 0 = 0$
$\Leftrightarrow P(-1 \cdot \cos\phi - 0 \cdot -\sin\phi) + R\cos\theta = 0$
$\Leftrightarrow P \cdot -\cos\phi - P \cdot 0 + R\cos\theta = 0$
$\Leftrightarrow R\cos\theta - P\cos\phi = 0$.
For the vertical component to balance,
$P\sin(180° - \phi) + R\sin\theta + W\sin 270° = 0$
$\Leftrightarrow P(\sin 180° \cos(-\phi) + \cos 180° \sin(-\phi)) + R\sin\theta + W \cdot -1 = 0$
$\Leftrightarrow P(0 \cdot \cos\phi + -1 \cdot -\sin\phi) + R\sin\theta = W$
$\Leftrightarrow P \cdot 0 + P \cdot \sin\phi + R\sin\theta = W$
$\Leftrightarrow R\sin\theta + P\sin\phi = W$.

(Responses continue on page 776.)

CHAPTER TWELVE

Vocabulary

Terms, symbols, and properties are listed by lesson to provide a checklist of concepts a student must know. Emphasize to students that they should read the vocabulary list carefully before starting the Progress Self-Test. If students do not understand the meaning of a term, they should refer back to the indicated lesson.

VOCABULARY

Below are the most important terms and phrases for this chapter. You should be able to give a general description and a specific example of each and a precise definition for those marked with an asterisk (*).

Lesson 12-1
vector
plane vector, two-dimensional vector
polar representation of a vector
magnitude, direction of a vector
standard position
component representation
x- and y-components
horizontal and vertical components
* norm of a vector, $|\vec{u}|$
zero vector
unit vector

Lesson 12-2
* sum of two vectors, $\vec{u} + \vec{v}$
force, resultant force
* opposite of a vector, $-\vec{v}$
difference of vectors, $\vec{u} - \vec{v}$
unit vector

Lesson 12-3
* parallel vectors
scalar
* scalar multiple, $k\vec{v}$
scalar multiplication
vector equation for a line
parametric equations for a line

Lesson 12-4
* dot product, $\vec{u} \cdot \vec{v}$
Angle Between Vectors Theorem
orthogonal vectors

Lesson 12-5
three-dimensional space, 3-space, xy-plane, xz-plane, yz-plane
Distance in Space Theorem
Equation of a Sphere Theorem

Lesson 12-6
sum, scalar multiples, dot product of three-dimensional vectors
cross product, $\vec{u} \times \vec{v}$

Lesson 12-7
vector equation for a line in 3-space
parametric equations for a line in 3-space
Equations for a Line in 3-Space Theorem
Equation for a Plane Theorem

776

Possible Responses, page 774

4. b. From part a, the following relationships hold:
(1) $R\cos\theta - P\cos\phi = 0$, and
(2) $R\sin\theta + P\sin\phi = W$.
From equation (1), $R\cos\theta = P\cos\phi$, so $R = \frac{P\cos\phi}{\cos\theta}$.
Substituting into equation (2),
$\frac{P\cos\phi}{\cos\theta} \cdot \sin\theta + P\sin\phi = W$
$\Leftrightarrow P\cos\phi\tan\theta + P\sin\phi = W$
$\Leftrightarrow P(\cos\phi\tan\theta + \sin\phi) = W$
$\Leftrightarrow P = \frac{W}{\cos\phi\tan\theta + \sin\phi}$.

c. i. $P = \frac{140}{\cos 45^\circ \tan 50^\circ + \sin 45^\circ}$
≈ 90.33 pounds,
$\frac{140}{2} = 70 < 90.33$, so this situation would be hard.

ii. $P = \frac{137}{\cos 45^\circ \tan 50^\circ + \sin 45^\circ}$
≈ 88.40 pounds,
$\frac{137}{2} = 68.5 < 88.40$, so this situation would be hard.

iii. $P = \frac{137}{\cos 30^\circ \tan 70^\circ + \sin 30^\circ}$
≈ 47.58 pounds,
$\frac{137}{2} = 68.5 > 47.58$, so this situation would not be hard.

d. Responses will vary.

PROGRESS SELF-TEST

Take this test as you would take a test in class. Then check the test yourself with the solutions at the back of the book.

9, 11) See margin.

In 1–5, let $\vec{u} = (3, -4)$ and $\vec{v} = (-5, 2)$, and compute.

1. $|\vec{v}|$ **$\sqrt{29}$** **2.** $\vec{u} - \vec{v}$ **(8, -6)** **3.** $-2\vec{u} + 5\vec{v}$ **(-31, 18)**

4. $\vec{u} \cdot \vec{v}$ **-23** **5.** the angle between $\vec{u}$ and $\vec{v}$ **≈ 149°**

In 6–9, let $\vec{s} = (-2, 0, 5)$ and $\vec{t} = (-4, 2, -2)$. Find the component representation of the indicated vector.

6. $\vec{s} + 3\vec{t}$ **(-14, 6, -1)**

7. a vector orthogonal to both $\vec{s}$ and $\vec{t}$ **(-10, -24, -4)**

8. a vector parallel to $\vec{s}$ **Sample: $2\vec{s}$ = (-4, 0, 10)**

9. Sketch the vectors $\vec{t}$ and $-\vec{t}$ in 3-space. How do their graphs compare?

10. **a.** Sketch the vector $\vec{v}$ from the point (-2, 7) to the point (-5, 3). **b) (-3, -4) c) ≈ [5, 233°]**

b. Find the component representation of $\vec{v}$.

c. Find the polar representation of $\vec{v}$.

11. Prove that if $\vec{v}$ and $\vec{w}$ are two-dimensional vectors and k is a real number, then $k(\vec{v} - \vec{w}) = k\vec{v} - k\vec{w}$.

12. Find z so that (2, -4, 3) is orthogonal to (3, -2, z). **$z = -\frac{14}{3}$**

10a)

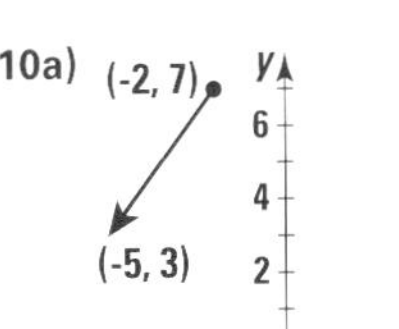

13b) The actual velocity of the plane is (-114, 260), which means the plane is traveling 114 mph west and 260 mph north.

13. According to its instrument panel, an airplane is traveling 25° west of north at an airspeed of 270 mph. Suppose a 15-mph wind is coming from the south.

a. Find the airplane's actual speed and direction.

b. Interpret the x- and y-components of the vector representing the airplane's actual velocity in terms of its motion. **See below left.**

a) Speed ≈ 284 mph, direction ≈ 23.7° west of north

In 14 and 15, sketch the resulting vectors, using the vectors drawn below. **See margin.**

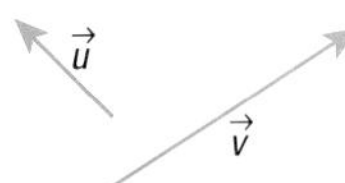

14. $\vec{u} + \vec{v}$ **15.** $\vec{u} - \vec{v}$

16. Write parametric equations for the line through the point $P = (-3, 2)$ parallel to the vector $\vec{v} = (4, -3)$. **See below.**

17. Let Q be the point (4, 0, -2) in 3-space, and $\vec{u}$ be the vector (1, 2, -3). Write an equation for the plane through Q perpendicular to $\vec{u}$.

18. Write an equation for the sphere with center (2, 0, -3) and radius 4. **$(x - 2)^2 + y^2 + (z + 3)^2 = 16$**

16) Sample: $\begin{cases} x = -3 + 4t \\ y = 2 - 3t \end{cases}$

17) $x + 2y - 3z = 10$

Progress Self-Test

For the development of mathematical competence, feedback and correction, along with the opportunity to practice, are necessary. The Progress Self-Test provides the opportunity for feedback and correction; the Chapter Review provides additional opportunities and practice. We cannot overemphasize the importance of these end-of-chapter materials. It is at this point that the material "gels" for many students, allowing them to solidify skills and understanding. In general, student performance should be markedly improved after these pages.

Assign the Progress Self-Test as a one-night assignment. Worked-out *solutions* for all questions are in the Selected Answers section of the student book. Encourage students to take the Progress Self-Test honestly, grade themselves, and then be prepared to discuss the test in class.

Advise students to pay special attention to those Chapter Review questions (pages 778–781) that correspond to questions missed on the Progress Self-Test.

Additional Answers

9.

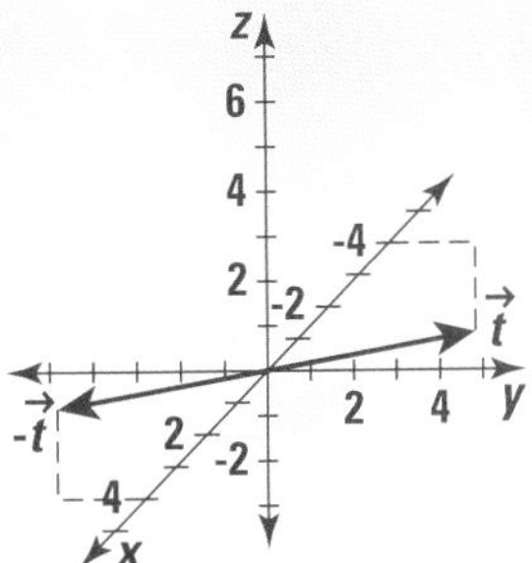

The graphs of the vectors have the same initial points and lengths but opposite directions.

11. left side $= k(\vec{v} - \vec{w})$
$= k(v_1 - w_1, v_2 - w_2)$
$= (kv_1 - kw_1, kv_2 - kw_2)$
$= k(v_1, v_2) - k(w_1, w_2)$
$= k\vec{v} - k\vec{w}$
= right side

14.

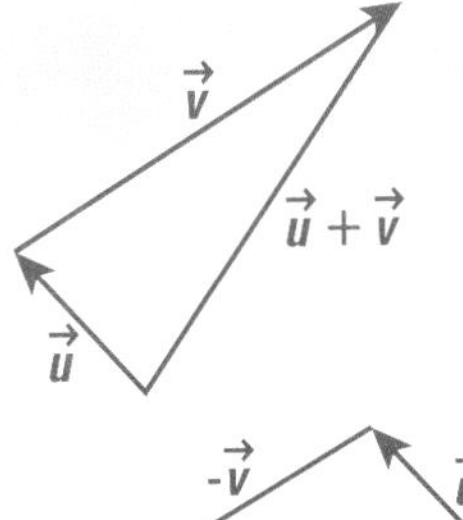

15.

Chapter 12 Review

Resources

From the ***Teacher's Resource File***

- Answer Master for Chapter 12 Review
- Assessment Sourcebook: Chapter 12 Test, Forms A–D Chapter 12 Test, Cumulative Form

Additional Resources

- TestWorks CD-ROM

The main objectives for the chapter are organized in the Chapter Review under the four types of understanding this book promotes—Skills, Properties, Uses, and Representations.

Whereas end-of-chapter material may be considered optional in some texts, in UCSMP *Precalculus and Discrete Mathematics* we have selected these objectives and questions with the expectation that they will be covered. Students should be able to answer these questions with about 85% accuracy after studying the chapter.

You may assign these questions over a single night to help students prepare for a test the next day, or you may assign the questions over a two-day period. If you work the questions over two days, then we recommend assigning the *evens* for homework the first night so that students get feedback in class the next day, then assigning the *odds* the night before the test, because answers are provided to the odd-numbered questions.

It is effective to ask students which questions they still do not understand and use the day or days as a total class discussion of the material which the class finds most difficult.

Additional Answers

23. $\vec{v} \cdot (\vec{u} \times \vec{v}) =$
$(-2, -3, 4) \cdot (11, 18, 19) =$
$-22 - 54 + 76 = 0$

CHAPTER TWELVE

CHAPTER REVIEW

Questions on SPUR Objectives

SPUR stands for **S**kills, **P**roperties, **U**ses, and **R**epresentations. The Chapter Review questions are grouped according to the SPUR Objectives for this chapter.

SKILLS DEAL WITH THE PROCEDURES USED TO GET ANSWERS.

Objective A: *Find the magnitude and direction of two-dimensional vectors.* *(Lesson 12-1)*

1. Find the magnitude and direction of the vector $(11, -3)$. **1, 2) See below.**

2. Find all possible directions for a vector whose x-component is three times its y-component.

3. Let $A = (2, 3)$, $B = (4, t)$, and $\vec{s}$ be the vector from A to B. If $|\vec{s}| = \sqrt{40}$, give the two possible values of t. **9 and -3**

4. Find the polar representation of the vector $(2, -5)$. **$\approx [\sqrt{29}, 292°]$**

Objective B: *Find sums, opposites, scalar products, and dot products of two-dimensional vectors.* *(Lessons 12-2, 12-3, 12-4)*

In 5–9, let $\vec{u} = (3, -2)$, $\vec{v} = (-5, 0)$, and $\vec{w} = (2, 6)$ and compute.

5. $\vec{u} + \vec{v}$ **(-2, -2)**
6. $-3\vec{u}$ **(-9, 6)**
7. $\vec{v} \cdot \vec{w}$ **-10**
8. $\vec{u} - \vec{w}$ **(1, -8)**
9. $4\vec{w} - 2\vec{u}$ **(2, 28)**

In 10–13, let $\vec{r} = [2, 35°]$, $\vec{s} = [3, 105°]$, and $\vec{t} = [5, 35°]$. Compute and express the answer in its polar representation. **See below for samples.**

10. $\vec{r} + \vec{s}$
11. $-\vec{s}$
12. $\vec{t} - \vec{r}$
13. $4\vec{t}$

14. If $\vec{v} = (3, -5)$ and $\vec{w} = (-2, 8)$, find the components of $\vec{u}$ so that $\vec{u} + \vec{v} = \vec{w}$. **(-5, 13)**

15. If $\vec{u}$ is the vector from $(-2, 6)$ to $(-5, 8)$, find the vector parallel to $\vec{u}$ and with half the magnitude. **Sample: $\left(-\frac{3}{2}, 1\right)$**

1) magnitude: $\sqrt{130}$; direction: $\approx$ -15.3°
2) $\approx$ 18.4° and 198.4°
10) [4.14, 78.0°] **11) [3, 285°]**
12) [3, 35°] **13) [20, 35°]**

16. Find a polar representation of a vector whose length is two-thirds that of $[12, 125°]$ and which has the opposite direction. **[8, 305°]**

Objective C: *Find sums, lengths, scalar products, dot products, and cross products of vectors in 3-space.* *(Lesson 12-6)*

In 17–22, let $\vec{u} = (-5, 2, 1)$ and $\vec{v} = (-2, -3, 4)$, and compute.

17. $\vec{u} + \vec{v}$ **(-7, -1, 5)**
18. $\vec{u} - \vec{v}$ **(-3, 5, -3)**
19. $2\vec{v} - 3\vec{u}$ **(11, -12, 5)**
20. $|\vec{u}|$ **$\sqrt{30}$**
21. $\vec{u} \cdot \vec{v}$ **8**
22. $\vec{u} \times \vec{v}$ **(11, 18, 19)**

23. For the vectors $\vec{u}$ and $\vec{v}$ in Questions 17–22, verify that $\vec{u} \times \vec{v}$ is orthogonal to $\vec{v}$.

24. Find a vector orthogonal to both $\vec{s} = (3, 0, -1)$ and $\vec{t} = (1, -2, 4)$. **Sample: (-2, -13, -6)**

23) See margin.

Objective D: *Find the measure of the angle between two vectors.* *(Lessons 12-4, 12-6)*

25. Find the measure of the angle between the vectors $\vec{u} = (-5, 3)$ and $\vec{v} = (1, -6)$.

26. Find the measure of the angle between the vectors $\vec{s} = (2, 0, -4)$ and $\vec{t} = (-3, 1, 2)$.

27. Let $\vec{u} = (1, 2, -3)$ and $\vec{v} = -3\vec{u}$. Find the measure of the angle between $\vec{u}$ and $\vec{v}$. What does your answer mean? **180°; they have opposite directions.**

25) $\approx$ 130.4°
26) $\approx$ 146.8°

778

CHAPTER TWELVE

PROPERTIES DEAL WITH THE PRINCIPLES BEHIND THE MATHEMATICS.

28–30, 32, 39) See margin.

Objective E: *Prove or disprove generalizations about vector operations.* (*Lessons 12-2, 12-3, 12-4, 12-6*)

28. If a is a real number and $\vec{u}$ and $\vec{v}$ are vectors in a plane, prove that $\vec{u} \cdot (a\vec{v}) = a(\vec{u} \cdot \vec{v})$.

29. Show that the vector $(1, m)$ is parallel to the vector from (x, y) to $(x + a, y + ma)$.

30. Prove that if $\vec{v}$ is a vector in 3-space and k and m are real numbers, then $(k + m)\vec{v} = k\vec{v} + m\vec{v}$.

31. When $\vec{u} = (1, 0, 1)$ and $\vec{v} = (0, 2, 3)$, does $\vec{u} \times \vec{v} = \vec{v} \times \vec{u}$? No

32. Let $\vec{u}$ and $\vec{v}$ be any vectors in 3-space, and let k be a nonzero real number. Prove that if $\vec{u}$ is orthogonal to $\vec{v}$, then $k\vec{u}$ is orthogonal to $\vec{v}$.

Objective F: *Identify parallel and orthogonal vectors.* (*Lessons 12-3, 12-4, 12-6*)

In 33–35, determine whether $\vec{u}$ and $\vec{v}$ are perpendicular, parallel, or neither.

33. $\vec{u} = (-7, 3)$ and $\vec{v} = (-2, -5)$ neither

34. $\vec{u} = (-6, 3)$ and $\vec{v} = (4, -2)$ parallel

35. $\vec{u} = (5, -3, 4)$ and $\vec{v} = (2, -2, -4)$ perpendicular

In 36 and 37, find x so that the vectors $\vec{s} = (x, 2, -4)$ and $\vec{t} = (15, -3, 6)$ have the indicated property.

36. $\vec{s}$ and $\vec{t}$ are orthogonal. 2

37. $\vec{s}$ and $\vec{t}$ are parallel. -10

38. Find all vectors orthogonal to $\vec{u} = (2, -3)$ with magnitude 5.
$\left(\frac{15}{13}\sqrt{13}, \frac{10}{13}\sqrt{13}\right)$ and $\left(-\frac{15}{13}\sqrt{13}, -\frac{10}{13}\sqrt{13}\right)$

USES DEAL WITH APPLICATIONS OF MATHEMATICS IN REAL SITUATIONS.

Objective G: *Use vectors in a plane to decompose motion or force into x- and y-components.* (*Lesson 12-1*)

39. A ship's velocity is represented by [16, 25°], where the magnitude is measured in miles per hour and the direction is in degrees north of east.

a. Sketch the vector for the velocity.

b. Give the vector in component form.

c. Interpret the components.

40. A kite is at the end of a 50-meter string. Its angle with the horizontal is 52°. Assume the string is straight.

a. Write a polar representation for the kite's position. [50, 52°]

b. Compute a component representation. b) (30.8, 39.4)

c. Interpret the components. The kite is 39.4 m above a spot on the ground, which is 30.8m away from the owner.

41a) 32.1 lb of force with direction 80.6° counterclockwise from the positive x-axis

Objective H: *Use addition of vectors in a plane to solve problems involving forces or velocities.* (*Lesson 12-2*)

41. George and Sarah push a go-cart containing Sam to the starting line of a race. George pushes with 20 lb of force, Sarah with 18 lb of force. Their angles with respect to a line behind the cart are shown.

a. What is the magnitude and direction of the resultant force? See below left.

b. Who contributes more to the forward force, George or Sarah? Sarah

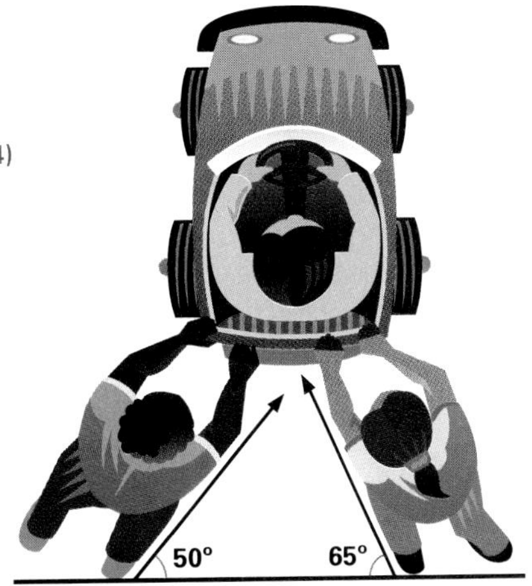

Assessment

Evaluation The Assessment Sourcebook provides five forms of the Chapter 12 Test. Forms A and B present parallel versions in a short-answer format. Forms C and D offer performance assessment. The fifth test is Chapter 12 Test, Cumulative Form. About 50% of this test covers Chapter 12, 25% of it covers Chapter 11, and 25% of it covers earlier chapters.

For information on grading, see *General Teaching Suggestions: Grading* in the *Professional Sourcebook*, which begins on page T20 in the Teacher's Edition.

Feedback After students have taken the test for Chapter 12 and you have scored the results, return the tests to students for discussion. Class discussion of the questions that caused trouble for the most students can be very effective in identifying and clarifying misunderstandings. You might want to have them write down the items they missed and work, either in groups or at home, to correct them. It is important for students to receive feedback on every chapter test, and we recommend that students see and correct their mistakes before proceeding too far into the next chapter.

Additional Answers

28. $\vec{u} \cdot (a\vec{v}) = (u_1, u_2) \cdot (av_1, av_2) = u_1av_1 + u_2av_2 = a(u_1v_1 + u_2v_2) = a(\vec{u} \cdot \vec{v})$

29. The vector from (x, y) to $(x + a, y + ma)$ is $(a, ma) = a(1, m)$. Therefore, by definition, the vectors are parallel.

30. $(k + m)\vec{v} = (k + m)(v_1, v_2, v_3) = (kv_1 + mv_1, kv_2 + mv_2, kv_3 + mv_3) = (kv_1, kv_2, kv_3) + (mv_1, mv_2, mv_3) = k\vec{v} + m\vec{v}$

32. $(k\vec{u}) \cdot \vec{v} = (ku_1, ku_2, ku_3) \cdot (v_1, v_2, v_3) = ku_1v_1 + ku_2v_2 + ku_3v_3 = k(u_1v_1 + u_2v_2 + u_3v_3) = k(\vec{u} \cdot \vec{v})$
Therefore, $k\vec{u}$ is orthogonal to $\vec{v}$ if $\vec{u}$ is orthogonal to $\vec{v}$.

39. a.

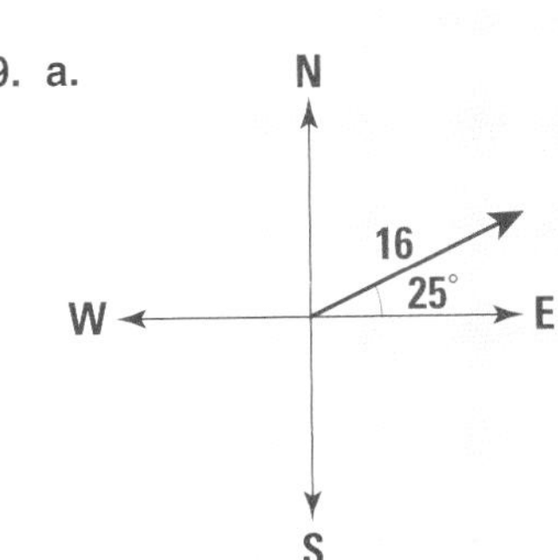

b. (14.5, 6.76)

c. The ship is going 14.5 mph towards the east and 6.76 mph towards the north.

Additional Answers

42. a, b.

[400, 135°] N a b W E [60, 270°] S

c. [360, 141.8°]; Relative to the ground, the plane's speed is 360 km/hr, and its heading is 38.2° North of West.

45. (-2.5, 4.3)

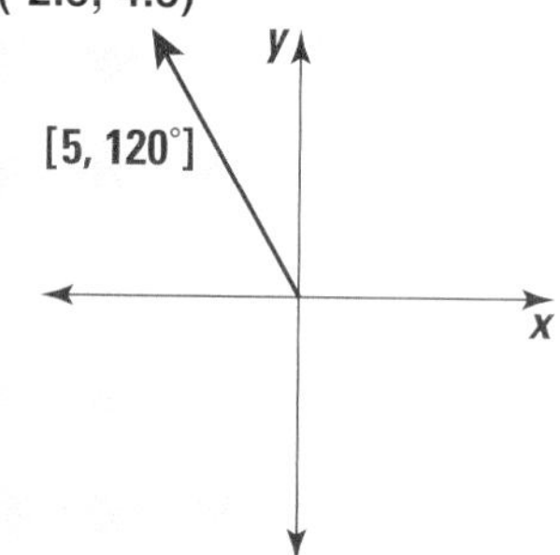

46.

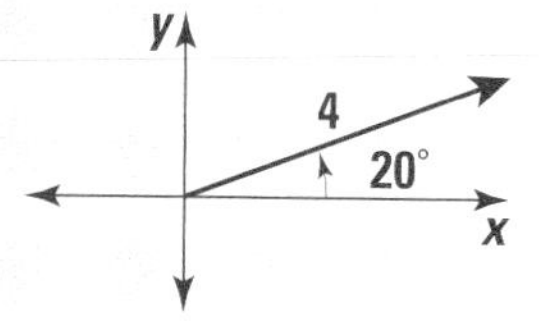

48. b.

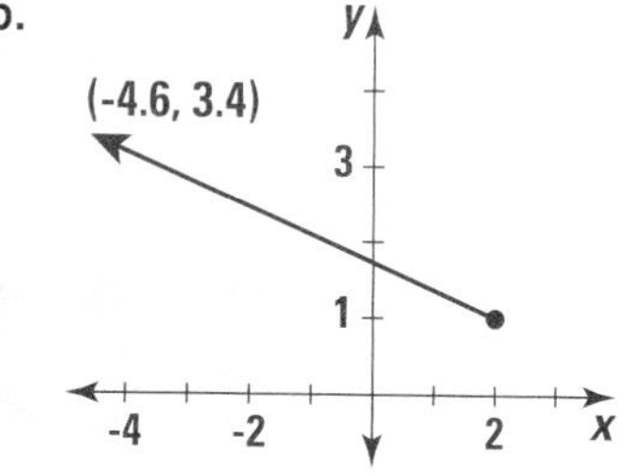

49. a.–d.

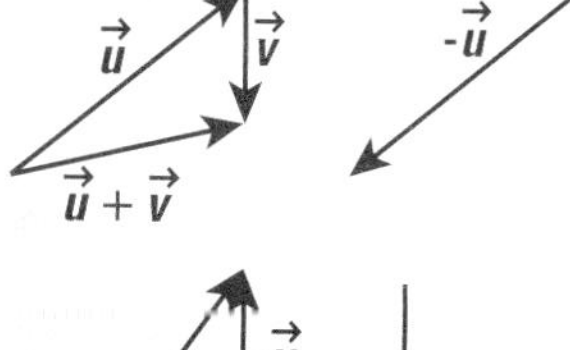

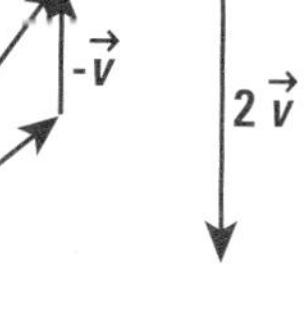

42. A plane travels at an airspeed of 400 km per hour with compass heading northwest. It encounters a 60 km/hr wind from the north.

a. Graph a vector for the plane's airspeed and compass heading, and another for the velocity of the wind.

b. Graph the resultant vector for the plane.

c. Compute and interpret the polar representation of the plane's actual velocity.

See margin.

43. A ferry leaves a pier for a dock one mile directly north across the river. The river current is 2 mph heading east. If the ferry boat captain maintains a speed of 10 mph in the direction 10° west of north, will the boat reach its destination? If so, how long will it take? **No**

44. An airplane pilot wishes to achieve an actual speed of 300 mph in the direction 25° south of east. If a 35-mph wind is blowing from the southwest, what airspeed and compass bearing should the pilot maintain on the instrument panel? **≈ 290 mph at 31.5° South of East**

REPRESENTATIONS DEAL WITH PICTURES, GRAPHS, OR OBJECTS THAT ILLUSTRATE CONCEPTS.

49–52, 53a, 53c, 54) See margin.

Objective I: *Represent two-dimensional vectors in their component or polar representation, or as directed segments.* *(Lessons 12-1, 12-3)*

45. Find the component representation of [5, 120°] and sketch the vector. **See margin.**

46. Sketch the vector described by (4 cos 20°, 4 sin 20°). **See margin.**

47. a. Find the component representation of the vector pictured below. **(6, 3)**

b. Find its length and direction. **length ≈ 6.7; direction ≈ 26.6°**

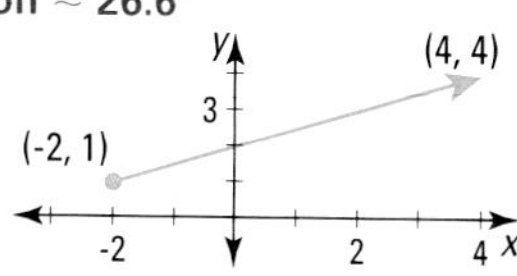

48. a. Give the endpoint of a vector which has polar representation [7, -200°] and initial point (2, 1). **≈ (-4.6, 3.4)**

b. Sketch the vector. **See margin.**

Objective J: *Represent addition, subtraction, and scalar multiplication of two-dimensional vectors graphically.* *(Lessons 12-2, 12-3)*

49. Given the vectors sketched at the right, sketch the following vectors.

$\vec{u}$ $\vec{v}$

a. $\vec{u} + \vec{v}$ **b.** $\vec{u} - \vec{v}$

c. $-\vec{u}$ **d.** $2\vec{v}$

50. Sketch the vectors $\vec{u}$ = [5, 30°] and $\vec{v}$ = [3, -60°]. Then sketch the following vectors.

a. $\vec{u} + \vec{v}$ **b.** $\vec{u} - \vec{v}$ **c.** $-\vec{v}$

Objective K: *Geometrically interpret three-dimensional vectors and their operations.* *(Lesson 12-6)*

In 51 and 52, let $\vec{u}$ = (5, 1, 3) and $\vec{v}$ = (-3, -4, 1).

51. Sketch the vectors $\vec{u}$ and $\vec{v}$ and the angle θ between them.

52. Find the components of $\vec{v} - \vec{u}$.

53. Given $\vec{u}$ = (3, 2, 0) and $\vec{v}$ = (-1, -2, 0).

a. Sketch the plane determined by $\vec{u}$ and $\vec{v}$.

b. Compute $\vec{v} \times \vec{u}$. **(0, 0, 4)**

c. Add $\vec{v} \times \vec{u}$ to your sketch.

Objective L: *Represent lines in a plane using vector or parametric equations.* *(Lessons 12-3, 12-4)*

54. A vector equation of a line is $(x - 1, y + 8) = t(3, 1)$.

a. Find the points on the line corresponding to each.

i. $t = 0$ **ii.** $t = 1$ **iii.** $t = -3$

b. Find a vector that is parallel to the line.

c. Sketch the line.

In 55 and 56, let $\vec{v}$ = (-5, 5) and P = (1, 2).

55. Write a vector equation for the line through P that is parallel to $\vec{v}$. **(x – 1, y – 2) = t(-5, 5)**

56. Write a vector equation for the line through P that is orthogonal to $\vec{v}$. **Sample: (x – 1, y – 2) = t(1, 1)**

50. a–c.

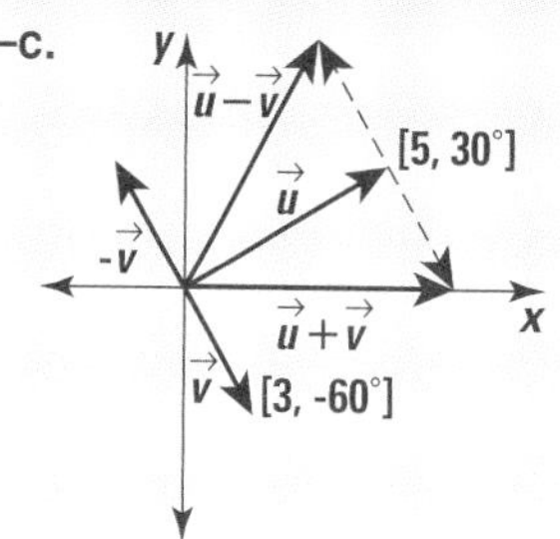

51.

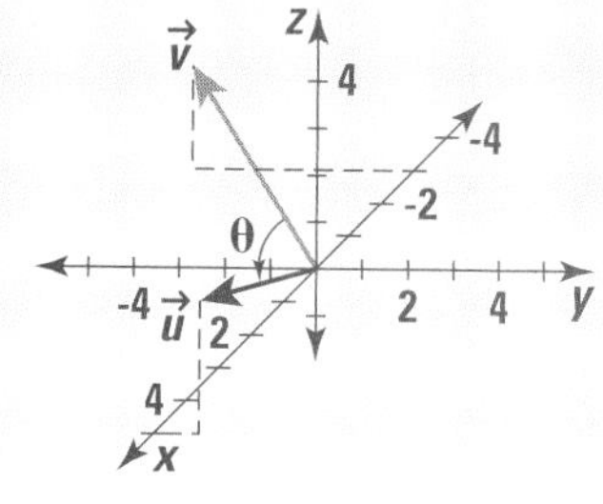

CHAPTER TWELVE

In 57 and 58, let $\vec{w}$ be the vector (-5, -3) and Q be the point (1, -2).

57. Find an equation of the line through Q perpendicular to $\vec{w}$. **$5x + 3y + 1 = 0$**

58. Find parametric equations for the line through Q parallel to $\vec{w}$. **See below.**

59. Find parametric equations for the line through (5, 0) that is parallel to the line with vector equation $(x - 2, y + 1) = t(3, -4)$. **See below.**

Objective M: *Represent lines, planes, and spheres in 3-space using parametric, vector, or coordinate equations.* *(Lessons 12-5, 12-7)*

60. Find the center and radius of the sphere with equation $x^2 + y^2 - 4y + z^2 + 8z = -15$.

61. Find the equations of two planes parallel to and 3 units away from the xz-plane. **$y = 3$ and $y = -3$**

60) center: (0, 2, -4); radius: $\sqrt{5}$

58) $\begin{cases} x = 1 - 5t \\ y = -2 - 3t \end{cases}$

59) $\begin{cases} x = 5 + 3t \\ y = -4t \end{cases}$

62) (6, 0, 0), (0, -4, 0), (0, 0, 12)

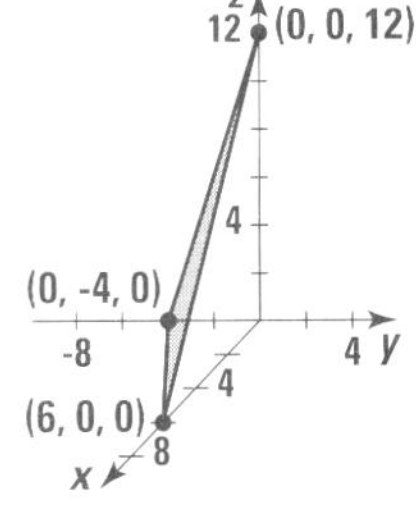

62. Use intercepts to sketch the plane with equation $2x - 3y + z = 12$. **See below left.**

63. Give a system of two linear equations that describes the z-axis in 3-space. **$x = 0$ and $y = 0$**

64. Find parametric equations for the line in 3-space through the point (3, 0, -1) that is parallel to the vector (2, -4, 0).

65. Find an equation for the plane containing the point (3, 0, -1) that is perpendicular to the vector (2, -4, 0). **$2x - 4y = 6$**

66. Find two vectors perpendicular to the plane given by $-3x + y + 5z = 8$.

67. Find a vector equation for the line through (5, -1, 2) that is perpendicular to the plane given by $2x - 6y + z = 7$.
$(x - 5, y + 1, z - 2) = t(2, -6, 1)$

64) $\begin{cases} x = 3 + 2t \\ y = -4t \\ z = -1 \end{cases}$

66) Sample: (-3, 1, 5) and (3, -1, -5)

54. a. i. (1, -8)
ii. (4, -7)
iii. (-8, -11)
b. Sample: (3, 1)
c.

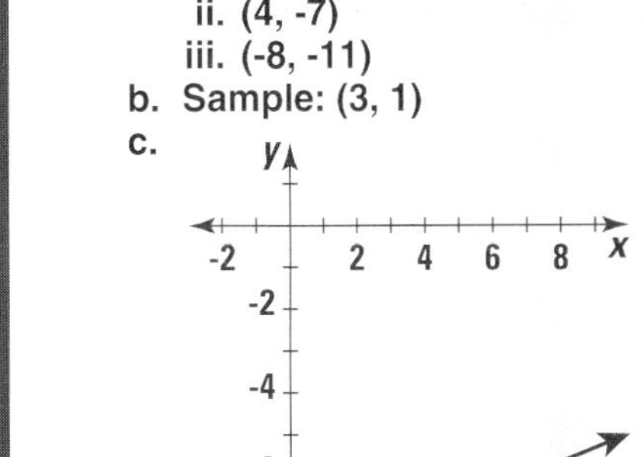

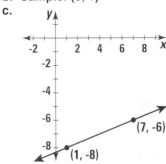

Additional Answers, page 780

52. (-8, -5, -2); This vector can be pictured by an arrow starting at the endpoint of $\vec{u}$ and ending at the endpoint of $\vec{v}$, providing $\vec{u}$ and $\vec{v}$ have the same initial points; or putting the vector in standard position, it is the diagonal of the figure having vertices (-3, -4, 1), (-5, -1, -3), (0, 0, 0), and (-8, -5, -2).

53. a, c.

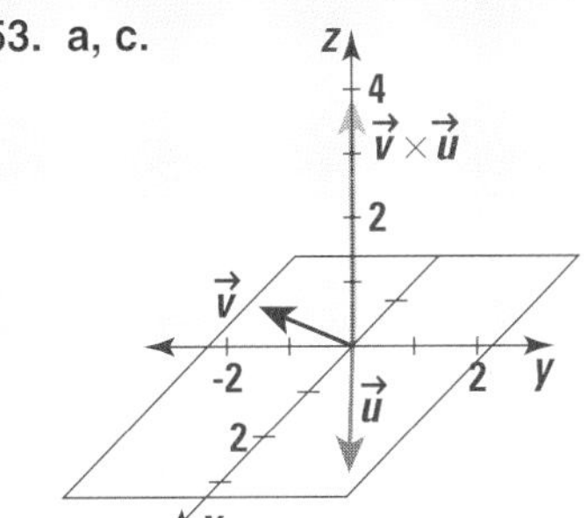

Adapting to Individual Needs

The student text is written for the vast majority of students. The chart at the right suggests two pacing plans to accommodate the needs of your students. Students in the Full Course should complete the entire text by the end of the year. Students in the Minimal Course will spend more time when there are quizzes and more time on the Chapter Review. Therefore, these students may not complete all of the chapters in the text.

Options are also presented to meet the needs of a variety of teaching and learning styles. For each lesson, the Teacher's Edition provides a section entitled *Adapting to Individual Needs.* This section regularly includes **Optional Activities, Challenge** problems, **English Language Development** suggestions, and suggestions for providing **Extra Help.** The Teacher's Edition also frequently includes an **Error Alert,** an **Extension,** and an **Assessment** alternative. The options available in Chapter 13 are summarized in the chart below.

Chapter 13 Pacing Chart

Day	Full Course	Minimal Course
1	13-1	13-1
2	13-2	13-2
3	13-3	13-3
4	13-4	13-4
5	Quiz*; 13-5	Quiz*; begin 13-5.
6	13-6	Finish 13-5.
7	13-7	13-6
8	Self-Test	13-7
9	Review	Self-Test
10	Test*	Review
11	Comprehensive Test*	Review
12		Test*
13		Comprehensive Test*

*in the Teacher's Resource File

In the Teacher's Edition...

Lesson	Optional Activities	Extra Help	Challenge	English Language Development	Error Alert	Extension	Cooperative Learning	Ongoing Assessment
13-1	●	●	●		●	●	●	Written
13-2	●	●	●		●	●	●	Written
13-3	●	●	●		●	●		Written
13-4	●	●	●		●	●		Quiz
13-5	●	●	●		●	●		Written
13-6	●	●	●		●	●	●	Written
13-7	●	●	●		●	●		

In the Additional Resources...

	In the Teacher's Resource File							
Lesson	Lesson Masters	Teaching Aids*	Answer Masters	Technology Sourcebook	Assessment Sourcebook	Visual Aids**	Technology	Explorations Software
13-1	13-1	147, 150, 151	13-1			147, 150, 151, AM		
13-2	13-2	147, 152, 153	13-2			147, 152, 153, AM		13-2
13-3	13-3	148, 154, 155	13-3	Calc 18		148, 154, 155, AM		
13-4	13-4	148, 156	13-4		Quiz	148, 156, AM		
13-5	13-5	149, 157	13-5	Calc 19		149, 157, AM		
In-class Activity			13-6					
13-6	13-6	149, 158	13-6			149, 158, AM		13-6
13-7		149	13-7			149, AM		
End of chapter					Tests			

*Teaching Aids are pictured on pages 782C and 782D.

**Visual Aids provide transparencies for all Teaching Aids and all Answer Masters.

Also available is the Study Skills Handbook which includes study-skill tips related to reading, note-taking, and comprehension.

Integrating Strands and Applications

	13-1	13-2	13-3	13-4	13-5	13-6	13-7
Mathematical Connections							
Number Sense	●	●	●	●	●		
Algebra	●	●	●	●	●	●	●
Geometry	●	●	●	●	●	●	●
Measurement	●	●	●	●	●	●	●
Logic and Reasoning	●	●	●	●	●	●	●
Patterns and Functions	●	●	●	●	●	●	●
Discrete Mathematics	●	●	●	●	●	●	
Interdisciplinary and Other Connections							
Science	●	●		●	●		
Social Studies	●			●	●		
Multicultural		●					
Technology		●	●		●	●	●
Career		●				●	
Consumer	●				●	●	
Sports			●				

Teaching and Assessing the Chapter Objectives

Chapter 13 Objectives (Organized into the SPUR catetgories—Skills, Properties, Uses, and Representations)	Lessons	Progress Self-Test Questions	Chapter Review Questions	In the Teacher's Resource File: Chapter Test, Forms A and B	Chapter Test, Forms C	Chapter Test, Forms D
Skills						
A: Calculate Riemann sums of functions over specified intervals.	13-2	2	1–3		1	
B: Evaluate definite integrals.	13-3, 13-4, 13-5	4, 5, 6	4–10		3	X
Properties						
C: Apply properties of definite integrals.	13-4	9, 11	12–15		2	X
D: Find the distance traveled by a moving object, given its rate.	13-1, 13-2, 13-5	10	16–18		4	
E: Use the definite integral to solve application problems.	13-4, 13-6	3	19–21			X
F: Estimate the distance under a velocity-time graph.	13-1	1	22–23			
Representations						
G: Express areas in integral notation.	13-3	7	24–26		3	
H: Find areas bounded by curves.	13-4, 13-5	8	27–29			
I: Find volumes of solids.	13-6	12	30–31		5	X

Assessment Sourcebook
Quiz for Lessons 13-1 through 13-4
Chapter 13 Test, Forms A–D
Chapter 13 Test, Cumulative Form
Comprehensive Test, Chapters 1–13

TestWorks CD-ROM

Teaching Aids

TEACHING AID 147

Warm-up
Lesson 13-1

A polygon has vertices (0, 0), (*a*, 0), (*a*, *b*), (*c*, *b*), (*c*, *d*), and (0, *d*), where *a*, *b*, *c*, and d are all positive.

1. If $c > a$ and $d > b$, what is the area of the polygon?
2. If $c < a$ and $d > b$, what is the area of the polygon?
3. If $c < a$ and $d < b$, what is the area of the polygon?

Warm-up
Lesson 13-2

In 1–3, find the value of the multiple of the series shown.

1. $1(1^2 + 2^2 + \ldots + 10^2)$
2. $0.5(0.5^2 + 1^2 + 1.5^2 + 2^2 + \ldots + 10^2)$
3. $0.25(0.25^2 + 0.5^2 + 0.75^2 + 1^2 + 1.25^2 + \ldots + 10^2)$
4. What might be the next sum in this sequence?
5. How is this sequence related to the reading of Lesson 13-2?

TEACHING AID 148

Warm-up
Lesson 13-3

On page 799 of the Student Edition, upper and lower Riemann sums for $f(x) = \sin x$ are pictured. Six intervals are used to calculate each sum, and each interval has length $\frac{\pi}{12}$.

1. Using a calculator, find the values used to calculate the number 1.12518 found for the upper Riemann sum.
2. Using a calculator, find the values used to calculate the number .86338 found for the lower Riemann sum.

Warm-up
Lesson 13-4

Consider the finite sequences $a_1, a_2, a_3, \ldots, a_{10}$ and $b_1, b_2, b_3, \ldots, b_{10}$.

Suppose the sum of all terms of the first sequence is *S* and the sum of all terms of the second sequence is *T*.

1. What is the sum of the sequence c, if for all *i*, $c_i = a_i + b_i$?
2. Write the results of Question 1 using Σ-notation.
3. What is the sum of the sequence d, if for all $i, d_i = 5a_i - b_i$?
4. Write the results of Question 3 using Σ-notation.

TEACHING AID 149

Warm-up
Lesson 13-5

In Lesson 13-5, the area bounded by the *x*-axis, the line $x = 1$, and the parabola $y = x^2$ is shown to be $\frac{1}{3}$. Use this result.

1. Find the area of the region bounded by the *y*-axis, the line $y = 1$, and the parabola $y = x^2$.
2. Find the area of the region bounded by the *y*-axis, the parabola $y = x^2$, the line $x = 1$, and the line $y = 4$.

Warm-up
Lesson 13-6

Each of these figures can be thought of as a surface of revolution. Name a possible generating curve and describe its relationship to the axis of revolution.

1. Sphere
2. Hemisphere
3. Cylinder
4. Torus (doughnut)

Warm-up
Lesson 13-7

Name several functions *f* that satisfy $f'(x) = 2x$.

TEACHING AID 150
Lesson 13-

Distance as Area

total distance = area of shaded region = 50 • 3.5 + 30 • 2 = 235 miles

total distance traveled = area of shaded region $= \sum_{i=1}^{10} r_i t_i$

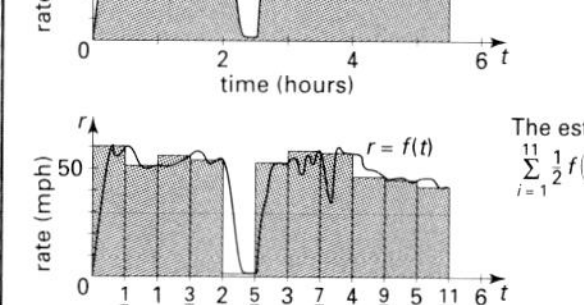

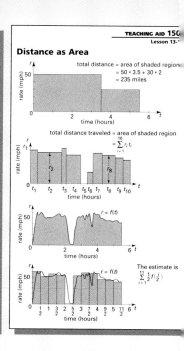

TEACHING AID 151
Lesson 13-1

Example 1

$g(x) = -.88(x - 10^2) + 88 \frac{\text{ft}}{\text{sec}}$

(10, 88), (8, 84.48), (6, 73.92), (4, 56.32), (2, 31.68)

rate (feet per second); time (seconds)

Example 2

(10, 88)

rate (feet per second); time (seconds)

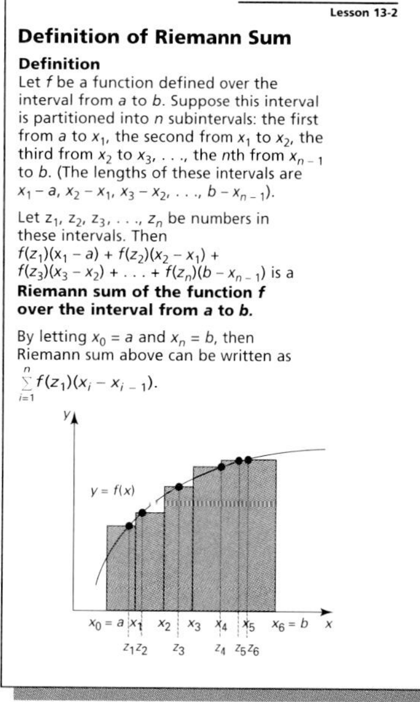

TEACHING AID 152
Lesson 13-2

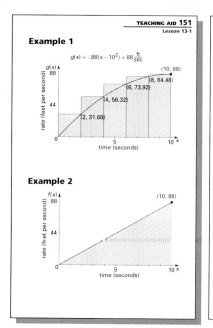

Definition of Riemann Sum

Definition

Let *f* be a function defined over the interval from *a* to *b*. Suppose this interval is partitioned into *n* subintervals: the first from *a* to x_1, the second from x_1 to x_2, the third from x_2 to x_3, . . ., the *n*th from x_{n-1} to *b*. (The lengths of these intervals are $x_1 - a, x_2 - x_1, x_3 - x_2, \ldots, b - x_{n-1}$).

Let $z_1, z_2, z_3, \ldots, z_n$ be numbers in these intervals. Then $f(z_1)(x_1 - a) + f(z_2)(x_2 - x_1) + f(z_3)(x_3 - x_2) + \ldots + f(z_n)(b - x_{n-1})$ is a **Riemann sum of the function *f* over the interval from *a* to *b*.**

By letting $x_0 = a$ and $x_n = b$, then Riemann sum above can be written as $\sum_{i=1}^{n} f(z_1)(x_i - x_{i-1})$.

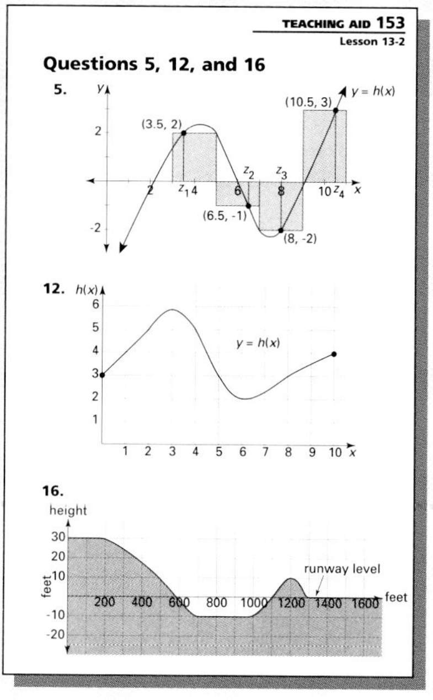

TEACHING AID 153
Lesson 13-2

Questions 5, 12, and 16

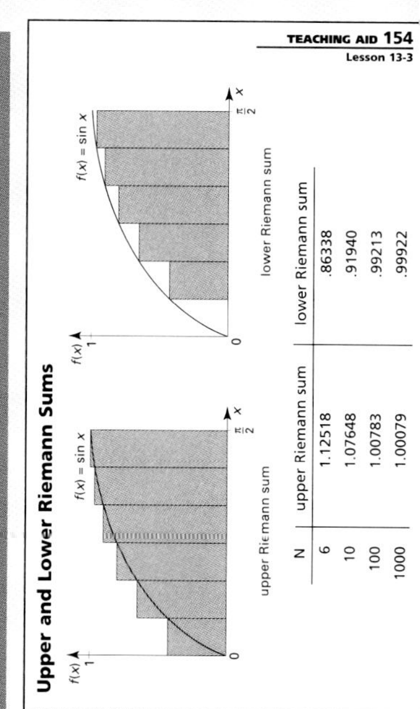

TEACHING AID 154
Lesson 13-3

Upper and Lower Riemann Sums

N	upper Riemann sum	lower Riemann sum
6	1.12518	.86338
10	1.07648	.91940
100	1.00783	.99213
1000	1.00079	.99922

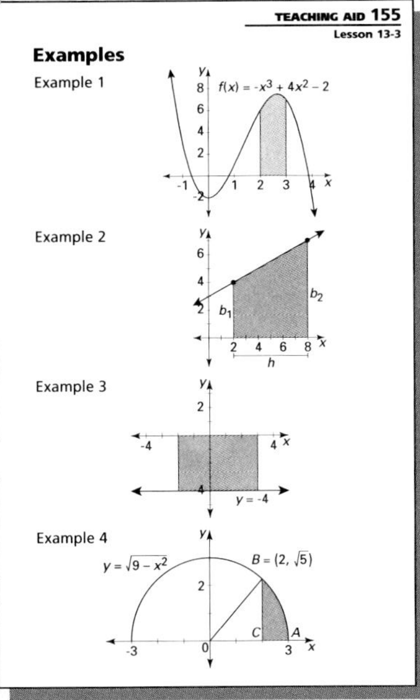
TEACHING AID 155
Lesson 13-3
Examples
Example 1
f(x) = -x^3 + 4x^2 – 2
Example 2
Example 3
y = -4
Example 4
y = √(9 – x^2)
B = (2, √5)

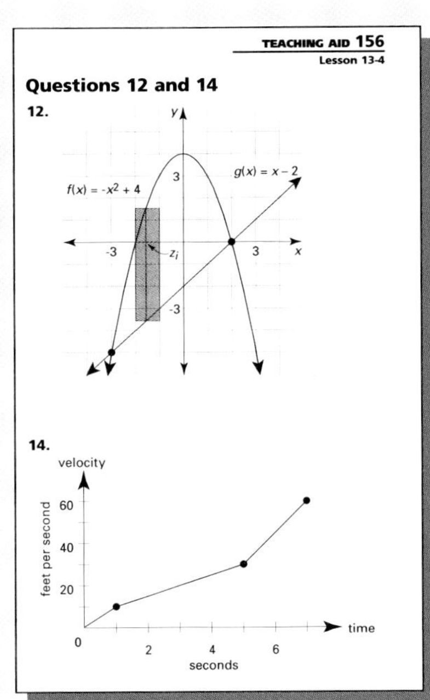
TEACHING AID 156
Lesson 13-4
Questions 12 and 14
12.
f(x) = -x^2 + 4
g(x) = x – 2
14.
velocity
feet per second
time
seconds

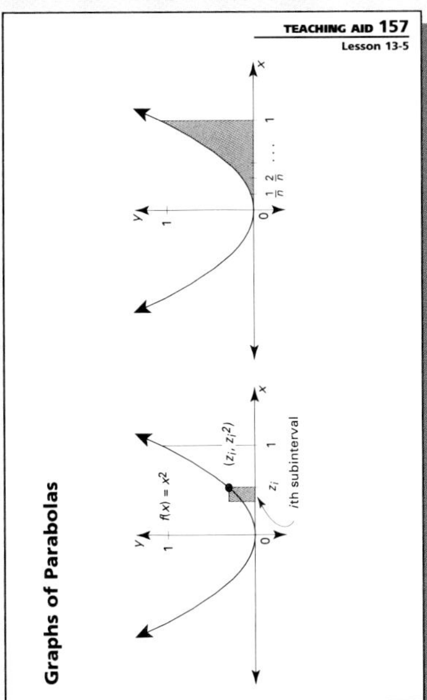
TEACHING AID 157
Lesson 13-5
Graphs of Parabolas
f(x) = x^2
ith subinterval

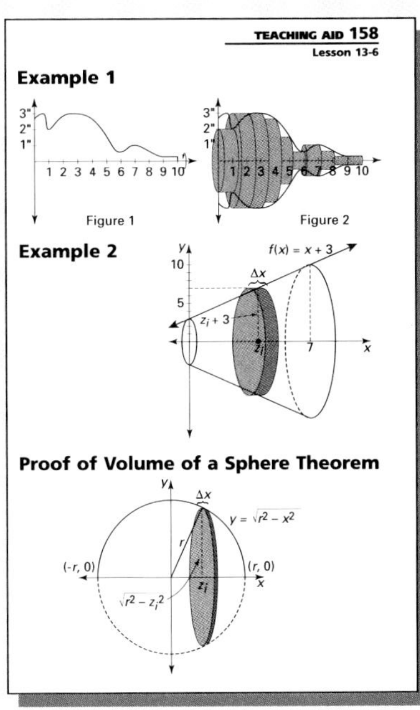
TEACHING AID 158
Lesson 13-6
Example 1
Figure 1
Figure 2
Example 2
f(x) = x + 3
Proof of Volume of a Sphere Theorem
y = √(r^2 – x^2)

Chapter Opener

Pacing

All lessons in this chapter are designed to be covered in one day. At the end of the chapter, you should plan to spend 1 day to review the Progress Self-Test, 1–2 days for the Chapter Review, and 1 day for a test. You may wish to spend a day on projects, and possibly a day is needed for quizzes and the In-class Activity. This chapter should therefore take 10–13 days.

Using Pages 782–783

Students have no doubt seen the integral sign. They may be excited by finding out what it means and how it can be calculated. Probe to see if they have any knowledge in this area. Point out to them that what they learn about integrals in this chapter will not be anything close to the detail that they would encounter in calculus, but it will prepare them well for that encounter.

CHAPTER 13

782

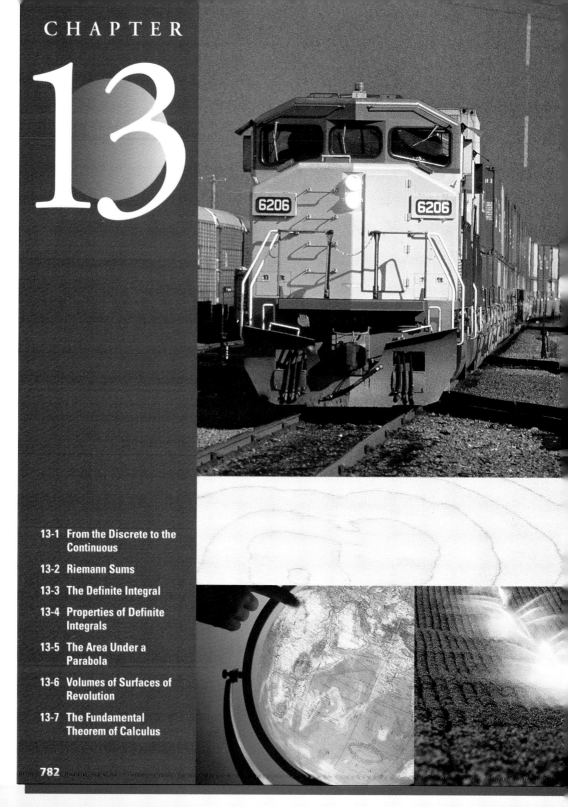

Chapter 13 Overview

This chapter introduces students to a fundamental idea in calculus, the integral. The approach taken is mathematically precise but informal. We feel that it is critical for success of students in calculus that they have encountered the basic concepts before they study a full course.

This chapter is a fitting chapter with which to close out the year for seniors; many of them will want to take calculus in their freshman year of college. If you do nothing more than give students a concrete meaning for the integral sign, $\int$, take the fear out of it, and show its importance, you will have achieved the goals of this chapter.

Mathematically, the integral is approached here through Riemann sums. In Lessons 13-1 and 13-2, Riemann sums are used to approximate the area under a curve and the distance traveled by a car whose speed at each instant is known. A computer program to evaluate Riemann sums is given in the second lesson. In Lesson 13-3, the definite integral is defined as the limit of a sequence of Riemann sums as the number of subintervals $n \to \infty$. Most examples deal with functions that are nonnegative or nonpositive on an interval. Students should be able to estimate whether a given Riemann sum or definite integral will be positive or negative on an interval.

The Integral in Calculus

The study of calculus has two main branches: differential calculus and integral calculus. In Chapter 9, you were introduced to differential calculus, whose fundamental concept is the derivative. The fundamental concept in integral calculus is that of the *integral*. The symbol for integral is $\int$, an elongated "s," which stands for sum. The symbol is used in recognition of the fact that an integral is a certain kind of limit of a sum. You will learn its specific meaning in this chapter.

The process of finding the integral of a function is called *integration*. Integration solves a variety of problems, and this chapter concentrates on four types.

1. Given the (changing) velocity of an object at every instant, find how far the object travels in a given time period.
2. (a more general form of type 1) Given the derivative of a function, determine the original function.
3. Find the area between the graph of a function and the x-axis, as illustrated in the diagram at the left below.

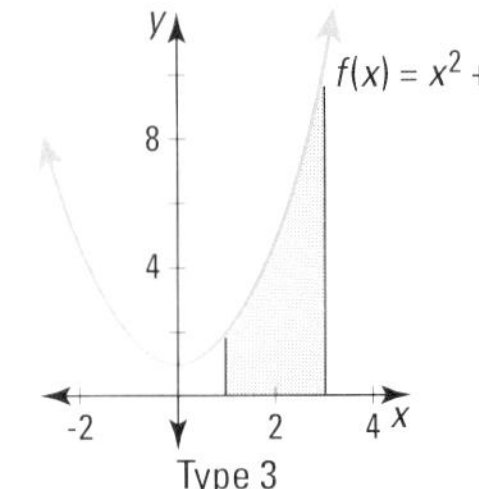

Type 3

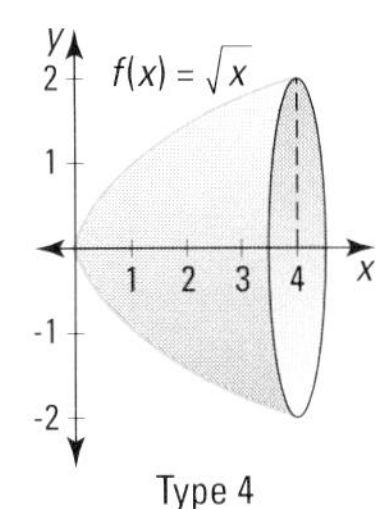

Type 4

4. (an extension of type 3) Find the volume of a solid of revolution, as illustrated in the diagram at the right above.

As with the derivative, the integral is a powerful tool. The connection of these two ideas, made by Isaac Newton and Gottfried Leibniz in the 17th century, paved the way for many of the advances in the physical sciences, engineering, and statistics which have taken place since then.

Photo Connections

The photo collage makes real-world connections to the content of the chapter: the integral in calculus.

Freight Train: Problems involving distance traveled by vehicles in continuous motion are discussed in Lesson 13-1. **Question 7** in that lesson deals with a freight train.

Runway: **Question 16** in Lesson 13-2 involves constructing an airport runway by filling in low points with dirt from the high points to form a level surface.

Wood: **Question 26** in the *Exploration* in Lesson 13-5 asks students to explain how Archimedes could use the weight of a parabolic region cut out of wood to arrive at a conjecture concerning the area bounded by a parabola.

Globe: In the *In-class Activity* on page 819, students are asked to explain how Earth can be thought of as a solid of revolution.

Irrigation: Under the conditions given in **Example 2** on page 807, students estimate the total amount of water used to irrigate a field. Then they use integral notation to represent the exact amount of water used.

Chapter 13 Projects

At this time, you might want to have students look over the projects on pages 832–833.

In some glimpses into calculus, students are given a formula, $\int_a^b$ for $x^n\,dx$ and then this formula is used to solve problems. It is, of course, a powerful tool. We do not do so in this chapter because we feel students will do too much by rote and ignore the underlying concepts. Emphasis is placed on properties that can be proved using what students know about area or sums of infinite series. Several general properties relating integrals are given in Lesson 13-4, and then some formulas are given in Lesson 13-5, culminating in a formula for $\int_0^a (c_2x^2 + c_1x + c_0)\,dx$ and its special cases, the constant and linear functions. In Lesson 13-6, volumes of solids of revolution are approximated by slicing the solid into sections approximated by cylinders and then adding up the volumes of those cylinders. One application yields an alternate derivation of the formula $V = \frac{4}{3}\pi r^3$ for the volume of a sphere.

The last lesson of the chapter introduces students to the Fundamental Theorem of Calculus, the theorem that relates derivatives to integrals. Its purpose is not only to conclude the text with an important theorem, but also to point out that major concepts of calculus are intimately related.

Lesson 13-1

Objectives

D Find the distance traveled by a moving object, given its rate.
F Estimate the distance under a velocity-time graph.

Resources

From the ***Teacher's Resource File***
- Lesson Master 13-1
- Answer Master 13-1
- Teaching Aids
  147 Warm-up
  150 Distance as Area
  151 Example 1 and Example 2

Additional Resources
- Visuals for Teaching Aids 147, 150, 151

Teaching Lesson 13-1

Warm-up

A polygon has vertices (0, 0), (a, 0), (a, b), (c, b), (c, d), and (0, d), where a, b, c, and d are all positive.

1. If $c > a$ and $d > b$, what is the area of the polygon?
   ab + cd − bc
2. If $c < a$ and $d > b$, what is the area of the polygon?
   ab + cd − bc
3. If $c < a$ and $d < b$, what is the area of the polygon?
   ab + cd − bc
   (Note: the area is the same regardless of the relative size of a, b, c, and d.)

LESSON

13-1

From the Discrete to the Continuous

Blue Ridge Parkway, North Carolina

Representing Distance as a Sum

If you travel for 3.5 hours at a constant speed of 50 miles per hour, the familiar formula $d = rt$ gives the total distance traveled, 175 miles. If your speed then changes to 30 miles per hour and you travel for an additional 2 hours, then the total distance traveled is

$$50 \cdot 3.5 + 30 \cdot 2 = 235 \text{ miles.}$$

The formula for the total distance could be written as $r_1t_1 + r_2t_2$, or $\sum_{i=1}^{2} r_it_i$, a sum of two terms. Here t_1 and t_2 add up to the total time and r_1 and r_2 are rates for the two parts of the trip.

Of course, few things travel at constant speeds for any long period of time—not cars, nor people, nor objects tossed into the air. To get a better approximation of the real situation, the total time can be split into n time intervals, $t_1, t_2, \ldots, t_n$. Then, if the rates in each interval of time are $r_1, r_2, \ldots, r_n$, the total distance traveled is

$$r_1t_1 + r_2t_2 + \ldots + r_nt_n, \text{ or } \sum_{i=1}^{n} r_it_i, \text{ a sum of } n \text{ terms.}$$

But even this still gives only an approximation. The rate of a moving object usually changes continuously. For instance, as the speed of an object changes from 50 to 30 mph, every number between 30 and 50 is a rate of the object at some time. So there are (in theory) infinitely many terms of the form r_it_i to add, one term for each different rate. The situation is continuous; the set of terms to add is not a discrete set. This problem of the distance traveled by objects in continuous motion is one of the kinds of problems that led to the invention of calculus.

Lesson 13-1 Overview

Broad Goals This lesson uses the context of distance, rate, and time to introduce the idea of the area between a curve and the x-axis.

Perspective The integral has interpretations under each of the SPUR categories and for each there is a move from discrete things students know to continuous ideas which may be new. The lesson begins with a Use—finding the total distance of a trip if times and speeds for each of a finite number of segments (subintervals) of it are known. The Representation of this distance is as the total area of a finite set of rectangles. The Skill is the calculation of the sum, which is of the form $\sum_{i=1}^{n} r_it_i$. The Properties of such sums and areas have been studied by students in previous chapters and previous courses.

If a car accelerates, then it's speed is not constant over any of its subintervals. Still, the distance traversed can be approximated by dividing the trip into more and more subintervals. As the number of subintervals of the trip increases, the sum has more terms, the rectangles have smaller widths, and the total distance represented by the sum becomes a more accurate approximation to the actual total distance. The examples of this lesson involve two different formulas for

Representing Distance as an Area

Graphically, when time is the x-coordinate and rate the y-coordinate, the distance traveled can be represented as the area under a rate curve. Here is a graph of the situation described in the first sentence of this lesson, where an object travels with constant speed.

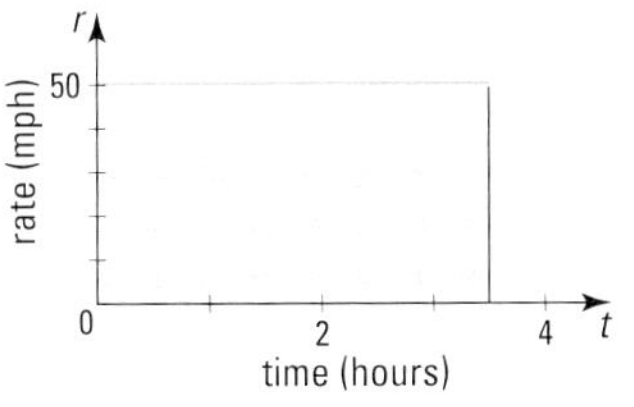

distance = area of rectangle
$= 50\,\frac{\text{mi}}{\text{hr}} \cdot 3.5$ hours
= 175 miles

Here is a graph of the situation in the second sentence of this lesson, in which part of the trip is at 50 mph, and the other part at 30 mph.

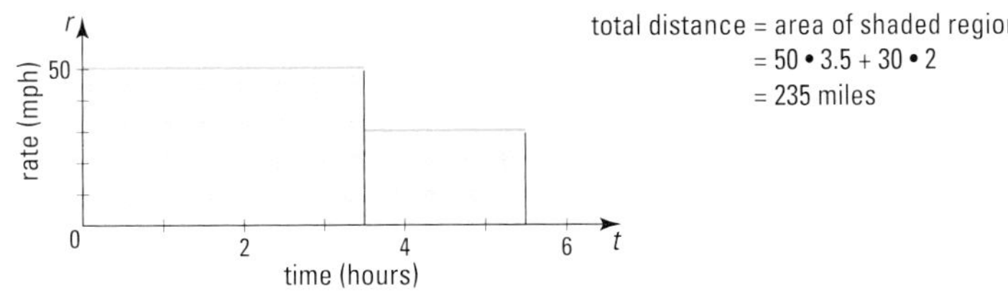

When there are 10 different constant rates $r_1, r_2, \ldots, r_{10}$ for time intervals of lengths $t_1, t_2, \ldots, t_{10}$, here is a possible graph. The height of each rectangle is just the rate for the corresponding time interval. (Note that r_5 is zero; the object is not moving during the time interval t_5.)

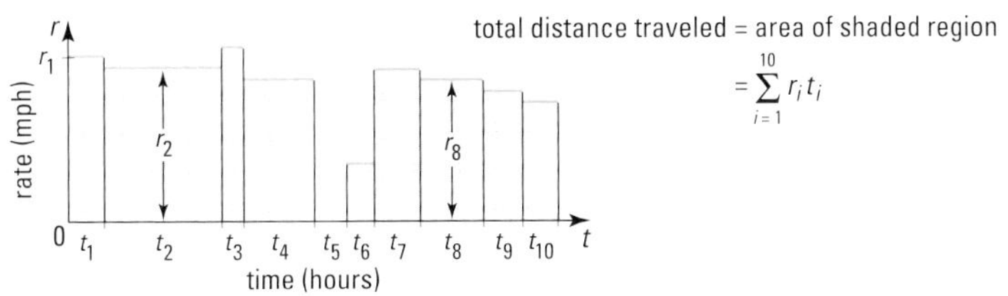

Now suppose $r = f(t)$ is the function giving the rate at which an object is moving at time t. For the functions represented by the three previous graphs, the range is a discrete set, containing 1, 2, and 10 elements, respectively. An actual situation is better modeled by a continuous function, as shown below. In this case, the range (the rates) consist of all real values from 0 to the maximum value of the function. Again, the area between the graph and the horizontal axis gives the total distance.

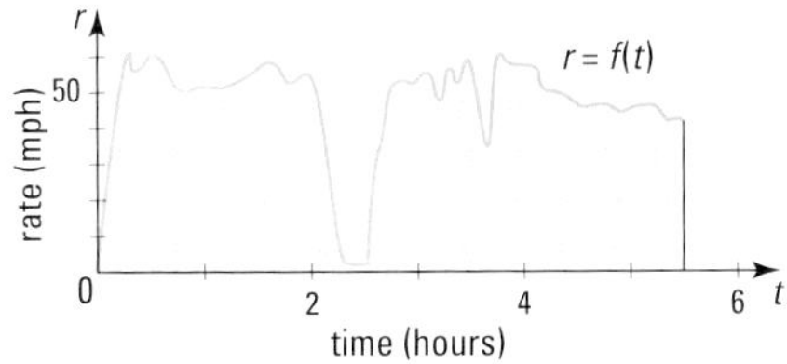

Notes on Reading

With five pages of reading, this is a long lesson, and you might wish to summarize it for students. The key applied idea is that distance traveled can be found by determining area under a speed curve. If the speed function is linear (and it will be if the acceleration is constant), the area can be computed exactly using familiar formulas. If the velocity function is non-linear, the area can be estimated by adding areas of rectangles.

After summarizing the lesson, examine each page in turn. Take particular care to make certain that students understand the use of summation notation in this context, as that notation is employed throughout the chapter. Students should be able to relate the notation to the appropriate graph. **Teaching Aid 150** is provided with some of the graphs on pages 785–786.

Social Studies Connection Under the National Highway System Designation Act of 1995, states were allowed to set their own highway speed limits. By late 1997, three states—Connecticut, Hawaii, and New Jersey—had kept the maximum speed limit on interstate highways at 55 miles per hour. Several states—Arizona, Colorado, Idaho, Nevada, New Mexico, Oklahoma, South Dakota, Utah, and Wyoming—had increased the maximum to 75 miles per hour. Montana set the daytime limit as "reasonable and prudent."

acceleration from 0 to 60 mph in 10 seconds.

The limit is easy to comprehend in both the contexts of the Use (the total distance traveled when the speed is known at each instant) and the Representation (the total area under a curve). The symbolic definition is, however, delayed until Lesson 13-3.

Optional Activities

You might use this activity after discussing the first situation described in the lesson. Ask students how the estimate of distance traveled would change if the speed were recorded as described at the right. [The approximation continues to get better as speed values are recorded at closer time intervals.] Then have students rewrite the formula given on page 784 for each situation.

1. Every $\frac{1}{20}$ hour $\left[\sum_{i=1}^{110} \frac{1}{20} f\left(\frac{i}{20}\right)\right]$
2. Every minute $\left[\sum_{i=1}^{330} \frac{1}{60} f\left(\frac{i}{60}\right)\right]$
3. Every second $\left[\sum_{i=1}^{19800} \frac{1}{19800} f\left(\frac{i}{19800}\right)\right]$

Error Alert Be sure students do not mistakenly assume that the speed functions g and f in **Example 1 and Example 2** are the only possible ways to accelerate from 0 to 60 $\frac{\text{mi}}{\text{hr}}$ (0 to 88 $\frac{\text{ft}}{\text{sec}}$). In fact, it is likely that an actual acceleration does not have such a simple formula.

Note that the answer to **Example 1** is larger than the answer to **Example 2.** Ask students why this should be so. [The car in **Example 1** is accelerating faster at first, so it should go farther.] **Teaching Aid 151** contains the graphs of **Example 1 and Example 2.**

To approximate this area, it is convenient to split the region under the graph of the function into rectangles whose horizontal dimensions (widths) are equal. For instance, with the function $r = f(t)$ on page 785, the area under the curve from $t = 0$ to $t = 5.5$ can be estimated by using rectangles with constant width $\frac{1}{2}$ and height equal to the value of f at the right side of the rectangle.

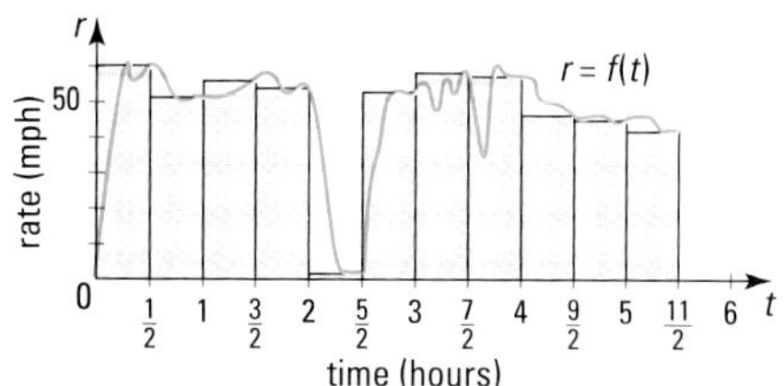

The estimate is $\frac{1}{2} \cdot f\left(\frac{1}{2}\right) + \frac{1}{2} \cdot f(1) + \frac{1}{2} \cdot f\left(\frac{3}{2}\right) + \ldots + \frac{1}{2} \cdot f\left(\frac{11}{2}\right) = \sum_{i=1}^{11} \frac{1}{2} f\left(\frac{i}{2}\right)$

This is like recording the speed every $\frac{1}{2}$ hour, assuming the rate was constant for the preceding $\frac{1}{2}$ hour, and calculating the total distance based only on this information. If the speed were recorded every $\frac{1}{10}$ hour, a better approximation of the distance traveled would be obtained. The width of each rectangle would be $\frac{1}{10}$, there would be 55 values in the 5.5 hours, and the estimate would be $\sum_{i=1}^{55} \frac{1}{10} f\left(\frac{i}{10}\right)$.

Estimating Distance as the Area Under a Curve

Now consider a situation in which there is a formula for the speed function. Imagine a car that accelerates from 0 to 60 mph $\left(88 \frac{\text{ft}}{\text{sec}}\right)$ in 10 seconds. If the acceleration is quicker at first (the driver presses hard on the pedal, then eases off), the speed $g(x)$ at time x might be given by the quadratic function $g(x) = -.88(x - 10)^2 + 88$. This results in the table and graph shown below.

x (seconds)	0	1	2	3	4	5	6	7	8	9	10
speed (ft/sec) after x seconds	0	16.72	31.68	44.88	56.32	66	73.92	80.08	84.48	87.12	88

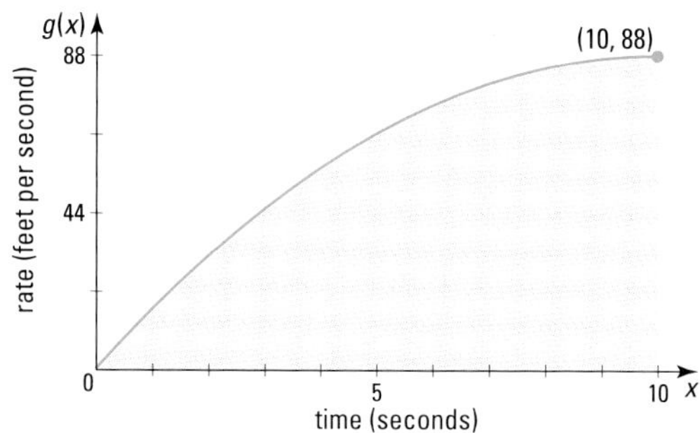

Adapting to Individual Needs

Extra Help
Students may wonder why we use $\frac{\text{ft}}{\text{sec}}$ rather than $\frac{\text{mi}}{\text{hr}}$ as the unit. If the latter were used, then the area would be in miles, and so the answers would be fractions of a mile. It's easier to use feet.

Challenge
Let C be a circle of radius r and let A_n be an inscribed regular polygon with n sides. Have students answer the following questions.

1. Connect the vertices of A_n to its center, dividing A_n into n congruent triangles. Let θ be the angle of each triangle at the center of the circle. What is the measure of θ? $\left[\frac{360^\circ}{n}\right]$
2. What is the area of each triangle? $\left[\frac{1}{2}r^2 \sin \frac{360^\circ}{n}\right]$
3. What is the total area of A_n in terms of n and r? $\left[\frac{n}{2}r^2 \sin \frac{360^\circ}{n}\right]$
4. Find the total area of A_n in terms of r for $n = 10, 50, 100$. What is the limit of A_n as n goes to infinity? $[\pi r^2]$

In this nonconstant acceleration situation, the speed curve is part of a parabola. The total distance traveled is given by the area between the parabola and the x-axis, but at this point you probably do not know any formula to find this area. Still, the total distance can be estimated.

Example 1

A car accelerates from 0 to 88 $\frac{\text{ft}}{\text{sec}}$ with a speed of $g(x) = -.88(x - 10)^2 + 88$ $\frac{\text{ft}}{\text{sec}}$ after x seconds. Estimate the distance the car travels in 10 seconds.

Solution

For our estimate, we choose to divide the interval $0 \le x \le 10$ into 5 subintervals. The distance the car travels is less than the sum of the areas of the 5 rectangles shown below. This area is

$$\sum_{i=1}^{5} 2 \cdot g(2i) = 2 \cdot 31.68 + 2 \cdot 56.32 + 2 \cdot 73.92 + 2 \cdot 84.48 + 2 \cdot 88$$
$$= 668.8 \text{ feet.}$$

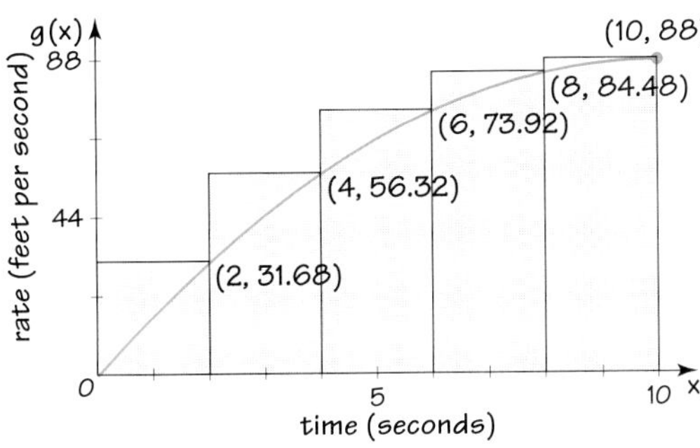

The estimate in Example 1 could be improved by splitting the interval into more subintervals. We found a high estimate for the area; a low estimate can be obtained by using rectangles that lie completely under the curve.

The narrower the rectangles, the closer the sum of their areas is to the area between the graph of g and the x-axis. In general, if f is a continuous function giving the rate at time t, then the total distance traveled equals the area between the graph of f and the x-axis over the time interval. In certain situations, this distance can be calculated exactly. So the narrower the rectangles, the closer the sum of their areas is to the total distance traveled.

Additional Examples

1. Suppose that a car accelerates from 0 to 88 $\frac{\text{ft}}{\text{sec}}$ in 10 seconds such that its speed y after t seconds is given by $y = .088t^3$.
   a. By splitting the interval from 0 to 10 into 5 intervals, drawing rectangles with the values of y at the midpoints of the intervals as heights of the rectangles, estimate the total distance traveled. **15.6 feet**
   b. Is this estimate too high or too low? **Too low**
2. A car accelerates from 0 to 88 $\frac{\text{ft}}{\text{sec}}$ in 11 seconds. If the acceleration is constant, how far will the car have traveled in that time? **484 feet**
3. Recall from Chapter 9 that, if the height (in feet) of a projectile after t seconds is given by $h(t) = 800t - 16t^2$, then its velocity is given by $h'(t) = v(t) = 800 - 32t$. Find the distance traveled between 8 and 20 seconds. **4224 feet**

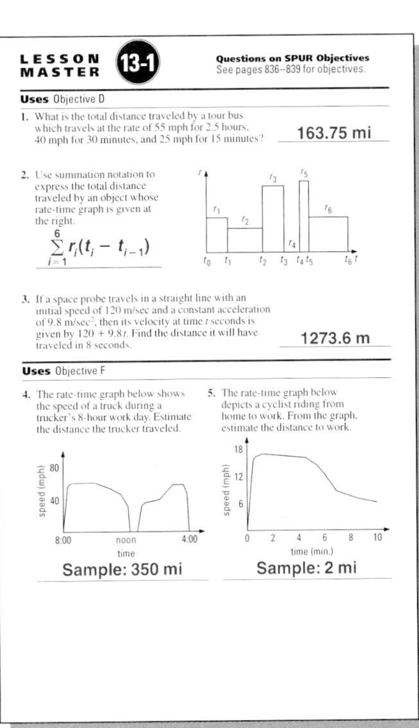

LESSON MASTER 13-1

Questions on SPUR Objectives
See pages 836–839 for objectives.

Uses Objective D

1. What is the total distance traveled by a tour bus which travels at the rate of 55 mph for 2.5 hours, 40 mph for 30 minutes, and 25 mph for 15 minutes? **163.75 mi**

2. Use summation notation to express the total distance traveled by an object whose rate-time graph is given at the right. $\sum_{i=1}^{6} r_i(t_i - t_{i-1})$

3. If a space probe travels in a straight line with an initial speed of 120 m/sec and a constant acceleration of 9.8 m/sec^2, then its velocity at time t seconds is given by $120 + 9.8t$. Find the distance it will have traveled in 8 seconds. **1273.6 m**

Uses Objective F

4. The rate-time graph below shows the speed of a truck during a trucker's 8-hour work day. Estimate the distance the trucker traveled.

Sample: 350 mi

5. The rate-time graph below depicts a cyclist riding from home to work. From the graph, estimate the distance to work.

Sample: 2 mi

Notes on Questions

Question 3 Be generous in allowing estimates. The important idea here is the method of estimating, not the accuracy of the estimate.

Question 4 This is the situation of **Example 2.** The car travels farther in the last 5 seconds because its speed is greater.

Question 6 This is the situation of **Example 1**. **Part b** may be easier to interpret in the form $\sum_{i=1}^{10} 1 \cdot g(i)$, where the constant 1 indicates a time interval of 1 second. If you have appropriate software, you could use it to show **part c.**

Question 7 This question brings home the idea that you can estimate how far a vehicle has traveled from taking speedometer readings even if you do not have its odometer (distance) readings. That is, from the rate function, you can determine the distance function. This suggests the relationship between the derivative and the integral that is summarized in the fundamental theorem of calculus. That idea is discussed in Lesson 13-7.

Additional Answers

3. A sample table is shown below.

$$\sum_{i=1}^{11} .5f(\tfrac{i}{2}) \approx 260.5 \text{ units}^2$$

i	$\frac{i}{2}$	$f\left(\frac{i}{2}\right)$	$.5\left(f\left(\frac{i}{2}\right)\right)$
1	0.5	60	30
2	1	51	25.5
3	1.5	57	28.5
4	2	54	27
5	2.5	2	1
6	3	52	26
7	3.5	58	29
8	4	57	28.5
9	4.5	45	22.5
10	5	44	22
11	5.5	41	20.5

2b)

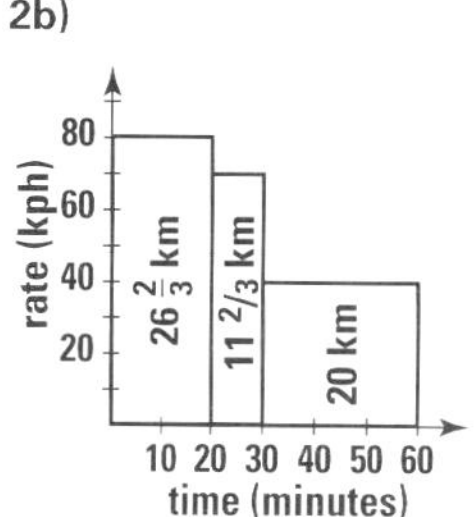

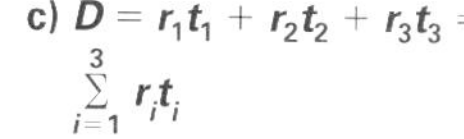
c) $D = r_1t_1 + r_2t_2 + r_3t_3 = \sum_{i=1}^{3} r_it_i$

Capetown, South Africa

Example 2

A car accelerates from 0 to 60 mph (88 $\frac{\text{ft}}{\text{sec}}$) in 10 seconds. If the acceleration is constant, how far will the car travel (in feet) in this time?

Solution

If the acceleration is constant, then the following table gives the speed after each second.

x (seconds)	0	1	2	3	4	5	6	7	8	9	10
speed (ft/sec) after x seconds	0	8.8	17.6	26.4	35.2	44	52.8	61.6	70.4	79.2	88

So the speed is given by the equation $f(x) = 8.8x$. This speed function is graphed below.

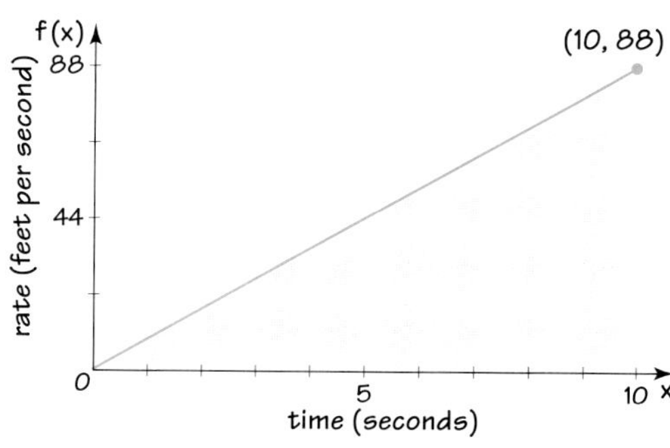

The total distance traveled by the car is given by the area between the graph of f and the x-axis. Using the formula $A = \frac{1}{2}bh$ for the area of a triangle, we find the distance to be $\frac{1}{2} \cdot 10$ seconds $\cdot\ 88 \frac{\text{ft}}{\text{sec}} = 440$ feet.

QUESTIONS

Covering the Reading

1. Of the 8 graphs of functions in this lesson, in how many is the range a discrete set? **3**

2. For 20 minutes, you travel on a highway at 80 kph. Then for 10 minutes, you travel at 70 kph as you near a city. Then for 30 minutes, you can average only 40 kph as you go through the city.
   a. What is the total distance traveled? **$58\frac{1}{3}$ km**
   b. Graph the rate over time and indicate the total distance on the graph.
   c. Generalize part **a** if you travel at a rate r_1 for a time of length t_1, r_2 for a time of length t_2, and r_3 for a time of length t_3. **b, c) See left.**

3. Estimate $\sum_{i=1}^{11} \frac{1}{2} f\left(\frac{i}{2}\right)$ for the function f on page 786 by first estimating values of the function from its graph. **See margin.**

788

4. A car accelerates from 0 to 88 feet per second in 10 seconds. Assume the acceleration is constant.

a. How far will the car travel in the first second? **4.4 ft**

b. How far will the car travel in the first five seconds? **110 ft**

c. How far will the car travel in the total time of ten seconds? **440 ft**

5. If a car accelerates from 0 to 28 meters per second in 8 seconds under constant acceleration, how far does it travel in those 8 seconds? **112 m**

6. A car accelerates from 0 to 88 feet per second with a speed of $g(x) = -.88(x - 10)^2 + 88\ \frac{\text{ft}}{\text{sec}}$ after x seconds.

a. Will this car or the car of Question 4 travel farther? **this car**

b. Estimate the distance the car travels in the 10 seconds by calculating $\sum_{i=1}^{10} g(i)$. **629.2 ft**

c. Trace the graph of g and draw the rectangles whose areas add to the estimate in part **b**. **See left.**

d. Is the estimate in part **b** better or worse than the estimate found in Example 1? **better**

e. Estimate the distance the car travels in the 10 seconds by calculating $\sum_{i=1}^{20} \frac{1}{2} g\left(\frac{i}{2}\right)$. **608.3 ft**

Applying the Mathematics

7. As a freight train travels eastward through Colorado, an instrument in the locomotive keeps a record of the train's velocity at any time on a paper scroll.

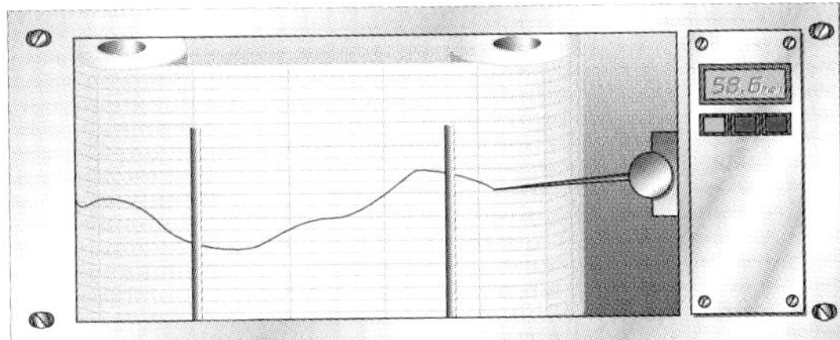

The velocity-time record for the trip is pictured below.

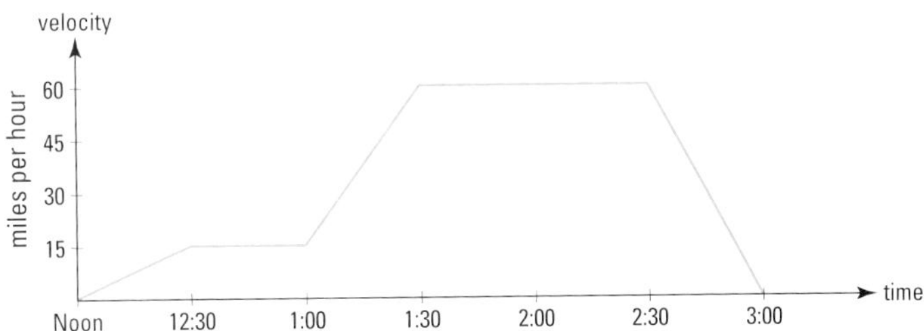

At 3:00, how far east of the starting point is the train? **105 mi**

Notes on Questions

Question 8a As with **Question 6b**, you may wish to write $\sum_{k=1}^{8} 1 \cdot f(k)$, where the constant 1 indicates a time interval of 1 minute.

Question 10 This formula will be used in Lesson 13-5, so it should be discussed here.

Question 14 This question is found in UCSMP *Transition Mathematics* and UCSMP *Algebra*.

Question 15 Discuss this question. Its ideas are important for Lesson 13-2.

8. The graph below shows the velocity of a rocket moving vertically during an eight-minute interval.

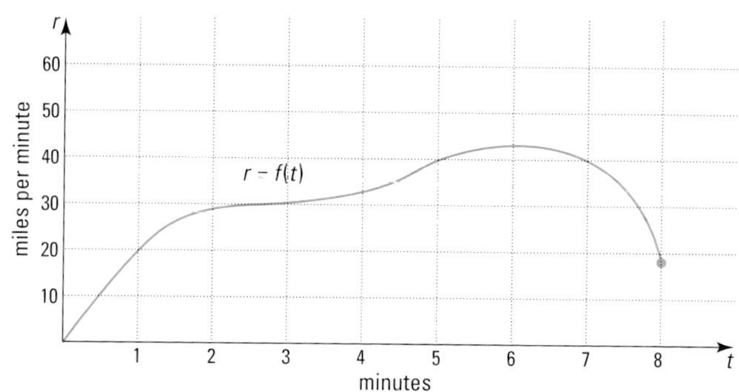

a. Estimate the distance traveled by evaluating $\sum_{k=1}^{8} f(k)$. **≈ 253 mi**

b. Estimate the distance traveled by evaluating $\sum_{k=1}^{4} 2f(2k)$. **≈ 246 mi**

c. Which estimate, the one from part **a** or the one from part **b**, is likely to be more accurate, and why? **the estimate from part a, because it has more rectangles, with a total area that is closer to that of the actual graph**

Review

9. Suppose that on a particular day during a flu epidemic, the probability that any given student has the flu is 20%. What is the probability that in a class of 25 students at least 3 have the flu? *(Lesson 10-6)* **≈ .9**

10. Use the formula $\sum_{i=1}^{n} i^2 = \frac{n(n+1)(2n+1)}{6}$ to find $1^2 + 2^2 + 3^2 + \ldots + 25^2$. *(Lesson 7-2)* **5525**

11. Solve the equation $2 \sin x = \cos x$ over the interval $-2\pi \le x \le 2\pi$. *(Lesson 6-8)* **$x \approx -5.82$ or $x \approx -2.68$ or $x \approx 0.46$ or $x \approx 3.61$**

12. a. Describe the end behavior of the function f, where $f(x) = \frac{2x^2 + 3x - 1}{x - 2}$.

b. Write equations for any horizontal, vertical, or oblique asymptotes. *(Lessons 5-4, 5-5)* **oblique asymptote: $y = 2x + 7$; vertical asymptote: $x = 2$ a) See left.**

13. a. Sketch the graph of a function with horizontal asymptote $y = 2$.

b. Sketch the result of transforming your graph by the scale change $S_{3,4}$.

c. Write an equation for the asymptote to your graph from part **b**.

d. Suppose a function has horizontal asymptote $y = k$. Write an equation of the asymptote when the graph is transformed by $S_{a,b}$. *(Lessons 2-4, 3-8)* **a, b) See left. c) $y = 8$ d) $y = bk$**

14. Explain why 60 miles per hour equals 88 feet per second. *(Previous course)* **See left.**

15. a. Suppose the interval from 3 to 7 is split into 5 equal parts. What are the endpoints of each of those parts? **3.0, 3.8, 4.6, 5.4, 6.2, 7.0**

b. Suppose the interval from 3 to 7 is split into n equal parts. What are the endpoints of the n parts? **$3 + (4k)/n$, where $k = 0, 1, \ldots, n$**

c. Suppose the interval from a to b is split into n equal parts. What is the length of each part? *(Previous course)* **$\frac{b-a}{n}$**

12a) $\lim_{x \to \infty} f(x) = \infty$; $\lim_{x \to -\infty} f(x) = -\infty$

13a, b) Sample:

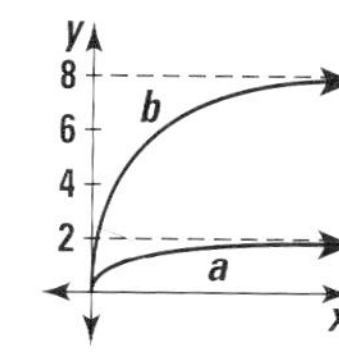

14) $60 \frac{mi}{hr} = 60 \frac{mi}{hr} \cdot 5280 \frac{ft}{mi} \cdot \frac{1}{3600} \frac{hr}{sec} = 88 \frac{ft}{sec}$

Exploration

16. The drawings below suggest two other solutions to Example 1.
   a. Obtain these estimates. **576 ft and 588 ft**
   b. Which do you think is a better estimate, and why? **Answers may vary.**

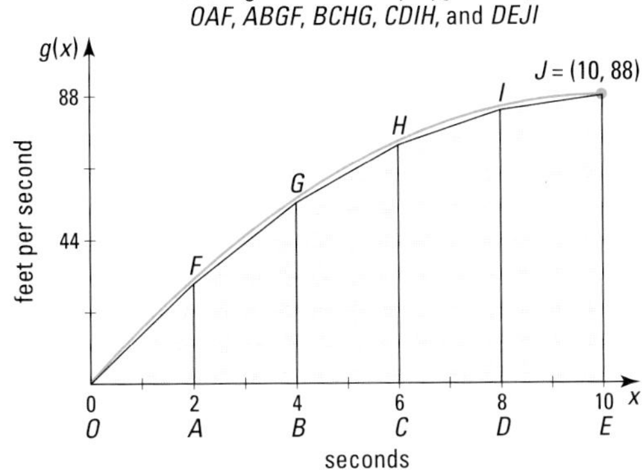

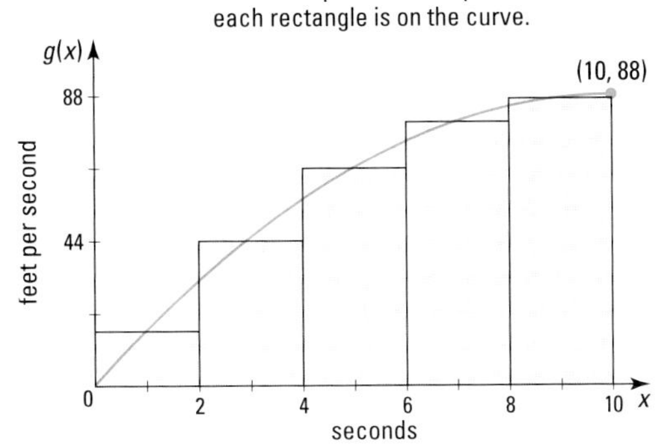

Follow-up for Lesson 13-1

Practice

For more questions on SPUR Objectives, use **Lesson Master 13-1** (shown on page 787).

Assessment

Written Communication Have students **work in groups** and complete **Question 16.** Ask students to devise at least one other estimate for the area under the curve, such as using smaller intervals. Then have the group compare and discuss all of the methods. [Students estimate the distance under a velocity-time graph.]

Extension

Have students suppose that a car accelerates from 0 to 88 ft/sec in 10 seconds according to the rule $h(x) = \frac{44\sqrt{10}}{5}\sqrt{x}$. Ask them to use rectangles of width 1 second to determine whether this car will travel more or less distance than the car in **Example 1.** [Slightly less, at $\approx$ 588.18 feet]

Setting Up Lesson 13-2

Discuss **Question 15,** obtaining the coordinates of each split.

Lesson 13-2

Objectives

A Calculate Riemann sums of functions over specified intervals.
D Find the distance traveled by a moving object, given its rate.

Resources

From the ***Teacher's Resource File***
- Lesson Master 13-2
- Answer Master 13-2
- Teaching Aids
  147 Warm-up
  152 Definition of Riemann Sum
  153 Questions 5, 12, and 16

Additional Resources
- Visuals for Teaching Aids 147, 152, 153
- Exploration 13-2

Warm-up

In 1–3, find the value of the multiple of the series shown.

1. $1(1^2 + 2^2 + \ldots + 10^2)$ **385**
2. $0.5(0.5^2 + 1^2 + 1.5^2 + 2^2 + \ldots + 10^2)$ **358.75**
3. $0.25(0.25^2 + 0.5^2 + 0.75^2 + 1^2 + 1.25^2 + \ldots + 10^2)$ **345.9375**
4. What might be the next sum in this sequence? **Sample: $0.125(0.125^2 + 0.25^2 + 0.375^2 + \ldots + 10^2)$**

LESSON

13-2 *Riemann Sums*

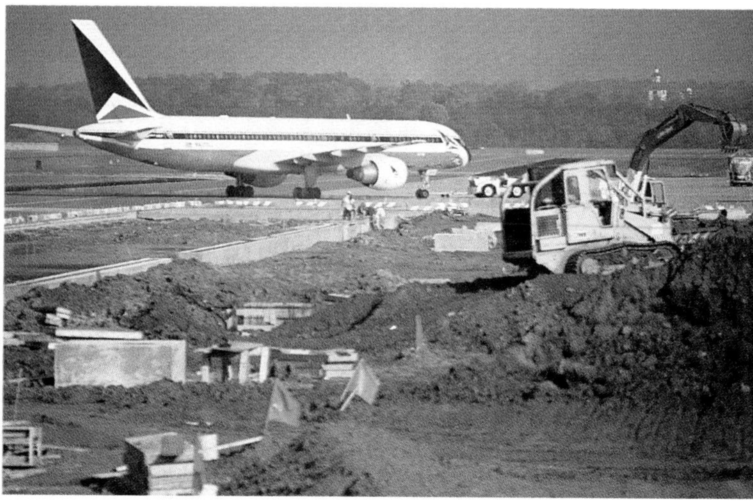

Taking the High Ground. *The amount of dirt to be hauled away can be estimated by using Riemann sums. See Question 16.*

In the last lesson, you saw that the total distance traveled by an object moving with a speed $f(x)$ during a time interval $a \le x \le b$ equals the area of the region between the graph of f and the x-axis over the interval from a to b. If f is a continuous function, then this distance (and this area) can be estimated by adding areas of rectangles. If more and more rectangles are used, the estimate can be made closer and closer to the area of the region.

For instance, consider the function used in Lesson 13-1 to describe a car accelerating from 0 to 88 feet per second in 10 seconds at the particular nonconstant rate such that $g(x) = -.88(x - 10)^2 + 88$.

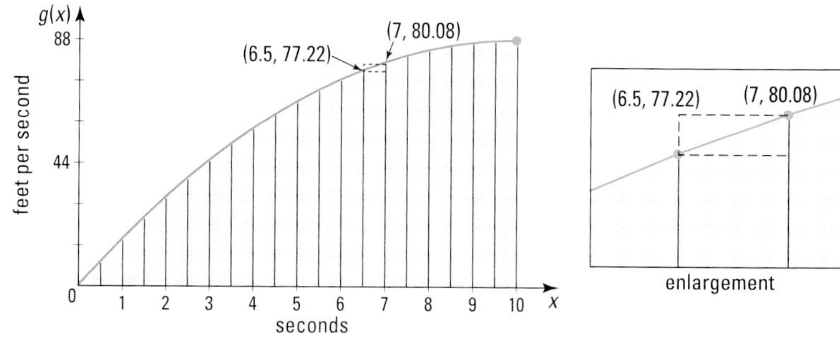

The area of each rectangle is an estimate of the distance traveled in that time interval. For instance, to calculate the distance traveled between 6.5 and 7 seconds, note that the rectangle has width 0.5 seconds. If the height of the graph on the right side of the interval is used, the height of the rectangle is $g(7) = 80.08$ ft/sec. If the height of the graph on the left

Lesson 13-2 Overview

Broad Goals The goal of this lesson is to understand the definition and notation of Riemann sums.

Perspective The lesson again begins with the total distance of a trip if times and speeds for each of a finite number of segments (subintervals) of it are known. If the speed is a function of time, that is, if $r = f(t)$, then the sum $\sum_{i=1}^{n} r_i t_i$ has the form $\sum_{i=1}^{n} f(z_i)(x_i - x_{i-1})$, where x_i and x_{i-1} are the endpoints of the subintervals, and where each z_i is a particular value in the ith subinterval. This is a *Riemann sum.* In this lesson, Riemann sums are defined with subintervals of any lengths, but all applications are done with equal subintervals. If the lengths of the subintervals are a constant Δx, the sum becomes $\sum_{i=1}^{n} f(z_i)\Delta x$. All of this is beginning to look more and more like the definite integral, which is defined in Lesson 13-3, but in this lesson all that is done is to calculate Riemann sums with various choices of the z_i from subintervals. Usually, the z_i are either the left endpoints, the right endpoints, or the midpoints of the intervals.

side of the interval is used, the height is $g(6.5) = 77.22$ ft/sec. Then the distance traveled between 6.5 and 7 seconds is estimated by

$$0.5 \text{ sec} \cdot 80.08 \tfrac{\text{ft}}{\text{sec}} = 40.04 \text{ feet} \quad \text{if } g(7) \text{ is used,}$$

or by

$$0.5 \text{ sec} \cdot 77.22 \tfrac{\text{ft}}{\text{sec}} = 38.61 \text{ feet} \quad \text{if } g(6.5) \text{ is used.}$$

Any other value for the height between $g(6.5)$ and $g(7)$ would give another estimate for the distance traveled.

Activity

Try $g(6.75)$ to see what estimate it gives for the distance traveled between 6.5 and 7 seconds. **See left.**

$g(6.75) = -.88(6.75 - 10)^2 + 88 = -9.295 + 88 = 78.705$. Then the distance is $.5 \text{ sec} \cdot 78.705 \frac{\text{ft}}{\text{sec}} = 39.3525$ ft.

An estimate of the total distance traveled in the 10 seconds is found by adding the areas of the 20 rectangles with width $\frac{1}{2}$. The expression $\sum_{i=1}^{20} \frac{1}{2} g(z_i)$, where the z_i are values in the 20 intervals, is an example of a *Riemann sum*, named in honor of the German mathematician Georg Friedrich Bernhard Riemann (1826–1866). In Question 6**e** of Lesson 13-1, you were asked to find the value of a Riemann sum, using the right endpoints of the intervals as the z_i.

The process described above can be generalized as follows:

> **Definition**
> Let f be a function defined over the interval from a to b. Suppose this interval is partitioned into n subintervals: the first from a to x_1, the second from x_1 to x_2, the third from x_2 to x_3, . . . , the nth from x_{n-1} to b. (The lengths of these intervals are $x_1 - a$, $x_2 - x_1$, $x_3 - x_2$, . . . , $b - x_{n-1}$).
>
> Let $z_1, z_2, z_3, \ldots, z_n$ be numbers in these intervals. Then
>
> $f(z_1)(x_1 - a) + f(z_2)(x_2 - x_1) + f(z_3)(x_3 - x_2) + \ldots + f(z_n)(b - x_{n-1})$
>
> is a **Riemann sum of the function f over the interval from a to b.**

By letting $x_0 = a$ and $x_n = b$, the Riemann sum above can be written as $\sum_{i=1}^{n} f(z_i)(x_i - x_{i-1})$. The points $z_1, z_2, \ldots, z_n$ in the intervals are called the **intermediate points** for the Riemann sum. Thus, the value of a Riemann sum depends not only on the function f and the interval from a to b, but also on the choice of the endpoints $x_0, x_1, \ldots, x_n$ of the subintervals and on the intermediate points $z_1, z_2, \ldots, z_n$ selected from these subintervals.

When you calculated Riemann sums in Lesson 13-1, the widths $x_i - x_{i-1}$ of the intervals were constant. This need not be the case, but it often is, and it eases computation. When the width is constant, it is often written as $\mathbf{\Delta x}$ (read "delta x"), the change in x. The Riemann sum is then

$$\sum_{i=1}^{n} f(z_i)\Delta x.$$

5. How is this sequence related to the reading of Lesson 13-2? **Sample: Suppose we wanted to estimate the area under $y = x^2$ from $x = 0$ to $x = 10$ by Riemann sums. If the lengths of the intervals began at 1 unit and split by half each time, and if right endpoints of each interval were used, these would be the sums.**

Notes on Reading

There is no new problem in this lesson. We show that the total distance can be represented by a Riemann sum, and we visualize the Riemann sum as the sum of the areas of rectangles.

The figure below illustrates such a Riemann sum $\sum_{i=1}^{n} (x_i - x_{i-1})f(z_i)$ with the following characteristics. The ith subinterval has left endpoint x_{i-1} and right endpoint x_i, and $\sum_{i=1}^{6} (x_i - x_{i-1})f(z_i)$ is the sum of the areas of the shaded rectangles. **Teaching Aid 152** is provided so that you can use this drawing in class. In this case, $n = 6$ and $(x_i - x_{i-1})$ is constant.

- z_3 is the midpoint of the 3rd subinterval.
- z_4 is the right endpoint of the 4th subinterval.
- z_6 is the left endpoint of the 6th subinterval.
- z_1, z_2, and z_5 are any values inside the subintervals.

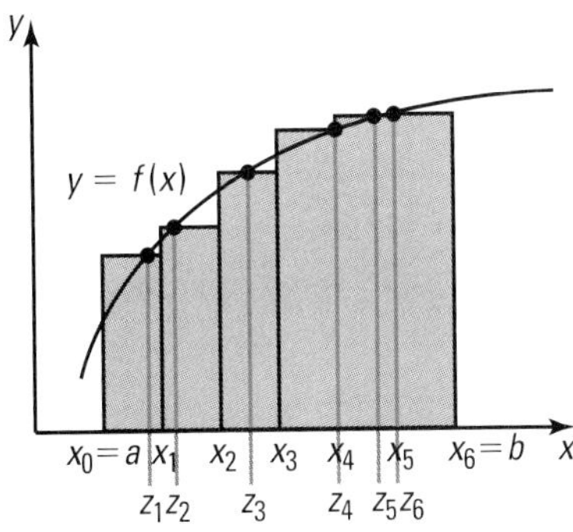

Emphasize that there are many Riemann sums for a given curve over a given closed interval, even if the subintervals are the same, because there are many choices of the z_i. However, if the function is continuous, the limit of those sums as the number of intervals $n \to \infty$ and the lengths of the intervals $\to 0$ is unique.

Optional Activities

Activity 1 Technology Connection
Materials: Explorations software

Students may use *Exploration 13-2: Riemann Sums,* as an alternative to the BASIC computer program in Lesson 13-2. Students can choose a function, an interval in the domain of the function, and a number of rectangular subintervals. The area under the curve will be calculated.

Activity 2 Writing
After completing the lesson, you might ask interested students to find out more about the 19th Century mathematician Georg Riemann and write a report about him.

In the example graphed at the beginning of this lesson, the entire interval from 0 to 10 was partitioned into 20 subintervals, so Δx was $\frac{10}{20} = \frac{1}{2}$. In general, if the interval from a to b is split into n subintervals of equal width then $\Delta x = \frac{b - a}{n}$, and a Riemann sum of g from a to b is

$$\sum_{i=1}^{n} g(z_i) \frac{b - a}{n}.$$

Most calculus software and some automatic graphers have the capability to calculate Riemann sums and to show graphically the rectangles whose areas are being calculated. It is also relatively easy to write programs to calculate Riemann sums. The BASIC computer program below computes Riemann sums for the function $g(x) = -.88(x - 10)^2 + 88$ using the right (upper) endpoints of the subintervals as the z_i.

❶
```
10   DEF FNF(X) = -.88*(X - 10)^2 + 88
20   PRINT "INPUT LEFT ENDPOINT"
30   INPUT A
40   PRINT "INPUT RIGHT ENDPOINT"
50   INPUT B
60   PRINT "INPUT NUMBER OF SUBINTERVALS"
70   INPUT N
80   REM CALCULATE DX, THE WIDTH OF EACH SUBINTERVAL
90   LET DX = (B - A)/N
100  LET SUM = 0
110  LET ZI = A
120  FOR I = 1 TO N
130     LET ZI = ZI + DX
140     LET ITHPRD = FNF(ZI) * DX
150     LET SUM = SUM + ITHPRD
160  NEXT I
170  PRINT "THE SUM IS"; SUM
180  END
```

We ran the above program several times for A = 0 and B = 10, and for increasingly larger values of N, the number of subintervals. Our output appears below.

N	Sum
10	629.2001
20	608.3
50	595.408
100	591.0519
500	587.5457
1000	587.1078
5000	586.753
10,000	586.7047

As N gets larger and larger, the Riemann sum gets closer and closer to the (theoretical) exact distance traveled by the car. It seems to be approaching a number slightly larger than 586. This is a good estimate of the distance traveled. In Lesson 13-5, the distance is calculated exactly.

❶ For the program on this page, the exact value of the limit is $586\frac{2}{3}$.

This program is used in the next lesson. As you discuss at least one of the lessons, give students time to explore tables of Riemann sum values as $n \to \infty$ using the program.

Software such as *Calculus* by TrueBASIC, Inc. and *The Calculus Toolkit* available from Addison-Wesley can be used to approximate areas under curves. Both pieces of software actually draw approximating rectangles and help students to visualize $\sum_{i=1}^{n} f(x_i)\, \Delta x$.

Error Alert Be aware that some calculus software may not be able to handle Riemann sums with as many as 500 intervals. (See Notes on **Questions 6–11.**)

LESSON MASTER 13-2

Questions on SPUR Objectives
See pages 836–839 for objectives.

Skills Objective A

1. Consider the function f with $f(x) = x^3 + 2$ over the interval from 0 to 10. Let z_i be the rightmost endpoint of the ith subinterval. Evaluate $\sum_{i=1}^{5} f(z_i)\Delta x$. **3620**

2. For the function g with $g(x) = 2x^3 - 3$, calculate the Riemann sum over the interval $0 \le x \le 2$ for $\Delta x = 0.25$ when

a. z_i = the left endpoint of the ith subinterval. **0.125**

b. z_i = the right endpoint of the ith subinterval. **4.125**

3. a. Let $h(x) = \frac{1}{2}\sin x$. Evaluate the Riemann sum $\sum_{i=1}^{n} h(z_i)\Delta x$ over the interval from 0 to $\frac{\pi}{2}$ when z_i is the right endpoint of the ith subinterval, the subintervals are of equal width, and n has the given value.

i. $n = 4$ **≈0.592** **ii.** $n = 8$ **≈0.547** **iii.** $n = 16$ **≈0.524**

b. Which value of n provides an answer that is nearest the area under the graph of h? Why?
n = 16; The more subintervals, the better the estimate.

c. To what value might you expect the Riemann sum to converge as n increases? **0.5**

3. Use a computer or programmable calculator to evaluate the Riemann sum for the function f with $f(x) = x^2(\cos 2x - \sin x)$ over the interval from 0 to π when z_i is the right endpoint of the ith subinterval of equal width and n has the given value.

a. $n = 10$ **≈ -2.615** **b.** $n = 50$ **≈ -3.983**
c. $n = 100$ **≈ -4.142** **d.** $n = 500$ **≈ -4.268**

Adapting to Individual Needs

Extra Help
Some students may have difficulty understanding the summation notations used to indicate Riemann sums. It might be helpful to discuss the notation $\sum_{i=1}^{n} f(z_i)\Delta x$ as it applies to **Example 1** in Lesson 13-1.

794

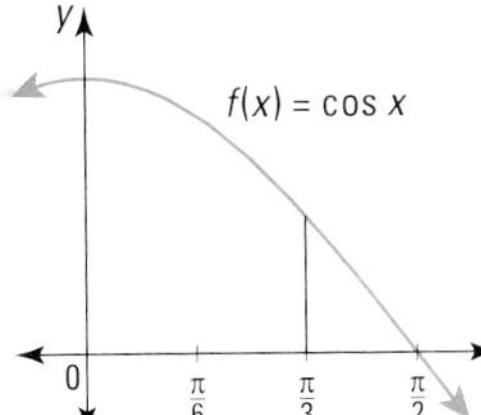

Example

Calculate Riemann sums for the function $f(x) = \cos x$ on the interval from 0 to $\frac{\pi}{3}$, using various numbers of subintervals and choosing z_i to be right endpoints of the subintervals.

Solution

This is tedious without a computer or programmable calculator. We used the program on page 794 with FNF(X) redefined to be COS(X). Here, A = 0 and B = $\frac{\pi}{3} \approx 1.0471976$. We let N = 10, 50, 100, and 500 and obtained the following output, rounded to five decimal places.

N	SUM
10	.83905
50	.86076
100	.86340
500	.86550

That is, the area under the function f(x) = cos x between x = 0 and x = $\frac{\pi}{3}$ is approximately 0.866.

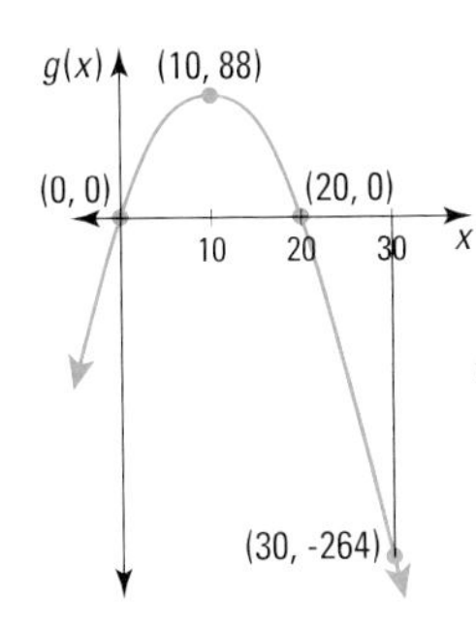

To use z_i = midpoint of ith subinterval, change line 110 in the program on page 794 to LET ZI = A – DX/2. You should try to run the program with this change for both of the functions defined in this lesson.

❷ If a continuous real function has negative values, then the value of the Riemann sum may be negative. For instance, the function $g(x) = -.88(x - 10)^2 + 88$ has negative values for $x > 20$, as shown in the graph at the left. To obtain a Riemann sum for the interval from 20 to 30 let A = 20 and B = 30 in the original program. For N = 10, the sum is -1306.8. This is negative because that part of the parabola lies below the x-axis. Its absolute value, 1306.8, is a good approximation to the area of the shaded region at the left.

If a Riemann sum is calculated for this function on the interval from 10 to 30, then it will have some positive terms and some negative terms. We found, using the program, that the sum is about -657.5313 when N = 50 and -593.7699 when N = 500.

QUESTIONS

Covering the Reading

In 1–3, use the velocity function $g(x) = -.88(x - 10)^2 + 88$ examined in this lesson.

1. Estimate the distance (in feet) traveled between 6.5 and 7 seconds by using one rectangle with a height of $g(6.75)$, as in the lesson's Activity. **39.3525 ft**
2. Give two estimates of the distance traveled between 3 and 3.5 seconds. **Sample: using $g(3)$: 22.44 ft; using $g(3.5)$: 25.41 ft**

❷ This discussion shows that Riemann sums can be negative. Thus, Riemann sums are a tool that can be employed to calculate area, but Riemann sums should not be equated with area. You might think of them as "directed area."

Additional Examples

Calculate the Riemann sum for the function f with $f(x) = x^3$ on the interval from 0 to 10 using the following numbers of subintervals and choosing the z_i as the right endpoints.

1. 10 **3025**
2. 100 **≈ 2550**
3. 500 **2510**
4. 1000 **≈ 2505**

The limit is 2500.

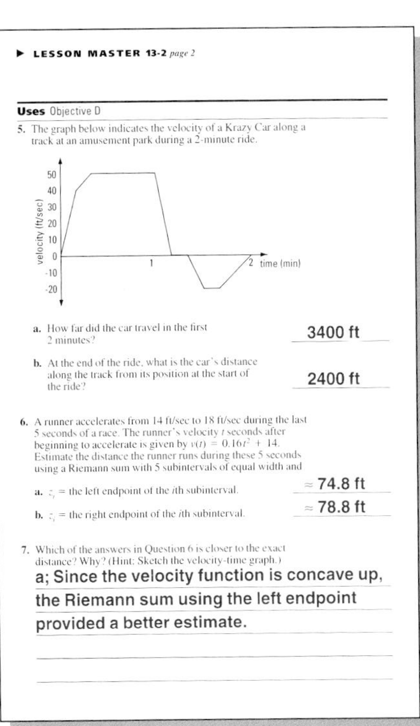

▶ **LESSON MASTER 13-2** *page 2*

Uses Objective D

5. The graph below indicates the velocity of a Krazy Car along a track at an amusement park during a 2-minute ride.

a. How far did the car travel in the first 2 minutes? **3400 ft**

b. At the end of the ride, what is the car's distance along the track from its position at the start of the ride? **2400 ft**

6. A runner accelerates from 14 ft/sec to 18 ft/sec during the last 5 seconds of a race. The runner's velocity t seconds after beginning to accelerate is given by $v(t) = 0.16t^2 + 14$. Estimate the distance the runner runs during these 5 seconds using a Riemann sum with 5 subintervals of equal width and

a. z_i = the left endpoint of the ith subinterval. **≈ 74.8 ft**

b. z_i = the right endpoint of the ith subinterval. **≈ 78.8 ft**

7. Which of the answers in Question 6 is closer to the exact distance? Why? (Hint: Sketch the velocity-time graph.)
a; Since the velocity function is concave up, the Riemann sum using the left endpoint provided a better estimate.

Adapting to Individual Needs

Challenge

Have students find the Riemann sum for the function f in the specified intervals with n partitions of uniform width. Let z_i be the right hand end point of each subinterval. Use summation formulas in this and other lessons to simplify the sums completely.

1. $f(x) = 2x + 1$, on [0, 2]. $[6 + \frac{4}{n}]$
2. $f(x) = x^2$, on [0, 2]. $[\frac{8n^3 + 12n^2 + 4n}{3n^3}]$
3. $f(x) = x^3$, on [0, 2]. $[\frac{4n^4 + 8n^3 + 4n^2}{n^4}]$

Notes on Questions

Question 5 The graph for this question is provided on **Teaching Aid 153.**

Questions 6–11 Encourage students to try both computer programs and available calculus software. The advantage of using calculus software is that most such software shows the rectangles being used in the calculations. However, the calculus software may not allow values of n as large as 500 or 1000, as required in **Questions 8, 10, and 11.**

Questions 12 and 16 The drawings can be found on **Teaching Aid 153.**

Question 16 Science Connection Airport runways must be constructed as level as possible with good drainage. In airports that handle large jet aircraft, runways are up to 14,000 feet long. Because thin air provides less lift at a given speed, runways built for similar aircraft must be longer at higher altitudes than at lower altitudes.

(Notes on Questions continue on page 798.)

3. Find the Riemann sum of g over the interval from 0 to 10, partitioning the interval into 5 subintervals and using the function values at the right endpoints of the subintervals for the heights of the rectangles. **668.8 ft**

4. If an interval with endpoints a and b is split into n subintervals of equal width, what is the width Δx of each subinterval? $\mathbf{\frac{b-a}{n}}$

5. A function h is defined by the graph below. The interval $3 \le x \le 11$ has been divided into 4 subintervals of equal width Δx. A point z_i has been chosen in each subinterval. Evaluate $\sum_{i=1}^{4} h(z_i)\,\Delta x$. **4**

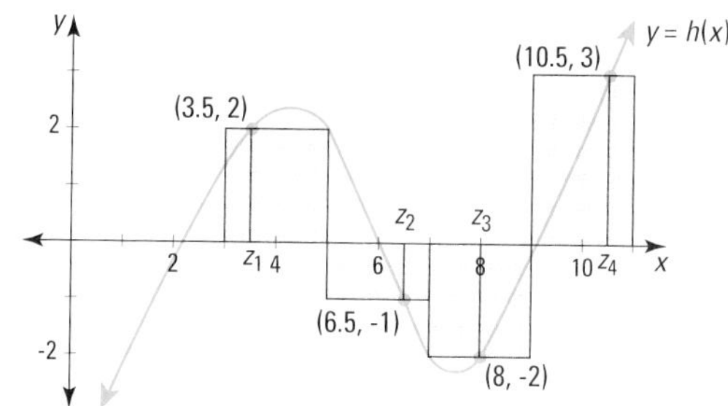

In 6–9, use the program of this lesson or another program that can calculate Riemann sums.

6. Repeat Question 3, using 200 subintervals. **588.8631**

7. a. Find the Riemann sum of $g(x) = -.88(x - 10)^2 + 88$ over the interval from -10 to 5, splitting the interval into 30 subintervals.

b. Why is the answer to part **a** a negative number?

a) -908.0501 (using right endpoints) b) See left.

8. Find the Riemann sum of $f(x) = \cos x$ over the interval from 0 to $\frac{\pi}{3}$, using 1000 equal-width subintervals, and letting z_i be the right endpoint of the ith subinterval. $\approx$ **0.8658**

7b) The region between the graph of g and the x-axis has more area below the x-axis than above.

10)

N	Sum
10	0.89141
50	0.87123
100	0.86864
500	0.86655

11)

N	Sum
10	541.2
20	564.3
50	577.808
100	582.252
500	585.786
1000	586.227

Applying the Mathematics

9. Repeat Question 8, letting z_i be the midpoint of the ith subinterval. $\approx$ **0.8655**

In 10 and 11, renumber line 130 of the computer program to be line 155. Then the function values at the left endpoints of the subintervals will be used for the heights of the rectangles.

10. Refer to the Example. Let z_i = the left endpoint of the ith subinterval. Evaluate $\sum_{i=1}^{n} f(z_i)\,\Delta x$ for n = 10, 50, 100, and 500. **See left.**

11. For the function $g(x) = -.88(x - 10)^2 + 88$ on the interval from 0 to 10, evaluate $\sum_{i=1}^{n} g(z_i)\,\Delta x$ for n = 10, 20, 50, 100, 500, and 1000 if z_i is the left endpoint of the ith subinterval. **See left.**

12. A graph of $y = h(x)$ is given below. Partition the interval from 0 to 10 into 5 subintervals of equal length Δx.

Evaluate $\sum_{i=1}^{5} h(z_i)\,\Delta x$, estimating each $h(z_i)$ to the nearest integer, for each of the following.

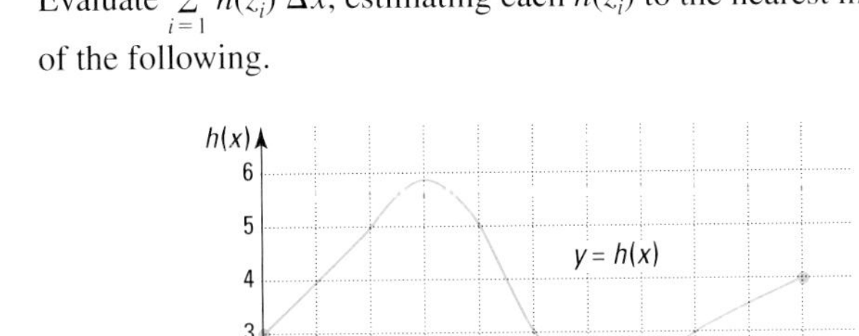
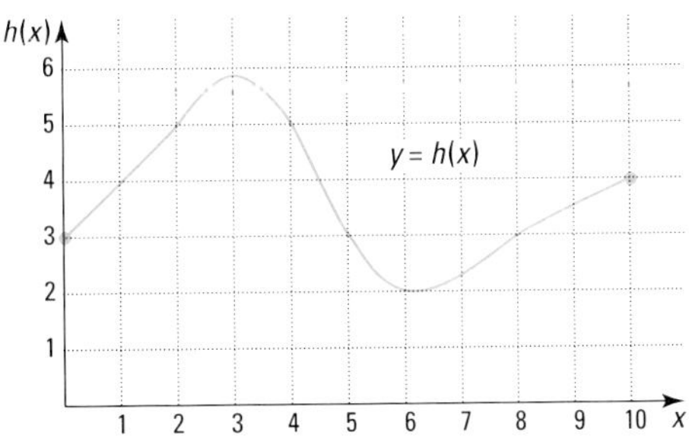

a. z_i = the right endpoint of the ith subinterval $\approx$ **38**
b. z_i = the left endpoint of the ith subinterval $\approx$ **36**
c. z_i = the midpoint of the ith subinterval $\approx$ **37.4**

In 13–15, a function is described. **a**. Sketch the function on the specified interval. **b**. Estimate whether the given Riemann sum will be positive, negative, or zero without actually computing it.

13. $f(x) = -x + 3$ on the interval $0 \le x \le 7$; $\Delta x = 1$; z_i = the midpoint of the ith subinterval; Riemann sum $= \sum_{i=1}^{7} f(z_i)\,\Delta x$ **a) See left. b) negative**

14. $g(x) = -x^2 + 4$ on the interval $0 \le x \le 3$; $\Delta x = 1$; z_i = the right endpoint of the ith subinterval; Riemann sum $= \sum_{i=1}^{3} g(z_i)\,\Delta x$
a) See left. b) negative

15. $h(x) = -x^2 + 4$ on the interval $0 \le x \le 3$; $\Delta x = 1$; z_i = the left endpoint of the ith subinterval; Riemann sum $= \sum_{i=1}^{3} h(z_i)\,\Delta x$
a) See left. b) positive

16. A construction company is building an airport runway and needs to level the ground. The low spots are to be filled in with some of the dirt from the high spots, and the rest of the dirt is to be hauled away. This plan shows a cross section of the region. Estimate the area above the dark line after the low spot below has been filled in. $\approx$ **10,000 ft²**

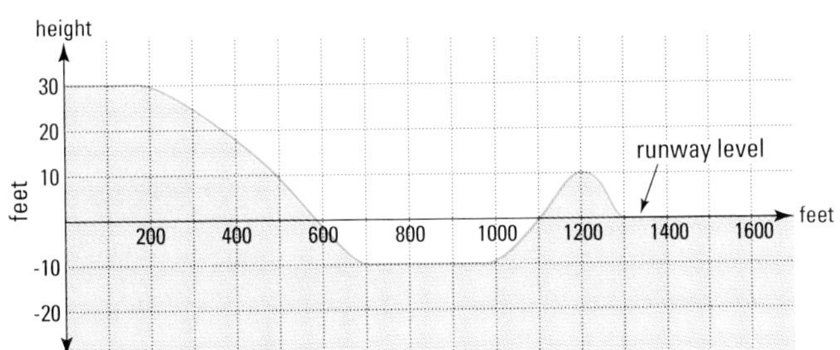

13a)

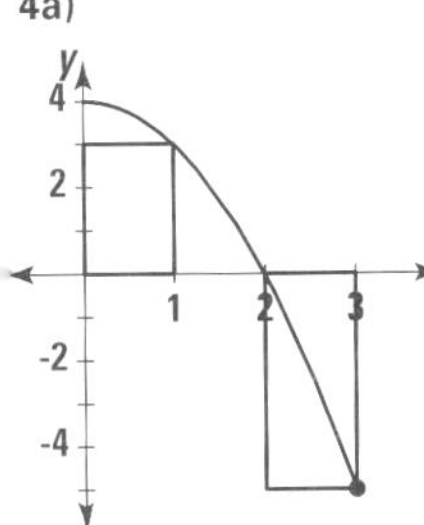

14a)

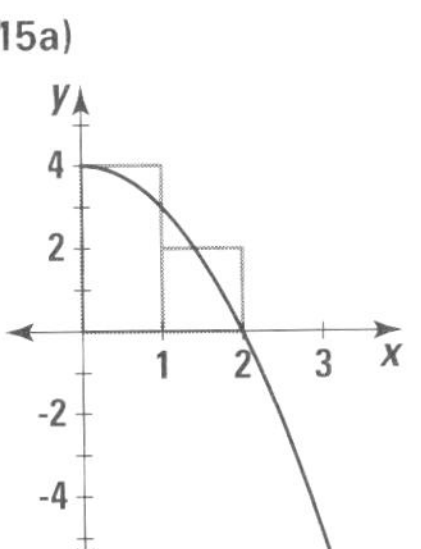

15a)

Follow-up for Lesson 13-2

Practice

For more questions on SPUR Objectives, use **Lesson Master 13-2** (shown on pages 794–795).

Assessment

Written Communication Have students **work in pairs.** Ask the partners to define a function and graph it on the interval $0 \le x \le 10$. Then have the pair adapt the BASIC program on page 794 for the new function and run the program for increasingly larger values of n. [Students calculate Riemann sums.]

Extension

Have students think of a function that has both positive and negative function values. [Sample: $y = \sin x$] Have them determine three different intervals, each including both positive and negative function values, such that the Riemann sum over the interval will be as follows.

1. Negative $\left[\text{From } a = \frac{2\pi}{3} \text{ to } b = \frac{5\pi}{3}\right]$
2. Zero [From $a = 0$ to $b = 2\pi$]
3. Positive $\left[\text{From } a = 0 \text{ to } b = \frac{7\pi}{6}\right]$

Project Update Project 1, *Programming Riemann Sums I,* Project 2, *Programming Riemann Sums II,* and Project 4, *Geographical Areas,* on pages 832–833, relate to the content of this lesson.

Notes on Questions

Questions 23–24 These are important for the next lessons as they allow the calculation of values of certain definite integrals when no formula is available.

Additional Answers

22.

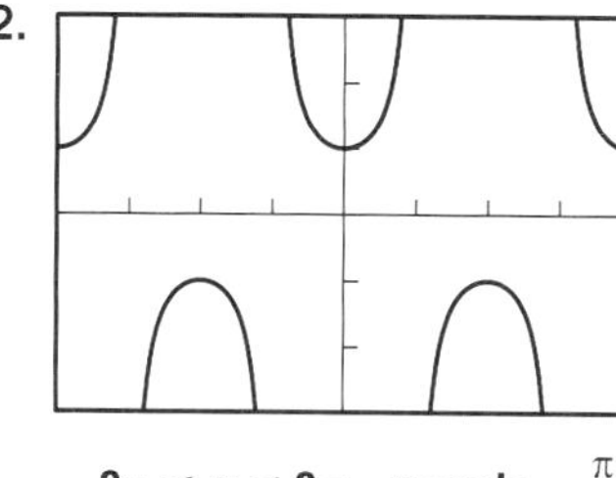

$-2\pi \le x \le 2\pi$, x-scale $= \frac{\pi}{2}$

$-3 \le y \le 3$, y-scale $= 1$

Review

17. The area between a velocity-time curve and the time axis represents what quantity? *(Lesson 13-1)* **distance**

18. A velocity-time graph for a freight train traveling along a straight stretch of track is pictured below. At the end of the trip, how far and in what direction is the train from its starting point? *(Lesson 13-1)* **22.5 miles ahead of where it started**

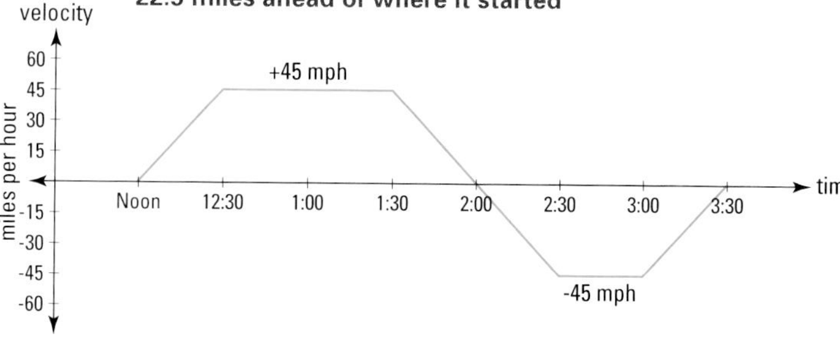

19a) Sample:

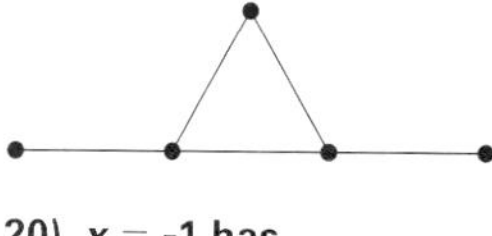

19. a. Draw a picture of a graph with exactly one circuit. **See left.**

b. Identify the length of the circuit. **Answers will vary.**

c. Identify each edge which could be removed while keeping the graph connected. How many such edges are there? *(Lesson 11-4)* **any single edge of the circuit**

20. Find all zeros and the corresponding multiplicities for the polynomial function g with $g(x) = x^4 - 5x^3 + 6x^2 + 4x - 8$. *(Lessons 4-4, 8-8)* **See left.**

20) $x = -1$ has multiplicity 1, and $x = 2$ has multiplicity 3.

21. Use the formula $\sum_{i=1}^{n} i^3 = \left[\frac{n(n+1)}{2}\right]^2$ to find $1^3 + 2^3 + \ldots + 25^3$. *(Lesson 7-2)* **105,625**

22. Use an automatic grapher to conjecture whether

$$(\tan\theta)(\sin\theta + \cot\theta\cos\theta) = \sec\theta$$

is an identity. If it appears to be an identity, prove it. If it is not, give a counterexample. *(Lessons 6-1, 6-2)* **See margin.**

In 23 and 24, find the area of the shaded region. *(Previous course)*

23.

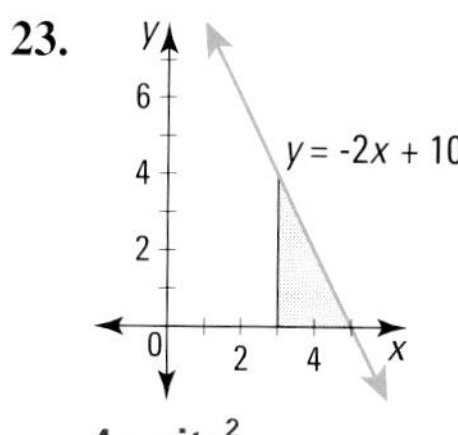

4 units^2

24.

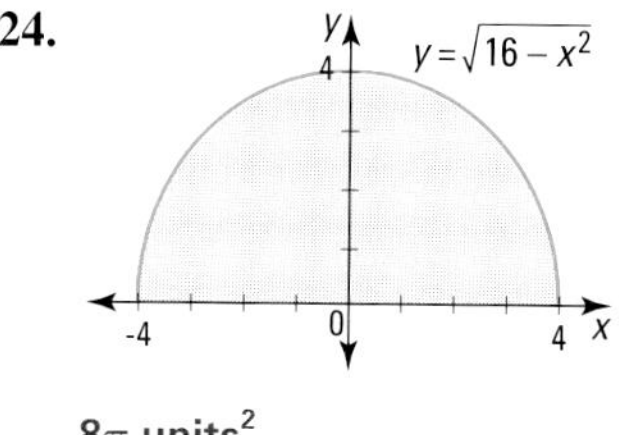

8π units^2

Exploration

25. Again consider the function $g(x) = -.88(x - 10)^2 + 88$, and use the program of this lesson to help you answer the following questions.

a. As $n \to \infty$, what seems to be the limit of Riemann sums of g over the interval from 0 to 30? **0**

b. Justify your answer to part **a**. **See left.**

25) The region between the graph of g and the x-axis has just as much area above the x-axis as below it.

It appears to be an identity.

$(\tan\theta)(\sin\theta + \cot\theta\cos\theta)$	$\sec\theta$	
$\left(\frac{\sin\theta}{\cos\theta}\right)\left(\sin\theta + \frac{\cos\theta}{\sin\theta}\cos\theta\right)$	$= \frac{1}{\cos\theta}$	Definition of tan, cot, and sec
$\left(\frac{\sin\theta}{\cos\theta}\right)\left(\frac{\sin^2\theta}{\sin\theta} + \frac{\cos^2\theta}{\sin\theta}\right)$		Common denominators
$\left(\frac{\sin\theta}{\cos\theta}\right)\left(\frac{1}{\sin\theta}\right)$		Pythagorean Identity
$\frac{1}{\cos\theta}$		Simplifying

$\therefore (\tan\theta)(\sin\theta + \cot\theta\cos\theta) = \sec\theta$

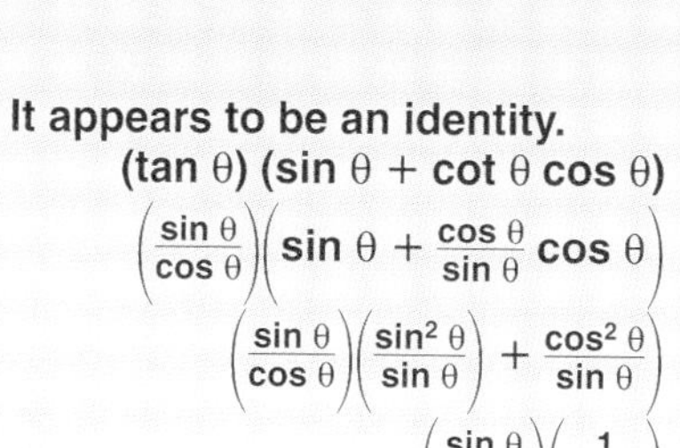

Setting Up Lesson 13-3

Be sure to discuss **Questions 23–24.** Point out that calculation of these areas does not require calculus, but in the next lesson Riemann sums will be used to calculate areas that could not easily be found by other means.

LESSON

13-3

The Definite Integral

In the two previous lessons, you calculated Riemann sums of functions over intervals. The algorithm you used for subintervals of equal length can be described as follows.

Step 1: Identify the function f.
2: Identify a and b, the endpoints of the interval.
3: Identify n, the number of subintervals. Then $\Delta x = \frac{b-a}{n}$.
4: Pick values $z_1, z_2, z_3, \ldots, z_n$ in each subinterval.
5: Calculate the Riemann sum $\sum_{i=1}^{n} f(z_i)\frac{b-a}{n} = \sum_{i=1}^{n} f(z_i)\Delta x$.

When $f(x) \geq 0$ for all x between a and b, the Riemann sum estimates the area between the graph of f and the x-axis. If f is a speed function, the Riemann sum estimates the total distance traveled. (It has other applications you have not yet studied.) When f is a continuous function on $a \leq x \leq b$, it can be proved that f has a largest and a smallest value on each of the subintervals involved in the Riemann sum. If each $f(z_i)$ is the largest value of the function on the subinterval, then the estimate is too high and the sum is called an **upper Riemann sum**. If each $f(z_i)$ is the smallest value on the subinterval, then the estimate is too low and the sum is called a **lower Riemann sum**.

For the increasing sine function $f(x) = \sin x$ on the interval $\left[0, \frac{\pi}{2}\right]$, taking the z_i to be the right endpoints of the subintervals yields an upper Riemann sum. Using the left endpoints yields a lower Riemann sum.

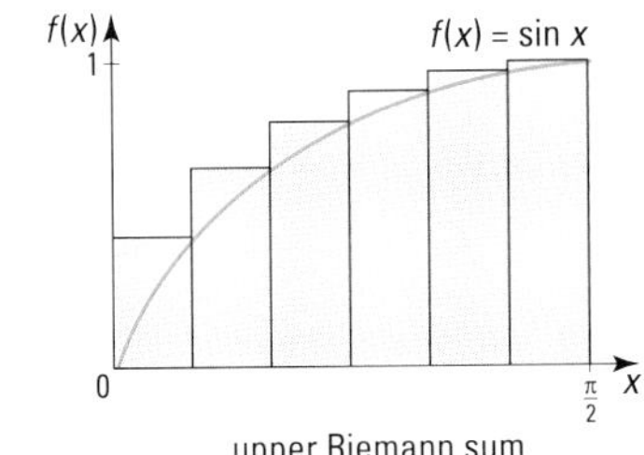

upper Riemann sum

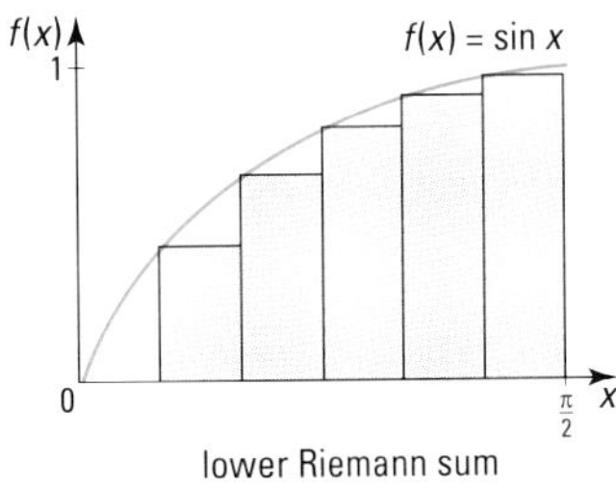

lower Riemann sum

We used the program from Lesson 13-2 to calculate these upper and lower Riemann sums from A = 0 to B = $\frac{\pi}{2}$ for N = 6, 10, 100, and 1000, and obtained the following results rounded to five decimal places.

N	upper Riemann sum	lower Riemann sum
6	1.12518	.86338
10	1.07648	.91940
100	1.00783	.99213
1000	1.00079	.99922

Lesson 13-3

Objectives

B Evaluate definite integrals.
G Express areas in integral notation.

Resources

From the ***Teacher's Resource File***
- Lesson Master 13-3
- Answer Master 13-3
- Teaching Aids
  - 148 Warm-up
  - 154 Upper and Lower Riemann Sums
  - 155 Examples 1–4
- Technology Sourcebook
  Calculator Master 18

Additional Resources
- Visuals for Teaching Aids 148, 154, 155

Teaching Lesson 13-3

Warm-up

On page 799, upper and lower Riemann sums for $f(x) = \sin x$ are pictured. Six intervals are used to calculate each sum, and each interval has length $\frac{\pi}{12}$.

1. Using a calculator, find the values used to calculate the number 1.12518 found for the upper Riemann sum.
   $1.12518 = \frac{\pi}{12}(\sin(\frac{\pi}{12}) + \sin(\frac{2\pi}{12}) + \ldots + \sin(\frac{6\pi}{12})) \approx \frac{\pi}{12}(.2588 + .5 + .7071 + .8660 + .9659 + 1)$
2. Using a calculator, find the values used to calculate the number .86338 found for the lower Riemann sum.
   $.86338 = \frac{\pi}{12}(\sin(\frac{\pi}{12}) + \sin(\frac{2\pi}{12}) + \ldots + \sin(\frac{5\pi}{12})) \approx \frac{\pi}{12}(.2588 + .5 + .7071 + .8660 + .9659)$

Notes on Reading

❶ **Teaching Aid 154,** with the drawings of upper and lower Riemann sums, can be used with this discussion.

Lesson 13-3 Overview

Broad Goals In this lesson, we look at Riemann sums as n approaches infinity and obtain definite integrals.

Perspective The definite integral is the limit of Riemann sums as $n \to \infty$. The definite integral is a number, whereas the indefinite integral, not discussed in this book, is a function. There is an analogy with the derivative at a point (a number) and the derivative of a function (a function).

With the development of the previous two lessons, the definite integral immediately has the following interpretations: it is the area under a curve; it yields the total distance. In this lesson, only the area application is considered.

Some calculus software draws the rectangles for Riemann sums for values of $n \le 300$ and lets the user look at upper sums, lower sums, and the difference between upper and lower sums. Using this or similar software enables students to visualize what happens to Riemann sums as $n \to \infty$. Note that, in the table on page 799, the upper Riemann sums appear to be decreasing toward a limiting value of 1 and that the lower Riemann sums appear to be increasing toward a limiting value of 1 as $n \to \infty$. That is, in this instance,

$$\lim_{n\to\infty} \sum_{i=1}^{n} \sin(z_i)\,\Delta x = \int_0^{\frac{\pi}{2}} \sin(x)\,dx = 1.$$

Point out to students that when they use a computer program to find upper and lower sums, they will first need to determine whether to use left or right endpoints. If a function is increasing on an interval, right endpoints give upper sums and left endpoints give lower sums. However, if a function is decreasing on an interval, the reverse is true.

Teaching Aid 155 has the graphs from **Examples 1–4.**

Ask students if they can discern the purpose for each example. Then discuss the purposes of the examples:

Example 1: to see if integral notation is understood;
Example 2: to point out that the integral of a linear function can be calculated exactly;
Example 3: to point out that the integral of a constant function can be calculated exactly;
Example 4: to point out that some other integrals can be calculated or estimated using area formulas from geometry.

G. F. B. Riemann

Note that as N increases, the upper and lower Riemann sums gets closer and closer to each other. This always happens when f is a continuous function. The choice of the z_i makes less and less of a difference, so that the upper and lower Riemann sums approach the same limit. This limit is called the **definite integral of f from a to b**, written

$$\int_a^b f(x)\,dx$$

and read "the integral of f from a to b." That is, if f is a continuous function, then $\int_a^b f(x)\,dx = \lim_{n\to\infty} \sum_{i=1}^{n} f(z_i)\,\Delta x$ for any choice of z_i in the subintervals.

The symbol "$\int$" is the integral sign. It is an elongated "s", which should remind you that the definite integral is a limit of sums. The a and b at the bottom and top of this symbol signify the endpoints of the interval. The symbol "dx" indicates that the independent variable is x.

While a Riemann sum, $\sum_{i=1}^{n} f(z_i)\,\Delta x$, usually approximates a quantity such as distance or area, the corresponding definite integral, $\int_a^b f(x)\,dx$, gives the *exact* value of this quantity.

Example 1

Express the area of the shaded region below with integral notation.

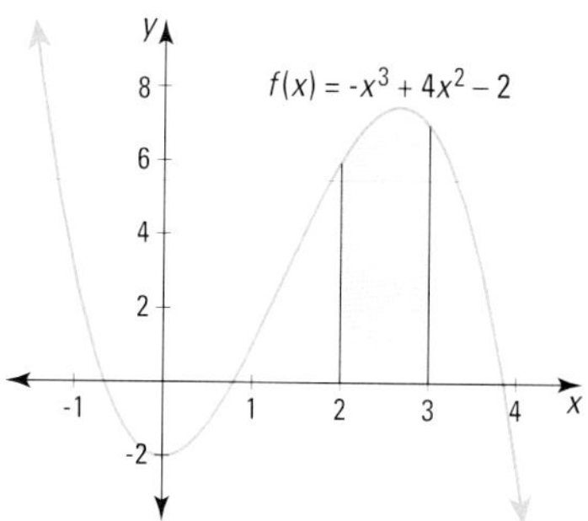

Solution

The shaded area is the limit of Riemann sums of the form $\sum_{i=1}^{n} (-z_i^3 + 4z_i^2 - 2)\,\Delta x$, from $x = 2$ to $x = 3$. This is written

$$\int_2^3 (-x^3 + 4x^2 - 2)dx.$$

If f is a constant or linear function, the exact value of $\int_a^b f(x)dx$ can be found using familiar area formulas.

Optional Activities

Activity 1 Technology Connection
In *Technology Sourcebook, Calculator Master 18,* students use a programmable calculator to determine upper and lower Riemann sums. Then they investigate the relationship between the number of subintervals of the Riemann sums and the error bound.

Activity 2 You might have students estimate the value of the definite integral in **Questions 4–6.** They should explain their method, noting the width of their subintervals and values for z_i in **Questions 4–5.**
[4. ≈ 6.6, using $\Delta x = 1$ and z_i = right endpoints (actual value is closer to 6.1)
5. ≈ 28, using $\Delta x = 1$ and z_i = right endpoints (actual value is 18);
6. $= 9$]

Activity 3 You might refer students to **Question 7** and have them do the following.
1. Find the exact value of the definite integral evaluated from -3 to 4. [24.5]
2. Explain why their result is smaller than the answer to **Question 7.** [The value is smaller because the area below the x-axis is considered negative.]

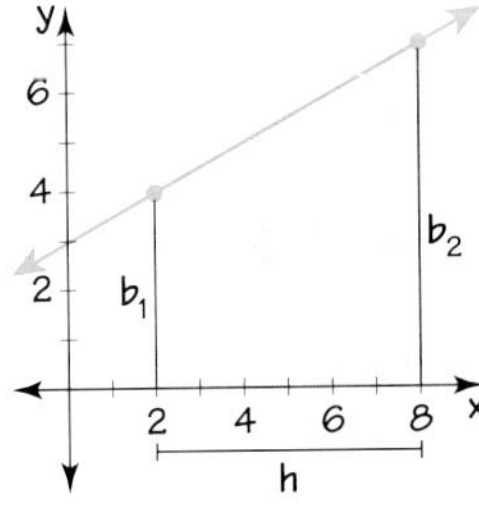

Example 2

Find the exact value of $\int_2^8 \left(\frac{1}{2}x + 3\right) dx$.

Solution

Sketch $y = \frac{1}{2}x + 3$ on the interval from $x = 2$ to $x = 8$. $\int_2^8 \left(\frac{1}{2}x + 3\right) dx$ = area under $y = \frac{1}{2}x + 3$ on this interval. The shaded region is a trapezoid with area

$$\frac{1}{2}(b_1 + b_2) \cdot h = \frac{1}{2}(f(2) + f(8)) \cdot 6$$
$$= \frac{1}{2}(4 + 7) \cdot 6 = 33.$$

Since a Riemann sum is negative when the function values are all negative, so is the value of the corresponding definite integral. As Example 3 illustrates, the definite integral represents the opposite of the area of the region if that region is below the x-axis.

Example 3

Find the exact value of $\int_{-2}^{3} -4\, dx$.

Solution

Graph $y = -4$ on the interval from $x = -2$ to $x = 3$. The region between the graph and the x-axis is a 5-by-4 rectangle with area 20. Since the region between $y = -4$ and the x-axis is below the x-axis, the value of the definite integral is negative.

$$\int_{-2}^{3} -4\, dx = 5 \cdot (-4) = -20$$

The formula for the area of a circle can help us find values of definite integrals of some other functions.

Example 4

Estimate $\int_2^3 \sqrt{9 - x^2}\, dx$.

Solution

The graph of $f(x) = \sqrt{9 - x^2}$ is a semicircle with radius 3. The given integral represents the area of the region bounded by the semicircle, the x-axis and the lines $x = 2$ and $x = 3$. Call the region ABC. (It is shaded at the right.) Then $m\angle AOB = \tan^{-1}\frac{\sqrt{5}}{2}$, and so $m\angle AOB \approx 48.2°$.

Thus the area of sector AOB is about $\frac{48.2}{360}$ of the area of the circle, or $\frac{48.2}{360} \cdot 9\pi$. The area of $\triangle OBC$ is $\frac{1}{2} \cdot 2 \cdot \sqrt{5} = \sqrt{5}$. Thus $\int_2^3 \sqrt{9 - x^2}\, dx \approx \frac{48.2}{360} \cdot 9\pi - \sqrt{5} \approx 1.55$.

If you discuss the program from Lesson 13-2 along with this lesson, give students time to work with both upper and lower Riemann sums so they can see the convergence of the sums to the same limit.

Error Alert Be sure students understand that the definite integral of a fraction from a to b could be negative if, for the given interval, more of the region between its graph and the x-axis is below the x-axis than above it. On the other hand, the sign of the integral is not affected by negative values of x because Δx is always positive.

Additional Examples

1. Express the area between the graph of $y = 16x - x^2$ and the x-axis with integral notation. $\int_0^{16} (16x - x^2)\, dx$
2. Find the exact value of $\int_4^{11} (3x + 1)\, dx$. **164.5**
3. Find the exact value of $\int_{-5}^{5} 7\, dx$. **70**
4. Estimate $\int_3^5 \sqrt{25 - x^2}$. $\approx$ **5.59**

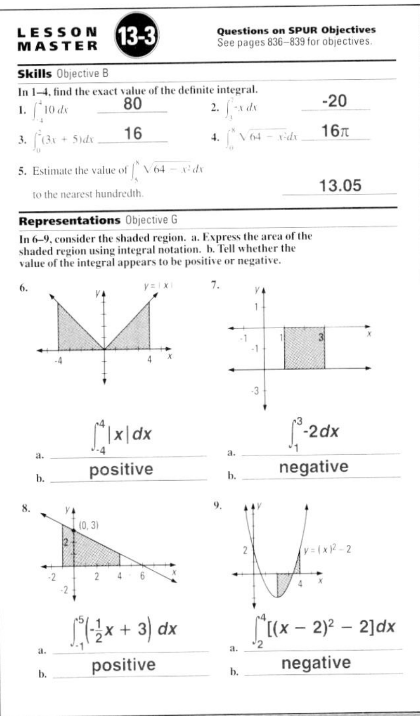
LESSON MASTER 13-3

Questions on SPUR Objectives
See pages 836–839 for objectives.

Skills Objective B

In 1–4, find the exact value of the definite integral.

1. $\int_{-4}^{4} 10\, dx$ 80
2. $\int_3^7 -x\, dx$ -20
3. $\int_0^2 (3x + 5)dx$ 16
4. $\int_0^8 \sqrt{64 - x^2}dx$ 16π
5. Estimate the value of $\int_5^8 \sqrt{64 - x^2}\, dx$ to the nearest hundredth. 13.05

Representations Objective G

In 6–9, consider the shaded region. a. Express the area of the shaded region using integral notation. b. Tell whether the value of the integral appears to be positive or negative.

6. a. $\int_{-4}^{4} |x|\, dx$ b. positive
7. a. $\int_1^3 -2dx$ b. negative
8. a. $\int_{-1}^{5} \left(-\frac{1}{2}x + 3\right) dx$ b. positive
9. a. $\int_2^4 [(x - 2)^2 - 2]dx$ b. negative

3. Find the values of $\int_1^4 |3x + 2|\, dx$ and $\int_{-3}^{4} |3x + 2|\, dx$. [There is no change in the value of the definite integral from 1 to 4; the value from -3 to 4 is $40\frac{5}{6}$.]

Adapting to Individual Needs

Extra Help

Some students may be troubled by the fact that the diagram for the lower Riemann sum on page 799 shows one less rectangle than the diagram for the upper Riemann sum. Explain that for both diagrams, $n = 6$. For the lower sum, however, the first rectangle "disappears" (its area is zero) because $f(z_1) = 0$. This will not happen for intervals in which $f(z_i) \neq 0$ for all i.

Notes on Questions

Questions 1–2 This parabola is the subject of Lesson 13-5, so these questions should be discussed in preparation for that lesson.

Questions 14–15 These formulas are used in later lessons, so should be discussed.

(Notes on Questions continue on page 804.)

QUESTIONS

Covering the Reading

In 1 and 2, use the parabola $y = x^2$ graphed below. Consider Riemann sums on the interval from 0 to 1.

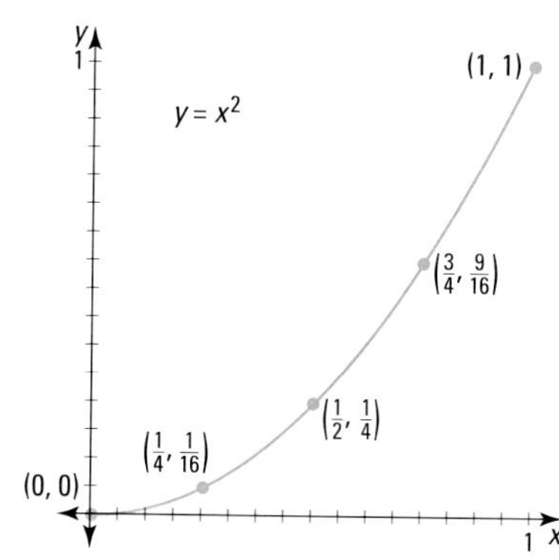

1. Give the values of the upper and lower Riemann sums with 4 equal-width subintervals. **upper sum: $\frac{15}{32}$; lower sum: $\frac{7}{32}$**
2. Use a program to find the upper and lower Riemann sums with the given number of subintervals.
   a. 100 **lower sum: 0.328350; upper sum: 0.338350**
   b. 1000 **lower sum: 0.332829; upper sum: 0.333828**
3. a. For continuous functions f, __?__ and __?__ Riemann sums on an interval $a \le x \le b$ always approach the same limit. **upper, lower**
   b. What is that limit called? **the definite integral of *f* from *a* to *b***

In 4–6, express the area of the shaded region as a definite integral. You do not have to find the value of the integral.

4. 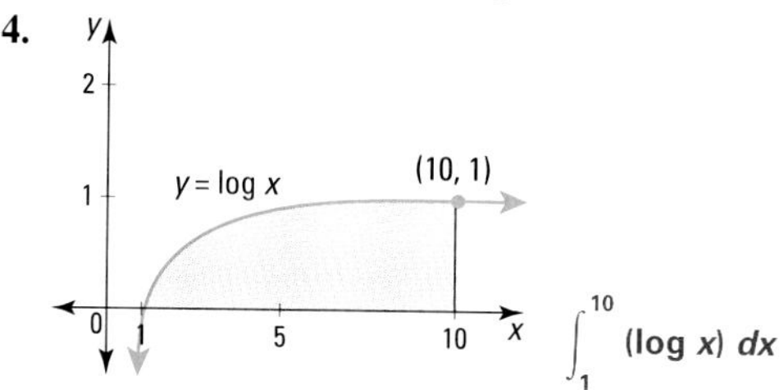

$\int_1^{10} (\log x)\, dx$

5. 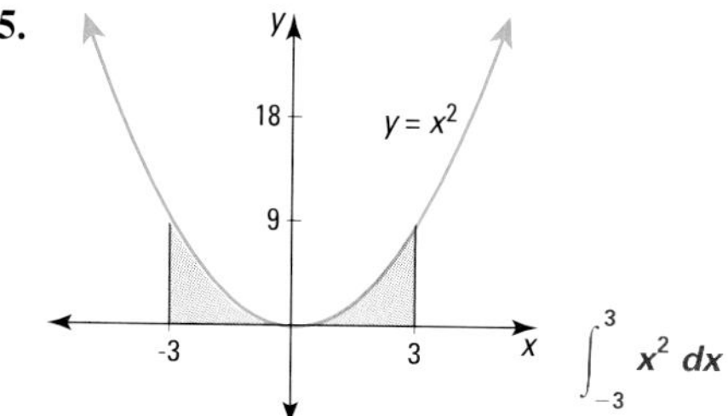

$\int_{-3}^{3} x^2\, dx$

Adapting to Individual Needs

Challenge

Have students evaluate these integrals.

1. Use the results of the Challenge on page 795 to evaluate the following.
   a. $\int_0^2 (2x + 1)\, dx$ [6]
   b. $\int_0^2 x^2\, dx$ $\left[\frac{8}{3}\right]$
   c. $\int_0^2 x^3\, dx$ [4]
2. Use graphs and area formulas to evaluate the following.
   a. $\int_{-\frac{\pi}{4}}^{\frac{\pi}{4}} \tan x\, dx$ [0]
   b. $\int_0^5 \sqrt{25 - x^2}\, dx)$ $\left[\frac{25\pi}{4}\right]$
   c. $\int_{-3}^{3} 2\sqrt{1 - \frac{x^2}{9}}\, dx$ $[3\pi]$

6.

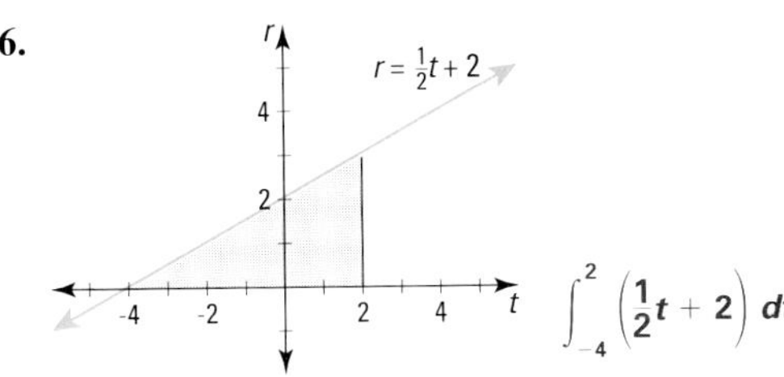

$\int_{-4}^{2} \left(\frac{1}{2}t + 2\right) dt$

In 7–9, find the exact value of the definite integral.

7. $\int_{1}^{4} (3x + 2)\, dx$ **28.5**

8. $\int_{-100}^{100} 3\, dx$ **600**

9. $\int_{-3}^{3} \left(-\sqrt{9 - x^2}\right) dx$ **-4.5π**

10. Estimate $\int_{1}^{5} \sqrt{25 - x^2}\, dx$. **14.67**

11a)

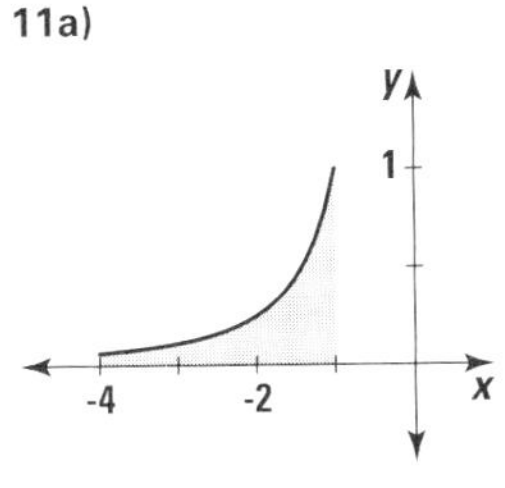

12a)

13a)

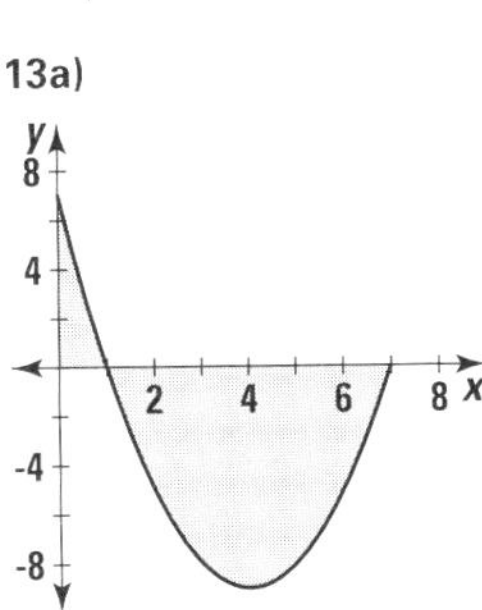

Applying the Mathematics

In 11–13, a definite integral of a function is given. **a**. Sketch the graph of the function over the indicated interval. **b**. Does the value of the integral appear to be positive or negative?

11. $\int_{-4}^{-1} \frac{1}{x^2}\, dx$ **a) See left. b) positive**

12. $\int_{2}^{4} (x^2 - 8x + 7)\, dx$ **a) See left. b) negative**

13. $\int_{0}^{7} (x^2 - 8x + 7)\, dx$ **a) See left. b) negative**

14. Find a formula for $\int_{0}^{a} mx\, dx$, where a and m are positive real numbers. $\mathbf{\frac{ma^2}{2}}$

15. Find a formula for $\int_{a}^{b} c\, dx$, where a, b, and c are positive and $a < b$. **$c(b - a)$**

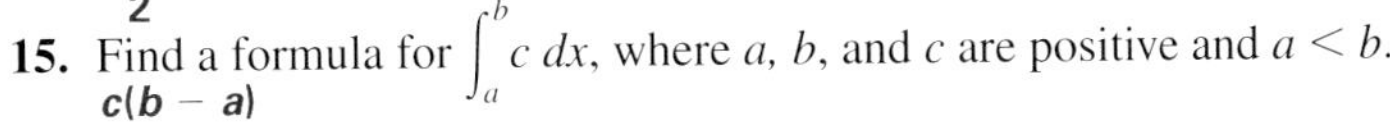

Follow-up for Lesson 13-3

Practice

For more questions on SPUR Objectives, use **Lesson Master 13-3** (shown on page 801).

Assessment

Written Communication Use integral notation to denote a definite integral as in **Questions 11–13.** Have students sketch the function and shade the region that corresponds to the integral. [Students relate integral notation to areas.]

Extension

Have students examine the definite integral from -*a* to *a* for odd functions and even functions. Ask them to make conjectures, supported by verbal or written arguments, for what they observe. [For odd functions, the definite integral from -*a* to *a* equals zero; since odd functions are symmetric about the origin, the two values of the definite integral (from -*a* to 0 and from 0 to *a*) above and below the *x*-axis will be equal and opposite in sign. For even functions, the definite integral from -*a* to *a* equals twice the definite integral from 0 to *a*; since even functions are symmetric about the *y*-axis, the two values of the definite integral (from -*a* to 0 and from 0 to *a*) both either above or both below the *x*-axis will be equal with the same sign.]

Project Update Project 2, *Programming Riemann Sums II,* on page 832, relates to the content of this lesson.

Notes on Questions

Question 20 This formula is used in Lesson 13-5 to obtain a formula for $\int_0^a x^2\,dx$).

Question 22 You might wish to discuss the following generalization of **Question 14** for the special case $m = 1$. $\int_a^b x\,dx = \frac{b^2}{2} - \frac{a^2}{2}$

Make certain that students realize that a and/or b could be negative.

For **Question 15,** a generalization is: $\int_a^b c\,dx = c(b - a)$.

Review

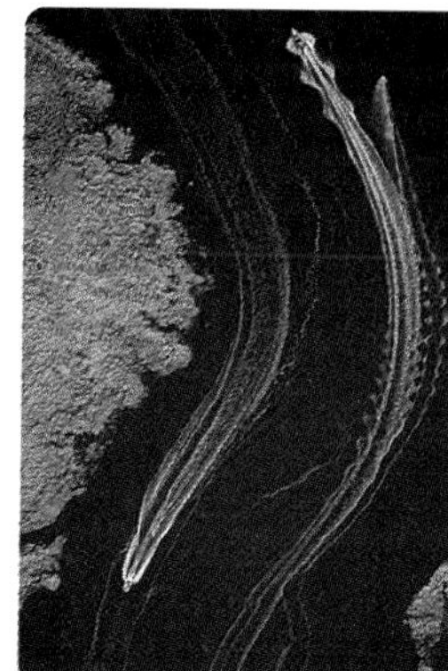

16. The graph shows the velocity of a boat traveling on a river over a five-hour interval.

a. Use a Riemann sum with 5 subintervals and the grid to find the approximate distance covered. Let z_i = the right endpoint of the ith subinterval. **≈ 156 miles**

b. What does the area between the graph of $r = f(t)$ and the t-axis represent? *(Lessons 13-1, 13-2)*

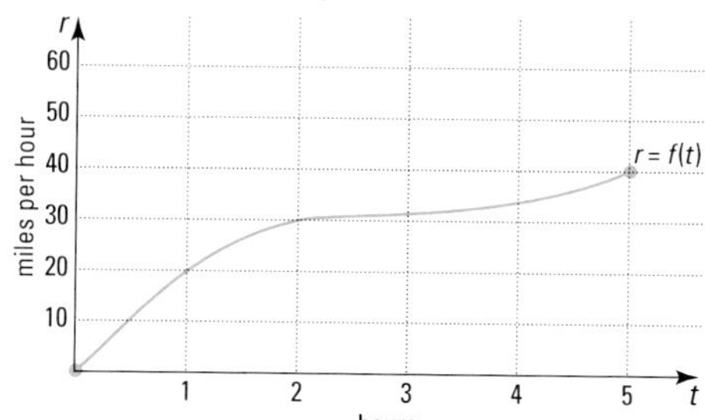

the distance from starting to ending point for the 5-hour period

17. A machine offers 6 kinds of snacks. In how many different ways can 4 snacks be selected under the given condition?

a. They must all be different kinds. **15**

b. More than one of the same kind can be chosen. *(Lessons 10-4, 10-7)* **126**

18. If a bank pays 6% interest, compounded continuously, then the amount A in an account t years after P dollars have been deposited is

$$A = Pe^{.06t}.$$

Find the average rate of change of the amount in the account from $t = 5$ years to $t = 10$ years if the indicated amount is deposited.

a. \$100 **\$9.45/yr** **b.** \$200 **\$18.89/yr** **c.** \$P *(Lesson 9-1)* **≈ .09445*P*/yr**

19)

19. Sketch the graph of the polar equation $r \sin \theta = 2$ and identify the figure you get. *(Lesson 8-4)* **See left. The graph is a line.**

20. Given that $\sum_{i=1}^{n} i^2 = \frac{n(n+1)(2n+1)}{6}$, find $100^2 + 101^2 + 102^2 + \ldots + 200^2$. *(Lesson 7-2)* **2,358,350**

21. A machine makes nails of length $1\frac{1}{2}$ inches. If the relative error can be no more than .5%, what nail lengths are acceptable? *(Lesson 3-9)* **$1.4925 \le \ell \le 1.5075$**

Exploration

22. In Questions 14 and 15, you used ideas of area to deduce a particular property of definite integrals. Based on your knowledge of graphs and transformations, conjecture one or more properties of definite integrals. Then use an area argument to explain why the property is true.

Sample: $k\int_0^a f(x)\,dx = \int_0^{a/k} f(x)\,dx$.

Under a vertical scale change of magnitude *k*, the area is multiplied by *k*.

Setting Up Lesson 13-4

For the next two lessons, it is critical that **Questions 4–10** on pages 802-803 be understood. You also should discuss **Questions 14–15** on page 803 so that students are familiar with a general property of integrals before they encounter Lesson 13-4.

LESSON

13-4

Properties of Definite Integrals

Irrigation Integration. *Definite integrals can be used to answer questions concerning varying rates of flowing water. See Examples 2 and 3.*

Because definite integrals can be interpreted as areas, properties of area can be used to deduce properties of these integrals. Four properties of definite integrals are developed in this lesson. The first two involve combining definite integrals of the same function over different intervals.

The sum of the areas under a curve over the adjacent intervals $[a, b]$ and $[b, c]$ equals the area under the curve over the union of the intervals $[a, c]$. If the curve is the graph of a continuous function f, then the following theorem, stated in the notation of definite integrals, holds.

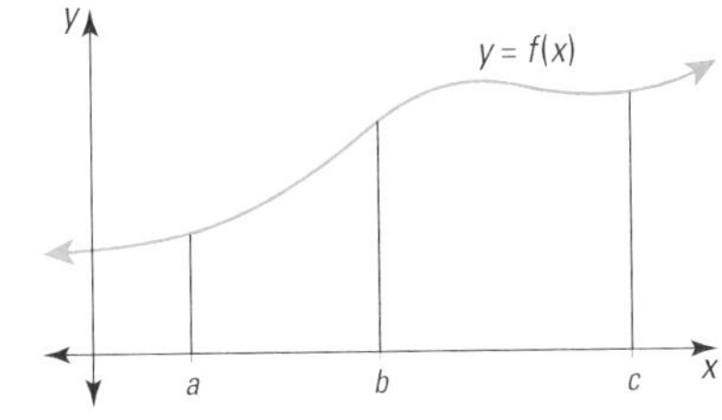

Theorem
If f is a continuous function on the interval $[a, c]$, and $a < b < c$, then
$\int_a^b f(x)\,dx + \int_b^c f(x)\,dx = \int_a^c f(x)\,dx.$

From this first theorem, a second theorem can be deduced. Substitute 0 for a, a for b, and b for c in the equation.

$$\int_0^a f(x)\,dx + \int_a^b f(x)\,dx = \int_0^b f(x)\,dx$$

Now subtract the left integral from both sides.

Lesson 13-4

Objectives
B Evaluate definite integrals.
C Apply properties of definite integrals.
E Use the definite integral to solve application problems.
H Find areas bounded by curves.

Resources
From the ***Teacher's Resource File***
- Lesson Master 13-4
- Answer Master 13-4
- Assessment Sourcebook: Quiz for Lessons 13-1 through 13-4
- Teaching Aids
  148 Warm-up
  156 Questions 12 and 14

Additional Resources
- Visuals for Teaching Aids 148, 156

Teaching Lesson 13-4

Warm-up
Consider the finite sequences $a_1, a_2, a_3, \ldots, a_{10}$ and $b_1, b_2, b_3, \ldots, b_{10}$.
Suppose the sum of all terms of the first sequence is S and the sum of all terms of the second sequence is T.
1. What is the sum of the sequence c, if for all i, $c_i = a_i + b_i$? $\mathbf{S + T}$
2. Write the results of Question 1 using Σ-notation.
$\sum_{i=1}^{10} c_i = \sum_{i=1}^{10} (a_i + b_i) = \sum_{i=1}^{10} a_i + \sum_{i=1}^{10} b_i$

(Warm-up continues on page 806.)

Lesson 13-4 Overview

Broad Goals This lesson shows four properties of definite integrals that follow rather immediately from the area interpretation of Riemann integrals. The goal of this lesson is for students to become familiar with the notation of definite integrals by using that notation in a variety of ways.

Perspective The area interpretation of integrals enables various properties of integrals to be deduced. In this lesson, there are four theorems relating integrals to each other.
1. The sum of the integrals of a function from a to b and from b to c equals the integral from a to c. This property enables an integral to be broken down into subintervals or built up from those subintervals.
2. The integral of a function from a to b equals the integral from 0 to b less the integral from 0 to a. Thus a general formula can be derived for an integral if a formula can be found for the special case over the interval from 0 to a.
3. The integral of the sum of two functions is the sum of the integrals of the functions; and
4. The integral of a constant multiple of a function is that constant multiple of the integral.

The last two of these properties are applied in the next lesson to obtain the definite integral of any quadratic function.

3. What is the sum of the sequence d, if for all i, $d_i = 5a_i - b_i$? $5S - T$

4. Write the results of Question 3 using Σ-notation.
$$\sum_{i=1}^{10} d_i = \sum_{i=1}^{10} (5a_i - b_i) =$$
$$\sum_{i=1}^{10} 5a_i - \sum_{i=1}^{10} b_i = 5\sum_{i=1}^{10} a_i - \sum_{i=1}^{10} b_i$$

Notes on Reading

The theorems on pages 805–806 have simple area interpretations, so one measure of student understanding of integral notation is their ability to give those interpretations. The interpretation of the first theorem precedes it; the interpretation of the second follows it.

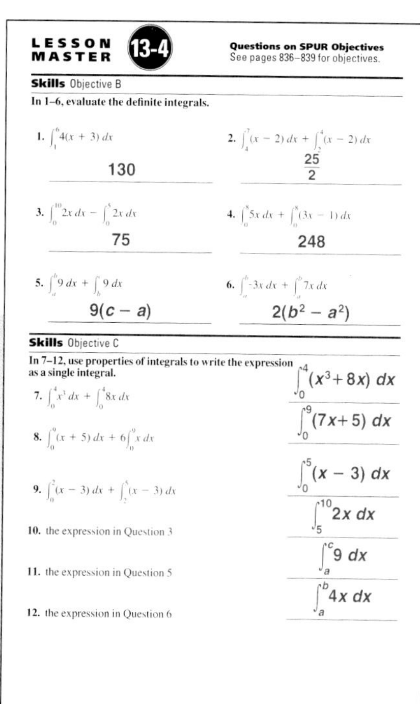
LESSON MASTER 13-4 Questions on SPUR Objectives
See pages 836–839 for objectives.

Skills Objective B

In 1–6, evaluate the definite integrals.

1. $\int_1^6 4(x+3)\,dx$ — 130
2. $\int_4^7 (x-2)\,dx + \int_2^4 (x-2)\,dx$ — $\frac{25}{2}$
3. $\int_0^{10} 2x\,dx - \int_0^5 2x\,dx$ — 75
4. $\int_0^8 5x\,dx + \int_0^8 (3x-1)\,dx$ — 248
5. $\int_a^b 9\,dx + \int_b^c 9\,dx$ — $9(c-a)$
6. $\int_a^b -3x\,dx + \int_a^b 7x\,dx$ — $2(b^2-a^2)$

Skills Objective C

In 7–12, use properties of integrals to write the expression as a single integral.

7. $\int_0^4 x^3\,dx + \int_0^4 8x\,dx$ — $\int_0^4 (x^3+8x)\,dx$
8. $\int_0^9 (x+5)\,dx + 6\int_0^9 x\,dx$ — $\int_0^9 (7x+5)\,dx$
9. $\int_0^2 (x-3)\,dx + \int_2^5 (x-3)\,dx$ — $\int_0^5 (x-3)\,dx$
10. the expression in Question 3 — $\int_5^{10} 2x\,dx$
11. the expression in Question 5 — $\int_a^c 9\,dx$
12. the expression in Question 6 — $\int_a^b 4x\,dx$

Theorem
If f is a continuous function on the interval $0 \le x \le b$, and $0 < a < b$, then
$$\int_a^b f(x)\,dx = \int_0^b f(x)\,dx - \int_0^a f(x)\,dx.$$

The area interpretation of this theorem is as follows: If the area under the curve over the interval $[0, a]$ is subtracted from the area over the interval $[0, b]$, then the result is the area under the curve over the interval from $[a, b]$. The importance of this theorem is that if a formula is known for the area between the graph of a curve and the x-axis over the interval $[0, b]$ for any b, then the formula can be utilized to find the area over any interval in the positive part of the x-axis.

Example 1

Verify the theorem above in the case that $a = 2$, $b = 7$, and $f(x) = 3x + 6$.

Solution

Sketch the function f over the interval $[0, 7]$. Then the three integrals in the theorem can be evaluated by finding areas of trapezoids.

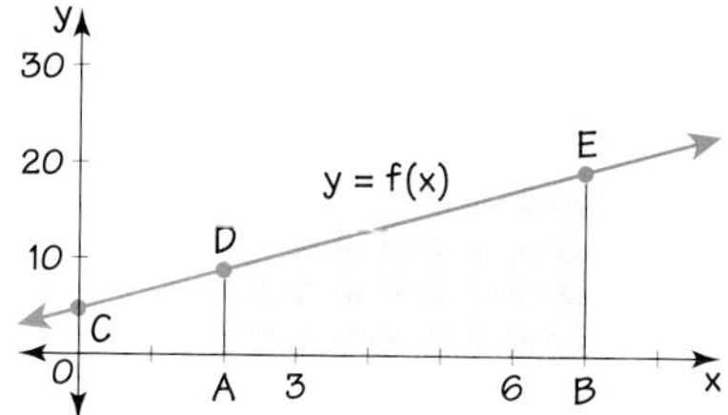

$$\int_a^b f(x)\,dx = \int_2^7 (3x+6)\,dx = \text{area of } ABED = \tfrac{1}{2}(f(2) + f(7)) \cdot 5$$
$$= \tfrac{1}{2}(12 + 27) \cdot 5 = 97.5$$
$$\int_0^b f(x)\,dx = \int_0^7 (3x+6)\,dx = \text{area of } OBEC = \tfrac{1}{2}(6 + 27) \cdot 7 = 115.5$$
$$\int_0^a f(x)\,dx = \int_0^2 (3x+6)\,dx = \text{area of } OADC = \tfrac{1}{2}(6 + 12) \cdot 2 = 18$$
$$\text{Then } \int_0^b f(x)\,dx - \int_0^a f(x)\,dx = 115.5 - 18 = 97.5 = \int_a^b f(x)\,dx.$$

The third and fourth properties concern integrals of different functions over the same interval. Consider the following situation, which involves the definite integral of the sum of two functions.

Optional Activities

Refer students to **Question 10.** Ask them to give an interpretation of **part a** in terms of a situation. [Sample: Let $f(x)$ represent the velocity of one truck over time and $g(x)$ represent the velocity of another truck. The difference in the definite integrals from a to b represents the difference in distance traveled by the two trucks from time a to time b.]

Example 2

Suppose a field in the Great Plains is irrigated by two pipes. Due to changes in water pressure, the rate of flow in these pipes varies and is recorded by devices attached to the pipes.

a. Given the rate-of-flow charts for these two pipes for a day, estimate the total amount of water used to irrigate the field for that 24-hour period.

b. If $f(t)$ and $g(t)$ represent the rates of flow $\left(\text{in } \frac{\text{gal}}{\text{hr}}\right)$ in the two pipes at time t, respectively, use integral notation to represent the exact amount of water used.

t	$f(t)$	$g(t)$	$(f+g)(t)$
0	500	200	700
2	450	250	700
4	400	300	700
6	400	350	750
8	450	350	800
10	500	400	900
12	550	350	900
14	500	250	750
16	450	250	700
18	450	300	750
20	450	350	800
22	400	350	750
24	400	350	750

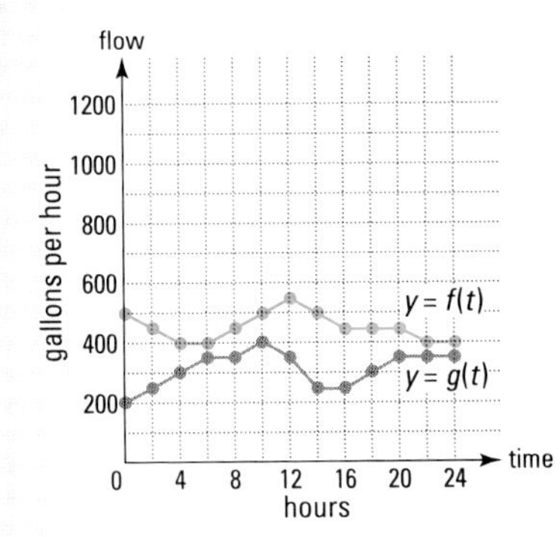

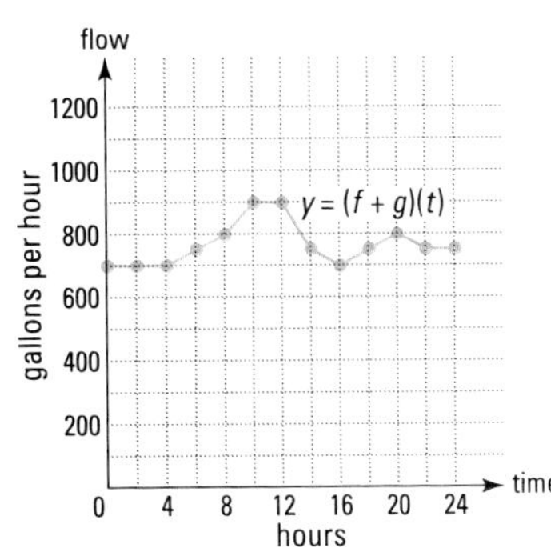

Solution

a. The rate-of-flow charts give some of the values of the functions f and g. The sum $f + g$ gives the gallons of water per hour flowing through both pipes together. The number of gallons used in a short time period can be approximated by multiplying the estimated rate of flow for that time period by the length of the time period: $\frac{\text{gal}}{\text{hr}} \cdot \text{hr} = \text{gal}$. The total amount of water is then approximated by the sum of these products. If Δt is the length of each time period, then the approximation for the total water is the Riemann sum

$$[f(z_1) + g(z_1)]\Delta t + [f(z_2) + g(z_2)]\Delta t + \ldots + [f(z_n) + g(z_n)]\Delta t$$
$$= \sum_{i=1}^{n} [f(z_i) + g(z_i)]\Delta t.$$

If $n = 12$ and the right endpoints of the intervals are used as the z_i, (so $z_1 = 2, z_2 = 4, \ldots, z_{12} = 24$), then $\Delta t = 2$ and the numbers $f(z_i) + g(z_i)$ are given in the right column of the table above. Thus, the approximation is

$$700 \cdot 2 + 700 \cdot 2 + 750 \cdot 2 + 800 \cdot 2 + \ldots + 750 \cdot 2 = 18{,}500 \text{ gallons.}$$

b. The exact amount of water used is the limit of the Riemann sum $\sum_{i=1}^{n} [f(z_i) + g(z_i)]\Delta t$ as n gets arbitrarily large. Thus, it is given by the definite integral

$$\int_0^{24} (f(t) + g(t))\, dt = \lim_{n \to \infty} \sum_{i=1}^{n} (f(z_i) + g(z_i))\Delta t.$$

Tell students that the situation of **Example 2** is quite realistic. Rate of flow is proportional to water pressure, so it can be known even if the total amount is not known. Point out the similarity between the following situations:

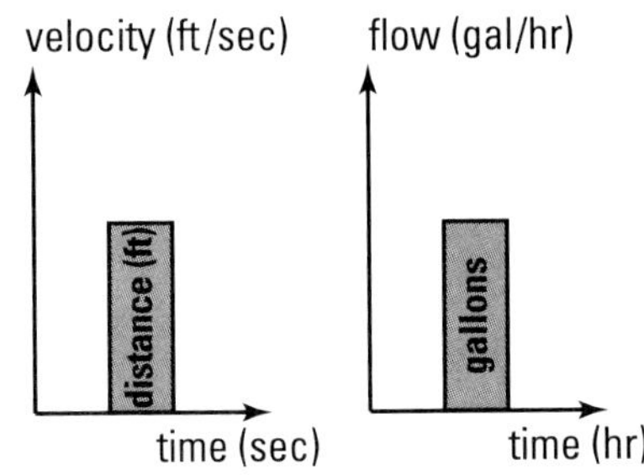

In the illustration, the situation shown on the left involves the units from Lesson 13-1; the situation on the right is from the example in this lesson.

Social Studies Connection
According to the U.S. Bureau of Census, *1992 Census of Agriculture,* 5.2% of all farm land in the United States was irrigated.

Adapting to Individual Needs

Extra Help
Sometimes students feel overwhelmed by symbolic notation. It might be helpful to summarize the four theorems of this lesson using the summary in the Perspective in the *Overview* on page 805. Then for each theorem, have a student make an appropriate area sketch on the board.

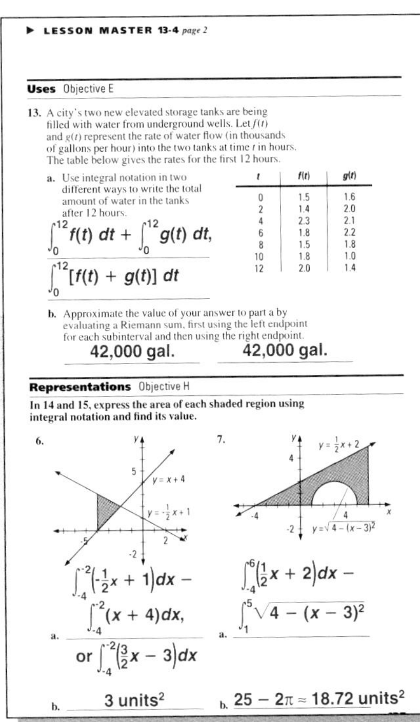

LESSON MASTER 13-4 *page 2*

Uses Objective E

13. A city's two new elevated storage tanks are being filled with water from underground wells. Let $f(t)$ and $g(t)$ represent the rate of water flow (in thousands of gallons per hour) into the two tanks at time t in hours. The table below gives the rates for the first 12 hours.

t	$f(t)$	$g(t)$
0	1.5	1.6
2	1.4	2.0
4	2.3	2.1
6	1.8	2.2
8	1.5	1.8
10	1.8	1.0
12	2.0	1.4

a. Use integral notation in two different ways to write the total amount of water in the tanks after 12 hours.
$\int_0^{12} f(t)\,dt + \int_0^{12} g(t)\,dt,$
$\int_0^{12} [f(t) + g(t)]\,dt$

b. Approximate the value of your answer to part a by evaluating a Riemann sum, first using the left endpoint for each subinterval and then using the right endpoint.
42,000 gal. 42,000 gal.

Representations Objective H

In 14 and 15, express the area of each shaded region using integral notation and find its value.

6. $y = x + 4$, $y = -\frac{1}{2}x + 1$
a. $\int_{-4}^{-2} \left(-\frac{1}{2}x + 1\right)dx - \int_{-4}^{-2} (x + 4)\,dx,$ or $\int_{-4}^{-2} \left(\frac{3}{2}x - 3\right)dx$
b. 3 units^2

7. $y = \frac{1}{2}x + 2$, $y = \sqrt{4 - (x-3)^2}$
a. $\int_{-4}^{6} \left(\frac{1}{2}x + 2\right)dx - \int_{1}^{5} \sqrt{4 - (x-3)^2}$
b. $25 - 2\pi \approx 18.72$ units^2

The Sum and Constant Multiple Properties are needed in the next lesson so should be discussed.

Additional Examples

If you use Additional Example 2, show both answers to exhibit the property that the integral of the difference of two functions is equal to the difference of the integrals of the individual functions. For Additional Example 3, show both answers to exhibit the Constant Multiple Property of Integrals.

1. Verify the first theorem of the lesson when $f(x) = 2x + 6$, $a = -3$, $b = 9$, and $c = 20$.
   $\int_{-3}^{9} (2x + 6)\,dx = 144$;
   $\int_{9}^{20} (2x + 6)\,dx = 385$;
   $\int_{-3}^{20} (2x + 6)\,dx = 529$,
   so the sum of the first two integrals equals the third.
2. Use the data from **Example 2** of the lesson.
   a. Estimate how much more water comes from the pipe with rate of flow $f(t)$ than from the pipe with rate of flow $g(t)$. **Splitting into 12 subintervals and using the right endpoints, an estimate is 3100 gallons.**
   b. Use integral notation to represent the exact difference.
   $\int_{0}^{24} (f(t) - g(t))\,dt$, or $\int_{0}^{24} f(t)\,dt - \int_{0}^{24} g(t)\,dt$
3. If, due to drought, the rate of flow in the pipes in **Example 2** is reduced to 75% of what it was, use integral notation to describe the total water used by the first pipe in the 24-hour period.
   $\frac{3}{4}\int_{0}^{24} f(t)\,dt$ or $\int_{0}^{24} \frac{3}{4}f(t)\,dt$

This integral can be computed in a different way, by adding the integrals of the individual functions. This can be seen as follows:

For each i, $[f(z_i) + g(z_i)]\Delta t = f(z_i)\Delta t + g(z_i)\Delta t.$

So,
$$\sum_{i=1}^{n} [f(z_i) + g(z_i)]\Delta t = \sum_{i=1}^{n} f(z_i)\Delta t + \sum_{i=1}^{n} g(z_i)\Delta t.$$

Consequently, in the limit,
$$\int_{0}^{24} [f(t) + g(t)]\,dt = \int_{0}^{24} f(t)\,dt + \int_{0}^{24} g(t)\,dt.$$

Thus the amount of water used to irrigate the field is also the sum of the two integrals based on the separate rate-of-flow functions for the individual pipes.

The property in Example 2**b** is an instance of a general property of definite integrals whose proof follows the ideas of the example.

Theorem (Sum Property of Integrals)
If f and g are continuous functions on the interval from a to b, then
$$\int_{a}^{b} (f(x) + g(x))\,dx = \int_{a}^{b} f(x)\,dx + \int_{a}^{b} g(x)\,dx.$$

Example 3

Suppose the field of Example 2 is irrigated by three computer-controlled pipes, all with the same rate of flow. If $y = f(t)$ represents the rate of flow of one pipe, use integral notation to describe the total water used by the three pipes in a period of 24 hours.

Solution

$3f(t)$ represents the rate of flow of the 3 pipes working simultaneously. Thus, the total amount of water used is $\int_{0}^{24} 3f(t)\,dt$. However, the total used by 3 pipes is 3 times the total used by 1 pipe, or $3\int_{0}^{24} f(t)\,dt$. Thus,
$$\int_{0}^{24} 3f(t)\,dt = 3\int_{0}^{24} f(t)\,dt.$$

The property in Example 3 is an instance of a fourth general property of definite integrals.

Theorem (Constant Multiple Property of Integrals)
If f is a continuous function on the interval from a to b, and c is a real number, then
$$\int_{a}^{b} c\,f(x)\,dx = c\int_{a}^{b} f(x)\,dx.$$

Adapting to Individual Needs

Challenge
Have students answer the following questions.

1. Compare the instruction "Evaluate $\int_{a}^{b} f(x)\,dx$" with the instruction "Find the area between the x-axis and the curve $y = f(x)$ on $[a, b]$." Are these the same questions? Why or why not?
   [They are the same if and only if $f(x)$ is nonnegative on $[a, b]$. If not, the area is $\int_{a}^{b} |f(x)|\,dx$.]
2. Evaluate $\int_{1}^{4} |x - 3|\,dx$. [2.5]

Proof
The graph of the function g, where $g(x) = c \cdot f(x)$, is a scale-change image of f. For every Riemann sum of f on the interval from a to b, there is a corresponding Riemann sum of g with the same subintervals and same z_i. The value of each term of the sum for g will be c times the value of the corresponding term of the sum for f. Consequently, the limit (the definite integral) for g will be c times the limit (the definite integral) for f.

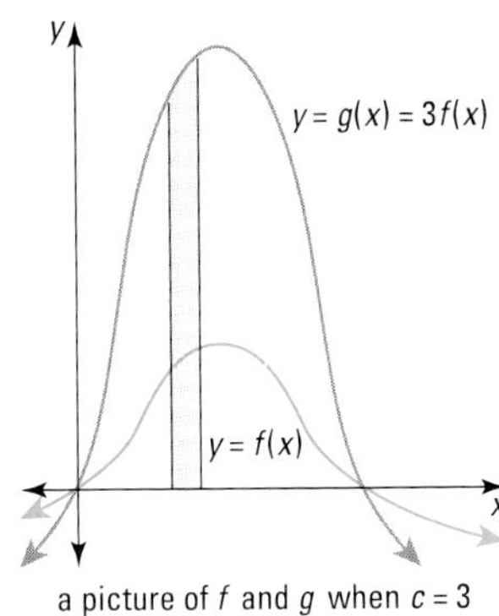

a picture of f and g when $c = 3$

QUESTIONS

Covering the Reading

1. Verify the first theorem of this lesson for the case $a = -2$, $b = 3$, $c = 4$, and $f(x) = 8 - 2x$. **See left.**

1) $\int_{-2}^{3} (8 - 2x)\,dx + \int_{3}^{4} (8 - 2x)\,dx = 35 + 1 = 36 = \int_{-2}^{4} (8 - 2x)\,dx$

2. Suppose g is a continuous function such that $\int_{-3}^{-1} g(x)\,dx = 2$, $\int_{-3}^{0} g(x)\,dx = 6$, and $\int_{0}^{2} g(x)\,dx = 5$. Find each.

a. $\int_{-3}^{2} g(x)\,dx$ **11** **b.** $\int_{-1}^{0} g(x)\,dx$ **4** **c.** $\int_{-1}^{2} g(x)\,dx$ **9**

In 3 and 4, refer to Example 2.

3. Give the units of t, $f(t)$, Δt, and $f(t)\Delta t$.
t hours, $f(t)$ gal/hr, Δt hours, $f(t)\ \Delta t$ gallons

4. a. Use the left endpoints of the 12 two-hour subintervals from 0 to 24 to calculate a Riemann sum for the given function. **See left.**
i. f **ii.** g **iii.** $f + g$
b. What do your answers to part **a** represent? **See left.**
c. How are they related to the answer found in Example 2**a**?
They are nearly equal.

4ai) 11,000 gal
ii) 7400 gal
iii) 18,400 gal
b) the amount of water that flowed through the pipes during the 24-hour period for each pipe and both pipes together.

5. Graph $f(x) = \sin x$ and $g(x) = 5 \sin x$ on the interval from 0 to π and use these graphs to explain why $\int_{0}^{\pi} g(x)\,dx = 5\int_{0}^{\pi} f(x)\,dx$. **See margin.**

Applying the Mathematics

In 6–8, use the properties of integrals to write the expression as a single integral.

6. $\int_{0}^{14} x^2\,dx - \int_{0}^{6} x^2\,dx$ **7.** $3\int_{a}^{b} \sin x\,dx - \int_{a}^{b} \sin x\,dx$

8. $\int_{3}^{4} \log x\,dx + \int_{3}^{4} (\log x^2)\,dx$ (Hint: Use properties of logarithms.)

6) $\int_{6}^{14} x^2\,dx$ 7) $2\int_{a}^{b} \sin x\,dx$ 8) $3\int_{3}^{4} \log x\,dx$

Notes on Questions

Question 1 After students see the details, the first theorem of this lesson becomes rather obvious.

Question 4 You could ask students to estimate the total amount of water used from, say, 4 AM to 10 AM by using a Riemann sum with $\Delta t = 2$ hours and $z_i =$ right endpoint of ith subinterval. Then $z_1 = 6$, $z_2 = 8$, and $z_3 = 10$, so $f(z_1) = 400$, $f(z_2) \approx 425$, $f(z_3) = 500$, $g(z_1) = g(z_2) = 350$, and $g(z_3) = 400$. Thus $(f + g)(z_1) = 750$, $(f + g)(z_2) = 775$, and $(f + g)(z_3) = 900$.

From this, $\sum_{i=1}^{3} f(z_i)\,\Delta t + \sum_{i=1}^{3} (z_i)\,\Delta t$
$= (400 + 425 + 500) \cdot 2 + (350 + 350 + 400) \cdot 2$
$= (750 + 775 + 900) \cdot 2$
$= \sum_{i=1}^{3} [f(z_i) + g(z_i)]\,\Delta t.$

Additional Answers

5.

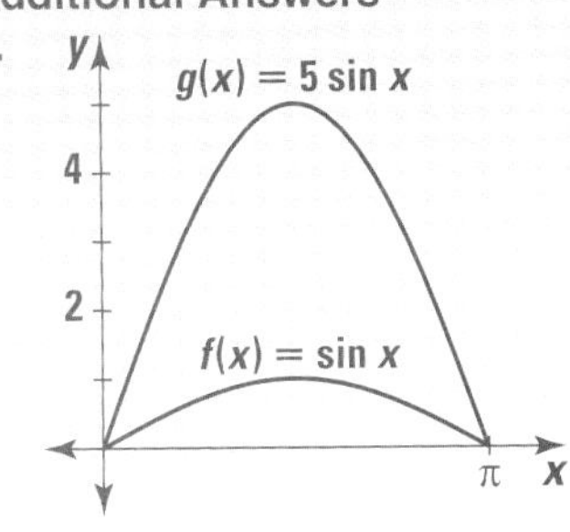

For each x_i, $g(x_i) = 5f(x_i)$, so $\int_{0}^{\pi} g(x)\,dx$, the area between $g(x)$ and the x-axis, will be $\int_{0}^{\pi} 5f(x)\,dx = 5\int_{0}^{\pi} f(x)\,dx$.

Notes on Questions

Question 10 A special case is given in Additional Example 2 on page 808.

Question 11 Finding these functions is rather easy. In fact, it is difficult to find functions f and g and a value of a for which equality holds.

Questions 12 and 14 Teaching Aid 156 contains these graphs.

Questions 12c Error Alert Students may write the integral as $\int_{-3}^{2}[g(x) - f(x)]\,dx$ in this type of problem, which would give a "negative area." This can happen especially if they do not reason carefully from a clear sketch of the two functions. Stress that the height of each rectangle in the Riemann sum is found by subtracting the y-value of g from the y-value of f, since g is below f throughout the region in question.

Questions 17–18 These are review for Lesson 13-6 and should be discussed.

Question 19 This exploration is helpful for the next lesson and might be used as a lead-in.

9c) answer from part b: $3 \cdot \frac{4^2}{2} + 7(4) = 52$; area of trapezoid: $4 \cdot \frac{7 + 19}{2} = 52$

10b) The area between the graphs of f and g (from a to b) is the area between f and the x-axis minus the area between g and the x-axis.

12a) $(f(z_i) - g(z_i))\,\Delta x$

b) $\sum_{i=1}^{n}(f(z_i) - g(z_i))\,\Delta x$

9. a. Use area formulas to evaluate the integrals $\int_0^a 7\,dx$ and $\int_0^a x\,dx$. **$7a$ and $a^2/2$**

b. Use your answers to part **a** and properties of integrals to evaluate $\int_0^a (3x + 7)\,dx$. **$3 \cdot \frac{a^2}{2} + 7a$**

c. Verify your answer to part **b** for $a = 4$ by finding the area of a trapezoid. **See left.**

10. a. Fill in the blank with a single integral.

$$\int_a^b f(x)\,dx - \int_a^b g(x)\,dx = \underline{\ ?\ } \quad \int_a^b [f(x) - g(x)]\,dx$$

b. Interpret your answer to part **a** in terms of area. **See left.**

11. Find functions f and g and a real number a for which

$$\int_0^a f(x)\,dx \cdot \int_0^a g(x)\,dx \neq \int_0^a (f \cdot g)(x)\,dx. \quad \textbf{See margin.}$$

12. Consider the region enclosed by the parabola $f(x) = -x^2 + 4$ and the line $g(x) = x - 2$. **a, b) See left.**

a. If the shaded rectangle at the right has width Δx, write its area in terms of $f(z_i)$, $g(z_i)$, and Δx.

b. Write a Riemann sum that approximates the area of the region between the graphs of f and g.

c. Write an integral which gives the exact area of the region.

$$\int_{-3}^{2} (f(x) - g(x))\,dx$$

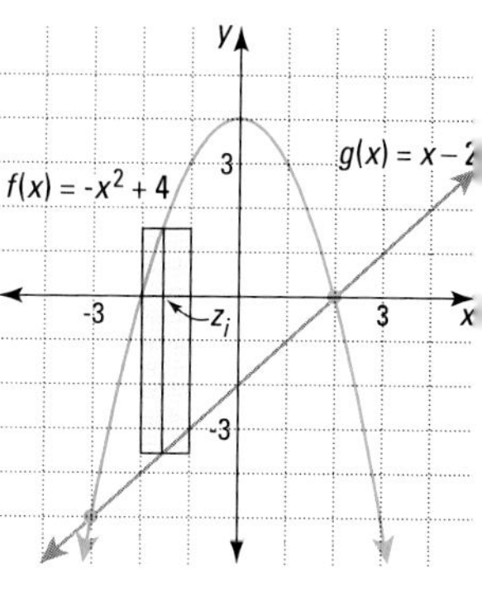

gyrfalcon, the largest species of hawk

Review

13. Find the value of the integral to the nearest hundredth. *(Lesson 13-3)*

a. $\int_{-5}^{5}\sqrt{25 - x^2}\,dx$ **39.27** **b.** $\int_{4}^{5}\sqrt{25 - x^2}\,dx$ **2.04**

14. After sighting its prey, a hawk descends with a velocity described by the graph at the right. Find the distance traveled by the hawk in this time. *(Lesson 13-1)* **175 feet**

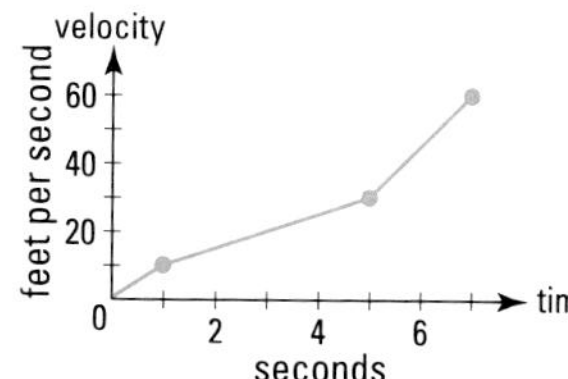

15a–c) Samples are given.

15. Let $P = (1, 2, -4)$, $Q = (-3, 0, 2)$, and $R = (2, -4, 2)$ be points in 3-space.

a. Find a vector orthogonal to vectors $\overrightarrow{PQ}$ and $\overrightarrow{PR}$. **(24, 30, 26)**

b. Find an equation of the plane M containing P, Q, and R.

c. Find parametric equations of the line through P orthogonal to M.

(Lessons 12-6, 12-7)

b) $12x + 15y + 13z = -10$ **c)** $\begin{cases} x = 1 + 12t \\ y = 2 + 15t \\ z = -4 + 13t \end{cases}$

Additional Answers

11. Sample: Let $f(x) = x$, $g(x) = x$, and $a = 1$.

Then $\int_0^1 x\,dx \cdot \int_0^1 x\,dx = \frac{1^2}{2} \cdot \frac{1^2}{2} = \frac{1}{4}$, but $\int_0^1 x^2\,dx = \frac{1^3}{3} = \frac{1}{3}$.

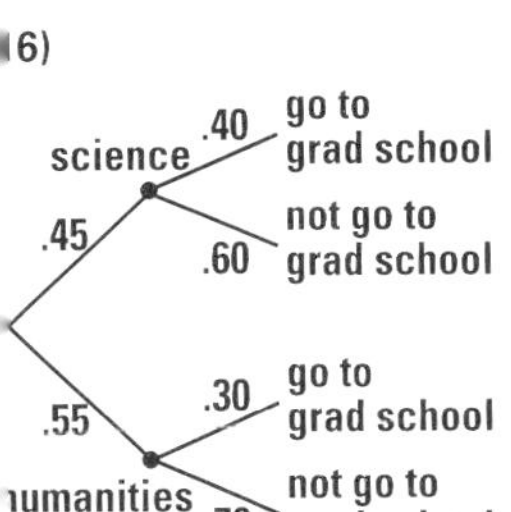

16. A survey of students at a college shows that 45% are science majors. Of the science majors, 40% plan to attend graduate school, compared to 30% of the humanities majors. Draw a graph which represents this situation, and find what percent of those who plan to attend graduate school are science majors. *(Lesson 11-1)* **See left. ≈ 52%**

In 17 and 18, use basic geometry formulas to find the volume of the figure. *(Previous course)*

17.

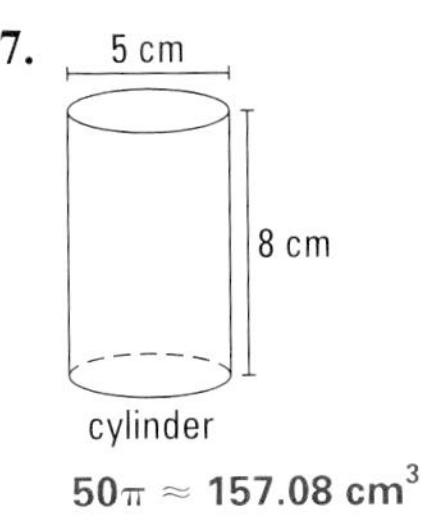

cylinder

$50\pi \approx 157.08$ cm^3

18.

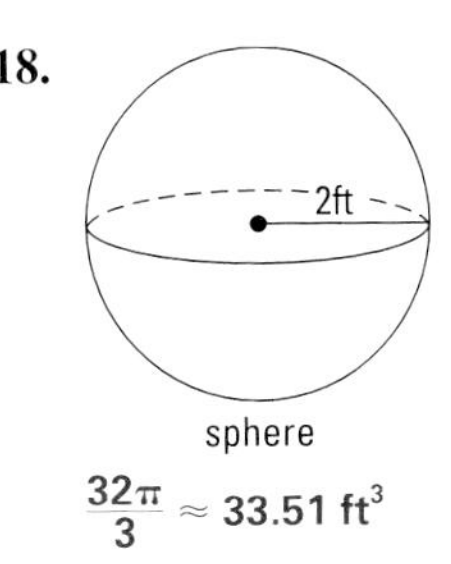

sphere

$\frac{32\pi}{3} \approx 33.51$ ft^3

Exploration

19. Develop a formula for $\int_0^a (mx + c)dx$.

(Hint: One way is to use the answers to Questions 14 and 15 of Lesson 13-3.)

$\frac{ma^2}{2} + ca$

Practice

For more questions on SPUR Objectives, use **Lesson Master 13-4** (shown on pages 806–807).

Assessment

Quiz A quiz covering Lessons 13-1 through 13-4 is provided in the *Assessment Sourcebook.*

Extension

Refer students to **Question 12.** Have students describe a general method for finding the area between two curves. Ask them what is important to specify about the two functions. [To find the area between two curves f and g, first find their points of intersection. Between any two points of intersection $(a, f(a) = g(a))$ and $(b, f(b) = g(b))$, the area will be $\int_a^b (f(x) - g(x))\,dx$, provided that $f(x) > g(x)$ for all x in the interval from a to b. If $g(x) > f(x)$ over the interval, then switch the order of subtraction.]

Setting Up Lesson 13-5

Students need to know the Sum and Constant Multiple Properties of Integrals. Also be sure to discuss **Questions 17–19.**

Lesson 13-5

Objectives
B Evaluate definite integrals.
D Find the distance traveled by a moving object, given its rate.
H Find areas bounded by curves.

Resources
From the ***Teacher's Resource File***
- Lesson Master 13-5
- Answer Master 13-5
- Teaching Aids
  149 Warm-up
  157 Graphs of Parabolas
- Technology Sourcebook
  Calculator Master 19

Additional Resources
- Visuals for Teaching Aids 149, 157

Teaching Lesson 13-5

Warm-up
In Lesson 13-5, the area bounded by the x-axis, the line $x = 1$, and the parabola $y = x^2$ is shown to be $\frac{1}{3}$. Use this result.
1. Find the area of the region bounded by the y-axis, the line $y = 1$, and the parabola $y = x^2$. $\frac{2}{3}$
2. Find the area of the region bounded by the y-axis, the parabola $y = x^2$, the line $x = 1$, and the line $y = 4$. $\frac{11}{3}$

LESSON

13-5 The Area Under a Parabola

Screwy Invention. *This Italian postage stamp shows Archimedes and the interior of an Archimedean Screw.*

Archimedes, who lived from about 287 to 212 B.C., is thought by many to have been the greatest mathematician of antiquity. He is certainly one of the brilliant minds of all time. He was known during his lifetime for his inventions, including the Archimedean screw (still used today in irrigation) and the catapult, and he made basic discoveries in physics. But he considered himself to be a mathematician, and he was the first person to find the area of a figure bounded by a parabola. It is said that he cut parabolic regions out of wood and weighed them to conjecture a formula, and then set about to deduce the formula. His methods were quite similar to the use of Riemann sums, calculating better and better approximations of the actual area, but he had none of today's notation.

Knowledge of parent functions can usually be extended to obtain knowledge about their offspring. So it is with integrals of functions. In a calculus course, you will learn how to obtain the integrals of all the parent functions you have studied in this course. Here, we examine the parent function with equation $y = x^2$, and begin by asking for the area between $x = 0$ and $x = 1$.
❶ That is, we find the definite integral

$$\int_0^1 x^2\, dx.$$

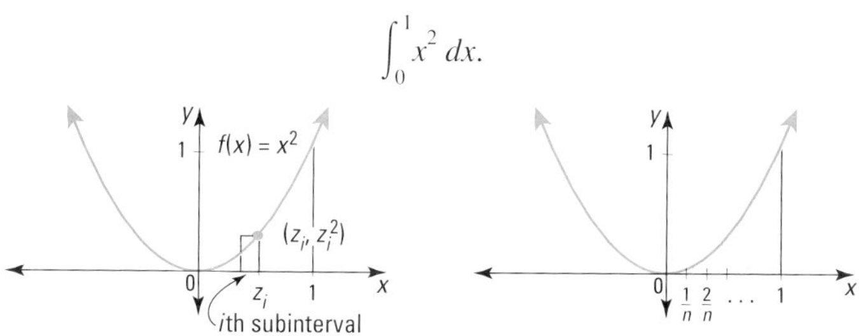

Since the integral is defined as the limit of Riemann sums, we begin by calculating those sums. Let

$$\sum_{i=1}^{n} f(z_i)\Delta x$$

be the Riemann sum obtained by dividing the interval $0 \le x \le 1$ into n equal subintervals, and let z_i be the right-hand endpoint of the ith subinterval. Since $\Delta x = \frac{1-0}{n} = \frac{1}{n}$, the n values (one for each subinterval) at which the function f will be evaluated are $z_1 = \frac{1}{n}, z_2 = \frac{2}{n}, z_3 = \frac{3}{n}, \ldots, z_n = \frac{n}{n} = 1$.

812

Lesson 13-5 Overview

Broad Goals This lesson first deduces a formula for $\int_0^a x^2\, dx$. Then the sum and constant multiple properties of integrals are employed to obtain a formula for the definite integral of a general quadratic over this interval.

Perspective By adding $\int_0^a c_0\, dx$, $\int_0^a c_1 x\, dx$ and $\int_0^a c_2 x^2\, dx$, the definite integral of any quadratic function over the interval from 0 to a can be found. The first two of these have been directly calculated in previous lessons using area formulas for rectangles and triangles, but the integral of the quadratic requires more work. That work is done on the first two pages of the lesson. Then the formula for the integral of the quadratic is applied to give an exact answer to a problem posed in Lesson 13-1, namely the distance traveled by a car when its speed is described by a quadratic function. A bonus is that the area of a region bounded by a parabola can now be calculated.

Therefore, for all i, $z_i = \frac{i}{n}$ and so $f(z_i) = \left(\frac{i}{n}\right)^2 = \frac{i^2}{n^2}$. Substituting into the Riemann sum formula above,

$$\sum_{i=1}^{n} f(z_i)\Delta x = \sum_{i=1}^{n}\left(\frac{i^2}{n^2} \cdot \frac{1}{n}\right) = \sum_{i=1}^{n} \frac{i^2}{n^3} = \frac{1}{n^3}\sum_{i=1}^{n} i^2.$$

(Since n is a nonzero constant with respect to the sum, so is $\frac{1}{n^3}$, and thus $\frac{1}{n^3}$ can be factored out of the sum.) In Lesson 7-3, it was proved that

$$\sum_{i=1}^{n} i^2 = \frac{n(n+1)(2n+1)}{6}.$$

Therefore,

$$\begin{aligned}\frac{1}{n^3}\sum_{i=1}^{n} i^2 &= \frac{1}{n^3} \cdot \frac{n(n+1)(2n+1)}{6} \\ &= \frac{n(n+1)(2n+1)}{6n^3} = \frac{(n+1)(2n+1)}{6n^2}.\end{aligned}$$

Although this result gives the Riemann sum, it is the limit of this sum that gives the value of the definite integral. To find the limit of this sum as $n \to \infty$, we rewrite the rightmost expression:

$$= \frac{1}{6} \cdot \frac{n+1}{n} \cdot \frac{2n+1}{n} = \frac{1}{6}\left(1 + \frac{1}{n}\right)\left(2 + \frac{1}{n}\right).$$

❷ Now take the limit of the Riemann sum above, using this new expression.

$$\begin{aligned}\lim_{n\to\infty} \sum_{i=1}^{n} f(z_i)\Delta x &= \lim_{n\to\infty} \frac{1}{n^3}\sum_{i=1}^{n} i^2 \\ &= \lim_{n\to\infty} \frac{1}{6}\left(1 + \frac{1}{n}\right)\left(2 + \frac{1}{n}\right) \\ &= \frac{1}{6} \cdot (1 + 0)(2 + 0) \qquad \text{since } \lim_{n\to\infty} \frac{1}{n} = 0 \\ &= \frac{1}{3}\end{aligned}$$

Since here $f(z_i) = z_i^2$ and the intervals are from 0 to 1, this limit is the definite integral of f over the interval from 0 to 1.

$$\int_0^1 x^2 dx = \frac{1}{3}$$

So the area under the parabola from 0 to 1 is $\frac{1}{3}$.

Using the program in Lesson 13-2 to approximate this integral with Riemann sums confirms this result. With 100 subintervals, the Riemann sum gives .33835, and with 1000 subintervals, it gives .33383.

When $a > 0$, the definite integral $\int_0^a x^2 dx$ can be evaluated if the same technique is used . This time, $\Delta x = \frac{a - 0}{n} = \frac{a}{n}$. Again, let z_i = right endpoint of the ith subinterval:

$$z_1 = \frac{a}{n},\ z_2 = \frac{2 \cdot a}{n},\ z_3 = \frac{3 \cdot a}{n}, \ldots, z_n = \frac{n \cdot a}{n} = a, \text{ and so for all } i,\ z_i = \frac{i \cdot a}{n}.$$

Thus

$$\begin{aligned}\sum_{i=1}^{n} f(z_i)\Delta x &= \sum_{i=1}^{n}\left(\frac{i \cdot a}{n}\right)^2 \cdot \frac{a}{n} = \sum_{i=1}^{n} \frac{i^2 \cdot a^3}{n^3} = \frac{a^3}{n^3}\sum_{i=1}^{n} i^2 \\ &= a^3\left[\frac{1}{n^3}\sum_{i=1}^{n} i^2\right].\end{aligned}$$

Notes on Reading

❶ These graphs are shown on **Teaching Aid 157.** Evaluating $\int_0^1 x^2\, dx$ as a limit of Riemann sums is difficult for some students. Part of the difficulty is reconciling the facts that the sum goes from 1 to n while the integral goes from 0 to 1. Remind students that n is the number of terms in the Riemann sum; the number of rectangles whose areas are being added.

The idea is first to write $\sum_{i=1}^{n} f(z_i)\ \Delta x$ in terms of n, and possibly some constants. This enables us to take the limit as n approaches infinity. To write that sum in terms of n, we must divide the interval from 0 to 1 into n subintervals—this is where the endpoints of the interval are utilized—pick the z_i in the subintervals and calculate the values of the $f(z_i)$. Obviously we try to pick the z_i so that there is a simple pattern for the $f(z_i)$. On page 812, we pick the right endpoints of the subintervals. Not surprisingly, given that $f(x) = x^2$, we are required to find a sum of squares. Fortunately, in an earlier chapter (and in earlier reviews in this chapter), we used mathematical induction to deduce a formula for the required sum. Thus the Riemann sum is expressed in terms of n. Finally, we take the limit of the Riemann sum as $n \to \infty$, and it turns out to be $\frac{1}{3}$.

❷ Here is an alternate way to evaluate the limit on this page:

$$\lim_{n\to\infty} \frac{(n+1)(2n+1)}{6n^2} = \lim_{n\to\infty} \frac{2n^2 + 3n + 1}{6n^2} = \lim_{n\to\infty} \frac{2 + \frac{3}{n} + \frac{1}{n^2}}{6} = \frac{2}{6} = \frac{1}{3}$$

Optional Activities

Activity 1 Technology Connection You might want to use *Technology Sourcebook, Calculator Master 19.* Students use a programmable calculator to approximate the areas of the petals of rose curves.

Activity 2 Have students look back through the chapter for integrals they can now evaluate exactly and evaluate them. You might suggest the following integrals.

1. In the Chapter Opener on page 783, the integral shown as Type 3 [$\frac{32}{3}$]
2. In Lesson 13-3, **Question 12–13** on page 803 [-$\frac{46}{3}$, -$\frac{98}{3}$]
3. In Lesson 13-4, **Question 6** on pages 809–810 [$\frac{2528}{3}$]

You may want to have students use the method illustrated to show that $\int_0^1 x\,dx = \frac{1}{2}$. If right endpoints are used for the n subintervals in the Riemann sum, then we obtain $\sum_{i=1}^{n} \frac{1}{n}\left(\frac{i}{n}\right)$. This is the sum of the integers from 1 to n, divided by n^2, and using $\sum_{i=1}^{n} i = \frac{n(n+1)}{2}$, we see that the sum is $\frac{n(n+1)}{2n^2}$. Taking the limit as $n \to \infty$ yields the desired value. More generally, you can show that $\int_0^a x\,dx = \frac{a^2}{2}$. This follows the procedure for $\int_0^1 x\,dx = \frac{1}{2}$ but with a constant multiple of a^2 in the sum, just as a^3 is found in the derivation of the theorem on this page.

The limits of the integral in the first theorem on page 814 are from 0 to a, but after the theorem there is deduced a formula for the area under the parabola from a to b. In **Question 16,** students are asked to find the corresponding formula $\int_a^b x\,dx = \frac{b^2}{2} - \frac{a^2}{2}$. In **Question 15** of Lesson 13-3, they found the formula $\int_a^b c\,dx = cb - ca$.

The limit of this expression is the value of the definite integral. Now use the result obtained on page 813.

$$\lim_{n\to\infty}\sum_{i=1}^{n} f(z_i)\Delta x = \lim_{n\to\infty} a^3\left[\frac{1}{n^3}\sum_{i=1}^{n} i^2\right] = a^3 \lim_{n\to\infty}\left[\frac{1}{n^3}\sum_{i=1}^{n} i^2\right] = a^3\cdot\frac{1}{3} = \frac{a^3}{3}$$

Thus $$\int_0^a x^2\,dx = \frac{a^3}{3}.$$

This argument proves the following theorem.

Theorem
If $a > 0$, $\int_0^a x^2\,dx = \frac{a^3}{3}$.

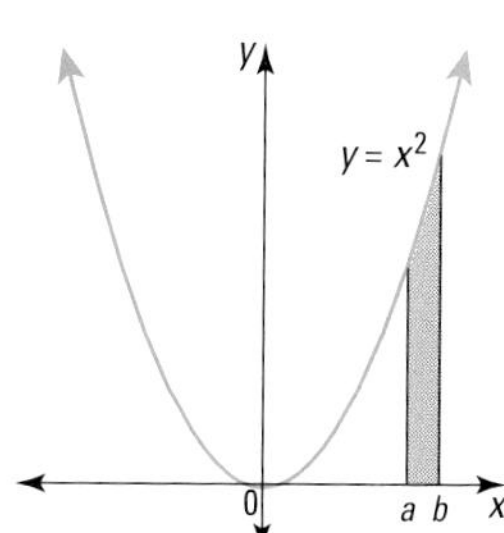

For instance, $\int_0^5 x^2\,dx = \frac{125}{3}$ and $\int_0^{15} x^2\,dx = \frac{15^3}{3} = 1125$.

To obtain a formula for $\int_a^b x^2\,dx$ when $0 < a < b$, apply the second theorem from Lesson 13-4.

$$\int_a^b x^2\,dx = \int_0^b x^2\,dx - \int_0^a x^2\,dx = \frac{b^3}{3} - \frac{a^3}{3} \text{ or } \frac{b^3 - a^3}{3}$$

One more result is needed to find the definite integral for all offspring of $f(x) = x^2$. Notice that the integral $\int_0^a x\,dx$ is the area of the triangle bounded by the x-axis, the line $y = x$, and the line $x = a$. This area is $\frac{1}{2}a \cdot a$, or $\frac{a^2}{2}$. Combined with the theorems of this and the previous lesson, the integral of the quadratic function $y = c_2x^2 + c_1x + c_0$ can be calculated.

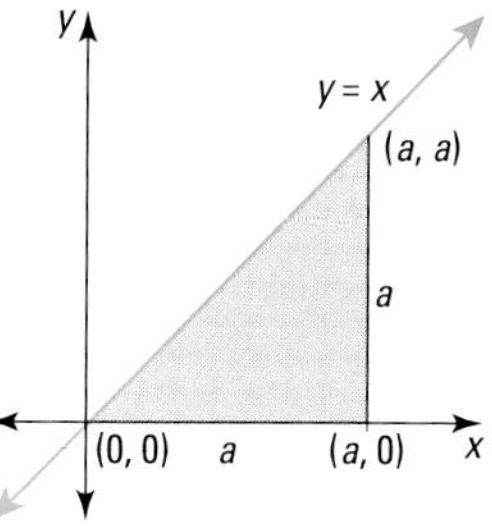

Theorem (Integral of a Quadratic Function)
If $a > 0$, $\int_0^a (c_2x^2 + c_1x + c_0)dx = c_2\frac{a^3}{3} + c_1\frac{a^2}{2} + c_0a$.

Proof
By the Sum Property and Constant Multiple Property of Integrals,

$$\int_0^a (c_2x^2 + c_1x + c_0)dx = c_2\int_0^a x^2dx + c_1\int_0^a x\,dx + \int_0^a c_0\,dx.$$

The first and second terms on the right side have been evaluated previously in this lesson. The third term is the area of the rectangle bounded by the line $y = c_0$, the x-axis, the y-axis, and the line $x = a$. So the area is c_0a. Thus

$$\int_0^a (c_2x^2 + c_1x + c_0)\,dx = c_2\frac{a^3}{3} + c_1\frac{a^2}{2} + c_0a.$$

Adapting to Individual Needs

Extra Help

You may want to emphasize that the last two terms of the Integral of a Quadratic Function Theorem, $c_1\frac{a^2}{2} + c_0a$, correspond to the terms $c_1x + c_0$ of the Quadratic Function. Since $f(x) = c_1x + c_0$ is a linear function, we now have a formula for the integral of any linear function: $\int_0^a (c_1x + c_0)\,dx = c_1\frac{a^2}{2} + c_0a$. You can verify this geometrically as shown at the right.

Total area

$= $ area of triangle $+$ area of rectangle

$= \frac{a \cdot c_1a}{2} + c_0a$

$= c_1\frac{a^2}{2} + c_0a$

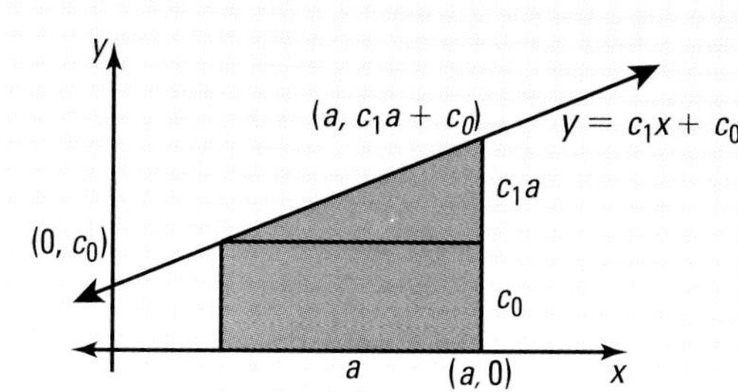

In the proof, we showed that $\int_0^a c_0\, dx = c_0 a$. More generally, the definite integral of the constant function f with $f(x) = c$ over the interval from a to b is $\int_a^b c\, dx = cb - ca$.

In Lessons 13-1 and 13-2 there was a question about the distance traveled by an object whose acceleration was not constant but was quicker at first. Because this particular rate function was quadratic, the question can now be answered exactly.

Example 1

Suppose a car accelerates from 0 to 88 $\frac{\text{ft}}{\text{sec}}$ in 10 seconds and its velocity in this time interval is given by $v = g(x) = -.88(x - 10)^2 + 88$. What is the total distance (in feet) traveled?

Solution

The distance is given by $\int_0^{10} g(x)\, dx$. Convert the formula for $g(x)$ into standard form.

$$\begin{aligned} g(x) &= -.88(x-10)^2 + 88 \\ &= -.88(x^2 - 20x + 100) + 88 \\ &= -.88x^2 + 17.6x \end{aligned}$$

Now use the Integral of a Quadratic Function Theorem with $a = 10$, $c_2 = -.88$, $c_1 = 17.6$, and $c_0 = 0$.

$$\begin{aligned} \int_0^{10} (-.88x^2 + 17.6x)\, dx &= -.88 \cdot \frac{10^3}{3} + 17.6 \cdot \frac{10^2}{2} + 0 \cdot 10 \\ &= \frac{-880}{3} + 880 \\ &= 586\frac{2}{3} \end{aligned}$$

This result agrees with the calculations done in Lesson 13-2.

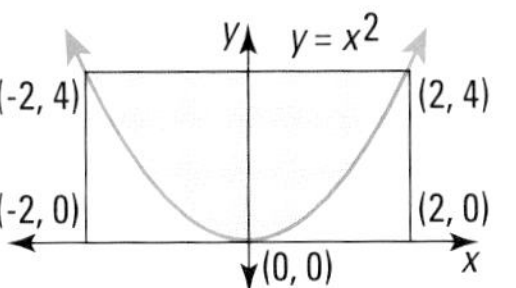

Example 2

Find the area of the shaded region at the left.

Solution

Subtract the area between the parabola and the x-axis from the area of the rectangle with vertices (-2, 4), (-2, 0), (2, 0), and (2, 4).

$$\begin{aligned} \text{Area of shaded region} &= \text{Area of rectangle} - \int_{-2}^{2} x^2 dx \\ &= \text{Area of rectangle} - 2\int_0^2 x^2\, dx \\ &= 16 - 2\left(\frac{2^3}{3}\right) \\ &= 16 - \frac{16}{3} \\ &= \frac{32}{3} \text{ square units} \end{aligned}$$

With all of this, the Integral of a Quadratic Function Theorem on page 814 can be generalized:
If $0 < a < b$,
then $\int_a^b (c_2x^2 + c_1x + c_0)dx = c_2\left(\frac{b^3}{3} - \frac{a^3}{3}\right) + c_1\left(\frac{b^2}{2} - \frac{a^2}{2}\right) + c_0(b - a)$.

You may wish to give this formula to students, but at this point we feel it is easier for many students simply to work with the integral from 0 to a.

Error Alert As we have returned several times to the acceleration formula used in **Example 1,** it bears reminding students that an actual acceleration would probably not have such a simple formula.

Additional Examples

1. Suppose that a car accelerates from 0 to 88 $\frac{\text{ft}}{\text{sec}}$ in 8 seconds such that its speed $f(t)$ after x seconds is given by $f(x) = -1.375(x - 8)^2 + 88$. Find the total distance traveled. **≈ 469.3 ft**
2. Find a formula for the area between the line $y = ax$ and the parabola $y = x^2$, when $a > 0$. $\frac{a^3}{6}$

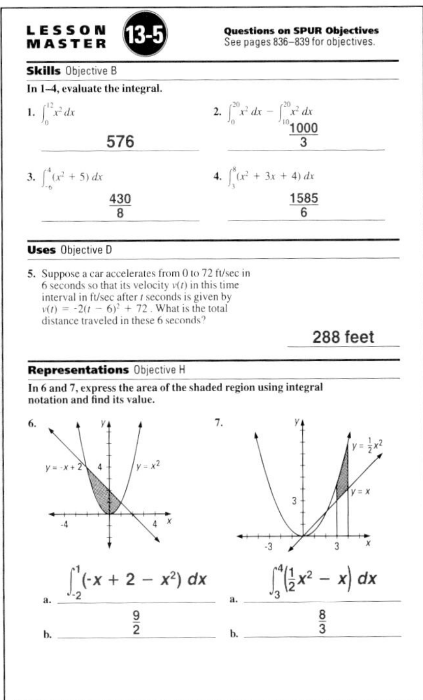
LESSON MASTER 13-5 Questions on SPUR Objectives
See pages 836–839 for objectives.

Skills Objective B

In 1–4, evaluate the integral.

1. $\int_0^{12} x^2\, dx$ 576
2. $\int_0^{20} x^2\, dx - \int_{10}^{20} x^2\, dx$ $\frac{1000}{3}$
3. $\int_{-6}^{4} (x^2 + 5)\, dx$ $\frac{430}{8}$
4. $\int_3^{8} (x^2 + 3x + 4)\, dx$ $\frac{1585}{6}$

Uses Objective D

5. Suppose a car accelerates from 0 to 72 ft/sec in 6 seconds so that its velocity $v(t)$ in this time interval in ft/sec after t seconds is given by $v(t) = -2(t - 6)^2 + 72$. What is the total distance traveled in these 6 seconds? 288 feet

Representations Objective H

In 6 and 7, express the area of the shaded region using integral notation and find its value.

6. a. $\int_{-2}^{1} (-x + 2 - x^2)\, dx$ b. $\frac{9}{2}$
7. a. $\int_3^4 \left(\frac{1}{2}x^2 - x\right) dx$ b. $\frac{8}{3}$

Notes on Questions

Question 5 Have students check the answer by evaluating the two integrals separately and then adding the results.

Question 11 It is intriguing to ask which areas can be found exactly and which only estimated, given formulas known to these students. The area under the parabola (in white) can be found exactly using the theorem of this lesson. The area of the quarter-circle can also be found exactly. So it is possible to get an exact value for the total shaded area. But to get an exact value for either part requires knowing a formula for $\int_0^a \sqrt{(1-x^2)}\,dx$, which is beyond the scope of this course.

Question 16 The given answer is in a form found when area has been used in the derivation of the formula. The equivalent $\frac{b^2}{2} - \frac{a^2}{2}$ is more familiar to those who know the formula for the integral of any polynomial.

4)

y 100 -10 10 x

QUESTIONS

Covering the Reading

1. Consider the problem of finding the area between the parabola $y = x^2$ and the x-axis, from $x = 0$ to $x = 1$.

a. Suppose the interval is divided into 25 subintervals. If the z_i are the right-hand endpoints of the subintervals, what are the values for z_i?

b. Give a Riemann approximation to this area, letting the z_i be the right endpoints of each interval. (Use the formula for $\sum_{i=1}^{n} i^2$ to help calculate the value.) **.3536 units²**

a) $i/25$, with $i = 1, 2, 3, \ldots, 25$

In 2 and 3, find the value of the integral.

2. $\int_0^3 x^2\,dx$ **9**

3. $\int_{-6}^{8} x^2\,dx$ **$242\frac{2}{3}$**

4. Find the area of the region bounded by the parabola $y = x^2$ and the line $y = 100$. (Hint: Sketch the region and use the model of Example 2.) **See left. $\frac{4000}{3}$ units²**

5. Consider the following sum: $\int_2^5 x^2\,dx + \int_5^6 x^2\,dx$.

a. Rewrite the sum as a single integral. **$\int_2^6 x^2\,dx$**

b. Evaluate the result from part **a.** **$\frac{208}{3}$**

In 6–10, evaluate the integral.

6. $\int_0^{15} 3\,dx$ **45**

7. $\int_{-200}^{400} dx$ **600**

8. $\int_0^7 x\,dx$ 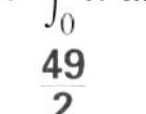 **$\frac{49}{2}$**

9. $\int_0^5 (3x^2 - 2x + 5)\,dx$ **125**

10. $\int_0^1 ax^2\,dx$ **$\frac{a}{3}$**

Applying the Mathematics

11. Consider the shaded portion of the graph at the right.

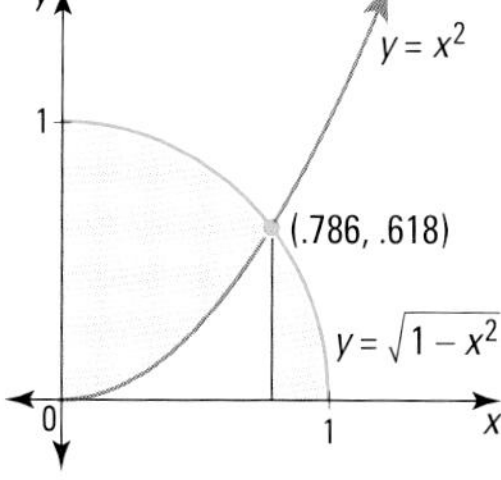

a. Evaluate $\int_0^1 \sqrt{1 - x^2}\,dx$.

(Hint: Use basic geometry formulas.) **$\frac{\pi}{4}$**

b. Evaluate $\int_0^{.786} x^2\,dx$. **≈ 0.162**

c. Use the results from parts **a** and **b** to find the area of the shaded portion. **≈ 0.624 units²**

Adapting to Individual Needs

Challenge

Have students answer the following questions.

1. Simpson's Rule approximates definite integrals:

$\int_a^b f(x)\,dx \approx \frac{b-a}{3n}[f(x_0) + 4f(x_1) + 2f(x_2) + 4f(x_3) + 2f(x_4) + \ldots + 2f(x_{n-2}) + 4f(x_{n-1}) + f(x_n)]$, where $a = x_0, x_1, x_2, \ldots$, and $x_n = b$ are n equally spaced values between a and b. Use this formula (with $n = 4$) to approximate the following. Then use a symbol manipulator to get the exact values.

a. $\int_0^1 e^{5x}\,dx$ [1.2974; $2(e^5 - 1)$]

b. $\int_0^1 \sin x\,dx$ [.4597; 1 − cos 1]

c. $\int_0^1 \frac{1}{x+3}\,dx$) [.28768; ln 4 − ln 3]

2. Evaluate: $\int_0^4 |x^2 - 4x + 3|\,dx$ [4]

3. Find the area of the region bounded by $y = x^2$ and $y = 2x - x^2$. $\left[\frac{1}{3}\right]$

12. A cylindrical barbeque grill has a base in the shape of a parabola, 1 foot high and 2 feet across. If the trough is 6 feet long, what is its volume? (Hint: You need to use the formula for the volume of a cylinder.) **8 ft^3**

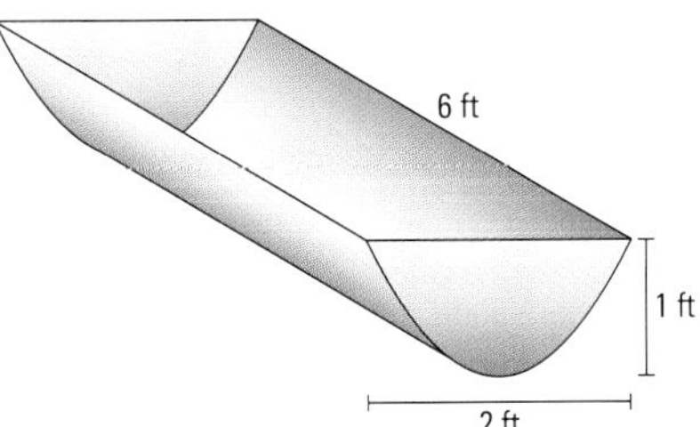

13. For what value of k is $\int_3^k x^2\,dx = 567$? **12**

14. Suppose the velocity (in feet per second) of an object at time t seconds is given by the function $f(t) = t^2$.

a. What integral gives the distance traveled by the object in 7 seconds?

b. Find the distance in part **a**.

a) $\int_0^7 t^2\,dt$ **b)** $\frac{7^3}{3} = 114.\overline{3}$

Review

15. Find the exact value of $\int_5^9 (4x + 1)\,dx$. *(Lesson 13-3)* **116**

16. Find a formula for $\int_a^b x\,dx$. (Hint: Draw a picture.) *(Lesson 13-3)* $\frac{(b + a)(b - a)}{2}$

See left.

17. Draw a directed graph whose adjacency matrix is

$$\begin{bmatrix} 0 & 1 & 0 & 1 \\ 0 & 0 & 0 & 0 \\ 1 & 0 & 2 & 2 \\ 1 & 0 & 1 & 0 \end{bmatrix}.$$

(Lesson 11-2) **See left.**

18. A salad bar contains 20 items besides lettuce. How many different salads can be created if 12 items, not counting the lettuce, are selected? *(Lesson 10-4)* **125,970**

19. a. Use the definition of derivative to compute the derivative of f when $f(x) = 2x^2 + 1$. $f'(x) = 4x$

b. Use your answer to part **a** to find the values of f at which a relative maximum or minimum could occur. $x = 0$

c. Check your answer to part **b** by graphing f. *(Lessons 9-3, 9-5)* **See left.**

16)

y
y = x
a
b
x

17) Sample:

v_1
v_2
v_3
v_4

19c)

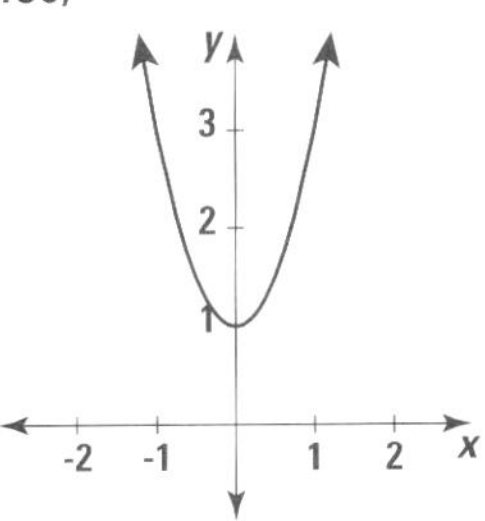

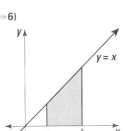

Notes on Questions

Question 27 The pattern is surprisingly simple, so much so that students might wonder why they did not learn such a formula in earlier courses. The reason is that most mathematics educators do not think it helps students merely to have a formula without knowing some way to derive it within any desired accuracy.

Follow-up for Lesson 13-5

Practice

For more questions on SPUR Objectives, use **Lesson Master 13-5** (shown on page 815).

Assessment

Written Communication Give students other problems like **Example 2** using various quadratic functions. [Students use integrals to find areas bounded by curves.]

Extension

Ask students to find the area between the graphs of $y = \sqrt{1 - x^2}$ and $y = x^2$. Refer them to **Question 11** of this lesson and **Example 4** of Lesson 13-3 for hints. [≈ 1.0665]

Project Update Project 1, *Programming Riemann Sums I*, Project 2, *Programming Riemann Sums II*, and Project 3, *Integrating by Weights*, on page 832, relate to the content of this lesson.

20b)

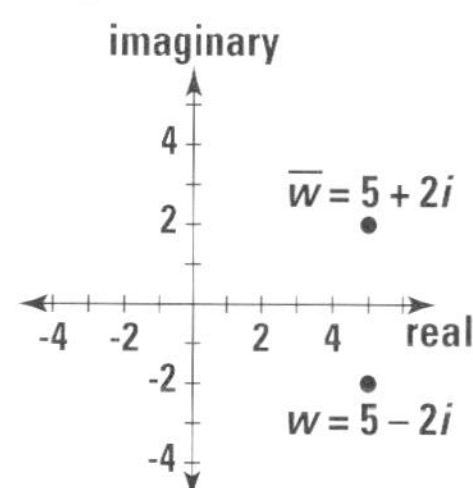

21a) $\sum_{i=1}^{7} (i^2 - 5i + 2) =$
$(-2) + (-4) + (-4) + (-2) + 2 + 8 + 16 = 14;$
$\sum_{i=1}^{7} i^2 = 140;\ \sum_{i=1}^{7} 5i = 140,$
$\sum_{i=1}^{7} 2 = 14$, so $\sum_{i=1}^{7} i^2 - \sum_{i=1}^{7} 5i + \sum_{i=1}^{7} 2 = 14.$

b) Sample:
$\sum_{i=1}^{n} (ai^2 + bi + c) = \sum_{i=1}^{n} ai^2 + \sum_{i=1}^{n} bi + \sum_{i=1}^{n} c$

20. Given the complex number $w = 5 - 2i$.
a. Give $\overline{w}$. $5 + 2i$
b. Graph w and $\overline{w}$ in the complex plane. *(Lesson 8-1)* See left.

21. a. Show by direct computation that
$$\sum_{i=1}^{7} (i^2 - 5i + 2) = \sum_{i=1}^{7} i^2 - \sum_{i=1}^{7} 5i + \sum_{i=1}^{7} 2.$$ See left.
b. Give the general property. *(Lesson 8-3)* See left.

In 22–24, evaluate without a calculator. *(Lessons 2-7, 2-9, 6-7)*

22. $e^{3 \ln x}\ (x > 0)$ x^3 **23.** $\log \sqrt{1000}$ 1.5 **24.** $\sin\left(\sin^{-1} \frac{\sqrt{2}}{2}\right)$ $\frac{\sqrt{2}}{2}$

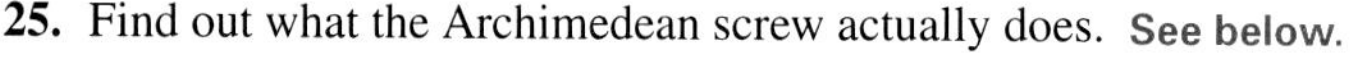

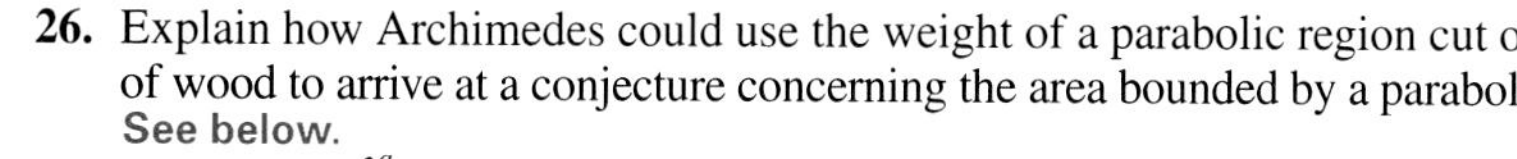

Exploration

25. Find out what the Archimedean screw actually does. See below.

26. Explain how Archimedes could use the weight of a parabolic region cut o[ut] of wood to arrive at a conjecture concerning the area bounded by a parabol[a]. See below.

27. Given: $\int_0^a dx = a$
$\int_0^a x\,dx = \frac{a^2}{2}$
$\int_0^a x^2 dx = \frac{a^3}{3}.$

a. Make a conjecture about $\int_0^a x^3 dx$. Sample: $\frac{a^4}{4}$
b. Test your conjecture for various values of a, using the BASIC program of Lesson 13-2 or another program to approximate the integral. Use various values of n. Answers may vary.

25) An Archimedean screw consists of a spiral passage within an inclined cylinder. It is used for raising water to a certain height. This is achieved by rotating the spiral within the cylinder.

26) Using wood with a reasonably consistent density, Archimedes could have weighed a rectangular piece of wood and measured its area. Then he could have cut out a parabolic region and weighed it. The weights of the parabolic region and the rectangular piece would be proportional to their areas.

Setting Up Lesson 13-6

Do the In-class Activity on page 819.

Introducing Lesson 13-6

Surfaces and Solids of Revolution

IN-CLASS ACTIVITY

When the line m is rotated in 3-space about the line ℓ, a two-napped cone results. This cone is an example of a **surface of revolution with axis ℓ**. The line m is the **generating curve** for the surface. Notice that each cross section of the surface by a plane perpendicular to the axis is a circle. If the region between the curve and the axis is revolved around the axis, then the perpendicular sections are disks rather than circles, and the figure is called a **solid of revolution with axis ℓ**. You can imagine surfaces and solids of revolution by thinking of spinning the generating curve or region about the axis. Work with a partner to answer these questions.

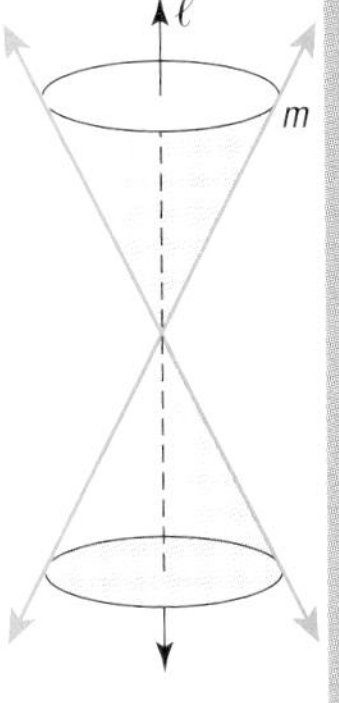

1a) A truncated cone with infinite lateral height.
b) A truncated cone with lateral height PQ.

1 Suppose that lines $\overleftrightarrow{PQ}$ and x are in the same plane. Let x be the axis. Describe the surface of revolution described by the indicated generating curve.

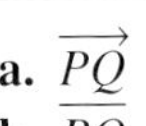

a. $\overrightarrow{PQ}$

b. $\overline{PQ}$

c. If $\overline{PQ}$ were parallel to x, how could you determine the volume of the surface of revolution it generates? **$v = \pi r^2 h$ where r = distance between x and $\overline{PQ}$, and h = length of $\overline{PQ}$**

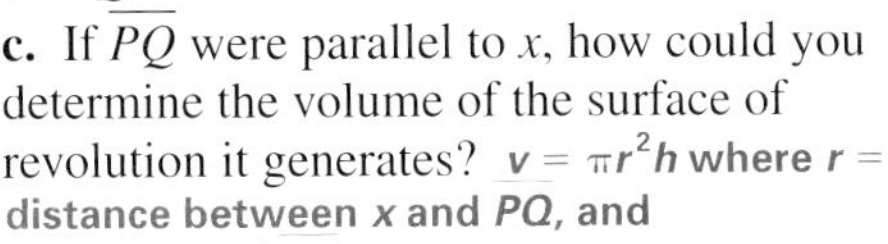

2 Let a circle C be the generating curve, and y be the axis for a surface of revolution. Describe this surface under the given condition.

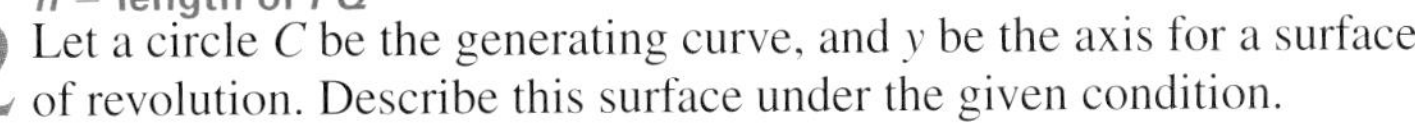

a. y contains a diameter of C. **sphere**

b. y does not intersect C, but y and C are coplanar.

c. y is perpendicular to the plane of C at its center. **circle C**

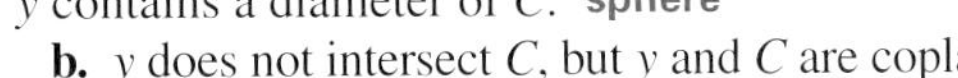

d. y is tangent to C and in the plane of C.

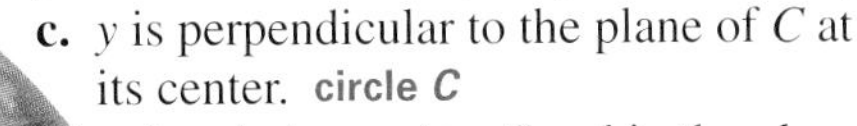

3 Explain how Earth can be thought of as a solid of revolution. **Sample: Earth rotates around its polar axis.**

2b) torus (doughnut)

2d) torus with no hole and width $2C$

In-class Activity

Resources

From the ***Teacher's Resource File***

- Answer Master 13-6

This activity deals with sets of points generated in space by a figure (the *generating curve*) rotating about an axis. In Task 1, the figure is a line. In Task 2, the figure is a circle. The purpose of the activity is to introduce students to the idea of a surface or solid of revolution. This prepares them for Lesson 13-6, in which the calculation of the volume of a surface or solid of revolution is examined.

Read through the directions carefully with the class to ensure that everyone understands the situation. Emphasize the second-to-last sentence in the paragraph and urge students to think of these questions as asking for the figure they would see if a spinner was formed using the figure and an axis.

Lesson 13-6

Objectives

E Use the definite integral to solve application problems.

I Find volumes of solids.

Resources

From the ***Teacher's Resource File***

- Lesson Master 13-6
- Answer Master 13-6
- Teaching Aids
  - 149 Warm-up
  - 158 Drawings for Examples 1–2, and for Proof of Volume of a Sphere Theorem

Additional Resources

- Visuals for Teaching Aids 149, 158
- Exploration 13-6

Teaching Lesson 13-6

Warm-up

Each of these figures can be thought of as a surface of revolution. Name a possible generating curve and describe its relationship to the axis of revolution.

1. Sphere
   Semicircle; line containing the diameter is the axis of revolution
2. Hemisphere
   Semicircle; symmetry line is the axis of revolution
3. Cylinder
   Segment; segment parallel to the generating segment and of the same length is the axis of revolution
4. Torus (doughnut)
   Circle; line in the same plane as the circle but not intersecting the circle is the axis of revolution

LESSON

13-6 *Volumes of Surfaces of Revolution*

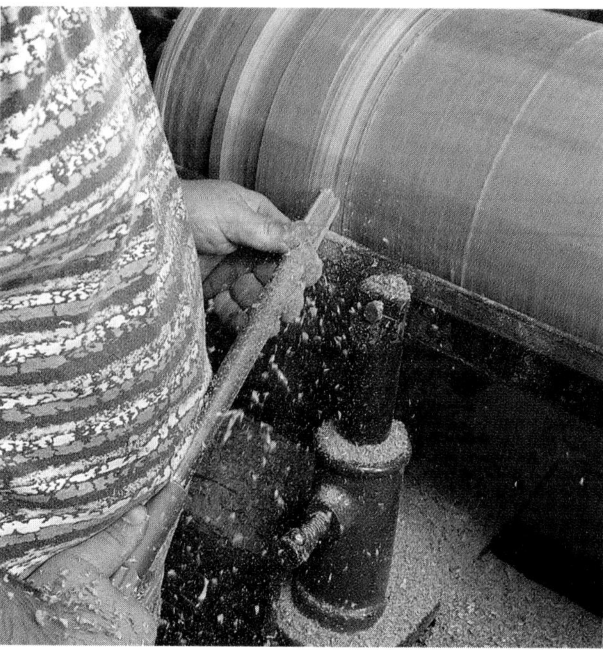

Spinning in Control. *A steady hand and a sharp tool can shape a piece of wood so its cross-sections are circular and vary in radius.*

You have seen that definite integrals can be used to compute areas and total distances. In fact, definite integrals can be used to compute many quantities, as long as those quantities can be approximated by Riemann sums of appropriate functions on appropriate intervals. This lesson illustrates how to use Riemann sums to find volumes of surfaces and solids of revolution.

Approximating the Volume of a Solid of Revolution

Example 1

A decorative chair leg is going to be shaped while spinning it about its axis. Use the figures below to approximate the volume of the chair leg. Dimensions are expressed in inches.

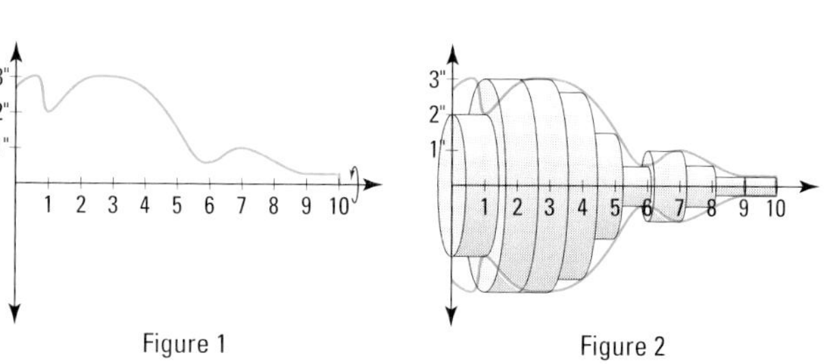

Figure 1 Figure 2

Lesson 13-6 Overview

Broad Goals This lesson shows how to use integrals to obtain the volume of a three-dimensional figure of revolution.

Perspective Integrals can be used to obtain volumes of solids in much the same way that they are employed to find areas of regions. Students who have studied Cavalieri's Principle (in UCSMP *Geometry* and other texts) will have seen figures split into thin cross sections as is done here.

The idea is to create a Riemann sum that approximates the volume and whose limit is that volume. In this lesson the only figures that are considered are solids of revolution, in particular, solids formed by rotating the region under a curve about the *x*-axis. Then, if the curve is sufficiently smooth, the solid can be sliced into 3-dimensional regions that are approximated by cylinders. The volume of the solid is approximately equal to the sum of the volumes of these regions.

Solution

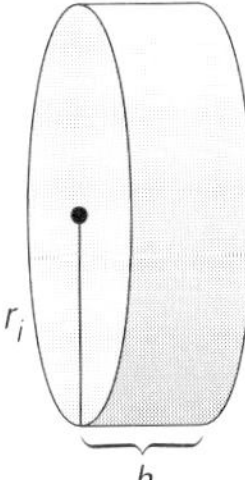

In Figure 1, the axis of the chair leg has been made to coincide with the x-axis in a 2-dimensional graph. Imagine generating the chair leg by rotating Figure 1 about the x-axis. Figure 2 shows a 3-dimensional approximation of the chair leg. Now, think of slicing the 3-dimensional figure into sections, each of which can be approximated by a cylinder. In Figure 2, there are 10 sections, and the radius r_i of the cylinder on the ith section is given by the height (to the nearest half inch) of the graph at the right endpoint of the ith subinterval. The volume ΔV_i of the cylinder on the ith subinterval is given by $\Delta V_i = \pi r_i^2 h$.

The height of each cylinder is the width of the subinterval, which is 1 inch.

i	1	2	3	4	5	6	7	8	9	10
r_i	2	3	3	2.5	1.5	.5	1	.7	.3	.3
ΔV_i	4π	9π	9π	6.25π	2.25π	$.25\pi$	1π	$.49\pi$	$.09\pi$	$.09\pi$

So the total volume of the chair leg is approximately

$$\sum_{i=1}^{10} \Delta V_i = 32.42\pi \approx 101.85 \text{ cubic inches.}$$

For all problems of this type, you can draw a sketch and analyze a representative ith subinterval, as was done in Example 1.

Finding the Exact Volume of a Surface of Revolution

Example 2

Consider the region bounded by the line $f(x) = x + 3$, the x- and y-axes, and the line $x = 7$. Find the volume of the solid generated by revolving this region about the x-axis.

Solution

Slice the solid into n sections which can be approximated by cylinders of width Δx. If $(z_i, 0)$ is a point contained in one of the cylinders, then the radius of the cylinder is $f(z_i)$, or $z_i + 3$. Thus the volume of the cylinder is $\pi(z_i + 3)^2 \Delta x$. The total volume of the solid can be approximated by the sum of the volumes of these cylinders, $\sum_{i=1}^{n} \pi(z_i + 3)^2 \Delta x$.

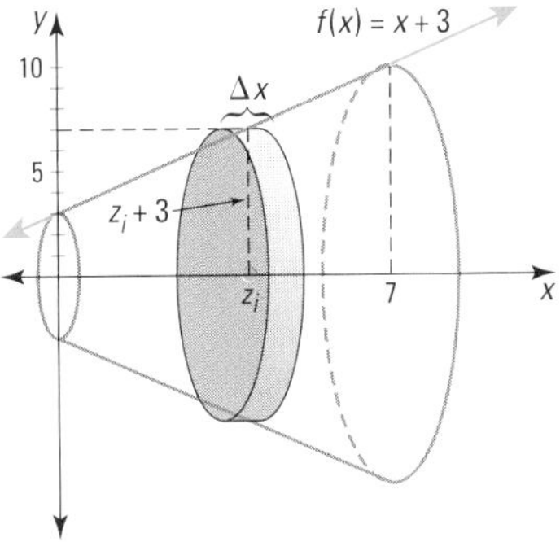

Notice that this is a Riemann sum for the function $f(x) = \pi(x + 3)^2$ on the interval $0 \le x \le 7$. As $n \to \infty$, that is, as more and more smaller slices are used, the sum becomes closer to the actual volume of the solid. Thus

$$\text{Volume} = \lim_{n\to\infty} \sum_{i=1}^{n} \pi(z_i + 3)^2 \Delta x.$$

Notes on Reading

Physical models can help students to visualize solids of revolution. Make a stack of pennies, nickels, dimes and quarters (in random order) and hold them between two fingers horizontally to illustrate how a solid can be made up of thin cylinders perpendicular to a horizontal axis. This model will resemble the chair leg in **Example 1** if the pennies, nickels, dimes and quarters are strategically placed. It is helpful to remove one coin and hold it flat so that students can see the proper relationships: Δx = width, or height, of cylinders, $f(z_i)$ = radius of cylinders, and so volume $= \pi r^2 h = \pi(f(z_i))^2 \Delta x$. **Teaching Aid 158** has the drawings of the chair leg.

Error Alert In the solution for **Example 1,** some students might lose sight of the fact they are finding volume because, in this case, $h = 1$.

The solid of **Example 2** is a truncated cone, and its volume could be found by standard Euclidean geometry formulas. In this example, note that the "width" of the cylinder is the cylinder's height for the purpose of calculating its volume. Also, the point $(z_i, 0)$ is on the axis of the cylinder, which is why $f(z_i)$ is the cylinder's radius. **Teaching Aid 158** has the drawing of this truncated cone.

The first example of this lesson creates and evaluates such a Riemann sum for a curve that is drawn and whose equation is not known. The second example shows how the method can be used to obtain the exact volume of the solid of revolution formed when a line is rotated about the x-axis. That requires taking the limit of the Riemann sum. The third example shows how the integral of a quadratic function can be applied to derive the volume formula for a sphere.

Optional Activities

Activity 1 Technology Connection
Materials: Explorations software

Students may use *Exploration 13-6: Volumes of Solids of Revolution,* as an alternative to **Example 2** in Lesson 13-6. Students can choose a function and an interval. Graphs show the region under the curve and a 3-D representation of the volume when the region is rotated around the x-axis. The computation using integration is shown.

Activity 2 You might have students check their answer to **Question 9b** using geometry. They must find the x-intercept of $f(x)$ to find the vertex of the cones involved. [The x-intercept of $f(x)$ is -4, so subtract the volume of the small cone (with base of radius 3 and height $4 + 2 = 6$) from the volume of the large cone (with base of radius 5 and height $4 + 6 = 10$) $= \frac{\pi 5^2(10)}{3} - \frac{\pi 3^2(6)}{3} = \frac{196\pi}{3}$]

❶ **Teaching Aid 158** shows the drawing for the Proof of the Volume of a Sphere Theorem. In the proof, you might note that it would also be possible to double the volume of half a sphere:

$V = 2[\pi\int_0^r (r^2 - x^2)\,dx]$.

If you do not have time to go through the details of the proof of the theorem for the volume of a sphere, you might give the general idea. The sphere is sliced into sections. Because the heights of these sections involve square roots of quadratic expressions, the volumes of the sections involve quadratic expressions. The limit of the sum then becomes an integral of a quadratic function and the formula of the preceding lesson can be applied; that formula indicated that the integral of a quadratic function is a cubic function. So here we have another reason why the formula for the volume of a sphere involves a cubic.

This is the limit of a Riemann sum for the function on the interval. Thus, the volume is an integral:

$$\text{Volume} = \int_0^7 \pi(x+3)^2\,dx = \pi\left[\int_0^7 (x^2 + 6x + 9)dx\right].$$

This can be evaluated by using the Integral of a Quadratic Function Theorem derived in Lesson 13-5, with $c_2 = 1$, $c_1 = 6$, and $c_0 = 9$:

$$\text{Volume} = \pi\left[\frac{7^3}{3} + 6 \cdot \frac{7^2}{2} + 9 \cdot 7\right] = \frac{973}{3}\pi.$$

Finding a Formula for the Volume of a Sphere

Definite integrals can help us obtain formulas for the volumes of some solid Here is a calculus proof of a theorem you may have first seen years ago.

Theorem
The volume of a sphere of radius r is $\frac{4}{3}\pi r^3$.

❶ **Proof**
This sphere can be obtained by revolving the semicircle $y = \sqrt{r^2 - x^2}$ about the x-axis.

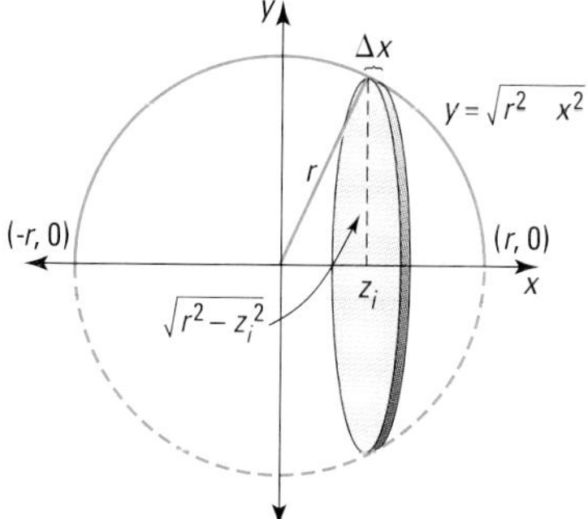

Slice the sphere into sections which can be approximated by cylinders of width Δx. If a section contains the point $(z_i, 0)$, its radius is approximately $\sqrt{r^2 - z_i^2}$, as shown in the drawing. Then from the formula for the volume of a cylinder, the volume of the section is approximately

$$\pi\left(\sqrt{r^2 - z_i^2}\right)^2 \Delta x = \pi(r^2 - z_i^2)\Delta x.$$

The sum of the volumes of these sections is

$$\sum_{i=1}^{n} \pi(r^2 - z_i^2)\Delta x.$$

The limit of this sum as $n \to \infty$ is the volume of the sphere. Also, this sum is a Riemann sum of the function $y = \pi(r^2 - x^2)$ over the interval $-r \le x \le r$. Thus its limit is an integral from $-r$ to r.

$$\text{Volume} = \lim_{n\to\infty} \sum_{i=1}^{n} (\pi(r^2 - z_i^2)\Delta x) = \int_{-r}^{r} \pi(r^2 - x^2)\,dx$$

Adapting to Individual Needs

Extra Help
You might wish to note the kinds of solids of revolution for which students can now find volumes. For any solid, if the solid can be placed as in **Example 1,** then its volume can be estimated. The methods of **Example 2** can be generalized to find the volume of any solid formed by revolving a line about the x-axis. The methods of the sphere volume theorem can be generalized to find the volume of any ellipsoid.

Using the Constant Multiple Property and Sum Property of Integrals, we get

$$\text{Volume} = \pi\left[\int_{-r}^{r} r^2\,dx - \int_{-r}^{r} x^2\,dx\right].$$

Now because r is a constant, the first integral is the integral of a constant function and can be evaluated by using $\int_a^b c\,dx = c(b-a)$. Also, by symmetry, $\int_{-r}^{r} x^2\,dx = 2\int_0^r x^2\,dx$. Thus,

$$\begin{aligned}\text{Volume} &= \pi\left[(r^2(r-(-r)) - \left(\frac{r^3}{3} - \frac{(-r)^3}{3}\right)\right] \\ &= \pi\left(r^2(2r) - \frac{r^3}{3} - \frac{r^3}{3}\right) \\ &= \pi\left(\frac{4}{3}r^3\right),\end{aligned}$$

which is equivalent to the formula $V = \frac{4}{3}\pi r^3$.

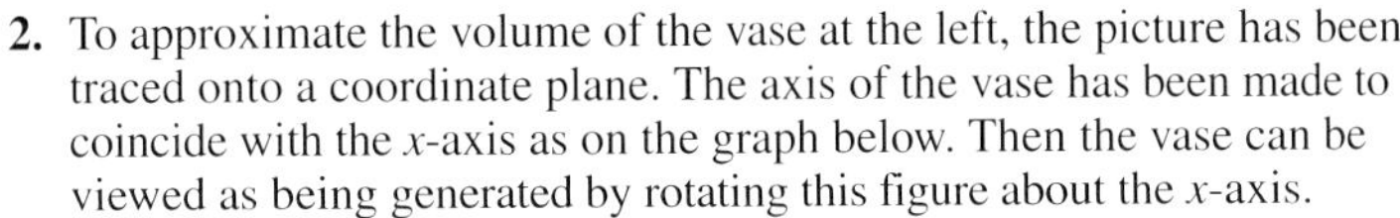

QUESTIONS

Covering the Reading

1. Refer to Example 1. Suppose r_i is given by the height (to the nearest half inch) of the graph at the left endpoint of the ith subinterval. Evaluate $\sum_{i=1}^{10} \Delta V_i$ in this case. **$41.25\pi \approx 129.59$ in^3**

2. To approximate the volume of the vase at the left, the picture has been traced onto a coordinate plane. The axis of the vase has been made to coincide with the x-axis as on the graph below. Then the vase can be viewed as being generated by rotating this figure about the x-axis.

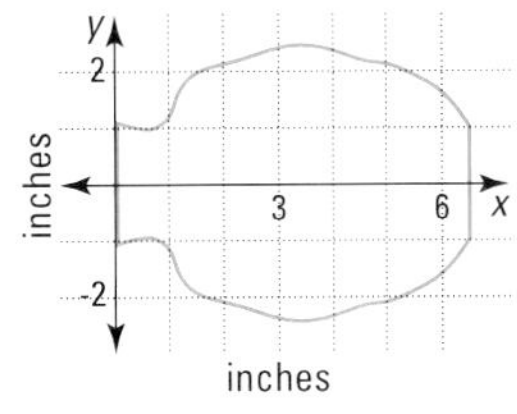

   a. If sections are formed as in Example 1 of this lesson, what figure does each section approximate? **cylinder**

   b. Using five subintervals, estimate the volume of the vase. (Take r_i to be the height, to the nearest fourth of an inch, of the graph at the right endpoint of the ith subinterval.) **$(17.375\pi)1.3 \approx 70.96$ in^3**

3. Consider the region bounded by the line $f(x) = x + 5$, the x- and y-axes, and the line $x = 4$. Find the volume of the solid generated by revolving this region about the x-axis. **$\frac{604\pi}{3} \approx 632.5$ units^3**

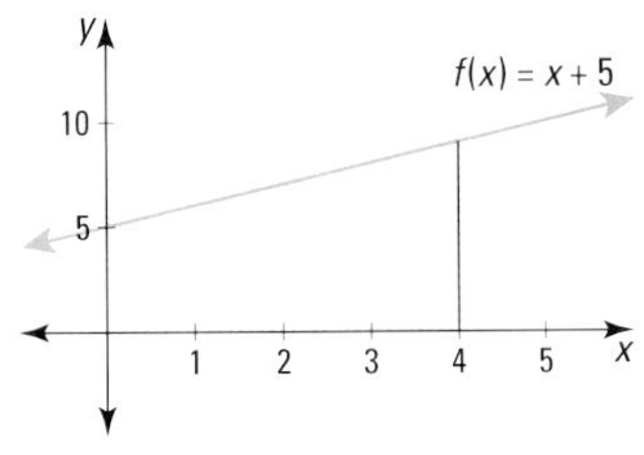

Additional Examples

1. Suppose that the region between the parabola $y = x^2$ and the x-axis, and between the y-axis and the line $x = 10$, is revolved about the x-axis.
   a. Split the region into five cylinders of equal width and use right endpoints of the subintervals to give an estimate for the volume of the solid generated. **$31{,}328\pi$**
   b. Repeat part a using 10 subintervals. **$25{,}333\pi$**
2. Find the volume generated when the area bounded by $y = \frac{1}{2}x$, the x-axis and $x = 6$ is revolved about the x-axis. **18π**

Notes on Questions

Question 2b Point out that here, unlike in **Example 2,** h in the volume formula is 1.3.

Question 3 This question is similar to **Example 2.** You can check the answer by noting that this solid is a truncated cone; the original cone had height 9 and radius 9 and the top 5 units of its height were cut off.

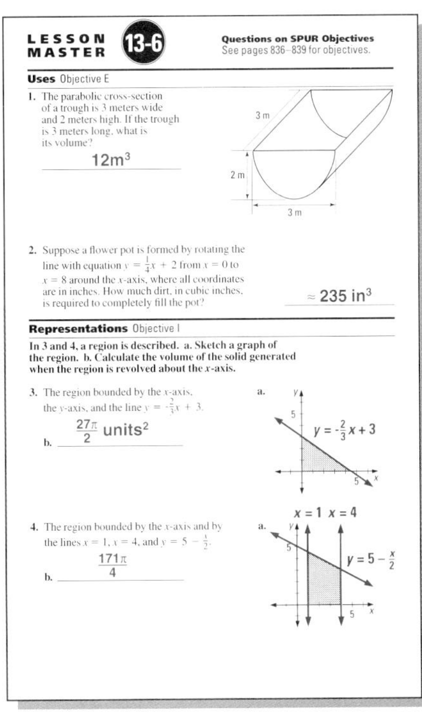

LESSON MASTER 13-6 — Questions on SPUR Objectives
See pages 836–839 for objectives.

Uses Objective E

1. The parabolic cross-section of a trough is 3 meters wide and 2 meters high. If the trough is 3 meters long, what is its volume? **12m^3**

2. Suppose a flower pot is formed by rotating the line with equation $y = \frac{1}{4}x + 2$ from $x = 0$ to $x = 8$ around the x-axis, where all coordinates are in inches. How much dirt, in cubic inches, is required to completely fill the pot? **≈ 235 in^3**

Representations Objective I

In 3 and 4, a region is described. a. Sketch a graph of the region. b. Calculate the volume of the solid generated when the region is revolved about the x-axis.

3. The region bounded by the x-axis, the y-axis, and the line $y = -\frac{2}{3}x + 3$.
   a. (graph) b. **$\frac{27\pi}{2}$ units^2**

4. The region bounded by the x-axis and by the lines $x = 1$, $x = 4$, and $y = 5 - \frac{x}{2}$.
   a. (graph) b. **$\frac{171\pi}{4}$**

Adapting to Individual Needs

Challenge

Have students find the volume when the region bounded by the x-axis and the semi-ellipse $y = 2\sqrt{\left(1 - \frac{x^2}{9}\right)}$ is revolved around the x-axis. [16π]

Notes on Questions

Question 5 Here each side has value $2r^3$.

Error Alert Students may not have realized the critical importance of "dx" in the calculation of definite integrals. Stress that it identifies the variable over which the integral is being considered. If the left side were $\int_{-r}^{r} r^2\, dr$, then the integral would be that of a quadratic, and would equal $\frac{2r^3}{3}$, while $\int_{-r}^{r} r^2\, dx\ r^2 \int_{-r}^{r} 1 \cdot dx = 2r^3$.

Additional Answers

9. a.

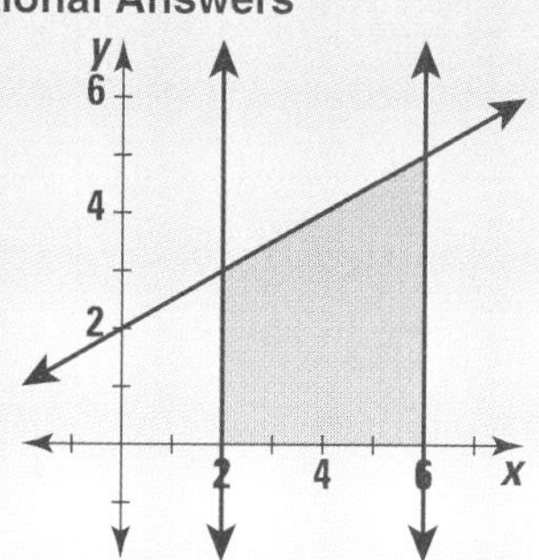

5) $\int_b^a kf(x)\, dx = k\int_b^a f(x)\, dx$ for k a constant. But r is a constant, so r^2 is a constant. So $\int_{-r}^{r} r^2\, dx = r^2\int_{-r}^{r} 1\, dx$ or $r^2\int_{-r}^{r} dx$.

7a)

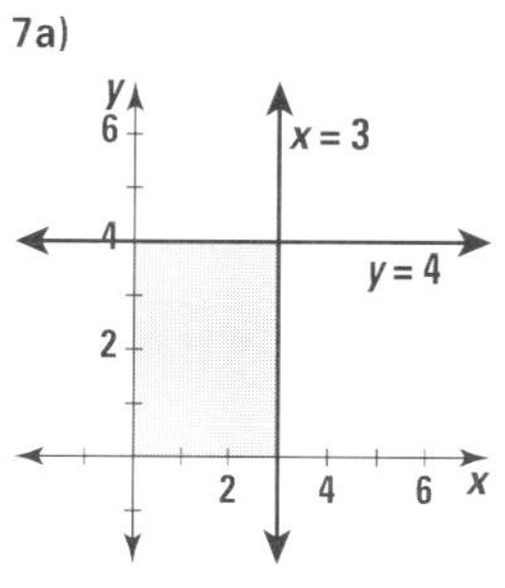

d) $\int_0^3 \pi r_i^2\, dx = 16\pi\int_0^3 dx = 48\pi$ units^3

8a)

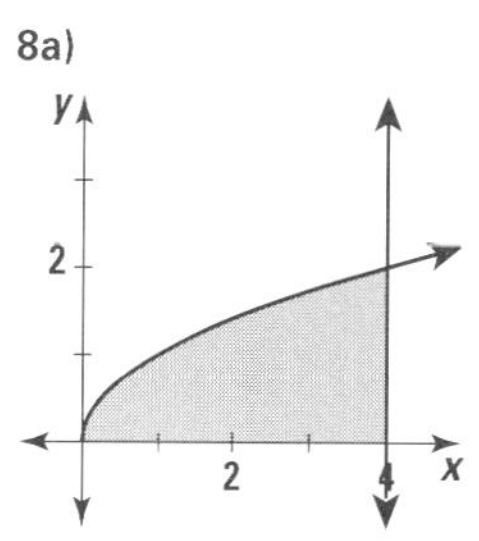

In 4–6, refer to the proof of the theorem on the volume of a sphere.

4. Explain why the cross-section containing the point $(z_i, 0)$ has radius equal to $\sqrt{r^2 - z_i^2}$. **The radius of the cross-section is the height of the graph where $x = z_i$, since $f(x) = \sqrt{r^2 - x^2}$, so $f(z_i) = \sqrt{r^2 - z_i^2}$.**

5. Explain why the following statement is true:

$$\int_{-r}^{r} r^2\, dx = r^2\int_{-r}^{r} dx.$$ **See left.**

6. Why are the two integrals in the proof evaluated from $-r$ to r? **$(-r, 0)$ and $(r, 0)$ are the left and right endpoints of the semicircle.**

Applying the Mathematics

7. Consider the region bounded by the x- and y-axes and the lines $y = 4$ and $x = 3$.

a. Sketch a graph of this region. **See left.**

b. Suppose the region is revolved about the x-axis. What type of solid is formed? **cylinder**

c. Let r_i be the radius of the cylindrical section on the ith subinterval. If r_i is the height of the graph at the right endpoint of the ith subinterval, find r_i. **4 units**

d. Find the volume of the solid in part **b** by setting up and evaluating an integral. **See left.**

e. Find the volume of the solid in part **b** by using theorems from geometry. **$\pi r^2 h = \pi(4^2)(3) = 48\pi$ units^3**

8. a. Sketch a graph of the region bounded by $f(x) = \sqrt{x}$, $x = 4$, and the x-axis. **See left.**

b. Calculate the volume of the solid generated when this region revolves about the x-axis. **8π units^3**

9. a. Sketch a graph of the region bounded by $f(x) = \frac{1}{2}x + 2$, $x = 2$, $x = 6$, and the x-axis. **See margin.**

b. Calculate the volume of the solid generated when this region revolves about the x-axis. **$\frac{196\pi}{3} \approx 205.25$ units^3**

Review

10. At the right is a graph of $y = 2x^2 - 16x + 33$.

a. Set up an integral that describes the area of the shaded region.

b. Evaluate your result in part **a**.

(Lessons 13-4, 13-5) **9 units^3**

a) $\int_2^5 (2x^2 - 16x + 33)\, dx$

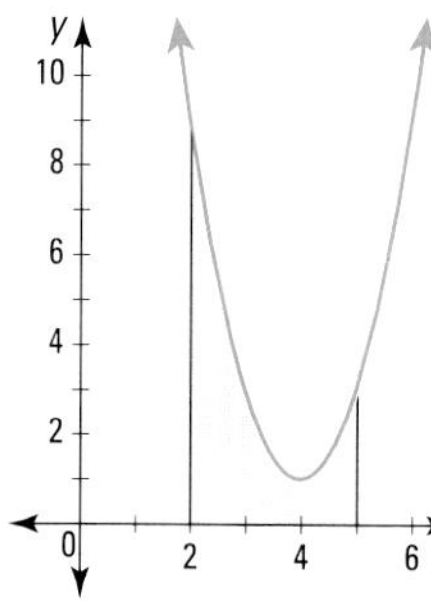

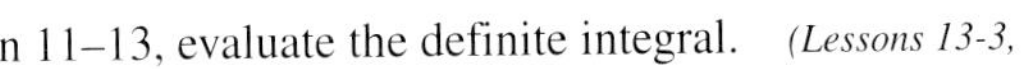

In 11–13, evaluate the definite integral. *(Lessons 13-3, 13-4, 13-5)*

11. $\int_0^7 5x\,dx$ **$\frac{245}{2}$**

12. $\int_2^3 (4x + 1)\,dx$ **11**

13. $\int_0^2 \sqrt{4 - x^2}\,dx$ **π**

14. Write as a single integral: $\int_3^{11} \log x^3\,dx + \int_3^{11} \log x^4\,dx$. *(Lesson 13-4)* **See left.**

15. The school bookstore carries only one size of three-ring binders but carries it in three colors: green, blue, and red. A student plans to purchase 5 binders. In how many different ways can the student do this? *(Lesson 10-7)* **21**

16. Let f be the function $f(x) = ax^2 + bx$. Calculate the average rate of change in f from x to $x + \Delta x$. *(Lesson 9-1)* **$2ax + b + a\Delta x$**

17. Consider the graph of the polynomial $p(x)$ at the right.

a. What does $\lim_{x \to \infty} p(x)$ appear to be? $-\infty$

b. What does $\lim_{x \to -\infty} p(x)$ appear to be? $-\infty$

c. What is the smallest possible degree of $p(x)$? *(Lesson 8-8)* **4**

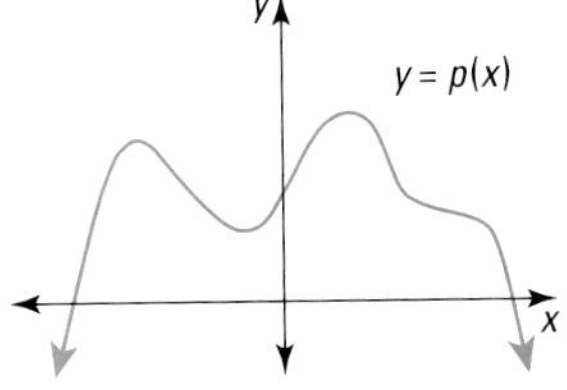

18. Prove the following identity:

$\forall$ *real numbers x for which* $\cos x \neq 0$, $\frac{\cos 3x}{\cos x} = 4\cos^2 x - 3$. *(Lessons 6-2, 6-4)* **See margin.**

19. Prove or disprove the following statement:

For all real numbers a, b, and c, if a is a factor of b and a is a factor of c, then a is a factor of bc. *(Lesson 4-1)* **See left.**

Exploration

20. Graphs of $y = 2$ and $y = \sqrt{x}$ appear below. Determine the volume of the solid generated when the shaded region is revolved about the x-axis. (Hint: Think of the solid as a cylinder out of which a bullet-shaped region has been cut.) **8π units^2**

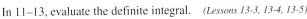

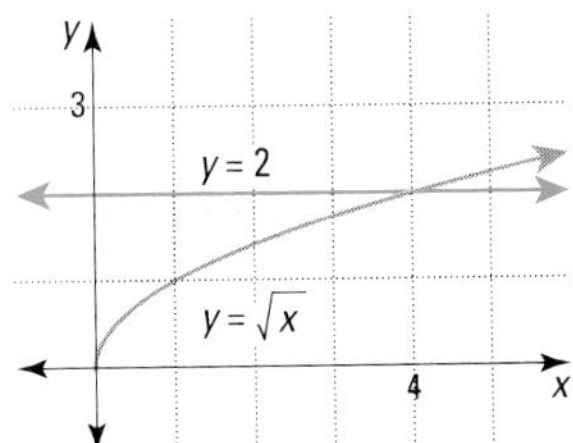

14) $\int_3^{11} \log x^7\,dx$ or $7\int_3^{11} \log x\,dx$

19) a is a factor of $c \Leftrightarrow c = am$ for some integer m. So $bc = b(am) = a(bm)$, so a is a factor of bc. (a is a factor of b is not needed.)

Follow-up for Lesson 13-6

Practice

For more questions on SPUR Objectives, use **Lesson Master 13-6** (shown on page 823).

Assessment

Written Communication Ask students to **work in pairs.** Have each student write a problem like **Question 2,** sketching a simple vessel that produces a curve over the interval $0 \leq x \leq 5$. Students should solve their partner's problem and discuss the solutions. [Students find the volumes of solids.]

Extension

Project Update Project 5, *Kepler,* on page 833 relates to the content of this lesson.

Additional Answers

18. Left side $= \frac{\cos 3x}{\cos x} = \frac{\cos(2x + x)}{\cos x} = \frac{\cos 2x \cos x - \sin 2x \sin x}{\cos x}$

$= \frac{(2\cos^2 x - 1)\cos x - (2\sin x \cos x)\sin x}{\cos x}$ Formulas for $\cos(\alpha + \beta)$ and $\sin(\alpha + \beta)$

$= \frac{2\cos^3 x - \cos x - 2\sin^2 x \cos x}{\cos x}$

$= 2\cos^2 x - 1 - 2\sin^2 x$ $\forall$ real numbers for which $\cos x \neq 0$

$= 2\cos^2 x - 1 - 2(1 - \cos^2 x)$ Since $\sin^2 x = 1 - \cos^2 x$

$= 4\cos^2 x - 3$

$=$ Right side

Lesson 13-7

Objectives

There are no SPUR Objectives for any reading lesson

Resources

From the ***Teacher's Resource File***
- Answer Master 13-7
- Teaching Aid 149: Warm-up

Additional Resources
- Visual for Teaching Aid 149

Teaching Lesson 13-7

Warm-up

Describe several functions f that satisfy $f'(x) = 2x$. **Sample:** $f(x) = x^2 + 1$, $f(x) = x^2 + 2$, $f(x) = x^2 + 3$

Notes on Reading

Error Alert Some students find it troubling at first that many functions have the same derivative, as illustrated in the *Warm-up*. The goal is for students to realize that functions that differ by a constant have the same derivative. To see this, have students trace and then sketch tangents to the two functions in the graph in the middle of page 827. Since corresponding tangents at each value of x are parallel, their slopes are equal and so the derivatives at each value of x are equal.

LESSON

13-7 *The Fundamental Theorem of Calculus*

That's the Way the Cookie Crumbles. *Eating certain foods may not help you learn calculus, but it might not hurt either.*

Who Discovered Calculus?

Archimedes and Johannes Kepler (the person who discovered that planets travel around the sun in elliptical orbits) used ideas of integration, and rates of change were studied by Galileo and others. However, Isaac Newton and Gottfried Leibniz are usually considered to be the founders or discoverers of calculus. Newton and Leibniz independently discovered that derivatives and integrals of functions are related in a simple way, and thus they created a unified branch of mathematics. Newton seems to have discovered this idea, which today we call the Fundamental Theorem of Calculus, in the 1660s, and Leibniz in the 1670s, but Leibniz published his work in 1684 and 1686, while Newton waited until 1687. The two men engaged in bitter quarrels about who was first, but today they are both generally credited with the discovery of calculus.

Examples of Related Derivatives and Integrals

You have seen a number of examples of the relationship between derivatives and integrals. In Chapter 9, you saw that the derivative of a position or distance function is a rate function. In this chapter, you saw that the integral of a rate function gives total distance.

Also in Chapter 9, you saw that if f is the function defined by $f(x) = ax^2 + bx$, then its derivative function f' is defined by $f'(x) = 2ax + b$. Now examine $\int_0^v (2ax + b)\,dx$. From the Sum Property and Constant Multiple Property,

$$\int_0^v (2ax + b)\,dx = 2a\int_0^v x\,dx + \int_0^v b\,dx$$
$$= 2a\left(\frac{v^2}{2}\right) + bv$$
$$= av^2 + bv.$$

Lesson 13-7 Overview

Broad Goals This lesson introduces the Fundamental Theorem of Calculus, which relates differentiation and integration.

Perspective We have tried to end all UCSMP texts with a lesson that involves many of the concepts found earlier in the book yet signals the future. This lesson follows that form: it serves to summarize this chapter and relate it to Chapter 9 by pointing out the nearly inverse relation between derivatives and integrals. At the same time, it demonstrates the wonderful unity of mathematics and prepares students for one of the major ideas in calculus.

So the integral of the derivative function $f'(x) = 2ax + b$ gives the original function when v is replaced by x.

In Lesson 13-2, you calculated a Riemann sum for $f(x) = \cos x$ on the interval from 0 to $\frac{\pi}{3}$. With $n = 500$, the value of that sum was approximately 0.8660, which is close to $\sin \frac{\pi}{3}$. In general,

$$\int_0^a \cos x\, dx = \sin a.$$

Do you recall from Chapter 9 that when $f(x) = \sin x$, $f'(x) = \cos x$? Thus the derivative of the sine function is the cosine function and, in a way (to be detailed below), the integral of the cosine function is the sine function.

The fact that many functions have the same derivative prevents derivatives and integrals from being related in a 1-1 manner. Specifically, adding a constant c to the values of a function merely translates the function up c units and does not affect any derivative.

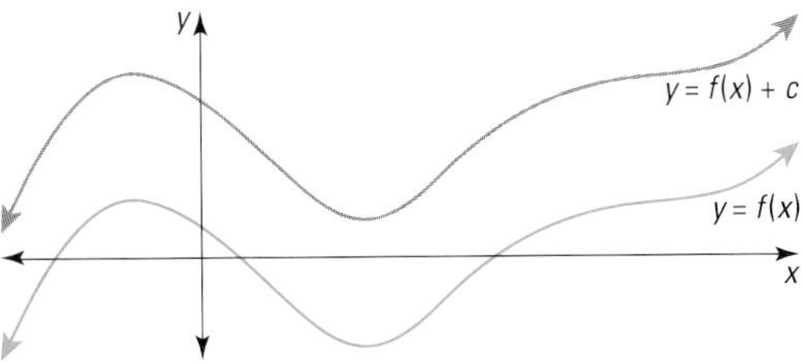

Still, the relationships between derivatives and integrals are most elegant.

The General Relationships Between Derivatives and Integrals

Fundamental Theorem of Calculus
Let f be a continuous function on the interval from a to b.

1. If g is a function whose derivative is f, then $\int_a^b f(x)\, dx = g(b) - g(a)$.
2. If $g(x) = \int_a^x f(t)\, dt$ for all x from a to b, then $g'(x) = f(x)$ for all such x.

The second part of the Fundamental Theorem of Calculus can be interpreted as saying that the derivative of the integral of a function is the original function. For instance, in Lesson 13-5, it was found that $\int_a^b x^2\, dx = \frac{b^3}{3} - \frac{a^3}{3}$. Let $x = t$ and $b = x$, and let $g(x) = \int_a^x t^2\, dt = \frac{x^3}{3} - \frac{a^3}{3}$. Then by Part 2 of the Fundamental Theorem, $g'(x) = x^2$.

To see why the second part of the theorem is true in general when f is a continuous function that is positive on the interval $a \le x \le b$, define a function g as follows: $g(x) = \int_a^x f(t)\, dt$ for all x on $a \le x \le b$. Then $g(x)$ is the area between the graph of f and the horizontal axis from a to x.

Another illustration of part (1) of the Fundamental Theorem of Calculus uses projectile motion. Recall that the position function $h(t) = 800t - 16t^2$ has as its derivative the velocity function $h'(t) = v(t) = 800 - 32t$. The distance traveled from $t = 8$ to $t = 20$ is given by the area under the velocity curve from 8 to 20, $\int_8^{20} v(t)\, dt$, which is $\int_8^{20} h'(t)\, dt$. But the distance traveled is also given by $h(20) - h(8)$. Therefore $\int_8^{20} h'(t)\, dt = h(20) - h(8)$.

Examples are critical for understanding the Fundamental Theorem of Calculus. For instance, you could prove (using the definition of derivative) that if $f(x) = \frac{1}{3}x^3$, then $f'(x) = x^2$. Now evaluate $\int_a^b x^2\, dx$ using the Fundamental Theorem of Calculus. It is $f(b) - f(a)$, or $\frac{b^3}{3} - \frac{a^3}{3}$. This evaluation, using the Fundamental Theorem, is quite simple and elegant compared with the derivation in Lesson 13-5, and gives many students an appreciation of the Fundamental Theorem.

Optional Activities

Activity 1 To ensure students have an understanding of the second part of the Fundamental Theorem of Calculus, you might have them explain why choices (a), (b), and (d) are incorrect in **Question 6.** [(a) is incorrect because the integral is from a to x; (b) is incorrect, but close: this result comes from doing the integration and evaluating, but then not taking the derivative; (d) is incorrect because the integration was not performed.]

Activity 2 Technology Some graphing calculators will allow the user to evaluate definite integrals. If your students' calculators have this capability, have them use this feature to check their answers to **Questions 3, 7, and 8.**

Activity 3 You might ask students to compute a Riemann sum for **Question 7** using 15 subintervals (of width 1). Have them compare their approximation with the exact answer to **Question 7.** [The Riemann sum yields an approximation of 1.5144, which is relatively close to the exact answer, $\ln(4) \approx 1.3863$.]

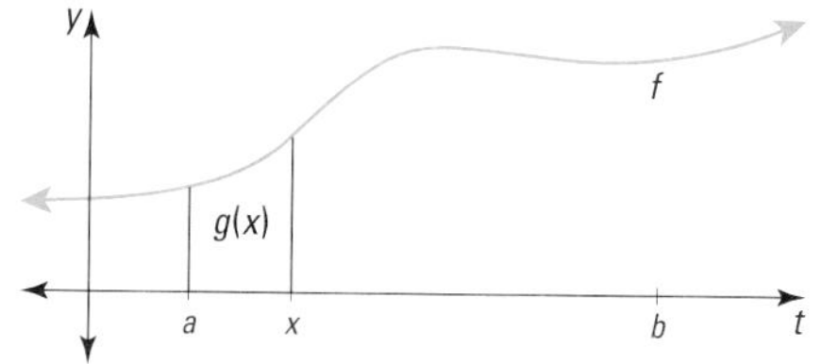

Remember that $g'(x) = \lim_{\Delta x \to \infty} \frac{g(x + \Delta x) - g(x)}{\Delta x}$. To evaluate the difference quotient when $\Delta x > 0$, notice that $g(x + \Delta x)$ is the area between the graph of f and the horizontal axis from a to $x + \Delta x$.

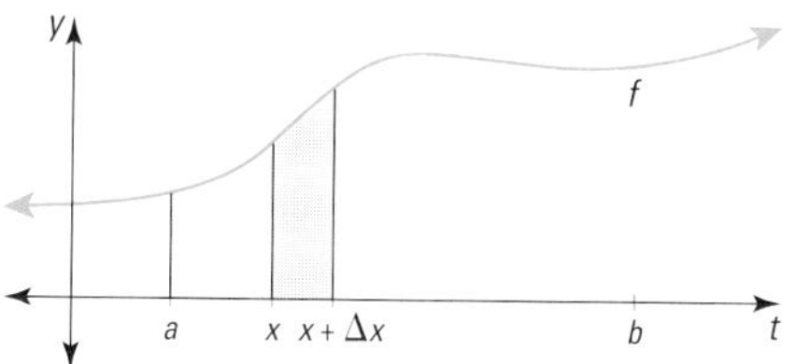

So $g(x + \Delta x) - g(x)$ is the area of the region between the graph of f and the horizontal axis from x to $x + \Delta x$.

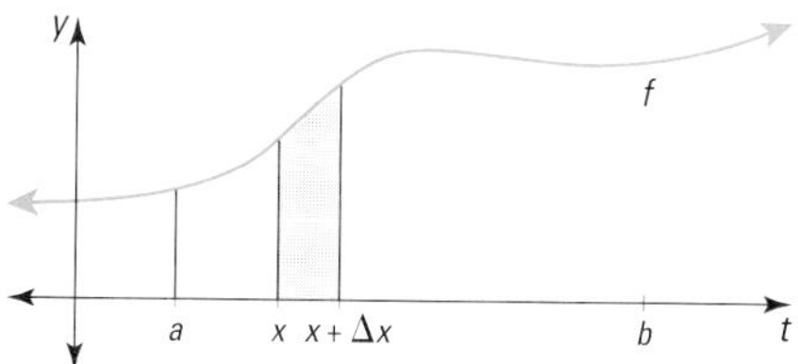

If Δx is small, then the region is nearly a rectangle, and if we divide this area by Δx, we are dividing by the width of the rectangle. The quotient is approximately the height of the rectangle, which, as Δx gets smaller and smaller, since f is continuous, approaches the value $f(x)$. That is, $\lim_{\Delta x \to \infty} \frac{g(x + \Delta x) - g(x)}{\Delta x} = f(x)$, or, in other symbols, $g'(x) = f(x)$.

In the case of the first part of the Fundamental Theorem of Calculus, g is called an **antiderivative** of f. This part indicates that the definite integral is found by evaluating an antiderivative. For instance, since the derivative of the sine is the cosine, if $f(x) = \cos x$, then one of its antiderivatives is $g(x) = \sin x$. Because of this,

$$\int_a^b \cos x \, dx = \sin b - \sin a.$$

Then
$$\int_0^{\pi/3} \cos x \, dx = \sin \frac{\pi}{3} - \sin 0 = \frac{\sqrt{3}}{2},$$

which agrees with the estimate found in the Example in Lesson 13-2.

Adapting to Individual Needs

Extra Help

As the lesson closes with reference to the many important theorems studied in this course, you might want to review the three "fundamental" theorems in this book: the Fundamental Theorem of Arithmetic (Lesson 4-7), the Fundamental Theorem of Algebra (Lesson 8-8), and the Fundamental Theorem of Calculus (Lesson 13-7). Interesting discussion might ensue. Are there other theorems which arguably could be considered more important in each of the three areas of mathematics? Are there any theorems from geometry or trigonometry that deserve the label of "fundamental?" [Answers will vary.]

Together, the two parts of the Fundamental Theorem of Calculus imply that if you have found the derivative of a function, then you can evaluate integrals of the derivative, and if you have the integral of a function, then you know the derivative of that integral.

Thus, integration and differentiation are almost inverse operations on functions. Perhaps this is not so surprising, for integrals can be interpreted as areas and volumes, which are basic models for multiplication. Derivatives are rates, and rate is a basic model of division. And, just as multiplication and division undo each other, so do integration and differentiation.

It is perhaps fitting that we have ended this book by discussing a very important theorem, for throughout this book you have studied some of the most important theorems in all of mathematics. Three of them even are called "fundamental"! If you take additional courses in mathematics, and we certainly hope you do, you will encounter the ideas in this course again and again, for discrete mathematics and the mathematics needed for calculus are found in virtually all fields of mathematics.

Why are mathematical ideas so interrelated? Perhaps because they originate from ideas in an inherently ordered world. No one knows for sure.

We hope that these and other ideas you have studied in this book have interested you and have stimulated your curiosity to learn more. And, of course, we hope you have enjoyed and learned much from this course.

QUESTIONS

Covering the Reading

1. What two mathematicians are credited with discovering calculus? **Isaac Newton and Gottfried Leibniz**
2. Why are derivatives and integrals not related in a 1-1 manner? **Many different functions have the same derivative.**
3. Use the first part of the Fundamental Theorem of Calculus to evaluate
$$\int_0^{\pi/2} \cos x \, dx.$$ **1**
4. You know that if $g(x) = x^2$ and $f(x) = 2x$, then $g'(x) = f(x)$. So g is called an _?_ of f. **antiderivative**
5. If $g(x) = \int_a^x \ln t \, dt$, then $g'(x) =$ _?_. **ln x**
6. *Multiple choice.* If $h(x) = \int_a^x (t^2 - 5t + 4)\, dt$, then $h'(x) =$ _?_. **c**
   (a) $t^2 - 5t + 4$
   (b) $\left(\frac{x^3}{3} - \frac{5x^2}{2} + 4x\right) - \left(\frac{a^3}{3} - \frac{5a^2}{2} + 4a\right)$
   (c) $x^2 - 5x + 4$
   (d) $(x^2 - 5x + 4) - (a^2 - 5a + 4)$

Notes on Questions

Question 3 Students are expected to use the result that if $f(x) = \sin x$, then $f'(x) = \cos x$.

Adapting to Individual Needs

Challenge
Have students answer these questions.

Let $f(x) = \int_1^x (t^2 + t + 1)\, dt$.

1. Use the first half of the Fundamental Theorem of Calculus to simplify $f(x)$ in terms of x. [$f(x) = \frac{1}{3}x^3 + \frac{1}{2}x^2 + x$]
2. From the result in part a, find $f'(x)$. [$f'(x) = x^2 + x + 1$]
3. Use the second half of the Fundamental Theorem of Calculus to find $f'(x)$. Do your answers agree? [$f'(x) = x^2 + x + 1$; yes]

Notes on Questions

Question 8 The derivative of the sine is the cosine; the derivative of the cosine is the opposite of the sine. Thus, the sequence of nth derivatives of the sine goes: sine, cosine, -sine, -cosine, sine, ..., repeating with a period of 4. It also means that the sine and cosine functions each satisfy the second order differential equation $f'' = -f$. This makes them very important in the study of such equations.

Question 17 You might inform students that there are tables of integrals and derivatives. There are also symbol manipulators and computer programs that can symbolically both integrate and differentiate.

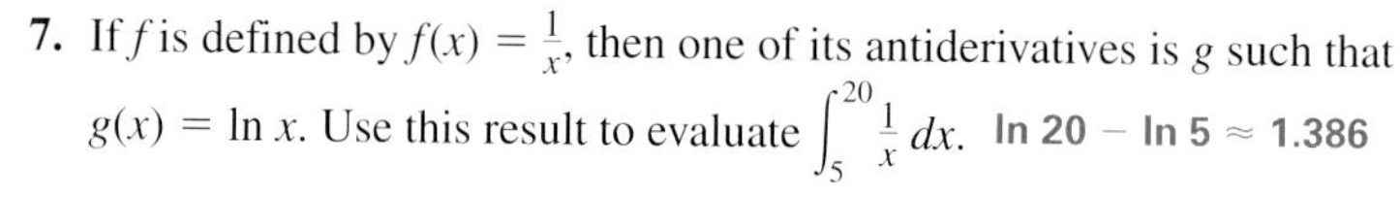

7. If f is defined by $f(x) = \frac{1}{x}$, then one of its antiderivatives is g such that $g(x) = \ln x$. Use this result to evaluate $\int_5^{20} \frac{1}{x}\,dx$. **$\ln 20 - \ln 5 \approx 1.386$**

8. If $f(x) = \sin x$, then one of its antiderivatives is $g(x) = -\cos x$.

a. Use this relationship to evaluate $\int_0^{\pi/3} \sin x\,dx$. **0.5**

b. Use a computer to approximate the integral, using a Riemann sum with 100 subintervals. How well does your result agree with the answer in part **a**? **0.5043; the result agrees very well; the relative error is only about 0.8%.**

9. What are the two other "fundamental theorems" discussed in this book? **See margin.**

10a)

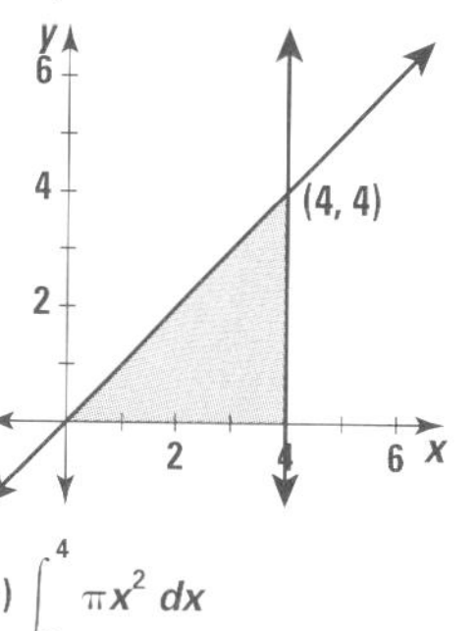

b) $\int_0^4 \pi x^2\,dx$

Review

10. a. Sketch the region bounded by the line $y = x$, the x-axis, and the line $x = 4$.

b. Write an integral that finds the volume of the solid formed when the region in part **a** is rotated about the x-axis. *(Lesson 13-6)*
a, b) See left.

11. A cylindrical trough has a base in the shape of a parabola, 4 feet high and 6 feet across. If the trough is 7 feet long, what is its volume? *(Lesson 13-5)* **112 ft^3**

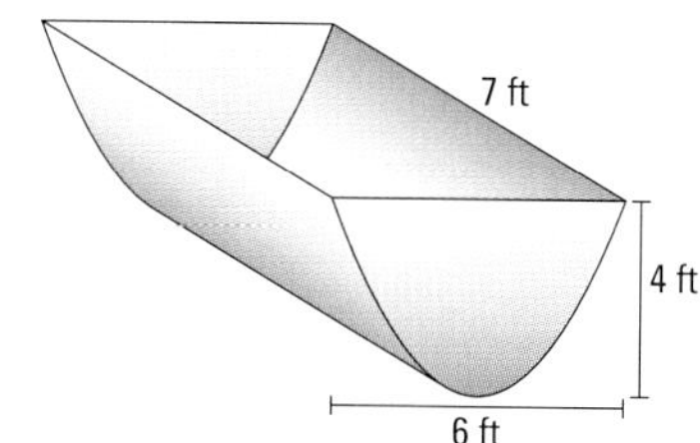

In 12 and 13, evaluate the definite integral. *(Lessons 13-3, 13-4, 13-5)*

12. $\int_{-3}^{2} (5x - 7)\,dx$ **-47.5**

13. $\int_1^2 (3x^2 + 4x)\,dx$ **13**

14. Express the shaded area below with integral notation. *(Lesson 13-3)* $\int_0^{\frac{5\pi}{4}} (1 + \sin 2x)\,dx$

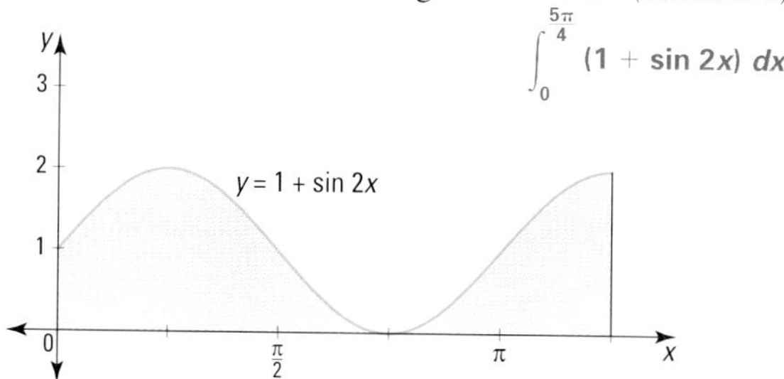

Additional Answers

9. **Fundamental Theorem of Arithmetic: Suppose that n is an integer and that $n > 1$. Then either n is a prime number or n has a prime factorization which is unique except for the order of the factors. Fundamental Theorem of Algebra: Every polynomial of degree $n \geq 1$ with real or complex coefficients has at least one complex zero.**

In 15 and 16, find an Euler circuit, if one exists. *(Lesson 11-4)*

15.

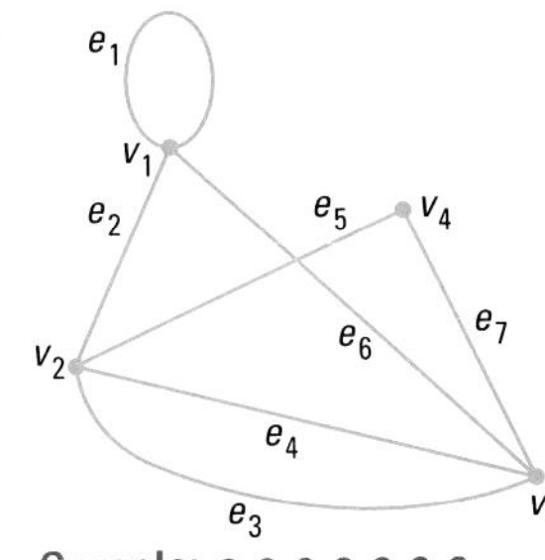

Sample: $e_1e_2e_3e_4e_5e_7e_6$

16.

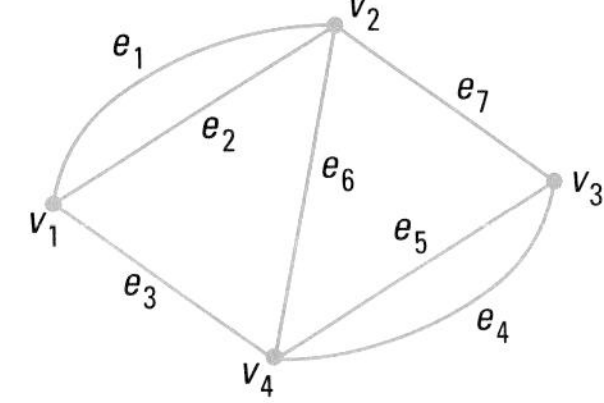

No Euler circuit exists.

Exploration

17. Given the following relationships:

if $f(x) = \tan x$	then	$f'(x) = \sec^2 x$
if $f(x) = \ln x$	then	$f'(x) = \frac{1}{x}$
if $f(x) = e^x$	then	$f'(x) = e^x$.

Make up one or more area problems to be evaluated through the use of the Fundamental Theorem of Calculus. Check your results by using a computer or calculator program to calculate Riemann sums with a larger and larger number of subintervals. Answers may vary.

Follow-up for Lesson 13-7

Extension

Following the second to last paragraph of this lesson, ask students for other examples of the interrelationships within mathematics. A discussion of why mathematical ideas are so interrelated could be quite interesting. There may be a wide range of opinions, but there is no "right" answer. It really is the case that no one knows why the extraordinary edifice of mathematics is so interconnected.

Project Update Project 6, *Du Châtelet,* on page 833, relates to the content of this lesson.

Chapter 13 Projects

The projects relate chiefly to the content of the lessons of this chapter as follows:

Project	Lesson(s)
1	13-2, 13-5
2	13-2, 13-3, 13-5
3	13-5
4	13-2
5	13-6
6	13-7

1 Programming Riemann Sums I This, along with Project 2, are straightforward, each culminating in a conjecture for a formula for a definite integral. You may wish to modify the BASIC program so that it works on a calculator.

2 Programming Riemann Sums II This project is quite similar to Project 1.

3 Integrating by Weights The directions for this project are quite specific so that the values found will be reasonably close to the theoretical values. Even so, this project takes quite a bit of work.

4 Geographical Areas The idea in this project is found in UCSMP *Geometry,* and students who have studied from that book are likely to remember it. The difference is that here, instead of counting squares inside, partly inside, and completely outside the region, one uses the grid as a coordinate axis.

5 Kepler Kepler has already been mentioned in this text for having used logarithms for calculations of orbits of planets.

PROJECTS 13 CHAPTER THIRTEEN

A project presents an opportunity for you to extend your knowledge of a topic related to the material of this chapter. You should allow more time for a project than you do for a typical homework question.

1 Programming Riemann Sums I

The BASIC program below approximates the area under the curve $y = x^2$ from 0 to 10 using Riemann sums with subintervals of equal width. The height of each rectangle is determined by the value of the function at the *midpoint* of the interval. The program below uses 100 rectangles for an interval from 0 to 10.

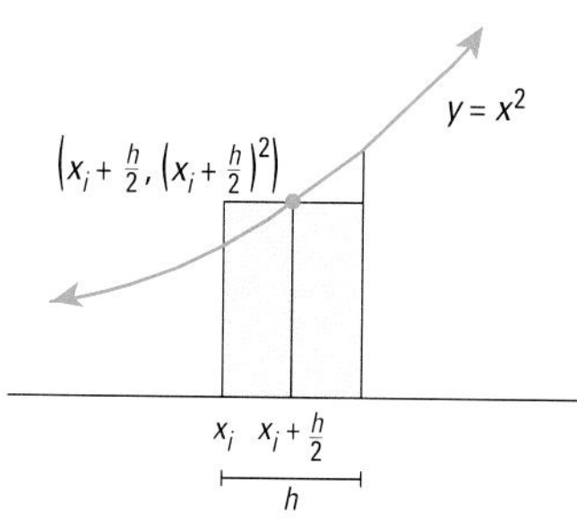


```
100  REM LEFT AND RIGHT ENDPOINTS
110  LET A = 0
120  LET B = 10
130  REM NUMBER OF SUBINTERVALS
140  LET N = 100
150  REM SUBINTERVAL SIZE
160  LET DX = (B - A)/N
170  REM INITIALIZE SUM
180  LET SUM = 0
190  REM LOOP THROUGH SUBINTERVALS
200  FOR I = 1 TO N
210    REM COMPUTE MIDPOINT OF
       SUBINTERVAL
220    M = A + (I-0.5)*DX
230    REM COMPUTE THE VALUE OF THE
       FUNCTION
240    V = M^2
250    REM INCREMENT THE SUM
260    SUM = SUM + V*DX
270  NEXT I
280  PRINT "SUM ="; SUM
290  END
```


a. Run the program and make a table of values for right endpoint values of $b = 1, 2, 3, 4, \ldots, 10$. Compare the values with the corresponding values of $\frac{b^3}{3}$.

b. Replace line 240 with V = M^3 to evaluate the area under the curve $y = x^3$. Mak a table as in part **a**. Make a conjecture as to the formula for the area under the curve from 0 to b.

2 Programming Riemann Sums II

Use the program in Project 1.

a. Investigate the area under $y = \sin x$ from 0 to b, where $b = \frac{\pi}{6}, \frac{\pi}{4}, \frac{\pi}{3}, \frac{\pi}{2}, \frac{2\pi}{3}, \frac{3\pi}{4}, \frac{5\pi}{6}, \pi$. Match your results to values of another trigonometric function and make a conjecture about the area under the curve $y = \sin x$ from 0 to b.

b. Investigate the area under $y = e^x$. Make a table for areas for $b = .5, 1, 1.5, 2, \ldots, 4$. Graph the curve $y = e^x$ and make a conjecture about a formula for the area under $y = e^x$ from 0 to b.

3 Integrating by Weights

Archimedes used physical models to make conjectures about areas under curves. You can do an experiment similar to his to find the area under the parabola $y = x^2$ from 0 to b. You will need an accurate scale such as those found in chemistry or physics laboratories. Take a piece of cardboard and draw a grid. If you have an 8.5×11 inch cardboard, mark it in centimeter squares. You will get 21 squares along the width and 27 along the length. Use the bottom edge of the width as your x-axis and mark centimeters on the width as $-5, -4, \ldots, 4, 5$. Graph $y = x^2$, using the height of the cardboard as your vertical dimension. You should be able to get the points $(-5, 25)$ and $(5, 25)$ on your graphs. Draw the parabola very carefully because you will be cutting it out later. Trim the cardboard so that you have a rectangle which is 10 units along the base and 25 units high. This has area 250 cm^2.

Possible Responses

1. a.

b	Area under $y = x^2$ from $x = 0$ to $x = b$	$\frac{b^3}{3}$
1	.33325	.33333
2	2.6666	2.66667
3	8.999773	9.00000
4	21.3328	21.33333
5	41.66562	41.66667
6	71.99818	72.00000
7	114.3305	114.33333
8	170.6624	170.66667
9	242.994	243.00000
10	333.325	333.33333

The area under $y = x^2$ approximated from the program is very close to $\frac{b^3}{3}$, as shown in the table at the left.

b. See table at the right. Conjecture: The area under the curve $y = x^3$ from $x = 0$ to $x = b$ is $\frac{b^4}{4}$.

b	Area under $y = x^3$ from $x = 0$ to $x = b$	$\frac{b^4}{4}$
1	.2499875	.25
2	3.999799	4.00
3	20.24899	20.25
4	63.99679	64.00
5	156.2422	156.25
6	323.9838	324.00
7	600.22	600.25
8	1023.949	1024.00
9	1640.168	1640.25
10	2499.875	2500.00

832

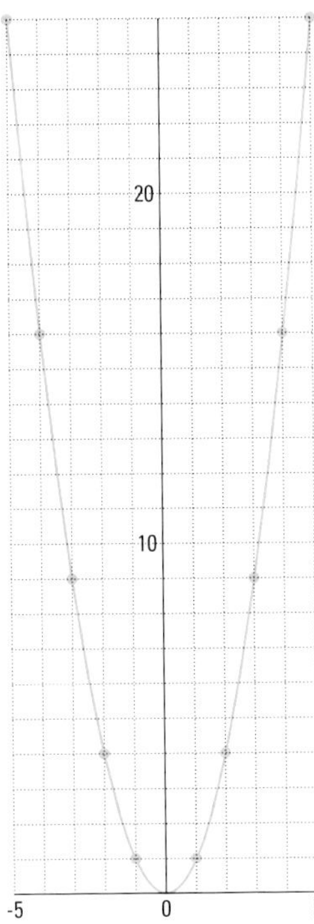

Weigh this piece of cardboard. You will get W grams. Record the weight, because you will need it to convert back to area later. (W grams corresponds to 250 cm^2.) Cut along the parabola from (-5, 25) through (0, 0) to (5, 25). Weigh this single, bullet-shaped piece. Suppose the weight is p grams. Then the area of the piece is $\frac{p}{w} \cdot 250$ cm^2. The area of the region under the curve is $250 - \frac{p}{w} \cdot 250$, and the area from 0 to 5 is one-half of that. You should compare your answer from this computation to $\frac{5^3}{3}$. One value is not sufficient, however. Carefully cut across the parabola from (-4, 16) to (4, 16). You can now weigh the parabola and deduce the area under the curve from 0 to 4. Repeat this process for 0 to 3 and 0 to 2. If you have a piece of the parabola left that seems to be big enough to handle, do 0 to 1. Compare each value to $\frac{b^3}{3}$ by plotting your data points, then graphing $y = \frac{x^3}{3}$.

4 Geographical Areas

Riemann sums are often used to calculate areas of irregular shapes. Below, the area of Hawaii can be estimated by adding up the areas above and below the x-axis. With a finer grid, the estimate becomes better. Find the area of your state, province, or country using Riemann sums. (Note: You may have to add and subtract different areas.)

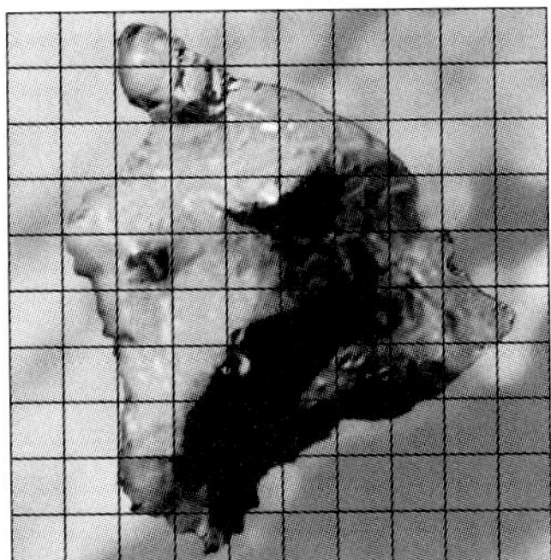

5 Kepler

Johannes Kepler (1571–1630) made significant contributions to the development of integral calculus. Write a short paper on his life and his work. Include his studies of wine barrels and the orbits of planets. Sources you might use include encyclopedias, Internet sites, calculus books, and books in your school or community library.

6 Du Châtelet

Emilie du Châtelet (1706–1749) translated the work of Newton into French and thus helped calculus to be known among the mathematicians of the European continent. Find out more about her life.

2. a.

b	Area under $y = \sin x$ from $x = 0$ to $x = b$	sin b	cos b	tan b
$\pi/6$	.13396695	.5	.866025	.577350
$\pi/4$	.2928828	.707107	.707107	1
$\pi/3$	.499984	.866025	.5	1.732051
$\pi/2$	.9999784	1	0	—
$2\pi/3$	1.499991	.866025	-.5	-1.732051
$3\pi/4$	1.707113	.707107	-.707107	-1
$5\pi/6$	1.866052	.5	-.866025	-.577350
π	2.000082	0	1	0

6 Du Châtelet Some people think that there were virtually no female mathematicians before this century because they did not possess the ability. A far more likely explanation is found from the fact that there were very few women in any profession. Not until the last half of this century has the number of female mathematicians become significant. It is unlikely that Du Châtelet could ever have obtained a university position, but she could be a patron and translator.

Project 2, continued

2. a. Sin, cos, and tan values can be compared as shown in the table above. Although no immediate match is apparent, it can be conjectured from the above table that the area under $y = \sin x$ from $x = 0$ to $x = b$ is equal to $1 - \cos b$.

b.

b	Area under $y = e^x$ from $x = 0$ to $x = b$
0.5	.6487206
1.0	1.718275
1.5	3.481657
2.0	6.38895
2.5	11.1822
3.0	19.08482
3.5	32.11382
4.0	53.59458

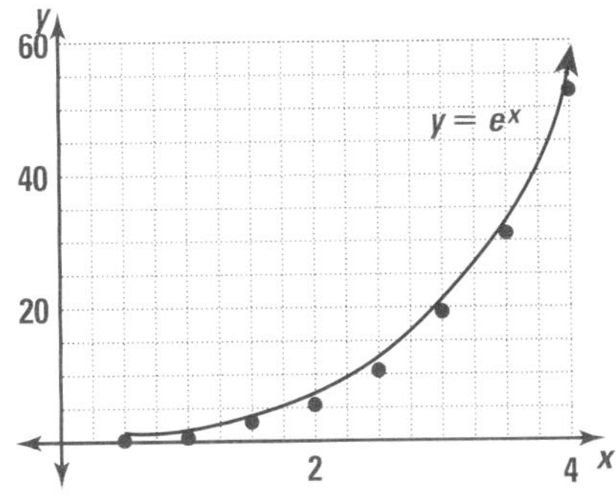

Conjecture: From the graph above, it appears that the area under $y = e^x$ from $x = 0$ to $x = b$ is $e^x - 1$.

(Responses continue on page 837.)

Summary

The Summary gives an overview of the entire chapter and provides an opportunity for students to consider the material as a whole. Thus, the Summary can be used to help students relate and unify the concepts presented in the chapter.

Vocabulary

Terms, symbols, and properties are listed by lesson to provide a checklist of concepts a student must know. Emphasize to students that they should read the vocabulary list carefully before starting the Progress Self-Test. If students do not understand the meaning of a term, they should refer back to the indicated lesson.

SUMMARY

This chapter has focused on calculus ideas related to integration, the second of the two main ideas of calculus studied in this text.

Four types of problems are studied in this chapter. The first involves finding the distance traveled by an object in a given time period when the velocity at each instant is known. If r_i is the constant velocity during time period t_i and there are n time periods, then the total distance is $\sum_{i=1}^{n} r_i t_i$. Graphically, the distance is the total area under a velocity-time graph.

A second type of problem involves finding the area between the graph of a function and the x-axis. This area can be expressed as a definite integral, defined to be the limit of Riemann sums. A Riemann sum for the area is obtained by partitioning the interval into subintervals. For each subinterval, a rectangle is formed whose height is the value of the function at some point in the subinterval. The Riemann sum is then the sum of the areas of these n rectangles. As the number of rectangles increases without bound, the sum gives a better and better approximation of the exact area, which is the definite integral.

An extension of the area problem involves finding the volume of the surface of revolution obtained when a curve revolves about the x-axis. The volume is partitioned into n nearly cylindrical sections, each of whose volume can be approximated. As the number of sections increases without bound, the sum of their volumes gives a better and better approximation of the exact volume, which is expressed as a definite integral.

A more general version of the distance, area, and volume problems involves finding the original function when its derivative is known. The Fundamental Theorem of Calculus describes the relationship between integration and differentiation.

VOCABULARY

Below are the most important terms and phrases for this chapter. You should be able to give a general description and a specific example of each and a precise definition for those marked with an asterisk (*).

Lesson 13-2
* Riemann sum of a function f over the interval from a to b
intermediate points for a Riemann sum, z_i
Δx

Lesson 13-3
upper Riemann sum
lower Riemann sum
* definite integral of f from a to b, $\int_a^b f(x)\,dx$

Lesson 13-4
Sum Property of Integrals Theorem
Constant Multiple Property of Integrals Theorem

Lesson 13-5
Integral of a Quadratic Function Theorem

Lesson 13-6
surface of revolution with axis ℓ
generating curve
solid of revolution with axis ℓ

834

Additional Answers, page 835

4. a.

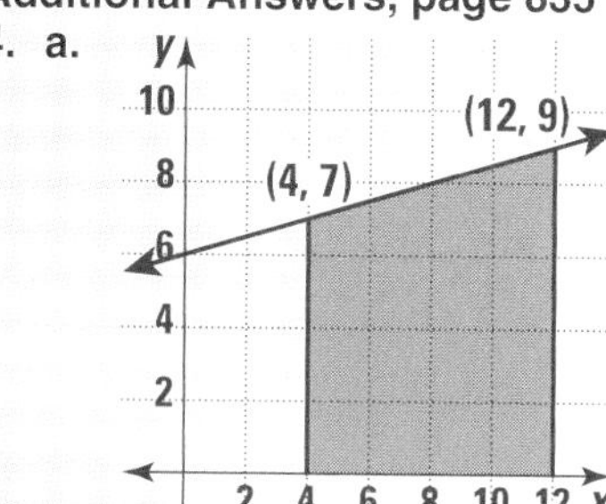

5. a.

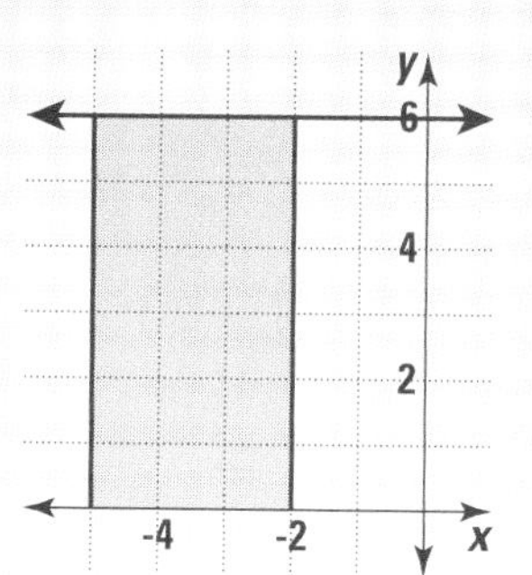

7.

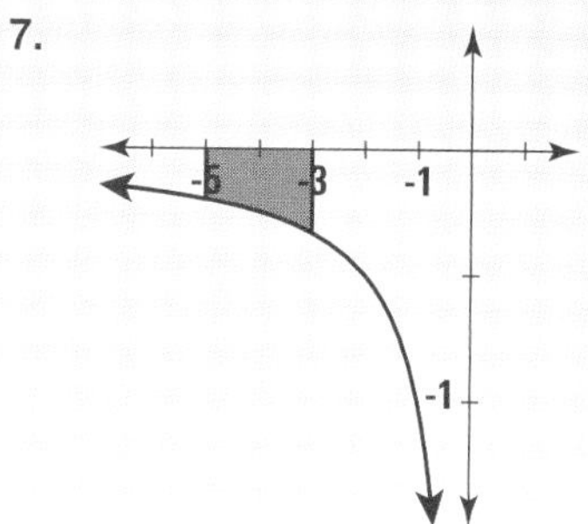

9.

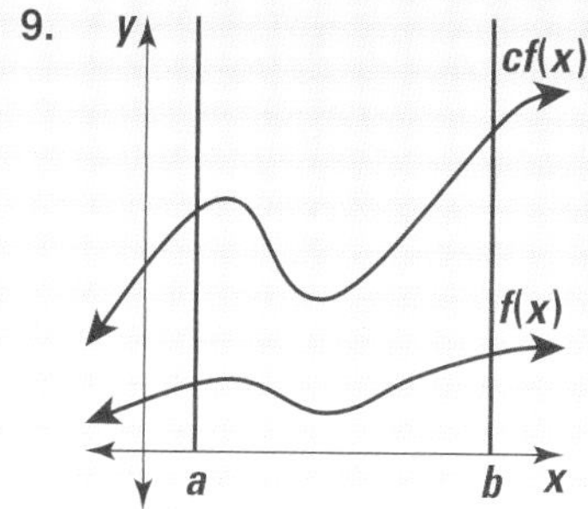

PROGRESS SELF-TEST

4a, 5a, 7, 9, 10a, 11, 12a) See margin.

Take this test as you would take a test in class. Then check the test yourself, using the solutions at the back of the book.

1. The velocity-time record for a train is given below. How far did the train travel from 8:00 A.M. to 1:00 P.M.? **175 miles**

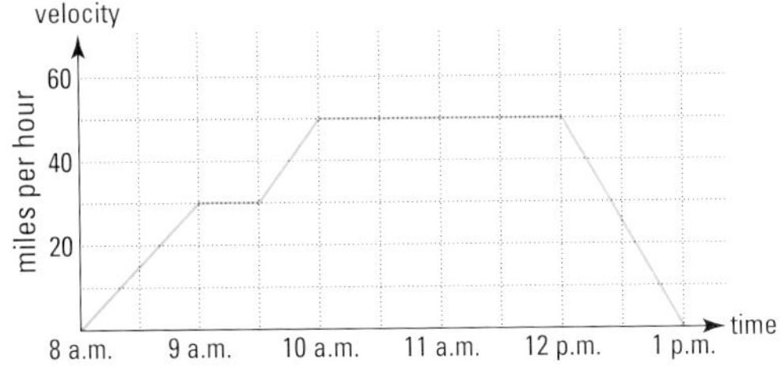

2. At the right is a graph of $y = t(x)$. Partition the interval from 0 to 4 into 4 subintervals of equal length, Δx. Let z_i = the right endpoint of the ith subinterval. Evaluate $\sum_{i=1}^{4} t(z_i)\Delta x$. **$\approx$ 7.5 units^2**

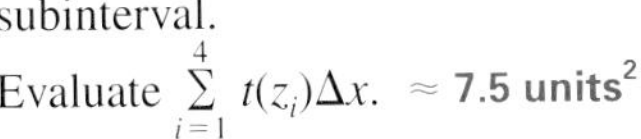

3. Use the grid and left endpoints of the rectangles to find a Riemann sum to estimate the volume of the nose cone at the right below. **49π units^3**

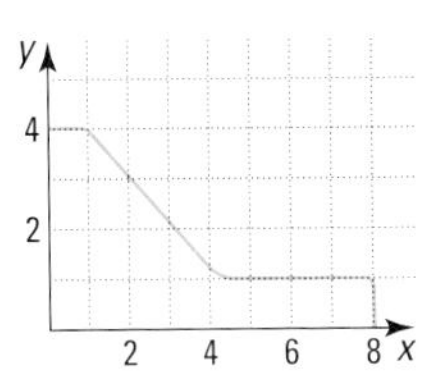

In 4 and 5, an integral is given. **a.** Sketch the region whose area is indicated by the integral. **b.** Find the exact value of the integral. **4b) 64**

4. $\int_4^{12} \left(\frac{1}{4}x + 6\right) dx$ **5.** $\int_{-5}^{-2} 6\, dx$ **b) 18**

6. Evaluate $\int_{-3}^{3} \sqrt{9 - x^2}\, dx$. **$\approx$ 14.137**

7. Sketch the region described by $\int_{-5}^{-3} \frac{1}{x}\, dx$. Does the value of the integral appear to be positive or negative? **negative. See margin for graph.**

8. Find the area of the shaded region below. **$\frac{650}{3}$ units^2**

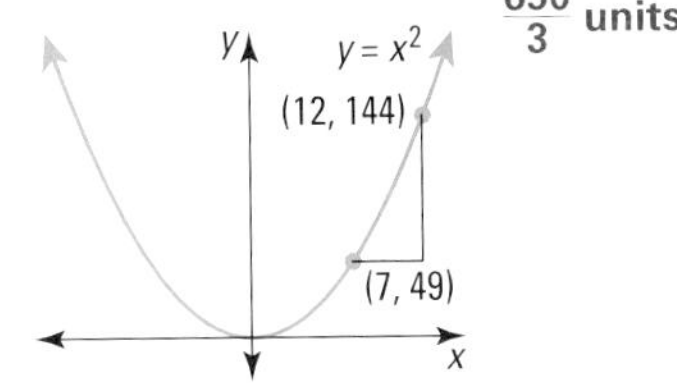

9. Consider the following theorem:

$$\int_a^b cf(x)\, dx = c\int_a^b f(x)\, dx.$$

Make a sketch and explain why the theorem is true when $f(x) \geq 0$ on the interval $[a, b]$.

10. Over a 15-second period, a car accelerates in such a way that its velocity (in feet per second) at any time t is given by $f(t) = -.4(t - 15)^2 + 90$.

a. What integral gives the distance traveled by the car in 15 seconds?

b. Find the distance in part **a**. **900 ft**

11. Rewrite as a single integral:

$$\int_0^{\pi/2} \cos x\, dx + \int_0^{\pi/2} 4\cos x\, dx.$$

12. a. Sketch the region bounded by the x-axis, the y-axis, and the line $y = 1 - x$.

b. Find the volume of the solid obtained when this region is revolved about the x-axis. **$\frac{\pi}{3}$ units^3**

Progress Self-Test

For the development of mathematical competence, feedback and correction, along with the opportunity to practice, are necessary. The Progress Self-Test provides the opportunity for feedback and correction; the Chapter Review provides additional opportunities and practice. We cannot overemphasize the importance of these end-of-chapter materials. It is at this point that the material "gels" for many students, allowing them to solidify skills and understanding. In general, student performance should be markedly improved after these pages.

Assign the Progress Self-Test as a one-night assignment. Worked-out *solutions* for all questions are in the Selected Answers section of the student book. Encourage students to take the Progress Self-Test honestly, grade themselves, and then be prepared to discuss the test in class.

Advise students to pay special attention to those Chapter Review questions (pages 836–839) that correspond to questions missed on the Progress Self-Test.

9. (Continued)
For every Riemann sum of f on the interval from a to b, there is a corresponding Riemann sum of $c \cdot f$ with the same subintervals and same z_i. The value of each term of the sum of $c \cdot f$ will be c times the value of the corresponding term of the sum of f.

$$\lim_{n\to\infty} \sum_{i=1}^{n} (c \cdot f(z_i)\,\Delta x) = c \cdot \lim_{n\to\infty} \sum_{i=1}^{n} (f(z_i)\,\Delta x),$$

$$\text{so } \int_a^b (c \cdot f(x))\, dx = c\int_a^b f(x)\, dx.$$

10. a. $\int_0^{15} (-.4(t - 15)^2 + 90)\, dt$

11. $\int_0^{\frac{\pi}{2}} \cos x\, dx + \int_0^{\frac{\pi}{2}} 4\cos x\, dx =$

$\int_0^{\frac{\pi}{2}} 5\cos x\, dx = 5\int_0^{\frac{\pi}{2}} \cos x\, dx$

12. a.

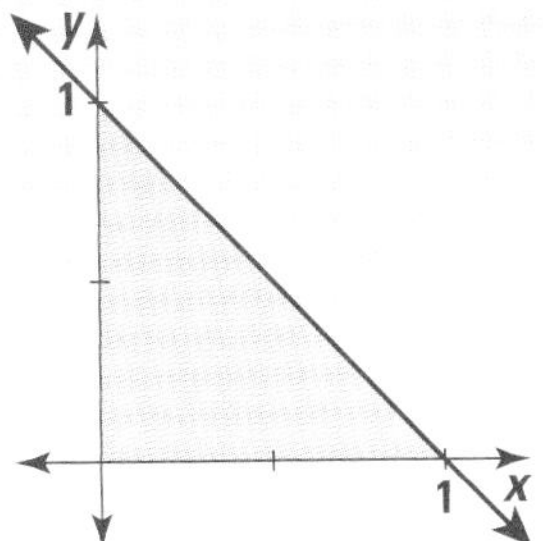

Chapter 13 Review

Resources

From the ***Teacher's Resource File***

- Answer Master for Chapter 3 Review
- Assessment Sourcebook: Chapter 13 Test, Forms A–D Chapter 13 Test, Cumulative Form Comprehensive Test, Chapters 1–13

Additional Resources

- TestWorks Software

The main objectives for the chapter are organized in the Chapter Review under the four types of understanding this book promotes—Skills, Properties, Uses, and Representations.

Whereas end-of-chapter material may be considered optional in some texts, in UCSMP *Precalculus and Discrete Mathematics* we have selected these objectives and questions with the expectation that they will be covered. Students should be able to answer these questions with about 85% accuracy after studying the chapter.

You may assign these questions over a single night to help students prepare for a test the next day, or you may assign the questions over a two-day period. If you work the questions over two days, then we recommend assigning the *evens* for homework the first night so that students get feedback in class the next day, then assigning the *odds* the night before the test, because answers are provided to the odd-numbered questions.

It is effective to ask students which questions they still do not understand and use the day or days as a total class discussion of the material which the class finds most difficult.

CHAPTER REVIEW

Questions on SPUR Objectives

SPUR stands for **S**kills, **P**roperties, **U**ses, and **R**epresentations. The Chapter Review questions are grouped according to the SPUR Objectives for this chapter.

SKILLS DEAL WITH THE PROCEDURES USED TO GET ANSWERS.

Objective A: *Calculate Riemann sums of functions over specified intervals.* *(Lesson 13-2)*

In 1 and 2, use the function f with $f(x) = x^3$ over the interval $[0, 10]$.

1. Let z_i = the right endpoint of the ith subinterval. Evaluate $\sum_{i=1}^{5} f(z_i)\Delta x$. **3600**

2. Let z_i = the left endpoint of the ith subinterval. Evaluate $\sum_{i=1}^{10} f(z_i)\Delta x$. **2025**

3. Let $g(x) = \sin x$ over the interval from $\frac{\pi}{3}$ to $\frac{\pi}{2}$. Let z_i = the right endpoint of the ith subinterval.

a. Write the appropriate Riemann sum for 100 subintervals. **See below.**

b. Use a program to evaluate the Riemann sum. **0.500**

a) $\sum_{i=1}^{100} \frac{\pi}{600} \sin\left(\frac{\pi}{3} + i\frac{\pi}{600}\right)$

Objective B: *Evaluate definite integrals.* *(Lessons 13-3, 13-4, 13-5)*

In 4–6, find the exact value of the definite integral.

4. $\int_3^7 (x + 3)\, dx$ **32**

5. $\int_{-3}^{-1} -x\, dx$ **4**

6. $\int_0^1 \sqrt{1 - x^2}\, dx$ $\frac{\pi}{4}$

7. a. Sketch a picture of the region described by $\int_3^5 \sqrt{25 - x^2}\, dx$. **See margin.**

b. Evaluate the integral. **≈ 5.59**

In 8–11, evaluate the integral.

8. $\int_0^6 x^2\, dx$ **72**

9. $\int_4^9 x^2\, dx$ **221.$\overline{6}$**

10. $\int_1^3 x^2\, dx + \int_3^4 x^2\, dx$ **21**

11. $\int_0^6 (4x^2 - 3x + 1)dx$ **240**

PROPERTIES DEAL WITH THE PRINCIPLES BEHIND THE MATHEMATICS.

Objective C: *Apply properties of definite integrals.* *(Lesson 13-4)*

In 12 and 13, rewrite each expression as a single integral.

12. $\int_4^7 2^x\, dx + \int_7^{10} 2^x\, dx$ $\int_4^{10} 2^x\, dx$

13. $\int_1^3 \cos^2 x\, dx + \int_1^3 \sin^2 x\, dx$ $\int_1^3 1\, dx$

14. *True or false.* **False**

$\int_0^a (f \cdot g)(x)\, dx = \int_0^a f(x)\, dx \cdot \int_0^a g(x)\, dx$

15. Use area to explain why the following property is true. If f is continuous and $f(x) \geq 0$ on $[a, b]$, and $a < c < b$, then

$$\int_a^c f(x)\, dx + \int_c^b f(x)\, dx = \int_a^b f(x)\, dx.$$

See margin.

Additional Answers

7. a.

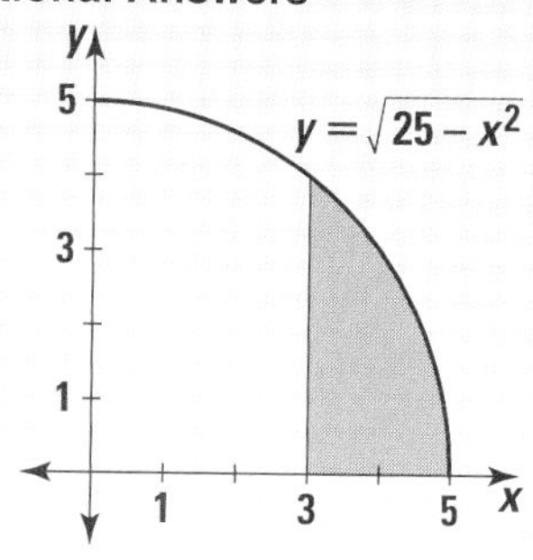

15.

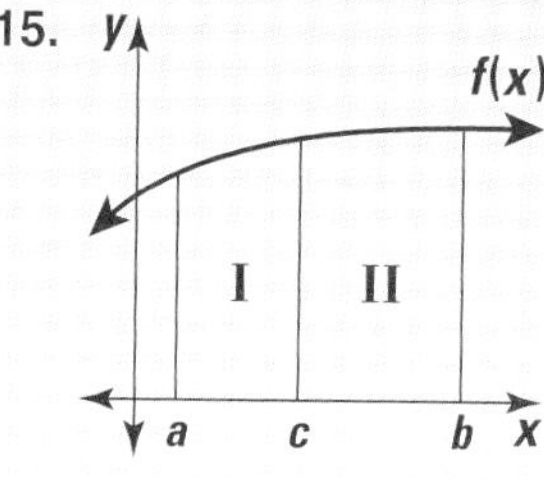

Area I is $\int_a^c f(x)\, dx$, Area II is $\int_c^b f(x)\, dx$, and the union of the regions represented by Areas I and II is $\int_a^b f(x)\, dx$. Since Area I + Area II equals the area of the union of the regions represented by Areas I and II, then

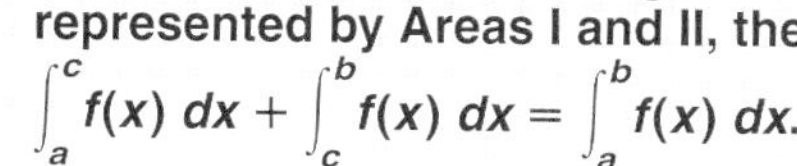

$\int_a^c f(x)\, dx + \int_c^b f(x)\, dx = \int_a^b f(x)\, dx.$

USES DEAL WITH APPLICATIONS OF MATHEMATICS IN REAL SITUATIONS.

Objective D: *Find the distance traveled by a moving object, given its rate.* *(Lessons 13-1, 13-2, 13-5)*

16. A car decelerates from $30\frac{\text{meters}}{\text{second}}$ to $18\frac{\text{meters}}{\text{second}}$ in 10 seconds. Assume the deceleration is constant.

a. How far will the car travel in the first second? **29.4 m** **b) 158.4 m**

b. How far will the car travel in six seconds?

c. How far will the car travel in the ten seconds? **240 m**

17. Another car decelerates from 88 ft/sec to 44 ft/sec in 5 seconds with the velocity at x seconds given by $h(x) = 1.76(x - 5)^2 + 44$. Subdivide the interval into five subintervals. Let z_i be the left endpoint of the ith subinterval. Use these values to estimate the distance traveled by the car in the five seconds.

18. The velocity (in ft/sec) of an object at t seconds is $3t^2 - 2t + 1$. Find the distance traveled by the object from $t = 7$ to $t = 12$ seconds.

17) 316.8 ft **18) 1295 ft**

Objective E: *Use the definite integral to solve application problems.* *(Lessons 13-4, 13-6)*

19. A cylindrical trough has a base in the shape of a parabola, 3 meters high and 4 meters across. If the trough is 12 meters long, what is its volume? **96 m³**

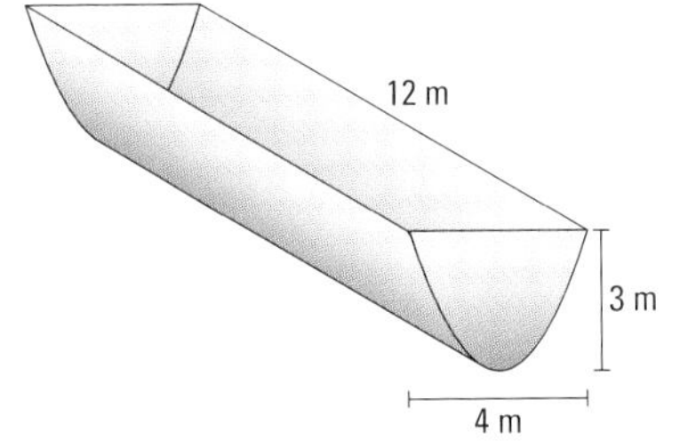

20. When a hard freeze is expected, strawberry farmers spray their fields with water so that a thin layer of ice covers the fruit; the ice insulates the fruit from temperatures below 32°F. The table below gives the rate of water flow through two sprayers for a 12-hour period.

t	$f(t)$	$g(t)$
0	3.5	2.0
2	3.0	2.5
4	2.75	3.0
6	3.25	2.75
8	3.0	3.5
10	3.5	2.0
12	2.5	1.5

a. Write an integral that describes the total amount of water used to spray the berries during this 12-hour period. **See below.**

b. Approximate the value of the integral by evaluating the appropriate Riemann sum, using the left endpoints as the z_i. **69.5 gal**

21. A lamp base has a shape as below. To find its volume, the outer curve of the lamp base is drawn on a two-dimensional graph as shown below. The shape is obtained by revolving the curve about the x-axis. Let the solid be divided into six sections approximating cylinders, each with height 3″. Using r_i as the height of the graph at the right endpoint of the ith subinterval, approximate the volume of the lamp base. **$51.75\pi \approx 162.58$ in³**

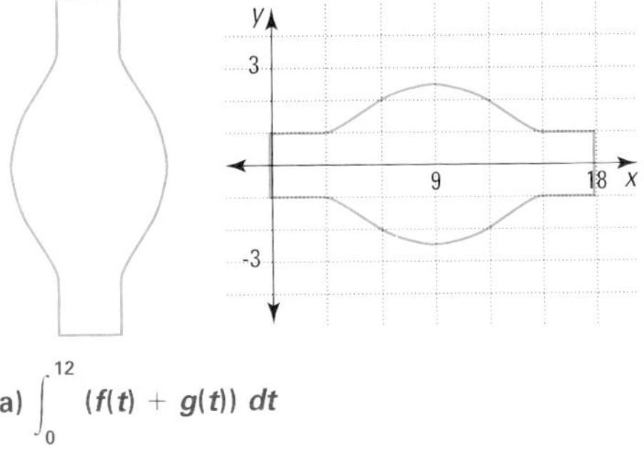

20a) $\int_0^{12} (f(t) + g(t))\, dt$

Assessment

Evaluation The Assessment Sourcebook provides six forms of the Chapter 13 Test. Forms A and B present parallel versions in a short-answer format. Forms C and D offer performance assessment. The fifth test is Chapter 13 Test, Cumulative Form. About 50% of this test covers Chapter 13, 25% of it covers Chapter 12, and 25% of it covers earlier chapters. In addition to these tests, Comprehensive Test Chapters 1–13 gives roughly equal attention to all chapters.

For information on grading, see *General Teaching Suggestions: Grading* in the *Professional Sourcebook,* which begins on page T20 in the Teacher's Edition.

Feedback After students have taken the test for Chapter 13 and you have scored the results, return the tests to students for discussion. Class discussion of the questions that caused trouble for the most students can be very effective in identifying and clarifying misunderstandings. You might want to have them write down the items they missed and work, either in groups or at home, to correct them. It is important for students to receive feedback on every chapter test.

Additional Responses, page 832

3.

b	weight of cardboard (grams)	Area under $y = x^2$ from $x = 0$ to $x = b$ calculated from experiment
2	0.5	2.3
3	2.0	4.3
4	3.5	24.2
5	7.25	42.6

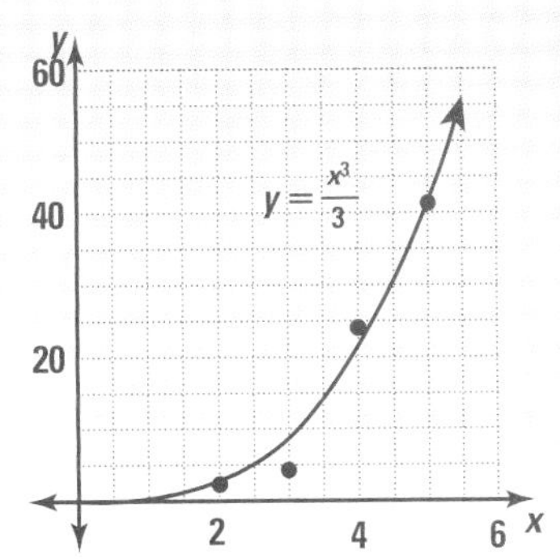

The values computed experimentally come close to the actual values as seen from the graph.

(Responses continue on page 838)

Objective F: *Estimate the distance under a velocity-time graph.* *(Lesson 13-1)*

22. A stunt driver is being filmed for a chase scene in a movie. The driver travels at a constant rate of speed as the cameras begin to roll. Two seconds into the scene the driver applies the brakes, going into a skid. Five seconds into the scene the vehicle comes to a stop. Use the velocity-time graph below to answer the following questions.

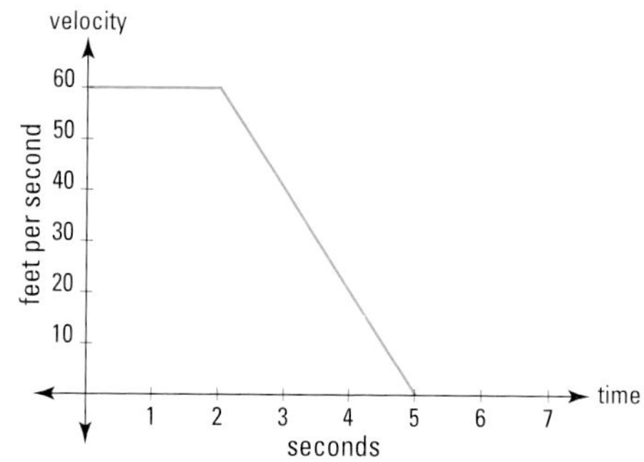

a. What was the driver's velocity before the brakes were applied? **60 ft/sec**

b. How far did the driver travel before applying the brakes? **120 ft**

c. How far did the driver travel after applying the brakes? **90 ft**

d. What is the total distance traveled by the driver? **210 ft**

23. A velocity-time graph for a skydiver is shown below. In this case the downward direction is taken to be positive. How high was the airplane if the skydiver lands 200 seconds after jumping? **4635 ft**

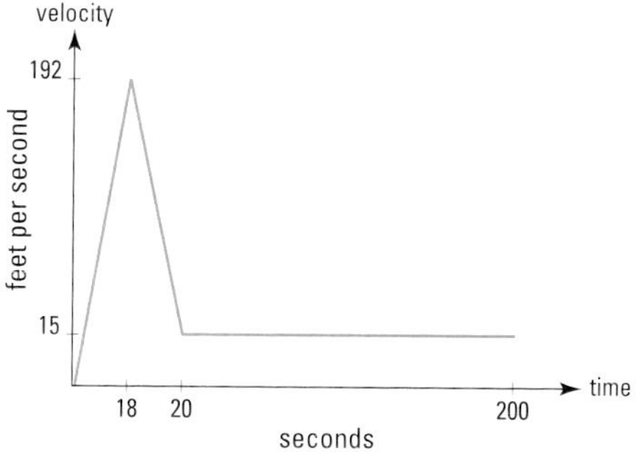

REPRESENTATIONS DEAL WITH PICTURES, GRAPHS, OR OBJECTS THAT ILLUSTRATE CONCEPTS.

Objective G: *Express areas in integral notation.* *(Lesson 13-3)*

In 24 and 25, express the shaded area with integral notation.

24.

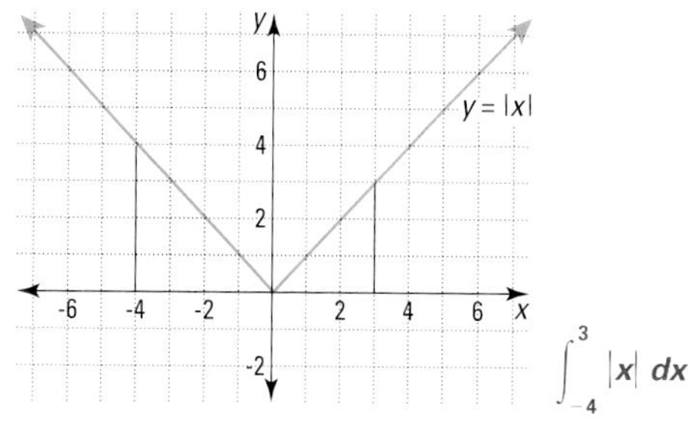

$$\int_{-4}^{3} |x|\, dx$$

25.

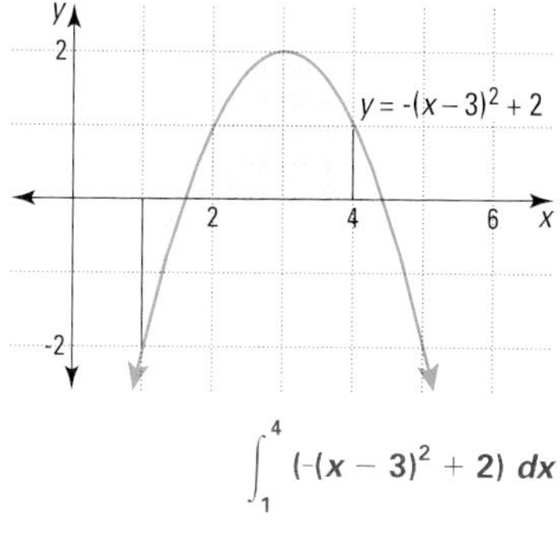

$$\int_{1}^{4} (-(x-3)^2 + 2)\, dx$$

Additional Responses, page 833

4. Sample (for Texas):

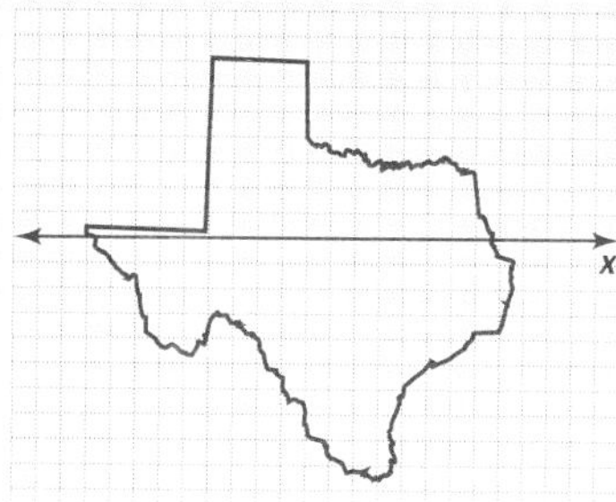

Using left endpoints, the area of the state above the x-axis is .7 + .6 + .5 + .4 + .3 + 4.3 + 7.2 + 7.2 + 7.1 + 7.0 + 3.6 + 3.6 + 3.0 + 3.0 + 3.0 + 3.0 + 2.6 = 57.1 square units.

Also using left endpoints, the area of the state below the x-axis is .8 + 1.8 + 4.2 + 4.5 + 3.4 + 3.4 + 4.0 + 5.5 + 6.6 + 8.9 + 9.2 + 9.5 + 6.0 + 5.2 + 4.8 + 4.0 + 3.6 = 85.4 square units.

1 unit ≈ 44 mi, so the total area of Texas is approximately
(57.1 sq units + 85.4 sq units) • $\frac{44^2 \text{ sq mi}}{\text{sq units}}$ = 275880 ≈ 276,000 sq mi.
(Note: actual area found in dictionary is 267,000 sq mi.)

CHAPTER THIRTEEN

26. Refer to the graph of g below.

a. Express the shaded area with integral notation. **See below.**

b. Does the value of the integral appear to be positive or negative? **negative**

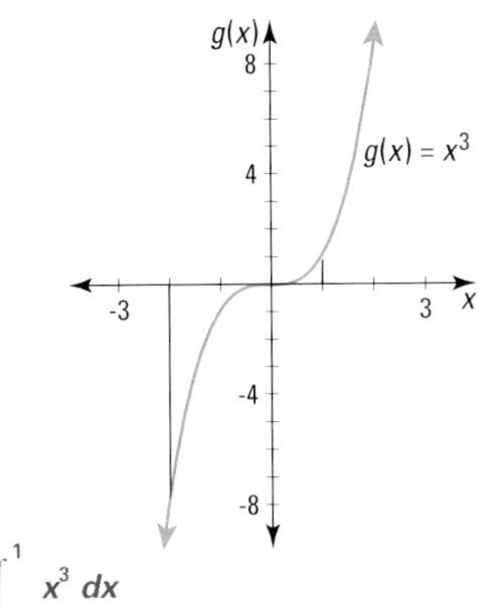

a) $\int_{-2}^{1} x^3\,dx$

Objective H: *Find areas bounded by curves.* *(Lesson 13-4, 13-5)*

27. Consider the shaded region below.

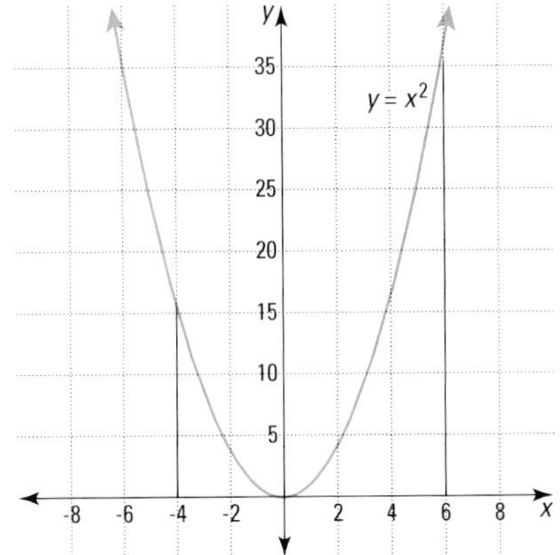

a. Approximate its area, using a Riemann sum with 5 equal subintervals and with z_i equal to the right endpoint of the ith subinterval.

b. Find the exact area, using an integral. **93.3 units²**

a) ≈ 120 units²

28. Find the area of the shaded region below. **37.3 units²**

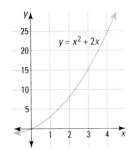

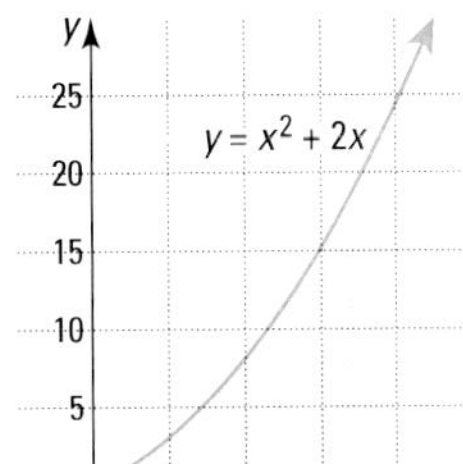

29. Consider the region bounded by the x-axis, the y-axis, the line $y = 3x + 2$, and the line $x = 4$.

a. Sketch the region. **See below.**

b. Set up and evaluate an integral that describes the area of this region.

$\int_0^4 (3x + 2)\,dx = 32$

Objective I: *Find volumes of solids.* *(Lesson 13-6)*

30. a. Sketch a graph of the region bounded by the x-axis, the line $x = 4$, and the line $y = x + 1$.

b. Find the volume of the solid obtained when the region of part **a** is revolved about the x-axis. **a, b) See margin.**

31. a. Sketch a graph of the region bounded by $y = \sqrt{x}$, the line $x = 2$, and the x-axis.

b. Calculate the volume of the solid generated when this region is revolved about the x-axis. **2π units³**

a) See margin.

29a)

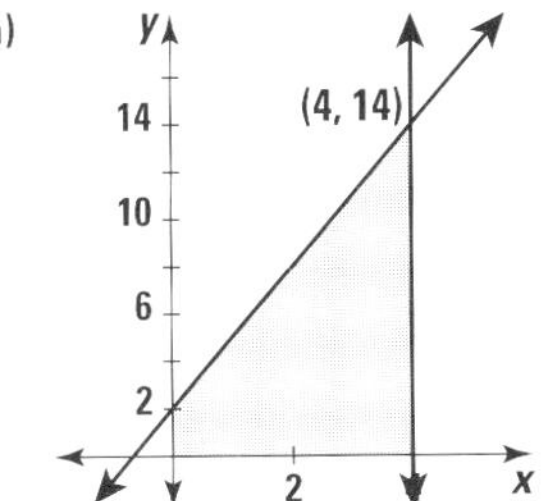

Additional Answers, page 839

30. a.

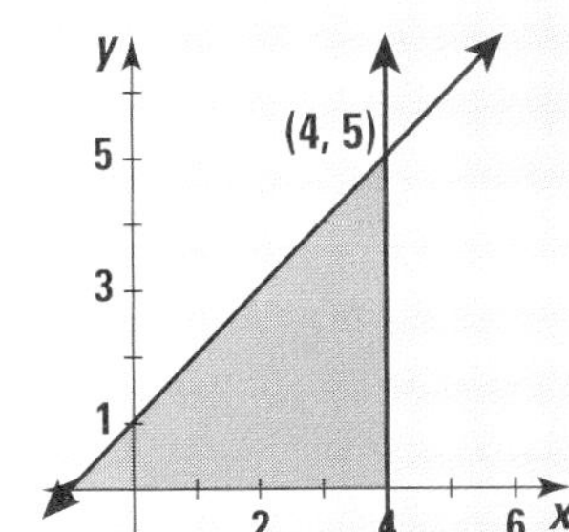

b. $\frac{125\pi}{3} \approx 130.9$ **units³**

31. a.

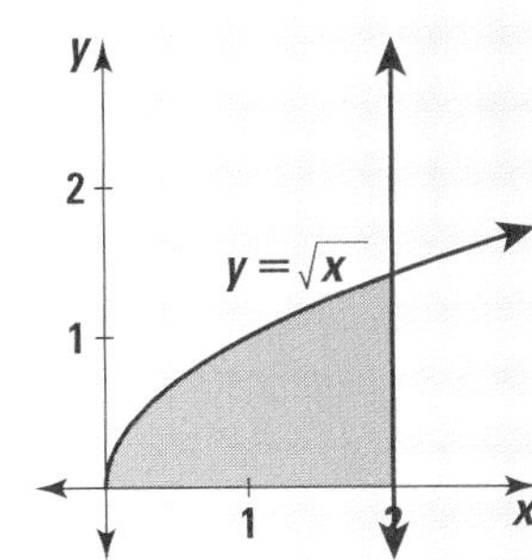

Additional Responses, page 833

5. Students' papers may include the following main points:
   a. Kepler's humble beginnings
   b. His education at the University of Tübingen
   c. His association with Tycho Brahe
   d. Kepler's law of planetary motion
   e. His study of wine barrels by using solids of revolution.

6. Students' reports may include the following main points:
   a. Emilie's interest in mathematics, physics, and philosophy
   b. Her association with Voltaire
   c. Her translation of Newton's *Principia Mathematica*
   d. Her own published works

Theorems and Properties

Chapter 1

Law of Substitution: If a universal statement is true for all elements of a given set, then it is true for each element of that set. *(Lesson 1-1, p. 7)*

The Negation of a Universal Statement Theorem: Let S be a set and $p(x)$ be a property that may or may not be true for elements x in S. The negation of $\forall x$ *in* S, $p(x)$. is $\exists x$ *in* S *such that not* $p(x)$. *(Lesson 1-2, p. 15)*

The Negation of an Existential Statement Theorem: Let S be a set and $p(x)$ be a property that may or may not be true for elements x in S. The negation of $\exists\, x$ *in* S *such that* $p(x)$. is $\forall x$ *in* S, *not* $p(x)$. *(Lesson 1-2, p. 16)*

De Morgan's Laws Theorem: For all statements p and q:

1. $\sim(p \text{ and } q) \equiv (\sim p) \text{ or } (\sim q)$
2. $\sim(p \text{ or } q) \equiv (\sim p) \text{ and } (\sim q)$ *(Lesson 1-3, p. 23)*

Negation of a Simple Conditional Theorem: The negation of the conditional statement *If* p *then* q. is p *and (not* q*)*. *(Lesson 1-5, p. 37)*

Negation of a Universal Conditional Theorem: Let S be a set and let $p(x)$ and $q(x)$ be statements that may or may not hold for elements x in S. The negation of $\forall x$ *in* S, *if* $p(x)$ *then* $q(x)$. is $\exists\, x$ *in* S *such that* $p(x)$ *and not* $q(x)$. *(Lesson 1-5, p. 38)*

Contrapositive Theorem: A conditional and its contrapositive are logically equivalent. That is, they always have the same truth values. *(Lesson 1-5, p. 39)*

Law of Detachment (*Modus Ponens*) Theorem: The following are valid forms of argument:

Simple form	Universal form
If p *then* q.	$\forall x$, *if* $p(x)$ *then* $q(x)$.
p	$p(c)$, *for a particular* c.
$\therefore q$.	$\therefore q(c)$.

(Lesson 1-6, p. 46)

The Law of Transitivity Theorem: The following are valid forms of argument:

Simple form	Universal form
If p *then* q.	$\forall x$, *if* $p(x)$, *then* $q(x)$.
If q *then* r.	$\forall x$, *if* $q(x)$, *then* $r(x)$.
$\therefore$ *If* p *then* r.	$\therefore \forall x$, *if* $p(x)$, *then* $r(x)$.

(Lesson 1-6, p. 47)

Law of Indirect Reasoning (*Modus Tollens*) Theorem: The following are valid forms of argument:

Simple form	Universal form
If p *then* q.	$\forall x$, *if* $p(x)$ *then* $q(x)$.
not q	*not* $q(c)$ *for a particular* c.
$\therefore$ *not* p.	$\therefore$ *not* $p(c)$.

(Lesson 1-6, p. 48)

Chapter 2

Theorem: The logarithm function $\log x$ is increasing on its domain $(0, \infty)$. *(Lesson 2-3, p. 94)*

Pythagorean Identity Theorem: For all θ, $\sin^2 \theta + \cos^2 \theta = 1$. *(Lesson 2-6, p. 113)*

Theorem: For any real numbers a and b with $a > 0$ and $b > 1$, the exponential function f with $f(x) = ab^x$ is increasing on the set $(-\infty, \infty)$ of all real numbers. *(Lesson 2-7, p. 118)*

Theorems: $\forall$ real numbers r and s and $\forall$ positive real numbers b, u, and v with $b \neq 1$,

Law of Exponents	Law of Logarithms
$b^r \cdot b^s = b^{r+s}$	$\log_b (u \cdot v) = \log_b u + \log_b v$ (Logarithm of a Product)
$\frac{b^r}{b^s} = b^{r-s}$	$\log_b \left(\frac{u}{v}\right) = \log_b u - \log_b v$ (Logarithm of a Quotient)
$(b^r)^s = b^{rs}$	$\log_b (u^s) = s \log_b u$ (Logarithm of a Power)

(Lesson 2-9, p. 132)

Change of Base Theorem: Let a and b be positive real numbers both unequal to 1, then for all $x > 0$, $\log_b x = \log_b a \cdot \log_a x$. *(Lesson 2-9, p. 133)*

Chapter 3

Theorem: A function has an inverse function if and only if it is a 1-1 function. *(Lesson 3-2, p. 157)*

Zero-Product Property: Let f, g, and h be functions. If there exists c such that $h(c) = 0$ and $h = f \cdot g$, then either $f(c) = 0$ or $g(c) = 0$. *(Lesson 3-3, p. 161)*

Addition Property of Equality: For any real expressions $f(x)$ and $g(x)$: if $f(x) = g(x)$, then $f(x) + c = g(x) + c$. *(Lesson 3-3, p. 161)*

Multiplication Property of Equality: For any real expressions $f(x)$ and $g(x)$: if $f(x) = g(x)$, then $f(x) \cdot c = g(x) \cdot c$. *(Lesson 3-3, p. 161)*

Function Composition and Equality Property: For any real functions f, g, and h, and values of x for which f, g, $h \circ f$, and $h \circ g$ are defined: if $f(x) = g(x)$, then $h(f(x)) = h(g(x))$. *(Lesson 3-3, p. 164)*

Reversible Steps Theorem: Let $f(x)$ and $g(x)$ be any real expressions. Then for all real expressions c and real functions h: (1) $f(x) = g(x) \Leftrightarrow f(x) + c = g(x) + c$. (2) $f(x) = g(x) \Leftrightarrow f(x) \cdot c = g(x) \cdot c$, provided $c \neq 0$. (3) $f(x) = g(x) \Leftrightarrow h(f(x)) = h(g(x))$, provided h^{-1} exists. *(Lesson 3-3, p. 165)*

The Intermediate Value Theorem: Suppose that f is a continuous function on the interval $[a, b]$. Then for every real number y_0 between $f(a)$ and $f(b)$, there is at least one real number x_0 between a and b such that $f(x_0) = y_0$. *(Lesson 3-4, p. 170)*

Addition Property of Inequality: For any real expressions $f(x)$ and $g(x)$: if $f(x) < g(x)$, then $f(x) + c < g(x) + c$. *(Lesson 3-5, p. 175)*

Multiplication Properties of Inequality: For any real expressions $f(x)$ and $g(x)$, where $f(x) < g(x)$: $f(x) \cdot c < g(x) \cdot c$, if $c > 0$; and $f(x) \cdot c > g(x) \cdot c$, if $c < 0$. *(Lesson 3-5, p. 175)*

Theorem: Suppose that f is a real function. If f is increasing throughout its domain, or if f is decreasing throughout its domain, then f is a 1-1 function. *(Lesson 3-5, p. 176)*

Corollary: If f is an increasing function throughout its domain, or if f is a decreasing function throughout its domain, then the inverse of f is a function. *(Lesson 3-5, p. 176)*

Theorem: Let f be a real function. (1) If f is increasing on its entire domain, then f^{-1} is increasing on its entire domain. (2) If f is decreasing on its entire domain, then f^{-1} is decreasing on its entire domain. *(Lesson 3-5, p. 177)*

Function Composition and Inequality Properties: or any real expressions $f(x)$, $g(x)$ and real function h, (1) $f(x) < g(x) \geq h(f(x)) < h(g(x))$, if h is an increasing function, and (2) $f(x) < g(x) \Leftrightarrow h(f(x)) > h(g(x))$, if h is a decreasing function. *(Lesson 3-5, p. 178)*

Reversible Steps Theorem for Inequalities: Let $f(x)$ and $g(x)$ be any real expressions. Then for all real expressions c and real functions h:
(1) $f(x) < g(x) \Leftrightarrow f(x) + c < g(x) + c$.
(2) $f(x) < g(x) \Leftrightarrow f(x) \cdot c < g(x) \cdot c$, if $c > 0$.
$f(x) < g(x) \Leftrightarrow f(x) \cdot c > g(x) \cdot c$, if $c < 0$.
(3) $f(x) < g(x) \Leftrightarrow h(f(x)) < h(g(x))$, if h is increasing.
$f(x) < g(x) \Leftrightarrow h(f(x)) > h(g(x))$, if h is decreasing.
(Lesson 3-5, p. 179)

Function Inequality Theorem: Suppose that f is a continuous real function. If f has zeros a and b and no zeros between a and b, then either $f(x) > 0$ for all x between a and b or $f(x) < 0$ for all x between a and b. *(Lesson 3-7, p. 190)*

Graph-Translation Theorem: In a relation described by a sentence in x and y, the following two processes yield the same graph: (1) replacing x by $x - h$, and y by $y - k$; (2) applying the translation $T_{h,k}$: $(x, y) \rightarrow (x + h, y + k)$ to the graph of the original relation. *(Lesson 3-8, p. 195)*

Graph Scale-Change Theorem: In a relation described by a sentence in x and y, the following two processes yield the same graph: (1) replacing x by $\frac{x}{a}$, and y by $\frac{y}{b}$; (2) applying the scale change $S_{a,b}$: $(x, y) \rightarrow (ax, by)$ to the graph of the original relation. *(Lesson 3-8, p. 196)*

Graph-Standardization Theorem: Suppose that G is the graph of a relation in x and y. Let h and k be any real numbers and let a and b be nonzero real numbers. Let G' be the image of G under the rubberband transformation $T: (x, y) \to (ax + h, by + k)$.

x-y form: If G is described by a rule relating x and y, then a rule for G' is found by replacing x by $\frac{x-h}{a}$ and y by $\frac{y-k}{b}$.

parametric form: If G is described by $\begin{cases} x = f(t) \\ y = g(t), \end{cases}$ then G' is described by $\begin{cases} x = af(t) + h \\ y = bg(t) + k. \end{cases}$

(Lesson 3-8, p. 198)

Theorem: For all real numbers x and a with $a > 0$, $|x| < a$ if and only if $-a < x < a$; that is, the solution set of $|x| < a$ is the interval $(-a, a)$ of real numbers. *(Lesson 3-9, p. 202)*

Theorem: For all real numbers x and a, $|x| > a$ if and only if $x < -a$ or $x > a$. *(Lesson 3-9, p. 205)*

Chapter 4

Transitive Property of Integer Factors Theorem: For all integers a, b, and c, if a is a factor of b and b is a factor of c, then a is a factor of c. *(Lesson 4-1, p. 226)*

Factor of an Integer Sum Theorem: For all integers a, b, and c, if a is a factor of b and a is a factor of c, then a is a factor of $b + c$. *(Lesson 4-1, p. 226)*

Theorems: For all polynomials $a(x)$, $b(x)$, and $c(x)$:

Transitive Property of Polynomial Factors: If $a(x)$ is a factor of $b(x)$ and $b(x)$ is a factor of $c(x)$, then $a(x)$ is a factor of $c(x)$.

Factor of a Polynomial Sum Theorem: If $a(x)$ is a factor of $b(x)$ and $a(x)$ is a factor of $c(x)$, then $a(x)$ is a factor of $b(x) + c(x)$. *(Lesson 4-1, p. 227)*

Factor of an Integer Product Theorem: For all integers m, n, and p, if m is a factor of n, then m is a factor of $n \cdot p$. *(Lesson 4-1, p. 229)*

Quotient-Remainder Theorem for Integers: If n is an integer and d is a positive integer, then there exist unique integers q (the **integer quotient**) and r (the **integer remainder**) such that $n = q \cdot d + r$ and $0 \le r < d$. *(Lesson 4-2, p. 232)*

Quotient-Remainder Theorem for Polynomials: If $p(x)$ is a polynomial and $d(x)$ is a nonzero polynomial, then there exist unique polynomials $q(x)$ (the **quotient**) and $r(x)$ (the **remainder**) such that $p(x) = q(x) \cdot d(x) + r(x)$ and either degree of $r(x) <$ degree of $d(x)$ or $r(x)$ is the zero polynomial. *(Lesson 4-2, p. 234)*

The Remainder Theorem: If a polynomial $p(x)$ of degree $n \ge 1$ is divided by $x - c$, then the remainder is the constant $p(c)$. That is, $p(x) = q(x)(x - c) + p(c)$. *(Lesson 4-3, p. 240)*

The Factor Theorem: For all polynomials $p(x)$, $x - c$ is a factor of $p(x)$ if and only if $p(c) = 0$, that is, if and only if c is a zero of $p(x)$. *(Lesson 4-4, p. 244)*

Theorem: If c_1 is a zero of a polynomial $p(x)$ and if c_2 is a zero of the quotient polynomial $q(x)$ obtained when $p(x)$ is divided by $x - c_1$, then c_2 is a zero of $p(x)$. *(Lesson 4-4, p. 245)*

Number of Zeros of a Polynomial Theorem: A polynomial of degree n has at most n zeros. *(Lesson 4-4, p. 246)*

Theorem: Let $p(x)$ be a polynomial of degree $n \ge 1$ with real coefficients. The graph of $y = p(x)$ can cross any horizontal line $y = k$ *at most n* times. *(Lesson 4-4, p. 246)*

Congruence Theorem: $\forall$ integers a and b and positive integers m, $a \equiv b \pmod{m}$ if and only if m is a factor of $a - b$. *(Lesson 4-5, p. 253)*

Properties of Congruence Theorem: Let a, b, c, and d be any integers and let m be a positive integer. If $a \equiv b \pmod{m}$ and $c \equiv d \pmod{m}$, then

Addition Property of Congruence

$$a + c \equiv b + d \pmod{m}$$

Subtraction Property of Congruence

$$a - c \equiv b - d \pmod{m}$$

Multiplication Property of Congruence

$$ac \equiv bd \pmod{m}.$$

(Lesson 4-5, p. 254)

Prime Factor Theorem: Every integer greater than 1 is either prime or has a prime factor. *(Lesson 4-7, p. 266)*

Validity of Proof by Contradiction Theorem: The following form of argument is valid.

If not s then (p and (not p)).

$\therefore s.$ *(Lesson 4-7, p. 266)*

Infinitude of Primes Theorem: There are infinitely many prime numbers. *(Lesson 4-7, p. 267)*

Factor Search Theorem: If an integer n has no prime factors between 1 and $\sqrt{n}$ inclusive, then n is prime. *(Lesson 4-7, p. 267)*

Fundamental Theorem of Arithmetic: Suppose that n is an integer and that $n > 1$. Then either n is a prime number or n has a prime factorization which is unique except for the order of the factors. *(Lesson 4-7, p. 268)*

Unique Factorization Theorem for Polynomials: Suppose that $p(x)$ is a polynomial with integer coefficients. Then either $p(x)$ is prime over the real numbers or $p(x)$ has a factorization into polynomials prime over the reals which is unique except for the order of the factors or multiplications by real constants. *(Lesson 4-7, p. 269)*

Chapter 5

Discontinuity Theorem: Given a rational function f with $f(x) = \frac{p(x)}{q(x)}$, where $p(x)$ and $q(x)$ are polynomials over the reals: If $\exists$ a real number c such that $q(c) = 0$ but $p(c) \neq 0$, then f has an essential discontinuity when $x = c$ and the line $x = c$ is a vertical asymptote to the graph of f. *(Lesson 5-4, p. 304)*

End Behavior of Rational Functions Theorem: Suppose $f(x) = \frac{a_m x^m + \ldots + a_1 x + a_0}{b_n x^n + \ldots + b_1 x + b_0}$ $\forall$ real numbers x for which the denominator is nonzero, where the a_i and b_i are real numbers $\forall$ i, $a_m \neq 0$, and $b_n \neq 0$. Then the end behavior of f is the same as the end behavior of the function g defined $\forall$ x by $g(x) = \frac{a_m}{b_n} x^{m-n}$. *(Lesson 5-5, p. 311)*

The Irrationality of $\sqrt{2}$ Theorem: $\sqrt{2}$ is irrational. *(Lesson 5-6, p. 316)*

Theorem: If a real number x can be written as a terminating or infinite repeating decimal, then x is a rational number. *(Lesson 5-6, p. 317)*

Rational Zero Theorem: Suppose that p is a polynomial function with integer coefficients: $p(x) = a_n x^n + a_{n-1} x^{n-1} + \ldots + a_1 x + a_0$, with $a_n \neq 0$. If $r = \frac{m}{k}$ is a rational number in lowest terms that is a zero of p, then m is a factor of the constant coefficient a_0 and k is a factor of the leading coefficient a_n. *(Chapter 5 Projects, p. 340)*

Chapter 6

Theorem: The functions defined by $y = b \sin\left(\frac{x-h}{a}\right) + k$ or $y = b \cos\left(\frac{x-h}{a}\right) + k$ have: amplitude $= |b|$, period $= 2\pi|a|$, phase shift $= h$, and vertical shift $= k$. *(Lesson 6-3, p. 363)*

Cosine of a Sum Theorem: For all real numbers α and β, $\cos(\alpha + \beta) = \cos\alpha\cos\beta - \sin\alpha\sin\beta$. *(Lesson 6-4, p. 367)*

Cosine of a Difference Theorem: For all real numbers α and β, $\cos(\alpha - \beta) = \cos\alpha\cos\beta + \sin\alpha\sin\beta$. *(Lesson 6-4, p. 369)*

Sine of a Sum Theorem: For all real numbers α and β, $\sin(\alpha + \beta) = \sin\alpha\cos\beta + \cos\alpha\sin\beta$. *(Lesson 6-5, p. 372)*

Sine of a Difference Theorem: For all real numbers α and β, $\sin(\alpha - \beta) = \sin\alpha\cos\beta - \cos\alpha\sin\beta$. *(Lesson 6-5, p. 373)*

Tangent of a Sum and Tangent of a Difference Theorem: For all real numbers α and β such that $\tan\alpha$, $\tan\beta$, and $\tan(\alpha + \beta)$ are defined, $\tan(\alpha + \beta) = \frac{\tan\alpha + \tan\beta}{1 - \tan\alpha\tan\beta}$, and $\tan(\alpha - \beta) = \frac{\tan\alpha + \tan\beta}{1 + \tan\alpha\tan\beta}$. *(Lesson 6-5, p. 373)*

Identities for cos 2x Theorem: For all real numbers x: $\cos 2x = \cos^2 x - \sin^2 x = 2\cos^2 x - 1 = 1 - 2\sin^2 x$. *(Lesson 6-6, p. 377)*

Identity for sin 2x Theorem: For all real numbers x, $\sin 2x = 2\sin x\cos x$. *(Lesson 6-6, p. 378)*

Chapter 7

Recursion Principle: Suppose that a recurrence relation defines x_{n+1} in terms of x_n and n for each integer $n \geq 1$. Then there is exactly one sequence X defined by this recurrence relation and the initial condition $x_1 = a$. *(Lesson 7-1, p. 406)*

Principle of Mathematical Induction: Let $S(n)$ be a sentence in n. If (1) $S(1)$ is true (the **basis step**), and (2) for all integers $k \geq 1$, the assumption that $S(k)$ is true implies that $S(k + 1)$ is true (the **inductive step**), then $S(n)$ is true for all positive integers n. *(Lesson 7-3, p. 418)*

Sum of the First *n* Powers Theorem: If $r \neq 1$, then $1 + r + r^2 + \ldots + r^{n-1} = \frac{1 - r^n}{1 - r}$ $\forall$ integers $n \geq 1$. *(Lesson 7-6, p. 435)*

Evaluation of a Finite Geometric Series Theorem: If a is any real number and r is any real number other than 1, then for all integers $n \geq 1$, $a + ar + ar^2 + \ldots + ar^{n-1} = a\left(\frac{1 - r^n}{1 - r}\right)$. *(Lesson 7-6, p. 436)*

Evaluation of an Infinite Geometric Series Theorem: If a is any real number and r is a real number with $0 < |r| < 1$, then $\sum_{k=0}^{\infty} ar^k = \frac{a}{1 - r}$. *(Lesson 7-6, p. 438)*

Principle of Mathematical Induction (Strong Form): Suppose that for each positive integer n, $S(n)$ is a sentence in n. If

(1) $S(1)$ is true, and

(2) for all integers, $k \geq 1$, the assumption that $S(1)$, $S(2)$, ..., $S(k - 1)$, $S(k)$ are all true implies that $S(k + 1)$ is also true, then $S(n)$ is true for all integers $n \geq 1$. *(Lesson 7-7, p. 442)*

Theorem: Every positive integer $n \geq 2$ is either a prime or a product of primes. *(Lesson 7-7, p. 446)*

Quicksort Theorem: For each integer $n \geq 0$, the Quicksort algorithm arranges any list of n distinct real numbers in increasing order. *(Lesson 7-8, p. 454)*

Chapter 8

Theorem: For any particular values of r and θ, the following polar coordinate representations name the same point.

a. $[r, \theta]$

b. $[r, \theta + 2\pi n]$, $\forall$ integers n

c. $[-r, \theta + (2n + 1)\pi]$, $\forall$ integers n *(Lesson 8-2, p. 481)*

Polar-Rectangular Conversion Theorem: If $[r, \theta]$ is a polar coordinate representation of a point P, then the rectangular coordinates (x, y) of P are given by $x = r \cos \theta$ and $y = r \sin \theta$. *(Lesson 8-2, p. 483)*

Geometric Addition Theorem: Let $z = a + bi$ and $w = c + di$ be two complex numbers that are not collinear with (0, 0). Then the point representing $z + w$ is the fourth vertex of a parallelogram with consecutive vertices $z = a + bi$, 0, and $w = c + di$. *(Lesson 8-3, p. 488)*

Geometric Multiplication Theorem: Let z and w be complex numbers. If $z = [r, \theta]$ and $w = [s, \phi]$, then $zw = [rs, \theta + \phi]$. That is, multiplying a complex number z by w applies to z the composite of a size change of magnitude s and a rotation of ϕ about the origin. *(Lesson 8-3, p. 490)*

DeMoivre's Theorem:

(Polar Form) For all positive integers n, if $z = [r, \theta]$, then $z^n = [r^n, n\theta]$.

(Trigonometric Form) For all positive integers n, if $z = r(\cos \theta + i \sin \theta)$, then $z^n = r^n(\cos n\theta + i \sin n\theta)$. *(Lesson 8-6, p. 508)*

Complex nth Roots Theorem:

(Polar Form) The n nth roots of $[r, \theta]$ are $\left[\sqrt[n]{r}, \frac{\theta}{n} + k \cdot \frac{2\pi}{n}\right]$, where $k = 0, 1, 2, \ldots, n - 1$.

(Trigonometric Form) The n nth roots of $r(\cos \theta + i \sin \theta)$ are $\sqrt[n]{r}\left(\cos\left(\frac{\theta}{n} + k \cdot \frac{2\pi}{n}\right) + i \sin\left(\frac{\theta}{n} + k \cdot \frac{2\pi}{n}\right)\right)$, where $k = 0, 1, 2, \ldots, n - 1$. *(Lesson 8-7, p. 515)*

Geometric nth Roots Theorem: When graphed in the complex plane, the n nth roots of any nonzero complex number z are the vertices of a regular n-gon whose center is at (0, 0). *(Lesson 8-7, p. 516)*

Theorem: Every polynomial of odd degree with real coefficients has at least one real zero. *(Lesson 8-8, p. 520)*

Fundamental Theorem of Algebra: If $p(x)$ is any polynomial of degree $n \geq 1$, with real or complex coefficients, then $p(x)$ has at least one complex zero. *(Lesson 8-8, p. 521)*

Theorem: If $p(x)$ is any polynomial of degree n with real or complex coefficients, then $p(x)$ has exactly n real or complex zeros provided that each zero of multiplicity m is counted m times. *(Lesson 8-8, p. 522)*

Conjugate Zeros Theorem: Let $p(x)$ be a polynomial with real coefficients. If $z = a + bi$ is a zero of $p(x)$, then its complex conjugate $\bar{z} = a - bi$ is also a zero of $p(x)$. *(Lesson 8-9, p. 526)*

Chapter 9

Derivative of a Quadratic Function Theorem: If $f(x) = ax^2 + bx + c$, where a, b, and c are real numbers and $a \neq 0$, then $f'(x) = 2ax + b$ for all real numbers x. *(Lesson 9-3, p. 572)*

Theorems: (Derivative of a Linear Function) If $f(x) = mx + b$, then $f'(x) = m$.
(Derivative of a Constant Function) If $\forall\, x, f(x) = k$, then $f'(x) = 0$. *(Lesson 9-3, p. 572)*

Theorem: Suppose f is a function whose derivative function f' exists for all x in the interval $a < x < b$.

(1) If $f'(x) > 0\ \forall\, x$ in the interval $a < x < b$, then f is increasing on the interval.

(2) If $f'(x) < 0\ \forall\, x$ *in the interval* $a < x < b$, then f is decreasing on the interval. *(Lesson 9-5, p. 581)*

Vertex of a Parabola Theorem: Let a, b, and c be real numbers with $a \neq 0$. Then the parabola that is the graph of $f(x) = ax^2 + bx + c$ has its vertex at the point where $x = -\frac{b}{2a}$. *(Lesson 9-5, p. 582)*

Chapter 10

The Multiplication Counting Principle: Suppose that strings result from a procedure which consists of k successive steps and that:

the 1st step can be done in n_1 ways,

the 2nd step can be done in n_2 ways,

⋮

and the kth step can be done in n_k ways.

Then the number of strings is $n_1 n_2 \cdot \ldots \cdot n_k$. *(Lesson 10-2, p. 609)*

Theorem: If repetition is allowed, the number of r-symbol strings that can be made from a set of n symbols is n^r. *(Lesson 10-2, p. 610)*

Permutation Theorem: There are $n!$ permutations of n different elements. *(Lesson 10-3, p. 616)*

***P*(*n*, *r*) Calculation Theorem:** The number $P(n, r)$ of permutations of n elements taken r at a time is given by $P(n, r) = \frac{n!}{(n-r)!}$. *(Lesson 10-3, p. 618)*

***C*(*n*, *r*) Calculation Theorem:** The number $C(n, r)$ of combinations of n elements taken r at a time is given by $C(n, r) = \frac{n!}{r!(n-r)!}$. *(Lesson 10-4, p. 623)*

Basic Properties of Combinations Theorem: For all n and r for which $C(n, r)$ is defined:

a. $C(n, r) = C(n, n-r)$, $\binom{n}{r} = \binom{n}{n-r}$;

b. $C(n, n) = C(n, 0) = 1$, $\binom{n}{n} = \binom{n}{0} = 1$.
(Lesson 10-4, p. 624)

The Binomial Theorem:
For all positive integers n and numbers x and y,

$$(x+y)^n = \binom{n}{0}x^n + \binom{n}{1}x^{n-1}y + \binom{n}{2}x^{n-2}y^2 + \ldots + \binom{n}{k}x^{n-k}y^k + \ldots + \binom{n}{n-1}xy^{n-1} + \binom{n}{n}y^n = \sum_{k=0}^{n}\binom{n}{k}x^{n-k}y^k.$$
(Lesson 10-5, p. 630)

Sum of Binomial Coefficients Theorem: $\forall$ integers $n \geq 0$,

$$\binom{n}{0} + \binom{n}{1} + \binom{n}{2} + \ldots + \binom{n}{k} + \ldots + \binom{n}{n} = \sum_{k=0}^{n}\binom{n}{k} = 2^n.$$
(Lesson 10-6, p. 633)

Theorem: Suppose that n and r are positive integers. The number of r-element collections that can be constructed from a set with n elements with repetitions allowed is given by $\binom{r+(n-1)}{r}$. *(Lesson 10-7, p. 642)*

Theorem: Let k and n be positive integers. In the expansion of $(x_1 + x_2 + \ldots + x_k)^n$, the coefficient of $x_1^{a_1}x_2^{a_2}\ldots x_k^{a_k}$ is $\frac{n!}{a_1!a_2!\ldots a_k!}$. *(Lesson 10-8, p. 645)*

Chapter 11

Total Degree of a Graph Theorem: The total degree of any graph equals twice the number of edges in the graph. *(Lesson 11-3, p. 674)*

Corollaries:

1. Total Degree is Even: The total degree of any graph is an even positive integer.
2. Number of Odd Vertices is Even: Every graph has an even number of vertices of odd degree.

(Lesson 11-3, p. 675)

Euler Circuit Theorem: If a graph has an Euler circuit, then every vertex of the graph has even degree. *(Lesson 11-4, p. 680)*

Sufficient Condition for an Euler Circuit Theorem: If a graph G is connected and every vertex of G has even degree, then G has an Euler circuit. *(Lesson 11-4, p. 682)*

Circuits and Connectedness Theorem: If a connected graph contains a circuit and an edge is removed from the circuit, then the resulting graph is also connected. *(Lesson 11-4, p. 683)*

Theorem: Let G be a graph with vertices $v_1, v_2, \ldots, v_m$, and let n be a positive integer. Let A be the adjacency matrix for G. Then the element a_{ij} in A^n is the number of walks of length n from v_i to v_j. *(Lesson 11-5, p. 689)*

Convergence of Powers Theorem: Let T be an $n \times n$ stochastic matrix with no zero entries. Then $\lim_{k\to\infty} T^k$ is a stochastic matrix with n identical rows. *(Lesson 11-6, p. 695)*

Theorem: Let G be a connected graph with no crossings, and let V, E, and F be the number of vertices, edges, and faces of G. The following alterations to G do not change the value of $V - E + F$:

(1) removing a vertex of degree 1 along with its adjacent edge, and

(2) removing an edge that is part of a circuit.
(Lesson 11-7, p. 702)

Theorem: Let G be a graph with at least one edge. If G has no circuits, then G has a vertex of degree 1. *(Lesson 11-7, p. 703)*

Euler's Formula: Let G be a connected graph with no crossings, and let V, E, and F be the number of vertices, edges, and faces of G. Then $V - E + F = 2$. *(Lesson 11-7, p. 703)*

Chapter 12

Theorem: If $\vec{u} = (u_1, u_2)$, then $|\vec{u}| = \sqrt{u_1^2 + u_2^2}$. *(Lesson 12-1, p. 724)*

Theorem: For all vectors $\vec{u}$, $[|\vec{u}|, \theta] = (|\vec{u}|\cos\theta, |\vec{u}|\sin\theta)$. *(Lesson 12-1, p. 724)*

Theorem:

a. If $\vec{v}$ is a vector with polar representation $[r, \theta°]$, then $-\vec{v} = [r, 180° + \theta°]$.

b. If $\vec{v}$ has component representation (v_1, v_2), then $-\vec{v} = (-v_1, -v_2)$. *(Lesson 12-2, p. 729)*

Theorem: Nonzero vectors $\vec{u}$ and $\vec{v}$ are parallel if and only if one of the vectors is a nonzero scalar multiple of the other. *(Lesson 12-3, p. 733)*

Theorem: A point $Q = (x, y)$ is on the line through $P = (x_0, y_0)$ parallel to the vector $\vec{v} = (v_1, v_2)$ if and only if there is a real number t with $\overrightarrow{PQ} = t\vec{v}$, or $(x - x_0, y - y_0) = t(v_1, v_2)$. *(Lesson 12-3, p. 734)*

Theorem: The line through (x_0, y_0) that is parallel to the vector $\vec{v} = (v_1, v_2)$ has parametric equations $\begin{cases} x = x_0 + tv_1 \\ y = y_0 + tv_2 \end{cases}$ where t may be any real number. *(Lesson 12-3, p. 734)*

Theorem: The dot product of a vector with itself equals the square of its length: For all vectors $\vec{w}$, $\vec{w} \cdot \vec{w} = |\vec{w}|^2$. *(Lesson 12-4, p. 740)*

Angle Between Vectors Theorem: Suppose that θ is the measure of the angle between two nonzero vectors $\vec{u}$ and $\vec{v}$ and $0 \le \theta \le \pi$. Then $\cos\theta = \frac{\vec{u} \cdot \vec{v}}{|\vec{u}|\,|\vec{v}|}$. *(Lesson 12-4, p. 741)*

Theorem: Two nonzero vectors $\vec{u}$ and $\vec{v}$ are perpendicular if and only if their dot product is zero. *(Lesson 12-4, p. 742)*

Theorem: The distance of the point (x, y, z) from the origin is $\sqrt{x^2 + y^2 + z^2}$. *(Lesson 12-5, p. 748)*

Distance in Space Theorem: The distance between $P = (x_1, y_1, z_1)$ and $Q = (x_2, y_2, z_2)$ is given by $PQ = \sqrt{(x_2 - x_1)^2 + (y_2 - y_1)^2 + (z_2 - z_1)^2}$. *(Lesson 12-5, p. 748)*

Equation of a Sphere Theorem: The sphere with center (a, b, c) and radius r has equation $r^2 = (x - a)^2 + (y - b)^2 + (z - c)^2$. *(Lesson 12-5, p. 749)*

Theorem: Let $\vec{u}$ and $\vec{v}$ be any three dimensional vectors and let θ be the measure of the angle between them. Then (1) $\cos\theta = \frac{\vec{u} \cdot \vec{v}}{|\vec{u}|\,|\vec{v}|}$, and (2) $\vec{u}$ and $\vec{v}$ are orthogonal $\Leftrightarrow \vec{u} \cdot \vec{v} = 0$. *(Lesson 12-6, p. 753)*

Equations for a Line in 3-Space Theorem: A point $Q = (x, y, z)$ is on the line ℓ through $P = (x_0, y_0, z_0)$ parallel to $\vec{v} = (v_1, v_2, v_3)$ if and only if there is a real number t such that

a. $\overrightarrow{PQ} = t\vec{v}$, or equivalently $(x - x_0, y - y_0, z - z_0) = t(v_1, v_2, v_3)$ (vector equation for ℓ) or

b. $\begin{cases} x = x_0 + tv_1 \\ y = y_0 + tv_2 \\ z = z_0 + tv_3 \end{cases}$

(parametric equations for ℓ). *(Lesson 12-7, p. 760)*

Equation for a Plane Theorem: The set of points $\{(x, y, z): ax + by + cz = d\}$, where at least one of the coefficients a, b, or c is nonzero, is a plane perpendicular to the vector $\vec{v} = (a, b, c)$. *(Lesson 12-7, p. 762)*

Chapter 13

Theorem: If f is a continuous function on the interval $[a, c]$, and $a < b < c$, then $\int_a^b f(x)\,dx + \int_b^c f(x)\,dx = \int_a^c f(x)\,dx$. *(Lesson 13-4, p. 805)*

Theorem: If f is a continuous function on the interval $0 \le x \le b$, and $0 < a < b$, then $\int_a^b f(x)\,dx = \int_0^b f(x)\,dx - \int_0^a f(x)\,dx$. *(Lesson 13-4, p. 806)*

Sum Property of Integrals Theorem: If f and g are continuous functions on the interval from a to b, then $\int_a^b (f(x) + g(x))\,dx = \int_a^b f(x)\,dx + \int_a^b g(x)\,dx$. *(Lesson 13-4, p. 808)*

Constant Multiple Property of Integrals Theorem: If f is a continuous function on the interval from a to b, and c is a real number, then $\int_a^b c\,f(x)\,dx = c\int_a^b f(x)\,dx$. *(Lesson 13-4, p. 808)*

Theorem: If $a > 0$, $\int_0^a x^2\,dx = \frac{a^3}{3}$. *(Lesson 13-5, p. 814)*

Integral of a Quadratic Function Theorem: If $a > 0$, $\int_0^a (c_2x^2 + c_1x + c_0)\,dx = c_2\frac{a^3}{3} + c_1\frac{a^2}{3} + c_0a$. *(Lesson 13-5, p. 815)*

Theorem: The volume of a sphere of radius r is $\frac{4}{3}\pi r^3$. *(Lesson 13-6, p. 822)*

Fundamental Theorem of Calculus: Let f be a continuous function on the interval from a to b.

1. If g is a function whose derivative is f, then $\int_a^b f(x)\,dx = g(b) - g(a)$.
2. If $g(x) = \int_a^x f(t)\,dt$ for all x from a to b, then $g'(x) = f(x)$ for all such x. *(Lesson 13-7, p. 827)*

Parent Functions and Their Graphs

Type of Function	Parent Function, f *	Graph of f	Inverse Function, f^{-1} †	Graph of f^{-1}
polynomial–constant	$f(x) = k$ domain: R range: $\{k\}$	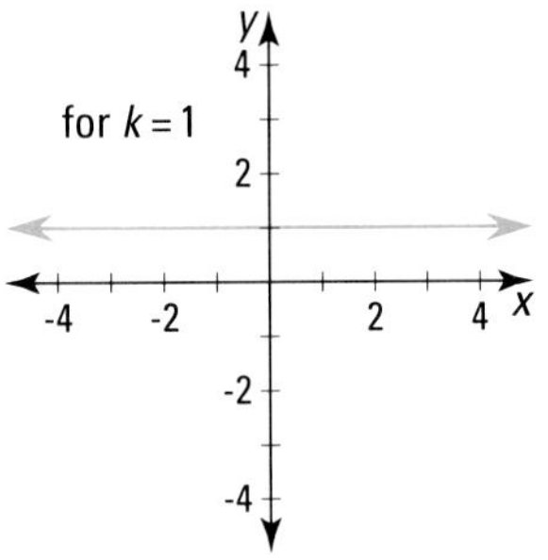 for $k = 1$	none	
polynomial–linear	$f(x) = x$ domain: R range: R	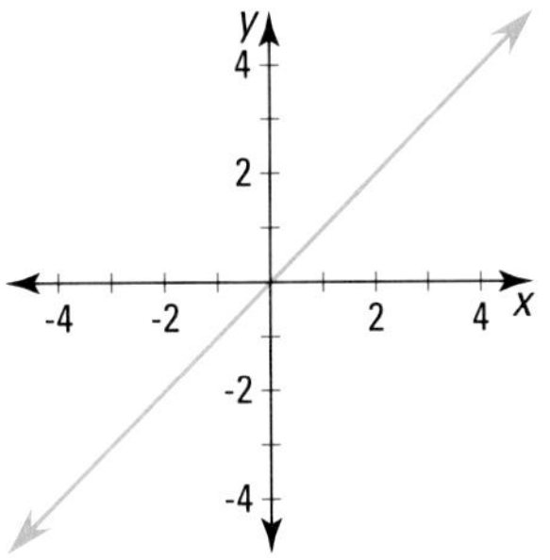	$f^{-1}(x) = x$	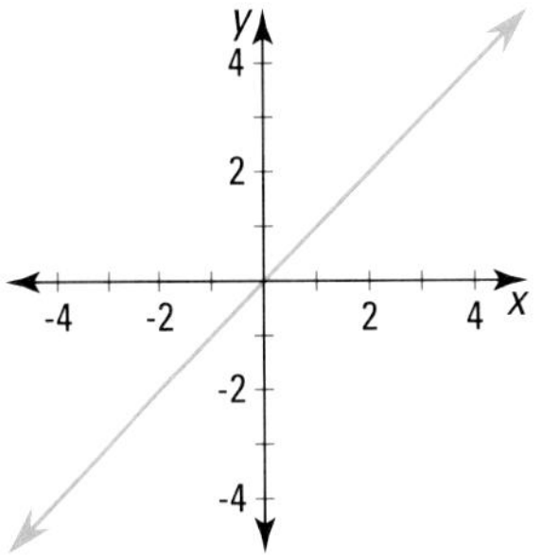
absolute value	$f(x) = \|x\|$ domain: R range: $R^+ \cup \{0\}$		none	
greatest integer	$f(x) = \lfloor x \rfloor$ domain: R range: set of integers	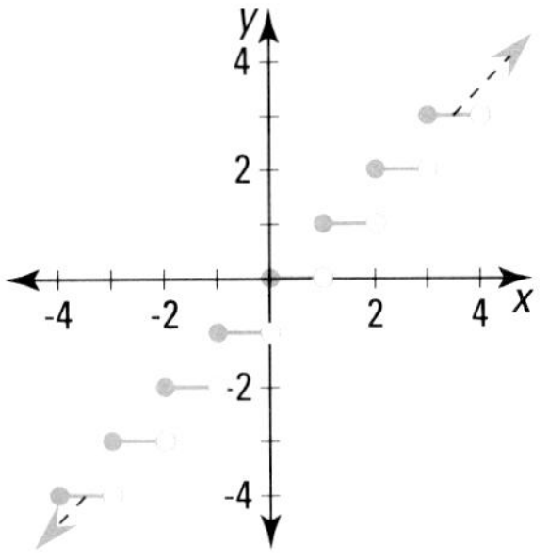	none	

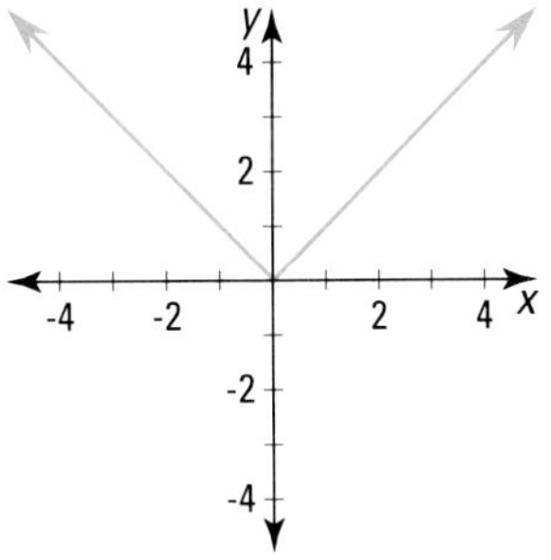

* R = set of real numbers, R^+ = set of positive real numbers.

† The domain and range of f^{-1} are the reverse of those for f except where indicated.

Type of Function	Parent Function, f *	Graph of f	Inverse Function, f^{-1} †	Graph of f^{-1}
polynomial–quadratic	$f(x) = x^2$ domain: R range: $R^+ \cup \{0\}$	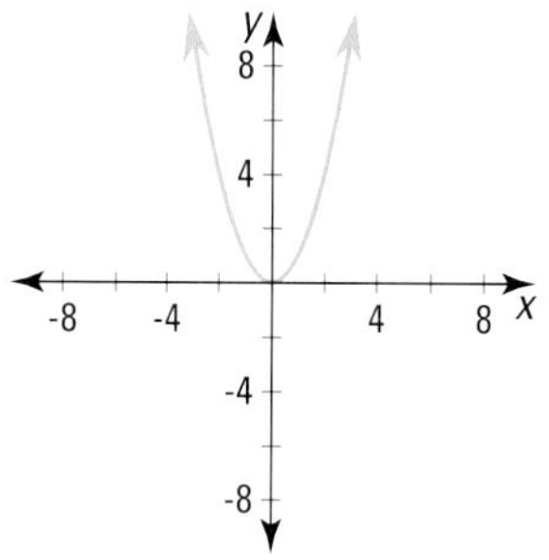	$f^{-1}(x) = \sqrt{x}$ domain: $R^+ \cup \{0\}$ range: $R^+ \cup \{0\}$	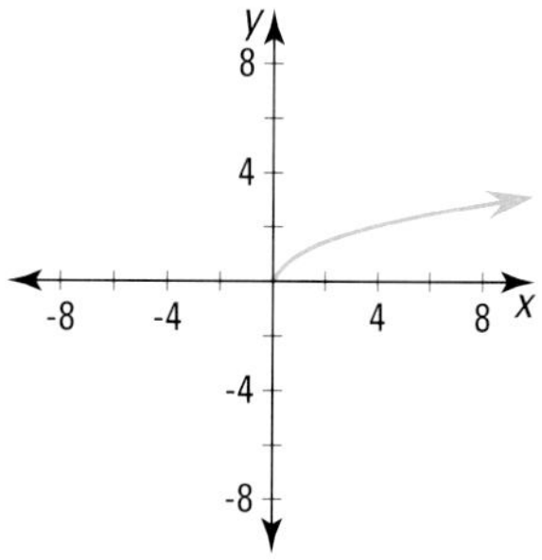
polynomial–cubic	$f(x) = x^3$ domain: R range: R	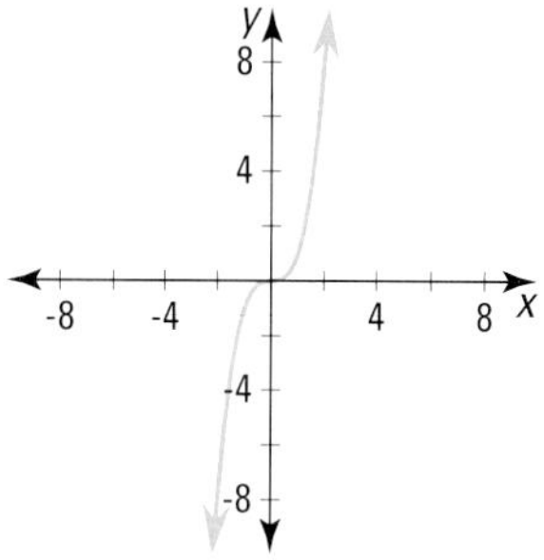	$f^{-1}(x) = \sqrt[3]{x}$	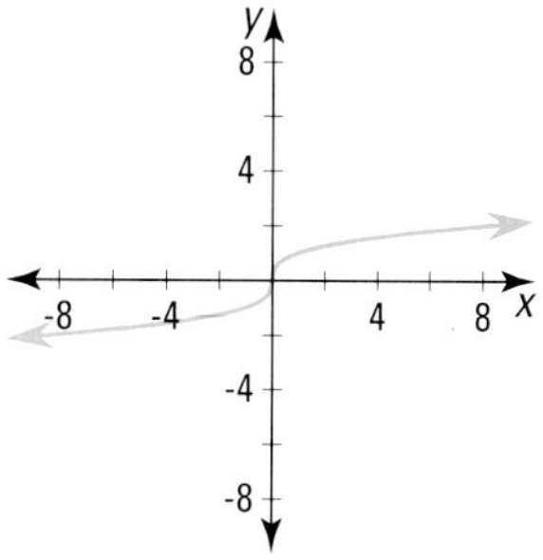
polynomial of higher degree	$f(x) = x^n$ n an odd integer domain: R range: R	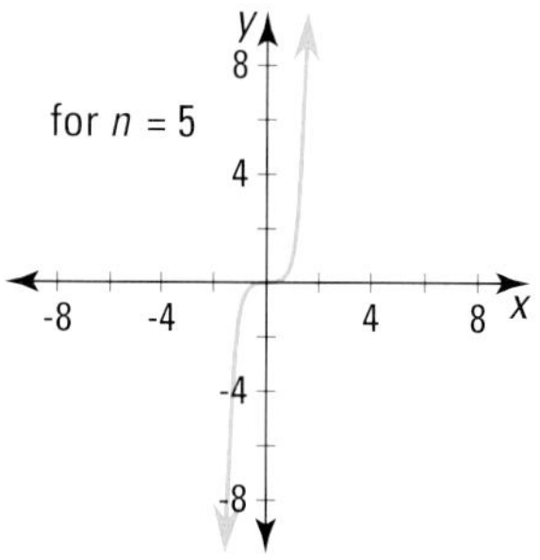 for $n = 5$	$f^{-1}(x) = \sqrt[n]{x}$	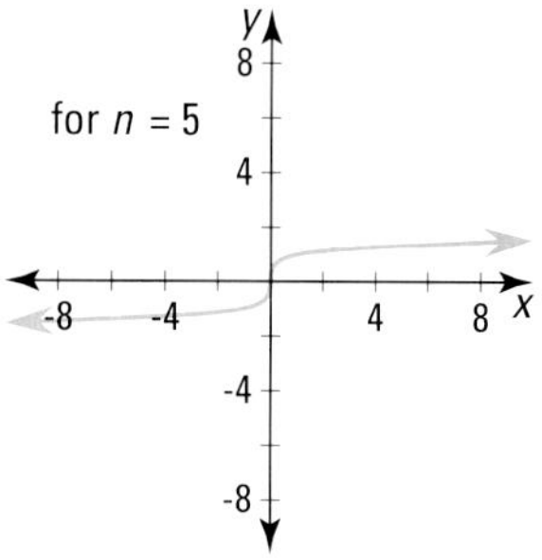 for $n = 5$
	$f(x) = x^n$ n an even integer domain: R range: $R^+ \cup \{0\}$	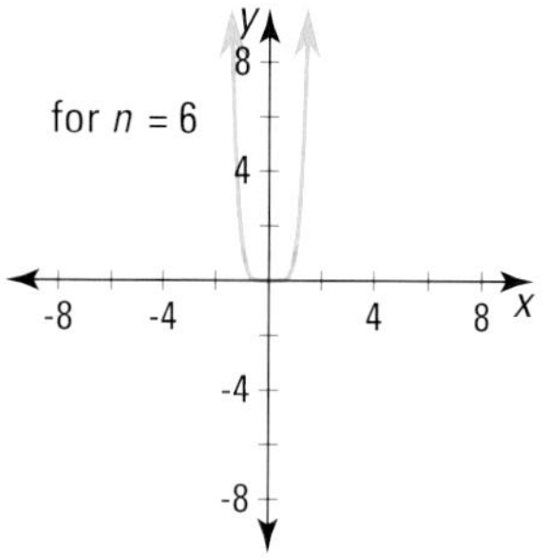 for $n = 6$	$f^{-1}(x) = \sqrt[n]{x}$ domain: $R^+ \cup \{0\}$ range: $R^+ \cup \{0\}$	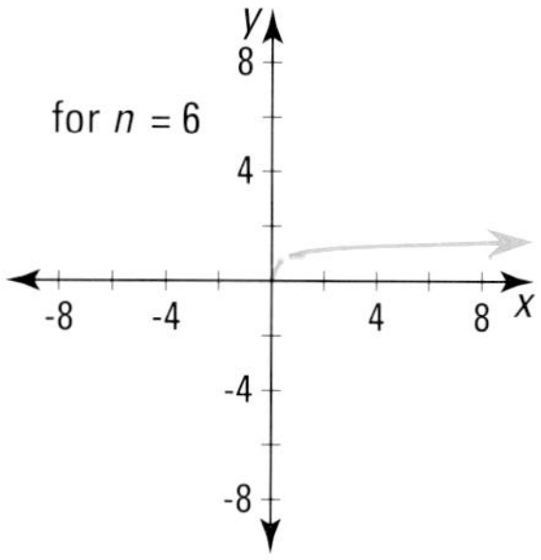 for $n = 6$

Type of Function	Parent Function, f *	Graph of f	Inverse Function, f^{-1} †	Graph of f^{-1}
hyperbola	$f(x) = \frac{1}{x}$ domain: set of nonzero reals range: set of nonzero reals	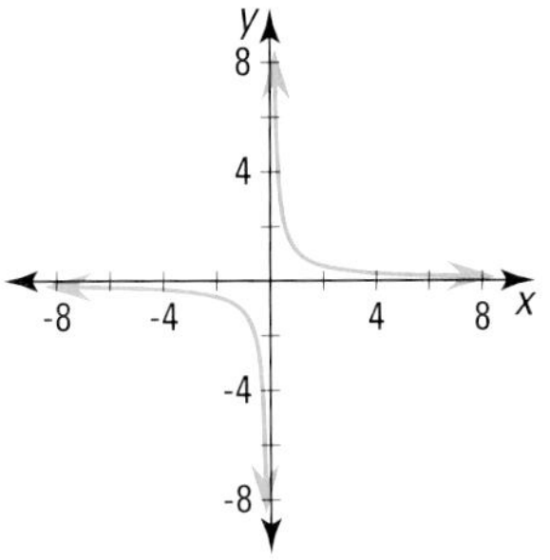	$f^{-1}(x) = \frac{1}{x}$	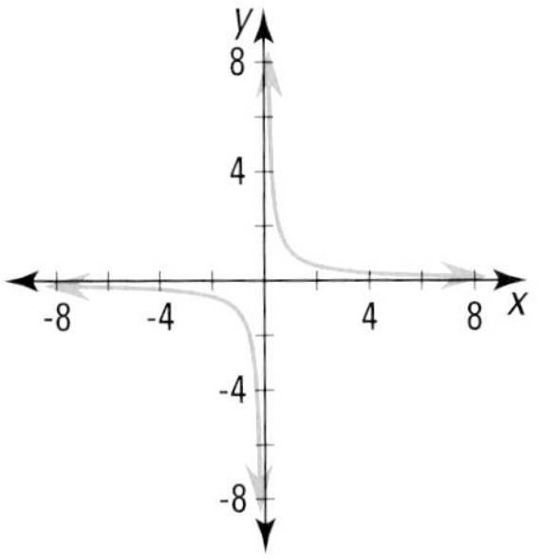
inverse-square	$f(x) = \frac{1}{x^2}$ domain: set of nonzero reals range: R^+	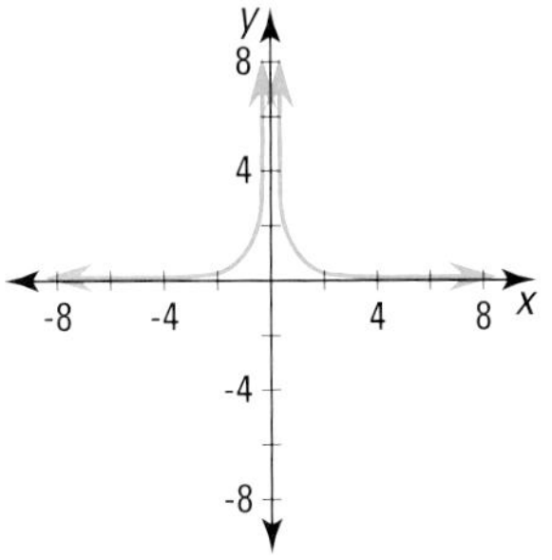	$f^{-1}(x) = \sqrt{\frac{1}{x}}$ domain: R^+ range: R^+	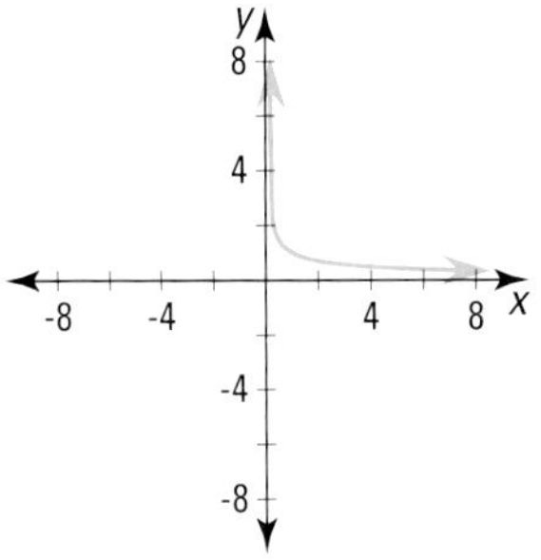
exponential any base	$f(x) = b^x$ $b > 1$ domain: R range: R^+	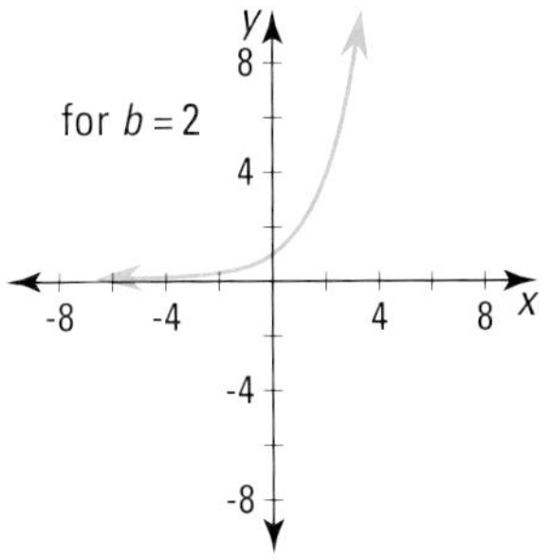 for $b = 2$	$f^{-1}(x) = \log_b x$	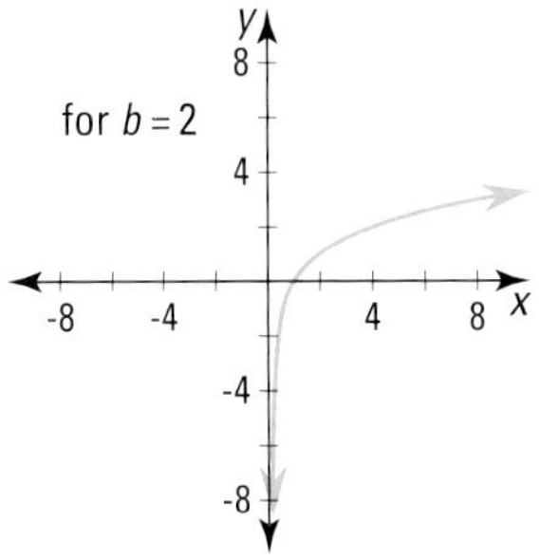 for $b = 2$
	$f(x) = b^x$ $0 < b < 1$ domain: R range: R^+	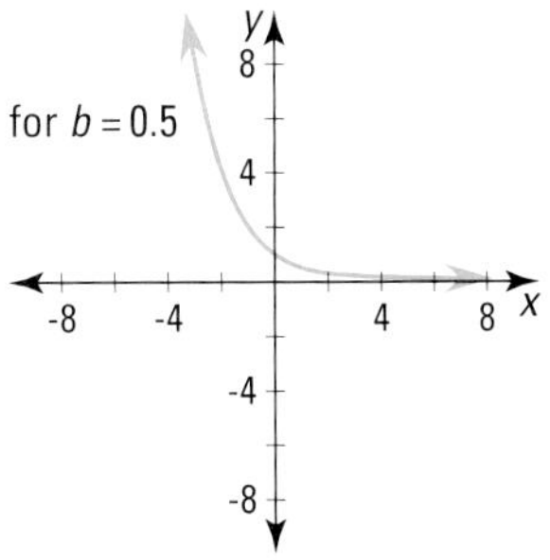 for $b = 0.5$	$f^{-1}(x) = \log_b x$	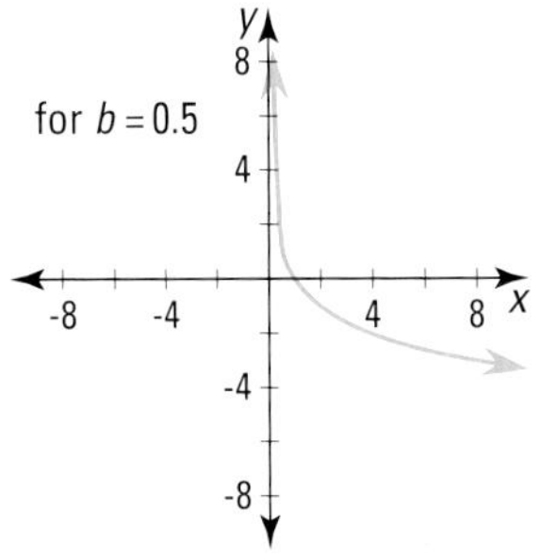 for $b = 0.5$

Type of Function	Parent Function, f *	Graph of f	Inverse Function, f^{-1} †	Graph of f^{-1}
exponential base e	$f(x) = e^x$ domain: R range: R^+	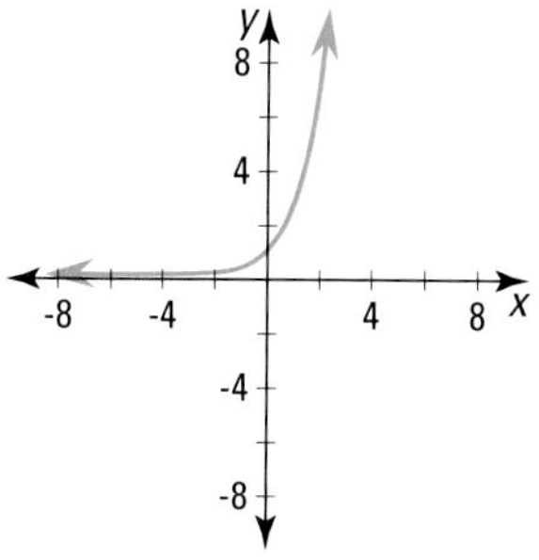	$f^{-1}(x) = \ln x$	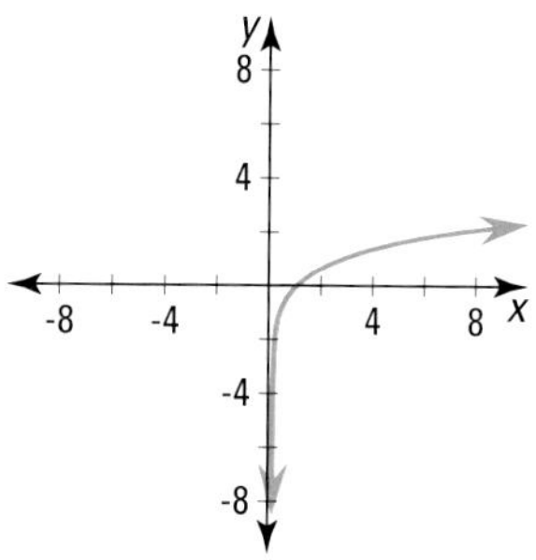
circular–sine	$f(x) = \sin x$ domain: R range: $\{y: -1 \leq y \leq 1\}$	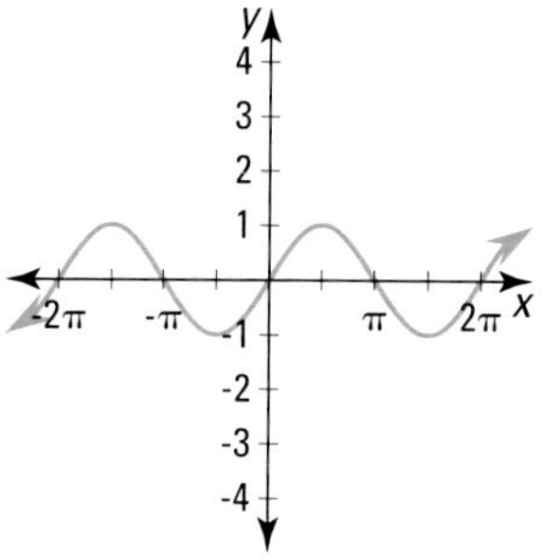	$f^{-1}(x) = \sin^{-1} x$ domain: $\{x: -1 \leq x \leq 1\}$ range: $\{y: \frac{\pi}{2} \leq y \leq \frac{\pi}{2}\}$	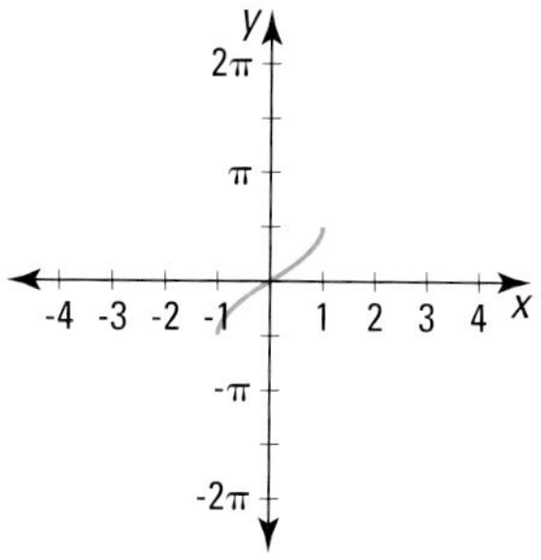
circular–cosine	$f(x) = \cos x$ domain: R range: $\{y: -1 \leq y \leq 1\}$	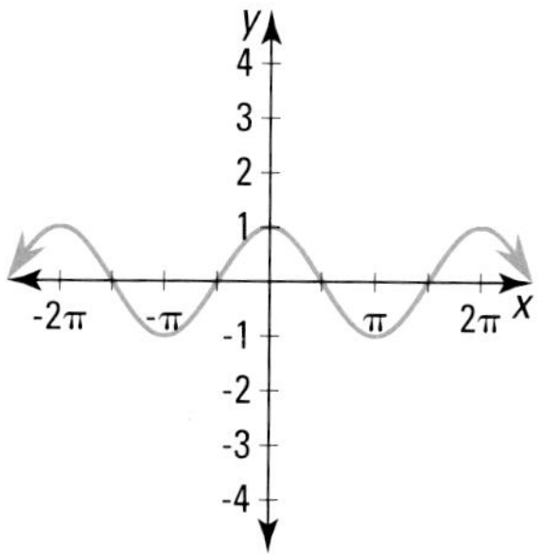	$f^{-1}(x) = \cos^{-1} x$ domain: $\{x: -1 \leq x \leq 1\}$ range: $\{y: 0 \leq y \leq \pi\}$	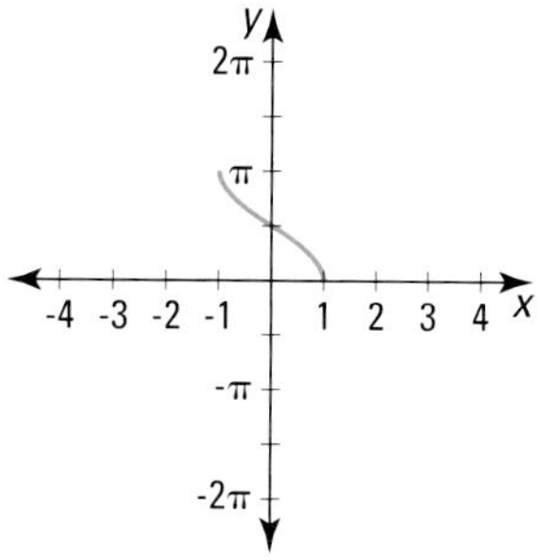
circular–tangent	$f(x) = \tan x$ domain: R except $\frac{\pi}{2} + n\pi$, n an integer range: R	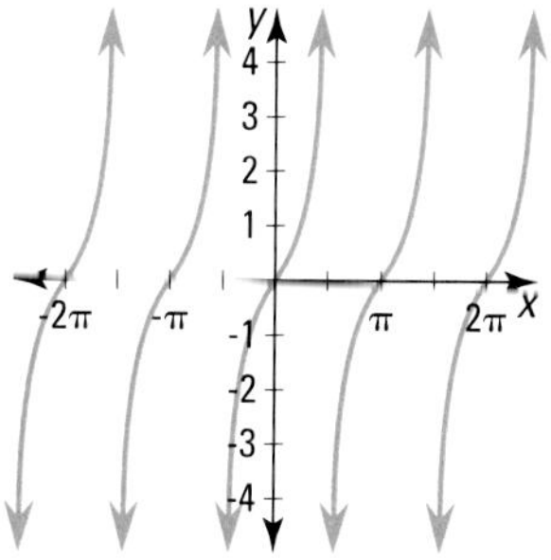	$f^{-1}(x) = \tan^{-1} x$ domain: R range: $\{y: -\frac{\pi}{2} < y < \frac{\pi}{2}\}$	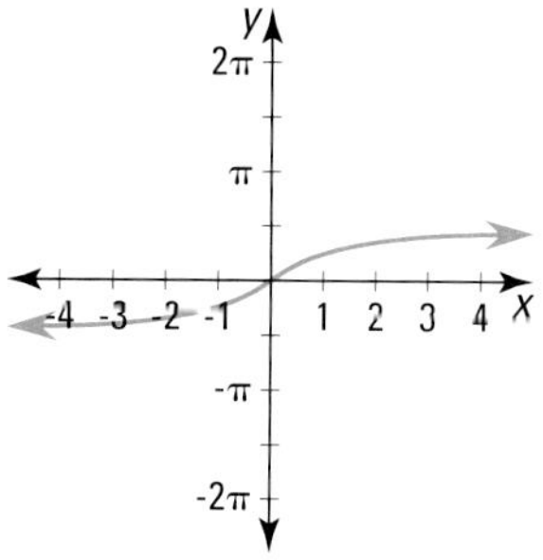

Type of Function	Parent Function, f	Graph of f
reciprocal circular–cosecant	$f(x) = \csc x = \frac{1}{\sin x}$ domain: set of reals except $n\pi$, where n is an integer range: $\{y: y \geq 1 \text{ or } y \leq -1\}$	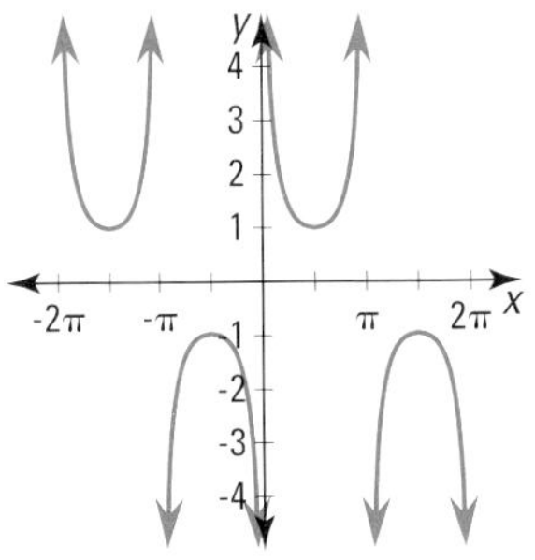
reciprocal circular–secant	$f(x) = \sec x = \frac{1}{\cos x}$ domain: set of reals except $\frac{\pi}{2} + n\pi$, where n is an integer range: $\{y: y \geq 1 \text{ or } y \leq -1\}$	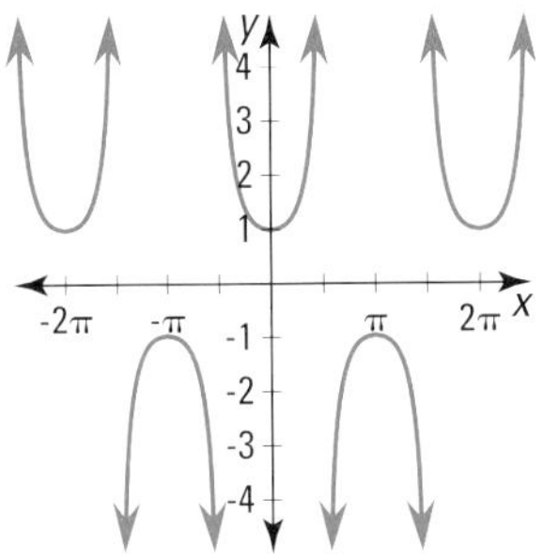
reciprocal circular–cotangent	$f(x) = \cot x = \frac{1}{\tan x}$ domain: set of reals except $n\pi$, where n is an integer range: R	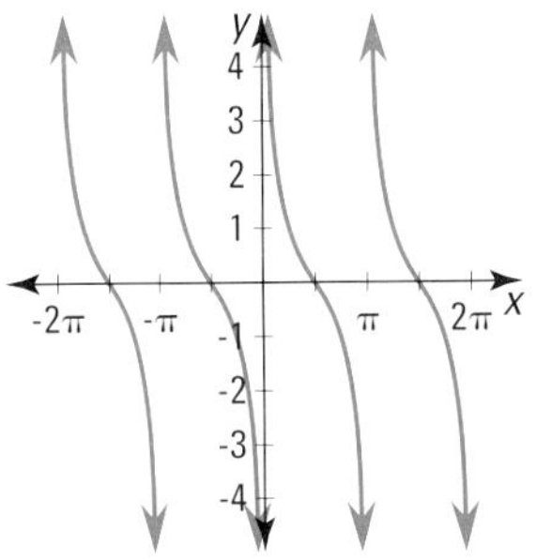
normal	$f(x) = e^{-x^2}$ domain: R range: $\{y: 0 < y \leq 1\}$	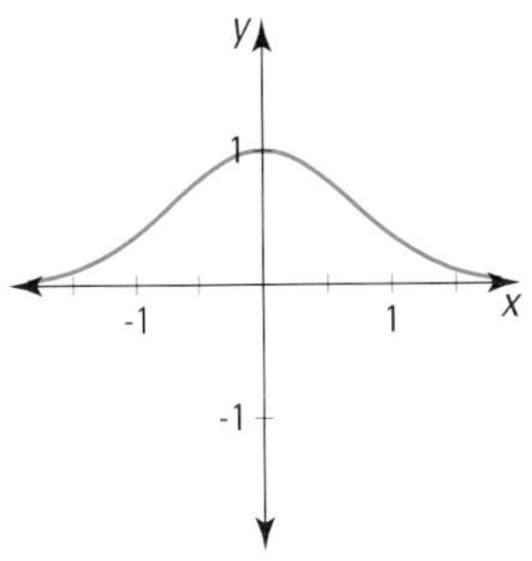

SELECTED ANSWERS

LESSON 7-1 (pp. 406–412)
9. $1, \frac{1}{2}, \frac{1}{3}, \frac{1}{4}, \frac{1}{5}, \frac{1}{6}$; $a_n = \frac{1}{n}$, $\forall$ integers $n \geq 1$ **11. a.** $a_1 = 2$; $a_{k+1} = 3a_k + 2$, $\forall$ integers $k \geq 1$ **b.** $a_n = 3^n - 1$, $\forall$ integers $n \geq 1$, conjectured from 2, 8, 26, 80, ... **c.** $a_1 = 3^1 - 1 = 2$, so the initial condition is met. $a_{n+1} = 3^{n+1} - 1 = 3 \cdot 3^n - 1 = 3 \cdot 3^n - 3 + 3 - 1 = 3(3^n - 1) + 2 = 3a_n + 2$, so the recursive relationship is met. Therefore, the explicit formula is correct. **13. a.** $\lim\limits_{x \to \infty} f(x) = 2$; $\lim\limits_{x \to -\infty} f(x) = 2$ **b.** There are essential discontinuities at $x = 3$ and $x = -3$. **c.** $x = 3, x = -3, y = 2$ **15.** $\frac{n+1}{n+2}$, for $n \neq -1, n \neq -2$ **17. a.** If there exists an x such that $p(x)$ is true and $q(x)$ is false. **b.** False

Lesson 7-2 (pp. 413–417)
11. It does.
13. Sample:
Let $a_n = 1\ \forall\ n$. Then $\sum\limits_{n=1}^{4} (a_n)^2 = 1^2 + 1^2 + 1^2 + 1^2 = 4$, and $\left(\sum\limits_{n=1}^{4} a_n\right)^2 = (1 + 1 + 1 + 1)^2 = 16$. **15.** explicit; -1, 1, -1, 1, -1, 1
17. $\frac{1}{2}, \frac{1}{3}, \frac{1}{4}, \frac{1}{5}, \frac{1}{6}, \frac{1}{7}$; $a_n = \frac{1}{n+1}$, $\forall$ integers $n \geq 1$
19.
$$\begin{aligned}\text{Left side} &= \sin^2 x - \sin^2 y\\ &= (1 - \cos^2 x) - (1 - \cos^2 y)\\ &= 1 - \cos^2 x - 1 + \cos^2 y\\ &= \cos^2 y - \cos^2 x\\ &= \text{Right side}\end{aligned}$$
$\therefore\ \forall$ real numbers x and y, $\sin^2 x - \sin^2 y = \cos^2 y - \cos^2 x$.
21. $(g \circ f)(k) = \frac{(k+1)(k+2)}{2}$

LESSON 7-3 (pp. 418–426)
7. a. $S(1)$: $1^2 = \frac{1(2)(3)}{6}$, so $S(1)$ is true. **b.** Assume that $S(k)$ is true for a particular but arbitarily chosen integer $k \geq 1$. $S(k)$: $1^2 + 2^2 + ... + k^2 = \frac{k(k+1)(2k+1)}{6}$. Show $S(k+1)$: $1^2 + 2^2 + ... + k^2 + (k+1)^2 = \frac{(k+1)(k+2)(2(k+1)+1)}{6}$ is true.
$1^2 + 2^2 + ... + k^2 + (k+1)^2 = \frac{k(k+1)(2k+1)}{6} + (k+1)^2 = \frac{k(k+1)(2k+1) + 6(k+1)^2}{6} = \frac{(k+1)(k(2k+1) + 6(k+1))}{6} = \frac{(k+1)(2k^2 + 7k + 6)}{6} = \frac{(k+1)(k+2)(2k+3)}{6} = \frac{(k+1)(k+2)(2(k+1)+1)}{6}$ **c.** Since $S(1)$ is true and $S(k) \Rightarrow S(k+1)$, then by mathematical induction, $S(n)$ is true $\forall$ integers $n \geq 1$. **9.** $S(n)$: $a_n = 2n^2 - 1\ \forall$ integers $n \geq 1$. (1) $a_1 = 1$ from the recursive definition; $a_1 = 2 \cdot 1^2 - 1 = 1$ from the explicit definition. Hence, $S(1)$ is true. (2) Assume $S(k)$: $a_k = 2k^2 - 1$ for some integer $k \geq 1$. Show $S(k+1)$: $a_{k+1} = 2(k+1)^2 - 1$ is true. $a_{k+1} = a_k + 4k + 2 = 2k^2 - 1 + 4k + 2 = 2(k^2 + 2k + 1) - 1 = 2(k+1)^2 - 1$. Therefore, $S(k+1)$ is true if $S(k)$ is true, and (1) and (2) prove by the Principle of Mathematical Induction that the explicit formula does describe the sequence. **11.** $\sum\limits_{i=1}^{n} \frac{i}{n}$ **13. a.** 1, 2, 3, 4, 5, 6

b. Sample: $a_n = n$, for all integers $n \geq 1$. **15. a.** Since $x - y$ is a factor of $x^4 - y^4$, and $x^4 - y^4$ is a factor of $x^5 - xy^4 = x(x^4 - y^4)$, then by the Transitive Property of Polynomial Factors, $x - y$ is a factor of $x^5 - xy^4$. **b.** $xy^4 - y^5 = y^4(x - y)$ **c.** Since $x - y$ is a factor of $x^5 - xy^4$ by part **a** and $x - y$ is a factor of $xy^4 - y^5$ by part **b**, then $x - y$ is a factor of $(x^5 - xy^4) + (xy^4 - y^5)$ by the Factor of a Polynomial Sum Theorem.

LESSON 7-4 (pp. 427–431)
7. $S(1)$ is true since $1^3 + 14 \cdot 1 + 3 = 18 = 3 \cdot 6$. Assume $S(k)$: 3 is a factor of $k^3 + 14k + 3$. Show $S(k+1)$: 3 is a factor of $(k+1)^3 + 14(k+1) + 3$ is true. $(k+1)^3 + 14(k+1) + 3 = k^3 + 3k^2 + 17k + 18 = (k^3 + 14k + 3) + 3k^2 + 3k + 15$. Since 3 is a factor of $k^3 + 14k + 3$ and $3(k^2 + k + 5)$, $S(k+1)$ is true. Hence, 3 is a factor of $n^3 + 14n + 3\ \forall\ n \geq 1$ by the Principle of Mathematical Induction. **9.** By Example 3 with $x = 2^2$ and $y = 1$, $x - y = 3$ is a factor of $x^n - y^n = 2^{2n} - 1$. **11.** $S(1)$ is true because $\sum\limits_{i=1}^{1} i^3 = 1^3 = 1$ and $\left[\frac{1(1+1)}{2}\right]^2 = 1^2 = 1$. Assume $S(k)$: $\sum\limits_{i=1}^{k} i^3 = \left[\frac{k(k+1)}{2}\right]^2$ is true for some integer $k \geq 1$. Show that $S(k+1)$: $\sum\limits_{i=1}^{k+1} i^3 = \left[\frac{(k+1)(k+2)}{2}\right]^2$ is true.
Now $\sum\limits_{i=1}^{k+1} i^3 = \sum\limits_{i=1}^{k} i^3 + (k+1)^3 = \left[\frac{k(k+1)}{2}\right]^2 + (k+1)^3 = \frac{k^2(k+1)^2}{4} + \frac{4(k+1)^3}{4} = \frac{(k+1)^2[k^2 + 4(k+1)]}{4} = \frac{[(k+1)(k+2)]^2}{4}$.
Since $S(1)$ is true and $S(k) \Rightarrow S(k+1)$, by the Principle of Mathematical Induction, $S(n)$ is true for all integers $n \geq 1$.
13. True
15.

Left side $= \frac{a^4 - b^4}{a - b}$	
$= \frac{(a^2 - b^2)(a^2 + b^2)}{a - b}$	Factoring
$= \frac{(a - b)(a + b)(a^2 + b^2)}{a - b}$	Factoring
$= (a + b)(a^2 + b^2)$	Division
$= a^3 + a^2b + ab^2 + b^3$	Multiplication

Therefore, $\frac{a^4 - b^4}{a - b} = a^3 + a^2b + ab^2 + b^3$ when $a \neq b$ by the Transitive Property.
17. $f(t) = 30 \cdot 3^t$

LESSON 7-5 (pp. 432–434)
9. Let $S(t)$ be the Statement: $3t^2 \geq 9t$
$S(3)$: $3 \cdot 3^2 = 27$, and $9 \cdot 3 = 27$, so $27 \geq 27$, and $S(3)$ is true
Assume $S(k)$. Then

$3k^2 \geq 9k$	
$3k^2 + 6k + 3 \geq 9k + 6k + 3$	Addition Property of Inequality
$3(k+1)^2 \geq 9(k+1) + 6k - 6$	Factor
$3(k+1)^2 \geq 9(k+1)$	Transitive Property, since $6k - 6 > 0$

Thus, $S(k) \Rightarrow S(k+1)$. So by the Principle of Mathematical Induction, $S(t)$ is true for all integers $t \geq 3$.

11. a. $\begin{cases} A_1 = 8000 \\ A_{n+1} = (1.008)a_n - 400 \quad \forall \text{ integers } n \geq 1 \end{cases}$
b. \$6639.79 **13. a.** Sample: $x = 12$ and $y = 10$, $xy = 120$ and $120(\text{mod } 7) \equiv 1(\text{mod } 7)$ **b.** Yes. $xy(\text{mod}7) \equiv 1(\text{mod } 7)$

LESSON 7-6 (pp. 435–441)

9. a. $a\left(\frac{1-r^n}{1-r}\right) = a \cdot \frac{-1}{-1} \cdot \frac{1-r^n}{1-r} = a\left(\frac{r^n-1}{r-1}\right)$
b. $a = 1, r = 2$:
Left side $= 1 \cdot \left(\frac{1-2^n}{-1}\right) = 2^n - 1$,
Right side $= 1 \cdot \left(\frac{2^n-1}{1}\right) = 2^n - 1$;
$a = 1, r = \frac{1}{2}$:
Left side $= 1 \cdot \left(\frac{1-\left(\frac{1}{2}\right)^n}{\frac{1}{2}}\right) = 2 - 2\left(\frac{1}{2}\right)^n$,
Right side $= 1 \cdot \left(\frac{\left(\frac{1}{2}\right)^n - 1}{-\left(\frac{1}{2}\right)}\right) = 2 - 2\left(\frac{1}{2}\right)^n$
c. the right side d. the left side
11. a. $a_1 = 3, a_k = \frac{1}{2}a_{k-1}$, for all integers $2 \le k \le 25$.
b. $a_n = 3\left(\frac{1}{2}\right)^{n-1}$ c. $\sum_{j=1}^{25} 3\left(\frac{1}{2}\right)^{j-1}$ d. ≈ 5.99999982 e. 6
f. The result confirms parts **d** and **e.**
13. Let $S(n)$: if $x > 1$, then $x^n > 1 \ \forall$ integers $n \ge 1$.
$S(1)$: $x^1 = x > 1$, is true since x is greater than 1.
Assume $S(k)$. If $x > 1$, then $x^k > 1$.

$x \cdot x^k > x \cdot 1$	M_x
$x^{k+1} > x$	Product of Powers
$x^{k+1} > 1$	Transitivity, since $x > 1$

Thus $S(k) \Rightarrow S(k+1)$. So by the Principle of Mathematical Induction, $S(n)$ is true for all positve integers.
15. a. The graph has shifted $\frac{\pi}{2}$ units to the right. **See below.**
b. $-\pi < \theta \le -\frac{\pi}{4}$ or $0 < \theta \le \frac{3\pi}{4}$

15. a.

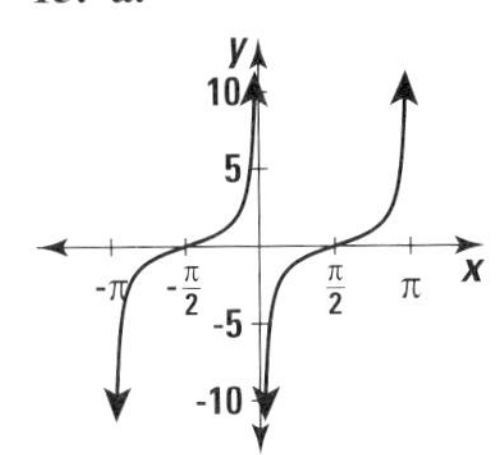

LESSON 7-7 (pp. 442–449)

5. a. 5, 15, 20, 35 b. $a_1 = 5$ and $a_2 = 15$ are multiples of 5. Assume $a_1, a_2, \ldots, a_k$ are all multiples of 5. Show that a_{k+1} is a multiple of 5. Now $a_{k+1} = a_k + a_{k-1}$. 5 is a factor of a_k and a_{k-1}, so it is factor of their sum, a_{k+1}. Hence, by the Strong Form of Mathematical Induction, a_n is a multiple of 5 $\forall$ integers $n \ge 1$.
7. a. $S(2)$: $L_2 = F_3 + F_1$. $3 = 2 + 1$, so $S(2)$ is true.
$S(3)$: $L_3 = F_4 + F_2$. $4 = 3 + 1$, so $S(3)$ is true.
b. $\forall$ integers j such that $2 \le j \le k$, $L_j = F_{j+1} + F_{j-1}$
c. $S(k+1)$: $L_{k+1} = F_{k+2} + F_k$
d. $L_{k+1} = L_k + L_{k-1} = (F_{k+1} + F_{k-1}) + (F_k + F_{k-2})$
e. $L_{k+1} = (F_{k-1} + F_{k-2}) + (F_{k+1} + F_k) = F_{k+2} + F_k$
9. Let $S(n)$: $n^3 + 3n^2 + 2n$ is divisible by 3. Then $S(1)$: $1^3 + 3 \cdot 1^2 + 2 \cdot 1$ is divisible by 3. $1 + 3 + 2 = 6$, which is divisible by 3, so $S(1)$ is true. Assume $S(k)$: $k^3 + 3k^2 + 2k$ is divisible by 3 is true for some integer $k \ge 1$.
Show $S(k+1)$: $(k+1)^3 + 3(k+1)^2 + 2(k+1)$ is divisible by 3 is true. $(k+1)^3 + 3(k+1)^2 + 2(k+1) =$
$k^3 + 3k^2 + 3k + 1 + 3k^2 + 6k + 3 + 2k + 2 =$
$k^3 + 6k^2 + 11k + 6 = (k^3 + 3k^2 + 2k) + 3(k^2 + 3k + 2)$.
$k^3 + 3k^2 + 2k$ is divisible by 3 by the inductive assumption, and $3(k^2 + 3k + 2)$ is divisible by 3; thus their sum is divisble by 3. Therefore, by mathematical induction, $n^3 + 3n^2 + 2n$ is divisible by 3 $\forall$ integers $n \ge 1$. 11. a. **See below.** b. $\tan x$
c. Left side $= \csc x \sec x - \cot x$

$= \frac{1}{\sin x} \cdot \frac{1}{\cos x} - \frac{\cos x}{\sin x}$	Definition of cosecant, secant, and cotangent
$= \frac{1}{\sin x \cos x} - \frac{\cos^2 x}{\sin x \cos x}$	Multiplication
$= \frac{1 - \cos^2 x}{\sin x \cos x}$	Subtraction of Fractions
$= \frac{\sin^2 x}{\sin x \cos x}$	Pythagorean Identity
$= \frac{\sin x}{\cos x}$	Simplifying fractions
$= \tan x$	Definition of tangent
$=$ Right side	

Therefore, $\csc x \sec x - \cot x = \tan x \ \forall \ x$ for which both sides are defined.
13. $x = -5, 2$

11. a.

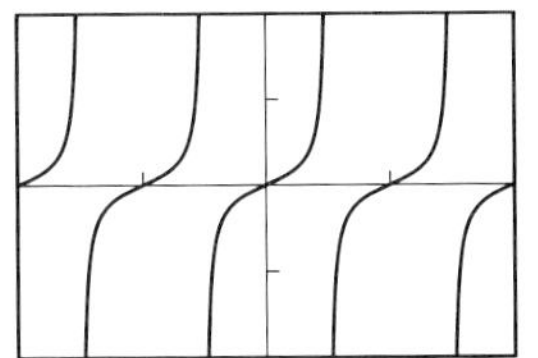

$-2\pi \le x \le 2\pi$, x-scale $= \pi$
$-10 \le y \le 10$, y-scale $= 5$

LESSON 7-8 (pp. 450–456)

7. If no interchanges are necessary, adjacent numbers are in order. Hence, by the Transitive Property, the entire list is in order.
9. Sample: 6, 5, 4, 3, 2, 1 11. Quicksort 13. $q = 14, r = 1$
15. a. $A_2 = \frac{1}{4}, A_3 = \frac{1}{16}$ b. $A_k = \frac{1}{4^{k-1}}$, for all integers $k \ge 1$
c. $\frac{4}{3}\left(1 - \left(\frac{1}{4}\right)^n\right)$ d. $\frac{4}{3}$ 17. a. $R = \frac{R_1R_2}{R_1 + R_2}$ b. $\frac{70}{17} \approx 4.12$ ohms

LESSON 7-9 (pp. 457–462)

7. **See below.** 9. Let $S(n)$: $a_n = 3n^2 + 5n - 3$. For $n = 1$, the formula yields $a_1 = 3 \cdot 1^2 + 5 \cdot 1 - 3 = 5$. This agrees with the initial condition, so $S(1)$ is true. Assume $S(k)$: $a_k = 3k^2 + 5k - 3$ is true for some positive integer k. Show that $S(k+1)$: $a_{k+1} = 3(k+1)^2 + 5(k+1) - 3$ is true. $a_{k+1} = 3(k+1)^2 + 5(k+1) - 3 = (3k^2 + 5k - 3) + 6k + 8 = a_k + 6k + 8$. This agrees with the recursive formula, so $S(k+1)$ is true. Hence, by mathematical induction, $S(n)$ is true for all integers $n \ge 1$, and so the explicit formula for the sequence is $3n^2 + 5n - 3$. 11. a. $a_n = 34 + 5(n-1)$ b. $\sum_{n=1}^{27}(34 + 5(n-1))$
13. a. not(p and (q or r)) b. Sample: $p = 0, q = 1, r = 0$

7.

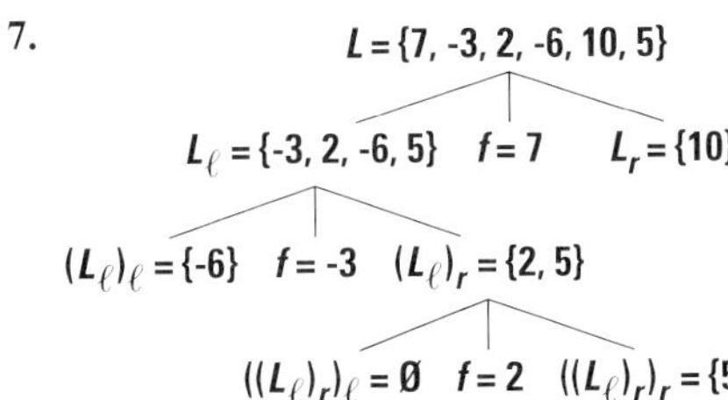

SELECTED ANSWERS

CHAPTER 7 PROGRESS SELF-TEST (p. 466)

1. a. 1, 2, 4, 8, 16 **b.** $a_n = 2^{n-1}$ $\forall$ integers $n \ge 1$ **2.** $r_1 = 5, r_n = 3r_{n-1}$, for $n \ge 2$ **3.** c **4.** $\sum_{i=1}^{k+1} i^2 = \left(\sum_{i=1}^{k} i^2\right) + (k+1)^2$ **5.** Let $S(n)$: $c_n = 3 \cdot 2n - 3$. $S(1)$: $c_1 = 3 \cdot 2^1 - 3$. This matches the recursive definition since $c_1 - 3$, so $S(1)$ is true. Assume $S(k)$: $c_k = 3 \cdot 2^k - 3$ is true for some arbitrary integer k. Show that $S(k+1)$: $c_{k+1} = 3 \cdot 2^{k+1} - 3$ is true. From the recursive definition, $c_{k+1} = 2c_k + 3 = 2(3 \cdot 2^k) - 3 = 3 \cdot 2^{k+1} - 3$. Therefore, $S(k+1)$ is true. Hence, by mathematical induction, $S(n)$ is true for all $n \ge 1$, and so the explicit formula $c_n = 3 \cdot 2^n - 3$ yields the correct definition of the sequence. **6. a.** ≈ 2.9999831 **b.** 3 **7. a.** recursive **b.** $b_1 = 1$; $b_{j+1} = 2b_j + 5$ for $j \ge 1$

8. Let $S(n)$: $\sum_{i=1}^{n} i^2 = \frac{n(n+1)(2n+1)}{6}$. (1) $\sum_{i=1}^{1} i^2 = 1^2 = 1$, $\frac{1 \cdot 2 \cdot 3}{6} = 1$ so $S(1)$ is true. (2) Assume that $S(k)$ is true for an arbitrary integer $k \ge 1$ where $S(k)$: $\sum_{i=1}^{k} i^2 = \frac{k(k+1)(2k+1)}{6}$.

Now use the assumption that $S(k)$ is true to prove $S(k+1)$ is true: $\sum_{i=1}^{k+1} i^2 = \left(\sum_{i=1}^{k} i^2\right) + (k+1)^2 = \frac{k((k+1)(2k+1))}{6} + \frac{6(k+1)^2}{6} =$ $\left(\frac{k+1}{6}\right) \cdot (2k^2 + k + 6k + 6) = \frac{(k+1)(k+2)(2k+3)}{6} = \frac{(k+1)((k+1)+1)(2(k+1)+1)}{6}$. Hence, $S(n)$ is true for all integers $n \ge 1$ by the Principle of Mathematical Induction.

9. Let $S(n)$: 4 is a factor of $2n^2 + 2n + 8$. (1) $2 \cdot 1^2 + 2 \cdot 1 + 8 = 12$ and 4 is a factor of 12 , so $S(1)$ is true. (2) Assume $S(k)$ is true. That is, 4 is a factor of $2k^2 + 2k + 8$ for some arbitrary integer $k \ge 1$. Show $S(k+1)$ is true. $2(k+1)^2 + 2(k+1) + 8 - 2k^2 + 4k + 2 + 2k + 2 + 8 = (2k^2 + 2k + 8) + 4k + 4 = (2k^2 + 2k + 8) + 4(k+1)$. 4 is a factor of $2k^2 + 2k + 8$ by inductive assumption, and 4 is clearly a factor of $4(k+1)$. Hence, 4 is a factor of $2(k+1)^2 + 2(k+1) + 8$ by the Factor of an Integer Sum Theorem. Therefore, $S(n)$ is true for all positive integers n by mathematical induction. So 4 is factor of $2n^2 + 2n + 8$ for all positive integers n. **10.** Assume $S(1), S(2), \ldots, S(k)$ are true for some integer $k \ge 1$. **11.** The sorted list is 1, 3, 7, 8, 10. **See below.**

11.

$L = \{8, 3, 10, 7, 1\}$

$L_\ell = \{3, 7, 1\}$ $f = 8$ $L_r = \{10\}$

$(L_\ell)_\ell = \{1\}$ $f = 3$ $(L_\ell)_r = \{7\}$

The chart below keys the questions on the **Progress Self-Test** to the objectives in the **Chapter Review** on pages 467–469 or to the **Vocabulary** (Voc.) on page 465. This will enable you to locate those **Chapter Review** questions that correspond to questions you missed on the **Progress Self-Test.** The lesson where the material is covered is also indicated on the chart.

Question	1	2	3	4	5	6	7	8	9	10
Objective	A, B	H	C	D	F	E	J	G	G	G
Lesson	7-1	7-1	7-2	7-2	7-3	7-6	7-1	7-3	7-4	7-7

Question	11
Objective	I
Lesson	7-8

CHAPTER 7 REVIEW (pp. 467–469)

1. 7, 13, 31, 85, 247 **3.** 0, 2, 2, 4, 4 **5.** 3, 5, -2, -24, -40 **7.** $-3c$ **9. a.** $1, \frac{1}{2}, \frac{1}{6}, \frac{1}{24}, \frac{1}{120}$ **b.** $a_n = \frac{1}{n!}$ for all integers $n \ge 1$ **11.** $I_n = n(n+1)$ **13. a.** $(n-3) + (n-2) + \ldots + (n+n)$ **b.** 9

15. $\frac{1}{7}$ **17.** $\sum_{i=1}^{n} \frac{1}{-i}$ **19. a.** $S(k)$: $\sum_{i=1}^{k} 2i = k(k+1)$ **b.** 202 **c.** $10100 + 202 = 10302$ and $101(102) = 10302$

21. $\sum_{j=1}^{k+1} (j-1)(2j+1) = \left[\sum_{j=1}^{k} (j-1)(2j+1)\right] + (k)(2k+3)$

23. a. $\frac{4t}{3}\left(1 - \left(\frac{1}{4}\right)^{n+1}\right)$ **b.** ≈ 2.6667 **25. a.** $S_n = 10\left(1 - \left(\frac{4}{5}\right)^n\right)$ **b.** ≈ 7.9029 **c.** 10 **27. a.** 0, 2, 6, 12, 20

b. Let $S(n)$: $b_n = n(n-1)$.

(1) $S(1)$: $b_1 = 1(1-1)$. $b_1 = 0$, so $S(1)$ is true.

(2) Assume $S(k)$. $b_k - k(k-1)$ is true for some arbitrary integer $k \ge 1$. Show that $S(k+1)$: $b_{k+1} = (k+1)((k+1)-1)$ is true.

From the recursive definition,

$$\begin{aligned} b_{k+1} &= b_k + 2k \\ &= k(k-1) + 2k \\ &= k^2 + k \\ &= (k+1)k \\ &= (k+1)((k+1)-1). \end{aligned}$$

Hence, by mathematical induction, $S(n)$ is true $\forall$ integers $n \ge 1$, and the explicit formula is correct.

29. (1) $S(1)$: $\sum_{i=1}^{1} 3i(i+2) = \frac{1 \cdot 2 \cdot 9}{2}$. $3 \cdot 1(1+2) = 9$ and $\frac{1 \cdot 2 \cdot 9}{2} = 9$, so $S(1)$ is true. (2) Assume that $S(k)$: $\sum_{i=1}^{k} 3i(i+2) = \frac{k(k+1)(2k+7)}{2}$ is true for some arbitrary integer $k \ge 1$. Show $S(k+1)$: $\sum_{i=1}^{k+1} 3i(i+2) = \frac{(k+1)(k+2)(2(k+1)+7)}{2}$ is true.

$\sum_{i=1}^{k+1} 3i(i+2) = \left(\sum_{i=1}^{k} 3i(i+2)\right) + 3(k+1)(k+3) = \frac{k(k+1)(2k+7)}{2} + (k+1)(3k+9) = \frac{k(k+1)(2k+7)}{2} +$

$\frac{(k+1)(3k+9)}{2} = \left(\frac{k+1}{2}\right)(2k^2 + 7k + 6k + 18)$
$= \left(\frac{k+1}{2}\right)(k+2)(2k+9) = \frac{(k+1)(k+2)(2(k+2)+7)}{2}$
Hence, by the Principle of Mathematical Induction, $S(n)$ is true $\forall$ integers $n \geq 1$.
31. (1) $S(2)$: 3 is a factor of $2 \cdot 2^3 - 5 \cdot 2.\ 16 - 10 = 6$, so $S(2)$ is true. (2) Assume that $S(k)$: is a factor of $2k^3 - 5k$ is true for some integer $k \geq 2$. Prove $S(k+1)$: 3 is a factor of $2(k+1)^3 - 5(k+1)$ is true. $2(k+1)^3 - 5(k+1) = 2k^3 + 6k^2 + 6k + 2 - 5k - 5 =$ $(2k^3 - 5k) + 3(2k^2 + 2k - 1)$ Since 3 is factor of $2k^3 - 5k$ and $3(2k^2 + 2k - 1)$. 3 is a factor of their sum by the Factor of an Integer Sum Theorem. Hence, by mathematical induction, $S(n)$ is true $\forall$ integers $n \geq 2$. **33.** (1) $S(2)$: $42 = 16 > 8 = 4(2)$. So $S(2)$ is true. (2) Assume $S(k)$. Show $S(k+1)$: $4^{k+1} > 4(k+1)$.

$4^k > 4k$	by the inductive assumption
$4 \cdot 4^k > 4 \cdot 4k$	M_4
$4^{k+1} > 16k$	Simplification
$4^{k+1} > 4(k+1) + 12k - 4$	Distributive Property
$4^{k+1} > 4(k+1) + 12(2) - 4$	Given $k \geq 2$
$4^{k+1} > 4(k+1)$	$4(k+1) < 4(k+1) + 20$

So $S(k) \Rightarrow S(k+1)$. Therefore by the Principle of Mathematical Induction, $S(n)$ is true for all integers $n \geq 2$.
35. a. 0, 4, 4, 16, 28 **b.** Let $S(n)$: 4 is a factor of b_n.
(1) $S(1)$: 4 is a factor of b_1. $b_1 = 0$, so $S(1)$ is true. $S(2)$: 4 is factor of b_2. $b_2 = 4$, so $S(2)$ is true. (2) Assume $S(1), S(2), \ldots,$ and $S(k)$ are true for some integer $k \geq 1$. So 4 is a factor of $b_1, b_2, \ldots, b_k$. Show $S(k+1)$: 4 is a factor of b_{k+1} is true. Since b_{k-1} and b_k have 4 as a factor, there exist integers p and q such that $b_{k-1} = 4p$ and $b_k = 4q$. Substituting into the recurrence relation,
$b_{k+1} = 4q + 3(4p) = 4q + 12p = 4(q + 3p)$. $q + 3p$ is an integer by closure properties, so 4 is a factor of b_{k+1}. Hence, by the Strong Form of Mathematical Induction, $S(n)$ is true for all integers $n \geq 1$.

37. a. $\begin{cases} A_1 = 80{,}000 \\ A_{k+1} = 1.01A_k - 900 \quad \text{for all integers } k \geq 1 \end{cases}$
b. \$79,489.90
39. a. initial order: 1, 3, 5, 2, 4 First pass: 1, 3, 2, 4, 5
Second pass: 1, 2, 3, 4, 5 **b.** 5, 4, 3, 2, 1
41. a. $a_1 = 1, a_{k+1} = \frac{1}{2}a_k$ for all integers $k \geq 1$ **b.** $a_n = \left(\frac{1}{2}\right)^{n-1}$ for all integers $n \geq 1$ **c.** $\sum_{i=1}^{20}\left(\frac{1}{2}\right)^{i-1}$ **d.** $S_{20} = 2\left(1 - \left(\frac{1}{2}\right)^{20}\right)$

LESSON 8-1 (pp.472–479)

13. a. $5 - 6i$ **b. See below.** **c.** parallelogram; Sample: slopes of opposite sides are equal. **15. a.** $\frac{5}{2} + 3i$ ohms **b.** $5i$ ohms
17. $(1+i)^2 - 2(1+i) + 2 = 1 + i + i + i^2 - 2 - 2i + 2 =$
$1 + i + i - 1 - 2 - 2i + 2 = 0$
So $1 + i$ is a solution of $z^2 - 2z + 2 = 0$.
19. $\frac{5}{29} + \frac{2}{29}i$; $z \cdot \frac{1}{z} = (5 - 2i)\left(\frac{5}{29} + \frac{2}{29}i\right) = \frac{25}{29} + \frac{10}{29}i - \frac{10}{29}i - \frac{4}{29}i^2 =$ $\frac{25}{29} + \frac{4}{29} = 1$ **21.** Suppose there is a smallest integer, s. Then $s - 1 < s$, and $s - 1$ is an integer. This contradicts the assumption that s is the smallest integer. So the assumption is false, and there is no smallest integer. **23. a.** -40° **b.** $-51.25°\text{F} \leq t \leq -28.75°\text{F}$

13. b.

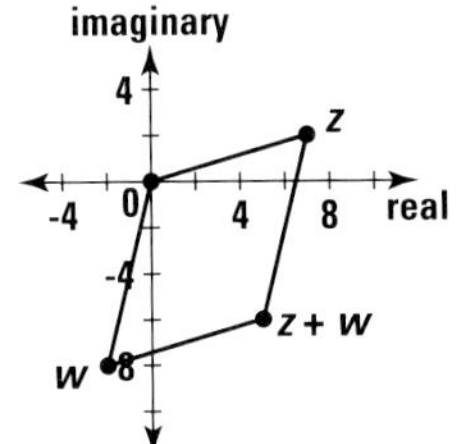

LESSON 8-2 (pp. 480–486)

11. a. sample: $\left[3, \frac{11\pi}{6}\right]$ **b.** sample: $\left[3, \frac{5\pi}{6}\right]$ **c.** sample: $\left[3, \frac{5\pi}{6}\right]$
13. a. sample: [1, 0°] **b.** sample: [1, 90°] **c.** sample: [11, 90°]
15. $P_1 = [3, 0°]$, $P_2 = [3, 30°]$, $P_3 = [3, 90°]$, $P_4 = [3, 120°]$, $P_5 = [3, 195°]$, $P_6 = [3, 240°]$, $P_7 = [3, 285°]$; $r = 3$
17. $-1.5 + \left(-1.5\sqrt{3}\right)i$ **19. a.** $z + w = (6 - 3i) + (2 + 4i) =$ $8 + i$, so $\overline{z + w} = 8 - i$. $\overline{z} = 6 + 3i$ and $\overline{w} = 2 - 4i$.
So $\overline{z} + \overline{w} = (6 + 3i) + (2 - 4i) = 8 - i$. $\therefore\ \overline{z + w} = \overline{z} + \overline{w}$.
b. $z \cdot w = (6 - 3i)(2 + 4i) = 24 + 18i$. So $\overline{z \cdot w} = 24 - 18i$.
$\overline{z} \cdot \overline{w} = (6 + 3i)(2 - 4i) = 24 - 18i$. $\therefore\ \overline{z \cdot w} = \overline{z} \cdot \overline{w}$.
c. $\frac{z}{w} = \frac{(6 - 3i)}{(2 + 4i)} = 0 - \frac{3}{2}i$, so $\overline{\left(\frac{z}{w}\right)} = 0 + \frac{3}{2}i$. $\frac{\overline{z}}{\overline{w}} = \frac{6 + 3i}{2 - 4i} = 0 + \frac{3}{2}i$.
$\therefore \overline{\left(\frac{z}{w}\right)} = \frac{\overline{z}}{\overline{w}}$. **21. a.** $\frac{400h}{26 + h}$ **b.** 6.5 mpg

LESSON 8-3 (pp. 487–492)

15. a. $|w| = \sqrt{5}$, $-\theta \approx -63.4°$ **b. See below.** **17. a.** $E' = 5 + i$, $F' = 1 + 4i$, $G' = 3 + 6i$ **b.** $EF = 5$, $EG = \sqrt{29}$, and $FG = 2\sqrt{2}$, while $E'F' = 5$, $E'G' = \sqrt{29}$, and $F'G' = 2\sqrt{2}$. So $\triangle EFG \cong \triangle E'F'G'$ by the SSS Congruence Theorem. **c.** $T_{1,1}$
19. a. See below. **b.** $x^2 + y^2 = 16$ **21.** Let $z = a + bi$, where a and b are real numbers. Then $\overline{z} = a - bi$.
$z + \overline{z} = (a + bi) + (a - bi) = 2a$. Since a is real, $2a$ is real. So for all complex numbers, the sum of the number and its complex conjugate is a real number. **23. a.** Yes **b.** domain: the set of real numbers; range: the set of integers

15. b.

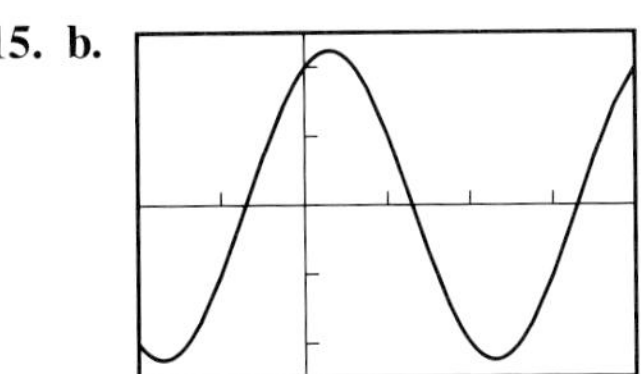

$-\pi \leq x \leq 2\pi$, x-scale $= \frac{\pi}{2}$
$-2.5 \leq y \leq 2.5$, y-scale $= 1$

19. a.

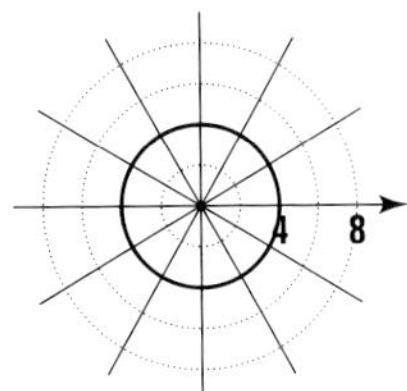

SELECTED ANSWERS

LESSON 8-4 (pp. 493–499)

7. a. $y + x = 1$ **b. See below.** **9.** periodic, sample: $0 \le \theta \le 2\pi$ **11. a.** The polar graph of $r = k \sin \theta$ is the graph of $r = \sin \theta$ taken through a scale change of k. **b.** It is a circle with radius $\frac{k}{2}$ and center $\left(0, \frac{k}{2}\right)$. **13. a.** $Z' = \left(-\frac{3}{2}, -9\right)$, $W' = \left(-\frac{9}{2}, -5\right)$ **b.** $T_{-\frac{7}{2}, -8}$ **c.** 5 **15. a.** $\frac{1}{2} - \frac{\sqrt{3}}{2}i$ **b.** They are complex conjugates. **c.** $z = \left[1, \frac{\pi}{3}\right]$; $w = \left[1, \frac{-\pi}{3}\right]$; their arguments are opposites. **17.** $\sum_{k=1}^{10} [k(2k + 1)]$

7. b.

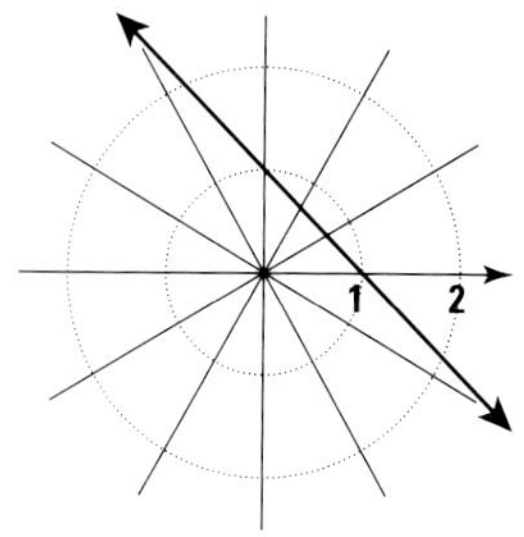

LESSON 8-5 (pp. 501–506)

7. a. $r = 2 \cos 5\theta$ or $r = 2 \sin 5\theta$ **b. See below.**

9. a. See above right. b.
$$r = \sqrt{2}\cos\left(\theta - \frac{\pi}{4}\right) = \sqrt{2}\left(\cos\theta \cos\frac{\pi}{4} + \sin\theta \sin\frac{\pi}{4}\right) = \sqrt{2}\left(\cos\theta \cdot \frac{\sqrt{2}}{2} + \sin\theta \cdot \frac{\sqrt{2}}{2}\right) = \cos\theta + \sin\theta$$

c. See above right.

$r = \cos\theta + \sin\theta \Rightarrow r = \frac{x}{r} + \frac{y}{r}$

$\Rightarrow \frac{x + y}{r} \Rightarrow r^2 = x + y$

$\Rightarrow x^2 + y^2 = x + y$

$\Rightarrow x^2 - x + y^2 - y = 0$

$\Rightarrow x^2 - x + \frac{1}{4} + y^2 - y + \frac{1}{4} = \frac{1}{2}$

$\Rightarrow \left(x - \frac{1}{2}\right)^2 + \left(y - \frac{1}{2}\right)^2 = \left(\frac{1}{\sqrt{2}}\right)^2$

Hence, the graph is a circle.

11. a. See above right. b. $[0, 0]$, $\left[2\sqrt{2}, \frac{\pi}{4}\right]$

13. a. $-20 - 10i$ volts **b.** $-9 - 2i$ volts

7. b.

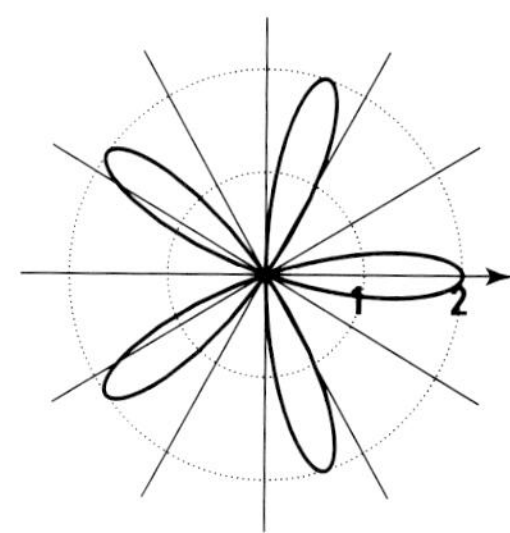

9. a.

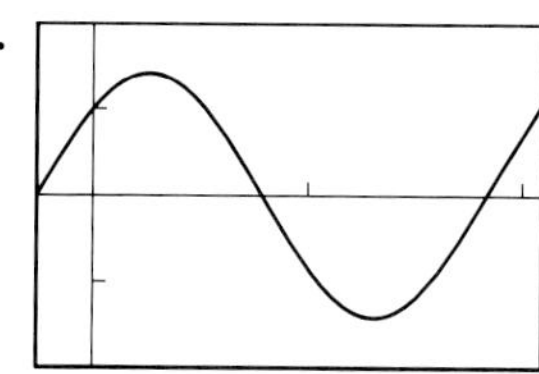

$-\frac{\pi}{4} \le x \le 2\pi$, x-scale = 3
$-2 \le y \le 2$, y-scale = 1

9. c.

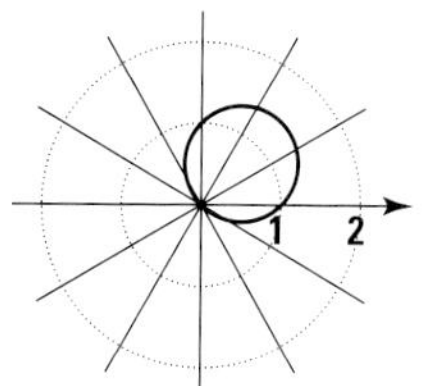

11. a.

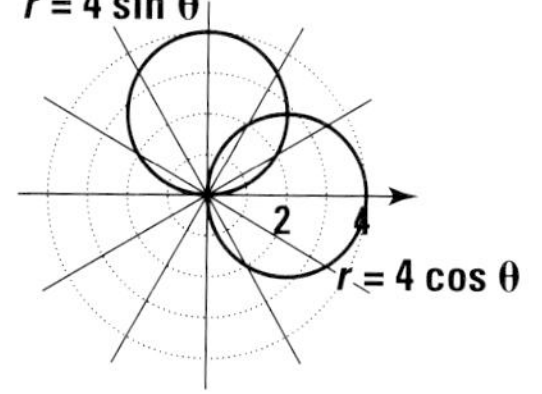

LESSON 8-6 (pp. 507–513)

11. a. $-128 - 128\sqrt{3}i$ **b.** $\left[4, \frac{\pi}{3}\right]^4 = \left[256, \frac{4\pi}{3}\right] = -128 - 128\sqrt{3}\,i$ **13. a.** $z^7 = \left[2^7, \frac{14\pi}{3}\right]$; $z^{13} = \left[2^{13}, \frac{26\pi}{3}\right]$; $z^{19} = \left[2^{19}, \frac{38\pi}{3}\right]$; $z^{25} = \left[2^{25}, \frac{50\pi}{3}\right]$ **b.** $\frac{14\pi}{3} = \frac{2\pi}{3} + 2(2)\pi$; $\frac{26\pi}{3} = \frac{2\pi}{3} + 2(4)\pi$; $\frac{38\pi}{3} = \frac{2\pi}{3} + 2(6)\pi$; $\frac{50\pi}{3} = \frac{2\pi}{3} + 2(8)\pi$ **15. a. See below.**

b. rose curve **17.** Let $z = a + bi$. Then $\overline{z} = a - bi$ and $z - \overline{z} = a + bi - (a - bi) = a + bi - a + bi = 0 + 2bi$ which is an imaginary number. **19.** (b) **21. a.** $\sqrt[3]{13}$ **b.** $-\sqrt[3]{13}$ **c.** $\sqrt[4]{13}, -\sqrt[4]{13}$ **d.** no real solution

15. a.

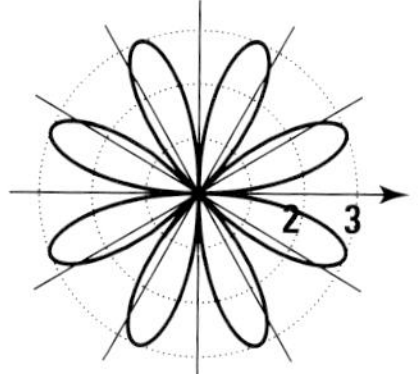

LESSON 8-7 (pp. 514–519)

9. -729; -9, $9(\cos 300° + i \sin 300°)$ **11. a. See page 875. b. See page 875. c.** They are the vertices of a regular n-gon, with center at the origin, and a vertex at (1,0). **13. a.** $z = \pm 3, \pm 3i$ **See page 875. b.** $\frac{3\sqrt{2}}{2} \pm \frac{3\sqrt{2}}{2}i, -\frac{3\sqrt{2}}{2} \pm \frac{3\sqrt{2}}{2}i$ **See page 875.**

15. The 3 cube roots of 8 are 2, -1 + $\sqrt{3}\,i$, -1 − $\sqrt{3}\,i$; their sum is 2 + (-1 + $\sqrt{3}\,i$) + (-1 − $\sqrt{3}\,i$) = 0 **17. See below.** The graph of $r = 3\theta$ is a spiral of Archimedes, and that of $r = 3^{\theta}$ is a logarithmic spiral. **19. a.** $a_n = 2^n + 1$ ∀ integers $n \geq 1$ **b.** $S(n)$: $a_n = 2^n + 1$. $S(1)$: $a_1 = 2^1 + 1 = 3$, so $S(1)$ is true. Assume $S(k)$: $a_k = 2^k + 1$. Then

$$\begin{aligned} a_{k+1} &= 2a_k - 1 \\ &= 2(2^k + 1) - 1 \\ &= 2^{k+1} + 2 - 1 \\ &= 2^{k+1} + 1 \end{aligned}$$

So $S(k) \Rightarrow S(k+1)$. Therefore by mathematical induction, $S(n)$ is true for all positive integers n. **21. a.** $x - 1$ **b.** -4 **c.** 1 **d.** 1 and -4, by the Transitive Property of Polynomial Factors

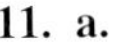

11. a.

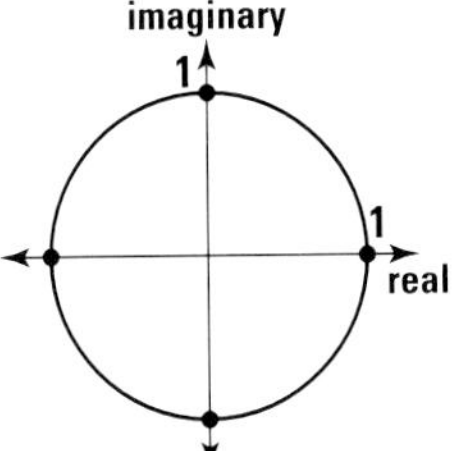

11. b.

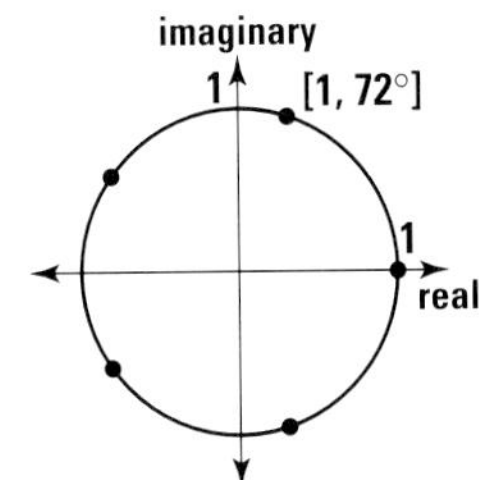

13. a.

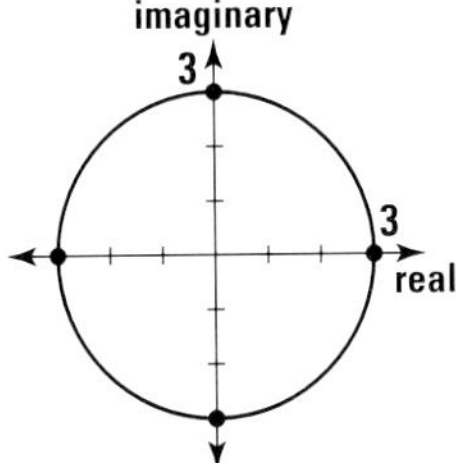

13. b.

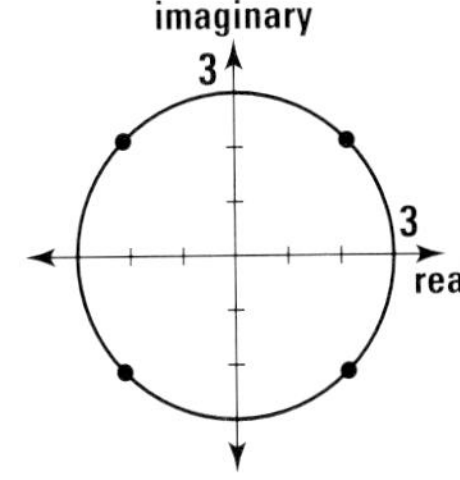

17.

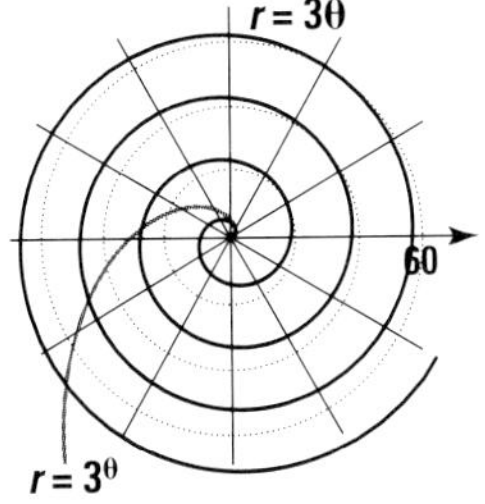

LESSON 8-8 (pp. 520–525)

9. a. 2 **b.** 3 **c.** 5 **d.** 7 **11.** It has three more zeros. There can be three more simple zeros, or one zero with multiplicity 3, or one simple zero and one zero with multiplicity 2. **13. a.** 256 **b. See above right.**

15. $(2 + i)^2 - 4(2 + i) + 5 = 4 + 4i - 1 - 8 - 4i + 5 = 0$; $(2 - 1)^2 - 4(2 + i) + 5 = 4 - 4i - 1 - 8 - 4i + 5 = 0$

17. a. 1, i, -1, $-i$, 1, i, -1, $-i$, 1 **b.** $i^{4k} = 1$, $i^{4k+1} = i$, $i^{4k+2} = -1$, and $i^{4k+3} = -i$ **c.** i. $-i$ ii. -1 iii. 1 **19. a.** i. 14 ii. 1 **b.** n DIV 7 **c.** c MOD 12

13. b.

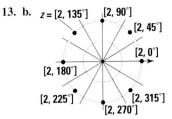

z = [2, 135°] [2, 90°] [2, 45°] [2, 0°] [2, 180°] [2, 225°] [2, 315°] [2, 270°]

LESSON 8-9 (pp. 526–533)

11. 1, -1, i, $-i$ **13.** Sample: $p(x) = 12x^3 - 8x^2 + 3x - 2$ **15.** zeros: $\pm\sqrt{3}i$ (each with multiplicity 2), 1 **17. See below.** **19. a.** 3 **b.** $2t^2 - 4t + 2$

17.

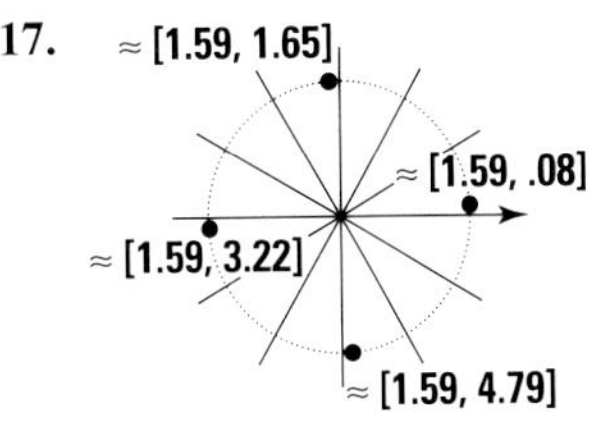

LESSON 8-10 (pp. 534–541)

11. Sample: $p(x) = x^4 - 4x^3 + 9x^2 - 10x$

13. $z_0 = 2\left(\cos\frac{\pi}{5} + i\sin\frac{\pi}{5}\right)$; $z_1 = 2\left(\cos\frac{7\pi}{10} + i\sin\frac{7\pi}{10}\right)$; $z_2 = 2\left(\cos\frac{6\pi}{5} + i\sin\frac{6\pi}{5}\right)$; $z_3 = 2\left(\cos\frac{17\pi}{10} + i\sin\frac{17\pi}{10}\right)$ **See below.** **15. a. See below.** **b.** $\theta = 0°$ **17.** $\frac{1152}{\pi^2} \approx 116.7$ feet

13.

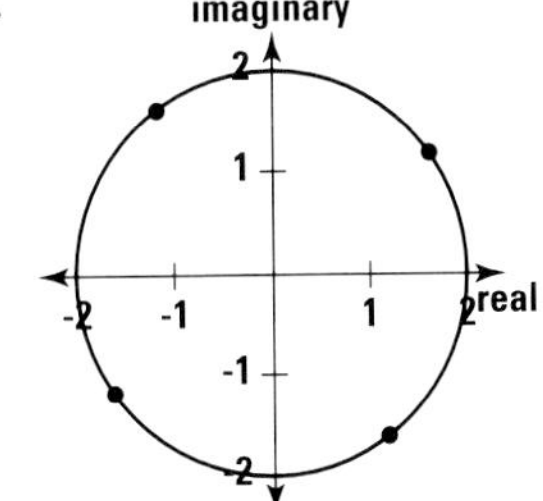

15. a.

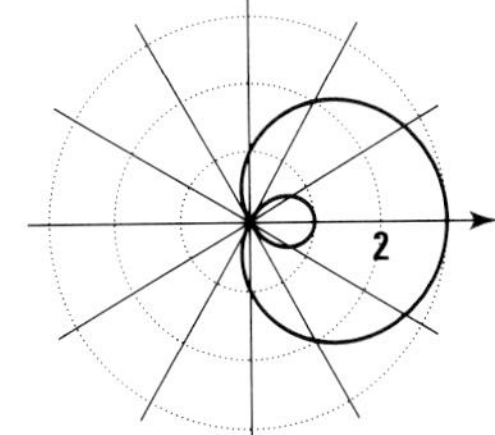

CHAPTER 8 PROGRESS SELF-TEST (p. 546)

1. a. $10 - 8i$ **b.** $-1 + 34i$ **c.** $-\frac{31}{13} - \frac{14}{13}i$ **d.** $-2 - 3i$ **2.** $(-4\sqrt{3}, 4)$
3. a. $(4\sqrt{3}, -4)$ **b.** 8 **c.** $\frac{11\pi}{6}$ **d.** $\left[8, \frac{11\pi}{6}\right]$ **4.** $-\frac{1}{2} - \frac{4}{3}i$ ohms
5. **See below.** **6. a.** $z^1 = 2\left(\cos\frac{\pi}{3} + i\sin\frac{\pi}{3}\right)$, $z^2 = 4\left(\cos\frac{2\pi}{3} + i\sin\frac{2\pi}{3}\right)$, $z^3 = 8(\cos\pi + i\sin\pi)$, $z^4 = 16\left(\cos\frac{4\pi}{3} + i\sin\frac{4\pi}{3}\right)$ **b. See below. c.** farther
7. a. $[3, 18°]$, $[3, 90°]$, $[3, 162°]$, $[3, 234°]$, $[3, 306°]$
b. See right. 8. zeros: -3 (with multiplicity 3), 3, $\pm 3i$
9. a. $a^2 - b^2 + 2abi$ **b.** $a^2 - b^2 - 2abi$
c. $\overline{z^2} = \overline{a^2 - b^2 + 2abi} = a^2 - b^2 - 2abi = (\overline{z})^2$
10. a. $-5i$, $1 + i$
b. $p(x) = (x - 2)(x - 5i)(x + 5i)(x - 1 - i)(x - 1 + i)$
11. See right. 12. a. See right. b. eight-leafed rose curve

5.

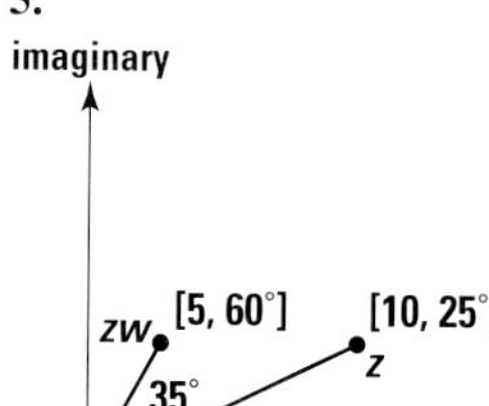

6. b.

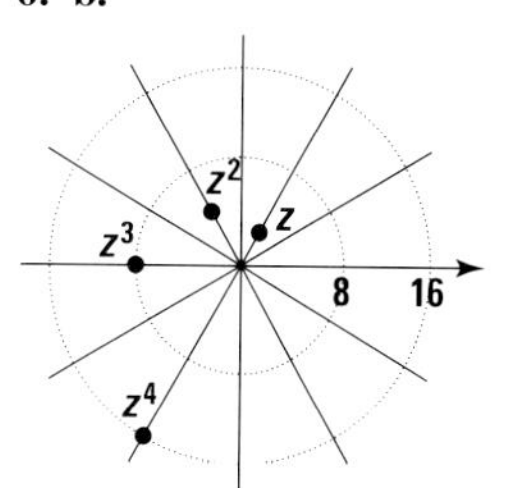

7. b.

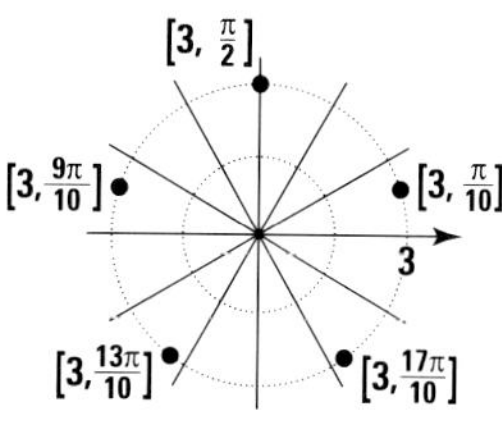

11.

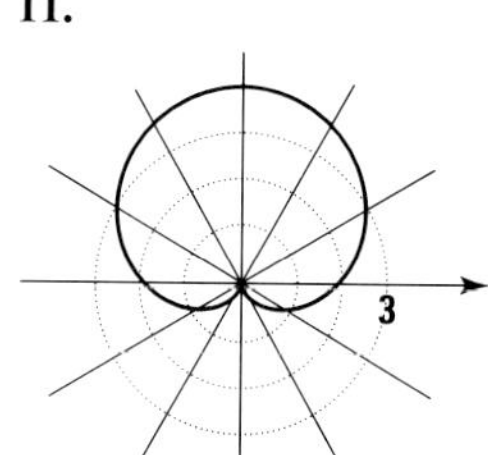

12. a.

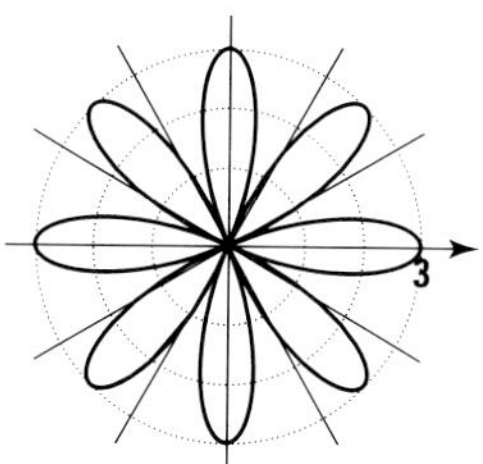

The chart below keys the questions on the **Progress Self-Test** to the objectives in the **Chapter Review** on pages 547–549 or to the **Vocabulary** (Voc.) on page 545. This will enable you to locate those **Chapter Review** questions that correspond to questions you missed on the **Progress Self-Test**. The lesson where the material is covered is also indicated on the chart.

Question	**1**	**2**	**3**	**4**	**5**	**6**	**7**	**8**	**9**	**10**
Objective	A	C	B	H	I	K	D, K	E	F	G
Lesson	8-1	8-2	8-3, 8-1	8-1	8-3	8-6	8-7	8-9	8-1, 8-6	8-8, 8-9
Question	**11**	**12**								
Objective	J	J								
Lesson	8-4	8-4, 8-5								

CHAPTER 8 REVIEW (pp. 547–549)

1. $(6\sqrt{3}, -6)$, $\left[12, \frac{11\pi}{6}\right]$, $12\left(\cos\frac{11\pi}{6} + i\sin\frac{11\pi}{6}\right)$
3. $2.5\cos 35° + 2.5i\sin 35°$, $(2.5\cos 35°, 2.5\sin 35°)$, $2.5(\cos 35° + i\sin 35°)$
5. $(-7, 5) \approx [\sqrt{74}, 144°]$, $\approx \sqrt{74}(\cos 144° + i\sin 144°)$
7. $|z| = 25$, $\theta \approx 163.7°$ **9. a.** Sample: $\left[4, \frac{\pi}{2}\right]$
b. Sample: $\left[4, -\frac{3\pi}{2}\right]$ **c.** $\left[4, \frac{\pi}{2} + 2n\pi\right]$, n an integer. **11.** $\frac{2}{3} - \frac{\sqrt{3}}{3}i$
13. $15 - 3i$ **15.** $\frac{5}{26} - \frac{7}{13}i$ **17.** 125 **19.** i
21. $\sqrt{21}(\cos 62° + i\sin 62°)$ **23. a.** $P = \left(\frac{1}{2}, \frac{\sqrt{3}}{2}\right)$, $Q = \left(\frac{1}{2}, -\frac{\sqrt{3}}{2}\right)$
b. True **25.** Sample: $\left[2, \frac{11\pi}{6}\right]$ **27.** $\approx 24.1 + 0i$

29. $\left[4, \frac{\pi}{6}\right]$, $\left[4, \frac{5\pi}{6}\right]$, $\left[4, \frac{3\pi}{2}\right]$
31. $2\cos\frac{\pi n}{5} + 2i\sin\frac{\pi n}{5}$, for $n = 0, 1, 2, \ldots, 9$ **33. a.** $[r^n, n\theta]$
b. $(r(\cos\theta + i\sin\theta))^n = r^n(\cos n\theta + i\sin n\theta)$
35. zeros: 0, 3, (both with multiplicity 2) **37.** $1 + i$, -3
39. $z - w = -1 + 3i$, so $\overline{z - w} = -1 - 3i$. $\overline{z} - \overline{w} = (3 - 2i) - (4 + i) = -1 - 3i$. So $\overline{z - w} = \overline{z} - \overline{w}$.
41. If $z = 0 + bi$ and $w = 0 + di$, then $zw = bdi2 = -bd = -bd + 0i$, which is a real number
43. a. $z^n = [r^n, n\theta]$; $z^m = [r^m, m\theta]$; $z^{n+m} = [r^{n+m}, (n+m)\theta]$
b. $z^n \cdot z^m = [r^n, n\theta] \cdot [r^m, m\theta] = [r^n \cdot r^m, n\theta + m\theta] = [r^{n+m}, (n+m)\theta] = z^{n+m}$ **45.** True **47.** $p(x)$ has real coefficients, so the conjugate of $2i$ would also be a zero. But $p(x)$ has degree 3 and so cannot have 4 zeros. **49.** Its multiplicity is at least 2.

51. $\frac{1}{5} - \frac{18}{5}i$ amps **53. a–d. See below. 55.** True **57. See below.**
59. $z + w = 3 - i$; vertices: $A = (0, 0)$, $B = (2, -5)$, $C = (3, -1)$, $D = (1, 4)$; slope of $\overline{AB}$ is $\frac{-5 - 0}{2 - 0} = -\frac{5}{2}$, slope of $\overline{AD} = \frac{4 - 0}{1 - 0} = 4$, slope of $\overline{DC} = \frac{4 - (-1)}{1 - 3} = -\frac{5}{2}$, slope of $\overline{BC} = \frac{-5 - (-1)}{2 - 3} = 4$ Since the slopes of opposite sides are equal, $ABCD$ is a parallelogram.

61.

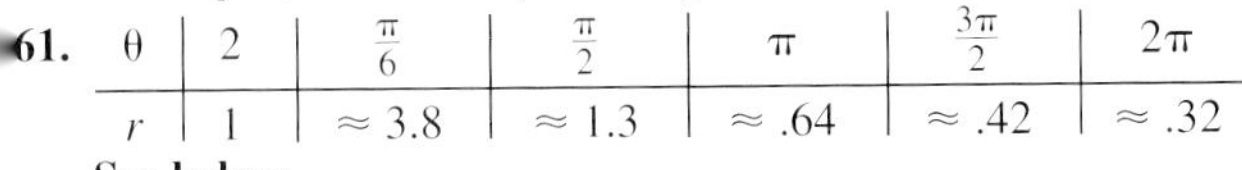

θ	2	$\frac{\pi}{6}$	$\frac{\pi}{2}$	π	$\frac{3\pi}{2}$	2π
r	1	≈ 3.8	≈ 1.3	$\approx .64$	$\approx .42$	$\approx .32$

See below.
63. See right. 8-leafed rose curve
65. See right. $r = 4^{\theta}$ is a logarithmic spiral, and $r = 4 + \theta$ is a spiral of Archimedes. **67. a. See right. b.** closer **69. See right.**

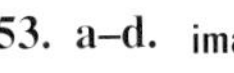

53. a–d.

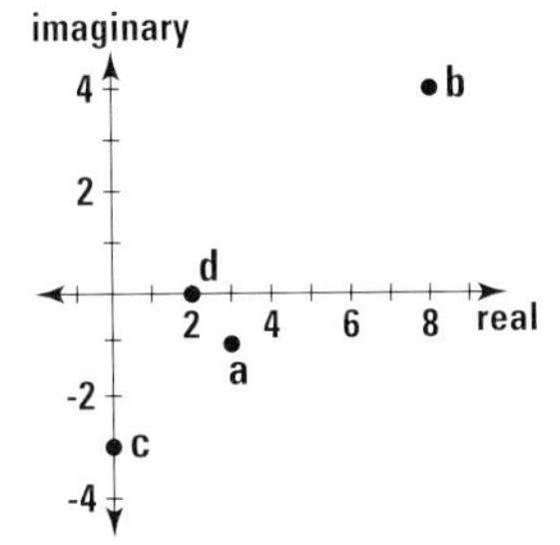

57.

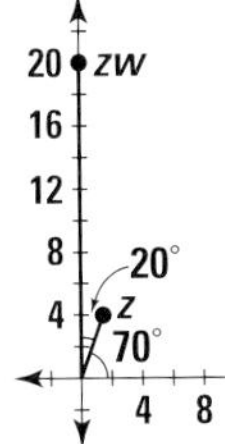

61.

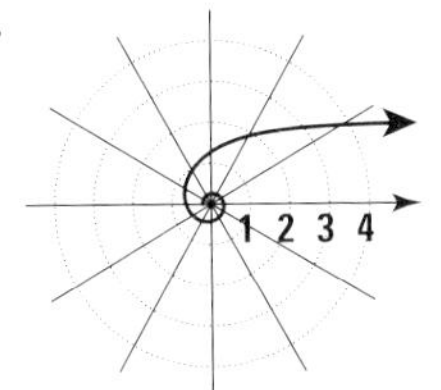

63.

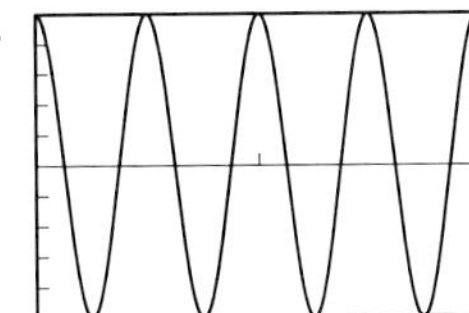

$0 \le x \le 2\pi$, x-scale = π
$-5 \le y \le 5$, y-scale = 1

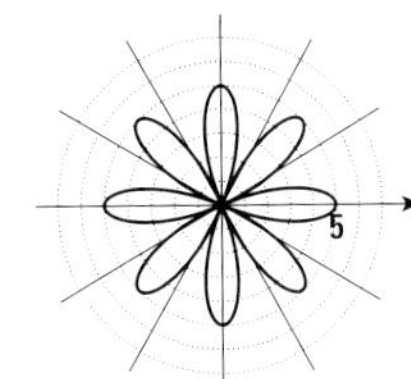

65.

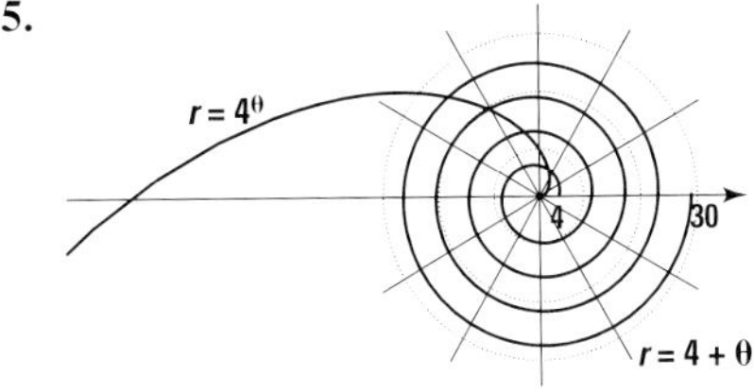

67. a.

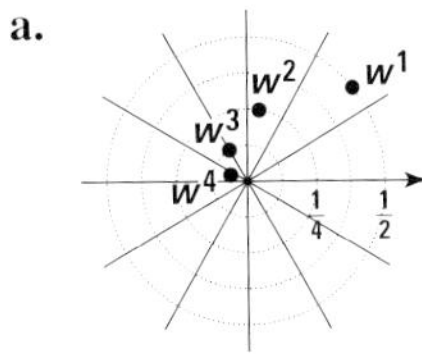

69.

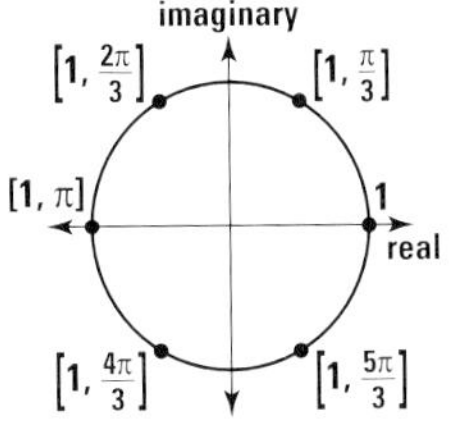

LESSON 9-1 (pps. 552–559)

13. 1 **15. a. See right. b.** \$25/computer **c.** \$12.50/computer **17. a.** 639.984 ft/sec **b.** 640 ft/sec **c.** $800 - 32t$ ft/sec **19.** $\frac{9x - x^2}{3 - 27x^2}$ **21. a.** $x > 3$ or $x < -3$ **b.** $-3 < x < 3$ **c.** -3, 3 **d.** $\{y: y \ge -9\}$

15.

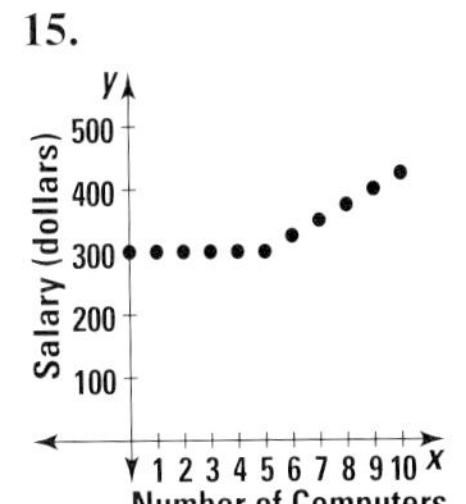

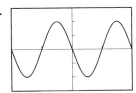

LESSON 9-2 (pp. 560–567)

11. a. 1 **b.** -1. **c.** $A'(0)$ is $\lim_{\Delta x \to 0} \frac{A(0 + \Delta x) - A(0)}{\Delta x}$; this limit does not exist because it has different values when approaching zero from the right and from the left. **13. a.** $f'(7{:}05) \approx -\frac{9}{7} \approx -1.3$ ft/min; $f'(7{:}15) \approx 1$ ft/min **b.** At 7:05, the water level is falling at about 1.3 ft/min; at 7:15, the water level is rising at about 1 ft/min.

15. a. $f(n) = \frac{180(n - 2)}{n}$ **b.** $f(20) = 162$, $f(24) = 165$ **c.** $\frac{3}{4}$
17. -0.5 **19.** $\frac{\pi}{3}$ **21.** π

LESSON 9-3 (pp. 569–575)

13. The graphs of f and g are almost identical. **See below. 15. a.** i **b.** Velocity as a function of time **17.** $x < -3$ **19.** -2 **21.** $\approx 21°$

13.

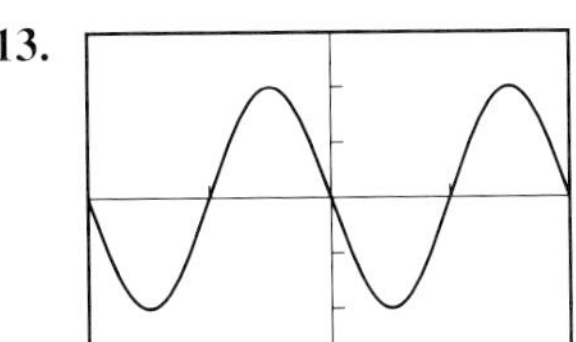

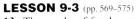

$-2\pi \le x \le 2\pi$, x-scale = π
$-1.5 \le y \le 1.5$, y-scale = 0.5

LESSON 9-4 (576–580)

9. $\frac{\text{degree Fahrenheit}}{\text{min}}$ per minute or degrees Fahrenheit/min^2
11. 7,742,000,000 **13.** $\frac{1}{2}$
15.
$\cos 2x = \cos^2 x - \sin^2 x$
$\cos 2x = (1 - \sin^2 x) - \sin^2 x$ Pythagorean Identity
$\cos 2x = 1 - 2\sin^2 x$ Addition
$2\sin^2 x = 1 - \cos 2x$
$\sin^2 x = \frac{1 - \cos 2x}{2}$

17. a. III **b.** IV **c.** II **d.** I

LESSON 9-5 (581–586)

9. See below. No; for example, consider the function $y = x^2$ graphed below. As x goes from -4 to -3 to -2 to -1 to 0, $f'(x)$ goes from -8 to -6 to -4 to -2 to 0. Those slopes are increasing, but the function is decreasing.
11. b **13. a.** The curve is increasing from April to July and from October to December. **See below. b.** i. True ii. False iii. True iv. False
15. $f'(1) = -2e^{-1} \approx -.74$ **17. a.** $\approx 4°$ **b. See right. 19.** .75

9.

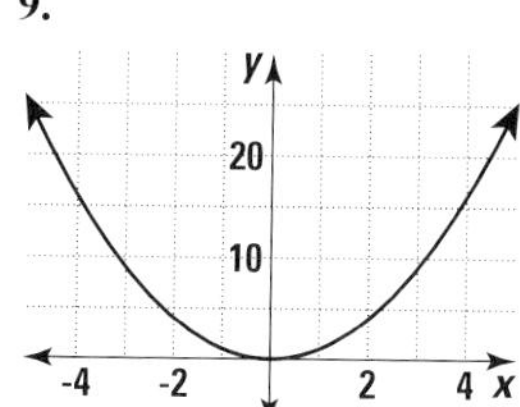

13a.

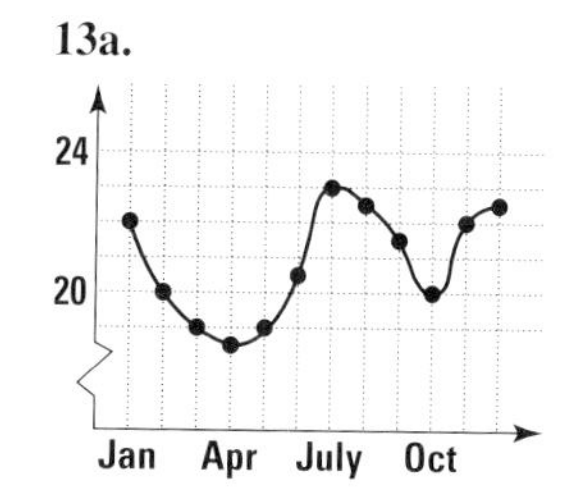

17b.

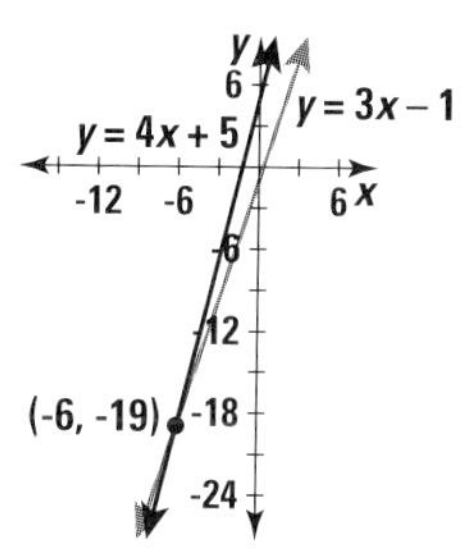

LESSON 9-6 (pp. 587–591)

7. $t < \frac{3}{4}$ sec **9. a.** -7.5 mph/sec, $\approx$ -4.2 mph/sec **b.** The car is decelerating more rapidly during the first four seconds of braking than during the last six seconds. **11.** $f'(1) = -1$ **13. a.** at about $t = 9.53$ seconds **b.** about 305 ft/sec **c.** about 208 mph
15. $n = 5$; $z = 32i$ **17.** 1000, 10000, 11000

PROGRESS SELF-TEST (pp. 594–595)

1. a. $-\frac{3}{2}$ **b.** $\frac{3}{4}$ **c.** Sample: $x = 0$ to $x = 2$
d. Samples: $x = -4$ to $x = -1$, $x = -1$ to $x = 2$ or $x = -4$ to $x = 2$
2. a. i. -.58% per year ii. -.03% per $-\frac{5}{2}$ year **b.** slower **c.** positive
3. a. $16 + 4\Delta x$ **b.** 16.4 **4. a.** $\frac{2}{3}$ **b.** $\frac{2}{3}$ **5. a.** $h'(x) = -4x + 1$
b. -11 **6.** c **7.** negative **See right. 8. a.** 32 ft/sec
b. -32 ft/sec^2; acceleration due to gravity **c.** 114 ft **d.** 0 ft/sec
9. f is increasing when $x < 0$. f is decreasing when $x > 0$.

7.

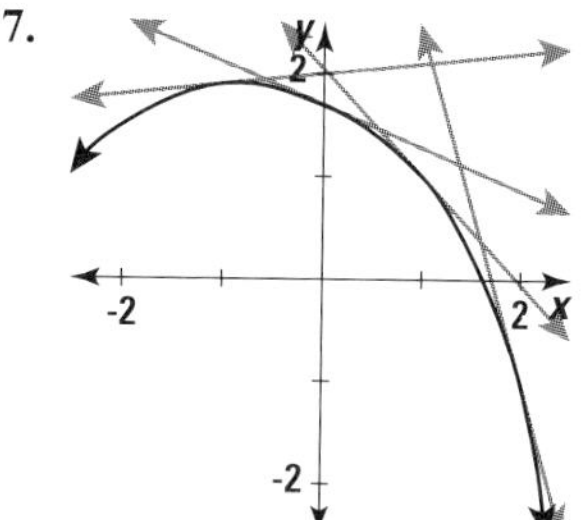

The chart below keys thequestions on the **Progress Self-Test** to the objectives in the **Chapter Review** on pages 596–599 or to the **Vocabulary** (Voc.) on page 593. This will enable you to locate those **Chapter Review** questions that correspond to questions you missed on the **Progress Self-Test**. The lesson where the material is covered is also indicated on the chart.

Question	1	2	3	4	5	6	7	8	9
Objective	G	D	A	H	B	I	I	E, F	C
Lesson	9-1	9-1	9-1	9-3	9-2	9-5	9-5	9-4,5	9-5

CHAPTER 9 REVIEW (pp. 596–599)

1. 9 **3. a.** $-4t + 5 - 2\Delta t$ **b.** -4 **5.** $f'(x) = -2x + 1$ **7.** $g'(x) = -6x$
9. False **11.** $f'(x) = 3x^2 + 3$. Since $x^2 \geq 0$ for all real x, $f'(x) = 3x^2 + 3 > 0$ for all real numbers. Since the derivative is positive, the slopes of the tangents to the curve are all positive, and the function is increasing for all real numbers.
13. a. i. $x < -2$ or $x > 3$ ii. $-2 < x < 3$ iii. $x = -2$ or $x = 3$
b. See right. 15. a. See right. b. increasing **c.** 1986–1987
17. a. -64 ft/sec **b.** -32 ft/sec^2 **c.** 2.5 sec **d.** -80 ft/sec
19. a. to the right **b.** slowing down **21. a.** $A(\theta) = \frac{1}{2}xy = \frac{1}{2}(4\cos\theta)(4\sin\theta) = 8\sin\theta\cos\theta = 4(2\sin\theta\cos\theta) = 4\sin 2\theta$
b. $\theta = \frac{\pi}{4}$ **23.** -3 **25. a.** $g'(-4) = -1$, $g'(-2) = 0$, $g'(0) = 2$, $g'(3) = 0$, $g'(5) = -3$ **b. See right. 27.** Sample: **See right.**
29. a. increasing: $x < -3$, $x > 1$; decreasing: $-3 < x < 1$
b. $x = -3$, $x = 1$ **c.** positive: $x > -1$; negative: $x < -1$

13b.

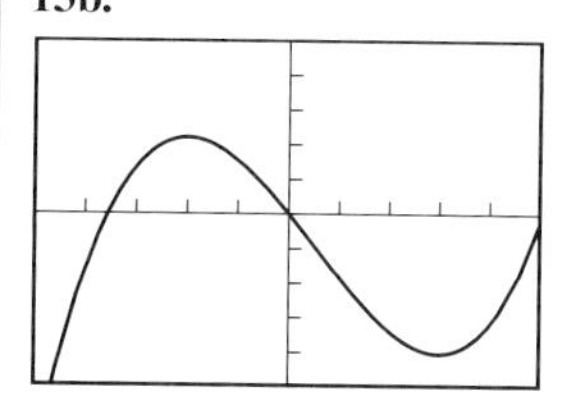

$-5 \leq x \leq 5$, x-scale = 1
$-50 \leq y \leq 50$, y-scale = 10

15. a.

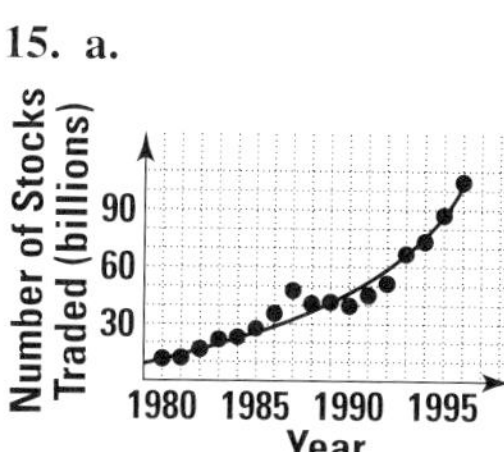

25b.

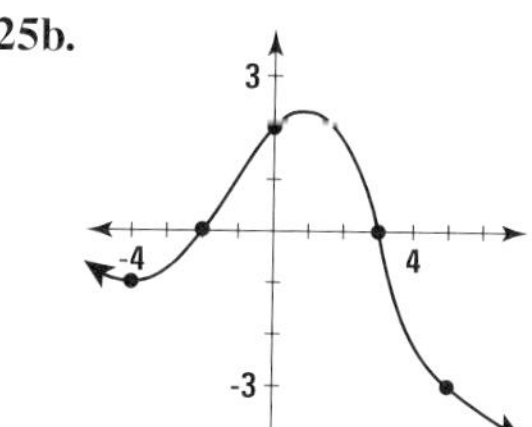

27.

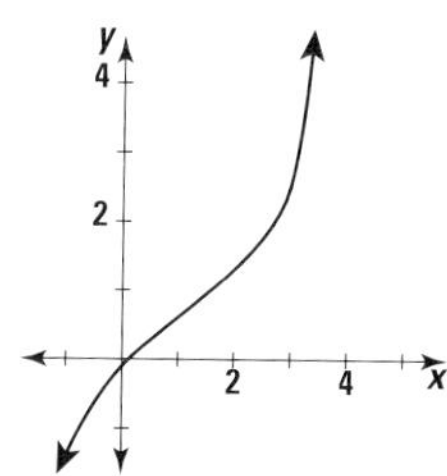

LESSON 10-1 (pp. 602–606)

11. Offices are unordered and repetition is not allowed.
13. Ordered symbols; repetition not allowed.
15. **See below.**

It is an identity.

$$\text{Left side} = (\tan\theta)(\sin\theta + \cot\theta\cos\theta)$$
$$= \frac{\sin\theta}{\cos\theta}\left(\sin\theta + \frac{\cos\theta\cos\theta}{\sin\theta}\right)$$
$$= \frac{\sin\theta}{\cos\theta}\left(\frac{\sin^2\theta + \cos^2\theta}{\sin\theta}\right)$$
$$= \frac{\sin\theta}{\cos\theta}\left(\frac{1}{\sin\theta}\right)$$
$$= \frac{1}{\cos\theta}$$
$$= \sec\theta$$
$$= \text{Right side}$$

17. a. 142 **b.** $\left\lfloor\frac{n}{d}\right\rfloor$ **19.** $\exists$ a positive integer n that is not prime.
21. $x^2 + 2xy + y^2$

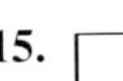
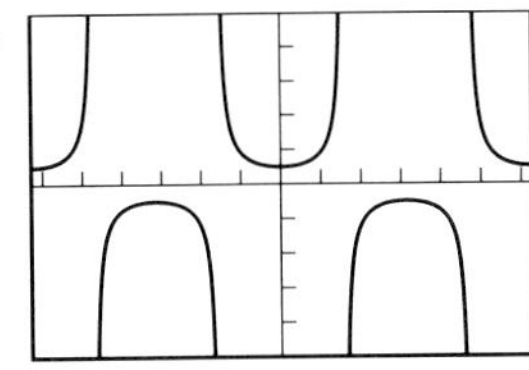

$-2\pi \le x \le 2\pi$, x-scale = 1
$-10 \le y \le 10$, y-scale = 2

LESSON 10-2 (pp. 607–614)

11. 1716 **13. a.** 555 **b.** $\approx$ 0.00375 **15.** s(1) is true, because the number of ways the first step can be done is n_1. Assume $s(k)$, the number of ways to do the first k steps, is $n_1 \cdot n_2 \cdot \ldots \cdot n_k$. Let m be the number of ways to do the first k steps and let n represent the number of ways to do the $(k + 1)$st step. Then by the inductive hypothesis, $m = n_1 \cdot n_2 \cdot \ldots \cdot n_k$ and $n = n_{k+1}$ so $mn = n_1 \cdot n_2 \cdot \ldots \cdot n_k \cdot n_{k+1}$. So $S(k + 1)$, the number of ways to do the $(k + 1)$ steps is $n_1 \cdot n_2 \cdot \ldots \cdot n_k \cdot n_{k+1}$. Thus $S(n)$ is true for all positive integers n. **17.** Ordered symbols; repetition is not allowed. **19. a.** 2485 **b.** 15,050 **c.** 49,495,500 **d.** $\frac{n}{2}(n + 1) - \frac{m}{2}(m - 1)$ **21.** $-\frac{6}{7}$

LESSON 10-3 (pp. 615–621)

9. a. $P(10, 9) = \frac{10!}{(10-9)!} = \frac{10!}{1!} = \frac{10!}{1} = \frac{10!}{0!} = \frac{10!}{(10-10)!} = P(10, 10)$
b. $\forall$ integers $n \ge 2$, $P(n, n - 1) = P(n, n)$ **11. a.** 120 **b.** 625 **13.** 28,800
15. a. $(n - 2)! = (n - 2)(n - 3)(n - 4)(n - 5)\ldots(2)(1) = (n - 2)[(n - 3)(n - 4)(n - 5)\ldots(2)(1)] = (n - 2)(n - 3)!$
b. $n = 7$ **17.** Sample: $n = 11$, $r = 9$ **19.** 6 trips **See below.**
21. $\frac{40}{3}$ cm **23.** $(x, y) \to (x - 1, 2(y + 7))$

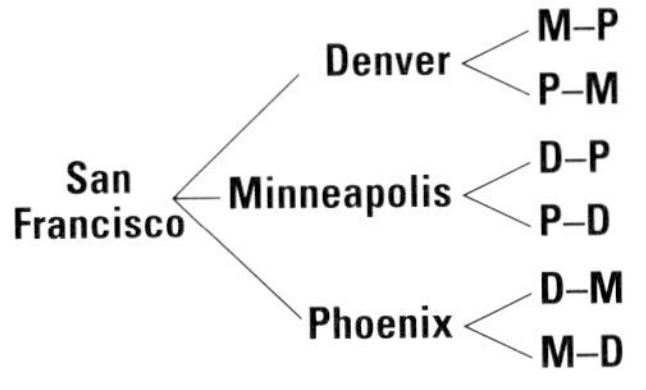

LESSON 10-4 (pp. 622–626)

11. 66 **13.** 301,644,000
15. a. i. $10 \cdot 9 \cdot 8 \cdot 7 = 5040 = (24)(210) = (4!)(210)$
ii. $33 \cdot 32 \cdot 31 \cdot 30 = 982{,}080 = (24)(40{,}920) = (4!)(40{,}920)$
iii. $97 \cdot 96 \cdot 95 \cdot 94 = 83{,}156{,}160 = (24)(3{,}464{,}840) = (4!)(3{,}464{,}840)$
b. $C(n, 4) = \frac{n!}{4!(n-4)!} = \frac{n(n-1)(n-2)(n-3)}{4!}$, and $C(n, 4)$ is an integer. So, the product of any 4 consecutive integers n, $n - 1$, $n - 2$, and $n - 3$ is divisible by 4! **17. a.** 7! = 5040 **b.** 2520 **c.** 16,807
19. **See below.**
21. a. $\sin(\alpha + \beta)\sin(\alpha - \beta)$
$= (\sin\alpha\cos\beta + \sin\beta\cos\alpha)(\sin\alpha\cos\beta - \sin\beta\cos\alpha)$
$= \sin^2\alpha\cos^2\beta - \sin\alpha\sin\beta\cos\beta\cos\alpha + \sin\alpha\sin\beta\cos\alpha\cos\beta - \sin^2\beta\cos^2\alpha$
$= \sin^2\alpha\cos^2\beta - \sin^2\beta\cos^2\alpha$
$= \sin^2\alpha\cos^2\beta - \cos^2\alpha\sin^2\beta$
b. $\sin^2\alpha\cos^2\beta - \cos^2\alpha\sin^2\beta$
$= \sin^2\alpha\cos^2\beta + \sin^2\alpha\sin^2\beta - \sin^2\alpha\sin^2\beta - \cos^2\alpha\sin^2\beta$
$= \sin^2\alpha(\cos^2\beta + \sin^2\beta) - \sin^2\beta(\sin^2\alpha + \cos^2\alpha)$
$= \sin^2\alpha - \sin^2\beta$
23. $x^3 + 3x^2y + 3xy^2 + y^3$

19.

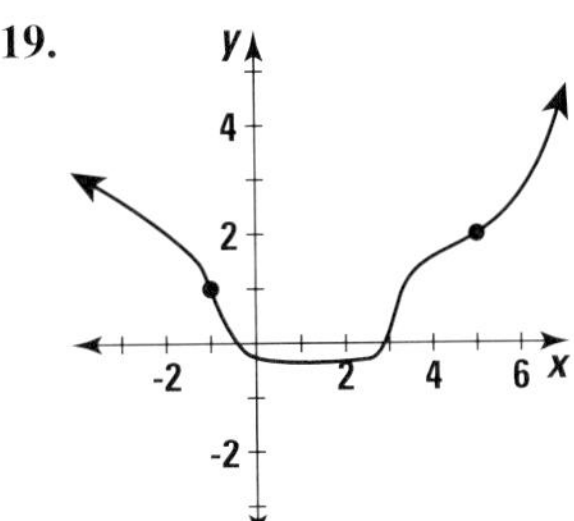

LESSON 10-5 (pp. 628–632)

7. a. -4 **b.** 16 **9.** $(x + 2)^7$ **11. a.** ${}_nC_r$ Calculation Theorem **b.** Forming a least common denominator **c.** Addition of fractions and distributive property **d.** $(n + 1)!$ **e.** ${}_nC_r$ Calculation Theorem **13.** 126 **15.** 70,073,640 **17. a.** Ordered symbols; repetition is not allowed. **b.** $\approx$ 1.0897 × 1010 **19.** c

LESSON 10-6 (pp. 633–638)

9. $\approx$ 0.088 **11. a.** The number of 5-element subsets of S_1 plus the number of 4-element subsets of S_1 is the number of 5-element subsets of S. **b.** Let S be a set of $n + 1$ elements and let S_1 be a set of n of these elements. Then every r-element subset of S is either an r-element subset of S_1 or an $(r - 1)$-element subset of S_1 along with the left-over element not in S_1. So $\binom{n+1}{r} = \binom{n}{r} + \binom{n}{r-1}$.
13. The expression $\binom{n}{0} - \binom{n}{1} + \binom{n}{2} - \binom{n}{3} + \ldots \pm \binom{n}{n}$ represents the coefficients of the expansion of $(x - y)^n$. Letting $x = y = 1$, $(x - y)^n = (1 - 1)^n = 0$, so the sum of the coefficients must be zero.
15. $128a^7 - 448a^6b + 672a^5b^2 - 560a^4b^3 + 280a^3b^4 - 84a^2b^5 + 14ab^6 - b^7$ **17.** Each style is available in 3000 fabrics.
19. a. **See page 880.**
b. eight-leafed rose curve
c. Point symmetry with respect to the origin, line symmetry with respect to $\theta = \frac{\pi}{8}$, $\theta = \frac{\pi}{4}$, $\theta = \frac{3\pi}{8}$, $\theta = \frac{\pi}{2}$, $\theta = \frac{5\pi}{8}$, $\theta = \frac{3\pi}{4}$, $\theta = \frac{7\pi}{8}$, $\theta = \pi$

19. a.

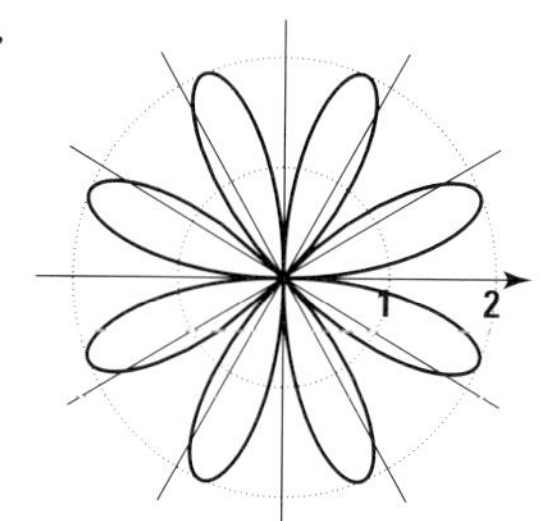

LESSON 10-7 (pp. 640–644)

13. 1820 **15.** 20 **17.** 1771 **19.** 448 **21. a.** 120 **b.** 48 **23.** 10
25. $((p \Rightarrow q) \text{ and } p) \Rightarrow q$

LESSON 10-8 (pp. 645–648)

9. 495 **11.** 4,838,400 **13.** $y \approx -4.47$; $\theta \approx 5.44$
15. a. The degree of $d(x)$ is one less than the degree of $p(x)$.
b. $p(x) = (3x + 2)\,d(x) + x + 2$, so some samples are:

$d(x)$	$p(x)$
x	$3x^2 + 3x + 2$
x^2	$3x^3 + 2x^2 + x + 2$
$x + 5$	$3x^2 + 18x + 12$

PROGRESS SELF-TEST (p. 652)

1. a. unordered symbols; repetition allowed **b.** 252
2. a. unordered symbols; repetition not allowed **b.** 140
3. 7 possible rolls **See right.** **4.** 132 **5.** 1,048,576 **6.** 73,440
7. 70 **8.** 1320 **9. a.** 2,284,880 **b.** 1,518,000 **10.** 84
11. $-5376x^6y^3$ **12.** 35 **13.** 232 **14.** 120
15. $P(n + 1, r + 1) = \dfrac{(n + 1)!}{(n + 1 - (r + 1))!} = \dfrac{(n + 1)}{(n - r)!}$;
$(n + 1) \cdot P(n, r) = (n + 1)\dfrac{n!}{(n - r)!} = \dfrac{(n + 1)!}{(n - r)!}$
So, $P(n + 1, r + 1) = (n + 1) \cdot P(n, r)$. **16.** ≈ 0.0317

3.

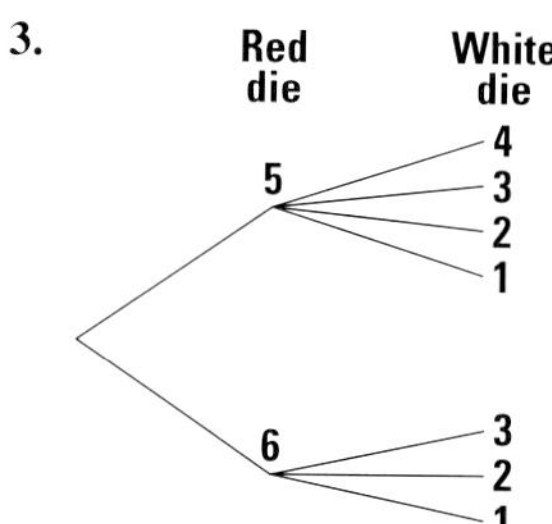

The chart below keys the questions on the **Progress Self-Test** to the objectives in the **Chapter Review** on pages 653–655 or to the **Vocabulary** (Voc.) on page 651. This will enable you to locate those **Chapter Review** questions that correspond to questions you missed on the **Progress Self-Test**. The lesson where the material is covered is also indicated on the chart.

Question	**1**	**2**	**3**	**4**	**5**	**6**	**7**	**8**	**9**	**10**
Objective	A,G	A,G	I	F	F	B	B	F	F	G
Lesson	10-1, 10-7	10-1, 10-4	10-2	10-2	10-2	10-3	10-4	10-2	10-2	10-4
Question	**11**	**12**	**13**	**14**	**15**	**16**				
Objective	C	H	E	G	D	H				
Lesson	10-5	10-6	10-6	10-7	10-3	10-6				

CHAPTER 10 REVIEW (pp. 653–655)

1. unordered symbols; repetition allowed **3.** ordered symbols; repetition not allowed **5.** ordered symbols; repetition allowed
7. 2002 **9.** 60,480 **11.** $x^8 + 8x^7y + 28x^6y^2 + 56x^5y^3 + 70x^4y^4 + 56x^3y^5 + 28x^2y^6 + 8xy^7 + y^8$ **13.** -10240
15. $C(n, r) = \dfrac{n!}{r!(n - r)!} = \dfrac{n!}{(n - (n - r))!(n - r)!} = C(n, n - r)$
17. For each of the $C(n, r)$ combinations of n objects taken r at a time, there are $r!$ arrangements. So $C(n, r) \cdot r! = P(n, r)$, or $P(n, r) = r!\,C(n, r)$. **19.** $\binom{20}{4}$ **21.** 5040 **23.** $\approx 1.2165 \times 10^{17}$
25. $\approx 1.40 \times 10^{10}$ **27.** 120 **29. a.** 1140 **b.** 8000 **31.** 210
33. 26 **35.** 66 **37. a.** ≈ 0.0163 **b.** ≈ 0.1814 **c.** ≈ 0.632538.
14 strings **39.** 14 outcomes **See right.**

39.

1 < 2—3, 4—3
2 < 1—4, 3—4
3 < 2—1, 4—1
4 < 1—2, 3—2

LESSON 11-1 (pp. 658–665)

11. Euler's **13. a.** $v = .90$; $w = .30$; $x = .50$; $y = .01$; $z = .45$ **b.** .24 **c.** .25 **d.** .10 **15.** See below. **17. a.** 4×3 **b.** 0 **c.** 4 **19.** 7

15.

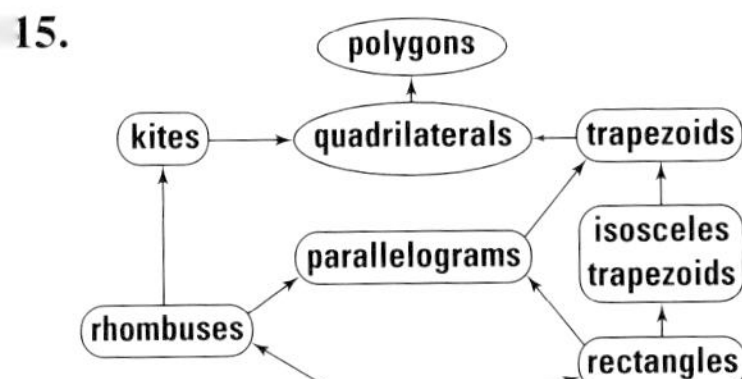

LESSON 11-2 (pp. 666–672)

11.

edge	endpoint
e_1	$\{v_1, v_2\}$
e_2	$\{v_2, v_4\}$
e_3	$\{v_2, v_4\}$
e_4	$\{v_3\}$

13. a. $\exists$ a graph G such that G does not have any loops and G is not simple. **b.** True: G could have parallel edges and no loops. **15.** The taster prefers A to C, and prefers C to P. But in a direct comparison of A and P, the taster prefers P. **17. a.** 18 **b.** 17 **c.** $V = E + 1$ **19.** quotient: $6x^3 - 42x^2 + 287x - 2006$; remainder: 14,043

LESSON 11-3 (pp. 673-678)

11. See below. **13.** See below. **15.** Impossible; one of the degree 3 vertices goes to each of the other vertices. But the other degree 3 vertex cannot connect to itself (the graph is simple), to the first degree 3 vertex (no parallel edges), or to the other two vertices (they already have one edge.) **17.** $\frac{n(n-3)}{2}$ **19.** "Twice the number of edges" must be an even number.

21.

	Miami	Milwaukee	Minn./St. Paul
Miami	0	1	2
Milwaukee	1	0	9
Minn./St. Paul	2	7	0

23. $x = \frac{\sqrt{5}}{5}, -\frac{\sqrt{5}}{5}, \frac{i\sqrt{3}}{2}, \frac{-i\sqrt{3}}{2}$ **25.** $\begin{bmatrix} 7 & 12 \\ 18 & 31 \end{bmatrix}$

11.

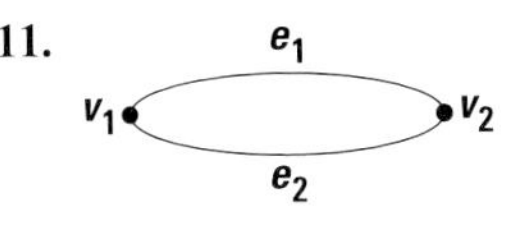

13.

LESSON 11-4 (pp. 680–686)

7. a. $e_1, e_2, e_3, e_4, e_5, e_6$ **b.** 2 **9.** Yes, if the graph is not connected, there is no way a circuit could contain every vertex. **11.** Yes; think of replacing each bridge by two bridges. Such a walk exists by the sufficient condition for an Euler Circuit Theorem, since every vertex will have an even degree. **13.** Yes, if the walk repeats an edge, then there is a circuit. Remove edges from the graph until there is no circuit. Then connect v to w.

15. $\begin{bmatrix} 0 & 1 & 1 & 1 \\ 1 & 0 & 1 & 1 \\ 1 & 1 & 0 & 1 \\ 1 & 1 & 1 & 0 \end{bmatrix}$ **17.** Leonhard Euler, eighteenth **19.** $\approx -.204$

LESSON 11-5: (pp. 687–692)

11. If the main diagonal is all zeros, there are no loops, and if all other entries are zero or one, there are no parallel edges, so the graph is simple. **13.** 4 **15.** No, add edge i. **See below. 17.** Yes **19. See below.**

21. Top network $\equiv \sim (p \text{ and } (q \text{ or } \sim r))$
$\equiv \sim p \text{ or } \sim (q \text{ or } \sim r)$
$\equiv \sim p \text{ or } (\sim q \text{ and } r)$
$\equiv$ Bottom network

Therefore, the two networks are equivalent.

15.

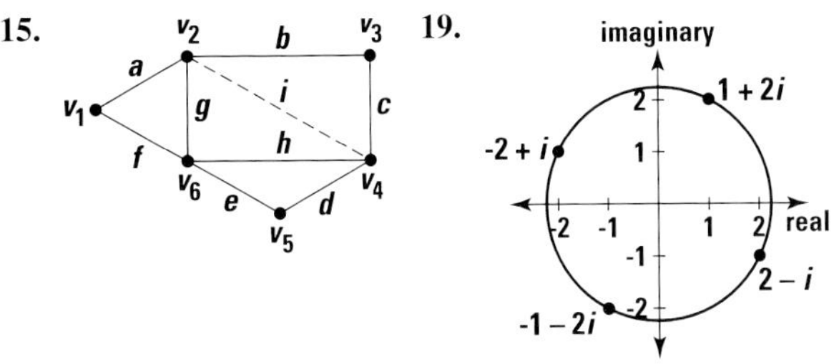

LESSON 11-6 (pp. 693–699)

9. See below.

11. Let $A = \begin{bmatrix} a_1 & a_2 \\ a_3 & a_4 \end{bmatrix}$, and $B = \begin{bmatrix} b_1 & b_2 \\ b_3 & b_4 \end{bmatrix}$. If A and B are stochastic, then each row sums to 1 and each entry is nonnegative. $AB = \begin{bmatrix} a_1b_1 + a_2b_3 & a_1b_2 + a_2b_4 \\ a_3b_1 + a_4b_3 & a_3b_2 + a_4b_4 \end{bmatrix}$. Row 1 sums to $a_1b_1 + a_2b_3 + a_1b_2 + a_2b_4 = a_1b_1 + a_1b_2 + a_2b_3 + a_2b_4 = a_1(b_1 + b_2) + a_2(b_3 + b_4) = a_1 + a_2 = 1$, since $b_1 + b_2 = b_3 + b_4 = a_1 + a_2 = 1$. Row 2 sums to $a_3b_1 + a_4b_3 + a_3b_2 + a_4b_4 = a_3b_1 + a_3b_2 + a_4b_3 + a_4b_4 = a_3(b_1 + b_2) + a_4(b_3 + b_4) = a_3 + a_4 = 1$, since $b_1 + b_2 = b_3 + b_4 = a_3 + a_4 = 1$. Each entry of AB is nonnegative since it is the sum of two terms, each of which is the product of two nonnegative numbers. Hence, the product of two 2×2 stochastic matrices is stochastic.

13. T stabilizes to $\begin{bmatrix} \frac{3}{7} & \frac{4}{7} \\ \frac{3}{7} & \frac{4}{7} \end{bmatrix}$. Proof: If $[a \quad b]\begin{bmatrix} .6 & .4 \\ .3 & .7 \end{bmatrix} = [a \quad b]$, then
$.6a + .3b = a \Rightarrow -.4a + .3b = 0$ and
$.4a + .7b = b \Rightarrow -.4a + .3b = 0.$

Since $a + b = 1$,

$$\begin{array}{l} -.4a + .3b = 0 \\ a + b = 1 \end{array} \Rightarrow \begin{array}{r} -.4a + .3b = 0 \\ .4a + .4b = .4 \\ \hline .7b = .4 \end{array}$$

$b = \frac{4}{7}$ and $a = \frac{3}{7}$

15. 15 **17.** No, a graph cannot have an odd number of odd vertices. **19.** no solution **21.** Let n, $n + 1$, $n + 2$, and $n + 3$ represent the four consecutive integers. By the Quotient-Remainder Theorem, $n = 4q + r$ where q is an integer and $r = 0, 1, 2,$ or 3. If $r = 0$, then n is divisible by 4. If $r = 1$, $n + 3 = (4q + 1) + 3 = 4(q + 1)$ is divisible by 4. If $r = 2$, $n + 2 = (4q + 2) + 2 = 4(q + 1)$ is divisible by 4. If $r = 3$, $n + 1 = (4q + 3) + 1 = 4(q + 1)$ is divisible by 4. So, exactly one of every four consecutive integers is divisible by 4.

9.

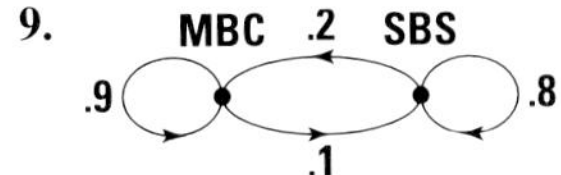

LESSON 11-7 (pp. 700–706)

15. a. **See right.**

b.

$$\begin{array}{c} \\ R \\ U \end{array}\begin{array}{cc} R & U \\ \left[\begin{array}{cc} .95 & .05 \\ .02 & .98 \end{array}\right] \end{array}$$

c. Urban ≈ 71%; Rural ≈ 29%

d. $.95a + .02b = a$

$$\begin{aligned} -5a + 2b &= 0 \\ 5a + 5b &= 5 \\ \hline 7b &= 5 \end{aligned}$$

$b = \frac{5}{7} \approx .714$; $a = \frac{2}{7} \approx .286$

17. a. No, there are two vertices with odd degrees.
b. **See right.** **19.** ≈ 20%

15. a.

Rural .05 Urban
.95 .98
.02

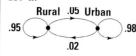

17. b.

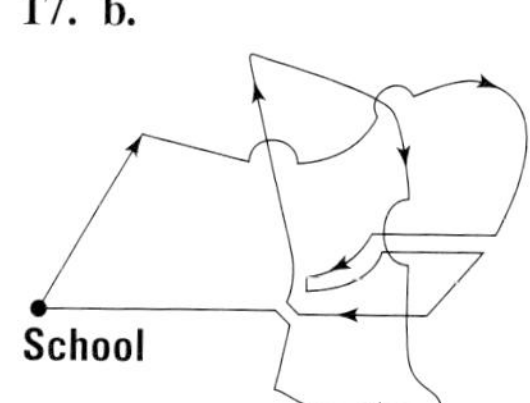

CHAPTER 11 PROGRESS SELF-TEST (pp. 711–712)

1. v_3 **2.** e_5 and e_6 **3.** Remove e_7 and e_8 and either e_5 or e_6. **4.** 5 **5.** 16 **6. a.** Yes **b.** Yes **c.** No **7.** all except e_3 **8.** No, there are vertices of odd degree. **9.** 2

10. a.

$$\begin{array}{c} \\ v_1 \\ v_2 \\ v_3 \\ v_4 \end{array}\begin{array}{cccc} v_1 & v_2 & v_3 & v_4 \\ \left[\begin{array}{cccc} 0 & 1 & 0 & 1 \\ 1 & 0 & 1 & 1 \\ 0 & 1 & 0 & 1 \\ 1 & 1 & 1 & 0 \end{array}\right] \end{array}$$

b. The numbers of 1-stop routes to Chicago, Pittsburgh, and New York are 1, 1, and 2, respectively.

11. No, this would be an Euler circuit, which is impossible since there are vertices with odd degree. **12.** **See right.** **13.** **See right.**

14. No, the total degree of a graph must be even.

15. a. **See right.**

b.

has HIV and test positive:	.00098
has HIV but tests negative:	.00002
doesn't have HIV but tests positive:	.001998
doesn't have HIV and tests negative:	.997002

c. ≈ 67%

16. A graph cannot have an odd number of odd vertices.

17. a. **See right.**

b.

$$\begin{array}{c} \\ Q \\ NQ \end{array}\begin{array}{cc} Q & NQ \\ \left[\begin{array}{cc} 0.0 & 1.0 \\ 0.5 & 0.5 \end{array}\right] \end{array}$$

c. $\frac{1}{3}$

12.

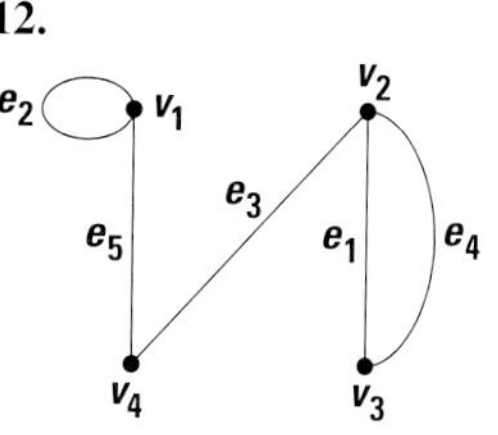

13.

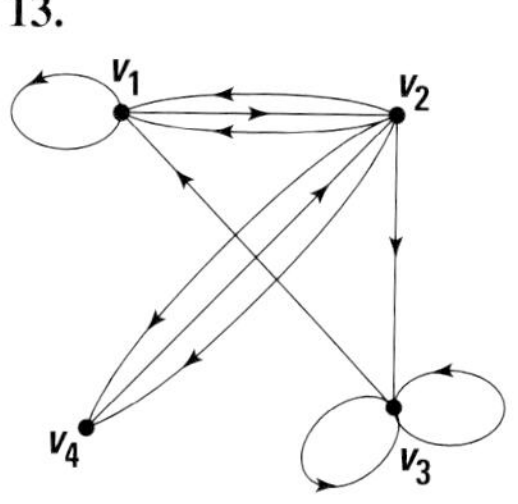

15. a.

Infected .98 Positive .00098
.02 Negative .00002
.001
Total Population
.999
Not Infected .002 Positive .001998
.998 Negative .997002

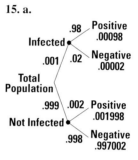

17. a.

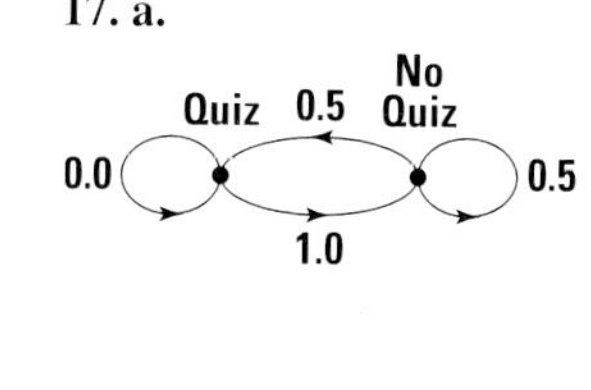

The chart below keys the questions on the **Progress Self-Test** to the objectives in the **Chapter Review** on pages 713–717 or to the **Vocabulary** (Voc.) on page 710. This will enable you to locate those **Chapter Review** questions that correspond to questions you missed on the **Progress Self-Test**. The lesson where the material is covered is also indicated on the chart.

Question	**1**	**2**	**3**	**4**	**5**	**6**	**7**	**8**	**9**	**10**
Objective	B	B	B	B	B	B	B	D	B	J
Lesson	11-2	11-2	11-2	11-3	11-3	11-4	11-4	11-4	11-4	11-5

Question	**11**	**12**	**13**	**14**	**15**	**16**	**17**
Objective	G	A	I	C	E	F	H
Lesson	11-4	11-2	11-2	11-3	11-1	11-3	11-6

CHAPTER 11 REVIEW (pp. 713–716)

1. a. Sample: **See right. b.** Yes, Sample: **See right.**
3. See right. 5. See right. 7. Yes
9. a. v_2, v_3, *and* v_5
b. e_2, e_4, e_6, e_7
c. none
d. e_1 and e_8
e. e_6
f. False
g. $\deg(v_1) = 4$; $\deg(v_2) = 3$; $\deg(v_3) = 2$; $\deg(v_4) = 4$; $\deg(v_5) = 3$
h. 16

11.

edge	endpoint
e_1	$\{v_1, v_5\}$
e_2	$\{v_1, v_2\}$
e_3	$\{v_1, v_3\}$
e_4	$\{v_2, v_3\}$
e_5	$\{v_2, v_4\}$
e_6	$\{v_4\}$
e_7	$\{v_4, v_5\}$
e_8	$\{v_1, v_5\}$

13. Sample: **See right. 15.** Impossible; a graph cannot have an odd number of odd vertices. **17.** The graph has an Euler circuit by the sufficient condition for an Euler Circuit Theorem, since it is connected and every vertex is of even degree. **19.** No, because v_2 and v_3 have odd degree. **21. a. See right. b.** ≈ 61.4%
23. a. See right. b. 33 hours **25.** No, a graph cannot have an odd number of odd vertices. **27. a.** Vertices *F* and *G* have odd degree, so there is not an Euler circuit. **b.** the edge between *F* and *G*
29. a. See right.
b.
$$\begin{array}{c} \\ B \\ NB \end{array}\begin{array}{c} \begin{array}{cc} B & NB \end{array} \\ \begin{bmatrix} .4 & .6 \\ .75 & .25 \end{bmatrix} \end{array}$$
c. $T^8 \approx \begin{bmatrix} .5557 & .4443 \\ .5554 & .4446 \end{bmatrix}$
They bowl on about 56% of the Tuesdays.
d. ≈ 56%

31.
$$\begin{array}{c} \\ v_1 \\ v_2 \\ v_3 \\ v_4 \end{array}\begin{array}{c} \begin{array}{cccc} v_1 & v_2 & v_3 & v_4 \end{array} \\ \begin{bmatrix} 0 & 1 & 2 & 0 \\ 0 & 0 & 1 & 1 \\ 0 & 0 & 2 & 1 \\ 2 & 0 & 0 & 0 \end{bmatrix} \end{array}$$

33. a. See right. b. No, the matrix is not symmetric.
35. a. 0 **b.** 0
37. a.
$$\begin{array}{c} \\ v_1 \\ v_2 \\ v_3 \end{array}\begin{array}{c} \begin{array}{ccc} v_1 & v_2 & v_3 \end{array} \\ \begin{bmatrix} 1 & 2 & 1 \\ 2 & 0 & 1 \\ 1 & 1 & 0 \end{bmatrix} \end{array}$$
b. 39
39. a. There are no walks of length 4 or more. **b. See right.**

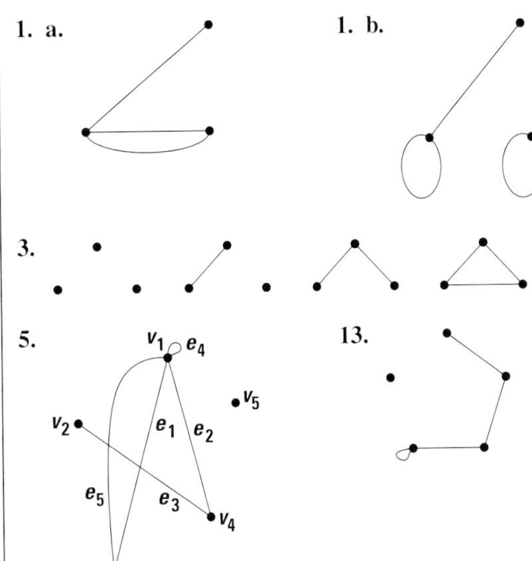

21. a.
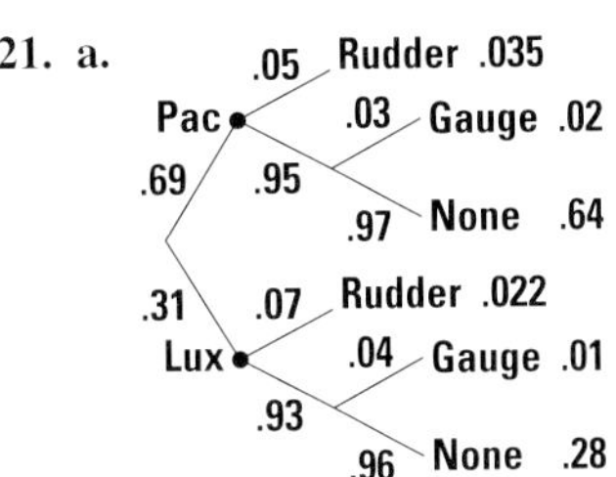

23. a.
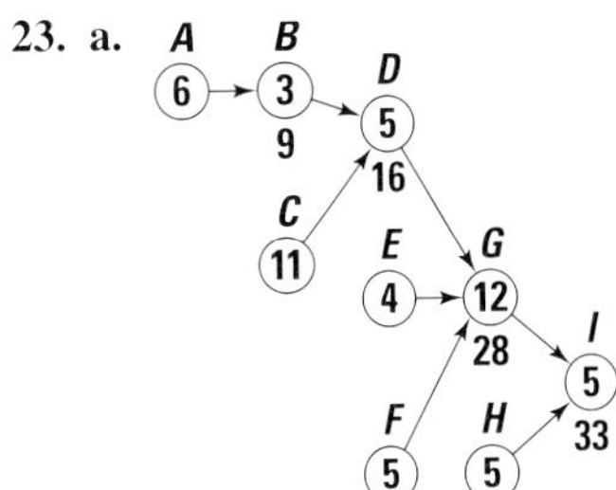

29. a.
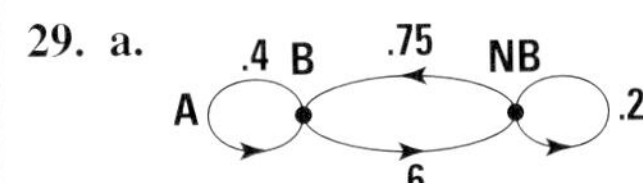

33. a.
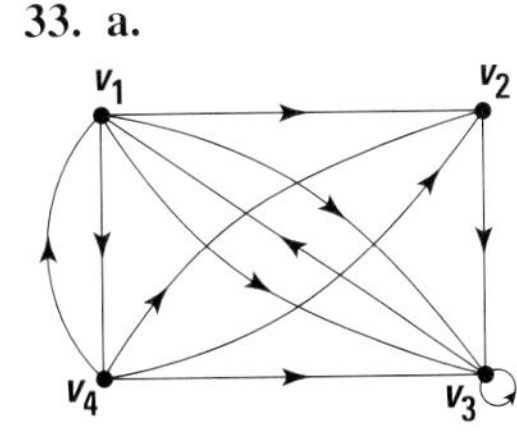

39. a.
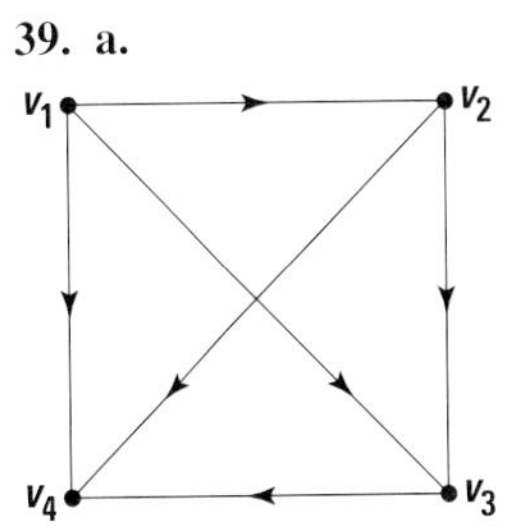

LESSON 12-1 (pp. 720–725)

11. The standard position arrow for the vector from (-1, 2) to (4, -1) has endpoint (4 − (-1), -1 − 2) = (5, -3); the standard position arrow for the vector from (3, -2) to (8, -5) has endpoint (8 − 3, -5 − (-2)) = (5, -3). So the vectors are the same. **13.** $\tan^{-1}\frac{1}{3} \approx 18.4°$ or 198.4° **15.** $\vec{w} = [5, 45°] = \left(\frac{5\sqrt{2}}{2}, \frac{5\sqrt{2}}{2}\right)$ **17. a.** $A_1 = 8000$; $A_2 = 7864$; $A_k = 1.008A_{k-1} - 200$ for $k > 1$. **b.** ≈ $7449.44 **19.** This is the graph of half a parabola whose y-intercept is (0,1). **21.** (-1,13), (-5, -1), (5, 1)

LESSON 12-2 (pp. 726–732)

11. Sample counterexample: If $\vec{u} = [1, 45°]$ and $\vec{v} = [1, 45°]$, then $\vec{u} + \vec{v} = [2, 45°] \neq [2, 90°]$. **13. a.** If $\vec{v} = (v_1, v_2)$, then $\vec{v} - \vec{v} = \vec{v} + \overrightarrow{-v}$ then $(v_1, v_2) + (-v_1, -v_2) = (v_1 + -v_1, v_2 + -v_2) =$ (0, 0), which is the zero vector. **b.** Sample: The arrow for $\vec{v} - \vec{v}$ is a point. **15. a.** The current is about 6.7 knots. **b.** The boat travels about 18.4 knots. **17.** 144 **19.** $\frac{x + 10}{(x + 4)(x - 2)(x + 1)}$

LESSON 12-3 (pp. 733-738)

7. Sample: $x = -1 - 5t$, $y = 5 - 5t$ **9.** Sample: $x = 2 + 3t$; $y = 8 + t$ **11. a.** (-15, 20) **b.** (-30, 40) **c.** (-30, 40) **d.** $a(b\vec{v}) = a(bv_1, bv_2) = (abv_1, abv_2) = ab(v_1, v_2) = (ab)\vec{v}$ **13.** about 360.6 lb in the direction about 26.3° **15.** (-2, 14), (2, -14) **17. a.** -0.267 words per sec; the subjects forget 8 words per 30 second period when the wait- time changes from 0 sec to 30 sec. **b.** -.13 words per sec; the subjects forget 4 words per 30-second period when the wait time changes from 30 sec to 60 sec. **19.** b

LESSON 12-4 (pp. 740–746)

11. a. $k(v_1)^2 + k(v_2)^2$ **b.** $|k|\,[(v_1)^2 + (v_2)^2]$ **c.** 0°, 180° **d.** If $k > 0$, $|k| \cdot \cos 0° = k \cdot 1 = k$; if $k < 0$, $|k| \cdot \cos 180° = -k \cdot -1 = k$ Hence, $|k| \cos\theta = k$

e.

$\cos\theta = \frac{\vec{u}\cdot\vec{v}}{\lvert\vec{u}\rvert \cdot \lvert\vec{v}\rvert}$	Angle Between Vectors Theorem
$\frac{k}{\lvert k\rvert} = \frac{\vec{u}\cdot\vec{v}}{\lvert\vec{u}\rvert \cdot \lvert\vec{v}\rvert}$	From part **d**, $\cos\theta = \frac{k}{\lvert k\rvert}$
$\frac{k}{\lvert k\rvert} = \frac{k(v_1)^2 + k(v_2)^2}{\lvert k\rvert\,[(v_1)^2 + (v_2)^2]}$	From parts **a** and **b**
$\frac{k}{\lvert k\rvert} = \frac{k[(v_1)^2 + (v_2)^2]}{\lvert k\rvert\,[(v_1)^2 + (v_2)^2]}$	Distributive Law
$\frac{k}{\lvert k\rvert} = \frac{k}{\lvert k\rvert}$	Simplify

Therefore, the Angle Between Vectors Theorem holds true for parallel vectors.

13. 8.13° **15. a.** (250 cos 55°, 250 sin 55°) ≈ (143, 205) **b.** Sample: $x = -50 + 143t$; $y = 30 + 205t$ **c.** (21.5, 132.5); it is 21.5 miles east and 132.5 miles north of Indianapolis. **17. a.** $\vec{u} + \vec{v}$ is 3; $\vec{u} - \vec{v}$ is 4 **b.** Sample: $\vec{u} = (3, 4)$ and $\vec{v} = (12, 5)$; $|\vec{u} + \vec{v}|^2 + |\vec{u} - \vec{v}|^2 = 306 + 82 = 388$; $2(|\vec{u}|^2 + |\vec{v}|^2) = 2(25 + 169) = 2(194) = 388$ **19.** The units digit of the fourth power of a number is the fourth power of the units, and 2^4, 4^4, 6^4, and 8^4 each have units digit 6.

LESSON 12-5 (pp. 747–751)

13. ≈ 79 cm **15.** $y = -2$ or $y = 6$ **17.** False **19. a. See right. b.** limaçon **21.** Left side $= \tan^2 x - \sin^2 x$

$$= \frac{\sin^2 x}{\cos^2 x} - \sin^2 x$$
$$= \frac{\sin^2 x - \sin^2 x \cos^2 x}{\cos^2 x}$$
$$= \frac{\sin^2 x(1 - \cos^2 x)}{\cos^2 x}$$
$$= \frac{\sin^2 x \sin^2 x}{\cos^2 x}$$
$$= \tan^2 x \sin^2 x$$
= Right Side

19. a.

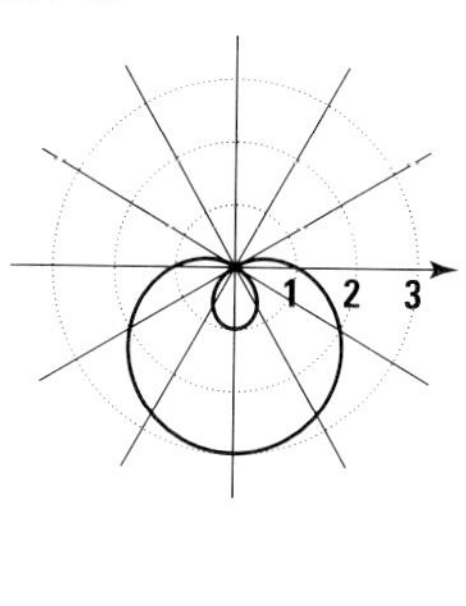

LESSON 12-6 (pp. 752–759)

15. a. $\vec{u} \cdot \vec{v} = u_1v_1 + u_2v_2 + u_3v_3 = v_1u_1 + v_2u_2 + v_3u_3 = \vec{v} \cdot \vec{u}$ **b.** commutative property of the dot product **17.** $(a\vec{u})(b\vec{v}) = (au_1, au_2, au_3) \cdot (bv_1, bv_2, bv_3) = abu_1v_1 + abu_2v_2 + abu_3v_3 = ab(u_1v_1 + u_2v_2 + u_3v_3) = ab(\vec{u} \cdot \vec{v})$ **19. a.** $\vec{u} = (-1, 0, 1)$, $\vec{v} = (0, -1, 3)$ **b.** Sample: (1, 3, 1) **c.** (-2, 4, 6) **d.** ≈ 0.645 **e.** 164 **21.** $(\sqrt{5}, 2\sqrt{5})$ and $(-\sqrt{5}, -2\sqrt{5})$ **23.** 255

LESSON 12-7 (pp. 760–766)

9. a. $7x - 2y + z = 6$ **b.** $7x - 2y + z = 6$ **11. a.** (3, -2, 1) and (1, 2, -1), the vectors perpendicular to the planes M_1 and M_2, are not parallel. **b.** Sample: $\left(\frac{7}{4}, 1, \frac{3}{4}\right)$ **c.** Sample: $x = \frac{7}{4}$; $y = 1 + 4t$; $z = \frac{3}{4} + 8t$ **13.** $p = \pm\sqrt{5}$ **15.** e **17. a.** $\sum_{j=1}^{n} \left(\frac{j}{n}\right)^2 \cdot \left(\frac{1}{n}\right)$ **b.** $\frac{(n + 1)(2n + 1)}{6n^2}$ **19. a. See below. b.** a cone **c.** $\frac{16\pi}{3}$ cubic units

19. a.

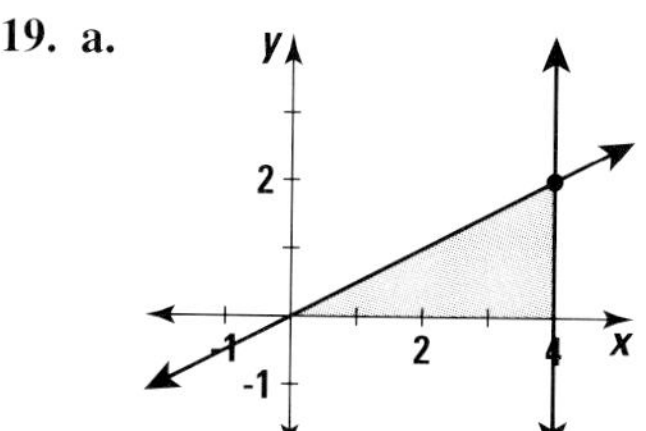

LESSON 12-8 (pp. 767–772)

15. $\begin{cases} x = -7 + 3t \\ y = 2 - 4t \\ z = -t \end{cases}$

17. $\vec{u_2} \times \vec{u_3}$ is perpendicular to both $\vec{u_2}$ and $\vec{u_3}$. $\vec{u_1} \cdot (\vec{u_2} \times \vec{u_3}) = 0$ if and only if $\vec{u_1}$ is also perpendicular to $\vec{u_2} \times \vec{u_3}$. Thus $\vec{u_1}$, $\vec{u_2}$ and $\vec{u_3}$ being all perpendicular to the same vector, are coplanar. **19.** Yes, it is an example of modus tollens.

CHAPTER 12 PROGRESS SELF-TEST (p. 777)

1. $\sqrt{(-5)^2 + 2^2} = \sqrt{25 + 4} = \sqrt{29}$ **2.** (3 − (-5), -4 − 2) = (8, -6) **3.** (-6, 8) + (-25, 10) = (-31, 18) **4.** 3 · (-5) + (-4) · 2 = -23 **5.** $|\vec{u_1}| = 5$, and $\theta = \cos^{-1}\left(\frac{\vec{u}\cdot\vec{v}}{|\vec{u}|\,|\vec{u}|}\right) = \cos^{-1}\left(\frac{-23}{5 \cdot \sqrt{29}}\right) \approx 149°$ **6.** (-2, 0, 5) + (-12, 6, -6) = (-14, 6, -1) **7.** $\vec{s} \times \vec{t} = (0(-2) - 5(2), 5(-4) - (-2)(-2), -2(2) - 0(4)) = (-10, -24, -4)$

8. Sample: $2\vec{s} = (-4, 0, 10)$ **9. See right.** The graphs of the vectors have the same initial points and lengths but opposite directions. **10. a. See right. b.** $\vec{v} = (-5, 3) - (-2, 7) = (-3, -4)$
c. $r = \sqrt{(-3)^2 + (-4)^2} = \sqrt{9 + 16} = \sqrt{25} = 5;$
$\theta = 180° + \tan^{-1}\left(\frac{-4}{-3}\right) \approx 180° + 53° = 233°;$
so $\vec{v} \approx [5, 233°]$.
11. Left side $= k(\vec{v} - \vec{w})$
$= k(v_1 - w_1, v_2 - w_2)$
$= (kv_1 - kw_1, kv_2 - kw_2)$
$= k(v_1, v_2) - k(w_1, w_2)$
$= k\vec{v} - k\vec{w}$
= Right side
$\therefore (\vec{v} - \vec{w}) = k\vec{v} - k\vec{w}$
12. $(2, -4, 3) \cdot (3, -2, z)$ must be zero.
$2 \cdot 3 + (-4)(-2) + 3 \cdot z = 0$, so
$3z = -8 - 6$, and $z = -\frac{14}{3}$.
13. a. $[270, 155°] + [15, 90°]$
$\approx (-114, 245) + (0, 15)$
$\approx (-114, 260)$
$\approx [284, 113.7°]$;
hence the speed is $\approx$ 284 mph, and the direction is $\approx 23.7°$ west of north.
b. The actual velocity of the plane is (-114, 260), which means the plane is traveling 114 mph west and 260 mph north.
14. See below. 15. See below. 16. Sample: $\begin{cases} x = -3 + 4t \\ y = 2 - 3t \end{cases}$
17. $1x + 2y - 3z = 1(4) + 2(0) - 3(-2) = 10$, so the plane is $x + 2y - 3z = 10$.
18. $(x - 2)^2 + y^2 + (z + 3)^2 = 16$

9.

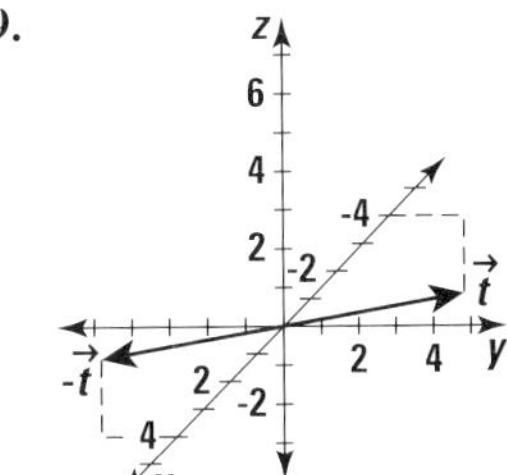

10. a.

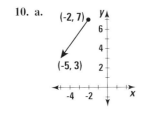

14.

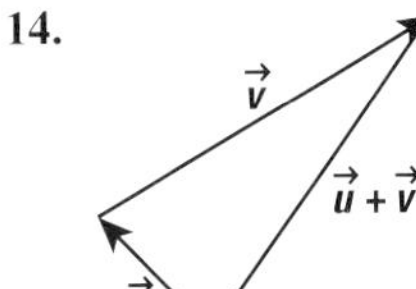

15.

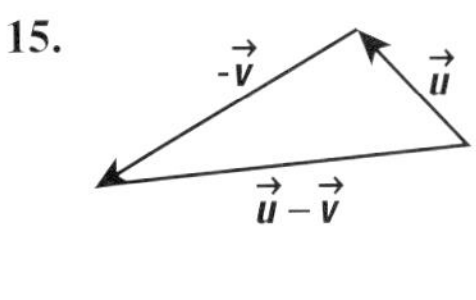

The chart below keys the questions on the **Progress Self-Test** to the objectives in the **Chapter Review** on pages 778–781 or to the **Vocabulary** (Voc.) on page 776. This will enable you to locate those **Chapter Review** questions that correspond to questions you missed on the **Progress Self-Test**. The lesson where the material is covered is also indicated on the chart.

Question	**1**	**2**	**3**	**4**	**5**	**6**	**7**	**8**	**9**	**10**
Objective	A	B	B	B	D	C	C	C	K	I
Lesson	12-1	12-2	12-3	12-4	12-4	12-6	12-6	12-6	12-6	12-3
Question	**11**	**12**	**13**	**14**	**15**	**16**	**17**	**18**		
Objective	E	F	H, G	J	J	L	M	M		
Lesson	12-3	12-6	12-1,12-2	12-2	12-2	12-3	12-7	12-5		

CHAPTER 12 REVIEW (pp. 778-781)

1. magnitude: $\sqrt{130}$; direction: $\approx -15.3°$ **3.** 9 and -3 **5.** (-2, -2) **7.** -10 **9.** (2, 28) **11.** Sample: [3, 285°] **13.** Sample: [20, 35°] **15.** Sample: $\left(-\frac{3}{2}, 1\right)$ **17.** (-7, -1, 5) **19.** (11, -12, 5) **21.** 8
23. $\vec{v} \cdot (\vec{u} \times \vec{v}) = (-2, -3, 4) \cdot (11, 18, 19) = -22 - 54 + 76 = 0$
25. $\approx 130.4°$ **27.** 180°; they have opposite directions.
29. The vector from (x, y) to $(x + a, y + ma)$ is $(a, ma) = a(1, m)$. Therefore, by definition, the vectors are parallel. $(kv_1, kv_2, kv_3) + (mv_1, mv_2, mv_3) = k\vec{v} + m\vec{v}$ **31.** No **33.** neither **35.** perpendicular **37.** -10 **39. a. See right. b.** (14.5, 6.76) **c.** The ship is going 14.5 mph towards the east and 6.76 mph towards the north. **41. a.** 32.1 lb of force with direction 80.6° counterclockwise from the positive x-axis **b.** Sarah **43.** No **45.** (-2.5, 4.3) **See right. 47. a.** (6, 3) **b.** length $\approx$ 6.7; direction $\approx 26.6°$ **49. a–d. See page 886. 51. See page 886.**
53. a., c. See page 886. b. (0, 0, 4) **55.** $(x - 1, y - 2) = t(-5, 5)$
57. $5x + 3y + 1 = 0$
59. $\begin{cases} x = 5 + 3t \\ y = -4t \end{cases}$
61. $y = 3$ and $y = -3$ **63.** $x = 0$ and $y = 0$
65. $2x - 4y = 6$ **67.** $(x - 5, y + 1, z - 2) = t(2, -6, 1)$

39. a.

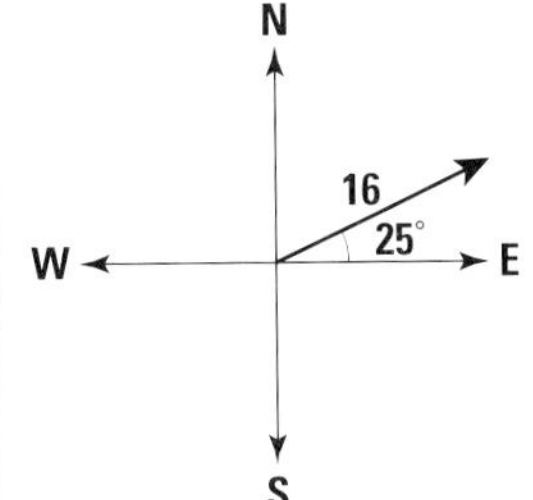

45.

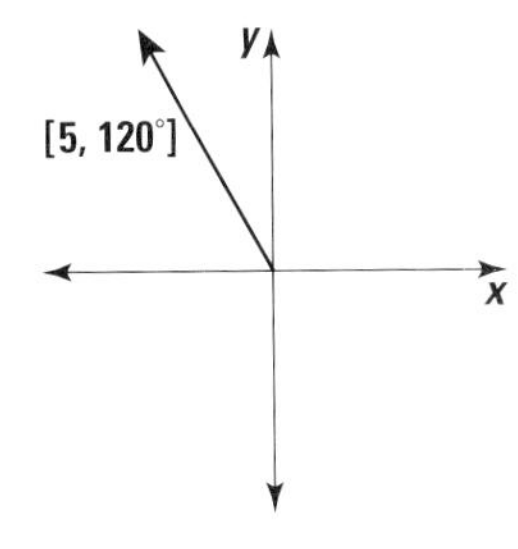

49. a.–d.

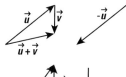

51.

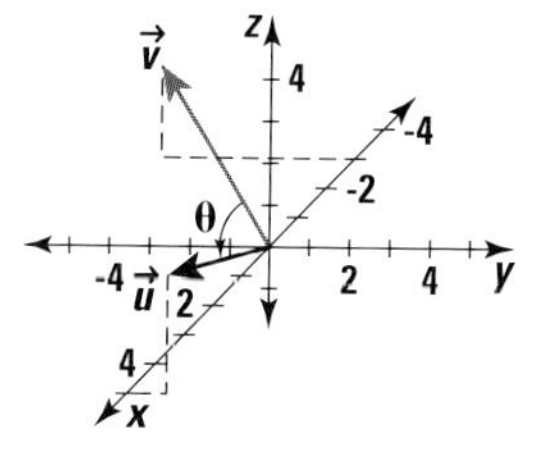

53. a., c.

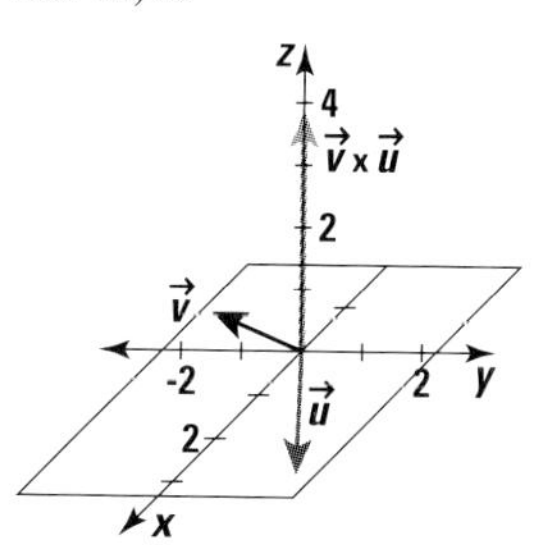

LESSON 13-1 (pp. 784–791)

7. 105 mi **9.** ≈.9 **11.** $x \approx -5.82$ or $x \approx -2.68$ or $x \approx 0.46$ or $x \approx 3.61$ **13. a., b.** Sample: **See below. c.** $y = 8$ **d.** $y = bk$ **15. a.** 3.0, 3.8, 4.6, 5.4, 6.2, 7.0 **b.** $3 + \frac{4k}{n}$, where $k = 0, 1, \ldots, n$ **c.** $\frac{b-a}{n}$

13. a., b. Sample:

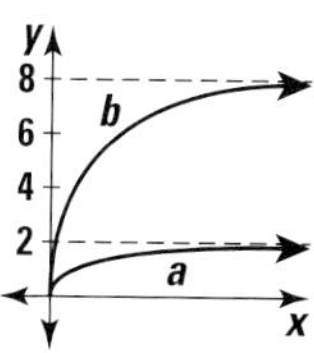

LESSON 13-2 (pp. 792–798)

9. ≈ 0.8655

11.

N	Sum
10	541.2
20	564.3
50	577.808
100	582.252
500	585.786
1000	586.227

13. a. See below. b. negative **15. a. See below. b.** positive **17.** distance **19. a.** Sample: **See below b.** Answers will vary. **c.** any single edge of the circuit **21.** 105,625 **23.** 4 units^2

13. a.

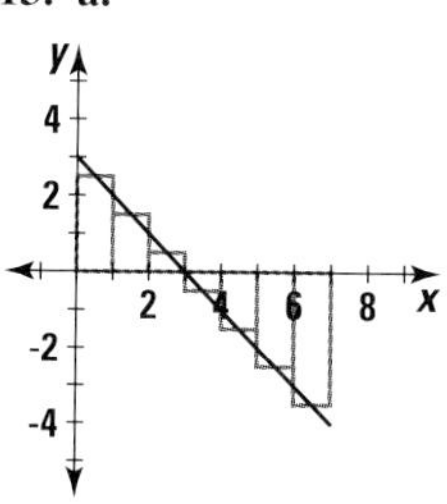

15. a.

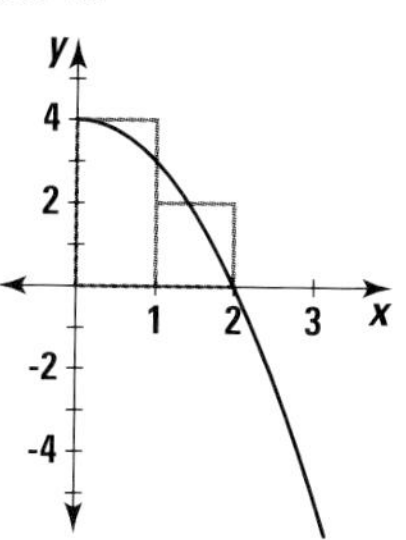

19. a.

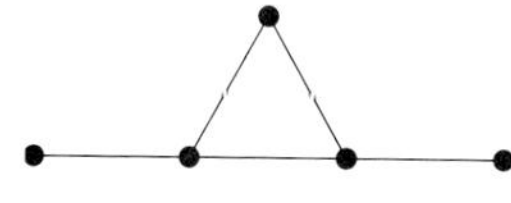

LESSON 13-3 (pp. 799–804)

11. a. See below. b. positive **13. a. See below. b.** negative **15.** $c(b - a)$ **17. a.** 15 **b.** 126 **19. See below.** The graph is a line. **21.** $1.4925 \le \ell \le 1.5075$

11. a.

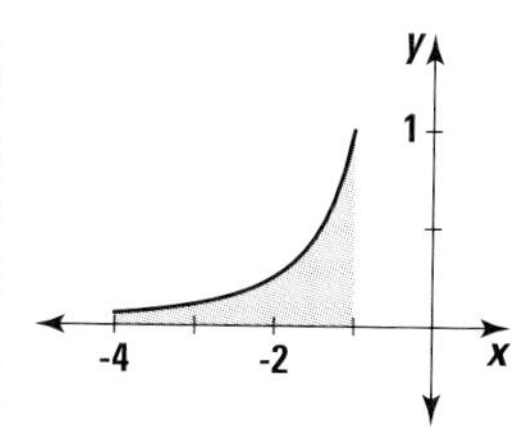

13. a.

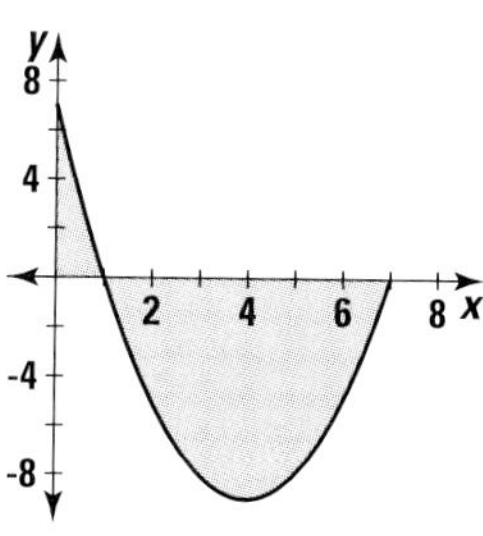

19.

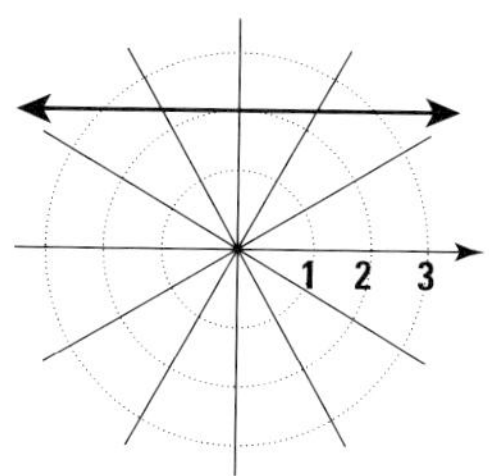

LESSON 13-4 (pp. 805–811)

7. $2\int_a^b \sin x\, dx$ **9. a.** $7a$ and $\frac{a^2}{2}$ **b.** $3 \cdot \frac{a^2}{2} + 7a$

c. answer from **b:** $3 \cdot \frac{4^2}{2} + 7(4) = 52$; area of trapezoid: $4 \cdot \frac{7 + 19}{2} = 52$ **11.** Sample: Let $f(x) = x$, $g(x) = x$, and $a = 1$. Then $\int_0^1 x\, dx \cdot \int_0^1 x\, dx = \frac{1^2}{2} \cdot \frac{1^2}{2} = \frac{1}{4}$, but $\int_0^1 x^2\, dx = \frac{1^3}{3} = \frac{1}{3}$.

13. a. 39.27 **b.** 2.04 **15.** Sample: **a.** (24, 30, 26) **b.** $12x + 15y + 13z = -10$

c. $\begin{cases} x = 1 + 12t \\ y = 2 + 15t \\ z = -4 + 13t \end{cases}$

17. $50\pi \approx 157.08$ cm^3

LESSON 13-5 (pp. 812–818)

11. a. $\frac{\pi}{4}$ **b.** ≈ 0.162 **c.** ≈ 0.624 units^2 **13.** 12 **15.** 116

17. **See below.** **19. a.** $f'(x) = 4x$ **b.** $x = 0$ **c.** **See below**

21. a. $\sum_{i=1}^{7} (i^2 - 5i + 2) = (-2) + (-4) + (-4) + (-2) + 2 + 8 + 16 - 14;$

$\sum_{i=1}^{7} i^2 = 140,\ \sum_{i=1}^{7} 5i = 140,\ \sum_{i=1}^{7} 2 = 14$, so $\sum_{i=1}^{7} i^2 - \sum_{i=1}^{7} 5i + \sum_{i=1}^{7} 2 = 14$

b. Sample:

$\sum_{i=1}^{n} (ai^2 + bi + c) = \sum_{i=1}^{n} ai^2 + \sum_{i=1}^{n} bi + \sum_{i=1}^{n} c$

23. 1.5

17. Sample:

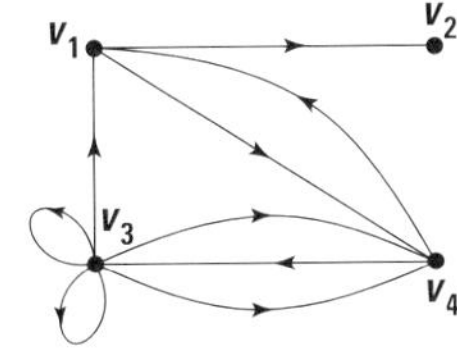

19. c.

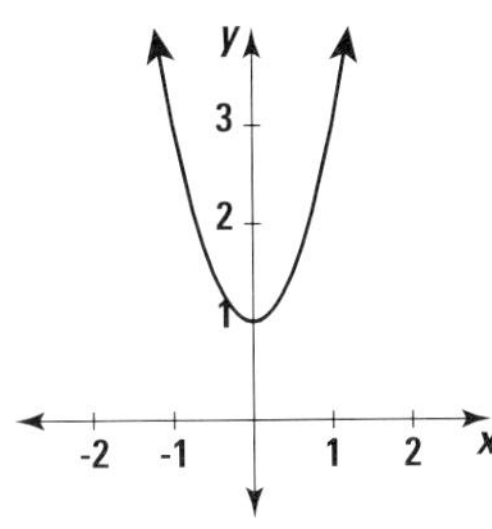

LESSON 13-6 (pp. 820–825)

7. a. **See below.** **b.** cylinder **c.** 4 units

d. $\int_0^3 \pi r^2\, dx = 16\pi \int_0^3 dx = 48\pi$ units^3

e. $\pi r^2 h = \pi(4^2)(3) = 48\pi$ units^3 **9. a.** **See below.**

b. $\frac{196\pi}{3} \approx 205.25$ units^3 **11.** $\frac{245}{2}$ **13.** π **15.** 21 **17. a.** $-\infty$

b. $-\infty$ **c.** 4 **19.** a is a factor of $c \Leftrightarrow c = am$ for some integer m. So $bc = b(am) = a(bm)$, so a is a factor of bc. (a is a factor of b is not needed.)

7. a.

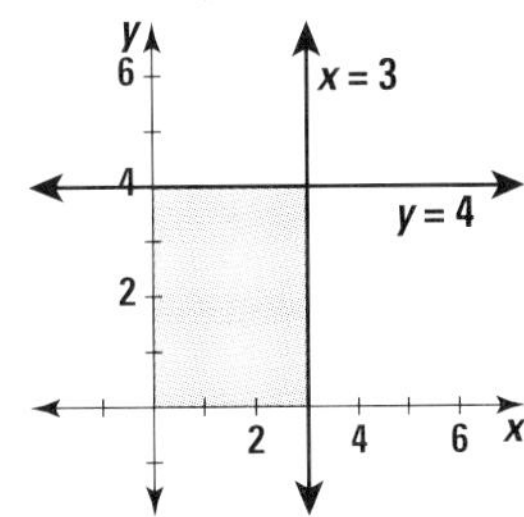

9. a.

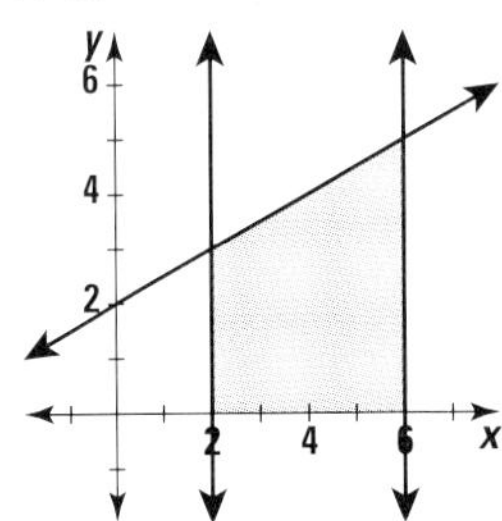

LESSON 13-7 (pp. 826–831)

11. 112 ft^3 **13.** 13 **15.** sample: $e_1 e_2 e_3 e_4 e_5 e_7 e_6$

CHAPTER 13 PROGRESS SELF-TEST (p. 835)

1. $\frac{1}{2} \cdot 1 \cdot 30 + \frac{1}{2} \cdot 30 + \frac{1}{2} \cdot \frac{1}{2}(30 + 50) + 2 \cdot 50 + \frac{1}{2} \cdot 50 \cdot 1$
$= 15 + 15 + 20 + 100 + 25$
$= 175$ miles

2. $1 \cdot 1 + 2.5 \cdot 1 + 3 \cdot 1 + 1 \cdot 1 \approx 7.5$ units^2

3. volume $\approx \sum_{i=1}^{8} \pi r_i^2 h$
$= \pi h \sum_{i=1}^{8} r_i^2$
$= \pi \cdot 1 \cdot (4^2 + 4^2 + 3^2 + 2^2 + 1^2 + 1^2 + 1^2 + 1^2)$
$= 49\pi$ ft^3

4. a. **See right.** **b.** $8 \cdot \frac{7 + 9}{2} = 8 \cdot 8 = 64$ **5. a.** **See right.**

b. $3 \cdot 6 = 18$ **6.** $\frac{1}{2}$ the area of the circle with radius 3 and center at the origin, hence $\frac{1}{2}\pi(3)^2 = 4.5\pi \approx 14.137$ **7.** negative; **See page 888.**

8. $\int_7^{12} x^2 dx - 49(12 - 7)$
$= \frac{1}{3}(12)^3 - \frac{1}{3}(7)^3 - 49 \cdot 5$
$= 576 - \frac{343}{3} - 245$
$= \frac{650}{3}$ units^2

9. For every Riemann sum of f on the interval from a to b, there is a corresponding Riemann sum of $c \cdot f$ with the same subintervals and same z_i. The value of each term of the sum of $c \cdot f$ will be c times the value of the corresponding term of the sum of f.

$\lim_{n\to\infty} \sum_{i=1}^{n} (c \cdot f(z_i)\, \Delta x) = c \cdot \lim_{n\to\infty} \sum_{i=1}^{n} (f(z_i)\, \Delta x)$

so $\int_a^b (c \cdot f(x))dx = c\int_a^b f(x)dx$. **See page 888.**

10. a. $\int_0^{15} (-.4(t - 15)^2 + 90)\, dt$

b. $\int_0^{15} (-.4(t^2 - 30t + 225) + 90)\, dt$
$= \int_0^{15} (-.4t^2 + 12t)\, dt$
$= \frac{-.4(15)^3}{3} + 6(15)^2 - 0$
$= -450 + 1350$
$= 900$ ft

11. $\int_0^{\pi/2} \cos x\, dx + \int_0^{\pi/2} 4\cos x\, dx = \int_0^{\pi/2} 5\cos x\, dx$
$= 5\int_0^{\pi/2} \cos x\, dx$

12. a. **See page 888.** **b.** volume $= \int_0^1 \pi(1 - x)^2\, dx$
$= \pi\int_0^1 (x^2 - 2x + 1)\, dx$
$= \pi\left(\frac{1^3}{3} - 1^2 + 1\right)$
$= \frac{\pi}{3}$ units^3

4. a.

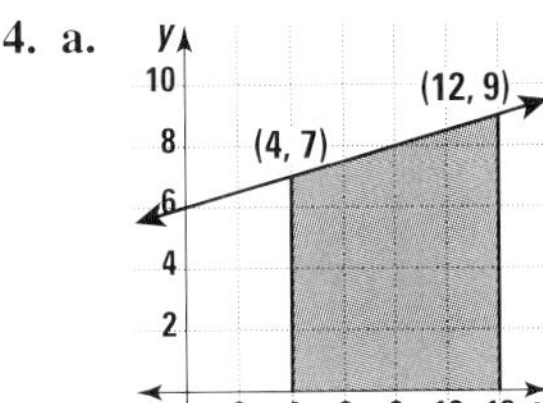

5. a.

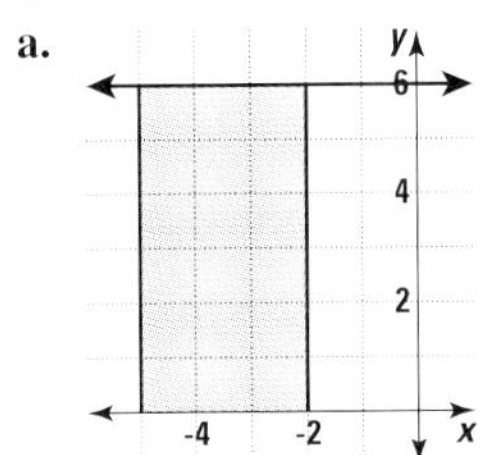

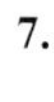

7.

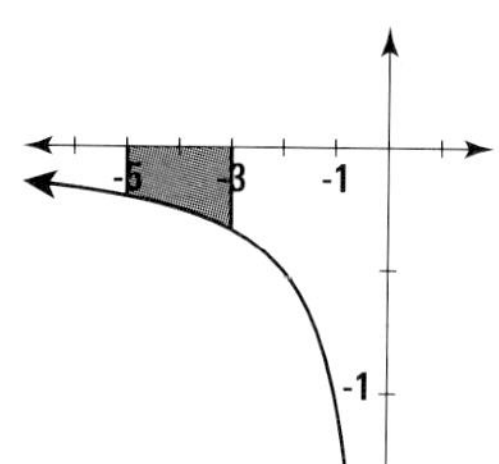

9.

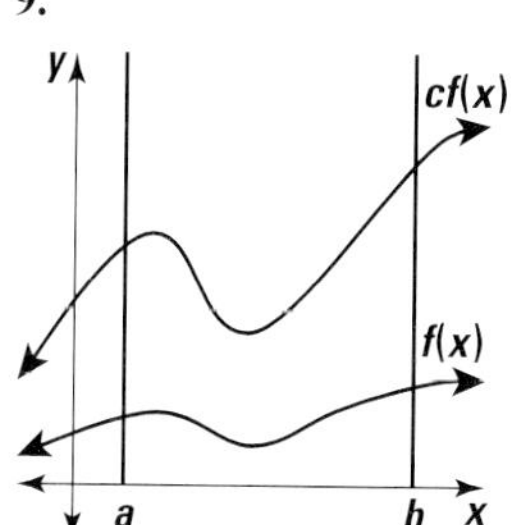

12. a.

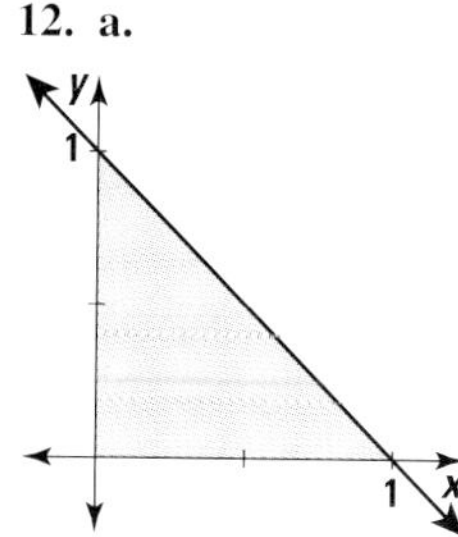

The chart below keys the questions on the **Progress Self-Test** to the objectives in the **Chapter Review** on pages 836–839 or to the **Vocabulary** (Voc.) on page 834. This will enable you to locate those **Chapter Review** questions that correspond to questions you missed on the **Progress Self-Test.** The lesson where the material is covered is also indicated on the chart.

Question	**1**	**2**	**3**	**4**	**5**	**6**	**7**	**8**	**9**	**10**
Objective	F	A	E	B	B	B	G	H	C	D
Lesson	13-1	13-2	13-6	13-3	13-3	13-5	13-3	13-4	13-4	13-5
Question	**11**	**12**								
Objective	C	I								
Lesson	13-4	13-6								

CHAPTER 13 REVIEW (pp. 836-839)

1. 3600 **3. a.** $\sum_{i=1}^{100} \frac{\pi}{600} \sin\left(\frac{\pi}{3} + i\frac{\pi}{600}\right)$ **b.** 0.500 **5.** 4
7. a. See right. b. ≈ 5.59 **9.** $221.\overline{6}$ **11.** 240 **13.** $\int_1^3 1\,dx$
15. Area I is $\int_a^c f(x)\,dx$, Area II is $\int_c^b f(x)\,dx$, and the union of the regions represented by Areas I and II is $\int_a^b f(x)\,dx$. Since Area I + Area II equals the area of the union of the regions represented by Areas I and II, then $\int_a^c f(x)\,dx + \int_c^b f(x)\,dx = \int_a^b f(x)\,dx$. **See right. 17.** 316.8 ft **19.** 96 m^3 **21.** $51.75\pi \approx 162.58$ in^3
23. 4635 ft **25.** $\int_1^4 (-(x-3)^2 + 2)\,dx$ **b.** negative **27.** a. 120 units^2
b. $93.\overline{3}$ units^2 **29. a. See right. b.** $\int_0^4 (3x + 2)\,dx = 32$
31. a. See right. b. 2π units^3

7. a.

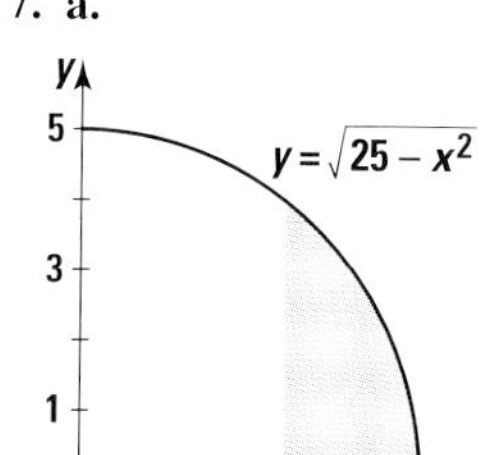
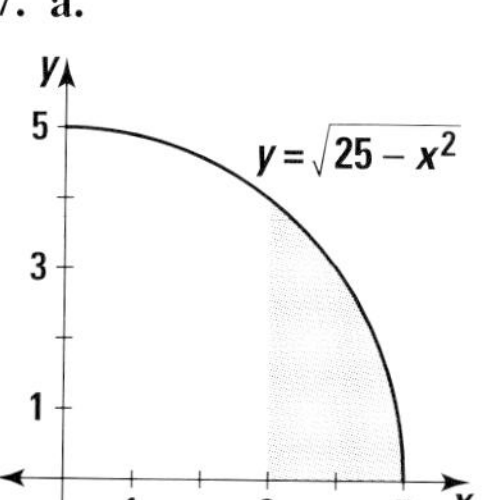

15.

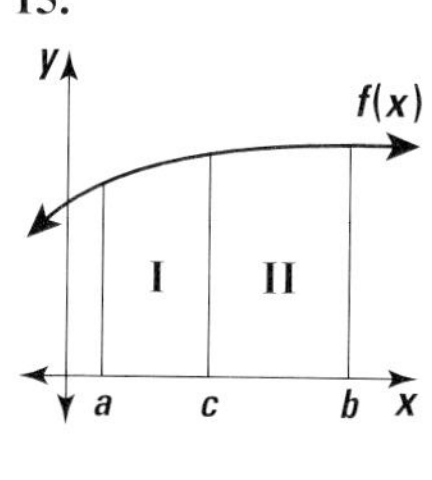

29. a.

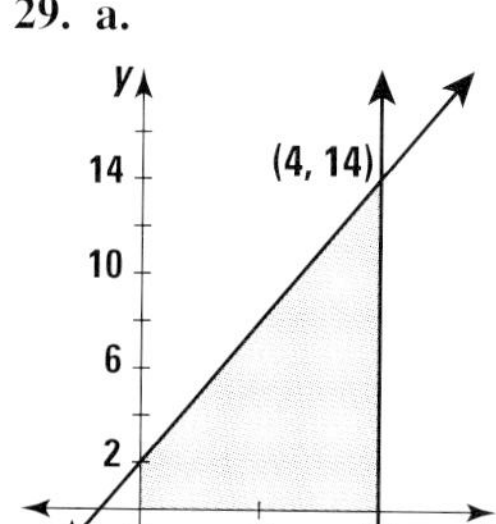

31. a.

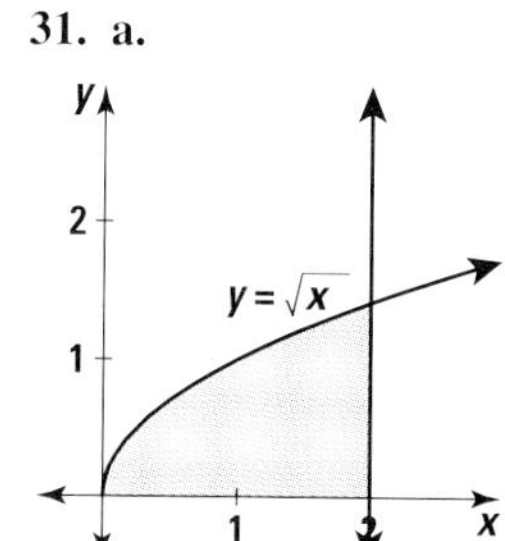

absolute error For an observed value o and an expected value e, $|o - e|$. (202)

absolute value, $|x|$ If $x \geq 0$, then $|x| = x$; if $x < 0$, then $|x| = -x$. Equivalently, $|x| = \sqrt{x^2}$. (202)

absolute value of a complex number, $|z|$ The distance from z to the origin or pole. Also called *modulus.* (489)

acceleration The rate of change of a rate of change. (576)

Addition Property of Equality For any real expressions $f(x)$ and $g(x)$, if $f(x) = g(x)$, then $f(x) + c = g(x) + c$. (161)

Addition Property of Inequality For any real expressions $f(x)$ and $g(x)$, if $f(x) < g(x)$, then $f(x) + c < g(x) + c$. (175)

adjacency matrix For a graph with vertices $v_1, v_2, \ldots, v_n$, the $n \times n$ matrix in which, $\forall$ i, j, the element in the ith row and jth column is the number of edges from vertex v_i to vertex v_j. (669)

adjacent edges Two edges of a graph with a common endpoint. (666)

adjacent vertices Two vertices of a graph connected by an edge. (666)

amplitude One-half the difference between the maximum and minimum values of a sine wave. (Previous course)

AND gate An input-output device for which the output signal is 1 if and only if the two input signals are 1. Otherwise, the output signal is 0. Schematically, the AND gate is represented by [AND gate symbol]. (28)

Angle Between Vectors Theorem Suppose that θ is the measure of the angle between two nonzero vectors $\vec{u}$ and $\vec{v}$ and $0 \leq \theta \leq \pi$. Then $\cos\theta = \frac{\vec{u} \cdot \vec{v}}{|\vec{u}|\,|\vec{v}|}$. (742)

antecedent p, in the conditional $p \Rightarrow q$. Also called *hypothesis.* (35)

antiderivative of f A function whose derivative is f. (828)

Arccos function See *inverse cosine function.*

Arcsin function See *inverse sine function.*

Arctan function See *inverse tangent function.*

argument A sequence of statements in which the final statement (the **conclusion**) is asserted to follow from preceding statements (the **premises**). (45)

argument of a complex number For the complex number $[r, \theta]$, θ. (489)

arithmetic sequence A sequence in which $\forall$ $n > 1$, $a_n = a_{n-1} + d$, where d is a constant. That is, each term beyond the first is d (the **constant difference**) greater than the preceding one. (123)

average rate of change For a function over the interval from x_1 to x_2, the slope of the line through $(x_1, f(x_1))$ and $(x_2, f(x_2))$. (553)

average speed Total distance divided by total time. (327)

average velocity The average rate of change of an object's directed distance from a fixed point (or the position of an object on a line) over a time interval. (554)

base 2 A representation of a number in which the digits are either a 0 or 1 and the place values are consecutive integral powers of 2. Also called *binary.* (258)

base 8 A representation of a number in which the digits can be any of the integers 0–7 and the place values are consecutive integral powers of 8. Also called *octal.* (258)

base 16 A representation of a number in which the digits can be any of the integers 0–9 or any of the letters A–F (representing the values 10–15) and the place values are consecutive integral powers of 16. Also called *hexadecimal.* (258)

base *b* notation The representation of a number as $d_n d_{n-1} \ldots d_1 d_0$, where each digit d_i is a particular integer from 0 through $b - 1$, and the value of the number is $d_n \cdot b^n + d_{n-1} \cdot b^{n-1} + \ldots + d_1 \cdot b^1 + d_0 \cdot b^0$. (260)

Basic Properties of Combinations Theorem For all n and r for which $C(n, r)$ is defined:

a. $C(n, r) = C(n, n - r)$, $\binom{n}{r} = \binom{n}{n-r}$;

b. $C(n, n) = C(n, 0) = 1$, $\binom{n}{n} = \binom{n}{0} = 1$. (624)

basis step See *Principle of Mathematical Induction.*

biconditional An *if and only if* statement. (40)

binary See *base 2.*

binary digit A single digit (0 or 1) in a base 2 representation of a number. Also called *bit.* (258)

binomial coefficients The coefficients in the series expansion of $(x + y)^n$; the combinations ${}_nC_k$. (628)

binomial probability The probability of k successes in n independent trials of a two-outcome experiment; given by the formula $\binom{n}{k} p^k q^{n-k}$, where p is the probability of success and $q = 1 - p$ is the probability of failure. (635)

Binomial Theorem For all positive integers n and numbers x and y, $(x + y)^n = \binom{n}{0} x^n + \binom{n}{1} x^{n-1} y + \binom{n}{2} x^{n-2} y^2 + \ldots + \binom{n}{k} x^{n-k} y^k + \ldots + \binom{n}{n-1} x y^{n-1} + \binom{n}{n} y^n = \sum_{k=0}^{n} \binom{n}{k} x^{n-k} y^k$. (630)

Bisection Method A method for obtaining zeros of a continuous function by splitting into successive intervals an interval which has the property that its endpoints produce function values with opposite signs. A zero will be between two such endpoints. At each step, the subinterval with this same property is split in half. By continuing to subdivide, the zero can be estimated to any degree of accuracy desired. (214)

bit See *binary digit.*

Boolean algebra An algebraic system in which the operations act similar to the logical operations of *and, or,* and *not* on statements. (31)

GLOSSARY

branch point A node of a tree corresponding to a step in which several choices or results are possible. (608)

Bubblesort A particular iterative sorting algorithm whereby terms are compared with neighboring terms and "bubble up" to the beginning of the list. (450)

byte A group of 8 bits. (260)

$C(n, r)$, $\binom{n}{r}$, $_nC_r$ The number of combinations of n elements taken r at a time. (622)

$C(n, r)$ Calculation Theorem $C(n, r) = \frac{n!}{r!(n-r)!}$. (623)

cardioid The polar graph of any equation of the form $r = a \pm \cos \theta$ or $r = a \pm \sin \theta$. (498)

Change of Base Theorem Let a and b be positive real numbers both unequal to 1; then for all $x > 0$, $\log_b x = \log_b a \cdot \log_a x$. (133)

chaos A property of a system in which small differences in the initial conditions for the system can lead to radically different results. (538)

chunking Treating an expression as if it were a single variable. (182)

circuit A path in a graph that starts and ends at the same vertex. (679)

Circuits and Connectedness Theorem If a connected graph contains a circuit and an edge is removed from the circuit, then the resulting graph is also connected. (683)

circuits connected in series Circuits connected in such a way that current flows through one circuit and then through the other. (476)

closed infinite interval, $[a, \infty)$ or $(-\infty, b]$ The set of numbers greater than or equal to a given number (a), or the set of numbers less than or equal to a given number (b), $\{x: a \le x\}$ or $\{x: x \le b\}$. (81)

closed interval, $[a, b]$ The set of numbers greater than or equal to one number (a) and less than or equal to a second larger number (b); $\{x: a \le x \le b\}$. (81)

closed with respect to an operation The property of a set S and an operation such that when the operation is applied to any element(s) of the set, the result is an element of the set. (284)

cofunction identity $\cos\left(\frac{\pi}{2} - x\right) = \sin x$ or $\sin\left(\frac{\pi}{2} - x\right) = \cos x$. (370)

collection A combination of items in which repetition is allowed and order makes no difference. (640)

combination of the n elements of the set S taken r at a time An r-element subset of a set S with n elements. (622)

combinatorics The science of counting. (601)

common logarithm, log A logarithm with base 10. (133)

complement of a subset A of a set S The elements of S that are not in A. (611)

complete graph A graph in which every pair of vertices is joined by exactly one edge. (673)

complex conjugates The complex numbers $a + bi$ and $a - bi$, where a and b are real numbers. (475)

complex fraction A fraction whose numerator or denominator contains a fraction. (286)

Complex nth Roots Theorem

Polar Form: The n nth roots of $[r, \theta]$ are $\left[\sqrt[n]{r}, \frac{\theta}{n} + k \cdot \frac{2\pi}{n}\right]$, where $k = 0, 1, 2, \ldots$, and $n - 1$.

Trigonometric Form: The n nth roots of $r(\cos \theta + i \sin \theta)$ are $\sqrt[n]{r} \cdot \left(\cos\left(\frac{\theta}{n} + k \cdot \frac{2\pi}{n}\right) + i \sin\left(\frac{\theta}{n} + k \cdot \frac{2\pi}{n}\right)\right)$, where $k = 0, 1, 2, \ldots$, and $n - 1$. (515)

complex number A number that can be written in the form $a + bi$ where a and b are real numbers and $i^2 = -1$. The **real part** of $a + bi$ is a and the **imaginary part** is b. (473)

complex number addition Let a, b, c, and d be real numbers and let $z = a + bi$ and $w = c + di$. Then $z + w = (a + c) + (b + d)i$. (474)

complex number multiplication Let a, b, c, and d be real numbers and let $z = a + bi$ and $w = c + di$. Then $zw = (ac - bd) + (ad + bc)i$. (474)

complex plane A coordinate plane for representing complex numbers. The horizontal axis of the complex plane is the **real axis** and the vertical axis is the **imaginary axis**. (476)

component representation For a vector $\vec{u}$, the ordered pair (u_1, u_2), the rectangular coordinates of the point at the tip of the standard position arrow for a vector. The numbers u_1 and u_2 are the ***x*-component** and ***y*-component** of $\vec{u}$, respectively, or the **horizontal** and **vertical components** of $\vec{u}$. (722)

composite, $f \circ g$ The function with the rule $(f \circ g)(x) = f(g(x))$, whose domain is the set of values of x in the domain of g for which $g(x)$ is in the domain of f. (154)

composition of functions The operation of first applying one function, then another. Denoted by the symbol $\circ$. (154)

conclusion q, in the conditional $p \Rightarrow q$. Also called *consequent*. (35)

conclusion of an argument See *argument*. (45)

conditional statement, $p \Rightarrow q$ A statement of the form *If p, then q.* Also read *p implies q.* $p \Rightarrow q$ is true except when p is true and q is false. (35)

congruence class For a given modulus, the set of numbers congruent to each other. (252)

Congruence Theorem $\forall$ integers a and b and positive integers m, $a \equiv b \pmod{m}$ if and only if m is a factor of $a - b$. (253)

congruent modulo m, $a \equiv b \pmod{m}$ a is congruent to b modulo m, denoted by $a \equiv b \pmod{m}$, if and only if a and b have the same integer remainder when they are divided by m (the **modulus** or **mod**). (252)

conjecture A statement believed to be true but not proved. (56)

Conjugate Zeros Theorem Let $p(x)$ be a polynomial with real coefficients. If $z = a + bi$ is a zero of $p(x)$, then its complex conjugate $\overline{z} = a - bi$ is also a zero of $p(x)$. (526)

connected graph A graph G such that $\forall$ vertices v and w in G, $\exists$ a walk from v to w. (681)

connected vertices Two vertices of a graph for which there is a walk from one to the other. (681)

consequent q, in the conditional $p \Rightarrow q$. Also called *conclusion.* (35)

constant difference See *arithmetic sequence.*

Constant Multiple Property of Integrals Theorem If f is a continuous function on the interval from a to b, and c is a real number, then $\int_a^b c\, f(x)\, dx = c \int_a^b f(x)\, dx$. (808)

constant polynomial A polynomial of degree 0, which has the form $p(x) = k \neq 0\ \forall\ x$. (225)

constant ratio See *geometric sequence.*

Continuous Change Model If a quantity grows or decays continuously at a periodic rate r, the amount $A(t)$ after t periods is given by $A(t) = Be^{rt}$ where $B = A(0)$. (120)

continuous function on an interval A function f on an interval $[a, b]$ such that the graph of $y = f(x)$ is an unbroken curve for values of x between a and b. (169)

contrapositive of $p \Rightarrow q$ $(\sim q) \Rightarrow (\sim p)$. (39)

Contrapositive Theorem A conditional and its contrapositive are logically equivalent. (39)

Convergence of Powers Theorem Let T be an $n \times n$ stochastic matrix with no zero entries. Then $\lim_{k\to\infty} T^k$ is a stochastic matrix with n identical rows. (695)

convergent series An infinite series whose sequence of partial sums has a finite limit. (439)

converse error An invalid argument of either of the following forms: (54)

Simple form	Universal form
If p then q.	*$\forall$x, if p(x) then q(x).*
q	*q(c), for a particular c.*
$\therefore$ p.	*$\therefore$ p(c).*

converse of $p \Rightarrow q$ $q \Rightarrow p$. (40)

convex polyhedron A polyhedron having the property that all points on the segment connecting any two points on the polyhedron lie on or in the interior of the polyhedron. (701)

cosecant of a real number x, csc x $\frac{1}{\sin x}$, $\forall\ x$ such that $\sin x \neq 0$. (322)

Cosine of a Difference Theorem For all real numbers α and β, $\cos(\alpha - \beta) = \cos \alpha \cos \beta + \sin \alpha \sin \beta$. (369)

cosine of a real number x, cos x The first coordinate of the image of (1, 0) under a rotation of magnitude x about the origin. (110)

Cosine of a Sum Theorem For all real numbers α and β, $\cos(\alpha + \beta) = \cos \alpha \cos \beta - \sin \alpha \sin \beta$. (367)

cotangent of a real number x, cot x $\frac{\cos x}{\sin x}$, $\forall\ x$ such that $\sin x \neq 0$. (322)

counterexample Given a universal statement $\forall$ *x in S, p(x)*, a value of x in S for which $p(x)$ is false. (9)

critical point A point at which the graph of a function changes from that of an increasing function to that of a decreasing function, or vice versa. (247)

cross product of three-dimensional vectors $\vec{u} = (u_1, u_2, u_3)$ and $\vec{v} = (v_1, v_2, v_3)$, $\vec{u} \times \vec{v}$ The vector $\vec{u} \times \vec{v} = (u_2v_3 - u_3v_2, u_3v_1 - u_1v_3, u_1v_2 - u_2v_1)$. (756)

crossing A place in a picture of a graph in which two edges seem to intersect not at their endpoints. (668)

current The rate of flow of electric charge through a circuit (measured in amps). (476)

deceleration Negative acceleration. (577)

decreasing function A function f such that $\forall\ x_1$ and x_2 in its domain, if $x_1 < x_2$ then $f(x_1) > f(x_2)$. (92)

definite integral of f from a to b The limit of upper and lower Riemann sums as the number of subintervals increases; denoted by $\int_a^b f(x)\, dx$. (800)

degree, ° A unit of measure of the magnitude of a rotation. 360 degrees is equivalent to one complete revolution. (109)

degree of a vertex, deg(v) The number of edges that have the vertex as an endpoint, with each edge that is a loop counted twice. (674)

DeMoivre's Theorem
Polar Form : For all positive integers n, if $z = [r, \theta]$, then $z^n = [r^n, n\theta]$.
Trigonometric Form : For all positive integers n, if $z = r(\cos \theta + i \sin \theta)$, then $z^n = r^n(\cos n\theta + i \sin n\theta)$. (508)

DeMorgan's Laws For all statements p and q,
1. $\sim$*(p and q)* $\equiv$ *($\sim$p) or ($\sim$q)*
2. $\sim$*(p or q)* $\equiv$ *($\sim$p) and ($\sim$q)*. (23)

dense One set is dense in another if there is an element of the first set as close as one wishes to every element of the second set. (538)

dependent variable The variable representing range values of a function. (78)

derivative function of f The function with the domain of f whose value at each point is the value of the derivative of f at that point. Denoted by f'. Also called *first derivative.* (570)

Derivative of a Constant Function Theorem If $\forall\ x$, $f(x) = k$, then $f'(x) = 0\ \forall\ x$. (572)

Derivative of a Linear Function Theorem If $f(x) = mx + b$, then $f'(x) = m$. (572)

Derivative of a Quadratic Function Theorem If $f(x) = ax^2 + bx + c$, where a, b, and c are real numbers and $a \neq 0$, then $f'(x) = 2ax + b$ for all real numbers x. (572)

derivative of a real function f at x Denoted by $f'(x)$ and given by $f'(x) = \lim_{\Delta x \to 0} \frac{f(x_1 + \Delta x) - f(x_1)}{\Delta x}$, provided this limit exists and is finite. (563)

difference equation For a sequence, an equation giving a general relation between the difference between one term of the sequence and the previous term. (124)

difference of two functions For two real-valued functions f and g with domain S, the function $f - g$ defined $\forall\ x$ in S by $(f - g)(x) = f(x) - g(x)$. (149)

GLOSSARY

difference of vectors, $\vec{u} - \vec{v}$ If $\vec{u} = (u_1, u_2)$ and $\vec{v} = (v_1, v_2)$, then $\vec{u} - \vec{v}$ is the vector $\vec{u} + (-\vec{v})$. (729)

difference quotient $\frac{f(x_1 + \Delta x) - f(x_1)}{\Delta x}$. (555)

differential calculus The study of rates of change in continuous functions. (551)

differential equation An equation involving functions and their derivatives. (589)

differentiation The process of finding derivatives of functions. (589)

digraph See *directed graph.*

direct proof A proof that proceeds directly from the antecedent (given) to the conclusion. (63)

directed graph A graph in which each edge has a direction. Also called *digraph.* (662)

direction of a vector The number θ in the polar representation $[r, \theta]$ of a vector. (721)

Discontinuity Theorem Given a rational function f with $f(x) = \frac{p(x)}{q(x)}$, where $p(x)$ and $q(x)$ are polynomials over the reals: if $\exists$ a real number c such that $q(c) = 0$ but $p(c) \neq 0$, then f has an essential discontinuity at $x = c$ and the line $x = c$ is a vertical asymptote to the graph of f. (304)

discrete dynamical system A set D together with a function f from D into itself that is repeatedly applied. (535)

discrete function A function whose domain is a discrete set. (82)

discrete set A set that can be put into 1-1 correspondence with a subset of the set of integers. (81)

Distance in Space Theorem The distance between $P = (x_1, y_1, z_1)$ and $Q = (x_2, y_2, z_2)$ is given by $PQ = \sqrt{(x_2 - x_1)^2 + (y_2 - y_1)^2 + (z_2 - z_1)^2}$. (749)

divergent series An infinite series whose sequence of partial sums does not have a finite limit. (439)

divisor See *factor.*

domain See *function.*

domain of an identity The set of all values of the variables for which both sides in an identity are defined. (285)

dot product of three-dimensional vectors $\vec{u} = (u_1, u_2, u_3)$ and $\vec{v} = (v_1, v_2, v_3)$, $\vec{u} \cdot \vec{v}$ The real number $\vec{u} \cdot \vec{v} = u_1v_1 + u_2v_2 + u_3v_3$. (753)

dot product of $\vec{u} = (u_1, u_2)$ and $\vec{v} = (v_1, v_2)$, $\vec{u} \cdot \vec{v}$ The real number $u_1v_1 + u_2v_2$. (741)

double-angle identities See *Identities for cos 2x Theorem* and *Identity for sin 2x Theorem.*

e The irrational number equal to $\lim_{x \to \infty} (1 + \frac{1}{x})^x$, which is approximately 2.71828 . . . . (119)

edge An arc on a graph. (658)

edge-endpoint function See *graph.*

efficiency of an algorithm The maximum number $E(n)$ of significant operations necessary for the algorithm to solve the given problem if it is of size n. (457)

elementary functions The basic functions from which more complicated functions may be defined, including polynomial, exponential, trigonometric, and logarithmic functions. (77)

end behavior A description of what happens to the values $f(x)$ of a function f as $x \to \infty$ and as $x \to -\infty$. (97)

End Behavior of Rational Functions Theorem Suppose $f(x) = \frac{a_mx^m + \cdots + a_1x + a_0}{b_nx^n + \ldots + b_1x + b_0}$ $\forall$ real numbers x for which the denominator is nonzero, where the a_i and b_i are real numbers $\forall$ i, $a_m \neq 0$, and $b_n \neq 0$. Then the end behavior of f is the same as the end behavior of the function g defined $\forall$ x by $g(x) = \frac{a_m}{b_n}x^{m-n}$. (311)

endpoint See *graph* and *interval.*

equality of complex numbers $a + bi = c + di$ if and only if $a = c$ and $b = d$. (474)

Equation for a Plane Theorem The set of points $\{(x, y, z): ax + by + cz = d\}$, where at least one of the coefficients a, b, or c is nonzero, is a plane perpendicular to the vector $\vec{v} = (a, b, c)$. (763)

Equation of a Sphere Theorem The sphere with center (a, b, c) and radius r has equation $r^2 = (x - a)^2 + (y - b)^2 + (z - c)^2$. (750)

Equations for a Line in 3-Space Theorem A point $Q = (x, y, z)$ is on the line ℓ through $P = (x_0, y_0, z_0)$ parallel to $\vec{v} = (v_1, v_2, v_3)$ if and only if there is a real number t such that

a. $\overrightarrow{PQ} = t\vec{v}$, or equivalently $(x - x_0, y - y_0, z - z_0) = t(v_1, v_2, v_3)$ (**vector equation for ℓ**) or

b. $\begin{cases} x = x_0 + tv_1 \\ y = y_0 + tv_2 \\ z = z_0 + tv_3 \end{cases}$

(**parametric equations for ℓ**). (761)

equivalent equations Two or more equations with the same solutions. (163)

equivalent graphs Two graphs for which there is a 1-1 correspondence between their vertices and edges under which the edge-endpoint function of one corresponds to the edge-endpoint function of the other. (659)

essential discontinuity A discontinuity that cannot be removed by insertion of a single point. (303)

essential features of a counting problem Whether order makes a difference in the objects to be counted, and whether or not the objects can be repeated. (602)

Euler circles See *Venn diagram.*

Euler circuit On a graph, a circuit that contains every edge and every vertex of the graph. (679)

Euler Circuit Theorem If a graph has an Euler circuit, then every vertex of the graph has even degree. (680)

Euler's formula Let G be a connected graph with no crossings, and let V, E, and F be the number of vertices, edges, and faces of G. Then $V - E + F = 2$. (703)

Evaluation of a Finite Geometric Series Theorem If a is any real number and r is any real number other than 1, then for all integers $n \geq 1$, $a + ar + ar^2 + \ldots + ar^{n-1} = a\left(\frac{1 - r^n}{1 - r}\right)$. (436)

Evaluation of an Infinite Geometric Series Theorem If a is any real number and r is a real number with $0 < |r| < 1$, then $\sum_{k=0}^{\infty} ar^k = \frac{a}{1 - r}$. (438)

even function A function such that $\forall$ x in its domain, $f(-x) = f(x)$. (101)

exclusive *or* One or the other but not both. (22)

existential statement A statement of the form *There exists x in S such that p(x)*, or, symbolically, $\exists$ *x in S such that p(x)*. (10)

expanded form of a polynomial A polynomial written in the form $p(x) = a_n x^n + a_{n-1}x^{n-1} + \ldots + a_1 x + a_0$. (225)

expanded form of a sum The form in which $\sum_{i=m}^{n} a_i$ is rewritten as $a_m + a_{m+1} + \ldots + a_n$. (413)

explicit formula for a sequence An equation which gives the nth term of a sequence in terms of n. (124)

exponential function with base *b* Any function defined by $f: x \to ab^x$, $\forall$ x, where the base b is a positive real number, $b \neq 1$, and a (the **initial value** of f) is a nonzero real number. (117)

exponential sequence See *geometric sequence.*

faces of a planar graph The regions of the plane into which the edges of the graph divide the plane. (701)

factor Given integers n and d with $d \neq 0$, d is a factor (or **divisor**) of n if and only if there is an integer q such that $n = q \cdot d$. (224)

Factor of a Polynomial Sum Theorem For all polynomials $a(x)$, $b(x)$, and $c(x)$, if $a(x)$ is a factor of $b(x)$ and $a(x)$ is a factor of $c(x)$, then $a(x)$ is a factor of $b(x) + c(x)$. (227)

Factor of an Integer Product Theorem For all integers m, n, and p, if m is a factor of n, then m is a factor of $n \cdot p$. (229)

Factor of an Integer Sum Theorem For all integers a, b, and c, if a is a factor of b and a is a factor of c, then a is a factor of $b + c$. (226)

Factor Search Theorem If an integer n has no prime factors between 1 and $\sqrt{n}$ inclusive, then n is prime. (267)

Factor Theorem For all polynomials $p(x)$, $x - c$ is a factor of $p(x)$ if and only if $p(c) = 0$; that is, if and only if c is a zero of $p(x)$. (244)

factored form of a polynomial A polynomial written as the product of two or more polynomials of lesser degree. (225)

Fibonacci numbers The integers 1, 2, 3, 5, 8, 13, 21, . . . , which are terms of the Fibonacci sequence. (125)

Fibonacci sequence The sequence defined by

$$\begin{cases} F_1 &= 1 \\ F_2 &= 1 \\ F_{n+1} &= F_n + F_{n-1} \text{ for all integers } n \geq \end{cases}$$

2.

(125, 410)

field of complex numbers The complex numbers together with the operations of addition and multiplication. (474)

field properties Addition and multiplication are closed, commutative, and associative. There is an identity for addition and a different identity for multiplication. Every number has an additive inverse and every number but the additive identity has a multiplicative inverse. Multiplication is distributive over addition. (474)

finite sequence A function whose domain is the interval of integers $[a, b]$. (124)

finite series The indicated sum of finitely many consecutive terms of a sequence. (435)

first derivative The derivative function or a value of that function. (578)

fixed point For a function f in a dynamical system, a value of x for which $f(x) = x$. (540)

force An influence that changes the velocity of an object. (727)

function A correspondence from a set A (the **domain**) to a set B in which each element in A corresponds to exactly one element of B. Also called *mapping.* (78)

Function Composition and Equality Property For any real functions f, g, and h, and values of x for which f, g, $h \circ f$, and $h \circ g$ are defined: If $f(x) = g(x)$, then $h(f(x)) = h(g(x))$. (164)

Function Inequality Theorem Suppose that f is a continuous real function. If f has zeros a and b and no zeros between a and b, then either $f(x) > 0$ for all x between a and b or $f(x) < 0$ for all x between a and b. (190)

functionally equivalent networks Two networks that produce the same output for each combination of input signals. (30)

fundamental period of a function The smallest positive number p such that $f(x + p) = f(x)$ for all x in the domain of f, if such a number exists. (113)

fundamental region See *tessellation.*

Fundamental Theorem of Algebra If $p(x)$ is any polynomial of degree $n \geq 1$, with real or complex coefficients, then $p(x)$ has at least one complex zero. (521)

Fundamental Theorem of Arithmetic Suppose that n is an integer and that $n > 1$. Then either n is a prime number or n has a prime factorization which is unique except for the order of the factors. (268)

Fundamental Theorem of Calculus Let f be a continuous function on the interval from a to b.

1. If g is a function whose derivative is f, then
$$\int_a^b f(x)\, dx = g(b) - g(a).$$
2. If $g(x) = \int_a^x f(t)\, dt$ for all x from a to b, then $g'(x) = f(x)$ for all such x. (827)

generating curve See *surface of revolution with axis ℓ.*

Geometric Addition Theorem Let $z = a + bi$ and $w = c + di$ be two complex numbers that are not collinear with (0, 0). Then the point representing $z + w$ is the fourth vertex of a parallelogram with consecutive vertices $z = a + bi$, 0, and $w = c + di$. (488)

GLOSSARY

Geometric Multiplication Theorem Let z and w be complex numbers. If $z = [r, \theta]$ and $w = [s, \phi]$, then $zw = [rs, \theta + \phi]$. That is, multiplying a complex number z by w applies to z the composite of a size change of magnitude s and a rotation of ϕ about the origin. (490)

Geometric *n*th Roots Theorem When graphed in the complex plane, the nth roots of any nonzero complex number z are the vertices of a regular n-gon whose center is at (0, 0). (515)

geometric sequence A sequence g in which $\forall\ n > 1$, $g_n = rg_{n-1}$, where r is a constant. That is, each term beyond the first is a constant r (the **constant ratio**) times the preceding term. Also called *exponential sequence*. (123)

geometric series The indicated sum of consecutive terms of a geometric sequence. (435)

Goldbach's conjecture A conjecture, originally made by Christian Goldbach in the middle of the 18th century, that every number greater than 2 can be written as the sum of two primes. (56)

graph A finite set of vertices, a finite set of edges, and a function (the **edge-endpoint function**) that maps each edge to a set of either one or two vertices (the **endpoints** of the edge). (666)

Graph Scale-Change Theorem In a relation described by a sentence in x and y, the following two processes yield the same graph: (1) replacing x by $\frac{x}{a}$ and y by $\frac{y}{b}$; (2) applying the scale change $S_{a,b}$: $(x, y) \to (ax, by)$ to the graph of the original relation. (196)

Graph-Standardization Theorem Suppose that G is the graph of a relation in x and y. Let h and k be any real numbers and let a and b be nonzero real numbers. Let G' be the image of G under the rubberband transformation T: $(x, y) \to (ax + h, by + k)$.
***x*-*y* form**: If G is described by a rule relating x and y, then a rule for G' is found by replacing x by $\frac{x-h}{a}$ and y by $\frac{y-k}{b}$.
parametric form:
If G is described by $\begin{cases} x = f(t) \\ y = g(t), \end{cases}$
then G' is described by $\begin{cases} x = af(t) + h \\ y = bg(t) + k. \end{cases}$ (198)

graph theory The study of graphs and their properties. (657)

Graph-Translation Theorem In a relation described by a sentence in x and y, the following two processes yield the same graph: (1) replacing x by $x - h$ and y by $y - k$; (2) applying the translation $T_{h,k}$: $(x, y) \to (x + h, y + k)$ to the graph of the original relation. (195)

half-adder A network of logic gates that takes two binary digits as input and produces the two digits of their sum as output. (261)

half-angle identities For all real numbers x, $\cos\left(\frac{x}{2}\right) = \pm\sqrt{\frac{\cos x + 1}{2}}$ or $\sin\left(\frac{x}{2}\right) = \pm\sqrt{\frac{1 - \cos x}{2}}$. (380)

half-open interval, (*a*, *b*] or [*a*, *b*) See *interval*.

handshake problem Suppose n people are at a party. If each person shakes hands with every other person, how many handshakes are required? (673)

hexadecimal See *base 16*.

horizontal asymptote A horizontal line to which the graph of a function gets closer and closer as $x \to \infty$ or as $x \to -\infty$. (97)

horizontal component of a vector See *component representation*.

hypothesis p, in the conditional $p \Rightarrow q$. Also called *antecedent*. (35)

Identities for cos 2*x* Theorem For all real numbers x; $\cos 2x = \cos^2 x - \sin^2 x = 2\cos^2 x - 1 = 1 - 2\sin^2 x$. (377)

identity An equation that is true for all values of the variables for which both sides are defined. (285)

Identity for sin 2*x* Theorem For all real numbers x, $\sin 2x = 2 \sin x \cos x$. (378)

identity function, *I* A function that maps each element of its domain onto itself. (157)

if and only if *p if and only if q* is denoted by $p \Leftrightarrow q$ and is equivalent to (*if p then q*) *and* (*if q then p*), or symbolically, $p \Rightarrow q$ *and* $q \Rightarrow p$. $p \Leftrightarrow q$ is true only when p and q are both true or both false. (40)

imaginary axis See *complex plane*.

imaginary number A number of the form bi, where b is a real number and i is the imaginary unit. (473)

imaginary part of a complex number See *complex number*.

imaginary unit, *i* The complex number $i = \sqrt{-1}$. (473)

impedance The opposition to the flow of current caused by components called resistors, coils, and capacitors (measured in ohms). (476)

implies See *conditional statement*.

improper induction Concluding a universal statement from instances of it. (55)

inclusive *or* One or the other or both. (21)

increasing function A function f such that $\forall\ x_1$ and x_2 in its domain, if $x_1 < x_2$ then $f(x_1) < f(x_2)$. (92)

independent variable A variable representing domain values of a function. (78)

index A subscript in summation notation. (413)

inductive assumption In mathematical induction, the assumption that $S(k)$ is true for an arbitrarily chosen integer $k \geq 1$. (419)

inductive step See *Principle of Mathematical Induction*.

infinite sequence A function whose domain is the interval of integers $[a, \infty)$. (124)

infinite series The indicated sum of the terms of an infinite sequence. (435)

infinite sum, $\sum_{k=1}^{\infty} a_k$ The limit of the partial sums of a sequence as $n \to \infty$, provided this limit exists and is finite. (437)

Infinitude of Primes Theorem There are infinitely many prime numbers. (267)

initial conditions See *recursive definition for a sequence*.

initial value of an exponential function The value of the exponential function f: $x \to ab^x$ when $x = 0$. (117)

input-output table A table indicating what the output will be from any possible combination of input signals. (28)

instantaneous acceleration The instantaneous rate of change of an object's velocity with respect to time. (577)

instantaneous rate of change of *f* at *x* The derivative of *f* at *x*. (564)

instantaneous velocity at time *x* The limit as $\Delta x \to 0$ of the average velocity of the object between times *x* and Δx, provided this limit exists and is finite. (561)

integer division Division where the result is expressed as an integer quotient and an integer remainder. (232)

integer quotient See *Quotient-Remainder Theorem for Integers.*

integer remainder See *Quotient-Remainder Theorem for Integers.*

Integral of a Quadratic Function Theorem If $a > 0$,

$$\int_0^a (c_2x^2 + c_1x + c_0)dx = c_2\frac{a^3}{3} + c_1\frac{a^2}{2} + c_0a.$$ (814)

intermediate points for a Riemann sum, z_i See *Riemann sum of a function f over the interval from a to b.* (793)

Intermediate Value Theorem Suppose that *f* is a continuous function on the interval [*a*, *b*]. Then for every real number y_0 between *f*(*a*) and *f*(*b*), there is at least one real number x_0 between *a* and *b* such that $f(x_0) = y_0$. (170)

interval The set of numbers between two given numbers, or greater than a number, or less than a number, possibly including the given numbers (the **endpoints**). (81)

invalid argument An argument or argument form for which there exist instances in which the premises are true and the conclusion is false. (53)

inverse A relation formed by reversing the ordered pairs of a given relation. (156)

inverse cosine (Arccos) function, $\cos^{-1}$ The function that maps *x* onto the number or angle *y* whose cosine is *x*, for $0 \le y \le \pi$. (386)

inverse error An invalid argument of either of the following forms: (55)

Simple form	Universal form
If p then q.	$\forall x$, *if p(x) then q(x).*
not p	*not p(c) for a particular c.*
$\therefore$ *not q.*	$\therefore$ *not q(c).*

inverse functions, $f = g^{-1}$ Two functions *f* and *g* such that $f \circ g(x) = x$ for all *x* in the domain of *g* and $g \circ f(x) = x$ for all *x* in the domain of *f*. (156)

inverse of $p \Rightarrow q$ $\sim p \Rightarrow \sim q$. (40)

inverse sine (Arcsin) function, $\sin^{-1}$ The function that maps *x* onto the number or angle *y* whose sine is *x*, for $-\frac{\pi}{2} \le y \le \frac{\pi}{2}$. (386)

inverse tangent (Arctan) function, $\tan^{-1}$ The function that maps *x* onto the number or angle *y* whose tangent is *x*, for $-\frac{\pi}{2} < y < \frac{\pi}{2}$. (386)

irrational conjugates The real numbers $c + \sqrt{d}$ and $c - \sqrt{d}$, where *c* and *d* are rational numbers and $\sqrt{d}$ is not a rational number. (319)

irrational number A real number that cannot be written as a ratio of two integers. (315)

isolated vertex A vertex of a graph that is not the endpoint of any edge. (667)

iterate To repeat a process over and over. (452)

iterative algorithm An algorithm in which the same steps are repeated again and again. (452)

justification A generalization, such as a postulate, definition, theorem, or law of logic, used in a proof. (61)

Königsberg bridge problem In the city of Königsberg (now Kaliningrad), two branches of the Pregol'a River come together. In the 1700s, parts of Königsberg were on the banks of the river, another part was on a large island in the middle, and a final part was between the two branches of the river. Seven bridges connected these four parts of the city. Is it possible for a person to walk around the city crossing each bridge exactly once, starting and ending at the same point? (657)

Law of Detachment, *modus ponens* A valid argument of either of the following forms: (46)

Simple form	Universal form
If p then q.	$\forall x$, *if p(x) then q(x).*
p	*p(c), for a particular c.*
$\therefore$ *q.*	$\therefore$ *q(c).*

Law of Indirect Reasoning, *modus tollens* A valid argument of either of the following forms: (48)

Simple form	Universal form
If p then q.	$\forall x$, *if p(x) then q(x).*
not q	*not q(c) for a particular c.*
$\therefore$ *not p.*	$\therefore$ *not p(c).*

Law of Substitution A law of logic that states that if a universal statement is true for all elements of a given set, then it is true for each element of that set. (7)

Law of Transitivity A valid argument of either of the following forms: (47)

Simple form	Universal form
If p then q.	$\forall x$, *if p(x) then q(x).*
If q then r.	$\forall x$, *if q(x) then r(x).*
$\therefore$ *If p then r.*	$\therefore \forall x$, *if p(x) then r(x).*

leaf See *rose curve.*

leaves The ends of the branches in a tree. (608)

length of a walk The number of edges in the walk. (687)

limaçon The polar graph of an equation of the form $r = a + b\cos\theta$ or $r = a + b\sin\theta$, where *a* and *b* are nonzero real numbers. (495)

limit of a function *f* as $x \to \infty$ or as $x \to -\infty$, $\lim_{x\to\infty} f(x)$ or $\lim_{x\to-\infty} f(x)$ The value that *f*(*x*) approaches as *x* gets larger and larger without bound, or smaller and smaller without bound. (97)

limit of a sequence, $\lim_{x\to\infty} s_n$ A number *L* such that, for any positive number *p*, there is an integer *N* such that $|s_n - L| < p$ for all $n \ge N$. (204)

limited growth model See *logistic model.*

$\lim_{x\to a^+} f(x)$ The limit of the function *f* as *x* approaches *a* from the right. (296)

$\lim_{x\to a^-} f(x)$ The limit of the function *f* as *x* approaches *a* from the left. (296)

GLOSSARY

logarithm function with base b The function $\log_b$ defined by the rule $x \to \log_b x$, for all positive real numbers x. (131)

Logarithm of a Power Theorem $\log_b (u^s) = s \log_b u$. (132)

Logarithm of a Product Theorem $\log_b (u \cdot v) = \log_b u + \log_b v$. (132)

Logarithm of a Quotient Theorem $\log_b \left(\frac{u}{v}\right) = \log_b u - \log_b v$. (132)

logarithm of x to the base b, $\log_b x$ The power to which the **base** b must be raised to equal x; that is, the number y such that $b^y = x$. (130)

logarithmic scale An ordinary measurement scale which has been transformed by a logarithmic function so that constant differences correspond to constant ratios in the untransformed scale. (138)

logarithmic spiral The polar graph of $r = ab^\theta$, where $a > 0$ and $b > 1$. (504)

logical expression A formula in which variables representing statements are combined in an unambiguous way with *and, or, not,* or *if-then.* (22)

logically equivalent expressions, $\equiv$ Two logical expressions with the same truth values for all substitutions of statements for their statement variables. (22)

logistic model A mathematical model of growth with a number which the growth cannot exceed. Also called a *limited growth model.* (127)

loop An edge of a graph whose endpoints are the same point. (666)

lower Riemann sum The Riemann sum of a function f where each $f(z_i)$ is the smallest value on the subinterval. (799)

lowest terms A fraction or rational expression in which the numerator and denominator have no common factor. (290)

magnitude of a vector The number r in the polar representation $[r, \theta]$ of a vector. (721)

main diagonal of a matrix For an $n \times n$ matrix, the diagonal consisting of all entries in the same row and the same column. (687)

mapping See *function.*

Markov chain Of a situation that can exist in only a finite number of states, when the probabilities of proceeding from one state to the next depend only on the first state. (44)

mathematical induction See *Principle of Mathematical Induction.*

mathematical proof A chain of logically valid deductions using agreed-upon assumptions, definitions, or previously proved statements. (61)

max-min problem A problem in which you need to find either the greatest or least value of a function. (86)

maximum value of a function f with domain S A number m such that $\exists$ x in S with $f(x) = m$ and $\forall$ x in S, $m \geq f(x)$. (88)

minimal spanning tree For a graph G in which each edge is labeled with a number, a spanning tree for G such that the sum of the labels on its edges has the smallest possible value. (707)

minimum value of a function f with domain S A number m such that $\exists$ x in S with $f(x) = m$ and $\forall$ x in S, $m \leq f(x)$. (88)

modulus See *absolute value of a complex number.*

modulus, mod See *congruent modulo m.*

modus ponens See *Law of Detachment.*

modus tollens See *Law of Indirect Reasoning.*

multinomial coefficient A coefficient in the series expansion of $(a_1 + a_2 + \ldots + a_k)^n$. (645)

multiple Given integers n and d with $d \neq 0$, n is a multiple of d if and only if d is a factor of n. (224)

Multiplication Counting Principle Suppose that strings result from a procedure which consists of k successive steps and that:

the 1st step can be done in n_1 ways,
the 2nd step can be done in n_2 ways,
⋮
and the kth step can be done in n_k ways.

Then there are $n_1 n_2 \cdot \ldots \cdot n_k$ possible strings. (609)

Multiplication Properties of Inequality For any real expressions $f(x)$ and $g(x)$, if $f(x) < g(x)$: then $f(x) \cdot c < g(x) \cdot c$ if $c > 0$; and $f(x) \cdot c > g(x) \cdot c$ if $c < 0$. (175)

Multiplication Property of Equality For any real expressions $f(x)$ and $g(x)$, if $f(x) = g(x)$, then $f(x) \cdot c = g(x) \cdot c$. (161)

multiplicity of a zero For a zero c of a polynomial $p(x)$ of degree at least 1, the largest positive integer m such that $(x - c)^m$ is a factor of $p(x)$. (521)

natural logarithm, ln A logarithm with base e. (133)

necessary condition "p is a necessary condition for q" means $q \Rightarrow p$. (42)

negation The statement, denoted **not p**, that, if true, exactly expresses what it would mean for p to be false. (14)

negation of $p \Rightarrow q$ *p and (not q).* (37)

negation of $\forall$ x in S, if $p(x)$ then $q(x)$ *$\exists$ x in S such that p(x) and not q(x).* (38)

network of logic gates NOT, AND, and OR gates connected in such a way that the output signals from some of the gates become input signals for other gates. (29)

Newton's Method A recursive method for obtaining zeros of a continuous function f by (1) finding the tangent line to the graph of the function at an initial point, (2) determining the x-intercept of this tangent line, and (3) finding the tangent line to the graph of the function for this new value of x. Steps (2) and (3) are then repeated until the zero of the function has been estimated to the desired degree of accuracy. (592)

node A vertex in a tree; corresponds to a step in which several choices or results are possible. (608)

nonreversible step A reasoning step in solving an equation or inequality whose converse is not true for some values of the variables for which the expressions in the equation are defined. (163)

norm of a vector The length of the vector; denoted by $|\vec{u}|$. (723)

NOT gate An input-output device for which the output signal is 0 if the input signal is 1, and the output signal is 1 if the input signal is 0. Schematically, the NOT gate is represented by [NOT gate symbol] (28)

not *p* See *negation.*

***n*th root** Of a complex number *w*, a number *z* such that $z^n = w$. (514)

***n*th term of a sequence** The value of the sequence corresponding to the domain value *n*. (124)

Number of Zeros of a Polynomial Theorem A polynomial of degree *n* has at most *n* zeros. (246)

***O*(*d*)** The orbit with initial point *d*. (535)

oblique asymptote An oblique line $y = mx + b$ which the graph of a function approaches as $x \to \infty$ or as $x \to -\infty$. (311)

octal See *base 8.*

odd function A function such that $\forall$ *x* in its domain, $f(-x) = -f(x)$. (101)

one-to-one function, 1-1 function A function *g* such that for all *u* and *v* in the domain of *g*, $g(u) = g(v) \Rightarrow u = v$. (157)

only if *p only if q* is equivalent to *if p then q*. (42)

open infinite interval, (*a*, ∞) or (-∞, *b*) The set of numbers greater than a given number (*a*), or the set of numbers less than a given number (*b*); $\{x: a < x\}$ or $\{x: x < b\}$. (81)

open interval, (*a*, *b*) The set of numbers greater than one number (*a*) and less than a second larger number (*b*); $\{x: a < x < b\}$. (81)

opposite of a vector, $-\vec{v}$ The vector with the same magnitude and direction opposite that of the given vector. (729)

optimization problem A problem in which the value of one variable is sought to obtain the most optimal, or desirable, value of another. (583)

OR gate An input-output device for which the output signal is 1 if one or both of the two input signals are 1. Otherwise, the output signal is 0. Schematically, the OR gate is represented by [OR gate symbol]. (28)

orbit with initial point *d* For a set *D* and a function $f: D \to D$ constituting a discrete dynamical system, the sequence $a_0, a_1, a_2, \ldots$ defined by

$$\begin{cases} a_0 = d \\ a_{k+1} = f(a_k) \text{ for integers } k \geq 0 \end{cases}$$

(585)

ordinate The second coordinate *b* of the ordered pair (*a, b*). (150)

orthogonal vectors Vectors whose directions are perpendicular. (743)

***P*(*n*, *r*), $_nP_r$** The number of permutations of *n* elements taken *r* at a time. (617)

***P*(*n*, *r*) Calculation Theorem** $P(n, r) = \frac{n!}{(n-r)!}$. (618)

parallel edges Two edges of a graph with both endpoints in common. (667)

parallel vectors Two vectors with the same or opposite directions. (733)

parameter An independent variable on which other variables (usually coordinates) depend. (103)

parametric equations A set of equations in which, in each equation, a different variable is expressed in terms of the same parameter. (103)

parametric form of an equation for a line A line through (x_0, y_0) that is parallel to the vector $\vec{v} = (v_1, v_2)$ has parametric equations $\begin{cases} x = x_0 + tv_1 \\ y = y_0 + tv_2 \end{cases}$ where *t* may be any real number. (735)

partial sum The sum of the first *n* terms of a sequence. (437)

Pascal's triangle A triangular array of binomial coefficients (equivalently, combinations) in which the *r*th element in row *n* is the sum of the $(r-1)$st and *r*th elements in row $n - 1$. (628)

	Row
1	0
1 1	1
1 2 1	2
1 3 3 1	3
1 4 6 4 1	4
1 5 10 10 5 1	5
⋮	⋮

path A walk from one vertex to another in which no edge is repeated. (679)

perfect number A positive integer that is equal to the sum of its proper divisors. (230)

period of a function Any positive number *p* such that $f(x + p) = f(x)$ for all *x* in the domain of *f*. (113)

periodic function A real function *f* with the property that there is a positive number *p* such that $f(x + p) = f(x)$ for all *x* in the domain of *f*. (113)

permutation A string of all of the symbols $a_1, a_2, \ldots, a_n$ without repetition. (615)

permutation of *n* elements of the set *S* taken *r* at a time A string of *r* elements from *S* without repetition. (617)

Permutation Theorem There are *n*! permutations of *n* different elements. (616)

petal See *rose curve.*

phase shift The least positive or the greatest negative horizontal translation that maps $y = \cos x$ or $y = \sin x$ onto its translation image. (Previous course)

plane vector See *two-dimensional vector.*

polar axis A ray, usually horizontal and drawn to the right, through the pole of a polar coordinate system, from which rotations are measured. (480)

GLOSSARY

polar coordinate system A system in which a point is identified by a pair of numbers $[r, \theta]$, where $|r|$ is the distance of the point from a fixed point (the **pole**), and θ is a magnitude of rotation from the polar axis. (480)

polar coordinates, $[r, \theta]$ Description of a point in a polar coordinate system. (480)

polar form of a complex number The representation of the number in polar coordinates. (489)

polar grid A background of circles and rays emanating from the pole, of use in sketching graphs in a polar coordinate system. (482)

polar representation of a vector The representation of a two-dimensional vector with positive **magnitude** r and **direction** θ by the polar coordinates $[r, \theta]$. (721)

Polar-Rectangular Conversion Theorem If $[r, \theta]$ is a polar coordinate representation of a point P, then the rectangular coordinates (x, y) of P are given by $x = r\cos\theta$ and $y = r\sin\theta$. (483)

pole See *polar coordinate system.*

polynomial division Division of polynomials, analogous to integer division, where the result is expressed in terms of a quotient polynomial and a remainder polynomial. (234)

polynomial of degree *n* A function P for which there are numbers $a_0, a_1, \ldots, a_n$, with $a_n \neq 0$, such that $P(x) = a_nx^n + a_{n-1}x^{n-1} + \ldots + ax + a_0$ for all x in the domain of P. (224)

possibility tree A diagram used to display the possible outcomes of an experiment. (608)

power function A function with an equation of the form $y = ax^n$. (99)

premises See *argument.*

prime An integer $n > 1$ whose only positive integer factors are 1 and n. (265)

Prime Factor Theorem Every integer greater than 1 is either prime or has a prime factor. (265)

prime factorization A representation of a number as a product of primes. (268)

prime over the real numbers A polynomial $p(x)$ of degree ≥ 1 whose only factors with real coefficients and leading coefficient 1 are constants or constant multiples of $p(x)$. (269)

Principle of Mathematical Induction Suppose that for each positive integer n, $S(n)$ is a sentence in n. If

(1) $S(1)$ is true (the **basis step**), and

(2) for all integers $k \geq 1$, $S(k)$ is true $\Rightarrow S(k + 1)$ is true (the **inductive step**), then $S(n)$ is true for all positive integers n. (418)

Principle of Strong Mathematical Induction Suppose that for each positive integer n, $S(n)$ is a sentence in n. If

(1) $S(1)$ is true, and

(2) for all integers $k \geq 1$, the assumption that $S(1), S(2), \ldots, S(k - 1), S(k)$ are all true implies that $S(k + 1)$ is also true, then $S(n)$ is true for all integers $n \geq 1$. (442)

probability tree A digraph in which each vertex represents an event, and the edge leading from vertex A to vertex B is labeled with the probability that event B occurs if A occurs. (662)

product of two functions For two real-valued functions f and g with domain S, the function $f \cdot g$ defined $\forall$ x in S by $(f \cdot g)(x) = f(x) \cdot g(x)$. (149)

proof by contradiction A proof in which, if s is the statement to be proved, one reasons from *not s* until a contradiction is deduced; from this it is concluded that *not s* is false, which means that s is true. (266)

Properties of Congruence (modular arithmetic) Let a, b, c, and d be any integers and let m be a positive integer. If $a \equiv b \pmod{m}$ and $c \equiv d \pmod{m}$, then

$a + c \equiv b + d \pmod{m}$ (Addition Property of Congruence)

$a - c \equiv b - d \pmod{m}$ (Subtraction Property of Congruence)

and $ac \equiv bd \pmod{m}$ (Multiplication Property of Congruence). (254)

Pythagorean Identity For all θ, $\cos^2\theta + \sin^2\theta = 1$. (113)

quantifier A phrase such as "for all" ($\forall$) or "there exists" ($\exists$) that is used to prefix a logical or mathematical sentence. (6)

Quicksort A particular recursive sorting algorithm whereby terms are divided into three sets and those sets are then sorted. (452)

Quicksort Theorem For each integer $n \geq 0$, the Quicksort Algorithm arranges any list of n distinct real numbers in increasing order. (454)

quotient The answer to a division problem. For integers n and d with $d \neq 0$, an integer q such that $n = q \cdot d$. (224)

quotient of two functions For two real-valued functions f and g with domain S, the function $\frac{f}{g}$ defined $\forall$ x in S by $\left(\frac{f}{g}\right)(x) = \frac{f(x)}{g(x)}$, provided $g(x) \neq 0$. (149)

Quotient-Remainder Theorem for Integers If n is an integer and d is a positive integer, then there exist unique integers q (the **integer quotient**) and r (the **integer remainder**) such that $n = q \cdot d + r$ and $0 \leq r < d$. (232)

Quotient-Remainder Theorem for Polynomials If $p(x)$ is a polynomial and $d(x)$ is a nonzero polynomial, then there exist unique polynomials $q(x)$ (the **quotient**) and $r(x)$ (the **remainder**) such that $p(x) = q(x) \cdot d(x) + r(x)$ and either degree of $r(x) <$ degree of $d(x)$ or $r(x) = 0$. (234)

radian A unit of measure of the magnitude of a rotation. 2π radians is equivalent to one revolution. (109)

range The set of possible values of the dependent variable of a function. Symbolically, for a function $f: A \to B$, the set of all elements y in B such that $\exists$ x in A with $f(x) = y$. (78)

rational equation An equation of the form $f(x) = g(x)$ where $f(x)$ and $g(x)$ are rational expressions. (329)

rational expression An algebraic expression of the form $\frac{p(x)}{q(x)}$, where $p(x)$ and $q(x)$ are polynomials with $q(x)$ not the zero polynomial. (289)

rational expression division Division of polynomials, analogous to rational division, where the result is expressed as a single rational expression. (234)

rational function A function f such that for all values of x in the domain of f, $f(x) = \frac{p(x)}{q(x)}$, where $p(x)$ and $q(x)$ are polynomials. (302)

rational number A real number such that there exist integers a and b ($b \neq 0$) such that $r = \frac{a}{b}$. (284)

rational number division Division where the quotient is expressed as a single rational number. (231)

Rational Zero Theorem Suppose that p is a polynomial function of degree n with integer coefficients: $p(x) = a_nx^n + a_{n-1}x^{n-1} + \ldots + a_1x + a_0$, with $a_0 \neq 0$. If $r = \frac{m}{k}$ is a rational number in lowest terms that is a zero of p, then m is a factor of the constant coefficient a_0 and k is a factor of the leading coefficient a_n. (341)

rationalizing the denominator Multiplying the numerator and the denominator of a fraction by the irrational conjugate of the fraction's denominator in order to remove the square root from the denominator. (319)

real axis See *complex plane*.

real function A function whose independent and dependent variables have only real number values. (80)

real part of a complex number See *complex number*.

real-valued function A function whose range is a set of real numbers. (80)

recurrence relation See *recursive definition for a sequence*.

Recursion Principle Suppose that a recurrence relation defines a unique value of S_{n+1} in terms of S_n and n for all integers $n \geq 1$. Then there is exactly one sequence S satisfying this recurrence relation and the initial condition $S_1 = k$. (406)

recursive algorithm An algorithm that refers back to a smaller version of itself. (452)

recursive definition for a sequence A definition of a sequence consisting of one or more initial terms of the sequence (the **initial conditions**) and an equation that relates each of the other terms of the sequence to one or more of the previous terms (a **recurrence relation** or **difference equation**). (406)

recursive formula A formula for a sequence in which the first term or first few terms are given, and the nth term is expressed in terms of the preceding term(s). (124)

regular polygon A convex polygon whose sides are all the same length and whose angles are all the same measure. (334)

regular polyhedron (plural *polyhedra*) A convex polyhedron whose faces are all congruent regular polygons. (336)

relative maximum value for a function *f* with domain *S* A number m such that $\exists\ x$ in S with $f(x) = m$ and f is $\geq m$ on some open interval containing x. (93)

relative minimum value for a function *f* with domain *S* A number m such that $\exists\ x$ in S with $f(x) = m$ and f is $\leq m$ on some open interval containing x. (93)

remainder See *Quotient-Remainder Theorem for Integers* or *Quotient-Remainder Theorem for Polynomials*.

Remainder Theorem If a polynomial $p(x)$ of degree ≥ 1 is divided by $x - c$, then the remainder is the constant $p(c)$. That is, $p(x) = q(x)(x - c) + p(c)$. (240)

removable discontinuity at *x* For a function f, the existence of a hole in the graph of f at x such that it is possible to redefine f at x in a way that removes that hole. (303)

resultant force The combined effect of two or more forces. (728)

reversible step A reasoning step in solving an equation or inequality whose converse is true for all values of the variables for which the expressions in the equation are defined. (163)

Reversible Steps Theorem Let $f(x)$ and $g(x)$ be any real expressions. Then for all real expressions c and real functions h,
(1) $f(x) = g(x) \Leftrightarrow f(x) + c = g(x) + c$.
(2) $f(x) = g(x) \Leftrightarrow f(x) \cdot c = g(x) \cdot c$, provided $c \neq 0$.
(3) $f(x) = g(x) \Leftrightarrow h(f(x)) = h(g(x))$, provided h^{-1} exists. (165)

Reversible Steps Theorem for Inequalities For any real expressions $f(x)$, $g(x)$ and real function h, $f(x) < g(x) \Leftrightarrow h(f(x)) < h(g(x))$ if h is an increasing function, and $f(x) < g(x) \Leftrightarrow h(f(x)) > h(g(x))$ if h is a decreasing function. (179)

Riemann sum of a function *f* over the interval from *a* to *b* The sum $f(z_1)(x_1 - a) + f(z_2)(x_2 - x_1) + f(z_3)(x_3 - x_2) + \ldots + f(z_n)(b - x_{n-1})$, where f is a function defined over the interval from a to b and the interval is partitioned into n subintervals: the first from a to x_1, the second from x_1 to x_2, the third from x_2 to x_3, . . . , the nth from x_{n-1} to b and each z_i (the **intermediate points**) is a value in the ith subinterval. Letting $x_0 = a$ and $x_n = b$, this Riemann sum can be written as $\sum_{i=1}^{n} f(z_i)(x_i - x_{i-1})$. (793)

Ringel's Conjecture Consider any connected graph which has no circuits and all of whose vertices have degree 1 or 3. Let n be the number of edges in the graph. Then the edges of the graph can be numbered from 1 to n in such a way that the sum of the numbers on the edges leading into any vertex of degree 3 is a constant. (707)

rose curve The polar graphs of equations of the form

$r = a \cos (n\theta)$, $a > 0$, n a positive integer
or
$r = a \sin (n\theta)$, $a > 0$, n a positive integer.

Each loop of a rose curve is called a **leaf** or **petal**. (502)

rubberband transformation A transformation that is the composite of scale changes and translations. (196)

Russell's Paradox A self-contradictory statement that can arise in set theory when sets are allowed to include themselves as elements. (67)

GLOSSARY

scalar A real number (used in conjunction with vectors, matrices, and transformations). (733)

scalar multiple of a three-dimensional vector $\vec{u} = (u_1, u_2, u_3)$ by a real number k The vector $k\vec{u} = (ku_1, ku_2, ku_3)$. (753)

scalar multiplication The operation of multiplying a vector $\vec{v} = (v_1, v_2)$ by a real number k (the **scalar**) resulting in a **scalar multiple** $k \cdot \vec{v} = (kv_1, kv_2)$ of the original vector. (733)

secant line for the graph of a function A line passing through two distinct points on the graph of a continuous function. (553)

secant line to a circle A line that intersects the circle at two distinct points. (553)

Secant Method A method for obtaining zeros of a continuous function by splitting into successive intervals an interval which has the property that its endpoints produce function values with opposite signs. A zero will be between two such endpoints. At each step, the subinterval with this same property is split into two parts by the x-intercept of the secant line joining the two points on the graph of the function determined by the endpoints of the subinterval. By continuing to subdivide, the zero can be estimated to any degree of accuracy desired. (213)

secant of a real number x, sec x $\frac{1}{\cos x}$, $\forall$ x such that $\cos x \neq 0$. (322)

second derivative The derivative function of a derivative function. (578)

sequence A function whose domain is the set of integers greater than or equal to a fixed integer. (124)

series The indicated sum of consecutive terms of a sequence. (435)

set An unordered list of symbols with no repetitions. (604)

significant operations The number of major operations needed in a problem. (457)

simple graph A graph with no loops and no parallel edges. (668)

simple zero Of a polynomial, a zero that has multiplicity 1. (521)

Simpson's Paradox A situation in which the averages of data sets $A_1, A_2, \ldots, A_n$ are each greater than the averages of corresponding data sets $B_1, B_2, \ldots, B_n$, yet the overall average of the B data sets is greater than the overall average of the A data sets. (341)

Sine of a Difference Theorem For all real numbers α and β, $\sin(\alpha - \beta) = \sin\alpha\cos\beta - \cos\alpha\sin\beta$. (373)

sine of a real number x, sin x The second coordinate of the image of (1, 0) under a rotation of magnitude x about the origin. (110)

Sine of a Sum Theorem For all real numbers α and β, $\sin(\alpha + \beta) = \sin\alpha\cos\beta + \cos\alpha\sin\beta$. (372)

sinusoidal curve The image of the graph of a sine or cosine function under a rubberband transformation. (363)

size of a problem The number of operations needed to do a problem, or an estimate of that number. (457)

solid of revolution with axis ℓ The three-dimensional solid that results when a generating region is rotated around a given axis ℓ. (819)

solving the difference equation The process of developing an explicit formula for a sequence from a difference equation for that sequence. (127)

sorting algorithm An algorithm whose purpose is to arrange or sort a given list of items in some desired order. (450)

spanning tree Given a connected graph G, a tree consisting of a subset of the edges of G but all of the vertices of G. (707)

spiral of Archimedes The polar graphs of $r = a\theta + b$, where a is positive and b is nonnegative. (503)

standard normal distribution A distribution described by a bell-shaped curve whose equation is $y = \frac{1}{\sqrt{2\pi}}e^{-x^2/2}$. (122)

standard position An arrow for a vector whose initial point is at the origin or pole of the coordinate system. (721)

standard prime factorization The prime factorization of an integer $n > 1$ in which all like factors are combined using exponents, and the prime factors are arranged in increasing order of magnitude. (268)

statement A sentence that is either true or false and not both. (6)

stochastic matrix A matrix in which each element is nonnegative, and the entries in each row add to 1. (694)

string An ordered list of symbols. (603)

Structure of a Direct Proof of a Universal Conditional Express the statement to be proved in the form $\forall$ *x in S, if p(x) then q(x)*. Start the proof by assuming the antecedent $p(x)$. Use the Law of Detachment, the definitions of the terms that appear in $p(x)$, and known properties to make a chain of deductions ending in $q(x)$. Use the Law of Transitivity to conclude the universal conditional. (63)

sufficient condition "p is a sufficient condition for q" means $p \Rightarrow q$. (42)

Sufficient Condition for an Euler Circuit Theorem If a graph G is connected and every vertex of G has even degree, then G has an Euler circuit. (682)

Sum of Binomial Coefficients Theorem $\forall$ integers $n \geq 0$, $\binom{n}{0} + \binom{n}{1} + \binom{n}{2} + \cdots + \binom{n}{k} + \cdots + \binom{n}{n} = \sum_{k=0}^{n}\binom{n}{k} = 2^n$. (633)

Sum of the First n Powers Theorem If $r \neq 1$, then $1 + r + r^2 + \ldots + r^{n-1} = \frac{1 - r^n}{1 - r}$ $\forall$ integers $n \geq 1$. (435)

sum of three-dimensional vectors $\vec{u} = (u_1, u_2, u_3)$ and $\vec{v} = (v_1, v_2, v_3)$ The vector $\vec{u} + \vec{v} = (u_1 + v_1, u_2 + v_2, u_3 + v_3)$. (753)

sum of two functions For two real-valued functions f and g with domain S, the function $f + g$ defined $\forall$ x in S by $(f + g)(x) = f(x) + g(x)$. (149)

sum of two vectors, $\vec{u} + \vec{v}$ If $\vec{u} = (u_1, u_2)$ and $\vec{v} = (v_1, v_2)$, then $\vec{u} + \vec{v}$ is the vector $(u_1 + v_1, u_2 + v_2)$. (727)

Sum Property of Integrals Theorem If f and g are continuous functions on the interval from a to b, then $\int_a^b (f(x) + g(x))dx = \int_a^b f(x)\,dx + \int_a^b g(x)\,dx$. (808)

summation notation, $\sum_{i=m}^{n}$ Suppose m and n are integers with $m < n$. Then $\sum_{i=m}^{n} a_i = a_m + a_{m+1} + \ldots + a_n$. (413)

surface of revolution with axis ℓ The surface that results when a curve (the **generating curve**) is rotated around a given axis ℓ. (819)

symmetric matrix A matrix whose element in row i, column j equals its element in row j, column i $\forall$ i, j. (688)

tangent line to the graph of a function at the point $(x, f(x))$ A line that intersects the graph of a function at $(x, f(x))$ and whose slope equals $\lim_{\Delta x \to 0} \frac{f(x_1 + \Delta x) - f(x_1)}{\Delta x}$. (561)

Tangent of a Difference Theorem For all real numbers α and β such that $\tan \alpha$, $\tan \beta$, and $\tan(\alpha - \beta)$ are defined, $\tan(\alpha - \beta) = \frac{\tan \alpha - \tan \beta}{1 + \tan \alpha \tan \beta}$. (373)

tangent of a real number x, $\tan x$ $\frac{\sin x}{\cos x}$ $\forall$ x such that $\cos x \neq 0$. (111, 322)

Tangent of a Sum Theorem For all real numbers α and β such that $\tan \alpha$, $\tan \beta$, and $\tan(\alpha + \beta)$ are defined, $\tan(\alpha + \beta) = \frac{\tan \alpha + \tan \beta}{1 - \tan \alpha \tan \beta}$. (373)

terminating decimal A number of the form $a_n 10^n + \ldots + a_1 10 + a_0 + a_{-1}10^{-1} + a_{-2}10^{-2} + \ldots + a_{-m}10^{-m}$, where all the a_i are digits from 0 to 9. (317)

tessellation A covering of the plane with congruent copies of the same region (the **fundamental region**), with no holes and no overlaps. (334)

Test-Point Method for Solving Inequalities A method for solving inequalities in which the real line is split into intervals by the zeros of an appropriate function, a value is chosen in each of these intervals, and the interval is part of the solution to the inequality if and only if the value satisfies the inequality. (190)

three-dimensional space, 3-space A space in which three numbers are needed to determine the position of a point. (753)

total degree of a graph The sum of the degrees of all the vertices of the graph. (674)

Total Degree of a Graph Theorem The total degree of any graph equals twice the number of edges in the graph. (674)

transition probability A probability that one event will be followed by another. (694)

Transitive Property of Integer Factors Theorem For all integers a, b, and c, if a is a factor of b and b is a factor of c, then a is a factor of c. (226)

Transitive Property of Polynomial Factors Theorem For all polynomials $a(x)$, $b(x)$, and $c(x)$, if $a(x)$ is a factor of $b(x)$ and $b(x)$ is a factor of $c(x)$, then $a(x)$ is a factor of $c(x)$. (227)

Traveling Salesman problem Given a graph in which each edge is associated with a number, the problem of finding a route through all the vertices that minimizes the total length of the edges. (708)

tree A connected graph that has no circuits. (707)

trial A probabilistic situation that is repeated in an experiment. (635)

trigonometric form of a complex number The form $r(\cos \theta + i \sin \theta)$ of the complex number $[r, \theta]$. (489)

truth table A table that gives the truth values for a logical expression for all possible truth values of the statements in that expression. (14)

two-dimensional vector A vector that can be characterized by two numbers. (721)

Unique Factorization Theorem for Polynomials Suppose that $p(x)$ is a polynomial. Then either $p(x)$ is prime over the real numbers or $p(x)$ has a factorization into polynomials prime over the reals which is unique except for the order of the factors or multiplications by constants. (269)

unit circle The circle with center (0, 0) and radius 1. (109)

unit fraction A fraction of the form $\frac{1}{n}$, where n is a positive integer. (334)

unit vector A vector whose length is 1. (724)

universal statement A statement asserting that a certain property holds for all elements in some set. A statement of the form *For all x in S, p(x), or, symbolically,* $\forall$ *x in S, p(x).* (7)

upper Riemann sum The Riemann sum of a function f where each $f(z_i)$ is the largest value of the function on the subinterval. (799)

valid argument An argument with the property that no matter what conditions are substituted in place of $p(x)$ and $q(x)$ in the premises, if the premises are both true, then the conclusion is true. (45)

valid conclusion The conclusion of a valid argument. (45)

vector A quantity that can be characterized by its direction and its magnitude. (720)

vector equation for a line The set of all points Q on the line through P parallel to $\vec{v}$ is given by the equation $\overrightarrow{PQ} = t\vec{v}$, or equivalently, $(x - x_0, y - y_0) = t(v_1, v_2)$ for some real number t. (735)

Venn diagram A graph that employs circles (sometimes called **Euler circles**) or closed curves to represent relations among sets in a logical argument. (60)

vertex A point on a graph. Also called *node*. (658)

Vertex of a Parabola Theorem Let a, b, and c be real numbers with $a \neq 0$. Then the parabola that is the graph of $f(x) = ax^2 + bx + c$ has its vertex at the point where $x = -\frac{b}{2a}$. (582)

vertical asymptote A vertical line $x = a$ which the graph of a function approaches as x approaches a either from the right or from the left. (296)

vertical component of a vector See *component representation*.

voltage The electrical potential between two points in a circuit (measured in volts). (476)

GLOSSARY

walk An alternating sequence of adjacent vertices and edges from one vertex of a graph to another. (679)

***x*-component of a vector** See *component representation.*

***xy*-plane** The set of points in 3-space for which the z-coordinate is 0; it has the equation $z = 0$. (748)

***xz*-plane** The set of points in 3-space for which the y-coordinate is 0; it has the equation $y = 0$. (748)

***y*-component of a vector** See *component representation.*

***yz*-plane** The set of points in 3-space for which the x-coordinate is 0; it has the equation $x = 0$. (748)

Zeno's Paradox A paradox dealing with the impossibility of adding up an infinite number of quantities to achieve a finite sum. (413)

zero function The function defined by $p(x) = 0 \; \forall \; x$. (225)

zero of a polynomial For a given polynomial $p(x)$, a number c such that $p(c) = 0$. (244)

zero vector The vector with same initial point and endpoint; denoted by $\vec{0}$. (724)

Zero-Product Property Let f, g, and h be functions. If there exists c such that $h(c) = 0$ and $h = f \cdot g$, then either $f(c) = 0$ or $g(c) = 0$. (161)

MATHEMATICAL SYMBOLS

Algebra

$\approx$	is approximately equal to
$\pm$	positive or negative
e	the base of the natural logarithms $\approx 2.71828\ldots$
π	pi
∞	infinity
!	factorial
$\lvert x \rvert$	absolute value of x
$\sqrt{x}$	positive square root of x
$\sqrt[n]{x}$	nth root of x
$a + bi$	complex number
(a, b)	rectangular coordinates; rectangular form of a complex number
$[r, \theta]$	polar coordinates; polar form of a complex number
$r(\cos\theta + i\sin\theta)$	trigonometric form of a complex number
$\bar{z}$	complex conjugate of a complex number
$\lvert z \rvert$	modulus of a complex number
i	imaginary unit, $\sqrt{-1}$
$\aleph_0$	the cardinality of a countably infinite set
c	the cardinality of an uncountable set

Logic

$\Rightarrow$	if-then (conditional)
$\Leftrightarrow$	if and only if (biconditional)
$\forall$	for all
$\exists$	there exists
$\sim$	negation
$\equiv$	logically equivalent
$\therefore$	therefore

Coordinates and Vectors

(x, y)	ordered pair
(x, y, z)	ordered triple
$[r, \theta]$	polar coordinate
$\overrightarrow{AB}$ or $\vec{v}$ or v	vector
(v_1, v_2)	component representation of vector
$[r, \theta]$	polar representation of vector
$k\vec{v}$	scalar k times vector
$\lvert\vec{v}\rvert$	length of vector
$\vec{0}$	zero vector
$\vec{u} \cdot \vec{v}$	dot product of vectors
$\vec{u} \times \vec{v}$	cross product of vectors

Geometry

$\overleftrightarrow{AB}$	line through A and B
$\overrightarrow{AB}$	ray from A passing through B
$\overline{AB}$	segment with endpoints A and B
AB	distance from A to B
$\angle ABC$	angle ABC
$m\angle ABC$	measure of angle ABC
$\triangle ABC$	triangle with vertices A, B, and C
$ABCD$	polygon with vertices A, B, C, and D
//	is parallel to
$\cong$	is congruent to
$\sim$	is similar to
$T_{h,k}$	translation of h units horizontally and k units vertically
$S_{a,b}$	scale change with horizontal magnitude a and vertical magnitude b

Functions and Sequences

$\lim\limits_{n\to\infty} a_n$	limit of sequence a as n approaches infinity
a_n	nth term of sequence a
$\sum\limits_{i=1}^{n} x_i$	summation notation; the sum $x_1 + x_2 + \ldots + x_n$
S_∞	sum of the infinite series S
$\log x$	common logarithm of x
$\log_b x$	logarithm of x to the base b
$\ln x$	natural logarithm of x
$\lfloor x \rfloor$	greatest integer function of x, or floor function of x
$\lceil x \rceil$	ceiling function of x
f^{-1}	inverse function of f
$f \circ g$	composite of functions f and g
$x \to \infty$	x approaches infinity
$x \to a^-$	x approaches a from the left
$x \to a^+$	x approaches a from the right
$\lim\limits_{x\to a} f(x)$	limit of function f as x approaches a
f'	first derivative of f
f''	second derivative of f
Δ	delta x, change in x
$\int_a^b f(x)\,dx$	definite integral of f from a to b

Combinatorics and Graphs

$P(n, r)$	permutations of n elements taken r at a time
${}_nP_r$	number of permutations of n elements taken r at a time
$C(n, r)$	combinations of n elements taken r at a time
${}_nC_r$ or $\binom{n}{r}$	number of combinations of n elements taken r at a time
$\deg(v)$	degree of vertex v
e_i	the ith edge of a graph
v_i	the ith vertex of a graph
K_n	complete graph with n vertices
mod	modulo
$\equiv$	modular congruence
Rn	modulo class n

Acknowledgments

Unless otherwise acknowledged, all photographs are the property of Addison Wesley Educational Publishers, Inc. Page abbreviations are as follows: (t) top, (c) center, (b) bottom, (l) left, (r) right.

ix Nick Dolding/Tony Stone Images **vi(r)** Dwight Kuhn **vii(r)** Carl Vanderschuitt/FPG International Corp. **vii(l)** Superstock, Inc. **viii** D. & J. Heaton/Westlight **x** Bruce Hands/Tony Stone Images **4(b)** Superstock, Inc. **4(c)** Superstock, Inc. **4(tr)** Brandon D. Cole/ENP Images **4(tl)** Superstock, Inc. **5(b)** Superstock, Inc. **6** © Edgerton Foundation, 1997, courtesy of Palm Press, Inc. **11** Simon Milliken **15** Tony Freeman/PhotoEdit **18** Alinari/Art Resource **20(t)** Tony Freeman/PhotoEdit **21** W. Metzen/H. Armstrong Roberts, Inc. **23** Rare Books and Manuscript Library/Columbia University **25** Library of Congress **28** Pete Saloutos/Stock Market **31** Library of Congress **35** Everett Collection, Inc. **41** Richard Martin/Agence Vandystadt **42** NASA **44** Frank Herholdt/Tony Stone Images **48** Library of Congress **53** Novastock/Photo Researchers **57** James D. Watt/Animals Animals **58** Jan Kanter **60** National Portrait Gallery, Washington, D.C./Art Resource **61** Carl Corey/Westlight **64** Randy Well/Tony Stone Images **67(b)** Drawings by John Tenniel **67(t)** Sidney Harris **69(b)** Stephen Dunn/Allsport **69(t)** Stouffer Enterprises, Inc./Animals Animals **70** Adrienne T. Gibson/Earth Scenes **71** NASA **74** Doug Pencincer/Allsport **76** Paul & Lindamarie Ambrose/FPG International Corp. **76(b)** David Lorenz Winston/ENP Images **76(cr)** Dwight Kuhn **76(t)** Glen Allison/Tony Stone Images **77(b)** De Wys/IFA/Leo de Wys, Inc. **78** Orion Press/Westlight **81** Thomas Porett/Photo Researchers **86** Mike Powell/Allsport **92** Texas Collection, Baylor University, Waco, Texas **93** A. & L. Sinibaldi/Tony Stone Images **96** W. Geiersperger/Stock Market **100** Jonathan Daniel/Allsport **102** Center for Image Processing in Education **104** David Leah/Allsport **109** Cleo/PhotoEdit **114** Onne Van Der Wal/Stock Newport **120** Deborah Davis/PhotoEdit **122(b)** Randy Wells/Tony Stone Images **122(t)** Superstock, Inc. **123** John Scheiber/Stock Market **124** Zig Leszczynski/Animals Animals **126** Zig Leszczynski/Animals Animals **129** Susan Ley/Animals Animals **130** New York Public Library, Astor, Lenox and Tilden Foundations **132** Robert Landen/Westlight **135** Gerard Lacz/Animals Animals/Earth Scenes **137** Mark Scott/FPG International Corp. **146(br)** Superstock, Inc. **146(bl)** Superstock, Inc. **146(c)** R. Kord/H. Armstrong Roberts, Inc. **146(t)** Superstock, Inc. **147(t)** Superstock, Inc. **148** Larry Lefever/Grant Heilman Photography **151** Bachmann/PhotoEdit **153** Jean Gaumy/Magnum Photos **160** Ted Horowitz/Stock Market **168** Jose L. Pelaez/Stock Market **170** Chicago Tribune photo by Bill Hogan **174** Dennis Degnan/Westlight **175** Superstock, Inc. **186** Mark Lewis/Tony Stone Images **187** James Blank/Stock Market **194** Superstock, Inc. **206** Willie L. Hill., Jr./Stock Boston **208** Brad Whitmore/Francis Schweizer, STScI/NASA **212** Metropolitan Museum of Art, Gift of Thomas F. Ryan, 1910(11.173.9) **214** Frozen Images, Inc. **220** "Happy Industrial Park" screen from SimCity™ ©1996 Maxis, Inc. **220(t)** Mark Segal/Tony Stone Images **222(b)** Superstock, Inc. **222(c)** Scott Kohn/Stock Connection **222(tr)** Craig Aurness/Westlight **222(tl)** Carl Vanderschuitt/FPG International Corp. **223(b)** Larry Downing/Woodfin Camp & Associates **224** Myrleen Ferguson/PhotoEdit **226** Steve Hill Photo **231** Superstock, Inc. **236** Superstock, Inc. **237** Otto Rogge/Stock Market **251** Kunio Owaki/Stock Market **252** Corbis-Bettmann **257** Marine Art Posters, Hull, U.K. **258** Scott Burns **260** Superstock, Inc. **261** Moore School of Engineering **264** AP/Wide World **265** Courtesy, Cray Computer **267** Los Alamos National Laboratory **270** Barbara Gerlach/Visuals Unlimited **271** Cydney Conger/Westlight **277** Dennis O'Clair/Tony Stone Images **280** Amy C. Etra/PhotoEdit **281** Cameramann International, Ltd. **282(b)** Robert Landau/Westlight **282(c)** Dean Siracusa/FPG International Corp. **282(tr)** Lois Ellen Frank/Westlight **282(tl)** D. & J. Heaton/Westlight **283(b)** Gary Conner/PhotoEdit **294** Bob Daemmrich/Stock Boston **295** Superstock, Inc. **300** Courtesy, BMW **302** Courtesy, BMW **306** Courtesy, General Motors Corporation **307** NASA **315** Photo: Christa Kopperman, Staatliche Antikensammlungen und Glyptothek, Munich **326** Janice Burkhardt/Westlight **327** Mike Sedam Photography **328** Ron Watts/Westlight **330** Bachmann/PhotoEdit **331** Mike Fizer/Check Six **334** ©1998 M. C. Escher/Cordon Art-Baarn-Holland. All rights reserved. **335** Alon Reininger/Stock Market **340** Ron Kimball **348(t)** Superstock, Inc. **348(br)** Ron Watts/Westlight **348(bl)** Kevin Anderson/Tony Stone Images **348(c)** Gerben Oppermans/Tony Stone Images **349(t)** Superstock, Inc. **360** Frank Siteman/Stock Boston **361** Zig Leszczynski/Animals Animals **363** Leonard Lee Rue III/Animals Animals/Earth Scenes **371** Granger Collection **376** Arthur C. Smith III/Grant Heilman Photography **377** Globus, Holway & Lobel/Stock Market **379** Superstock, Inc. **383** Victoria McCormick/Earth Scenes **390** Joe Towers/Stock Market **391** Superstock, Inc. **398** Ken Reid/FPG International Corp. **402** Craig Aurness/Westlight **404(b)** Anne-Marie Weber/FPG International Corp. **404(cr)** Right Image/Stock Connection **404(cl)** Patrick Cocklin/Tony Stone Images **404(t)** Nourok/PhotoEdit **405(b)** W. Cody/Westlight **417** David Young Wolff/PhotoEdit **431** Steve Chenn/Westlight **434** Gabe Palmer/Stock Market **436** Granger Collection **442** Jeff Mangiat/Stock Market **456** Tom McCarthy/PhotoEdit **461** Cary Wolinski/Stock Boston **462** Sidney Harris **463** Ron Kimball **470(b)** FourByFive/Superstock, Inc. **470(cr)** Frank Saragnese/FPG International Corp. **470(cl)** Mark Newman/Stock Connection **470(t)** Superstock, Inc. **471(t)** James L. Amos/Stock Connection **472** Adam H Davis/SPL/Photo Researchers **473** Giraudon/Art Resource **474** Granger Collection **478** H.Schneebeli/SPL/Photo Researchers **480** Gregory G. Dimijian/Photo Researchers **485** Onne Van Der Wal/Stock Newport **486** Pek Parviainen/SPL/Photo Researchers **488** W. Geiersperger/Stock Market **491** Tim Davis/Photo Researchers **495** Peter Weimann/Animals Animals **498** Frank Burek/Earth Scenes **501, 502** Patti Murray/Earth Scenes **505** Bruce Iverson **506** W. Gregory Brown/Animals Animals **507** Westlight **508** Granger Collection **510** Oxford Scientific Films/Animals Animals **526** Worldsat International Inc./Photo Researchers **534** Naoki Okamoto/Stock Market **539** Milt & Patti Putnam/Stock Market **540** Courtesy, Edward Lorenz **542(b)** Superstock, Inc. **542(c)** PhotoDisc, Inc. **542(t)** Japack/Leo de Wys, Inc **543** PhotoDisc, Inc. **550(b)** CNRI/Phototake **550(c)** David Hanover/Tony Stone Images **550(tr)** Mark J. Barrett/Stock Connection **550(tl)** Jamie Squire/Allspo **551(c)** Japack/Leo de Wys, Inc. **552** Tom Van Sant/Geosphere Project, Santa Monica/SPL/Photo Researchers **554** NASA **558** G. McLaughlin/Stock Market **559** Tony Stone Images **560** Globus Brothers, Inc./Stock Market **562** Nancy Dudley/Stock Boston **567** Leo Mason/Sports Illustrated **569** Superstock, Inc. **576** NASA **579** Mendola Ltd./Stock Market **580** Robert E. Daemmrich/Tony Stone Images **583** Dale O'Dell/Stock Market **587** Superstock, Inc. **590(b)** Jim Steinberg/Photo Researchers **592** Superstock, Inc. **594** Grant Heilman/Grant Heilman Photography **600(br)** Randy Faris/Westlight **600(bl)** Miguel S. Salmeron/FPG International Corp. **600(c)** R. Fukuhara/Westlight **600(t)** Joe Sohm/Chromosohm/Stock Connection **601(c)** Nick Dolding/Tony Stone Image **602** Bob Daemmrich/Stock Boston **604** Superstock, Inc. **607** Don Mason/Stoc Market **610** Secretary of State Office, Illinois **612** AP/Wide World **615** Fredric Ichinose **618** Superstock, Inc. **627** Superstock, Inc. **631** Hand-colored by Che Kucharzak **636** Robert E. Daemmrich/Tony Stone Images **647** Superstock, Inc **648** Robin Smith/Tony Stone Images **650** L. Gervais/Westlight **650** Gary Buss/FPG International Corp. **654(b)** AP/Wide World **655** David M. Grossman/Photo Researchers **656(b&c)** Ron Chapple/FPG International Corp. **656(tr)** Bill Deering/FPG International Corp. **656(tl)** Richard Niebel/Stock Connection **657(b)** Superstock, Inc. **661** Bonnie Kamin/PhotoEdit **664** James Wells/Tony Stone Images **673** Bob Daemmrich/Stock Boston **677** Robert E. Daemmrich/Tony Stone Images **678** David R. Frazier/Tony Stone Images **679** Fritz Hoffmann/Image Works **687** Kartographischer Verlag, Innsbruck, Austria **691** Superstock, Inc. **693** Akira Fujii **696** Rich Iwasaki/Tony Stone Images **699** David Young-Wolff/PhotoEdit **700** Superstock, Inc. **706** Anthony Edgeworth, Inc./Stock Market **708** Adamsmith Productions/Westlight **711** Superstock, Inc. **712** Reprinted by permission of United Feature Syndicate **715** Jim Brown/Stock Market **716** Paul Merideth/Tony Stone Images **718(b)** Chuck O'Rear/Westlight **718(cr)** Superstock, Inc. **718(cl)** Anne-Marie Weber/FPG International Corp. **718(t)** Antony Nagelmann/FPG International Corp. **719(t)** Superstock, Inc. **720** Superstock, Inc. **721** Superstock, Inc. **726** J Corwin/Tony Stone Images **728** Arthur Tilley/Tony Stone Images **731** Keith Wood/Tony Stone Images **732** Superstock, Inc. **733** Robert A. Mitchell/Tony Stone Images **736** Superstock, Inc. **744** NASA **751** Courtesy, Lear **752** NASA **754** Andrew Sacks/Tony Stone Images **771, 772** Superstock, Inc. **773** Adamsmith/FPG International Corp. **774** Warren Bolster/Tony Stone Image **777** Baron Wolman/Tony Stone Images **782(br)** David R. Frazier/Stock Solution **782(bl)** Superstock, Inc. **782(c)** H. D. Thoreau/Westlight **782(t)** Bruce Hands/Tony Stone Images **783(t)** Susan Benson/Stock Connection **784** Superstock, Inc. **788** Superstock, Inc. **789** Hans Halberstadt/Stock Market **792** Michael Newman/PhotoEdit **800** Ward/Corbis-Bettmann, Hand-colored by Cheryl Kucharzak **804** Henley & Savage/Stock Market **805** Grafton M. Smith/Stock Market **808** Joe Gator/Stock Market **810** Daniel J. Cox/Tony Ston Images **817** Dean Abramson/Stock Boston **818** Corbis-Bettmann, Hand-colore by Cheryl Kucharzak **819** Superstock, Inc. **820** Gary Wagner/Stock Boston **821** Eleanor Thompson/Stock Market **827** David Ulmer/Stock Boston **833(t)** PhotoDisc, Inc. **833(b)** Library of Congress **835** Craig Aurness/Westlight **837** Jim Foster/Stock Market **838** Superstock, Inc.

LESSON 7-5, pp. 433–434

9. Let $S(t)$ be the statement: $3t^2 \geq 9t$.
$S(3)$: $3 \cdot 3^2 = 27$, and $9 \cdot 3 = 27$, so $27 \geq 27$, and $S(3)$ is true.
Assume $S(k)$. Then $3k^2 \geq 9k$.

$3k^2 + 6k + 3 \geq 9k + 6k + 3$ — Addition Property of Inequality

$3(k+1)^2 \geq 9(k+1) + 6k - 6$ — Factor

$3(k+1)^2 \geq 9(k+1)$ — Transitive Property, since $6k - 6 > 0$

Thus, $S(k) \Rightarrow S(k+1)$. So by the Principle of Mathematical Induction, $S(t)$ is true for all integers $t \geq 3$.

10. Let $S(n)$ be the statement: 3 is a factor of $n^3 + 14n$.
$S(1)$: $1^3 + 14(1) = 15$; since 3 is a factor of 15, $S(1)$ is true.
Assume $S(k)$. Then 3 is a factor of $k^3 + 14k$. Show $S(k+1)$: 3 is a factor of $(k+1)^3 + 14(k+1)$ is true.
$(k+1)^3 + 14(k+1) =$
$k^3 + 3k^2 + 17k + 15 =$
$(k^3 + 14k) + 3(k^2 + k + 5)$
By the Factor of an Integer Sum Theorem $S(k) \Rightarrow S(k+1)$. Thus, by the Principle of Mathematical Induction $S(n)$ is true for all integers greater than zero.

11. a. $\begin{cases} A_1 = 8000 \\ A_{n+1} = (1.008)A_n - 400 \end{cases}$
$\forall$ integers $n \geq 1$

b. \$6639.79

CHAPTER 7 PROJECT 4, p. 464

4. a. 1, 1, 2, 3, 5, 8, 13, 21, 34, 55, 89, 144

b. i. $3 \cdot 5$, $5 \cdot 8$, $8 \cdot 13$

ii. $S(n)$: $\sum_{i=1}^{n} F_i^2 = F_n \cdot f_{n+1}$

iii. Sample (for $n = 7$):
$1^2 + 1^2 + 2^2 + 3^2 + 5^2 + 8^2 + 13^2 = 273 = 13 \cdot 21$

iv. (1) $1^2 = 1 \cdot 1 = F_1 \cdot F_2$, so $S(1)$ is true.
(2) Assume $S(k)$ is true for some Integer k. Must show $S(k+1)$ is true.
$F_1^2 + F_2^2 + F_3^2 + \ldots + F_k^2 + F_{k+1}^2$
$= F_k \cdot F_{k+1} + F_{k+1}^2$ — Since $S(k)$ is true
$= F_{k+1}(F_k + F_{k+1})$ — Distributive Prop.
$= F_{k+1} + F_{k+2}$ — Def. of Fibonacci sequence
$\therefore$ By the Principle of Mathematical Induction, $S(n)$ is true for all natural numbers n.

c. i. 7, 12, 20

ii. $S_n = \sum_{i=1}^{n+1} F_i$. $S(n)$: $S_n = S_{n-1} + S_{n-2} + 1$

iii. Sample (for $n = 6$):
$S_6 = 1 + 1 + 2 + 3 + 5 + 8 + 13 = 33 = 20 + 12 + 1$
$= S_5 + S_4 + 1$

iv. (1) $S_2 + S_1 + 1 = 4 + 2 + 1 = 7 = S_3$, so $S(3)$ is true. (2) Assume $S(k)$ is true for some positive integer $k \geq 3$. Must show $S(k+1)$ is true.

$S_{k+1} = \sum_{i=1}^{k+2} F_i$ — Definition of S

$= F_{k+2} + \sum_{i=1}^{k+1} F_i$ — Rewrite summation

$= F_{k+2} + S_k$ — Definition of S

$= F_{k+2} + S_{k-1} + S_{k-2} + 1$ — By the inductive assumption

$= F_{k+1} + F_k + S_{k-1} + S_{k-2} + 1$ — Def. of Fibonacci Seq.

$= (F_{k+1} + S_{k-1}) + (F_k + S_{k-2}) + 1$ — Commutativity

$= (F_{k+1} + \sum_{i=1}^{k} F_i) + (F_k + \sum_{i=1}^{k-1} F_i) + 1$ — Definition of S

$= (\sum_{i=1}^{k+1} F_i) + (\sum_{i=1}^{k} F_i) + 1$ — Rewrite summation

$= S_k + S_{k+1} + 1$ — Def. of S

$\therefore$ By the Principle of Mathematical Induction, $S(n)$ is true for all natural numbers $n \geq 3$.

d. i. 5, 13, 34, 89

ii. $S_n = \sum_{i=1}^{n} (F_i^2 + F_{i+1}^2)$.
$S(n)$: $S_n = 3S_{n-1} - S_{n-2}$

iii. Sample (for $n = 6$):
$S_6 = 8^2 + 13^2 = 233 = 267 - 34 = 3(89) - 34 = 3S_5 + S_4$

iv. (1) $3S_2 + S_1 = 3(5) - 2 = 15 - 2 = 13 = 4 + 9 = 2^2 + 3^2 = S_3$, so $S(3)$ is true.
(2) Assume $S(k)$ is true for some positive integer $k \geq 3$. Must show $S(k+1)$ is true.

$S_{k+1} = \sum_{i=1}^{k+1} (F_i^2 + F_{i+1}^2)$

$= F_{k+1}^2 + F_{k+2}^2 + \sum_{i=1}^{k} (F_i^2 + F_{i+1}^2)$

$= F_{k+1}^2 + F_{k+2}^2 + S_k$

$= F_{k+1}^2 + F_{k+2}^2 + 3S_{k-1} - S_{k-2}$

$= F_{k+1}^2 + (F_k + F_{k+1})^2 + 3S_{k-1} - S_{k-2}$

$= F_{k+1}^2 + F_k^2 + 2F_kF_{k+1} + F_{k+1}^2 + 3S_{k-1} - S_{k-2}$

$= 2F_{k+1}^2 + F_k^2 + 2F_kF_{k+1} + 3S_{k-1} - S_{k-2}$

$= 2F_{k+1}^2 + F_k^2 + 2F_k(F_k + F_{k-1}) + 3S_{k-1} - S_{k-2}$

$= 2F_{k+1}^2 + F_k^2 + 2F_k^2 + 2F_kF_{k-1} + 3S_{k-1} - S_{k-2}$

$= 2F_{k+1}^2 + 2F_k^2 + F_k^2 + 2F_kF_{k-1} + F_{k-1}^2 - F_{k-1}^2 + 3S_{k-1} - S_{k-2}$

$= 2F_{k+1}^2 + 2F_k^2 + (F_k + F_{k-1})^2 - F_{k-1}^2 + 3S_{k-1} - S_{k-2}$

$= 2F_{k+1}^2 + 2F_k^2 + F_{k+1}^2 - F_{k-1}^2 + 3S_{k-1} - S_{k-2}$

$= 3F_{k+1}^2 + 2F_k^2 - F_{k-1}^2 + 3S_{k-1} - S_{k-2}$

$= 3F_{k+1}^2 + 2F_k^2 + F_k^2 - F_k^2 - F_{k-1}^2 + 3S_{k-1} - S_{k-2}$

$= 3F_{k+1}^2 + 3F_k^2 - F_k^2 - F_{k-1}^2 + 3S_{k-1} - S_{k-2}$

$= 3(F_{k+1}^2 + F_k^2) - (F_k^2 + F_{k-1}^2) + 3S_{k-1} - S_{k-2}$

$= 3(F_{k+1}^2 + F_k^2) + 3S_{k-1} - (F_k^2 - F_{k-1}^2) - S_{k-2}$

$= 3(F_{k+1}^2 + F_k^2) + 3\sum_{i=1}^{k-1} (F_i^2 + F_{i+1}^2) - (F_k^2 + F_{k-1}^2) - \sum_{i=1}^{k-2} (F_i^2 + F_{i+1}^2)$

$= 3\sum_{i=1}^{k} (F_i^2 + F_i + 1^2) - \sum_{i=1}^{k-1} (F_i^2 + F_{i+1}^2)$

$= 3S_k - S_{k-1}$

$\therefore$ By the Principle of Mathematical Induction, $S(n)$ is true for all natural numbers $n \geq 3$.

e. Sequence defined by
$S_k = \sum_{i=1}^{k} (-1)^{i+1} F_{i+1}$
$1 = 1$
$1 - 2 = -1$
$1 - 2 + 3 = 2$
$1 - 2 + 3 - 5 = -3$
$1 - 2 + 3 - 5 + 8 = 5$
$1 - 2 + 3 - 5 + 8 - 13 = -8$
Claim: $S(n)$: $S_n = (-1)^{n+1} F_n$
(1) $S_1 = 1 \cdot 1 = (-1)^2 F_2$, so $S(1)$ is true. (2) Assume $S(k)$ is true for some integer k. Must show $S(k+1)$ is true.

$S_k + 1 = \sum_{i=1}^{k+1} (-1)^{i+1}F_{i+1}$

Definition of S_{k+1}

$= S_k + (-1)^{k+2}F_{k+2}$

Simplify

$= (-1)^{k+1}F_k + (-1)^{k+2}F_{k+2}$

Since S_k is true

$= (-1)^{k+1}F_k + (-1)^{k+2}(F_k + F_{k+1})$

Def. of Fibonacci Seq.

$= (-1)^{k+1}F_k - (-1)^{k+1}F_k - (-1)^{k+1}F_{k+1}$

Distributive Prop.

$= -(-1)^{k+1}F_{k+1}$

Subtraction

$= (-1)^{k+2}F_{k+1}$

$\therefore$ By the principle of Mathematical Induction, $S(n)$ is true for all natural numbers.

CHAPTER 7 PROJECT 5, (continued), p. 464

5. c. Sample triangle shown:

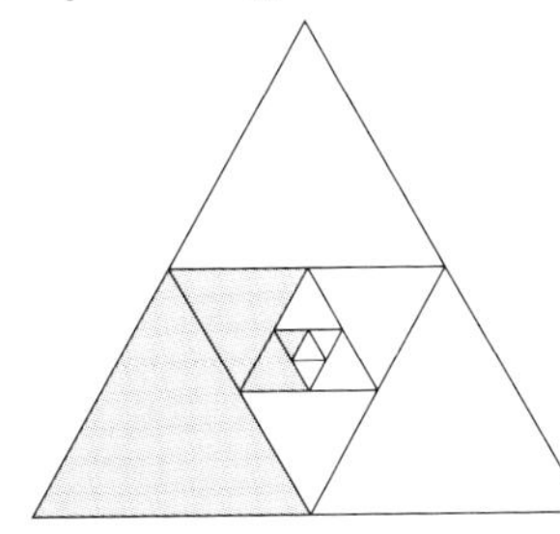

$p(1) = 3s$ $\quad p(2) = \frac{3s}{2}$

$p(3) = \frac{3s}{4}$ $\quad p(4) = \frac{3s}{8}$

$p(5) = \frac{3s}{16}$

It can be seen that $p(i)$ is a geometric sequence with

$p(k+1) = (\frac{1}{2})p(k)$.

So with $p(1) = 3s$ and $r = \frac{1}{2}$, the sum

$\sum_{i=1}^{\infty} p(i) = \frac{4s}{1 - \frac{1}{2}} = \frac{4s}{\frac{1}{2}} = 8s.$

$A(1) = \frac{\sqrt{3}s^2}{8}$ $\quad A(2) = \frac{\sqrt{3}s^2}{32}$

$A(3) = \frac{\sqrt{3}s^2}{128}$ $\quad A(4) = \frac{\sqrt{3}s^2}{512}$

$A(5) = \frac{\sqrt{3}s^2}{2048}$

It can be seen that $A(i)$ is a geometric series with

$A(k+1) = \frac{1}{4}(A(k))$.

So with $A(1) = \frac{\sqrt{3}s^2}{8}s$ and $r = \frac{1}{4}$, the sum

$\sum_{i=1}^{\infty} A(i) = \frac{\frac{\sqrt{3}s^2}{8}}{1 - \frac{1}{4}} = \frac{\frac{\sqrt{3}s^2}{8}}{\frac{3}{4}} = \frac{\sqrt{3}s^2}{6}.$

CHAPTER 7 PROJECT 6, p. 464

6. a. $M = \begin{bmatrix} 1 & 1 \\ 1 & 0 \end{bmatrix}$

$M^2 = \begin{bmatrix} 2 & 1 \\ 1 & 1 \end{bmatrix}$

$M^3 = \begin{bmatrix} 3 & 2 \\ 2 & 1 \end{bmatrix}$

$M^4 = \begin{bmatrix} 5 & 3 \\ 3 & 2 \end{bmatrix}$

$M^5 = \begin{bmatrix} 8 & 5 \\ 5 & 3 \end{bmatrix}$

$M^6 = \begin{bmatrix} 13 & 8 \\ 8 & 5 \end{bmatrix}$

b. Conjecture: $S(n)$:

$M^n = \begin{bmatrix} F_{n+1} & F_n \\ F_n & F_{n-1} \end{bmatrix}$ for $n \geq 2$.

c. (1) $M^2 =$

$\begin{bmatrix} 2 & 1 \\ 1 & 1 \end{bmatrix} = \begin{bmatrix} F_3 & F_2 \\ F_2 & F_1 \end{bmatrix}$

(2) Assume $S(k)$ is true for some integer k. Show $S(k+1)$ is true.

$M^{k+1} = M^k \cdot M$ Matrix mult.

$= \begin{bmatrix} F_{k+1} & F_k \\ F_k & F_{k-1} \end{bmatrix}\begin{bmatrix} 1 & 1 \\ 1 & 0 \end{bmatrix}$

Since $S(k)$ is true

$= \begin{bmatrix} F_{k+1} + F_k & F_{k+1} \\ F_k + F_{k-1} & F_k \end{bmatrix}$

Matrix multiplication

$= \begin{bmatrix} F_{k+2} & F_{k+1} \\ F_{k+1} & F_k \end{bmatrix}$

Definition of Fibonacci sequence.

$\therefore$ By the Principle of Mathematical Induction, $S(n)$ is true for all natural numbers n.

d. $N = \begin{bmatrix} 2 & 1 \\ 1 & 0 \end{bmatrix}$

$N^2 = \begin{bmatrix} 5 & 2 \\ 2 & 1 \end{bmatrix}$

$N^3 = \begin{bmatrix} 12 & 5 \\ 5 & 2 \end{bmatrix}$

$N^4 = \begin{bmatrix} 29 & 12 \\ 12 & 5 \end{bmatrix}$

Sequence: 2, 5, 12, 29, 70, 169, ...

e. $G_n = 2G_{n-1} + G_{n-2}$ for $n \geq 2$.

f. The sequence generated by $\begin{bmatrix} a & 1 \\ 1 & 0 \end{bmatrix}$ may be recursively defined $G_n = aG_{n-1} + G_{n-2}$ for $n \geq 2$.

CHAPTER 7 REVIEW, pp. 468–469

31. (1) $S(2)$: 3 is a factor of $2 \cdot 2^3 - 5 \cdot 2$. $16 - 10 = 6$, so $S(2)$ is true.
(2) Assume that $S(k)$: is a factor of $2k^3 - 5k$ is true for some integer $k \geq 2$. Prove $S(k+1)$: 3 is a factor of $2(k+1)^3 - 5(k+1)$ is true.
$2(k+1)^3 - 5(k+1) =$
$2k^3 + 6k^2 + 6k + 2 - 5k - 5 =$
$(2k^3 - 5k) + 3(2k^2 + 2k - 1)$.
Since 3 is factor of $2k^3 - 5k$ and $3(2k^2 + 2k - 1)$, 3 is a factor of their sum by the Factor of an Integer Sum Theorem. Hence, by mathematical induction, $S(n)$ is true $\forall$ integers $n \geq 2$.

32. Let $S(n)$ be the statement: If $0 \leq x \leq 1$, then $0 \leq x^n \leq x$.
(1) $S(1)$: $x^1 = x$, so $S(1)$ is true, since $x \geq 0$ by the given statement.
(2) Assume $S(k)$ for some arbitrary integer. Show $S(k+1)$: If $0 \leq x \leq 1$, then $0 \leq x^{k+1} \leq x$. $0 \leq x^k \leq x$.
By the inductive assumption
$x \cdot 0 \leq x \cdot x^k \leq x \cdot x$ $\quad M_x$
$0 \leq x^{k+1} \leq x^2$
Product of powers
$0 \leq x^{k+1} \leq 1 \cdot 1$
Given $x \leq 1$
$0 \leq x^{k+1} \geq 1$
Simplification
$0 \leq x^{k+1} \leq x$
Given $x \leq 1$
Hence, $S(k) \Rightarrow S(k+1)$. Therefore, by mathematical induction $S(n)$ is true for integers $n \geq 1$.

33. (1) $S(2)$: $4^2 = 16 > 8 = 4(2)$. So $S(2)$ is true.
(2) Assume $S(k)$. Show $S(k+1)$: $4^{k+1} > 4(k+1)$.
$4^k > 4k$ by the inductive assumption
$4 \cdot 4^k > 4 \cdot 4k$ $\quad M_4$
$4^{k+1} > 16k$ Simplification
$4^{k+1} > 4(k+1) + 12k - 4$ Distributive Property
$4^{k+1} > 4(k+1) + 12(2) - 4$ Given $k \geq 2$
$4^{k+1} > 4(k+1)$
$4(k+1) < 4(k+1) + 20$
So $S(k) \Rightarrow S(k+1)$. Therefore by the Principle of Mathematical Induction, $S(n)$ is true for all integers $n \geq 2$.

34. a. $S(1)$: $(1 - \frac{1}{2}) = \frac{1}{2} = \frac{1}{1+1}$, so $S(1)$ is true.

b. Assume $S(k)$:
$(1 - \frac{1}{2})(1 - \frac{1}{3}) \ldots (1 - \frac{1}{k+1})$
$= \frac{1}{k+1}$ for some integer $k \geq 1$.

c. $S(k+1)$: $(1 - \frac{1}{2})(1 - \frac{1}{3}) \ldots$
$(1 - \frac{1}{k+1})(1 - \frac{1}{k+2}) = \frac{1}{k+2}$

d. $(1 - \frac{1}{2})(1 - \frac{1}{3}) \ldots$
$(1 - \frac{1}{k+1})(1 - \frac{1}{k+2})$
$= S(k)(1 - \frac{1}{k+2})$
$= (\frac{1}{k+1})(1 - \frac{1}{k+2})$
$= (\frac{1}{k+1})((\frac{k+2}{k+2}) - (\frac{1}{k+2}))$
$= (\frac{1}{k+1})(\frac{k+1}{k+2}) = \frac{1}{k+2}$
Hence, $S(k) \Rightarrow S(k+1)$. Therefore, by the Principle of Mathematical Induction, $S(n)$ is true for all integers $n \geq 1$.

35. a. 0, 4, 4, 16, 28

b. Let $S(n)$: 4 is a factor of b_n. (1) $S(1)$: 4 is a factor of b_1. $b_1 = 0$, so $S(1)$ is true. $S(2)$: 4 is factor of b_2. $b_2 = 4$, so $S(2)$ is true. (2) Assume $S(1)$, $S(2)$, ... and $S(k)$ are true for some integer $k \geq 1$. So 4 is a factor of $b_1, b_2, \ldots, b_k$. Show $S(k + 1)$: 4 is a factor of b_{k+1} is true. Since b_{k-1} and b_k have 4 as a factor, there exist integers p and q such that $b_{k-1} = 4p$ and $b_k = 4q$. Substituting into the recurrence relation, $b_{k+1} = 4q + 3(4p) = 4q + 12p = 4(q + 3p)$. $q + 3p$ is an integer by closure properties, so 4 is a factor of b_{k+1}. Hence, by the Strong Form of Mathematical Induction, $S(n)$ is true for all integers $n \geq 1$.

36. a. $C_2 = 1$, $C_3 = 3$, $C_4 = 6$

b. $C_{k+1} = k + C_k$, for $k \geq 2$

c. 28

37. a. $\begin{cases} A_1 = 80{,}000 \\ A_{k+1} = 1.01A_k - 900 \end{cases}$ for all integers $k \geq 1$

38. a. $\begin{cases} b_1 = 2 \\ b_{k+1} = 2b_k, \text{ integers } k \geq 1 \end{cases}$

39. a. initial order: 1, 3, 5, 2, 4
First pass: 1, 3, 2, 4, 5
Second pass: 1, 2, 3, 4, 5

40.

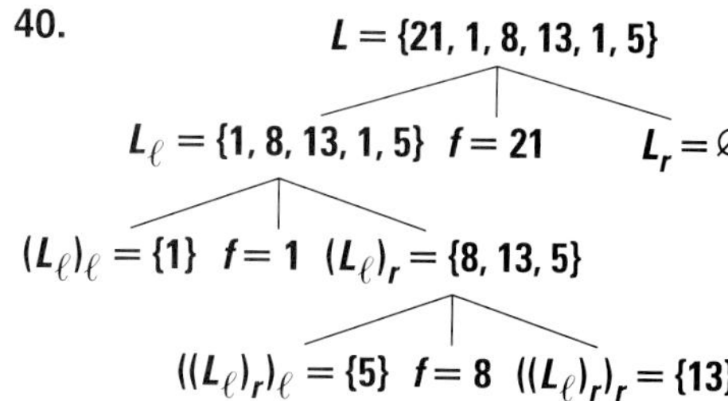

41. a. $a_1 = 1$, $a_{k+1} = \frac{1}{2}a_k$ for $k \geq 1$

c. $\sum_{i=1}^{20} (\frac{1}{2})^{i-1}$

d. $S_{20} = 2(1 - (\frac{1}{2})^{20})$

42. b. Explicit; the nth term of the sequence is given as a function of n in line 20.

LESSON 8-3, p. 492

21. Let $z = a + bi$, where a and b are real numbers. Then $\bar{z} = a - bi$. $z + \bar{z} = (a + bi) + (a - bi) = 2a$. Since a is real, $2a$ is real. So for all complex numbers, the sum of the number and its complex conjugate is a real number.

26. Geometric Division Theorem: Let z and w be complex numbers. If $z = [r, \theta]$ and $w = [s, \phi]$, then $\frac{z}{w} = [\frac{r}{s}, \theta - \phi]$ $(s \neq 0)$. That is, dividing a complex number z by w applies to z a size change of magnitude $\frac{1}{s}$ and a rotation of $-\phi$ about the origin.

LESSON 8-4, p. 499

19. b. $r = a + b\cos\theta$, where $a < b$

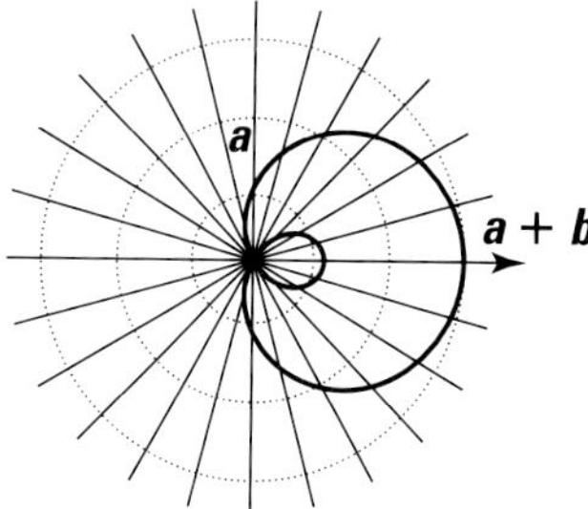

$r = a + b\cos\theta$, where $a = b$

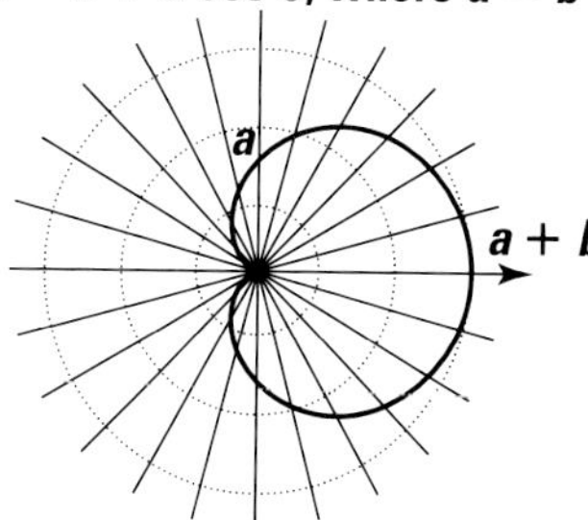

$r = a + b\cos\theta$, where $a > b$

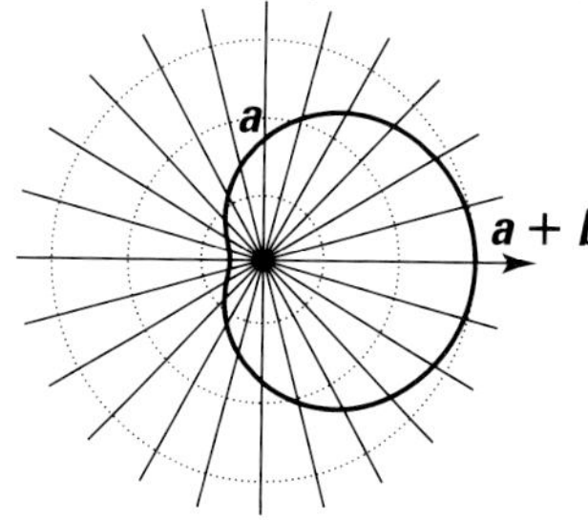

IN-CLASS ACTIVITY, p. 500

5. a.

$0 \leq \theta \leq 2\pi$, θ-step $= \frac{\pi}{6}$
$-2 \leq x \leq 2$, x-scale $= 1$
$-2 \leq y \leq 2$, y-scale $= 1$

b. By definition, $r = \sec\theta = \frac{r}{x}$ so $r = \frac{r}{x}$ or $x = \frac{r}{r}$, and so $x = 1$, which is the equation for a vertical line through the point (1, 0).

c. The graph of $r = \csc\theta$ will be a horizontal line through the point (0, 1) because by definition, $\csc\theta = \frac{r}{y}$, so $r = \frac{r}{y}$ or $y = \frac{r}{r}$, and so $y = 1$ which is the equation of a horizontal line through the point (0, 1).

LESSON 8-7, p. 519

22. Sample:

```
5   REM ENTER A COMPLEX
    NUMBER, A + BI, AND
    DESIRED ROOT, N
10  PRINT "WHAT IS THE REAL
    COMPONENT, A, OF THE
    COMPLEX NUMBER";
20  INPUT A
30  PRINT "WHAT IS THE
    IMAGINARY COMPONENT, B";
40  INPUT B
50  PRINT "WHICH ROOT DO YOU
    WANT";
60  INPUT N
70  LET PI = 3.14159265359
80  IF A = 0 AND B = 0 THEN
    PRINT "0 IS THE ONLY
    ROOT.":GOTO 190
85  REM CALCULATE THE
    ARGUMENT, D, IN RADIANS,
    OF A + BI
90  IF A = 0 AND B < 0 THEN LET
    D = -PI/2
100 IF A = 0 AND B > 0 THEN LET
    D = PI/2
110 IF A > 0 THEN LET D =
    ATN(B/A)
120 IF A < 0 THEN LET D =
    ATN(B/A) + PI
125 REM CALCULATE THE
    ABSOLUTE VALUE OF A + BI
130 LET L = SQR(A * A + B * B)
135 REM OUTPUT THE N NTH
    ROOTS OF A + BI
140 PRINT "THE ABSOLUTE
    VALUE OF EACH ROOT
    IS";L^(1/N)
150 PRINT "THE ARGUMENTS
    ARE"
160 FOR I = 0 TO (N - 1)
170 PRINT (D/N) + I*(2 * PI/N)
180 NEXT I
190 END
```

CHAPTER 8 PROJECTS, p. 543

7. a. sample:

```
10  REM ORBITS OF
    DYNAMICAL SYSTEMS
20  REM A is the number of
    terms
30  REM The window
    displayed will have corners
    (-MAX, -MAX) and
    (MAX, MAX)
40  A = 100:MAX = 2
50  DIM ORE(A), OLM(A)
60  INPUT "ENTER C";CR, CI
70  INPUT "ENTER D";DR, DI
80  ZR = DR:ZI = DI
90  REM Draw axes then plot
    points
100 LINE (0,128) - (512,128) :
    LINE (256,0) - (256,256)
110 FOR N = 1 TO A
120 ZR = ZR*ZR - ZI*ZI + CR
130 ZI = 2*ZR*ZI + CI
```

```
140 ORE(N) = ZR: OLM(N) =
    ZI:PR = (128/MAX)*ZR:PI =
    (128/MAX)*ZI
150 IF (PR < -256) OR (PR >
    256) OR (PI < -128) OR (PI
    > 128) THEN 170
160 PSET (256 + PR, 128 − PI)
170 NEXT N
180 REM Output list of values in
    orbit
190 INPUT "HIT <RETURN>";A$
200 FOR N = 1 TO A
210 PRINT ORE(N);"+";
    OLM(N);"i"
220 NEXT N
230 END
```

b. sample (for $c = -.39054 - .58679i$, $d = 0$):

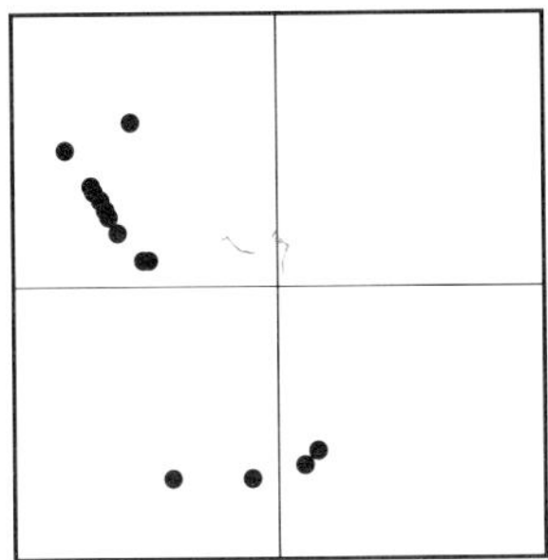

sample (for $c = .11 + .67i$, $d = 0$)

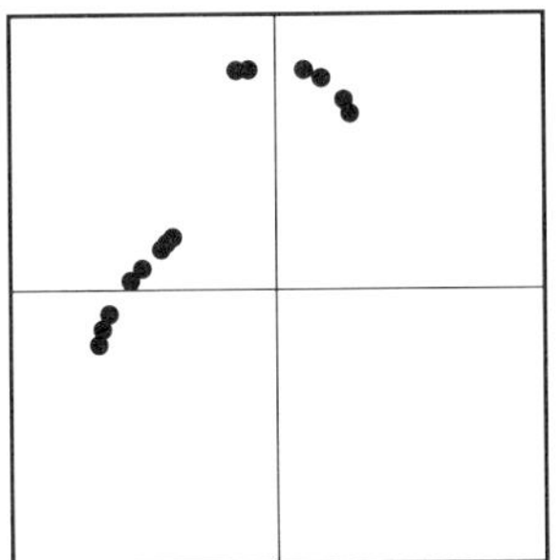

c. sample (for c = -.39054 − .58679i)

sample (for $c = -.11 + .67i$)

d. sample (for c = -2 − 1.25i)
See page T198 for program.

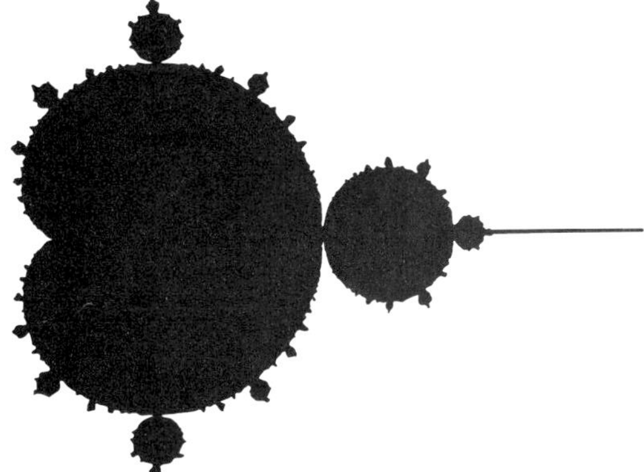

d. The Mandelbrot Set is the set of all complex numbers which when iterated by the rule $z \to z^2 + c$ do not diverge, where c is the complex number being tested.

sample program:

```
10  REM MANDELZOOM
20  INPUT "ENTER THE REAL
    AND IMAGINARY PARTS
    OF C:",ACORNER,
    BCORNER
30  INPUT "ENTER THE SIZE
    OF THE VIEWING
    WINDOW:",SIZE
40  CLS
50  P = 200
60  GAP = SIZE/P
70  FOR J = 1 TO P
80  FOR K = 1 TO P
90  AC = ACORNER + J*GAP
100 BC = BCORNER + K*GAP
110 AZ = 0: BZ = 0
120 FOR COUNT = 1 TO 200
130 OLDAZ = AZ
140 AZ = AZ*AZ − BZ*BZ + AC
150 BZ = 2*OLDAZ*BZ + BC
160 MAGZ = SQR(AZ*AZ +
    BZ*BZ)
170 IF MAGZ > 2 THEN 200
180 NEXT COUNT
190 PSET (J, P–K)
200 NEXT K
210 NEXT J
220 END
```

sample (for $c = -2 - 1.25i$):

CHAPTER 8 REVIEW, p. 549

60.

θ	0°	30°	45°	60°	90°	120°	135°	180°	240°	270°
r	6	≈5.2	≈4.2	3	0	-3	≈-4.2	-6	-3	0

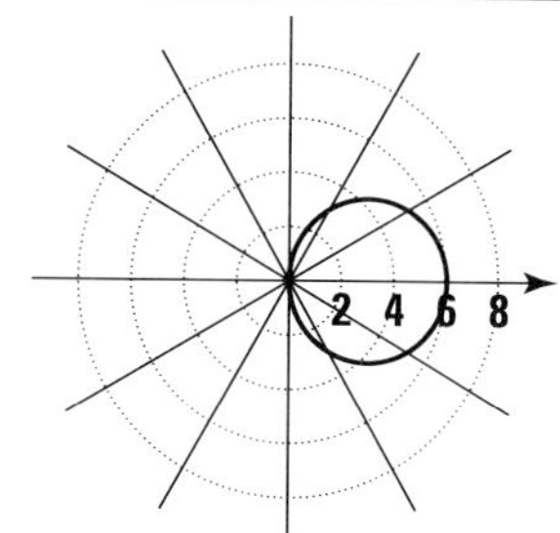

61.

θ	2	$\frac{\pi}{6}$	$\frac{\pi}{2}$	π	$\frac{3\pi}{2}$	2π
r	1	≈3.8	≈1.3	≈.64	≈.42	≈.32

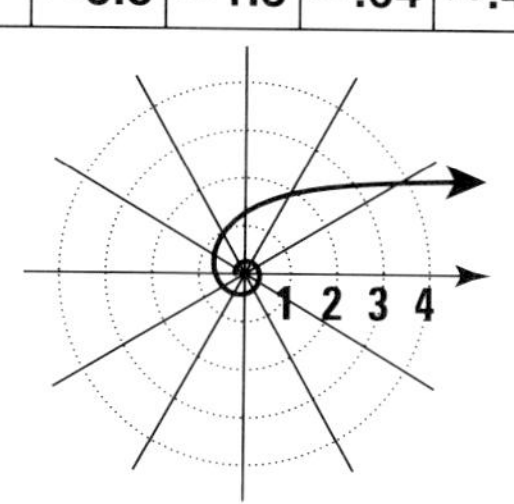

62.

θ	0°	30°	60°	120°	180°	330°
r	5	≈5.8	10	-10	-5	≈5.8

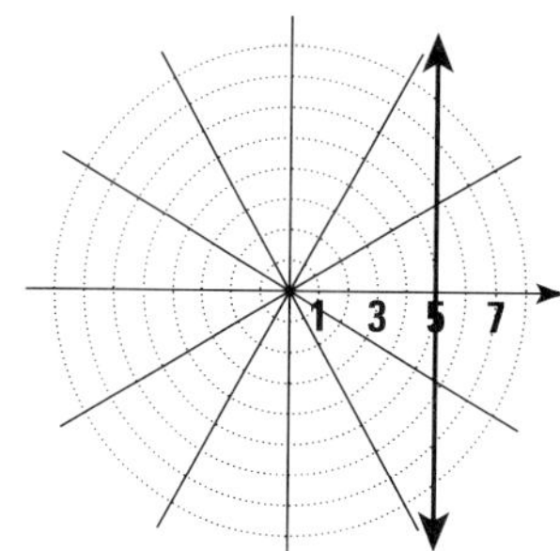

63.

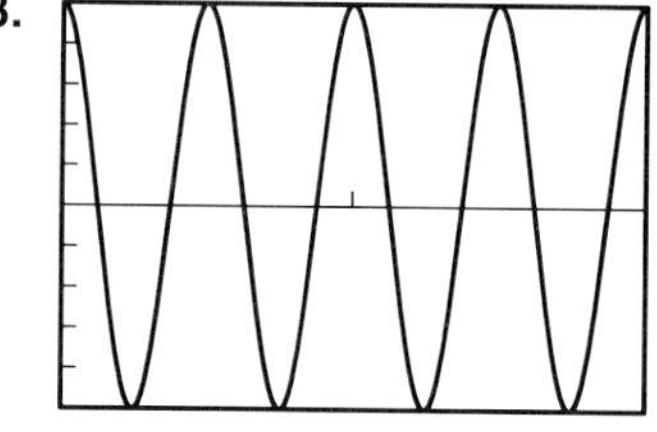

$0 \le x \le 2\pi$, x-scale $= \pi$
$-5 \le y \le 5$, y-scale $= 1$

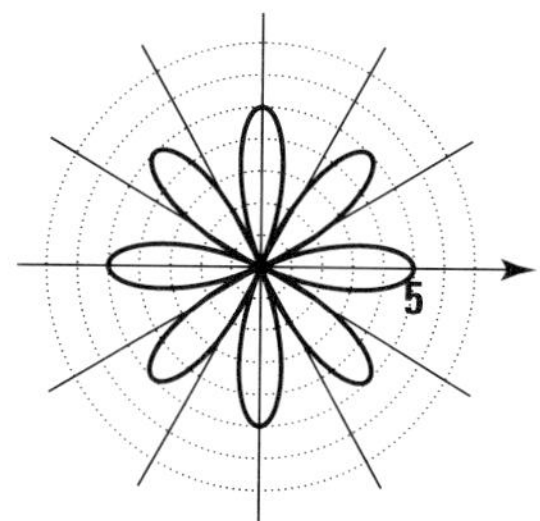

8-leafed rose curve

64.

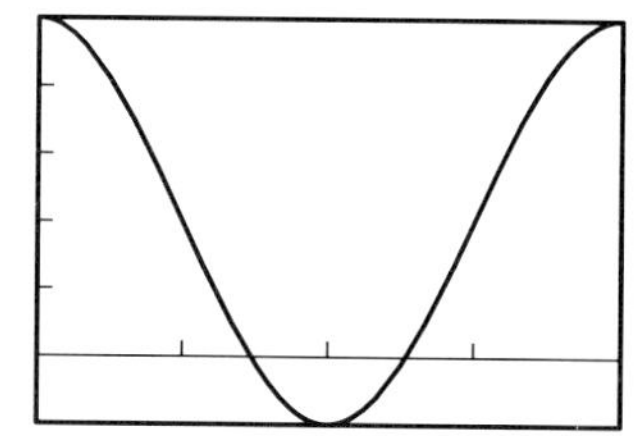

$0 \le x \le 2\pi$, x-scale $= \frac{\pi}{2}$
$-1 \le y \le 5$, y-scale $= 1$

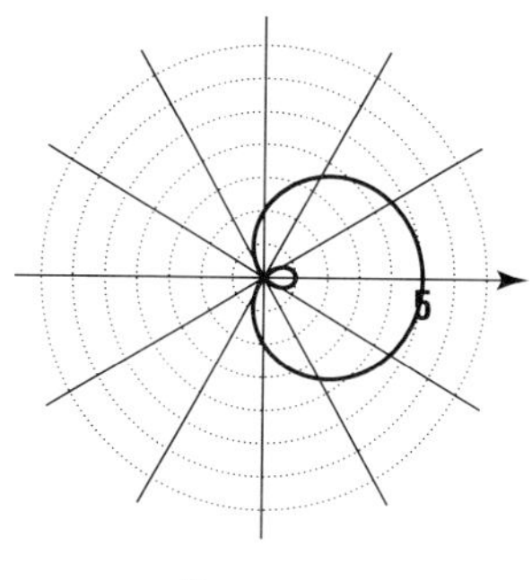

limaçon

65.

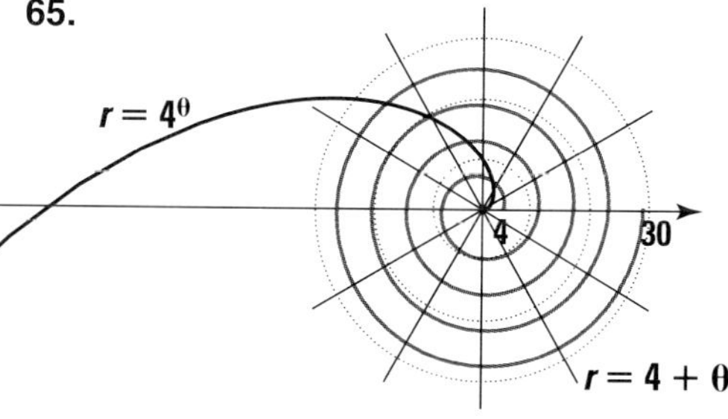

$r = 4^\theta$ is a logarithmic spiral, and $r = 4 + \theta$ is a spiral of Archimedes.

66. a.

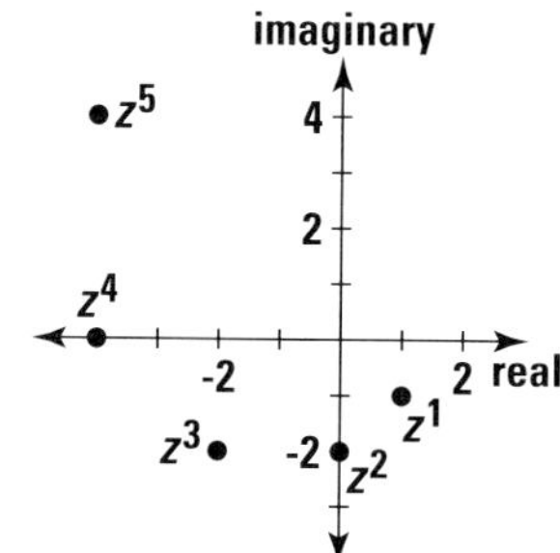

b. farther

67. a.

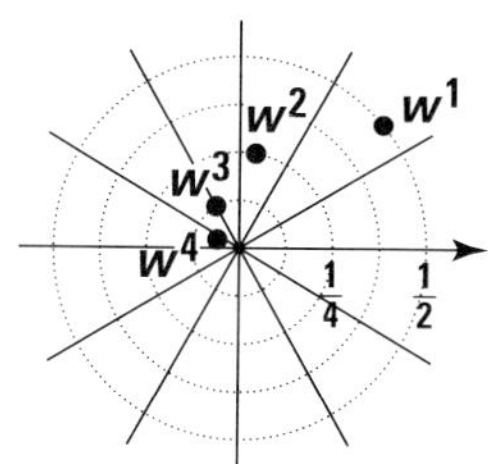

b. closer

68. a. a pentagon

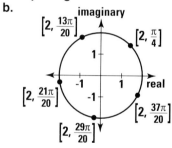

b. imaginary; $\left[2, \frac{13\pi}{20}\right]$; $\left[2, \frac{\pi}{4}\right]$; 1; -1; 1; real; -1; $\left[2, \frac{21\pi}{20}\right]$; $\left[2, \frac{37\pi}{20}\right]$; $\left[2, \frac{29\pi}{20}\right]$

69.

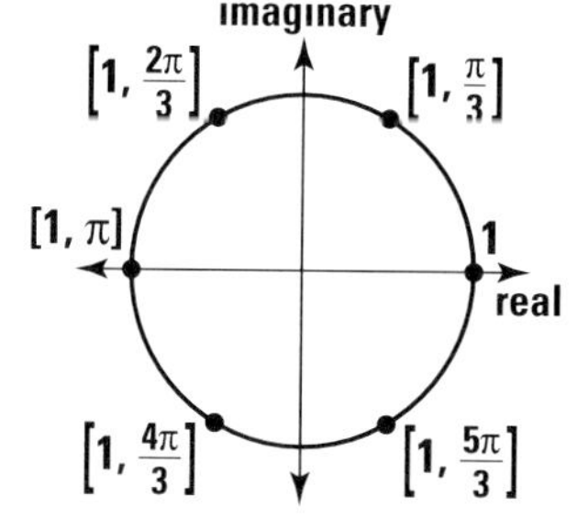

CHAPTER 10 PROJECT 3, p. 649

3. a. $(x+y+z)^3$
$= (x+y+z)(x+y+z)^2$
$= (x+y+z)(x^2+2xz+z^2+2yz+y^2+2xy)$
$= x^3+3x^2z+3xz^2+6xyz+3xy^2+3x^2y+3yz^2+3y^2z+y^3+z^3$

So the fourth layer is

$1z^3$

$3xz^2 \quad 3yz^2$

$3x^2z \quad 6xyz \quad 3y^2z$

$1x^3 \quad 3x^2y \quad 3xy^2 \quad 1y^3$.

b. Calculated similarly are the fifth and sixth layers shown below.

fifth layer:

$1z^4$

$4xz^3 \quad 4yz^3$

$6x^2z^2 \quad 12xyz^2 \quad 6y^2z^2$

$4x^3z \quad 12x^2yz \quad 12xy^2z \quad 4y^3z$

$1x^4 \quad 4x^3y \quad 6x^2y^2 \quad 4xy^3 \quad 1y^4$;

sixth layer:

$1z^5$

$5xz^4 \quad 5yz^4$

$10x^2z^3 \quad 20xyz^3 \quad 10y^2z^3$

$10x^3z^2 \quad 30x^2yz^2 \quad 30xy^2z^2 \quad 10y^3z^2$

$5x^4z \quad 20x^3yz \quad 30x^2y^2z \quad 20xy^3z \quad 5y^4z$

$1x^5 \quad 5x^4y \quad 10x^3y^2 \quad 10x^2y^3 \quad 5xy^4 \quad 1y^5$

c. As positioned in the text, powers of *z* increase from the bottom to the top of each layer. Powers of *x* increase from right to left, and powers of *y* increase from left to right. A coefficient in the center of a layer is equal to the sum of the three coefficents in the previous layer which form a triangle immediately above it. The students' models might be constructed out of cardboard, light wood, or plastic. The triangular layers would be of increasing sizes and could be connected with string for a mobile style or solid pillars for a free standing version.

e. Pascal's triangle appears on each of the 3 side faces of the tetrahedron but not on the base. One represents $(x+y)^n$, another $(x+z)^n$, and the third $(y+z)^n$.

NOTES

NOTES

NOTES

NOTES

NOTES

NOTES

NOTES

NOTES

NOTES